International Atomic Weights

International atomic weights. Parenthetical weights refer … ber, not the atomic weight, of the isotope with the longest half-lif…

Name	Symbol	Atomic number	Atomic weight
Actinium	Ac	89	(227)
Aluminum	Al	13	26.9815
Americium	Am	95	(243)
Antimony	Sb	51	121.75
Argon	Ar	18	39.948
Arsenic	As	33	74.9216
Astatine	At	85	(210)
Barium	Ba	56	137.34
Berkelium	Bk	97	(247)
Beryllium	Be	4	9.0122
Bismuth	Bi	83	208.98
Boron	B	5	10.811[a]
Bromine	Br	35	79.904
Cadmium	Cd	48	112.40
Calcium	Ca	20	40.08
Californium	Cf	98	(249)
Carbon	C	6	12.01115[a]
Cerium	Ce	58	140.12
Cesium	Cs	55	132.905
Chlorine	Cl	17	35.453
Chromium	Cr	24	51.996
Cobalt	Co	27	58.9332
Copper	Cu	29	63.546
Curium	Cm	96	(247)
Dysprosium	Dy	66	162.50
Einsteinium	Es	99	(254)
Erbium	Er	68	167.26
Europium	Eu	63	151.96
Fermium	Fm	100	(253)
Fluorine	F	9	18.9984
Francium	Fr	87	(223)
Gadolinium	Gd	64	157.25
Gallium	Ga	31	69.72
Germanium	Ge	32	72.59
Gold	Au	79	196.967
Hafnium	Hf	72	178.49
Helium	He	2	4.0026
Holmium	Ho	67	164.930
Hydrogen	H	1	1.00797[a]
Indium	In	49	114.82
Iodine	I	53	126.9044
Iridium	Ir	77	192.2
Iron	Fe	26	55.847
Krypton	Kr	36	83.80
Kurchatovium(?)	Ku(?)	104	(260)
Lanthanum	La	57	138.9
Lawrencium	Lw	103	(257)?
Lead	Pb	82	207.19
Lithium	Li	3	6.939
Lutetium	Lu	71	174.97
Magnesium	Mg	12	24.305
Manganese	Mn	25	54.9380
Mendelevium	Md	101	(256)
Mercury	Hg	80	200.59
Molybdenum	Mo	42	95.94
Neodymium	Nd	60	144.24
Neon	Ne	10	20.179
Neptunium	Np	93	(237)
Nickel	Ni	28	58.71
Niobium	Nb	41	92.906
Nitrogen	N	7	14.0067
(Nobelium)	No	102	(256)
Osmium	Os	76	190.2
Oxygen	O	8	15.9994[a]
Palladium	Pd	46	106.4
Phosphorus	P	15	30.9738
Platinum	Pt	78	195.09
Plutonium	Pu	94	(242)
Polonium	Po	84	(210)
Potassium	K	19	39.102
Praseodymium	Pr	59	140.907
Promethium	Pm	61	(145)
Protactinium	Pa	91	(231)
Radium	Ra	88	(226)
Radon	Rn	86	(222)
Rhenium	Re	75	186.2
Rhodium	Rh	45	102.905
Rubidium	Rb	37	85.47
Ruthenium	Ru	44	101.07
Samarium	Sm	62	150.35
Scandium	Sc	21	44.956
Selenium	Se	34	78.96
Silicon	Si	14	28.086[a]
Silver	Ag	47	107.868
Sodium	Na	11	22.9898
Strontium	Sr	38	87.62
Sulfur	S	16	32.064[a]
Tantalum	Ta	73	180.948
Technetium	Tc	43	(99)
Tellurium	Te	52	127.60
Terbium	Tb	65	158.924
Thallium	Tl	81	204.37
Thorium	Th	90	232.038
Thulium	Tm	69	168.934
Tin	Sn	50	118.69
Titanium	Ti	22	47.90
Tungsten	W	74	183.85
Uranium	U	92	238.03
Vanadium	V	23	50.942
Xenon	Xe	54	131.30
Ytterbium	Yb	70	173.04
Yttrium	Y	39	88.905
Zinc	Zn	30	65.37
Zirconium	Zr	40	91.22

[a] These atomic weights are known to be variable because of natural variations in isotopic composition. The observed ranges are: B ± 0.003, C ± 0.00005, H ± 0.00001, O ± 0.0001, Si ± 0.001, S ± 0.03.

CHEMICAL SYSTEMS

Energetics
Dynamics
Structure

A Series of Books in Chemistry
LINUS PAULING, Editor

CHEMICAL

With special chapters by TAD A. BECKMAN
STEPHEN V. FILSETH
KENNETH M. HARMON
MITSURU KUBOTA
PHILIP C. MYHRE
WILLIAM G. SLY
ROY A. WHITEKER
HARVEY MUDD COLLEGE
NEAL W. CORNELL
POMONA COLLEGE

W. H. FREEMAN AND COMPANY
San Francisco

SYSTEMS

Energetics
Dynamics
Structure

J. A. CAMPBELL
HARVEY MUDD COLLEGE
CLAREMONT, CALIFORNIA

CHEMICAL SYSTEMS

Printed in the United States of America
Library of Congress Catalog Card Number: 75-75627
International Standard Book Number: 0-7167-0145-6

To Karin and Dawn
and their generation

Preface

TO THE STUDENT

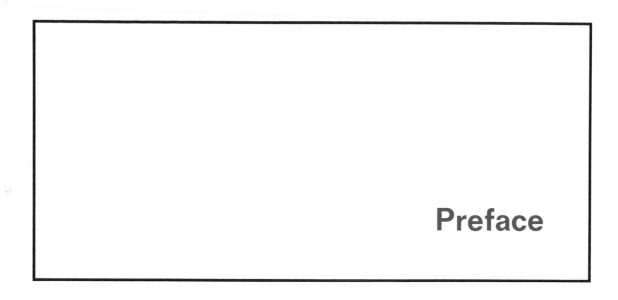

Every human production, whether material or ideological, is based on certain assumptions. This book is no exception. You may find using it easier, and even exciting, if you know what some of its underlying assumptions are.

I assume that you are interested in science and that you wish to explore what chemists do, what they think is important, what points of view they tend to emphasize, and what they feel the limitations and future of chemistry are. The systems with which chemists work are generally more complicated than those of major interest to the physicist, just as those of the physicist are generally more complicated than those of the mathematician. Thus the level of rigor decreases and the emphasis on intuition and qualitative argument increases as a person moves from mathematics to physics to chemistry. The trend continues as he goes into engineering, the life sciences, the social sciences, and the humanities. We shall therefore assume that you not only have adequate mathematical skill to follow the more rigorous treatments but also enough intuition to follow a qualitative discussion when rigor is less possible.

Each concept will be interpreted briefly as it is first introduced. We assume that you have at least had high school courses in chemistry, in physics, and in mathematics through algebra and geometry. (The use of calculus is deferred until Chapter 6.) From chemistry you should have acquired some ability to handle chemical symbols, atomic weights, molar quantities, the periodic table, and chemical formulas; some knowledge of dynamic equilibrium, solubility, acid-base and redox reactions, equilibrium constants, modern descriptive chemistry, the nature of bonding, and the importance of structure. From physics you are assumed to have gained some familiarity with wave and particle theories of light ($E = h\nu$), Coulomb's Law ($F = q_1q_2/r^2$), the existence and properties of electrons, the nuclear atom, kinetic energy ($= mv^2/2$), force, pressure, momentum, and absolute temperature. A prior, or concurrent, course in college physics will make this course in chemistry much more rewarding. And from studying mathematics you should be able to solve simple algebraic equations, to translate problems written in English into algebraic language for a solution and then retranslate the algebra into a conclusion expressed as an English sentence. It is also assumed from Chapter 6 on, that you either have had or are concurrently taking a course in calculus.

Laboratory experimentation done by you with *real* chemical systems is assumed to be essential to the comprehension of chemistry and many appropriate experiments are outlined in the text. Such experiments can profitably precede classroom discussion: when they do, they are truly experiments rather than demonstrations of already known facts and ideas.

Problem solving is just as essential. More than 350 solved exercises are included as guides. Special care has been used to produce an additional 700 problems that call for thought—and sometimes original thought—on your part. Approximate answers are given to many of these for rough checks on your work. Relatively few problems are of the "plug-in" type. Many problems are "cumulative," requiring more information for their successful solutions than may be obtained by merely searching through the chapter in which they appear. Most chapters are followed by three sets of problems. You should be able to solve each problem in the first set in less than 10 minutes, and each problem in the second set in less than 20. Those in the third set sometimes take longer.

There is ordinarily no substitute for completely working out a problem on paper, step by step; if you cannot write out a solution your comprehension is inadequate. Once a solution is obtained, examine it. Is it reasonable? What does it teach? What other problems does it raise? The more competent you become, the more you will use each "solution" as a source of questions that will lead to further knowledge.

It is strongly suggested that you look over the entire table of contents and the appendices before beginning Chapter 1. You will, from such a survey, get a better idea of the science of chemistry and its subject matter than any short discussion could give. You will also obtain an inkling of the plan of attack and the sequence of subjects to be studied.

A similar mode of study is suggested for each chapter. Try skimming each chapter first, reading only the titles of the sections, looking at the figures and tables and their legends, and reading at least the first section of the problems at the end. The framework thus provided will make subsequent reading of the chapter easier and more rewarding. A goal will have been established in your mind, a rough path to it plotted, and you will have formulated a series of questions that will facilitate learning. Your second reading should be deliberate but not slow, and you should concentrate more on the development of ideas than on details. Study of a sample of the problems (especially those in the first set) should follow, with special emphasis on any problem assigned by the instructor. Finally, detailed study of the chapter, with special attention to the points raised by your earlier readings and by the problems, should yield the comprehension and confidence that form part of the goal of a college education. From then on a brief review of problems, figures, tables, and section headings should suffice to reinforce your knowledge and understanding, with only occasional reference to the details of particular sections.

The object is to "explore" a series of workable models for use in solving problems, not to collect equations into which numbers may be inserted. The most important equations have been printed in color—not to facilitate memorization—but only to emphasize their importance. It seems as important that these models be useful for qualitative comprehension and rough prediction of "order of magnitude" effects as that they be capable of embodying the most accurate data available. It also is important that you comprehend the experimental bases of these models, that you see the methods by which theories grow, why one theory is used to extend or even replace another, and that you learn the general techniques that have led to the present "solutions" of many major problems.

We hope you achieve from this study a firmly grounded tentativity. Your knowledge of chemistry should be firmly grounded in that you understand the experimental evidence and can apply the models confidently, tentative in that you understand the limitations of present knowledge, know that it will inevitably change, and recognize that accepted ideas may occasionally be overthrown.

The book is so organized as to interweave continually the experimental and theoretical material. Sections containing the most fundamental information have headings printed in color, the least essential sections are set in smaller type. Ideas are usually introduced in an experimental context, especially in the early chapters. Alternate interpretations of chemical phenomena are presented whenever feasible, especially if current data do not allow a definitive choice between them. The theoretical interpretations are then applied, as soon as possible, to real chemical systems, and to enough systems to enable you to see that each is a generalization that is valid under the specified conditions. Many of these applications, in turn, lead to recognition of further theoretical patterns.

The sequence followed in the text has been set by the desire to emphasize experimental observations, to interpret them as quickly, as thoroughly, and as adequately as possible, and then continually to reapply the principles established in the interpretation to further systems and further experiments. A major idea should be something that is used, not just carried around in the head because it is good to know. Ideas that are not used become isolated and divorced from reality—powerful in potentiality but puny in practice.

By the end of the course you should have become at least semiskilled in the observation, interpretation, and correlation of chemical systems in terms of kinetics, thermodynamics, quantum states, structure, and electrical interactions. May your reaction rates be high, your entropy production low, and your structural integrity increased.

TO THE TEACHER

The keynote of this book is flexibility. Designed for a three-semester college course for students with a good background in high school science who intend to major in science or engineering, the book was written with the intention of combining a thorough introduction to general chemistry with enough physical chemistry to serve as background for all further undergraduate courses in chemistry, physics, engineering, and applied mathematics.

The exposure to chemistry that students now entering college have had is notably varied. Some students come from excellent high school courses, others from ones that gave only a minimal introduction. But the native abilities of the science-oriented students are higher than ever. Part of the flexibility of this volume lies in its interweaving of three books to fit these varied needs. One book, marked by section headings printed in color, teaches basic chemistry and provides an adequate background for mathematicians, engineers, and physicists (as well as for chemistry students who have arrived at college with minimal backgrounds and must concentrate on the fundamentals). The second book, whose section headings are printed in black, contains material that amplifies the first and rounds out the discussions for those with better backgrounds and for those with a serious interest in chemistry and its broader coverage. The third book, set in smaller type, is intended for those who, either consistently or from time to time, wish to dig deeper into the material under discussion and penetrate beyond the level typically found in general chemistry and elementary physical chemistry at the undergraduate level: the additional readings of Appendix IV are also intended for these students.

We have attempted to obtain even greater flexibility by organizing the text into seven parts that address themselves to seven questions:

1. What models are useful in describing molecular behavior?
2. What holds molecules together?
3. To what extent do reactions occur?
4. How do reactions occur?
5. Why do net reactions occur?
6. How does structure affect properties?
7. How are chemical reactions used?

Each part is relatively self-contained, and reordering the sections to some extent and eliminating portions of a section that are of little interest to the instructor and the class are possible. Of course, the book is so written that a body of information is being built that is used as the reader proceeds. It should be clear, for example, that Part 6 is especially dependent on the thermodynamics of Part 5. Furthermore, chapters on descriptive, experimental chemistry have been developed as transitions between sections.

Experimental and descriptive approaches are alternated with interpretive and theoretical discussions. The most commonly used ideas from energetics, dynamics, and structure are introduced in an experimental context, are applied to simple situations, are investigated theoretically, are treated again in terms of other systems, and are reiterated in the text, exercises, and problems of later material. In addition to the quantitative methods of stoichiometry, thermodynamics, kinetics, and structure analysis, continual use is made of such qualitative ideas as acid-base theory, redox theory, and electron structure to underline the dual emphasis in chemistry on rigorous calculation and intuitive generalization. I think it important for students to realize that chemists must be capable of both rigorous and intuitive decision making, and that, for this reason, they must seek to develop not only the skills of the more rigorous physicists but also those of the more intuitive life scientists.

If any one thing may be said to characterize the chemists of today it is probably the general emphasis they place on the interpretation of macroscopic phenomena in terms of behavior at the molecular level—it is this emphasis that we have favored. It is also this emphasis that seems to create the greatest problems for students. Macroscopic phenomena may be readily observable, but direct observations of molecular events are comparatively rare. For this reason much of the emphasis early in the book is on the observation and interpretation of spectroscopic data. In few cases can a more direct tie between observable phenomena and molecular behavior be made than in rotational, vibrational, and electronic spectra of simple substances: the ideas and concepts thus developed are later used in interpreting kinetic, thermodynamic, and structural data.

One of the difficulties with an approach that emphasizes molecular behavior is the tendency to lose sight of reaction chemistry. Reactions are central to chemistry, but their interpretation is not "intuitively obvious": after all, most net reactions are complicated, even though the individual steps are simple. For this reason a large fraction of the 350 exercises in the chapters and the 700 problems at the ends of the chapters emphasize reaction chemistry, for it is in this area that chemistry and chemists can make their greatest contribution to human knowledge and wisdom. Chemists study reactions, and control reactions, and one of their major tools is comprehension at the molecular level.

ACKNOWLEDGMENTS

Many of the coauthors have contributed appreciably to material throughout the book, but especially to the chapters headed by their names. To each of them goes credit for the major content, organization, imagination, and clarity of these chapters and to me goes the blame if alterations, additions, and deletions have clouded their presentation.

Few authors have had the benefit of as much student comment as received by me between 1964 and 1969. To the hundreds of students at Tulane, at Montana State, and at Harvey Mudd and to their venturesome professors Hans Jonassen, Reed Howald, and the Harvey Mudd chemists, go thanks for hundreds of improvements. The editorial suggestions of John Quinlan of Pomona College, William Eberhardt of Georgia Institute of Technology, and Linus Pauling were of great value. And finally, the superb typing and cross-checking of Betty Lumpkin were major factors in the completion of the book. May you be as incisive and direct in sending me criticisms as they have been.

Claremont, California
December, 1969

J. A. Campbell

Contents

CHEMICAL SYSTEMS

Energetics
Dynamics
Structure

Prologue

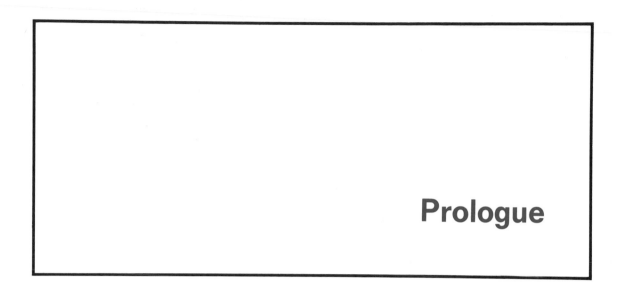

No man is free to choose
unless he knows the choices.

Chemistry is an experimental science, and, like all experimental sciences, consists of methods of phrasing questions and seeking answers to them by study of natural systems. A large number of chemical problems are practical, or applied, and relate to immediate, often pressing, human problems. Many others are "pure" and relate to no known practical problem. The largest number of chemical problems, however, combine pure and applied aspects, and require both immediate remedial measures and long-term solutions.

Pressing problems cannot wait for ultimate solutions. They require palliative measures chosen from those immediately available. A conviction is growing, however, that long-term solutions may most often be found through analysis of complex situations into simpler components. In most cases the simpler components of apparently unrelated problems bear remarkable similarity to one another; they may even follow the same "scientific laws." We shall, therefore, look first at some of mankind's pressing problems on which scientists are shedding some direct light. We shall then spend the major part of our discussion on much simpler systems, systems that may be at least partially comprehended in terms of molecular behavior—the terms that characterize the work of many present-day chemists.

TIME SCALES

All of man's problems and their solutions, whether pertaining to the individual or the human race, involve time, and intelligent solutions require an understand-

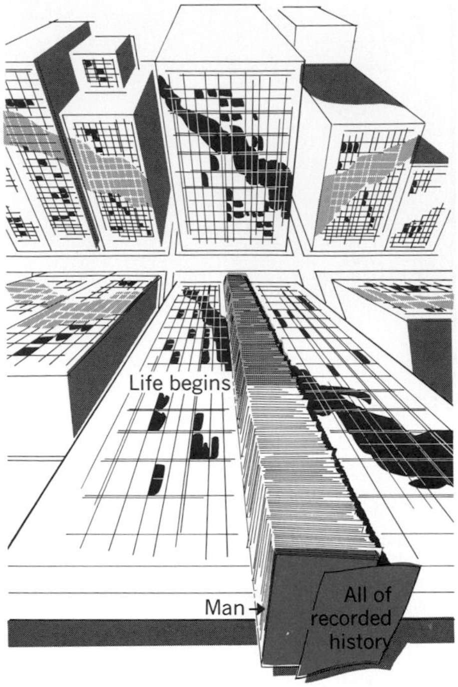

Figure 1 Geologic time.

ing of time scales. Many of man's current problems result from a lack of appreciation of the time scale and his resultant reliance on short-term solutions. We now have, thanks to the geological record, astronomical observations, and long-range dating methods based largely on nuclear transmutations, a very good idea both of the "length of the past" and the "extent of the future." Some of these dating methods are discussed in Chapters 2, 5, and 22.

It is now believed that the universe has been in roughly its present condition for something less than ten billion years (10^{10} years),* that life has existed on earth for a few billion years, and manlike beings for a few hundred thousand years. Written history is less than ten thousand years old and experimental science is a few hundred years old.

Figure 1 puts these figures in more comprehensible terms. If the total history of the earth, in roughly its present form, were written on a pile of paper a thousand feet high, there would be no record of life in the bottom half of the pile. The first hint of man would come about one foot from the top, with man appearing in the last inch. All of written history would be found on the top sheet and the contributions of experimental science would be represented by the dust on top of the total pile. Man, his problems, and his search for solutions have had a short life compared to that of the earth itself.

Just as important, the evidence is strong that there will be a time span of at least another ten billion years during which the earth and the solar system will remain essentially unchanged. Man can not only learn a great deal by studying the past; he can plan with considerable confidence on a long future—unless he himself shortens it.

* Throughout this book the exponential system will be used to express large and small numbers. See Appendix I.

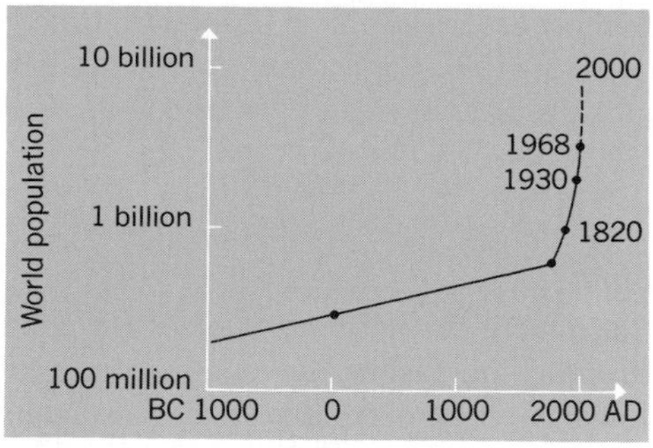

Figure 2 The growth of world population from 1000 BC to 2000 AD.

THREATS TO EXISTENCE

Each generation feels threatened. Current threats include nuclear war, mass starvation, gross pollution of water and air, depersonalization of universities and governments, rising costs of living (even more rapidly rising taxes), the disappearance of natural resources. Each threat is severe, and the sum is such that many people feel this to be the most threatened generation in human history.

But let me at this point use a standard scientific method, that of suggesting a thesis: if we are more threatened than men have been at any other time in history, we are also better equipped to understand and meet the threats. We are freer than ever before because of the many choices available to us; choices that were unknown only a few years ago.

Let us explore some threats and some choices. The exploration may provide insight into the relationships between pure and applied science, including chemistry.

POPULATION

Figure 2 is one of the most dramatic graphs available for consideration. For most of written history the rate of human population growth was about 0.04% per year and the time required for doubling the total human population about 2000 years. The present worldwide average rate is 50 times as great (about 2 percent per year), giving a doubling time of about 35 years (See Table 1). The growth rate in the United States (1.4 percent) is not far below the average.

It is increasingly clear that the world's population cannot continue to increase much longer. Had there been only a dozen people alive at the time of Christ, and had the population increased at the present rate for the past 2000 years, there would now be about 10^{17} people on earth—a population density of one hundred people per square foot over both land and water.

Table 1 Doubling time of a population is inversely proportional to percent rate of growth.

Rate of growth (percent)	0.1	0.5	1	2	3	4
Doubling time (years)	700	140	70	35	24	18

Population control is probably the most crucial problem of modern times. Many other problems are directly related to rapid population growth and if growth increases much longer it seems unlikely that they can ever be solved.

THREE CHOICES

We have realized for a long time that there were three broad choices for controlling population: decreasing the birth rate, increasing the death rate, and "shipping people out." For all three we now have controls that were not available as recently as ten years ago. Even more effective measures will soon be feasible.

Birth control methods are now approaching a reliability of 100 percent (though that figure will almost certainly never be reached because of chemical variations from one individual to another). Cheaper and more effective methods will soon be possible. For example, there will almost certainly be a subcutaneous capsule that will reduce the chances of conception to less than 1 percent over a period of as long as twenty years; such a capsule could be removed at any time a child was desired.

In many primitive societies "death control" has long been used to maintain the necessary balance between population size and available resources: nomadic tribes leave behind those unable to keep up with the rest; other, more static societies kill unwanted children at birth. Few people today advocate a planned increase in death rates, though war is sometimes excused as being a population control device. Instead, as our knowledge of human physiology grows, "death control" means postponing death, and accelerates population growth by increasing life spans. Research now underway is expected to extend life expectancies to a hundred years or more—a pleasing prospect for some individuals but a potentially disastrous one for the human race.

Whereas to "ship people out" once meant to send them to Australia or New Caledonia, both of which got the ancestors of much of their present human populations from assigned emigration, present technological capacity makes it possible to think of sending people to the moon and the planets. The minimum energy required to get a man to the moon is one million (10^6) kcal (present cost $20 in terms of cheap electric power). This would be for a man with no support, no food, no protection. Any reasonable estimate would increase this amount by a factor of at least 10^3, to give 10^9 kcal per person, or about thirty man-years of energy at current rates. (World energy consumption now runs about $3 \cdot 10^7$ kcal per person per year.) There surely must be some simpler and cheaper method of population control.

Customarily these are said to be the only three choices available. We shall find there is a fourth alternative—one that has been commonly used by past generations—but shall defer discussing it for the present, and turn now to some limits that are placed on human population by those things that are necessary for human life, such as air, water, food, weather, and health, rather than the raw materials such as copper, iron, and salt, that we need to maintain our present standards. We shall, in what follows, assume that each individual will require the same amounts of necessities that the average American uses today.

AIR

Man perishes quickly from lack of air, so it is pertinent to ask how many humans the earth's air supply can support. Air exerts a pressure of about 15 pounds per square inch; the total area of the earth is 200 million square miles. Thus the atmosphere contains about 10^{15} tons of oxygen and $5 \cdot 10^{15}$ tons of nitrogen.

At present each person in the United States uses some 200 million kilocalories (kcal) of energy per year (mostly from fossil fuels); this means an expenditure of about 10^2 tons of oxygen per person per year. The present rate of cycling of oxygen through the atmosphere is estimated to be once per 3000 years, making 10^{12} tons available per year—in the assumed steady state, enough for 10^{10} people, only three times the present world population.

Nitrogen is an essential element in food, and is present mainly in the form of protein. The per person consumption of protein nitrogen per year in the United States is about 25 pounds (10^{-2} tons). The cycling time for nitrogen is estimated at 10^8 years, giving $2 \cdot 10^8$ tons per year, or enough for about 10^{10} people.

These figures, like most of the simple calculations we shall make in this prologue, are approximate and involve both optimistic and pessimistic numerical assumptions. The attempt here is to give as realistic a maximum population estimate as possible within the simplifications. For example, the United States already finds it necessary to synthesize nitrogen compounds at the rate of 50 pounds of nitrogen per person per year in order to supply the fertilizer required for current crop yields (see Chapters 12 and 36). The corresponding figures for the rest of the world are 10 pounds of synthetic and 30 pounds of natural compounds, a total of 40. We optimistically estimated 25 pounds of protein nitrogen above. Clearly atmospheric nitrogen is already inadequate in the face of population pressures. The shortage can be relieved only if synthetic chemical methods are used to shorten the nitrogen cycle.

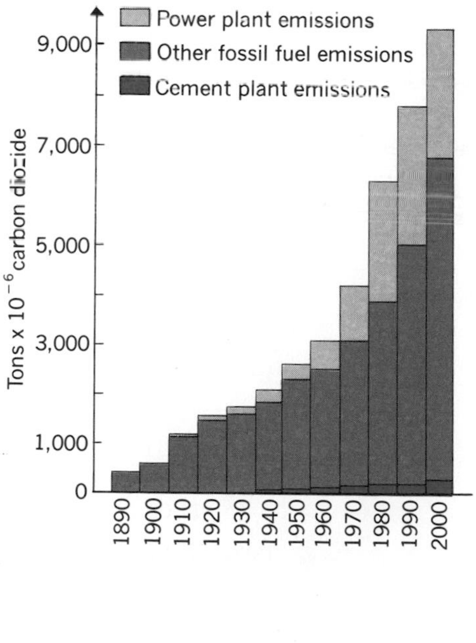

Figure 3 Carbon dioxide injection into the atmosphere from industrial operations. [F. A. Rohrman et al., *Science*, 156 (1967), 931. © 1967 by the American Association for the Advancement of Science.]

The atmosphere is not only a source of oxygen and nitrogen; it is also a sink into which we pump many substances. Smog is one result, carbon dioxide build-up another. Smog effects are so well known that we shall not discuss them here, but Problem 6.28 and the discussion in Chapter 22 are directed to their consideration.

Carbon dioxide build-up is illustrated in Figure 3. It is interesting to note that the famous chemist Svante Arrhenius predicted in 1903 that combustion of fossil fuels might lead to an abnormal rise in atmospheric CO_2. The average temperature of the earth's surface appears already to have risen 0.2°C and that of the stratosphere 2°C as a result of carbon dioxide build-up and the fact that CO_2 is transparent to most solar radiation but not to heat radiated out from the earth (see Chapters 8 and 31). It is estimated that further heating may cause ocean levels to rise several hundred feet as the polar icecaps melt.

But we have new choices. Nitrogen compounds are widely synthesized and may soon become cheaper, as mentioned in Chapter 37. Nuclear fuels, which neither consume oxygen nor release carbon dioxide, are rapidly becoming available, and the direct conversion of sunlight to storable energy is a bright, long-term prospect.

WATER

The total annual rainfall on earth is about $2 \cdot 10^{19}$ liters. Much falls into the ocean, and much runs off in places inaccessible to man. About $3 \cdot 10^{17}$ liters are actually available per year. At the current average rate of use in the United States of 10^7 liters per person per year, this amount of rain would support a worldwide population of $3 \cdot 10^{10}$. Modern technology of water reuse multiplies the supply by a factor of 5 or 6, and large-scale desalination of seawater can soon multiply it by another factor of 10. The cost of desalination is coming down rapidly, as is seen in Figure 4, and is approaching the thermodynamic limit discovered by "pure science" years ago (see Chapter 35).

Available water is unequally distributed over the earth's surface, making it likely that there will continue to be severe local water shortages, but there is little threat of a worldwide shortage.

Lakes, streams, and oceans are not merely sources of water. They are, like the atmosphere, sinks into which we pour great quantities of waste. When the waste input (usually chemical reducing agents) exceeds the amount of oxygen in

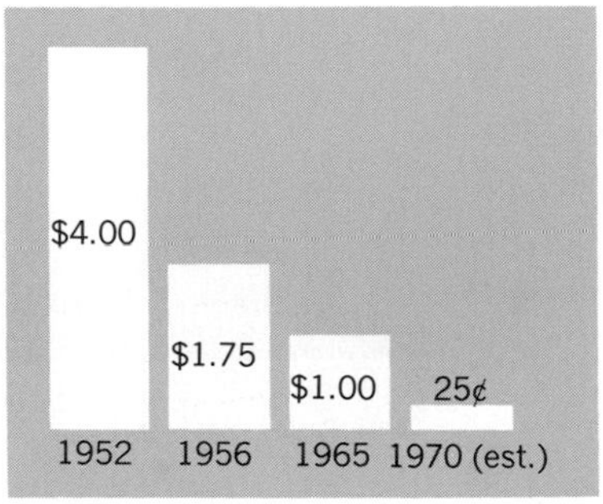

Figure 4 Decreasing cost of desalinating water.

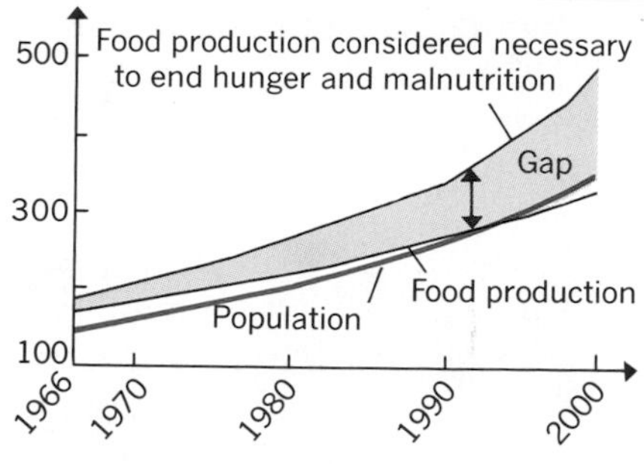

Figure 5 Population and food projections. Population and food production as of 1940 = 100.

the water, much of the aquatic life is destroyed, swimming is unhealthy, and chlorination and similar treatment must be increased just to make the water barely palatable for human consumption. This in spite of the fact that our present knowledge of water supplies seems great enough, if used, to make any gross water contamination nonsensical. Lake Erie is an outstanding example of a large body of water badly contaminated by human waste.

FOOD

A well-fed person consumes about 3000 kcal (Calories to the dietician) per day. The minimum human requirement appears to be about 1000 kcal per square meter of body area (the approximate size of the average person). Figure 5 presents data on recent projections of food production and population change. It is apparent that, if present trends are not altered, the entire population of the earth (on the average) will be underfed by the end of this century: half is underfed today.

Food production is more efficient in some parts of the world than in others, and could be increased almost everywhere. Figure 6 illustrates agricultural performance in the United States in recent years. The amount of cropland has remained about constant (though only about half of the area that could be cultivated is used), but food production has doubled. Note, however, that this has re-

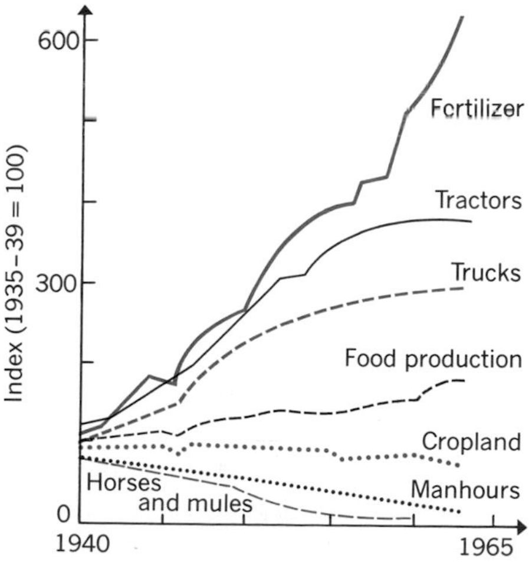

Figure 6 Growth of agricultural technology in the United States. [*International Science and Technology*, March 1967, p. 77.]

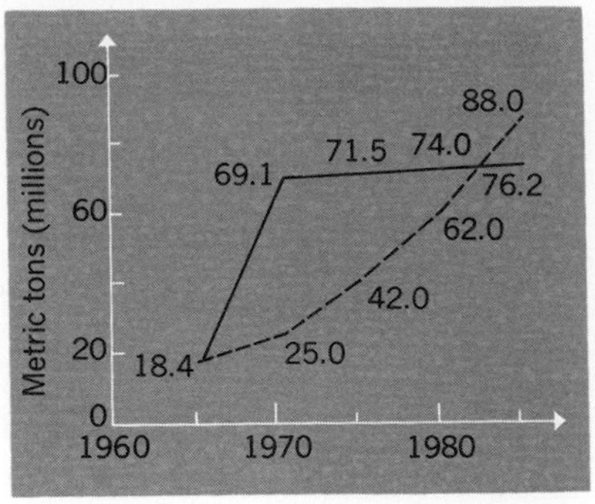

Figure 7 United States food production and world needs. *Solid line:* Grain that the United States could produce beyond domestic use and commercial export needs. *Dashed line:* Food aid needs of 66 developing countries. [U. S. Dept. of Agric.]

quired a threefold increase in the use of trucks, fourfold in tractors, and sixfold in chemical fertilizer. Only the contributions of humans and of horses and mules have decreased. Not shown is the very large increase in the use of chemical herbicides and pesticides (some are mentioned in Chapter 21), many of whose long-term effects are of considerable current concern.

Yet agriculture in the United States is now at the place where it would be impossible to feed even the nation's own population if it were denied chemical controls of pests and chemical fertilizers. Such chemical assistance, much of which is based on a rather detailed knowledge of molecular behavior in living systems, will certainly increase as it becomes safer for the human consumers. Our available choices will continue to increase as our knowledge of biological systems and their chemistry becomes more detailed. But even if this country's production increases in accord with the optimistic estimates indicated in Figure 7 it will shortly become impossible to continue to provide food to the rest of the world. Figure 7 assumes a rapid expansion of agriculture in the United States, a most unlikely event. This would give a surplus until about 1985, but the surplus would be used up within the next ten years or so.

The solutions must clearly involve, in addition to population control, major agricultural reform in most of the countries of the world, and a higher and higher dependence on chemical assistance. But note again: solutions are available, choices can be made. For example, available methods of food preservation and enrichment could lead to great net gains in the effective food supply, as Problem 1.25 suggests.

WEATHER

The range and efficiency of life are strongly influenced by the weather, especially by the temperature and the humidity. (See Problems 26.11, 26.12, 26.14, 26.16, and 26.17) Man's ability to construct shelter and to use fire has given him a great advantage over other forms of life by extending his habitable range and increasing his biological efficiency. Air conditioning is an extension of these efforts, as is present research in long-range weather forecasting and, indeed, control. For example, it is already possible to influence rainfall chemically under favorable circumstances (the best available method seems to be the generation of colloidal silver iodide to nucleate rain formation; see Chapter 32). Even the feasibility of air conditioning whole cities is seriously discussed.

Figure 8 illustrates another way in which man is already changing the weather (unintentionally and undesirably, in this instance). The data are for Washington, D.C. but similar effects are produced in any highly populated area by the large quantity of heat released by human activity. Atmospheric and water pollution also affect weather. But the reports and analyses, necessary for control are improving as the new weather satellites allow us quickly to measure the formation and spread of largescale weather patterns.

One interesting natural adaptation that has enabled man to overcome a weather problem is illustrated by the correlation between skin color, vitamin D synthesis, and population distribution. Vitamin D is synthesized in humans by subcutaneous cells, which obtain the required energy from sunlight. Too little vitamin D leads to death from rickets, too much to death by vitamin D poisoning. Dark-skinned persons may obtain too little vitamin D from sunlight in northern latitudes, and light-skinned persons exposed to tropical sunlight may synthesize too much of the vitamin—hence the historical distribution of man by color. Eskimos get vitamin D from their fish diet and thus survive with very little sunlight in spite of their skin pigmentation. Enough modern foods are enriched by the addition of vitamin D to make availability of sunlight no longer a dominant factor in relating population distribution and skin color.

HEALTH

The longevity and death rate of a species are determined by many factors. Apparently most of them are chemical and have to do with the rates of critical chemical reactions, which show up in what we call aging, sickness, and health. We shall discuss rates of reaction in simple systems in Chapters 22 and 23 and some rates in biological systems in Chapter 40.

For most of man's existence the principal sources of sickness, especially among children, have been viral and bacterial infections. Figure 9 illustrates recent progress in handling four virus diseases chemically. Similarly dramatic curves are available for many bacterial infections, and it seems safe to predict a contin-

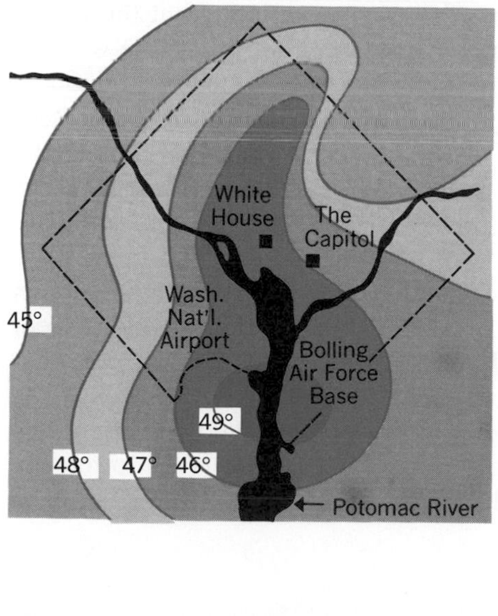

Figure 8 Human activity and temperature in Washington, D. C. (It is not the politicians that generate most of the hot air.)

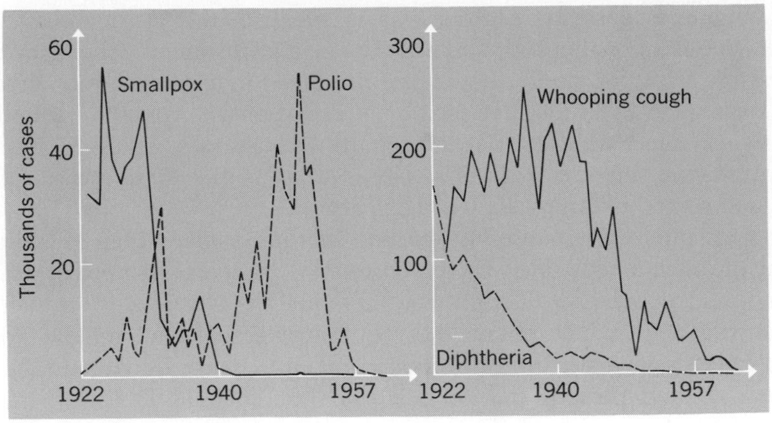

Figure 9 Decline of four viral diseases. No cases of smallpox have been reported since 1957. [New York Times, Nov. 20, 1966. © 1966 by the New York Times Company. Reprinted by permission.]

uing decrease in deaths due to infection. Great progress is also being made in treating functional diseases of the heart and other vital organs, and serious investigation is underway into controlling the aging process itself. We shall almost certainly have an increasing ability to control the rate of death and the average age at which death takes place.

The effect of death control measures on the genetic pool is the subject of much current research. It is possible, for example, that each blue-baby operation, which prolongs a life by heart surgery, increases the chance that there will be more babies born with defective hearts, necessitating more and more such operations as time passes. The age distribution of the population is also influenced by death control. As available controls continue to grow in number, it will become ever more important to consider the long-term results of the choices made.

SPACE

The total area of the world is about 200 million square miles; about 60 million square miles is dry land. The present average population density of the world is the same as that of the United States: 50 persons per square mile of land. Some of the most densely populated countries are the Netherlands, about 1000 persons per square mile; Japan, 700; India, 400. Australia and Canada are among the countries having the lowest density, with about 5 persons per square mile. If we assume that the whole world could be as populous as the Netherlands, we get a total population of 60 billion, a level that will be achieved about the year 2100 (when your grandchildren will still be alive) unless present growth rates decrease. Figure 10 presents a correlation between present population density and present adequacy of food supply. Coupled with Figure 10, Figure 11 correlates hunger and growth rate.

It is, of course, to be remembered that cities may have population densities of over 100,000 per square mile (like Harlem), but it is also well to remember that deserts and other "uninhabitable" lands cover perhaps one-quarter of the earth's surface.

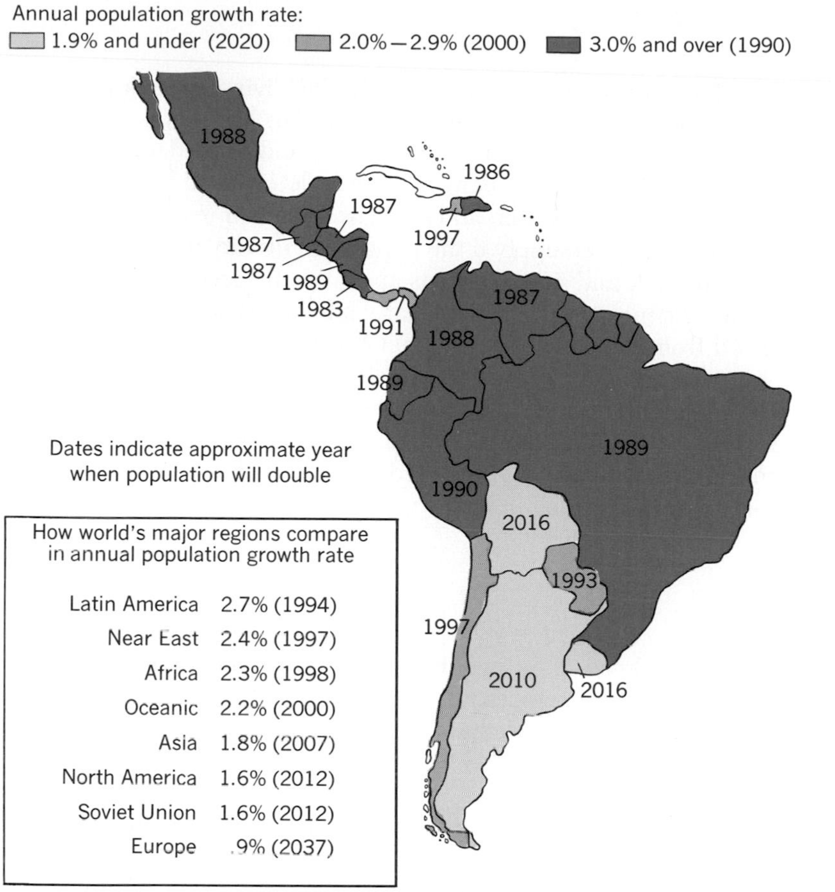

Figure 10 Population growth, in Latin America, where the rate of growth is the highest in the world. [New York Times, Sept. 17, 1967. © 1967 by the New York Times Company. Reprinted by permission.]

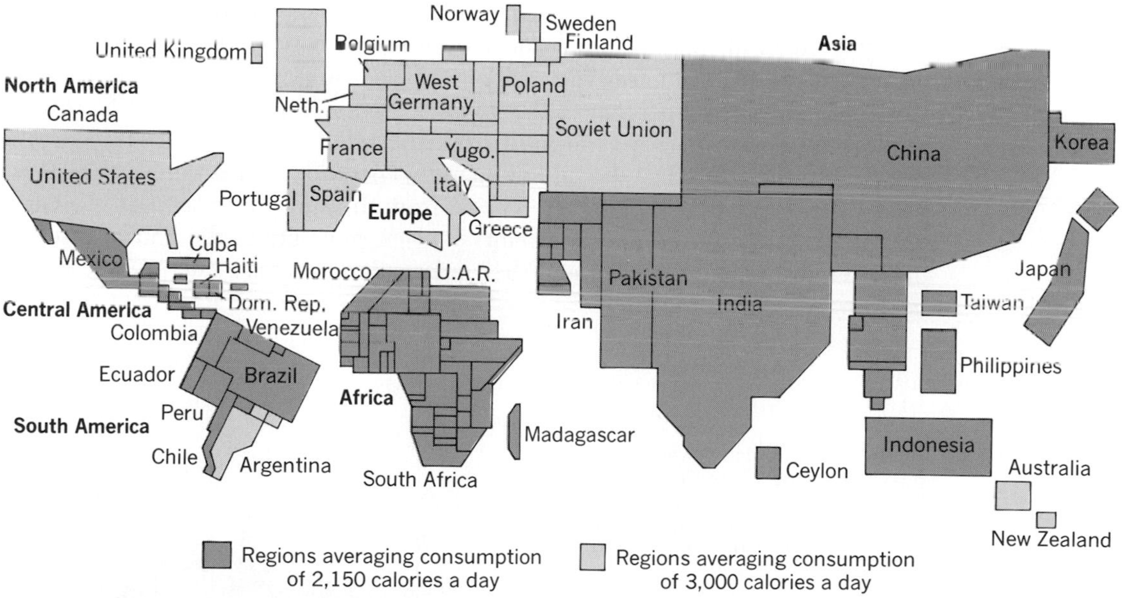

Figure 11 Nutritional status of the world. In this stylized map the size of land areas is proportional to their population. Note that, since less than 2500 calories a day is considered inadequate, more than half the world's population is malnourished. [New York Times, Jan. 1, 1967. © 1967 by the New York Times Company. Reprinted by permission.]

Evidence has been accumulating recently that living species require a certain average minimum area for health and growth. This has been known to be true of plants for a long time (especially desert plants), and of predatory animals. It now appears that the minimum for many animals is determined by needs other than such raw materials as food, water, and sunlight. Rats will resort to cannibalism even with an adequate food supply if the population density in a cage exceeds a rather well-defined limit, and similar effects appear to be present in other species. There is some evidence that man is similarly affected; it seems that there is a variation in need from one culture to another but that the minimum requirement for space is real and may already be operative in some crowded places. Clearly, we shall soon know more about these variables, and again our range of possible choices will grow. The effect of crowding can almost certainly be minimized by chemical means—say by pills called "space pacifiers." But nevertheless, the available space will remain limited.

ENERGY

Each of the problems outlined so far may be solved in a variety of already established ways and our number of choices in most areas is still increasing with time, though this will hardly continue indefinitely. But most of the solutions share a common feature. They all require energy. We shall discuss energy and energy flow extensively in Chapters 26 to 29.

Most, if not all, of the useful energy supply on earth comes from the sun. Some comes in the form of direct sunlight (at the rate of about 10^{21} kcal per year of which about 50 percent is immediately reflected back to space, 50 percent is absorbed as heat then quickly radiated to space, and some 0.1 percent, or 10^{18} kcal year^{-1}, is converted into earth-bound energy, as in wood. Some energy comes from fossil fuels (of which our consumption rate is now about 10^{17} kcal year^{-1}); some from nuclear fuels and hydroelectric power, although currently these add only a few percent to the supply. Figure 12 projects these figures for the United States. Perhaps the most dramatic interpretation of these figures is that before the year 2100 the rate of energy generation by man on earth will exceed the present rate of energy retention from the sun. From then on the earth will be operating on an energy deficit. Table 2 summarizes the known reserves of the largest energy sources, and their exhaustion periods if the present rate of use continues.

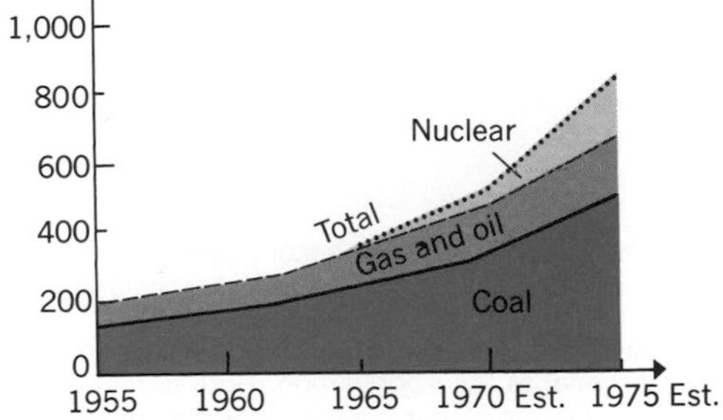

Figure 12 Projected power sources in the United States: in millions of tons of coal, or equivalent. [New York Times, Aug. 28, 1966. © 1966 by the New York Times Company. Reprinted by permission.]

Table 2 **Known reserves of the largest energy sources and their exhaustion periods at present use rate.**

Fuel	Reserve (kcal)	Annual use (kcal)	Years until exhaustion at present use rates	
Oil	10^{18}	$3 \cdot 10^{16}$	30	
Oil shale	10^{19}	—	300	
Coal and gas	$3 \cdot 10^{19}$	10^{17}	300	
Nuclear fission	10^{21}	—	1000	If each were sole source of energy.
Nuclear fusion	10^{26}	—	10^{8}	
Solar energy	10^{20} yr^{-1}	—	10^{10}	

Table 3 **Relation between population and projected demand for water and electric power.**

	1964	1980	2000
People (millions)	49	70	108
Water (10^9 gal day^{-1})	218	254	365
Electric power (10^6 kw)	53	150	440

The interpretation of Table 2 is complicated by the factor illustrated in Table 3 for the western United States, where a technologically based population is growing rapidly. As population increases, some demands (for water, for example) increase in a roughly linear fashion. But other demands, especially for energy, increase much more rapidly. We shall use present population and demand figures but the nonlinear relationship must be constantly remembered.

The present energy consumption in this country is about $2 \cdot 10^8$ kcal per person per year. At this rate the fossil fuels listed in Table 2 would last about 10^{11} person years, or about thirty years for the present world population. Additional fossil fuels will be discovered, but it is doubtful whether the supply will be doubled and extremely unlikely that it will ever increase tenfold. As a matter of fact, the discovery rate has decreased in recent years. It is clear that fossil fuels cannot supply the long-term energy needs and are going to decline rapidly in the near future as a prime source of energy. Many chemists would argue, even now, that oil, gas, and coal are of more potential value as chemicals for synthetic purposes than they are as energy sources. Yet their projected consumption as fuel continues to increase, as shown in Figure 13.

The long-term energy picture for the world is rather favorable, however. Nuclear fission is now controllable and is already contributing appreciably to the available energy (see Figure 12). Fission products are difficult to handle, but so is the carbon dioxide from fossil fuels. Nuclear fusion is beginning to look feasible (as in Problem 26.13) and may produce only helium, which seems a most innocuous potential contaminant. The direct conversion of sunlight to electricity is also a promising source of energy that may produce no chemical contaminants at all. A principal problem now is to find a cheap material for covering large areas—for example, sheet plastic, as discussed in Chapter 39. The energy received on a single desert in Chile, 180 by 100 miles in area, could supply the total energy

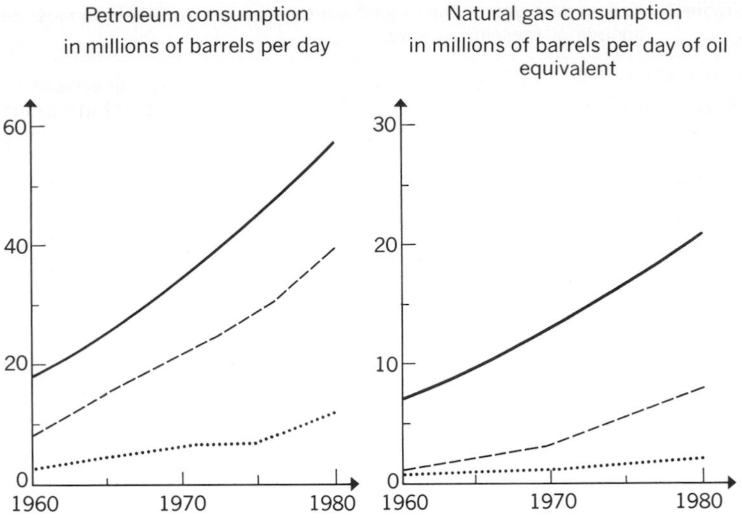

Figure 13 Projected fossil fuel use. *Solid line:* United States. *Dashed line:* Other developed nations (Canada, Europe, Japan, Australia). *Dotted line:* Developing nations.

needs of the present world population—10^{17} kcal year^{-1}—if it were all captured and converted to useful forms instead of reradiating to the sky. Similarly, an average house and lot in the United States receives enough sunlight to supply all the needs of a family if the energy could be captured and used efficiently.

Our knowledge of energy sources is reaching the point at which it should soon be possible to have much more energy available and to harness it much more cheaply. Since energy is required to solve most of man's problems, its increasing availability is most encouraging.

HEAT

One result of scientific research that is of considerable import to any discussion of human affairs and energy production is the observation that energy turns into heat as it is used. Thus energy flows from concentrated sources like the sun to relatively cool places like the earth, with most of the energy on earth turning into heat and warming the earth (as summarized in the second law of thermodynamics). We have already discussed the heating that has resulted from the increasing carbon dioxide content of the atmosphere as well as that due to the large energy outputs in our cities.

The steady-state heat supply on earth has, for the past few thousand years at least, been made up of about $2 \cdot 10^{17}$ kcal year^{-1} from radioactive and other thermal processes inside the earth, and about $5 \cdot 10^{20}$ kcal year^{-1} of solar energy. The sum of these has just balanced the radiative heat losses to space, and the earth's average temperature has been about constant. Now man is adding about 10^{17} kcal year^{-1} to the total.

Man's present energy output of 10^{17} kcal per year is sufficient to warm all the water in all the oceans about 10^{-4}°C per year. This is not a negligible amount of heating, and, of course, the heat is not uniformly distributed through the ocean waters. As production and use of energy from fossil and nuclear fuels increases, the rate of heating will also increase. The present rate of increase of temperature in the earth's atmosphere probably runs about 0.01°C per year, but projected carbon dioxide injections and fuel consumption, as outlined in Figures 3 and 12, may shortly raise this to 0.1°C per year, or 10°C per 100 years. It is extremely doubtful that the earth could support a large human population if such a rise continued for long.

It is true that there are methods for increasing the rate of heat loss from the earth's surface, but none presently known can increase the rate of loss as fast as man is increasing the rate of production of heat.

Thus, in all likelihood, heat production will be a primary limiting factor on human activity and population. It also seems likely that the present rate of heat generation is near the maximum tolerable rate: it may even be too high for a tolerable steady-state situation. However, if the rate of heat generation is slowed, changes due to the rising temperature will also be slowed. The heat will have a chance to diffuse through the oceans, markedly lowering the rate at which atmospheric temperature rises, and the temperatures of ocean, land, and air may change so slowly that living organisms will be able to adapt to the change and to the new, slightly higher average temperatures. In fact, there is considerable geological evidence that the temperature of the oceans has fluctuated several degrees in the past. It will probably slowly do so again in the future, and the changes need not even be uncomfortable for mankind. But if the fluctuations become a monotonic trend fed by larger and larger human energy production, the ecological results will almost certainly be catastrophic.

Already we have a great deal of ecologic evidence, from heating of streams by nuclear power plants, from geological records of past temperature cycles, and from laboratory experiments, on the effects of temperature changes of a few degrees or less. The situation is already serious enough to have been the subject of hearings before a United States Congressional committee discussing the location of large power plants. It is almost certainly time to consider the whole question of rate of heat production.

The dissipation of heat is one area in which we seem to have few choices, their number being limited by the laws of thermodynamics, as you will see in this course. Nor does it seem likely that the number of choices will increase in the future unless we are badly mistaken about the nature of heat and heat transfer. Of all the threats to the existence of human society, of humankind itself, the most serious—except for the unceasing growth of population—is probably that from the steady increase in the temperature of man's environment. Yet a leveling off or decrease in energy use would have the immediate effect of exacerbating the present tensions in society.

At the moment, the best solution to the heat problem seems to be more intensive use of sunlight. Even now, about 50 percent of sunlight is converted to heat without doing useful work and is then radiated into space. If this unused energy were converted to work, it would probably increase the amount of useful energy by a factor of from 2 to 10 without adding appreciably to the heat that is not radiated into space. And this, of course, would make unnecessary the production of energy in ways that increase the earth's increment of heat. Why should we not spend as much effort on the direct conversion of sunlight as we now spend on developing nuclear fusion? The actual current effort is minimal,

Table 4 Estimates of population that could be supported at present U.S. levels by existing resources. Present world population $3 \cdot 10^9$: will reach 10^{10} about 2030.

Resource	Population	Resource	Population
Air	10^{10}	Space	10^{11}
Water	10^{12}	Energy	10^{11}
Food	10^{11}	Heat	10^{10}

but even so is producing results which promise real choices for minimizing the heat problem at the present population level.

THE STEADY STATE

Table 4 summarizes our discussion so far by giving likely steady-state populations in terms of each variable resource that limits the population. Consideration of all the data indicates that the steady-state population can hardly exceed ten billion, and may be even lower. World population will probably reach this level not later than 2050, when some of you will still be alive.

FOURTH CHOICE

Past experience shows that problems will not be solved—perhaps not even recognized—unless a sequence of steps similar to the following is followed: (1) the current situation is discussed, (2) possible problems are identified, (3) possible solutions are outlined, (4) the effects of each of the possible solutions are predicted, and (5) the most promising solution is selected for trial. Human freedom rests in large measure on the ability to carry out this process, for it is certainly true that no man is free to choose unless he knows the choices. This is one of the main goals of education—to free man by making him aware of the available choices, the methods of increasing the number of those choices, and the methods of evaluating the results of the choice he has made.

Since the severity of each problem we have outlined increases in proportion to increase in population, we may well look once again at the possible solutions to population growth. We have mentioned three: decrease the birth rate, increase the death rate, and "ship people out." But our search for solutions would be incomplete if we did not recognize that there is a fourth solution—one that has commonly been used by man when past situations have become threatening. It is to stop thinking of certain individuals—usually ethnic or social groups of individuals—as human beings, and to stop treating them as such.

When individuals are no longer treated as people it is not necessary to consider them in arriving at decisions on survival any more than one would domestic animals or plants, or even wild animals and plants. The birth rate and death rate among them is considered to be of no consequence to anyone except themselves.

There is ample evidence that this fourth solution has been accepted many times in history: the helots of Sparta, the Christians of ancient Rome, the Indians of the Americas, the serfs of czarist Russia, the Jews and gypsies of Nazi

Germany—these are but a few examples of groups that have been considered "lesser breeds without the law." Even today, in many "advanced" countries the birth records of cows and horses are more carefully kept than the birth records of minority groups, and the amount of money spent on pet food comes close to that spent on the prevention of human starvation. In any case, this chauvanistic or *laissez faire* solution has at least as great historical precedent as any of the other three. Would you advocate it now?

THE ROLE OF CHEMISTRY

You may well be asking what this prologue has to do with chemistry. The answer is that chemistry is one way of viewing man, his environment, and his problems. Chemists discover solutions to certain of these problems and throw light on the probable effect of applying the various solutions. But, if these solutions proposed by chemists—or by those engaged in any form of scientific research—are to be properly evaluated, they must be viewed in the context of all other suggested solutions. Otherwise they may be accepted or rejected on inadequate grounds.

We shall, in this book, spend the great majority of our time exploring rather simple chemical systems. Most of them will seem remote from the problems discussed in this prologue, even unrelated to them. Yet almost every solution we have mentioned here—and they are many and increasing in number—stems from exploration of systems in terms of their simpler components. The role of scientists in illuminating human problems and their possible solutions is bound to increase. There is no difference between the systems studied in the laboratory and the systems found in the "real" world. Relationships are found in the most unlikely circumstances, and discoveries based on "pure" science have remarkable practical applications. Any study of science in general, and of chemistry in particular, should be viewed as part of a total study of man and his environment. Without such perspective, much if not most of the value that can accrue from the efforts of scientists will be lost.

CHEMISTRY AND LEARNING

Now consider a very personal chemical problem. It may surprise you to know that the suggestions to the student concerning effective study methods (see the Preface) are themselves based on understanding certain chemical processes. Almost overwhelming evidence now exists that learning and retention of information occur when electric signals, generated by chemical processes in the five types of sense receptors (sight, hearing, taste, smell, and touch—including heat sensors), are transmitted to the brain by the chemical systems we call nerve cells, and are there converted into protein structures that constitute our memory storage units.

Recall and thought then bring into play an electrical search mechanism that, when it functions efficiently, finds the appropriate combination of the 10^{10} nerve cells of the brain (each connected to about a thousand other nerve cells), collects electric signals from their protein, and transmits these signals to the hand, mouth, or other signal generators with which we communicate to the world outside ourselves. The acceptance of information, the storage of information, and the recall, use, and combination of information all involve chemical systems and changes in them. The available evidence indicates that these chemical systems and their changes involve the same phenomena and laws as those that apply to nonliving systems. Thus your ability to learn chemistry is strongly influenced by your own body chemistry; it is to you as a unique chemical system that suggestions concerning study are directed.

The chemistry of learning is not yet clearly understood but it is well established that learning can be of at least two kinds—short-term and long-term. Looking up a telephone number and using it immediately is an example of short-term learning. Memories of childhood are examples of long-term learning. Education is a process of instilling long-term learning that can be recalled selectively and used intelligently.

Much is already known about both short-term and long-term learning, but it is sufficient here to point out that long-term learning, and hence education, is most effective if the following conditions are met.

1. The learner is alert when exposed to new ideas (receptors active).
2. The learner is supplied with clear, storable ideas (signals).
3. The learner is interested and sees some usefulness in the new ideas (internal reward).
4. The learner is rewarded quickly for learning the new ideas (external reward).
5. The learner's retention is reinforced by repeated exposure to the new ideas, preferably from slightly different points of view (establishing the brain circuits).
6. The learner is allowed immediate opportunities to clarify the signal and check his responses to it (feedback).

The suggestions to students are based on maximizing the effectiveness of these conditions and the resulting chemical changes within you that lead to learning, memory, recall, and education.

There is, however, remarkable chemical variation from individual to individual, and you should therefore experiment with various learning techniques to see how best to accomplish your own education. But it is doubtful, indeed, that you will find ways that do not involve the above conditions, and it will pay to note that each of them includes active participation by the observer; it is not sufficient merely to be exposed to an outside stimulus. The role of the teacher—part of the surrounding system—includes providing clear "signals," rewarding performance, and reinforcing important ideas, but the rate-determining step in the process of education is usually the alertness of the internal system—that is, the student.

See page 1090 for a list of references and readings in the recent chemical literature related to the material in this chapter.

Science can not discover truth, but is an excellent means of discovering error. The residuum left after errors are eliminated is usually called scientific truth.
—*Kenneth Boulding* (1969).

PART 1

Energy, Atoms and Molecules

WHAT ARE MOLECULES DOING?

CHAPTER 1

Conservation and Change

Were everything conserved there could be no change.

Chemical reactions are involved in most observed changes. To interpret, understand, and control these changes most effectively, we need to understand chemical reactions. Changes are generally observed as variations in the bulk properties of substances. But a chemist thinks of and correlates these observations of large phenomena in terms of the behavior of molecules, atoms, electrons, and nuclei, all of which are very tiny indeed.

CHEMICAL REACTIONS

Some chemical reactions take place between readily identifiable substances and produce obviously new substances. Here are some examples.

a) Atomic hydrogen and atomic chlorine (both gases) unite to form molecular hydrogen chloride (another gas).
b) Liquid gasoline burns in oxygen to give carbon dioxide and water, plus a great deal of energy.
c) Metallic iron rusts in moist oxygen to give a red-brown hydrated oxide.
d) Metallic iron corrodes in hot oxygen to give a black oxide.
e) Metallic copper placed in aqueous silver nitrate produces metallic silver and a blue solution.
f) Gaseous hydrogen sulfide and sulfur dioxide react at the mouth of a volcano to produce sulfur and water.
g) Calcium oxide added to hard water causes calcium carbonate to precipitate.

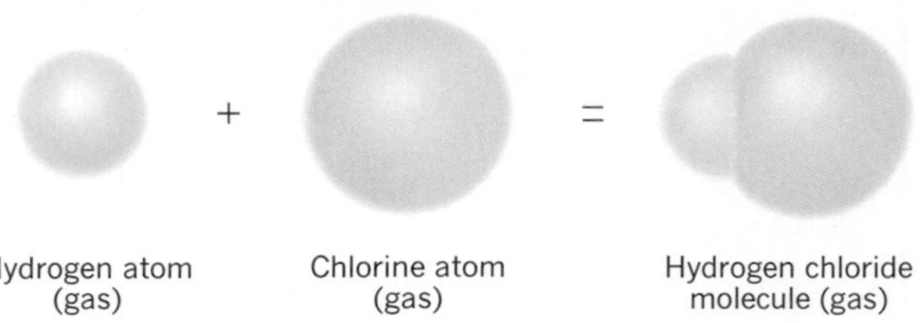

Figure 1.1 Chemical reaction represented by space-filling models.

Some reactions are produced solely by heating or cooling.

h) Baking soda gives carbon dioxide when heated.
i) Sugar decomposes to carbon and water when heated.
j) Nitrogen dioxide, a brown gas, becomes dinitrogen tetroxide (colorless) when cooled.

Sometimes we cannot readily name or describe all the reactants and products, but we still attribute the change to a chemical reaction.

k) An egg is cooked by heating.
l) A headache is cured by aspirin.
m) Automobile engine performance is improved when gasoline contains lead tetraethyl.
n) Iron is made harder by the addition of carbon.

And our level of sophistication tempts us to view some changes as though no chemical reaction were involved, no new products were formed, and no molecular changes occurred.

o) Heated water turns to steam.
p) Salt dissolves in water.
q) Mothballs (para-dichlorobenzene) dissolve in benzene.
r) An apple falls from a tree.
s) A coat fabric rips.

Yet surely liquid water and gaseous water (or crystalline sodium chloride and aqueous sodium chloride) are very different substances with different behavior at the molecular level. Close analysis of the changes in the apple or coat show that molecular behavior changes during the fall or tear. Thus all these changes—indeed, almost all changes—can be of interest to chemists. In turn, chemical knowledge of

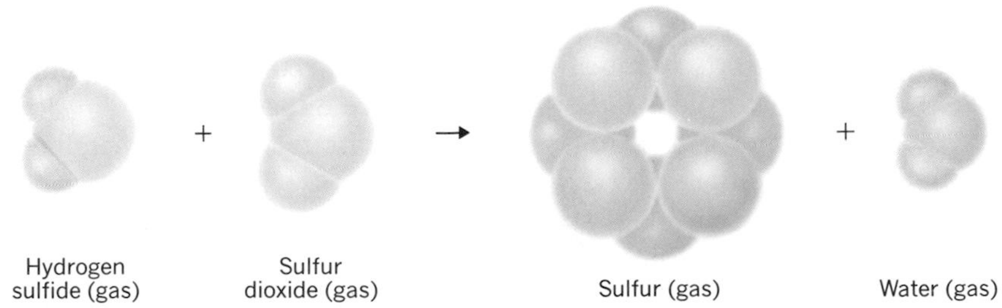

Figure 1.2 Chemical reaction represented by space-filling models.

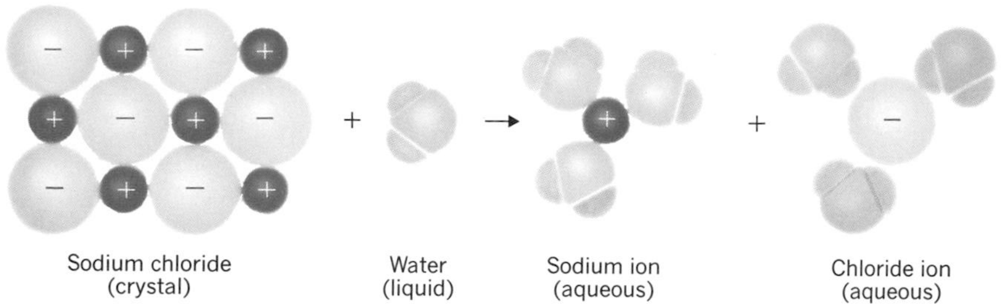

Figure 1.3 Solution of salt in water represented by space-filling models.

molecular behavior can make all of these changes more understandable, and thus more controllable. For example, we can develop fabrics which do not tear easily, and apples which do not fall before picking time nor bruise readily.

CHEMICAL SYMBOLISM

Much is now known about the details of molecular and atomic constitution and behavior. All the reactions listed above can be represented in much greater detail. For instance, we may represent reaction *a* as in Figure 1.1, where the smaller sphere represents an atom of hydrogen, the larger sphere an atom of chlorine. The product, hydrogen chloride, is represented by the same two spheres, but now interpenetrating or overlapping. Clearly this graphic representation, which is consistent with many of our observations of the system, contains more information than *a*.

The changes in reaction *f* might be represented in terms of similar "space-filling" models, as in Figure 1.2.

Clearly we have changed the numbers of atoms in our representation of the reaction: Figure 1.2 is therefore not an equation, since the atomic content of the reactants is not equal to the atomic content of the products.

The changes in reaction *p* could be represented as in Figure 1.3.

Again this is clearly not an equation. But something new has been added—a representation of electric charge (+ or −), indicating that here some of the atoms and molecular aggregates have a net electric charge other than zero.

Reaction *s* may be represented as in Figure 1.4.

The space-filling representations in Figures 1.2 and 1.3 do not show that the number of atoms remains constant in a chemical reaction. But atoms are conserved in chemical reactions. We can use our space-filling models to show this, as was done in Figure 1.1, by studying the models for reaction *f*, used in Figure 1.5.

All the hydrogen and oxygen atoms of the reactants must end up in water molecules, each containing 1 oxygen atom and 2 hydrogen atoms. Thus, the ratio of hydrogen atoms to oxygen atoms among the reacting molecules must also be 2 to 1, or 2 hydrogen sulfide molecules must react for each sulfur dioxide molecule

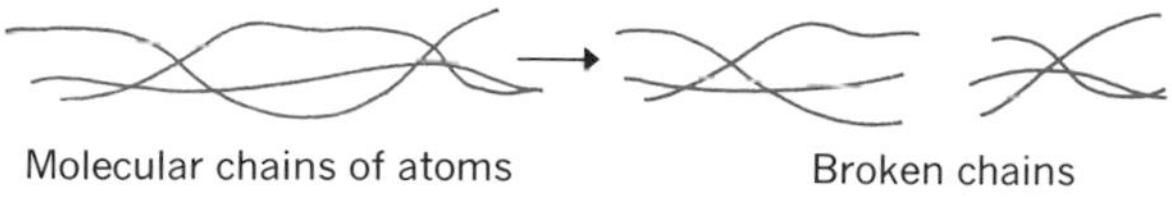

Figure 1.4 Tearing a fabric represented as breaking of molecular chains.

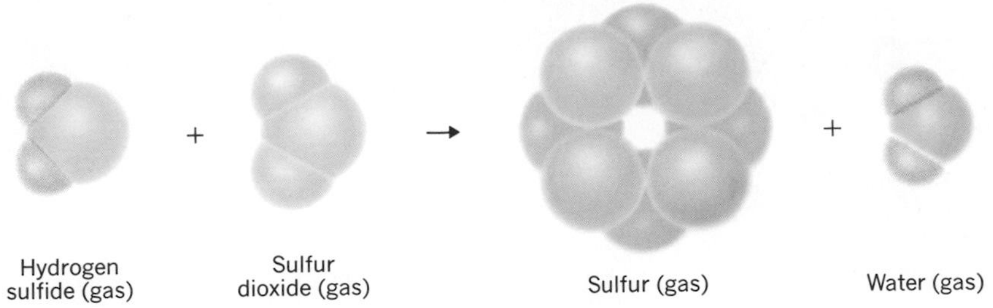

Figure 1.5 Chemical reaction represented by space-filling models.

that reacts. Thus if 2 hydrogen sulfide molecules do react with 1 sulfur dioxide molecule, it is possible to produce exactly 2 molecules of water and 3 atoms of sulfur. But the sulfur molecule contains 8 atoms per molecule. If we do not care to do further arithmetic, we can represent the equation as in Figure 1.6 or we can "clear fractions" to get Figure 1.7.

These space-filling models can give considerable insight (more than is apparent from a mere examination of the figures) into molecular changes accompanying chemical reactions. They are, however, time-consuming to prepare and, as we have shown, they do not necessarily or easily give the chemical equation for the reaction.

Many simpler representations of atoms and molecules have been suggested since Democritus first postulated the existence of atoms about 400 B.C. Some alchemical symbols from about 500 A.D. are shown in Figure 1.8. Even in these early symbols, the idea that elements are simpler than compounds was often indicated by symbols like that for iron oxide, which is more complex than that for iron.

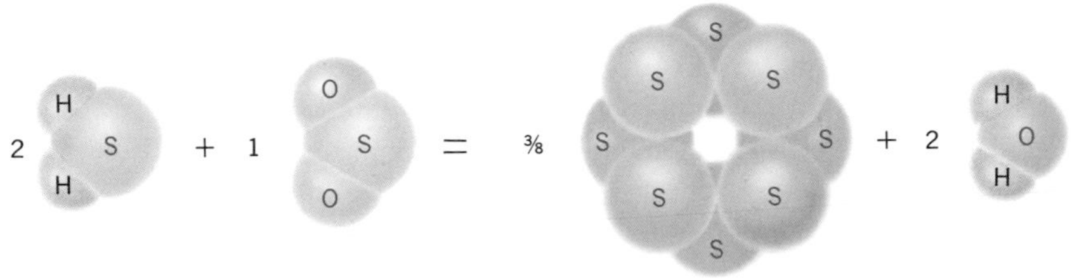

Figure 1.6 Chemical equation represented by space-filling models.

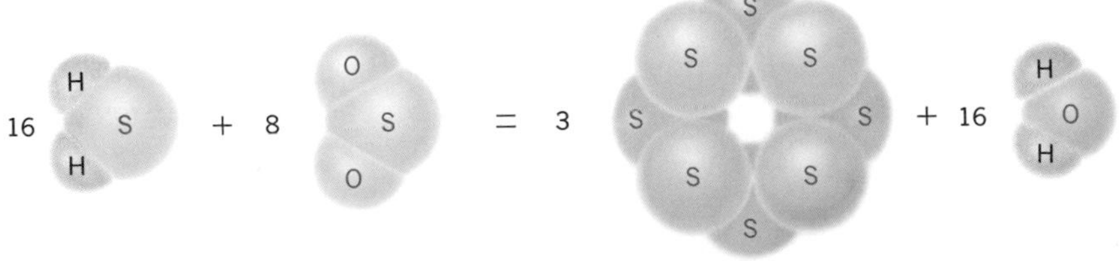

Figure 1.7 Chemical equation represented by space-filling models.

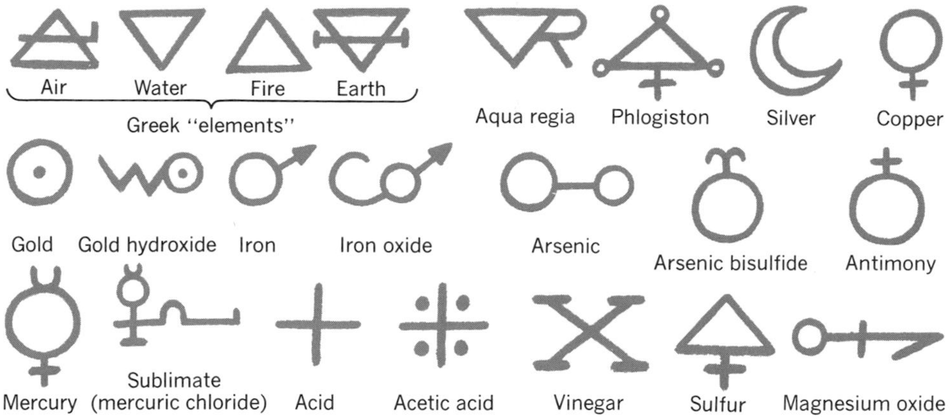

Figure 1.8 Some alchemical symbols. Note the relationships existing between some of the symbols.

Exercise 1.1

What information does the symbolic representation for sulfur in Figures 1.2, 1.5, 1.6, and 1.7 impart? *Answer:* Elementary sulfur exists as puckered rings of eight atoms (four up, four down). The atoms tend to behave like overlapping spheres. Sulfur atoms are larger than hydrogen or oxygen atoms.

ATOMIC SYMBOLS

In the course of the past hundred years, chemists throughout the world have agreed to use a set of Roman letter symbols similar to those first suggested by Berzelius about 1810. Some of the more commonly confusing ones are shown in Table 1.1, and the complete set is given in Table 1.2. We may think of a single elementary symbol as representing one atom of that element: H indicates one atom of hydrogen, Cl one atom of chlorine, Na one atom of sodium, and so on. The suffix -ium in the name of an element usually indicates it is a metal.

Exercise 1.2

Name the elements corresponding to the following symbols: Na, Au, Mg, Mn, C, Ca, N, Ni, Fe. *Answer:* See Tables 1.1 and 1.2.

Table 1.1 Common Berzelius symbols not derivable from the English name, and the name from which each symbol does come.

Antimony	Sb	stibium	Potassium	K	kalium
Copper	Cu	cuprum	Silver	Ag	argentum
Gold	Au	aurum	Sodium	Na	natrium
Iron	Fe	ferrum	Tin	Sn	stannum
Lead	Pb	plumbum	Tungsten	W	wolfram
Mercury	Hg	hydrargyrum			

Table 1.2 International atomic weights. Parenthetical weights refer to radioactive elements; the mass number, not the atomic weight, of the isotope with the longest half-life is given.

Name	Symbol	Atomic number	Atomic weight	Name	Symbol	Atomic number	Atomic weight
Actinium	Ac	89	(227)	Mendelevium	Md	101	(256)
Aluminum	Al	13	26.9815	Mercury	Hg	80	200.59
Americium	Am	95	(243)	Molybdenum	Mo	42	95.94
Antimony	Sb	51	121.75	Neodymium	Nd	60	144.24
Argon	Ar	18	39.948	Neon	Ne	10	20.179
Arsenic	As	33	74.9216	Neptunium	Np	93	(237)
Astatine	At	85	(210)	Nickel	Ni	28	58.71
Barium	Ba	56	137.34	Niobium	Nb	41	92.906
Berkelium	Bk	97	(247)	Nitrogen	N	7	14.0067
Beryllium	Be	4	9.0122	(Nobelium)	No	102	(256)
Bismuth	Bi	83	208.98	Osmium	Os	76	190.2
Boron	B	5	10.811[a]	Oxygen	O	8	15.9994[a]
Bromine	Br	35	79.904	Palladium	Pd	46	106.4
Cadmium	Cd	48	112.40	Phosphorus	P	15	30.9738
Calcium	Ca	20	40.08	Platinum	Pt	78	195.09
Californium	Cf	98	(249)	Plutonium	Pu	94	(242)
Carbon	C	6	12.01115[a]	Polonium	Po	84	(210)
Cerium	Ce	58	140.12	Potassium	K	19	39.102
Cesium	Cs	55	132.905	Praseodymium	Pr	59	140.907
Chlorine	Cl	17	35.453	Promethium	Pm	61	(145)
Chromium	Cr	24	51.996	Protactinium	Pa	91	(231)
Cobalt	Co	27	58.9332	Radium	Ra	88	(226)
Copper	Cu	29	63.546	Radon	Rn	86	(222)
Curium	Cm	96	(247)	Rhenium	Re	75	186.2
Dysprosium	Dy	66	162.50	Rhodium	Rh	45	102.905
Einsteinium	Es	99	(254)	Rubidium	Rb	37	85.47
Erbium	Er	68	167.26	Ruthenium	Ru	44	101.07
Europium	Eu	63	151.96	Samarium	Sm	62	150.35
Fermium	Fm	100	(253)	Scandium	Sc	21	44.956
Fluorine	F	9	18.9884	Selenium	Se	34	78.96
Francium	Fr	87	(223)	Silicon	Si	14	28.086[a]
Gadolinium	Gd	64	157.25	Silver	Ag	47	107.868
Gallium	Ga	31	69.72	Sodium	Na	11	22.9898
Germanium	Ge	32	72.59	Strontium	Sr	38	87.62
Gold	Au	79	196.967	Sulfur	S	16	32.064[a]
Hafnium	Hf	72	178.49	Tantalum	Ta	73	180.948
Helium	He	2	4.0026	Technetium	Tc	43	(99)
Holmium	Ho	67	164.930	Tellurium	Te	52	127.60
Hydrogen	H	1	1.00797[a]	Terbium	Tb	65	158.924
Indium	In	49	114.82	Thallium	Tl	81	204.37
Iodine	I	53	126.9044	Thorium	Th	90	232.038
Iridium	Ir	77	192.2	Thulium	Tm	69	168.934
Iron	Fe	26	55.847	Tin	Sn	50	118.69
Krypton	Kr	36	83.80	Titanium	Ti	22	47.90
Kurchatovium(?)	Ku(?)	104	(260)	Tungsten	W	74	183.85
Lanthanum	La	57	138.9	Uranium	U	92	238.03
Lawrencium	Lw	103	(257)?	Vanadium	V	23	50.942
Lead	Pb	82	207.19	Xenon	Xe	54	131.30
Lithium	Li	3	6.939	Ytterbium	Yb	70	173.04
Lutetium	Lu	71	174.97	Yttrium	Y	39	88.905
Magnesium	Mg	12	24.305	Zinc	Zn	30	65.37
Manganese	Mn	25	54.9380	Zirconium	Zr	40	91.22

[a] These atomic weights are known to be variable because of natural variations in isotopic composition. The observed ranges are: B $\pm$ 0.003, C $\pm$ 0.00005, H $\pm$ 0.00001, O $\pm$ 0.0001, Si $\pm$ 0.001, S $\pm$ 0.03.

IONS AND NEUTRAL MOLECULES

Most substances made up only of nonmetallic elements are composed of neutral molecules. Thus most of the millions of known compounds containing only carbon, hydrogen, oxygen, nitrogen, and the halogens are made up of electrically neutral molecules. Examples are carbon dioxide, CO_2; sugar, $C_{12}H_{22}O_{11}$; octane, C_8H_{18}; DDT, $C_{14}H_9Cl_5$; water, H_2O.

On the other hand, most compounds consisting of both metallic and nonmetallic elements are composed of electrically charged atoms or groups of atoms. These electrically charged species are called ions. Examples are: sodium chloride, Na^+Cl^-; barium sulfate, $Ba^{++}SO_4^=$; aluminum chloride, $Al^{+3}(Cl^-)_3$; potassium hydroxide, $K^+(OH^-)$; calcium hydroxide, $Ca^{++}(OH^-)_2$; aluminum oxide, $(Al^{+3})_2(O^=)_3$. Note that the relative numbers of positive and negative ions are always such that the total electrical charge in the substance is zero.

One of the first questions you should ask yourself in writing and using chemical formulas is: "How ionic is the substance?" Electrical properties affect chemical behavior in important ways.

Forces between electrically neutral species are often so small that crystalline substances melt, and even boil, at low temperatures (less than 200°C), as well as dissolving readily in solvents similar to themselves. Forces between ions are greater than those between neutral molecules at the molecular distances found in crystals and liquids. Thus most ionic substances have rather high melting and boiling points and dissolve readily only in liquids that are also ionic, or sometimes in water. Water is a bent molecule, shaped somewhat like a boomerang, with its hydrogen ends electrically positive and its center negative. It is thus able to orient favorably both to positive and negative ions and allow them to separate from one another and remain in solution. These aquated, or hydrated, ions can act quite independently of one another, so it is very common to see their formulas used in describing chemical systems. Examples are: sodium ion, $Na^+_{(aq)}$; hydrogen ion, $H^+_{(aq)}$; calcium ion, $Ca^{++}_{(aq)}$; chloride ion, $Cl^-_{(aq)}$; sulfate ion, $SO_4{}^=_{(aq)}$; nitrate ion, $NO_3{}^-_{(aq)}$.

CHEMICAL EQUATIONS

We may now rewrite equations for many of our original reactions *a* to *s*, using these new symbols. We shall use an equal sign (=) to indicate a chemical equation that shows the relative numbers of atoms and molecules reacting to give a certain set of products. We indicate the phase of each substance by subscripts, using *(g)* for gases, *(l)* for liquids, *(c)* for crystals, *(aq)* for aqueous (water) solutions, and (*name of solvent*) for other solutions. If no coefficient is given in front of a formula, the coefficient is understood to be one. For gases, liquids, molecular crystals, and solutions, the molecular formula of the actual molecules present is given, when it is known. Examples: gases, $H_{(g)}$, $HCl_{(g)}$, $O_{2(g)}$, $N_2O_{4(g)}$; liquids, $C_8H_{18(l)}$, $C_6H_{6(l)}$; molecular crystals, $C_{12}H_{22}O_{11(c)}$, $C_6H_4Cl_{2(c)}$; solutions, $Ag^+_{(aq)}$, $Cu^{++}_{(aq)}$, $Cl^-_{(aq)}$, $C_6H_4Cl_{2(benzene)}$. Otherwise, and especially in the case of nonmolecular crystals such as $Fe_{(c)}$ or $NaCl_{(c)}$, the simplest (or empirical) formula is used.

a′) $H_{(g)} + Cl_{(g)} = HCl_{(g)}$ (or any other set of coefficients in the ratio 1/1/1.

b′) $C_8H_{18(l)} + 12\frac{1}{2}O_{2(g)} = 8CO_{2(g)} + 9H_2O_{(g)}$ (or any other coefficients in the ratio $1/12\frac{1}{2}/8/9$).

c′) $2Fe_{(c)} + \frac{3}{2}O_{2(g)} + nH_2O_{(g)} = Fe_2O_3 \cdot nH_2O_{(c)}$. (The formula $Fe_2O_3 \cdot nH_2O$ indicates that the actual composition is not known, or that the amount of water per mole of Fe_2O_3 is variable.)

d′) $3Fe_{(c)} + 2O_{2(g)} = Fe_3O_{4(c)}$ + energy. (Energy changes accompany all chemical reactions. We shall only indicate them occasionally, but the energy involved is most important in accomplishing the reaction and must be considered in any *complete* description of a reaction.)

e′) $Cu_{(c)} + 2Ag^+{}_{(aq)} = Cu^{++}{}_{(aq)} + 2Ag_{(c)}$.

f′) $2H_2S_{(g)} + SO_{2(g)} = \frac{3}{8}S_{8(c)} + 2H_2O_{(g)}$.

g′) $CaO_{(c)} + HCO_3^-{}_{(aq)} = CaCO_{3(c)} + OH^-{}_{(aq)}$.

h′) energy + $NaHCO_{3(c)} = Na_2CO_{3(c)} + H_2O_{(g)} + CO_{2(g)}$.

i′) energy + $C_{12}H_{22}O_{11(c)} = 12C_{(c)} + 11H_2O_{(g)}$.

j′) $2NO_{2(g)} = N_2O_{4(g)}$ + energy.

k′ to m′) Too little has been discovered as yet for us to write chemical equations for these changes, but chemists believe that ultimately such equations will be discovered.

n′) $2Fe_{(c)} + C_{(c)} = Fe_3C_{(c)}$ (plus many other possibilities).

o′) energy + $H_2O_{(l)} = H_2O_{(g)}$.

p′) $NaCl_{(c)} = Na^+{}_{(aq)} + Cl^-{}_{(aq)}$. (Note that H_2O present as a solvent is indicated by the subscript (*aq*), meaning aqueous.)

q′) $p\text{-}C_6H_4Cl_{2(c)} = p\text{-}C_6H_4Cl_{2(benzene)}$. (Note that "p" must be used to indicate which isomer is referred to, here the "para" form,

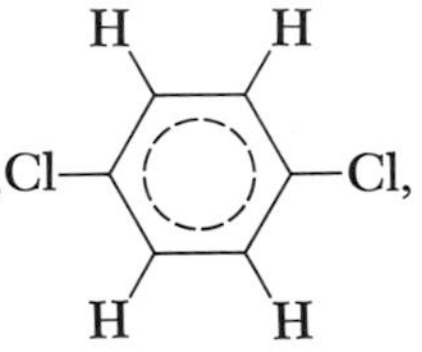

where the chlorines are opposite one another and attached to a benzene ring of six carbon atoms.)

r′ and s′) Again insufficient knowledge is at hand to write the chemical equations for these processes, but the search for the equations is intense.

Exercise 1.3

Check all the above (*a′* through *q′*) for the conservation of atoms. Two of the representations are not printed as equations. Correct them. All the formulas are correct, so change only the coefficients.

WRITING CHEMICAL EQUATIONS

A chemical equation represents the ratio in which substances will react to give products, if such a reaction occurs. Thus, we must first have formulas that adequately represent the elementary composition of the substances involved. In such formulas—for instance, $Na_2Cr_2O_7 \cdot 2H_2O$—the letter symbols indicate the elements from which the substance might be made: sodium, Na; chromium, Cr; oxygen, O; hydrogen, H. The subscripts indicate the relative numbers of atoms present: 2 sodiums, Na, for every 2 chromiums, Cr, for every 7 oxygens, O. The small dot and 2 after the $Na_2Cr_2O_7$ part of the formula and just before the H_2O, is read "plus two" and indicates that for every $Na_2Cr_2O_7$ unit present there are a certain number of additional molecules present, here 2 water molecules. The formula H_2O indicates that each molecule of water is composed of 2 hydrogen atoms and 1 oxygen atom.

In order to write an equation you need first to know the formulas of the reactants and products. This is the most important part of the chemistry. The equation then results from careful bookkeeping to ensure that our representation of the reaction—the equation—satisfies the conservation laws. Only two of the conservation laws need be applied to obtain the usual chemical equation. They are the law of conservation of charge and the law of conservation of atoms.

BALANCING BY HALF-REACTIONS

Consider the reaction between crystals of sodium dichromate (orange), $Na_2Cr_2O_7 \cdot 2H_2O$, and aqueous hydrogen peroxide, H_2O_2, in acid solution (a solution containing $H^+{}_{(aq)}$, aqueous hydrogen ions). Experiment shows that oxygen gas is evolved, the orange crystals disappear, and a green solution, $Cr^{+++}{}_{(aq)}$, is formed. We summarize this statement in chemical formulas, using an arrow, $\longrightarrow$, to indicate the direction of the reaction:

$$\underset{\text{orange}}{Na_2Cr_2O_7 \cdot 2H_2O_{(c)}} + H_2O_{2(aq)} + H^+{}_{(aq)} \longrightarrow O_{2(g)} + \underset{\text{green}}{Cr^{+++}{}_{(aq)}} \qquad (1.1)$$

Clearly this is not an equation; there are no sodium atoms among the products and neither atoms nor electric charges are conserved. Nor does quick inspection resolve the problem.

There are many ways of finding the equation, but one of the most general and powerful is the method of half-reactions. In this method we choose a pair of substances—one reactant and one product—which are clearly interrelated in terms of containing atoms of the same element, and write an equation for their interconversion. The equation is so written that atoms are conserved, and then charges are conserved very simply by arbitrarily adding an appropriate number of negative charges (represented as electrons, e^-) to the equation. We might choose the hydrogen peroxide and oxygen as our pair of compounds:

$$H_2O_{2(aq)} \longrightarrow O_{2(g)} \qquad (1.2)$$

When, as here, hydrogen atoms are "left over," we write them by convention among the products as H^+ *(aq)*. Thus,

$$H_2O_{2(aq)} \longrightarrow O_{2(g)} + 2H^+{}_{(aq)} \qquad (1.3)$$

Atoms are now conserved. Charge will also be conserved if we add 2 negative charges (electrons) to the products:

$$H_2O_{2(aq)} = O_{2(g)} + 2H^+{}_{(aq)} + 2e^- \qquad (1.4)$$

This is now an equation, so we use an equal sign. It is called a half-equation* (or equation for a half-reaction) because it contains electrons. No complete chemical equation contains electrons. Unlike most chemicals, electrons cannot be bottled and stored in any large quantity, though they certainly may be involved in the reactions. Thus we must write another half-reaction to show where these electrons "go."

Another pair of related substances is certainly

$$Na_2Cr_2O_7 \cdot 2H_2O_{(c)} \longrightarrow Cr^{+++}{}_{(aq)} \tag{1.5}$$

One can progress to the half-equation in many ways. The important criteria are the conservation of atoms and charges. We shall assume, in considering half-reactions, that "extra" oxygens unite with $H^+{}_{(aq)}$ to form H_2O, and that metallic ions such as Na^+ remain unchanged, unless we have experimental evidence to the contrary. Then

$$Na_2Cr_2O_7 \cdot 2H_2O_{(c)} \longrightarrow 2Cr^{+++}{}_{(aq)} + 2Na^+{}_{(aq)} + 7H_2O + 2H_2O \tag{1.6}$$

or, adding $H^+{}_{(aq)}$ to conserve atoms completely, we get

$$Na_2Cr_2O_7 \cdot 2H_2O_{(c)} + 14H^+{}_{(aq)} \longrightarrow 2Cr^{+++}{}_{(aq)} + 2Na^+{}_{(aq)} + 9H_2O_{(l)} \tag{1.7}$$

Atoms are now conserved and we may conserve charges by adding 6 electrons:

$$Na_2Cr_2O_7 \cdot 2H_2O_{(c)} + 14H^+{}_{(aq)} + 6e^- = 2Cr^{+++}{}_{(aq)} + 2Na^+{}_{(aq)} + 9H_2O_{(l)} \tag{1.8}$$

This half-equation uses up electrons, whereas the peroxide half-equation generates them. We must now add the two half-equations, to give the net equation, but we must do this in such a way that the electrons produced in one half-equation exactly equal those used in the other. [We will neglect for the moment all the subscripted phase descriptions such as *(c)* or *(g)*.]

$$3(H_2O_2 = O_2 + 2H^+ + 2e^-)$$

or

$$3H_2O_2 = 3O_2 + 6H^+ + 6e^-$$

plus

$$Na_2Cr_2O_7 \cdot 2H_2O + 14H^+ + 6e^- = 2Cr^{+++} + 2Na^+ + 9H_2O$$

Net:

$$Na_2Cr_2O_7 \cdot 2H_2O + 14H^+ + 3H_2O_2 = 3O_2 + 6H^+ + 2Cr^{+++} + 2Na^+ + 9H_2O \tag{1.9}$$

This last equation can be simplified by subtracting $6H^+{}_{(aq)}$ from each side so that only species which change are listed. (We will also reintroduce the phase descriptions.)

Net:

$$\underset{\text{orange}}{Na_2Cr_2O_7 \cdot 2H_2O_{(c)}} + 8H^+{}_{(aq)} + 3H_2O_{2(aq)} = 3O_{2(g)} + \underset{\text{green}}{2Cr^{+++}{}_{(aq)}} + 2Na^+{}_{(aq)} + 9H_2O_{(l)} \tag{1.10}$$

A quick check shows that the number of atoms of each element and the total electrical charge are conserved. Equation (1.10) agrees with the experimental observations that an orange solid reacts with an acidic colorless solution to produce a

* A half-equation always contains electrons (to balance electrical charges). Complete equations may be obtained by adding two half-equations in such a manner that the electrons cancel out.

colorless gas and a green solution. It also indicates the composition and relative amounts of each species. Whether the equation describes the actual reaction can be determined only by experiment. In this case there is a good chance it will since we knew all the reactants and most of the products before starting to balance the equation [see Equation (1.1)].

Exercise 1.4

Balance the following, adding H^+, H_2O, and OH^- as required:

$MnO_4^- + SO_3^= \longrightarrow Mn^{++} + SO_4^=$. *Answer:* (I) $\underset{c}{5e^-} + \underset{b}{8H^+} + MnO_4^- = Mn^{++} + \underset{a}{4H_2O}$

(II) $\underset{a}{H_2O} + SO_3^= = SO_4^= + \underset{b}{2H^+} + \underset{c}{2e^-}$ (*a*, *b*, *c* indicate order of entries).

Net: Add 2I + 5II, cancel H^+'s and H_2O's to get $6H^+ + 2MnO_4^- + 5SO_3^= = 5SO_4^= + 2Mn^{++} + 3H_2O$.

BALANCING BY INSPECTION

Chemical equations may be balanced with half-reactions; many, however, are easily balanced by inspection, which should always be tried first. Note the following examples.

(*a*)
$$La^{+++}{}_{(aq)} + F^-{}_{(aq)} \longrightarrow LaF_{3(c)}$$

By inspection of atoms and charges we see that $La^{+++}{}_{(aq)} + 3F^-{}_{(aq)} = LaF_{3(c)}$.

(*b*)
$$Na_{(c)} + Hg_{(l)} \longrightarrow Na_{11}Hg_{(c)}$$

By inspection we see that $11Na_{(c)} + Hg_{(l)} = Na_{11}Hg_{(c)}$.

(*c*)
$$C_7H_{16(g)} + Cl_{2(g)} \longrightarrow C_7H_{14}Cl_{2(l)} + HCl_{(g)}$$

By inspection, since each C_7H_{16} loses 2 H's (to form 2 HCl's on the right side) and gains 2 Cl's, we see that $C_7H_{16(g)} + 2Cl_{2(g)} = C_7H_{14}Cl_{2(l)} + 2HCl_{(g)}$.

(*d*)
$$Cr^{+++}{}_{(aq)} + Zn_{(c)} \longrightarrow Cr^{++}{}_{(aq)} + Zn^{++}{}_{(aq)}$$

By inspection, since each Zn acquires 2 positive charges and each Cr^{+++} loses 1 positive charge, we see that $2Cr^{+++}{}_{(aq)} + Zn_{(c)} = 2Cr^{++}{}_{(aq)} + Zn^{++}{}_{(aq)}$.

Correct formulas of substances and correct equations describing the reactions between substances are essential to the solution of many chemical problems. Obtaining correct formulas is much the harder job; writing the equations is merely bookkeeping. *Conclusion:* First get the formulas correct.

Chemical equations are written in a three-step process.

1. Correct formulas for known reactants and products are written.
2. Electric charges on ions are indicated by superscripts and phase designations by subscripts.
3. Atoms and electric charges are conserved by inspection or by use of half-equations.

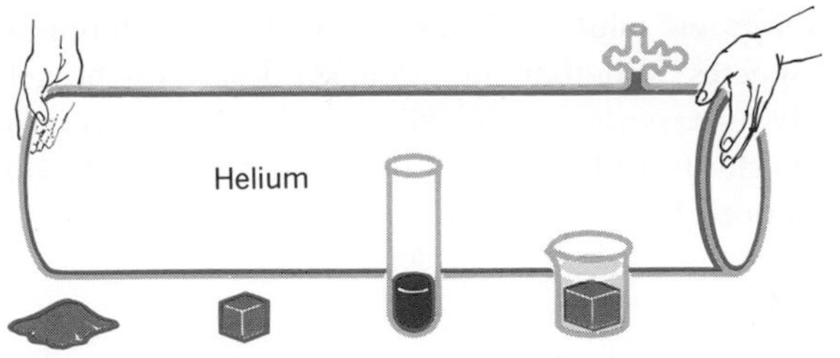

Figure 1.9 One mole, $6.02 \cdot 10^{23}$ atoms, of several elements in the forms found at ordinary laboratory conditions. The molar volumes are: S = 16 cm^3, U = 13 cm^3, He = $2.5 \cdot 10^4$ cm^3, Hg = 15 cm^3, K = 39 cm^3. The molar volumes of most of the solid and liquid elements run from 5–50 cm^3. The molar volume of the gases is constant at about $2.5 \cdot 10^4$ cm^3 at ordinary laboratory conditions. (Substances like potassium, which react with air, are often stored under oil, if they do not react with it, since air is very slightly soluble in oil.)

THE MOLE CONCEPT AND CHEMICAL MEASUREMENT

We may view chemical symbols as representing atoms, and chemical equations as describing the ratios in which atoms in substances exist and react, but it is not easy in the laboratory to measure small numbers of atoms directly. Just as it is easier in a hardware store to measure nails by the pound than by counting them, so in a chemical laboratory it is easier to measure chemicals by weight than by the number of atoms. Yet it is clear that in both the hardware store and the chemical laboratory there is a simple relationship between the number of individual objects (nails or atoms) and the bulk property of weight. If the weights of the individual objects vary, the number per unit weight will vary, but there is a constant ratio of weight to number if the objects are identical.

The weight ratio of equal numbers of two kinds of atoms is independent of the numbers of atoms. Any given number of hydrogen atoms weighs $\frac{1}{12}$ as much as the same number of carbon atoms.

The most common number of atoms referred to by chemists is that represented by the mole, which is defined as: "A mole is an amount of a substance, of specified chemical formula, containing the same number of formula units (atoms, molecules, ions, electrons, quanta, or other entities) as there are in 12 grams (exactly) of the pure nuclide C^{12}."*

According to the best available measurements—

One mole of atoms contains $6.0225 \cdot 10^{23}$ atoms

Thus the elementary chemical symbols commonly stand for one mole ($6.0225 \cdot 10^{23}$) of atoms, as well as for individual atoms and molecules. The number of formula units in a mole is called Avogadro's number and is symbolized by N_0. We shall usually work with three significant figures so that you will most commonly see $6.02 \cdot 10^{23}$ used for N_0.

In any equation, the elementary symbols always represent the *same* num-

* International Union of Pure and Applied Chemistry, Bulletin 24, 1965.

ber of atoms (or moles) of each of the elements represented. The subscripts and coefficients then indicate how many of these units will be involved if the reaction represented actually occurs.

The mole number, $N_0 = 6.02 \cdot 10^{23}$, is selected in such a way that an atomic weight in grams of any element contains $6.02 \cdot 10^{23}$ atoms. Each of the following contains $6.02 \cdot 10^{23}$ atoms: 4.00 g of helium, He; 32.0 g of sulfur, S; 238 g of uranium, U; and so on for all the elements. See Figure 1.9.

The chemical formula of any substance indicates the relative number of atoms that combine to make the substance. Thus, sulfuric acid, formula H_2SO_4, could be made from atoms of hydrogen (H), sulfur (S), and oxygen (O) in the ratio 2/1/4. (Note that the "1" is not actually written in the formula, but is understood in the absence of any other subscript.) It follows that a mole of sulfuric acid molecules ($6.02 \cdot 10^{23}$ molecules) could be made from 2 moles of hydrogen atoms ($2 \cdot 6.02 \cdot 10^{23}$ atoms), 1 mole of sulfur atoms ($6.02 \cdot 10^{23}$ atoms), and 4 moles of oxygen atoms ($4 \cdot 6.02 \cdot 10^{23}$ atoms). See Figure 1.10.

The molecular weight, M, must always be the sum of the atomic weights of the atoms present in the molecule, and the molecular weight of any substance, measured in grams, must contain one mole of molecules. The following all contain $6.02 \cdot 10^{23}$ molecules: 18.0 g of water, H_2O; 146 g of sulfur hexafluoride, SF_6; 27.7 g of diborane, B_2H_6; or the molecular weight of any substance measured in grams. These are called molar weights, and each equals M grams.

Some substances, such as sodium chloride, NaCl, calcium carbonate, $CaCO_3$, or silicon carbide, SiC, do not contain separated molecules. They are said to be lattice compounds, or macromolecular substances. Applied to such compounds, the term mole is unambiguous only when it is associated with a particular chemical formula. Thus a mole of NaCl contains 1 mole of sodium ions, Na^+, and 1 mole of chloride ions, Cl^-, and weighs 23.0 g (1 mole of sodium ions) plus 35.5 g (1 mole of chloride ions), or 58.5 g. In the same way, 100 g of $CaCO_3$ (40 g Ca, 12 g C, 48 g O) contains 1 mole of $CaCO_3$ (see Figure 1.11).

For some purposes (mass spectra, very large molecules) it is convenient to use atomic mass units, called amu or daltons.

$$1 \text{ amu} = 1 \text{ g}/6.0225 \cdot 10^{23} = 1.16604 \cdot 10^{-24} \text{ g} = 1 \text{ dalton}$$

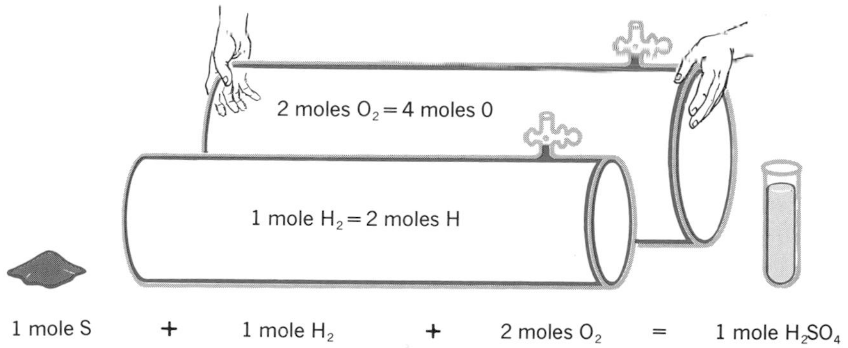

Figure 1.10 Volumes and numbers of moles in a chemical reaction. Relative volumes are: $H_2 = 2.5 \cdot 10^4$ cm³, S = 16 cm³, $O_2 = 5.0 \cdot 10^4$ cm³, H_2SO_4 = 54 cm³.

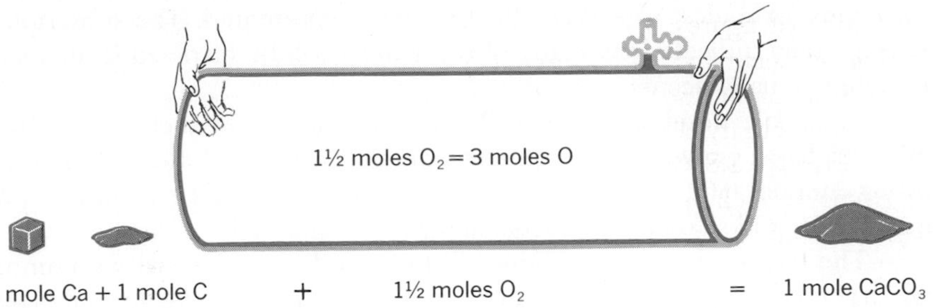

Figure 1.11 Volumes and numbers of moles in a chemical reaction. Relative volumes: Ca = 26 cm^3, C = 5 cm^3, O_2 = $3.8 \cdot 10^4$ cm^3, $CaCO_3$ = 37 cm^3.

Exercise 1.5

Interpret the equation $2Al_{(c)} + 6HBr_{(g)} = Al_2Br_{6(c)} + 3H_{2(g)}$. *Answer:* Crystalline aluminum reacts with gaseous hydrogen bromide to give crystalline aluminum bromide and gaseous hydrogen.

$2Al_{(c)}$	+	$6HBr_{(g)}$	=	$Al_2Br_{6(c)}$	+	$3H_{2(g)}$
2 moles	+	6 moles	gives	1 mole	+	3 moles
$2 \cdot 27$ g	+	$6(1 + 80)$ g	gives	$(2 \cdot 27 + 6 \cdot 80)$ g	+	$3(2 \cdot 1)$ g
54 amu	+	486 amu	gives	534 amu	+	6 amu
$2 \cdot 6.02 \cdot 10^{23}$ atoms	+	$6 \cdot 6.02 \cdot 10^{23}$ molecules	gives	$6.02 \cdot 10^{23}$ molecules	+	$3 \cdot 6.02 \cdot 10^{23}$ molecules

SIGNIFICANT FIGURES

You may have noted in the preceding section that Avogadro's number was expressed in two different sets of digits, 6.0225 and 6.02, each times 10^{23}. The figure $6.0225 \cdot 10^{23}$ is the most accurate statement and is given to five significant figures (6.0225 consists of five experimentally measured digits). Not very many measurements are made to this accuracy. Since no arithmetical result involving multiplication and division can be more accurate than the least accurate datum involved, it is common to round off numbers to this minimum number of significant figures before performing these arithmetical operations. Most data in this course will be given to three significant figures so, for example, the value of N_0 you will most often use is $6.02 \cdot 10^{23}$, but you might use 6.023, 6.0, or 6, times 10^{23}, depending on the accuracy of other data in the problem.

Appendix I gives the value $6.02252 (\pm 0.00028) \cdot 10^{23}$ as the best value of N_0. This symbolism means that all acceptable measurements agree on the first four significant figures but the fifth is in doubt; N_0 is in doubt by ± 0.0003 or $\pm 0.005\%$. No number obtained by multiplying or dividing by N_0 can have an uncertainty less than $\pm 0.005\%$, and such a number should not be written with more digits than this limitation allows. A rough rule is to say that the number of significant figures in the result of any arithmetical operation involving only division and multiplication cannot exceed the number of significant figures in the least accurately known datum. Initial and final zeroes are not significant if they are present only to locate the decimal point. Other zeroes are significant. Thus, each of the following contains three significant figures: 755, 0.0543, 2370, 4.10, 206, $3.00 \cdot 10^6$. Since the actual limitation on accuracy is the percentage of uncertainty, not merely numbers of digits, it is common not to count initial "1's" as significant figures. The following examples may clarify the situation.

I. $2.02 \cdot 1.896 \cdot 3.0 = 11.48976$ if all numbers are treated as exact. But 3.0 is given to only 2 significant figures. Assuming the uncertainty is ± 0.1, or $\pm 3\%$ in 3.0, the product cannot be known to better than $\pm 3\%$. Since 11.48976 starts with "1" we would round it off to 11.5 as the arithmetically acceptable product. The same result may be achieved more quickly by rounding off before doing the arithmetic to get: $2.0 \cdot 1.90 \cdot 3.0 = 11.4$, which equals 11.5 within the inherent uncertainty of $\pm 3\%$. Many scientists prefer to keep an "extra" significant figure as long as possible; then they round off the answer. They would multiply $2.02 \cdot 1.896 \cdot 3.0 = 11.5$.

II. No initial rounding: $1.5 \cdot 2.53 \cdot 4.126 = 15.6817 = 16$.
Initial rounding: $1.5 \cdot 2.5 \cdot 4.1 = 15$.
Retain one extra figure: $1.5 \cdot 2.53 \cdot 4.13 = 15.6 = 16$.

Note that all results agree within the 1.5 ± 0.1 or $\pm 7\%$ uncertainty of the least well known datum.

You will save large amounts of time, gain considerable insight into data, and avoid deluding yourself on the accuracy of your answers if you observe significant figures. Suggested procedure in division and multiplication: (1) Determine the number of significant figures in the least accurate datum. (2) Round off all data to one more than this number of significant figures. You may prefer not to count initial "1's." (3) Carry out the arithmetic. (4) Round off the answer.

CHEMICAL FORMULAS FROM ANALYTICAL DATA

Although the mole is the most common unit of quantity that chemists use, actual samples of substances seldom involve integral numbers of moles. Yet in every sample of a pure substance, regardless of size, the atoms of the constituent elements must be present in the same ratio they would have in a sample containing one mole of the substance. The determination of the relative numbers of the different kinds of atoms in any sample of a pure substance allows us to calculate the formula of the substance. Remember—the formula gives this ratio.

One of the most common measurments made by chemists is weight. Weights can be measured quickly, precisely, and accurately by using modern single-pan analytical balances. For samples weighing a few grams an accuracy of 1 part in 100,000 can be obtained by experienced persons, and an accuracy of 1 part in 1,000 ($\pm 0.1\%$) is possible for neophytes. Thus gravimetric analysis (analysis in terms of weights) is one of the most frequently employed chemical techniques, especially if high accuracy is desired.

Consider the following example. A 0.8546-g sample of europium chloride (yellow) is dissolved in water, and sufficient aqueous silver nitrate is added to precipitate the chloride ion quantitatively. The silver chloride precipitate is carefully filtered, dried, and weighed. The weight of the AgCl is 1.0910 g. Now we may calculate a formula for the europium chloride. Since one mole of AgCl weighs

107.880 + 35.453 = 143.333 g (or, to the same precision as the weight of AgCl, 143.33 g), we get

$$1.0910 \text{ g AgCl is } \frac{1.0910 \text{ g } \cancel{\text{AgCl}}}{143.33 \text{ g } \cancel{\text{AgCl}}/\text{mole AgCl}} = 7.613 \cdot 10^{-3} \text{ moles AgCl}$$

which contains $7.613 \cdot 10^{-3}$ moles of chloride. All this chloride comes from the europium chloride, so it must also have contained $7.613 \cdot 10^{-3}$ moles of chloride. Since one mole of chloride weighs 35.453 g (or 35.45 g), we get

$$7.613 \cdot 10^{-3} \cancel{\text{moles Cl}} \cdot 35.45 \text{ g Cl}/\cancel{\text{mole Cl}} = 0.2770 \text{ g Cl}$$

Thus the 0.8546 g sample of europium chloride contained 0.2770 g of chlorine and 0.8546 − 0.2770 = 0.5776 g of europium. One mole of europium is 152.0 g, which gives us $0.5776 \cancel{\text{g Eu}}/151.96 \cancel{\text{g Eu}} \cdot (\text{mole Eu})^{-1} = 3.800 \cdot 10^{-3}$ moles of europium in the original sample. Thus the original sample contained $3.800 \cdot 10^{-3}$ moles of europium and $7.613 \cdot 10^{-3}$ moles of chlorine. We could write the formula as $Eu_{3.800 \cdot 10^{-3}}\,Cl_{7.613 \cdot 10^{-3}}$, but we prefer subscripts that are small whole numbers. The ratio here is

$$\frac{7.613 \cdot 10^{-3} \text{ moles Cl}}{3.800 \cdot 10^{-3} \text{ moles Eu}} = 2.003 \text{ moles Cl per mole Eu}$$

The 2.003 is, within experimental uncertainty (±0.0001 g in each weighing), equal to exactly 2. Thus we write the formula as $EuCl_2$.

In the same way, any gravimetric weight data can be converted to moles by using the known atomic weights. From the resulting mole ratios, formulas can be deduced.

Analytical data can also be obtained with volumetric equipment. Beginners can easily achieve accuracies of ±0.2% with these techniques, but even experts seldom can do better than ±0.02%, as contrasted to the ±0.001% that is possible gravimetrically. What is lost in accuracy is gained in convenience and speed. Transfer problems are minimized, and lengthy processes of precipitation, filtration, and drying are often avoided. Another advantage of volumetric techniques is that, in many cases, they make it possible to measure quantities too small to be weighed accurately on readily available balances. Chemists almost always prefer volumetric to gravimetric techniques.

Here is an example. A solution known to contain aqueous strontium nitrate, $Sr(NO_3)_2$, gives a precipitate of strontium sulfate when 0.1426 *F** sodium sulfate solution is added from a buret. Careful observation shows that no additional precipitation occurs after 37.46 ml of the sulfate is added. How much strontium, as Sr^{++}, was in the original solution?

The equation for the precipitation reaction is

$$Sr^{++}_{(aq)} + SO_4{}^{=}_{(aq)} = SrSO_{4(c)}$$

Each mole of Sr^{++} requires one mole of $SO_4{}^{=}$ for precipitation. Thus the number of moles Sr^{++} = the number of moles $SO_4{}^{=}$. The number of moles $SO_4{}^{=}$ = 0.1426

*A one formal (1 *F*) solution contains one formula weight in grams (one mole) of the dissolved substance in one liter of solution. Thus 1.00 *F* $HCl_{(aq)}$ contains 36.5 g of HCl dissolved in enough water to give one liter of solution.

(moles $SO_4^{=}$/~~ℓ soln~~) · 0.03746 ~~ℓ soln~~ = 0.005342 moles $SO_4^{=}$ = 0.005342 moles Sr^{++}. Thus the original solution must have contained 0.005342 moles of strontium nitrate.

Exercise 1.6

A 0.2033-g sample of uranium fluoride contains 0.0492 g of fluorine. What is the formula of the compound? *Answer:* Moles fluorine = 0.0492 g F/19.0 g F $mole^{-1}$ = 0.00261, moles uranium = (0.2043 – 0.0492) g U/238 g U $mole^{-1}$ = 0.000652. Mole ratio = 0.00261 moles F/0.000652 moles U = 4.00. Formula = UF_4. (Note three significant figures throughout.)

DETERMINATION OF CHEMICAL FORMULAS BY THE METHOD OF MIXTURES

A particularly simple and quite powerful method of determining chemical formulas was outlined by Job in 1928.*

Consider the general equation for a net reaction (with an example in parentheses):

$$M + nY = MY_n \qquad (Cu^{++}{}_{(aq)} + 4NH_{3(aq)} = Cu(NH_3)_4{}^{++}{}_{(aq)})$$

where the species may be either electrically neutral or charged. The equilibrium constant** for such an equation is

$$K = \frac{[MY_n]}{[M][Y]^n} \qquad \left(K = \frac{[Cu(NH_3)_4{}^{++}]}{[Cu^{++}][NH_3]^4}\right)$$

Suppose that the system is always set up in such a way that the sum of the total initial formal concentrations, $[M]_t$ and $[Y]_t$, in the mixture before reaction is a constant, $c = [M]_t + [Y]_t$.

If the equilibrium formal concentrations are [M], [Y], and $[MY_n]$, we can write the equations as

$$[M] = [M]_t - [MY_n],\ [Y] = [Y]_t - n[MY_n] = c - [M]_t - n[MY_n]$$

$$K = \frac{[MY_n]}{[M][Y]^n} = \frac{[MY_n]}{([M]_t - [MY_n])(c - [M]_t - n[MY_n])^n} \qquad (1.11)$$

Let us now explore the dependence of $[MY_n]$ on $[M]_t$ in this equation. That is, how does the equilibrium concentration, $[MY_n]$, of "product" vary when the sum of the initial concentrations of the reagents, c, is kept constant as described?

Consider first the case where K is very large and approaches infinity. All the M and Y that can react to give MY_n will do so, and the final concentration of MY_n will be determined by the reagent which is present in deficient quantity. Thus the final amount of MY_n can never exceed the initial amount of M, and will not even equal it if there is insufficient Y to react with all

* P. Job, *Ann. Chim.* (10), **9**, 113 (1928).

** The equilibrium constant for any chemical equation can readily be written as a fraction whose numerator contains a term equal to the concentration of each product and whose denominator contains a term equal to the concentration of each reactant, each term raised to a power equal to its coefficient in the net equation. The whole fraction equals K, the equilibrium constant. We shall use a symbol in square brackets to represent concentrations in moles per liter: [M] = moles per liter of species M.

the M initially present. Or, vice versa, the maximum amount of MY_n will be determined by the initial amount of Y if M is in excess. To produce the maximum amount of MY_n at equilibrium under these conditions, the necessary mathematical restriction is that $[Y]_t/[M]_t = n$.

Thus at maxima,

$$n = \frac{[Y]}{[M]} \left[\equiv \frac{[Y]_t}{[M]_t} \text{ at these stoichiometric ratios only} \right]$$

A plot of $[MY_n]$ versus $[M]_t$ for such a system will give a series of peaks. Each peak corresponds to a compound formed by M and Y, with the peak occurring at that value of $[M]_t$ for which $[Y]_t/[M]_t = n$ for that compound. Sharp peaks are obtained if K is large; as K diminishes the peaks become more and more rounded.

The maximum amount of reaction between the two components may be detected in many ways. Each of the components may be colorless and the compound colored, so that intensity of color measures the amount of compound formed. Or the compound may be insoluble, so that the amount formed is proportional to the amount of insoluble substance in each tube. The temperature change

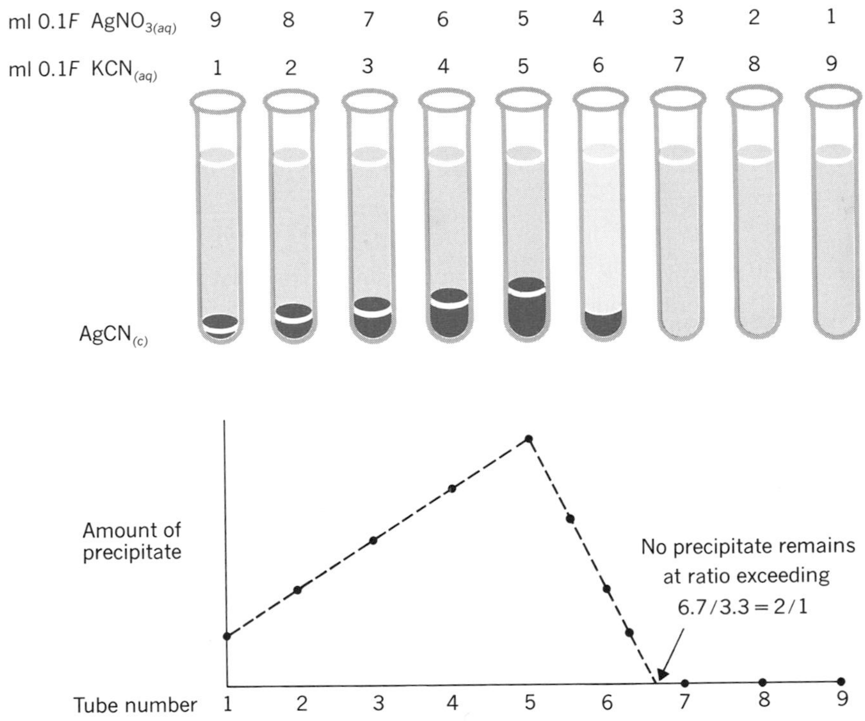

Figure 1.12 The method of mixtures (Job's method) applied to the Ag^+-CN^- system. Maximum precipitation occurs at equiformal amounts of $AgNO_{3(aq)}$ and $KCN_{(aq)}$, indicating precipitate contains equal numbers of moles of Ag^+ and CN^-. It has the formula $AgCN_{(c)}$. The tube 5–6 line (with data added from two more tubes) intersects the zero precipitate line at $CN^-/Ag^+ = 6.7/3.3 = 2/1$, indicating maximum reaction to give $Ag(CN)_2{}^-{}_{(aq)}$. [The murkiness in some tubes is caused by small particles of crystalline AgCN which have adsorbed some of the excess cyanide (or silver) ions on their surface. The resulting net charges keep the particles from colliding and settling.]

during reaction may also be noted, since maximum extent of reaction will give maximum temperature change. Many other observations are possible.

A particularly simple way of proceeding is to prepare equiformal solutions of the two reactants (approximately 0.1 F to start) and place the two solutions in 50-ml burets. To nine different test tubes then add 1, 2, 3, 4, 5, 6, 7, 8, and 9 ml of solution M respectively. Use the other buret containing Y to increase the total volume in each test tube to 10 ml by adding 9, 8, 7, 6, 5, 4, 3, 2, and 1 ml to the respective tubes. The total concentration of reactants is now the same in each tube. Shake the tubes and interpret the observed changes in terms of the ideas above. Intermediate measurements and/or use of different concentrations will then allow exact peak positions to be determined.

Figure 1.12 shows the result of carrying out this experiment with solutions of silver nitrate and potassium cyanide.

CONSERVATION LAWS

The conservation laws are most used in calculating "balances." We balanced, or conserved, both charges and numbers of atoms in writing equations. We balanced masses in calculating chemical formulas. In a similar fashion, chemists often use conservation laws dealing with such properties as energy, momentum, electron spin, and nuclear spin. Energy is the only one of these properties we shall deal with frequently in this course. The difficulty of measuring energy effects, in contrast to the easier counting of atoms and charges, explains the absence of energy terms in most equations.

It is widely recognized now that some of the conservation laws are intimately linked. For example, mass-energy is conserved more closely than either mass or energy alone.* This is another way of saying that the properties we call mass (as measured on a balance) and energy (as measured on a calorimeter) are two different aspects of the same property (mass-energy) and are readily converted back and forth into one another. They are related by the

EINSTEIN EQUATION: $$\Delta E = -c^2 \, \Delta m$$

where ΔE and Δm represent the related changes in energy, E, and mass, m. The conversion factor is c^2.** Dry ice and gaseous carbon dioxide may be used as an analogy. We may observe and measure dry ice and gaseous carbon dioxide with different devices (a balance for dry ice or a manometer for the gas), but the two substances are readily interconverted in several ways.

The conservation laws are also powerful in sorting possible changes from impossible ones. They are not very useful in selecting probable reactions from among all the possible ones. The equation, $H_3^- + He_2^- = H_2He^- + HeH^-$, is possible. It clearly satisfies the conservation of atoms, mass, and charge (and does not violate any other conservation laws), but the reaction will probably never be detected experimentally. Each species is highly improbable.

---

*Mass is measured either in terms of gravitational attraction or in terms of resistance of a particle to change in motion (momentum). Energy is usually measured in terms of ability to do work or to change the temperature of a system.

**If mass is measured in grams and E is measured in ergs, then c is the velocity of light in cm sec^{-1}, or $3.00 \cdot 10^{10}$ cm sec^{-1}.

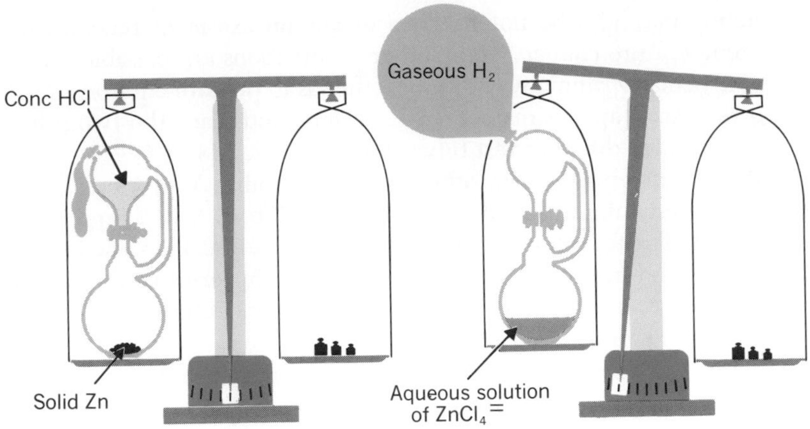

Figure 1.13 Change and conservation. *Conserved:* mass and charge (and some other quantities not specifically measured in the experiment). *Changed:* color, volume, physical state (and other quantities not specifically measured in the experiment).

In the actual experiment, conducted as shown, the balance will shift. The weight pan drops, the pan containing the reaction flask rises. What causes the shift in the balance? *Answer:* The volume of the reaction container increases (the balloon fills with H_2) during the reaction. The apparent change in weight during the reaction equals the difference between the weight of the hydrogen and the weight of the air displaced (Archimedes principle). However, there is no detectable change in mass during the reaction:

$$Zn_{(c)} + 4HCl_{(aq)} = ZnCl_4{}^{=}{}_{(aq)} + 2H^+{}_{(aq)} + H_{2(g)}$$

Nor are the conservation laws helpful in deciding the probable direction of a chemical reaction. Chemical equations, whether written "forward" or "backward," are consistent with the conservation laws, but the likelihood of the reaction proceeding with equal probability in both directions is small.

A little thought should lead to the realization that were everything conserved there could be no change. Since change is apparent all about us, there must be properties or quantities that are not conserved, but are changing. See Figure 1.13. It is to the nonconserved properties we must look for guidance with respect to change.

Exercise 1.7

Can a system lose energy and still conserve atoms? Can a system lose atoms and still conserve energy? *Answer:* Energy can be lost by radiation or conduction, neither of which involves loss of atoms, so energy can be gained or lost by a system which conserves atoms. On the other hand, loss of atoms always involves loss of energy: (1) the mass of the atom is itself an energy equivalent ($\Delta E = -c^2\,\Delta m$), and (2) the translational energy of the atom would be lost (except at 0°K, where no changes could occur).

ENTHALPY AND CHANGE

As far as the conservation laws can predict, any reaction for which one can write a chemical equation may occur sometime. But the reaction may be very improbable. How, then, do we know which reactions are probable and which are improbable?

The sure method is to try each reaction under every conceivable set of conditions and to tabulate the results. Early work proceeded in this manner. Clearly this is enormously time-consuming, and it may even lead to serious error if the reaction is not studied under all possible conditions. It would be much simpler if we could find some simple criteria related to reaction probability, which applied to all reactions over as wide a range of conditions as possible.

One of the earliest attempts to find such criteria culminated toward the end of the nineteenth century in the idea that reactions that generate heat as they proceed are the probable ones. Such systems, if maintained at constant temperature, must lose heat as reaction proceeds. Their change in heat content, ΔH (more usually called change in enthalpy) is negative.* Such changes are said to be exothermic. The data available led many chemists to assume that only exothermic reactions could occur spontaneously. Endothermic reactions (ΔH positive) would occur only if energy was supplied from the surroundings. ΔH seemed a possible predictor of spontaneity.

Although it is true that the great majority of the reactions we see about us each day are exothermic—the combustion of fuels, the operation of animal systems, solar reactions—there are many others that are endothermic. The reaction

$$CaCO_{3(c)} = CaO_{(c)} + CO_{2(g)}$$

is endothermic but spontaneous at high temperatures. You have certainly noted the cooling effect of the evaporation of a liquid, an endothermic process. The process of solution of a crystal in a liquid is usually endothermic. The shortening of a stretched rubber band is a spontaneous endothermic process. No informed person can any longer believe that all spontaneous reactions are exothermic. Furthermore many exothermic reactions are not spontaneous. The reaction

$$2NO_{2(g)} = N_2O_{4(l)}$$

is exothermic, as is the condensing of gaseous water to liquid, but both reactions are improbable at, for example, 150°C and 1 atm pressure.

ENTROPY, PROBABILITY, AND CHANGE

The currently accepted solution to the problem of identifying probable changes was suggested in 1824 by the French engineer Sadi Carnot. Almost a hundred years went by before his idea was widely applied to chemical processes. Today Carnot's suggestion has been formalized in terms of entropy changes—one of the most powerful generalizations known to mankind. It is called the second law of thermodynamics.

The second law of thermodynamics may be stated in many ways, as shown in Appendix III. For the moment we shall use the first statement there:

"Every system which is left to itself will, on the average, change toward a condition of maximum probability."—G. N. Lewis

---

* We shall use the delta symbol, Δ, to mean "change in." Thus, if the enthalpy of a system changes from H_1 to H_2, we say that $\Delta H = H_2 - H_1$.

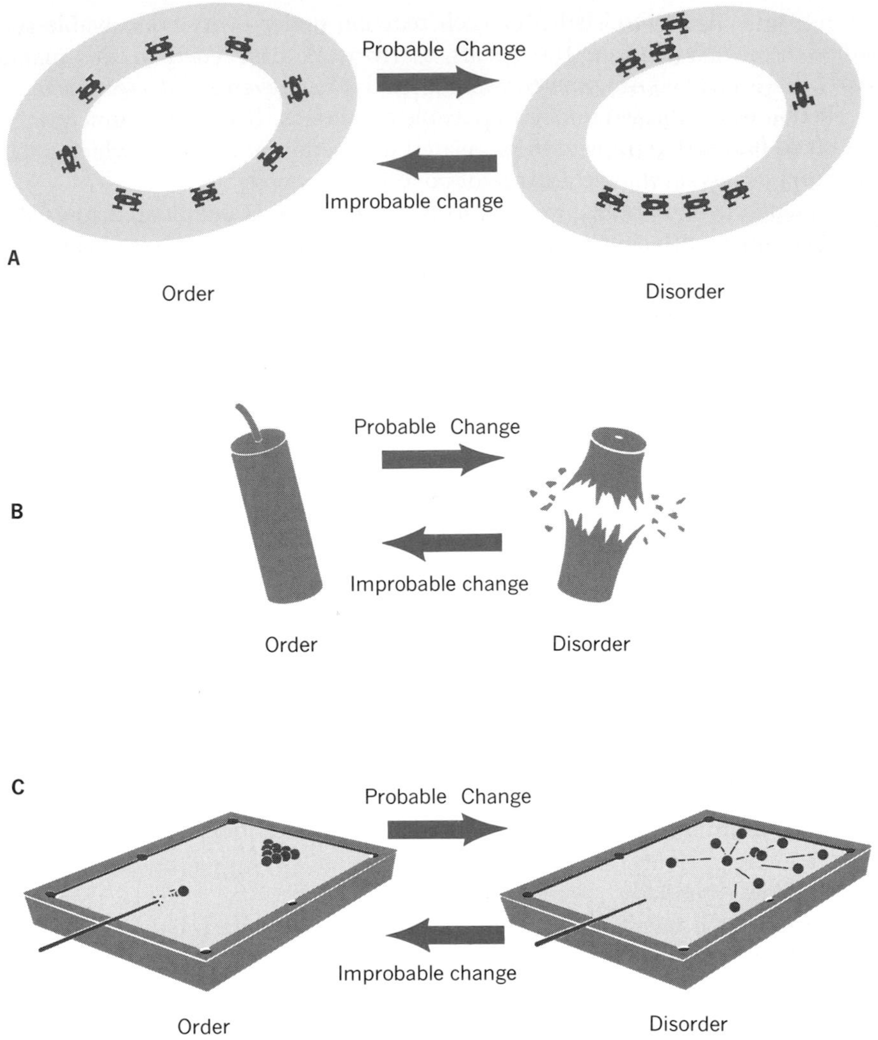

Figure 1.14 Probable changes lead to disorder.

We shall discuss probability and its relation to entropy at considerable length in Chapters 9, 10, and 28. For the moment, qualitative relationships will be sufficient, plus the definition that increase in probability means increase in entropy and vice versa. Since systems left to themselves "change toward a condition of maximum probability" such spontaneous changes must involve an increase in the entropy. ΔS is positive for all spontaneous changes in a system left to itself.

An improbable state is one which can be achieved in only a few ways. A probable state can be achieved in many ways. For example, regular spacing of cars on a racetrack or a freeway, as in Figure 1.14, is improbable since it can be achieved in only one way—all distances the same. Disordered sequences of cars separated by various distances are much more probable; they can be achieved in many ways. A firecracker is more ordered before it explodes than afterwards. The parts initially are related in an ordered way to one another. After explosion they are scattered randomly and the pieces and energy are dissipated through a larger volume; they are more disordered. Racked-up pool balls about to be hit by the cue ball are a much less probable arrangement than the resulting distribution of balls rolling around the table. Again both the particles and the energy are more widely distributed in the final state.

You have no doubt seen motion pictures run backwards. The most amusing sequences are normally those in which order increases, rather than those in which things merely reverse their directions. We are so used to the general trend toward more probable (less ordered) states, that apparently spontaneous reversals in this trend seem humorous.

Consider some of the simpler examples mentioned in the preceding section, changes occurring at the molecular level. The reaction

$$CaCO_{3(c)} = CaO_{(c)} + CO_{2(g)}$$

produces a gas and a crystal from a crystal. Disorder increases since gases are more disordered than crystals. When a liquid evaporates (an endothermic process), it goes from a condensed drop in which there are a relatively small number of ways in which the molecules can arrange themselves, to a diffuse gas in which there are many possible arrangements and positions available to each molecule. When a crystalline substance dissolves in a liquid, the molecules move from the tightly packed, highly ordered crystalline structure to the much more diffuse, more disordered, more probable distribution throughout the liquid. When a rubber band shortens, the molecules move from the extended, or stretched, configuration in which each molecule is forced to be more or less linear, to a relaxed or coiled position in which each molecule can assume many configurations. The coiled condition is much more probable, since there are many ways of coiling a molecule but only one of stretching it out linearly. Remember that all these reactions are endothermic. Complete examination of all endothermic reactions shows that only those are spontaneous which involve a change from an ordered to a disordered system.

Many exothermic systems also produce disorder in the local system. The combustion of gasoline, $C_7H_{16(l)} + 11O_{2(g)} = 7CO_{2(g)} = 8H_2O_{(g)}$, produces 15 moles of gas from 11 moles of gas and one of liquid. The reaction of Figure 1.13, $Zn_{(c)} + 2H^+_{(aq)} = Zn^{++}_{(aq)} + H_{2(g)}$, produces a gas and consumes a crystal, the ions staying in solution. ΔS is positive for both systems. But many exothermic reactions produce local order in the reacting system so that ΔS of the system is negative. Consider $2NO_{2(g)} = N_2O_{4(l)}$ + heat, or $NH_{3(g)} + HCl_{(g)} = NH_4Cl_{(c)}$ + heat, or the crystallization of any pure liquid. All these are exothermic reactions (ΔH positive) with an increase in local molecular order (ΔS negative for the system). No such endothermic reactions are known. The interpretation of this fact may remind you of the equivalence of mass and energy in the conservation laws. A similar parallelism between matter and energy is shown in entropy changes.

CONFIGURATIONAL AND THERMAL ENTROPY

Entropy can change: (1) due to a change in configurational entropy (for example, increase in particle or molecular disorder as by the dissipation of matter into a larger volume), or (2) due to a change in thermal entropy (for example, an increase in thermal disorder as by dissipation of heat into a larger volume or as by dissipation of potential energy as heat). In the $N_2O_{4(l)}$, $NH_4Cl_{(c)}$, and crystallizing liquid cases in the last paragraph, the molecular order increases, but is always accompanied by a large increase in the thermal disorder (much heat generated). This heat either raises the temperature of the system or escapes to the surroundings or both. In each case the increase in thermal disorder is more than enough to offset the decrease in molecular order of the system. When this condition is no longer met, net reaction ceases; the entropy of the universe has reached a maximum.

THE SYSTEM, SURROUNDINGS, AND UNIVERSE

According to the second law, the total entropy change for a spontaneous reaction must be positive, usually stated as "the entropy of the universe increases." But it is often convenient to divide the universe into the system of immediate interest and its surroundings. Then

$$\Delta S_{univ} = \Delta S_{sys} + \Delta S_{sur}$$

ΔS_{univ} must be positive, but either ΔS_{sys} or ΔS_{sur} may be negative as long as their algebraic sum is positive. In discussing values of ΔS it is essential to specify which ΔS is meant and to define the system clearly. Similarly, either in the system or in the surroundings, the configurational entropy change and the thermal entropy change may have either the same or opposite signs. The important limitation is that only those reactions will be spontaneous for which the sum of all the accompanying entropy changes is positive. If calculations show that ΔS_{univ} is negative for a reaction, we know the reaction will be improbable. The more negative the value of ΔS_{univ}, the more improbable the reaction. The more positive the value of ΔS_{univ}, the more probable the reaction.

For any reaction there are at least three values of ΔS which might be of interest: ΔS_{univ}, ΔS_{sur}, and ΔS_{sys}. In most cases it is ΔS_{sys} to which one refers. Thus the simple, unsubscripted form, ΔS, usually refers to the entropy change in the system under discussion. The most common system in this course will be one undergoing a chemical reaction. Such a system is usually composed of the reactants and the products listed in the chemical equation.

It is interesting to note that entropy effects were discussed by Carnot before the discovery of the conservation of energy. Yet we call the conservation of energy the first law and the entropy principle the second law of thermodynamics, reversing their historical order.

Exercise 1.8

Apply the concept of increasing entropy (order $\longrightarrow$ disorder) to several common changes. *Answer:* (1) Writing with a pen spreads ink from the pen over a large surface and leads to evaporation of the solvent. (2) Living, for animals, involves ingesting highly ordered, complicated molecules (starches, carbohydrates) and excreting mostly small molecules, such as disordered gaseous carbon dioxide and water. (3) Burning gasoline in a car also produces smaller molecules and also distributes the energy produced over a large volume.

THE ESTIMATION (SIGN) OF ΔH

We have seen that ΔH is a useful property for estimating probability of reaction because of its relation to thermal entropy and ΔS. Let us see how ΔH can be measured.

The formation of a bond between any two atoms is always exothermic and the breaking of a bond is always endothermic. ΔH will be negative if stronger bonds form among the products than are broken among the reactants. Thus guessing ΔH requires considerable chemical background and intuition concerning bond strengths. But the sign of ΔH can be determined merely by noting if the system warms ($\Delta H = -$) or cools ($\Delta H = +$) when reaction occurs faster than heat can leave or enter the system.

As a matter of fact, the numerical measurement of ΔH is quite simple in many cases, since $\Delta H = C\Delta T$ (assuming constant values of the heat capacity, C*, over the temperature range ΔT). If known quantities of the reactants are mixed in the correct proportion for reaction according to the equation, and if the reaction proceeds almost completely, then a simple measurement of the change in temperature often allows an estimation of the heat of reaction at constant pressure, ΔH. Suppose that 50.0 ml each of 0.200 F hydrogen chloride and sodium hydroxide are mixed. The observed temperature rise is 1.35°C (or °K). Assuming the heat capacity to be the same as that of the 100 ml of water present, a total of 135 calories of heat are liberated. The reaction occurs between 0.0100 mole of hydrogen ion and the same number of moles of hydroxide ion to form 0.01 mole of water, and liberates 135 calories:

$$H^+_{(aq)} + OH^-_{(aq)} = H_2O_{(l)} + 135 \text{ calories per } 0.0100 \text{ mole}$$

or, for one mole reacting,

$$H^+_{(aq)} + OH^-_{(aq)} = H_2O_{(l)} + 13.5 \text{ kcal mole}^{-1}$$

The accepted value for ΔH is -13.345 kcal mole^{-1}, which is in good agreement with our figure. Note that ΔH will be negative, since heat must be *lost* from the system if T is to remain constant. The diffusion of the escaping energy to the surroundings increases ΔS_{sur} and tends to make the reaction a probable one.

One handy generalization in guessing the sign of ΔH is that bonds between unlike atoms tend to be stronger than bonds between like atoms. Thus we would guess ΔH to be negative for all the following reactions at constant T.

$SO_{2(g)} + \frac{1}{2}O_{2(g)} = SO_{3(g)}$	S—O bond stronger than O—O bond
$2H_{2(g)} + O_{2(g)} = 2H_2O_{(g)}$	H—O bond stronger than average of H—H and O—O bond
$H_{2(g)} + C_2H_{4(g)} = C_2H_{6(g)}$	C—H bond stronger than average of H—H and C—C bond

*The heat capacity, C, is the amount of heat required to raise the temperature of a system one degree. The most common units in chemistry are cal per degree Centigrade, cal (°C)$^{-1}$, which is identical to cal per degree Kelvin, cal (°K)$^{-1}$. Molar heat capacity, C, is usually in units of cal (°K)$^{-1}$ mole^{-1}. The calorie is defined in terms of electrical units, but for all practical purposes one calorie will heat one gram of water one degree Centigrade.

$H_{2(g)} + Cl_{2(g)} = 2HCl_{(g)}$	H—Cl bond stronger than average of H—H and Cl—Cl bond
$2Br_{(g)} = Br_{2(g)}$	Br—Br bond forms

For the moment, guessing and/or a thermometer will guide you with regard to ΔH, but there is much accurate data tabulated: for example, the National Bureau of Standards Circular 500 by Rossini et al., and the National Bureau of Standards Technical Note 270 by Wagman et al. See also Table 27.1.

Exercise 1.9

Is ΔH positive if a system tends to heat up during a given change? *Answer:* If the system tends to heat up, it will also tend to lose energy to its surroundings. Loss of energy means a negative ΔH, an exothermic change. If ΔH is positive, the change will tend to cool the system.

CHANGES IN CLOSED SYSTEMS AT CONSTANT TEMPERATURE AND CONSTANT PRESSURE

Many chemical changes in the laboratory take place in a system which conserves atoms (such a system is called a closed system), at conditions of constant temperature and constant pressure. The pressure, P, is often kept constant by leaving the system open to the atmosphere (but not letting matter escape). The temperature, T, is often kept constant by letting energy escape (if the reaction is exothermic) or supplying energy by heating (if the reaction is endothermic). From our previous discussion it should be clear that exothermic reactions tend to be the more probable ones, since they tend to diffuse energy concentrated in the system to a more probable state in which it is spread through the surroundings. Endothermic reactions, on the contrary, tend to concentrate energy within the system, and thus are more improbable. Note again the emphasis on defining the system. In a closed system at constant T a change which is exothermic for the system, and hence tends to be probable for the system, is of course endothermic with respect to the surroundings.

At the same time, changes within the system which increase molecular disorder are also probable, since they increase the configurational entropy; changes which increase molecular order in the system are improbable, since these tend to decrease the configurational entropy. One must consider both enthalpy and entropy effects to determine the actual probability of reaction.

The exact statement of the above generalizations, combining the effects due to enthalpy and entropy, is given in thermodynamic terms as the

FREE ENERGY EQUATION:

$$\Delta G = \Delta H - T\Delta S \qquad (1.12)$$

Only those reactions for which ΔG is negative are probable in closed systems at constant T and P. Improbable reactions are those for which ΔG is positive. ΔG is called the change (Δ) in the Gibbs free energy (G); ΔH is the change in the heat content (H), preferably called the enthalpy; T is the Kelvin temperature; and ΔS is the change in the entropy (S) of the closed system.

Table 1.3 Effect of signs of ΔH and ΔS on ΔG (hence tendency of reaction to occur) in $\Delta G = \Delta H - T\,\Delta S$.

	ΔH	ΔS	ΔG		
Exothermic	−	+	−	always;	reaction goes as written
	−	−	−	at low T;	reaction goes as written at low T
Endothermic	+	+	−	at high T;	reaction goes as written at high T
	+	−	+	always;	reaction occurs in reverse direction

It should be clear that negative values of ΔH, and/or positive values of ΔS (especially at high temperatures) tend to give negative values of ΔG, which indicate possible reactions. These relations are summarized in Table 1.3.

Exercise 1.10

What combination of signs for ΔH and ΔS will surely produce a positive value for ΔG and so ensure that the change will not occur in a closed system at constant T and P? *Answer:* A positive value of ΔH (endothermic reaction) and a negative value of ΔS (since T is always positive) make ΔG positive. Thus no probable changes are known for which ΔH is positive and ΔS is simultaneously negative in a closed system at constant T and P.

CHANGES STARTING FROM THE STANDARD STATE

The sign of ΔS for the system may be guessed in many cases by inspection of the equation for the net reaction. Thus, solution of crystals in a liquid will probably result in an increase in configurational entropy. Similarly, liberation of a gas from a solution will probably result in an increase in the configurational entropy. Both these types of reaction are probable ones.

In the most general case, the formation of any new molecules increases the number of ways the atoms could be distributed, and thus increases the disorder and increases the entropy. The change of any system of "pure reactants" toward forming products represented by a chemical equation *must* involve an increase in entropy and must, therefore, be a probable reaction.

This possibility of creating molecules not previously present in the system is a sufficient logical basis for the statement: all possible reactions (all reactions for which a chemical equation can be written) will occur. Since all possible reactions will occur, though perhaps only to a very slight extent, we have a case of trivial interest in most instances. Note that the formation of one new molecule from a mole of reactants ($6.02 \cdot 10^{23}$ molecules) would be a most unlikely reaction indeed. It would also be undetectable. Many possible reactions are even less likely than this example.

A more interesting problem at this stage in your chemical knowledge is the likelihood of reaction if all the reactants and all the products listed in the chemical equation are initially mixed. In this case, no new types of molecules will form and we can discuss the likelihood that the atoms present in the closed system will react and redistribute themselves in mole ratios different from the ratios used in making up the initial system. Such reactions are called reactions in the standard state. The standard state we will use is defined as one containing all the reactants and products (1) in the pure state if they are crystalline substances or liquids, (2) at one atmosphere pressure if they are gases, (3) at 1 *F* concentration (one formula weight in grams per liter of solution) if they are dissolved in a solvent, and (4) at a specified temperature.

It is customary to write the criterion for change from a standard state as the

FREE ENERGY EQUATION: $$\Delta G_T{}^0 = \Delta H_T{}^0 - T\,\Delta S^0 \tag{1.13}$$

The superscript zeroes enable one to read the equation as "delta *G* standard equals delta *H* standard minus *T* delta *S* standard." The sub *T* indicates the constant temperature.

If ΔG^0 for the reaction is positive, that reaction is unlikely in the standard state. But note one important corollary. A positive value of ΔG^0 means that the reverse reaction ("products" to give "reactants") *is* likely in the standard state, since ΔG^0 for this reverse reaction will be negative. That is to say, the signs of ΔG, ΔH, and ΔS reverse when a reaction is reversed, but their numerical values are unchanged. Table 1.3 summarizes the contributions of ΔH and ΔS to ΔG. Remember that ΔG^0 must be negative for a net reaction to occur in the standard state in the direction indicated by the chemical equation.

Exercise 1.11

Define the standard state for the reaction, $Zn_{(c)} + 2H^+{}_{(aq)} = H_{2(g)} + Zn^{++}{}_{(aq)}$. *Answer:* In the standard state you would have an aqueous solution which was 1 *F* in hydrogen ion (perhaps from aqueous HCl), 1 *F* in zinc ion (perhaps from aqueous $ZnSO_4$), and in contact with both pure, crystalline zinc and gaseous hydrogen at one atmosphere pressure of hydrogen, all at a specified *T*.

THE ESTIMATION (SIGN) OF ΔS^0

For most reactions, ΔH as measured by simple thermometer experiments such as just described is very nearly equal to ΔH^0. But ΔS varies greatly with the state of the system.

If often turns out to be quite easy to guess the sign of ΔS^0 from the net equation. For example, gases are much more disordered than condensed phases. Thus reactions in which the number of moles of gaseous molecules increase tend to have positive values of ΔS^0.

	ΔS^0 (entropy units = cal mole^{-1} °K^{-1} = eu)
$Br_{2(g)} = 2Br_{(g)}$	+25.0; moles of gas increase, $\Delta n = +1$
$2H_2O_{(g)} = 2H_{2(g)} + O_{2(g)}$	+21.2; moles of gas increase, $\Delta n = +1$
$2HCl_{(g)} = H_{2(g)} + Cl_{2(g)}$	−4.8; no change in number of moles of gas, $\Delta n = 0$
$SO_{2(g)} + \frac{1}{2}O_{2(g)} = SO_{3(g)}$	−22.7; moles of gas decrease, $\Delta n = -\frac{1}{2}$
$H_{2(g)} + C_2H_{4(g)} = C_2H_{6(g)}$	−28.8; moles of gas decrease, $\Delta n = -1$

We have already discussed the sign of ΔH for these reactions.

Solutions are more disordered than pure phases. Thus reactions in which substances disperse into one another tend to have positive values for ΔS^0. Conversely, the formation of pure condensed phases such as precipitates tends to give negative signs to ΔS^0.

	ΔS^0 (entropy units = cal mole^{-1} °K^{-1} = eu)	
$NH_4Cl_{(c)} = NH_4^+{}_{(aq)} + Cl^-{}_{(aq)}$	+18.0	The ions have less order (greater randomness) in the solution than in the corresponding crystal. (Note that these entropy changes are smaller than those in which a mole of gas is formed, even though two moles of ions form in each instance here.)
$AgCl_{(c)} = Ag^+{}_{(aq)} + Cl^-{}_{(aq)}$	+7.9	
$AgBr_{(c)} = Ag^+{}_{(aq)} + Br^-{}_{(aq)}$	+11.5	
$AgI_{(c)} = Ag^+{}_{(aq)} + I^-{}_{(aq)}$	+16.4	

If a reaction proceeds in a condensed phase (as do many reactions in aqueous solutions, for example), condensation of several species into a smaller number tends to give a negative sign to ΔS^0, and net dissociation of substances into a larger number of fragments tends to give a positive sign to ΔS^0.

A difficulty that arises here is that net equations often give few clues as to changes in the interactions between the solvent and the dissolved materials. Thus the reaction of an acid and a base in water, as in the net equation

$$H^+{}_{(aq)} + OH^-{}_{(aq)} = H_2O, \qquad \Delta S^0 = 19.28 \text{ eu}$$

might have been guessed to involve a negative ΔS^0, since condensation of two particles to one occurs. However, each of the ions interacts strongly with surrounding water molecules. These interactions are destroyed during the reaction, freeing the previously bound water molecules and increasing their entropy. This, of course, tends to give a positive sign to ΔS^0 for the reaction. The observed value, +19.28 entropy units (eu = cal mole^{-1} °K^{-1}) indicates the importance of the solvent interaction on the entropy term. This effect is most severe when H^+ ions are involved, since they interact very strongly indeed with water. With most solvents and most solutes the effect of solvent-solute changes on ΔS^0 is much smaller than the other effects discussed and often negligible.

For ΔS^0, as for ΔH^0, standard compilations of data exist. Some typical data are listed in Table 27.1. For the present you should learn to guess signs for ΔH^0 and ΔS^0.

Starting with the equation for the net reaction, one may get considerable insight into the sign of ΔG^0 from a guess as to the signs of ΔS^0 and ΔH^0. Remember that the sign of T is always positive, for T equals the Kelvin temperature at which the experiment is performed. A negative sign for ΔG^0 indicates that the reaction in the standard state is probable as written. A positive sign for ΔG^0 indicates that the reaction in the standard state is probable in the direction reverse to that written in the net equation.

Exercise 1.12

Estimate the sign of ΔS^0 for the reaction $CaCO_{3(c)} + 2H^+{}_{(aq)} = Ca^{++}{}_{(aq)} + H_2O + CO_{2(g)}$. *Answer:* Entropy is increased by the solution of the crystalline $CaCO_3$, by the formation of gaseous CO_2, and by the freeing of hydrated water from the $H^+{}_{(aq)}$. Entropy is decreased by the hydration of water by $Ca^{++}{}_{(aq)}$, and, possibly, by the uniting of hydrogen ions into water molecules. Net effect should be an increase in entropy due to dominance of crystal and gas effects.

THE PRECIPITATION OF $CaCO_3$

A very common reaction in nature is the formation of calcium carbonate, $CaCO_3$, from aqueous solutions containing calcium ions and carbonate ions. Formation of pearls, shells, and limestone caves all involve precipitation of $CaCO_3$. We may represent the net reaction as

$$Ca^{++}_{(aq)} + CO_3{}^{=}_{(aq)} = CaCO_{3(c)}, \qquad \Delta G^0 = -11.38 \text{ kcal}$$

Our simple rules would lead us to predict that ΔS^0 is negative (since 2 moles of dispersed ions form 1 mole of crystal) and ΔH^0 is negative (since the bonds between closely packed ions in a crystal are stronger than the bonds between the same ions in the solution). Actually $\Delta S^0 = +48.1$ cal °K^{-1} and $\Delta H^0 = +3.0$ kcal per mole of $CaCO_{3(c)}$ for this reaction. Why would both our simple guesses be incorrect?

The answer lies in the very strong interaction between the ions, especially the calcium ions, and the water. The increase in entropy due to the release, or freeing, of water bound to the ions more than offsets the loss in entropy due to crystallization. Furthermore, the energy required to break the water molecules free from the ions is greater than the energy released when the ions crystallize and the freed water molecules interact. Figure 1.15 shows these effects and their trends for all of the alkaline earth carbonates. Note that ΔH and ΔS both get smaller as the positive ion gets larger, and hence less tightly hydrated.

Thus the low solubility of calcium carbonate in water is due even more to the low entropy of the hydrated ions in solution than to the strong bonding in the solid. Figure 4.9 shows that Ca^{++} is one of the smallest ions. This, plus its +2 electric charge, gives high charge density on the ions and large interactions with surrounding water molecules. You should anticipate similar effects with other small, highly charged ions. See Table 27.1 for further data.

PROPERTIES AND CHANGE

Direct observation of many substances can be made by anyone. We see color, size, shape, and texture. We smell a wide range of odors, hear a wide range of sounds, and sense tactilely a large variety of such sensations as heat, roughness, and wetness. But we appear to differentiate only four or five types of taste.

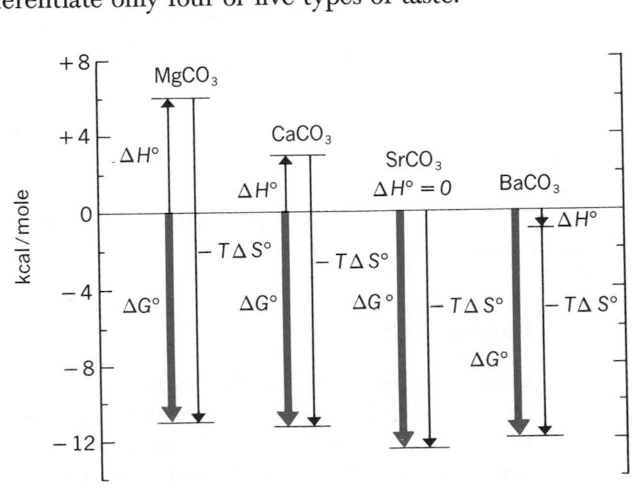

Figure 1.15 $\Delta G^0 = \Delta H^0 - T\Delta S^0$ for $M^{++}_{(aq)} + CO_3{}^{=}_{(aq)} = MCO_{3(c)}$ at 25°C (M = Mg^{++}, Ca^{++}, Sr^{++}, Ba^{++}). Note trends. [Strong and Stratton, *Chemical Energy*, Reinhold, 1965.]

One of the problems of the chemist is to translate these sense impressions, often aided by more or less complex instruments, into descriptions expressed in terms of atomic and molecular behavior. He does this usually by finding a property that is constant under certain laboratory conditions, but which changes when conditions change. He thus often combines measurements made in a static or unchanging initial condition with measurements made in a dynamic, changing condition, and interprets both in terms of atomic-molecular properties. But it should not be assumed that static bulk properties, such as color, require static atoms and molecules. Many systems that are apparently static at the bulk level are highly dynamic at the molecular level.

This combination of dynamics and statics is one reason that many chemical systems are too complicated to be completely understood at present. For example, very few chemical systems can be rigorously described in the mathematical terms available today. Some of the appropriate mathematical equations can be written, but not solved: some of the equations are not even known. Yet a great number of problems can be solved analytically, and mathematical approaches are becoming more and more useful in chemistry.

The present lack of suitable mathematical techniques forces chemists to combine a qualitative, intuitive approach with a more exact quantitative one. In this respect the chemist stands between the physicist (and his more mathematically tractable systems) and the biologist (with his more complicated systems). One of the most useful concepts for the chemist is that of the nuclear atom, all treatments of which are partly qualitative and partly quantitative. We shall explore some of these treatments in Chapter 2.

SUMMARY

Three of the most common problems for chemists are to determine (1) chemical formulas, (2) chemical equations, and (3) probabilities of chemical reaction. Formulas are obtainable from analytical data, equations from formulas plus further experiments on reacting ratios, and reaction probabilities from direct experiment or from tabulated data on enthalpies, entropies, and free energies of reaction.

The conservation laws tell us what changes are possible. Chemical equations explicitly describe the conservation of atoms and charge, the usual unit being one mole, or $6.02 \cdot 10^{23}$ units (atoms, molecules, charges). Many chemical equations also explicitly describe the conservation of energy. In chemical terms, any reaction for which an equation can be written is not only possible but will actually happen. But the conservation laws alone do not tell how probable the reaction is. They give no guidance to the relative likelihood of various reactions nor to the time required to produce reaction. Thus most reactions for which equations can be written are very unlikely and will not be detectable.

Though all possible changes will happen sometime, only those changes are probable which are accompanied by an entropy increase in the universe. In a closed system at constant temperature and pressure (one of the most common laboratory conditions) the likelihood of reaction is interpreted in terms of the

FREE ENERGY EQUATION: $$\Delta G = \Delta H - T\Delta S$$

Probable reactions have negative values of ΔG, the Gibbs free energy. Negative values of ΔG occur when the reactions are exothermic (negative value of ΔH, stronger bonds form than are broken) and/or when the reactions have positive values of ΔS for the system under consideration (local disorder increases). The Kelvin temperature also influences the probability of reaction as shown in the equation. All these terms can be measured quantitatively, allowing the calculation of numerical values for ΔG; but we shall, for awhile, be satisfied with estimating the signs of ΔH and ΔS and so guessing the sign of ΔG and the probable direction of the reaction. The likelihood of a correct guess is increased by dealing with reactions in the standard state.

Chemical equations delimit the possible reactions, and the sign and magnitude of the entropy, heat content, and free energy changes, and the temperature define the probability of reactions. But these terms alone do not give information on the rate of reactions. The rate of a reaction depends on other factors which we shall explore later.

I think that anyone who asks the question about scientific effectiveness will also conclude that much of the mathematizing in physics and chemistry today is irrelevent if not misleading.
Many—perhaps most—of the great issues of science are qualitative, not quantitative, even in physics and chemistry. Equations and measurements are useful when and only when they are related to proof; but proof or disproof comes first and is in fact strongest when it is absolutely convincing without any quantitative measurement
—John R. Platt, Science, **146,** 351 (1964).

PROBLEMS

Each chapter is followed by problems, usually three sets. The groups differ primarily in the time you might be expected to spend on a single problem (or part of a multiple problem). Perhaps a dozen from group I, or five to eight from group II, or two or three from group III might make up a typical one-hour examination. You can, thus, estimate your own performance while working on them. Within each group there may be three types of problems; colored numbers designate those dealing with the most important sections of the text, large black numbers those based on intermediate sections, and small black numbers those dealing with portions of the text in small type. The ability to work readily and correctly at least half of the color-numbered problems in each of the first groups will indicate that you have at least a minimal competence in using the techniques chemists employ to approach new situations. Approximate answers to many problems are given in parentheses.

1.1. All the following formulas are correct. Apply the ideas of conservation of atoms and of charge to obtain equations.

(*a*) $B_4H_{10(g)} + O_{2(g)} \longrightarrow B_2O_{3(c)} + H_2O_{(g)}$

(*b*) $Sc(NO_3)_{3(c)} + H_2PO_4^-{}_{(aq)} \longrightarrow ScPO_{4(c)} + H^+{}_{(aq)} + NO_3^-{}_{(aq)}$

(*c*) $Pt(CN)_6{}^{-4}{}_{(aq)} + O_{2(g)} + H_2O \longrightarrow Pt(CN)_6{}^{-2}{}_{(aq)} + OH^-{}_{(aq)}$
(*d*) $La_2(SiO_3)_{3(c)} + HF_{(g)} \longrightarrow LaF_{3(c)} + SiF_{4(g)} + H_2O_{(g)}$
(*e*) $H_2O_{(l)} + F_{2(g)} \longrightarrow HF_{(aq)} + O_{3(g)}$
(*f*) $S_2O_8{}^{=}{}_{(aq)} + BiO^+{}_{(aq)} + H_2O_{(l)} \longrightarrow Bi_2O_{4(c)} + SO_4{}^{=}{}_{(aq)} + H^+{}_{(aq)}$
(*g*) $NH_3OH^+{}_{(aq)} + HNO_{2(aq)} \longrightarrow$
$N_2O_{4(g)} + N_2H_5{}^+{}_{(aq)}$ (add H_2O and $H^+{}_{(aq)}$ as needed)
(*h*) $RhO^{++}{}_{(aq)} + SbO^+{}_{(aq)} \longrightarrow$
$Rh^{+++}{}_{(aq)} + Sb_2O_{4(c)}$ (add H_2O and H^+ as needed)
(*i*) $Pd[C_2H_4(NH_2)_2]_2Cl^+{}_{(aq)} + MnO_4{}^-{}_{(aq)} \longrightarrow$
$PdO^{++}{}_{(aq)} + CO_{2(g)} + N_{2(g)} + H_2O + Cl_{2(g)} + Mn^{++}{}_{(aq)}$
(add H_2O and H^+ as needed)
(*j*) $H_2O_{2(l)} + O_{3(g)} \longrightarrow H_2O_{(l)} + O_{2(g)}$ (*Note:* There are many different ratios of coefficients which will give an equation here. Can you see why?)

1.2. Find an alchemical symbol in addition to that for iron oxide which indicates that the alchemists knew the substance was a "compound."

1.3. Why do both a stopcock and a side tube connect the upper and lower glass bulbs in Figure 1.13?

1.4. Complete the following table for the reaction indicated.

	$CaH_{2(c)}$ +	$2H_2O_{(g)}$	=	$Ca(OH)_{2(c)}$ +	$2H_{2(g)}$
(*a*) (moles)	2 moles +	______	$\longrightarrow$	______ +	______
(*b*) (grams)	42 g +	______	$\longrightarrow$	______ +	______
(*c*) (atoms of hydrogen)	$6.02 \cdot 10^{23}$ +	______	$\longrightarrow$	______ +	______
(*d*) (ft³ of gas)		10 ft³	$\longrightarrow$		______

1.5. Which of the following equations, as written, describe probable reactions? Justify your answers as completely as possible. All formulas and descriptions of physical state are correct. Which reactions will become more probable as *T* increases? (For example, *a* will.)
(*a*) $2H^+{}_{(aq)} + CaCO_{3(c)} = Ca^{++}{}_{(aq)} + CO_{2(g)} + H_2O$
(*b*) $CH_{4(g)} + 2O_{2(g)} = CO_{2(g)} + 2H_2O_{(g)}$
(*c*) $C_{12}H_{22}O_{11(c)} = 12C_{(c)} + 11H_2O_{(g)}$
(*d*) $MgO_{(c)} = Mg_{(c)} + \frac{1}{2}O_{2(g)}$

1.6. Which of the following probably result in a decrease in the entropy of the system (negative ΔS^0) at constant *T* and *P* (all gases)? (For example, *a* does.)

(*a*) $H_2C{=}CH{-}CH_2{-}CH_3 \longrightarrow$ 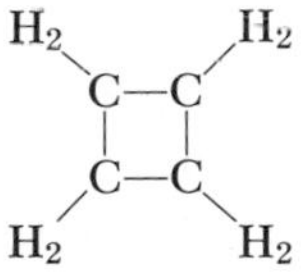

(*b*) $H_2C{=}CH{-}CH_2{-}CH_3 + H_2 \longrightarrow H_3C{-}CH_2{-}CH_2{-}CH_3$
(*c*) $H_2C{=}CH{-}CH_2{-}CH_3 \longrightarrow H_2C{=}CH{-}CH{=}CH_2 + H_2$
(*d*) $H_2C{=}CH{-}CH_2{-}CH_3 \longrightarrow H_3C{-}CH_2{-}CH{=}CH_2$
(*e*) $H_2C{=}CH{-}CH_2{-}CH_3 \longrightarrow H_3C{-}CH{=}CH{-}CH_3$

1.7. 0.9418 g of oxygen will exactly combine with 1.0582 g of aluminum. 10 g of aluminum are burned in 10 g of oxygen until one of the reagents is consumed. Is either aluminum or oxygen present in excess? What weight of aluminum oxide is formed? (19 g Al_2O_3.)

1.8. 6.20 g of a certain compound was burned in a stream of chlorine gas. The products were collected and identified to be 21.9 g HCl, 30.8 g CCl_4, and 10.3 g SCl_2. Assuming that the compound contains only carbon, hydrogen, and sulfur, what is its simplest formula?

1.9. Use arguments based on ΔH^0 and ΔG^0 to answer the following (consider high and low T).
(*a*) Will H_2 react with C_4H_8 to give C_4H_{10} (all gases)?
(*b*) Will gaseous SF_6 intermingle with gaseous Xe?
(c) Will crystalline $C_{10}H_8$ burn in air to give CO_2 and H_2O?
(*d*) Will oxygen react with crystalline rhodium?

II

1.10. A thermometer is inserted into each of the following closed systems at the moment that almost complete reaction occurs, at constant pressure, to form 0.0100 moles of product in 100 ml of water. The temperature changes, ΔT, are given in °K.
(*a*) Calculate ΔH for each reaction in kcal mole^{-1}.
(*b*) Guess the sign of ΔS^0 for each reaction from the net equation. Give the reasons for your guess.
(*c*) Indicate which sign or signs of ΔS^0 are certain to be as you have guessed them. Give your reasons.

	ΔT	ΔH	ΔS^0	Certain?
i) $Ag^+_{(aq)} + I^-_{(aq)} = AgI_{(c)}$	+1.44			
ii) $CaCO_{3(c)} + 2H^+_{(aq)} = Ca^{++}_{(aq)} + H_2O + CO_{2(g)}$	+2.40			
iii) $AgCN_{(s)} + CN^-_{(aq)} = Ag(CN)_2{}^-_{(aq)}$	~0			

1.11. Prepare a list of six to ten quantities which (*a*) are conserved during chemical reactions, and (*b*) are not conserved. In which list do you find most of the quantities you actually use to observe changes?

1.12. A pure sample of manganese dioxide, formula MnO_2, weighing 0.435 g is heated. Only oxygen is evolved and another pure oxide is formed weighing 0.382 g. What is the formula of the second oxide? Write an equation for the reaction.

1.13. 0.302 g of a hydrate of yttrium oxalate [formula of the anhydrous salt is $Y_2(C_2O_4)_3$] loses 0.081 g on heating to constant weight. What is the formula of the hydrate?

1.14. Estimate the number of molecular layers lost by an automobile tire (tread thickness $\frac{3}{8}$ inch) per revolution.

1.15. Calcium hypochlorite, formula $Ca(OCl)_2$, might be used to chlorinate swimming pools. How many grams should be added to a 20 × 40 × 6 foot pool to raise the chlorine level from 0.1 to 1 part per million by weight?

1.16. 230 mg of $Al(OH)_3$ was weighed into a flask and water was added. Then 0.1240 *F* HCl solution was added from a buret, and the insoluble hydroxide began to dissolve as it reacted with the acid. How many milliliters of HCl were required for complete reaction? Write an equation for the reaction. (About 7 ml.)

1.17. K. S. Harmon and colleagues (1962) carried out a reaction involving *t*-butyliodide, cycloheptatriene, and mercuric iodide. From the reaction mixture two compounds were obtained: (1) a red crystalline material which melted at 166–67°C and (2) a yellow crystalline material which melted at 150°C. After considerable work it was decided that possible formulas for the compounds were as follows:

$$C_7H_7HgI_3, \quad (C_7H_7)_2HgI_4, \quad \text{and} \quad C_7H_7Hg_2I_5$$

An ultraviolet spectrophotometric analysis of the yellow substance showed that it contained 8.3% tropenium (C_7H_7). Which of the above formulas best represents the yellow compound?

1.18. Potassium dichromate, formula $K_2Cr_2O_7$, can be used to determine quadripositive uranium, U^{+4}, by oxidizing it to the uranyl ion, UO_2^{++}, while being reduced to chromic ion, Cr^{+++}. How many ml of a 0.0200 *F* $K_2Cr_2O_7$ solution would be required to oxidize 100 ml of a 0.0100 *M* U^{+4} solution? (About 17 ml.)

1.19. Commercially available acetic acid, formula CH_3COOH, has a specific gravity of 1.06. 0.5% of the solution is water, and the balance is acetic acid. If 3.00 ml of the acetic acid solution is diluted with sufficient water to make 250 ml of solution, what is the formality of this resultant solution? (About 0.2 *F*.)

III

1.20. Which is better fuel per pound of total fuel carried, CH_4 or C_2H_6, (*a*) if oxygen is obtained from the surroundings, (*b*) if oxygen must be carried (as in a rocket)? Molar heats of combustion: CH_4, 212.798 kcal; C_2H_6, 372.820 kcal.

1.21. A rocket engineer designed a missile based on a fuel of average composition C_3H_8. The fuel delivered and used had a composition corresponding to C_2H_4. Enough liquid oxygen was carried in the rocket to burn fuel of composition C_3H_8. Assuming that the fuels are equally effective per given weight, and that 1000 pounds of fuel is used, what increase in the weight of pay load would have resulted from carrying the correct amount of oxygen for the fuel used? (About 200 lbs.)

Equations:

$$C_3H_8 + 5O_2 \longrightarrow 3CO_2 + 4H_2O$$
$$C_2H_4 + 3O_2 \longrightarrow 2CO_2 + 2H_2O$$

1.22. 1.000 g of an oxide of uranium is treated with fluorine to produce oxygen and 1.267 g of uranium hexafluoride, UF_6. What is the simplest formula of the oxide?

1.23. A plant is producing 2700 tons of 100% H_2SO_4 per day. How many tons of sulfur are required per day? Design a storage capacity for the sulfur and the sulfuric acid ample for one month of operation. List assumptions and estimate their validity in practice.

1.24. Quicklime, $CaO_{(c)}$, is made by heating limestone, $CaCO_{3(c)}$. The carbon dioxide released may be used to make dry ice. Design a gas storage tank for a plant producing 1000 tons of quicklime a day and needing enough gas storage to last a week?

1.25. Human beings utilize the eight essential amino acids in the ratio they occur in eggs. If any food is deficient in an amino acid, compared to egg, the excesses of the other amino acids are used only for energy, not for protein synthesis. The figure on the next page shows the amino acid profiles for rice and egg adjusted to the fact that lysine is the limiting reagent in rice, in which it is present to about 0.2%. Thus, about half the protein in rice is useless for human protein synthesis. Suggest a means of rectifying this situation. Any application to human needs?

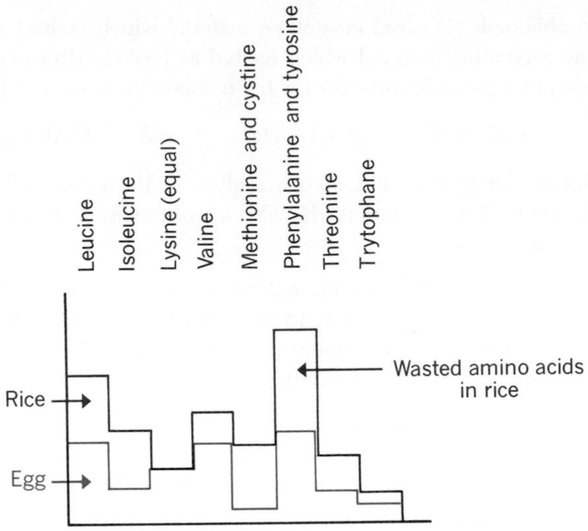

1.26. Treatment of 0.200 g of ZO_2 with HCl gives 0.475 g of ZCl_4. What is the atomic weight of Z? (O = 16.0, Cl = 35.5) (Less than 50.)

1.27. Criticize briefly the definition: "Chemistry is the science which deals with the deep-seated, permanent changes in matter."

1.28. A group of scientists develop a complete system of chemistry and physics based on a unit of mass—the gaggle. They adopt as a standard for atomic weights the element quizzium, which is assigned the relative weight 67.000 . . . . The element quizzium is what we call sodium. The gaggle is a rather heavy unit of mass, equaling 418.1 g. What is the equivalent value of Avogadro's number? Which is correct, their value of ______ or our value of $6.023 \cdot 10^{23}$?

See page 1090 for a list of references and readings in the recent chemical literature related to the material in this chapter.

CHAPTER 2

The Nuclear Atom

It is probable that most, if not all, theories in all fields of knowledge are incomplete. We use theories because they help us to remember and correlate past discoveries and to predict areas and experiments for further investigation.

Any student who has studied even elementary chemistry probably *believes* firmly in the "nuclear atom." Your own concept of "nuclear" may be slightly garbled or unclear, but you *believe*. You probably know that neutrons, protons, and electrons can be considered as the "building blocks" of the chemical elements. And you may be delighted, as most chemists are, that often only these three particles are invoked in interpreting the bulk properties of matter. "Three particles go together to make the 100+ elements, which combine to give the millions of compounds that intermingle to produce our varied universe." What a delightfully simple progression!

We shall here review very briefly the discovery of the nuclear model for atoms, and then go on to some of its properties of importance to chemists.

ATOMIC THEORIES

The earliest recorded speculation about the ultimate nature of substances is that of the Greeks, about 400 B.C. Some scholars of that time contended that matter was continuous in nature, but changed properties as it gained and lost "essences." Some contended that substances were illusions created by human senses. Some held, as do contemporary scientists, that substances consisted of small particles called atoms (from the Greek word for indivisible). The atomic idea was strongly espoused by Democritus, born about 460 B.C. Democritus is remembered because he turned

Table 2.1 **"Atomic weights" from Dalton's notebooks (H = 1.0, by definition). Dalton's "atomic weights" are often fractions of present values ($\frac{1}{2}$, $\frac{1}{3}$, $\frac{1}{4}$), because of confusion in interpretation of data.**

Date	H	O	N	S	P
Sept. 6, 1803	1	5.66	4	17	—
Sept. 19, 1803	1	5.66	4	14.4	7.2
Aug. 14, 1806	1	7	5	22	9.3
1810	1	7	5	13	9
Factor to convert to present values	1	2	3	2	3
Atomic weights from Table 1.2	1	16	14	32	30

out, as much by good fortune as by merit of proof or logical argument, to be "right."

The Greek theories were not given the thorough experimental evaluation we now expect until after Francis Bacon (1561–1626) had emphasized the importance of experiment, and scientists such as Lavoisier (1743–1794) had introduced and used the chemical balance. By 1805 sufficient data existed—even though the experimental uncertainties were usually ±5% or even greater—for Dalton to see that an atomic theory was consistent with the data, whereas no other known theory was. The Daltonian suggestion was opposed by many scientists, especially those who did not understand the nature and size of the experimental uncertainties in their data. Table 2.1 shows some of the data accumulated by Dalton. Note the variation with time and the wide deviations from comparable values used today. Because of their uncertainty, it is hardly surprising that many scientists did not accept Dalton's ideas.

Dalton's atomic theory readily interpreted the following experimental facts.

1. The compositions of many substances are fixed in a certain weight ratio of the constituent elements, no matter how the substances are made or in what weight ratio the appropriate ingredients are mixed. For example, all samples of ammonia contain nitrogen and hydrogen in the same 5 to 1 ratio by weight.
2. When two elements form more than one compound (as H_2O and H_2O_2), the different weights of one element that combine with a constant weight of the other have a simple numerical relationship. For example, the hydrogen/oxygen weight ratio in water is 1/7, in hydrogen peroxide 1/3.5.
3. If x g of element X combine with 1 g of some substance (say oxygen), and y g of element Y also combine with 1 g of the same substance (here oxygen), very often X and Y combine with some further substance, W, or with one another in the same x/y ratio. These weights, calculated by Dalton in terms of unit weight of hydrogen, are known as combining weights. It is these combining weights that are given in Table 2.1. For example, 1 g of hydrogen can combine with either 7 g of oxygen or 9 g of phosphorus, and 7 g of oxygen can combine with 9 g of phosphorus.

Dalton's ideas become much more intelligible to a modern student when phrased in terms of moles (meaning number of atoms) rather than in terms of weight, as Dalton expressed them.

1′. The compositions of many substances are fixed in a certain mole ratio of the constituent elements, no matter how the substances are made or in what mole ratio the appropriate ingredients are mixed. (Silver and chlorine combine in the ratio of 1 mole of Ag atoms to 1 mole of Cl atoms, no matter how the compound is made.)

2′. When two elements form more than one compound, the numbers of moles of one element that combine with one mole of the other have a simple numerical relationship: CH_4, C_2H_2, C_2H_4, $C_{10}H_{22}$, C_6H_6; N_2O, NO, N_2O_3, NO_2, N_2O_5.

3′. If x moles of element X combine with 1 mole of substance Z and y moles of Y also combine with 1 mole of substance Z, very often X and Y will combine with some further substance, W, or with one another in the same mole ratio x/y: MgO, Cl_2O, $MgCl_2$; H_2O, CO_2, CH_4; $CaCO_3$, $Y_2(CO_3)_3$, $CaCl_2$, YCl_3; H_2S, CuS, H_2O, CuO, NH_3, HCl, NCl_3.

Dalton's suggestions prompted many attempts to measure the relative weights of atoms. Berzelius published his first atomic-weight table in 1813. By 1815 enough atomic weights had been accurately determined that Prout could suggest that all atomic weights were integral multiples of the weight of the lightest known atom—hydrogen. Many of these early "atomic weights" were actually combining weights, the weight of the element that would combine or react with a unit weight of hydrogen. This confusion between atomic weights and combining weights was not removed until Cannizzaro's ideas became accepted, following 1860 (see p. 126). Prout further suggested that all atoms were composed of subatomic units of hydrogen atoms. Prout, like Dalton, attributed deviations from his "rule" to experimental uncertainty. Unfortunately for Prout, the experimentalists had improved their methods so much that he was quickly shown to be wrong (see Table 2.2). Many atomic weights were far from integral multiples of that of hydrogen—for example, chlorine. However, so many of the atomic weights were close to integral multiples of the atomic weight of hydrogen that Prout's idea was not forgotten, even though his subatomic hydrogen units were much derided. Nevertheless, the Daltonian idea of indivisible atoms became one of the most strongly established concepts in science.

By 1868–1870 Mendeleev and Lothar Meyer had developed the periodic table, showing that elements occurred in families with similar properties and that the elements fell into the table in order of increasing atomic weight of the element —with two or three small exceptions that could not be explained away as experimental uncertainties (see pp. 127–128). The order number in the table, starting with 1 for hydrogen, was called the atomic number. The relative weights of the atoms were expressed as atomic weights.

Table 2.2 Combining weights from *Elementary Chemistry* by Fownes, published in 1865, just before Mendeleev (O = 8, by definition). The 1965 values of the corresponding atomic weights are in parentheses. The marked improvement from Table 2.1 is due mainly to better analytical data. Cannizzaro's ideas (see p. 126) were still not universally applied, nor was the law of Dulong and Petit (see p. 125).

O = 8 (16)	P = 31 (31)	Cu = 31.7 (63.5)	Br = 80 (80)	Hg = 100 (201)
H = 1 (1)	Cl = 35.5 (35.5)	Pb = 103.7 (207)	Cd = 56 (112)	Li = 6.95 (6.94)
N = 14 (14)	I = 127 (127)	Ag = 108 (108)	Ca = 40 (40)	Mn = 27.6 (55)
C = 6 (12)	K = 39 (39)	Al = 13.7 (27)	F = 19 (19)	Pd = 53.3 (107)
S = 16 (32)	Fe = 28 (56)	As = 75 (75)	Mg = 12 (24)	Na = 23 (23)

Many bases have been used for atomic weights, among them hydrogen = 1, oxygen = 100, oxygen = 16. The current universally accepted convention is to assign atoms of the most common isotope of carbon a mass of exactly 12. This is the basis used in this book.

In 1897 J. J. Thomson achieved the first definite proof of subatomic units when he showed that all substances tested, when placed in a strong electric field, could yield particles having masses about 1/2000 that of a hydrogen atom. These particles also had a negative electrical charge. We now call them electrons. At about the same time, the Curies and others discovered that all the elements with atomic weights greater than bismuth were spontaneously emitting particles of very high energy and turning into lead. Three types of high-energy radiation were discovered. Initially called alpha (α), beta (β), and gamma (γ) rays, they were soon identified as doubly positive helium atoms (α), electrons (β), and high-energy X-rays (γ). (It is interesting to note that Mendeleev, one of the great chemical innovators with his periodic table, rejected the idea of subatomic particles. For example, he tried to account for Thomson's results in terms of an element of very low atomic weight, which he called chemical ether.)

Intensive interest was aroused in subatomic properties. Researches like those of Thomson and the Curies showed that atoms could emit less massive particles and undergo change. Then how were the atoms constituted? Were atoms uniform but able to eject pieces of themselves in various forms? Or did atoms contain subatomic units that could be detached from one another to form the observed products? Or were there other possibilities?

Many suggestions were presented, many false starts made, and many profitless experiments done before Rutherford suggested to his students Geiger and Marsden that they probe atoms by bombarding them with high energy alpha particles. In 1911 he announced his astonishment at the results. Not only did most of the alpha particles penetrate the thin elementary samples, as predicted, but a readily measured fraction were bounced back toward the source of the alphas. Calculations showed that the particles causing the alphas to rebound must (*a*) be about 10^{-13} cm in diameter, (*b*) contain more than 99% of the mass of the atom, and (*c*) have a positive electrical charge (measured as multiples of the electron charge) roughly half the atomic weight. Van den Broek suggested in 1913 that the central charge was equal to the atomic number, Z, of the element in the periodic table. Rutherford's initial conclusions on the nuclear atom were based on data with an experimental uncertainty of about ±20%. Conclusive proof was later obtained for statement *c*, by Chadwick. See Table 2.3, where the uncertainty is only about 1%.

Table 2.3 Chadwick's alpha scattering results, 1920.

Element	Cu	Ag	Pt
Experimental value of Z	29.3	46.3	77.4
Presently accepted value of Z	29	47	78

SOURCE: J. Chadwick, *Phil. Mag.*, **40,** 734 (1920).

THE NUCLEAR ATOM

All data available today are consistent with the idea that a mole of any element, formula X, contains $6.02 \cdot 10^{23}$ nuclei. Each nucleus is about 10^{-13} cm in diameter and bears a positive electrical charge equal to the atomic number, Z, of the element: +1 (in units of electron charge) for hydrogen, +8 for oxygen, through +82 for lead, and so on. The volume of a mole of many solid elements is about 20 cm^3 (cubic centimeters) and, of course, contains $6.02 \cdot 10^{23}$ nuclei. Thus the volume per nucleus is about [$20\ cm^3/6.02 \cdot 10^{23}$ nuclei] or about $30 \cdot 10^{-24}\ cm^3$/nucleus. This means that the internuclear distance must be about $(30 \cdot 10^{-24}\ cm^3)^{1/3}$, or somewhat more than 10^{-8} cm.

Thus nuclei are spaced very widely apart compared to their own size, the distance being 10^{-8} cm or more between nuclei of radius only 10^{-13} cm. The volume occupied by a nucleus—about $(10^{-13})^3 = 10^{-39}\ cm^3$—is a minute fraction of the space between the nuclei, about $(10^{-8})^3 = 10^{-24}\ cm^3$. About one millionth of a billionth of the total bulk volume is "occupied" by nuclei. Nuclear mass densities must be approximately 10^{15} times as great as bulk densities. Nuclear electrical charge densities are also very high compared to bulk charge densities, and again the factor is about 10^{15}. It was these high electrical and mass densities which forced the alpha particles in Rutherford's experiment to bounce back.

Nuclei are electrically positive. Since bulk matter is electrically neutral, there must be negative electrical charges present to balance the positive nuclear charge. It was Millikan, in the period 1906 to 1916, who showed that electrical charge, whether positive or negative, is always found in multiples of a single unit, which he called the electron charge. No exceptions to this idea have yet been discovered. The value of the electron charge is $1.6012 \cdot 10^{-19}$ coulombs (also given as $4.803 \cdot 10^{-10}$ esu), but we shall usually refer to this charge as unity: −1 for electrons, +1 for protons.

Every nucleus has a positive charge equal to the electron charge times its atomic number. For a collection of atoms to be electrically neutral, as we observe bulk matter normally to be, every nucleus must be associated with enough negative charge to balance electrically its own positive charge. But charge always appears to come in units of the electron charge, + or −. Thus every electrically neutral atom must contain a number of negative electron charges equal to its positive nuclear charge, or equal to its atomic number. Electrically charged atoms are formed if any electrically neutral atom gains or loses electrons.

The requirement of electrical neutrality in bulk matter is met if every atom contains a number of electrons equal to its positive nuclear charge, where the number of electrons = Z. The highest known nuclear charge, Z, is just over 100, so at most only about 100 electrons are required. Thomson showed that the mass of an electron is about 1/2000 that of a hydrogen atom, so 100 electrons add only 1/20 of an atomic weight unit to that represented by the nucleus. This is consistent with Rutherford's conclusion that more than 99% of the atomic mass is concentrated in the nucleus.

But it could also be true that the negative electrical charge is present in a diffuse cloud that surrounds the nucleus but does not contain identifiable particles such as electrons. An analogy would be a large drop of water falling through the atmosphere. Addition of energy to the drop can cause smaller drops to break off. The large drop contains all the essentials to make a set of smaller drops except the required energy, yet there are no small drops present until after the energy is absorbed. Before investigating extranuclear electrons, let us round out our discussion of the nucleus itself.

ISOTOPES

Ever since Prout suggested that atoms might be composed of units of hydrogen, scientists have been intrigued by the many approximately integral atomic weights. This interest was greatly heightened when J. J. Thomson (in 1913) and Aston, Dempster, and others (after 1919) showed that Prout was closer to being correct than even he thought. Before 1913, it was possible to weigh only large aggregates of atoms, and so obtain only average atomic weights, but in that year Thomson invented the mass spectrometer, in an attempt to determine the masses of individual atoms.

Most mass spectrometers are arranged to produce a beam of high-energy, electrically positive atoms (see Figure 2.1). The charged atoms are usually formed by bombarding a well-defined stream of some gas with electrons. The bombardment expels electrons from the gaseous atoms. The resulting charged atoms may be accelerated to a known velocity by an electric field, proceeding in a straight-line path until they come to electric and/or magnetic fields. In such fields the charged particles are bent in a predictable fashion from their straight-line paths and may be detected individually. The amount of deflection depends on the strengths of the

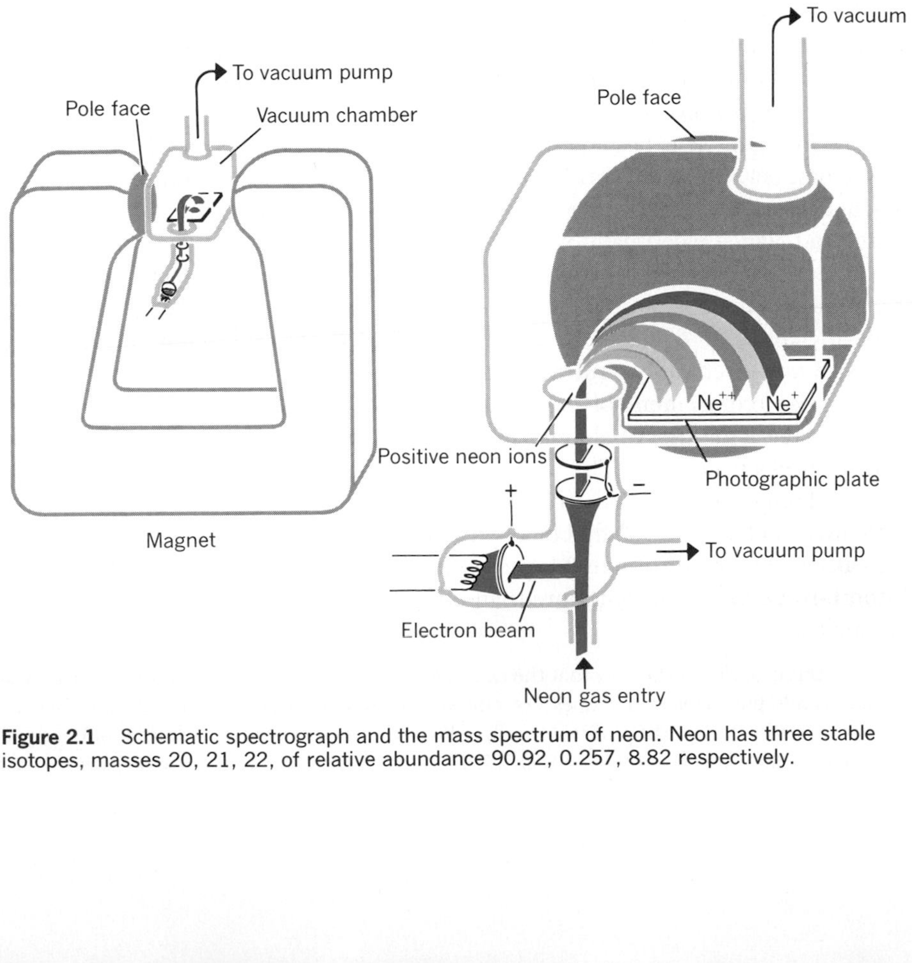

Figure 2.1 Schematic spectrograph and the mass spectrum of neon. Neon has three stable isotopes, masses 20, 21, 22, of relative abundance 90.92, 0.257, 8.82 respectively.

electric and magnetic fields, the electrical charge of the atoms, the velocity of the atoms, and their masses. All but the mass may be rather readily fixed by adjusting the instrument. The amount of deflection then varies only with the mass. From the amount of deflection the mass, A, is calculated in atomic mass units. An early experiment on atomic chlorine showed atomic masses of 35 and 37. The relative amounts of each atom were such (75.53% Cl 35 and 24.47% Cl 37) as to give the previously observed average atomic weight of 35.46. Rapid examination of almost all the elements followed. Without exception the actual atomic weights fell very close to integral numbers, as Prout had guessed. Such atoms, having the same nuclear charge (and all, hence, of the same element) but differing in mass, are said to be isotopes. Elements having naturally occurring isotopes often have average atomic weights quite different from integers.*

Prout, like Democritus, is remembered because he made a guess and presented a theory. Although his guess was not supported by enough experimental evidence to convince his contemporaries that he was correct, later evidence supported his suggestions and made his theory acceptable. History is full of instances where luck and intuition have won out over immediate logic and "facts." It will be interesting to see how many current suggestions will have a similar fate. But it is wise to remember that history is even more full of triumphs for experimental observations over intuition. Science, however, uses *all* available means of solving problems. Every technique is applied, and time winnows success from failure.

Exercise 2.1

Assuming that naturally occurring carbon consists only of two isotopes of mass exactly 12 and exactly 13, what atomic percent of carbon 13 exists in nature? *Answer:* See Table 1.2, which indicates that this percent varies with the sample. If x = fraction carbon 13, using the average value for the atomic weight of carbon, 12.01115, gives $12.01115 = x13 + (1 - x)12, \quad x = \dfrac{12.01115 - 12}{13 - 12} = 0.01115$ or 1.115%. (*Note:* We can have four significant figures for the answer, since 12 and 13 are assumed to be exact numbers, actually 13 is not exact. (See Table 2.5).

THE NEUTRON-PROTON THEORY

In 1932 the neutron, a particle of zero electrical charge and atomic weight 1, was discovered by Chadwick. Chadwick bombarded boron isotopes of mass 11 with alpha particles and obtained nitrogen atoms and another particle, which he identified as having mass 1 and no electrical charge. Such a particle had been postulated previously and, indeed, named the neutron, so Chadwick adhered to the name. The equation of the reaction is $B^{11} + He^{4} = N^{14} + n^{1}$.** It was immediately hypothesized that nuclei were made up of neutrons of charge 0, mass 1, and hydro-

* The average atomic weights of elements that have naturally occurring isotopes are often found to vary slightly, depending on the source of the sample. Many processes in nature (such as vaporization or solution) cause slight segregation of the isotopes, thus causing the average, or chemical, atomic weights to vary. This effect is usually less than 0.01% in the chemical atomic weight (see Table 1.2).

** The superscripts indicate the nuclear mass numbers, A, of the particles. Note that mass number is conserved in nuclear reactions.

gen nuclei (called protons) of charge +1, mass 1. This neutron-proton theory readily accounted for the observed charges and masses of the known atoms. Nuclear mass number (A) equaled the sum of the number of protons (Z) and the number of neutrons, (N):

$$A = Z + N$$

[Since neutrons and protons each weigh about 1 atomic mass unit, A closely approximates the nuclear mass (see Table 2.5). The application of the law of conservation of mass-energy accounts exactly for the small deviations from exact multiples of the hydrogen mass found in nuclear masses.]

Most scientists look at 1932 as the year in which the structural model of matter was at its simplest. All nuclei appeared to contain characteristic numbers of neutrons and protons, all atoms contained a simple nucleus and a characteristic number of electrons, all molecules contained a characteristic arrangement of atoms, all pure substances contained characteristic molecules, and all objects contained mixtures of pure substances. Thus three fundamental particles—neutrons, protons, and electrons—could be used to synthesize all matter and to account for the observed changes in matter.

Since 1932, life for scientists who deal with subatomic fields has become more and more complicated. We shall return to some of these problems later, but for all scientists except those actively engaged in nuclear research the neutron-proton theory is still adequate, and we shall use it in accounting for all the systems with which we will deal.

It is probable that most, if not all, theories in all fields of knowledge are incomplete. We use theories because they help us to remember and correlate past discoveries and to predict areas and experiments for future investigation. We change theories when new observations can be explained only by doing so. But to any particular problem we apply that theory and accompanying reasoning which is simplest and involves the fewest assumptions, yet which produces results that accord with experiment. Philosophically, this method of using the simplest theory, involving the fewest assumptions, is known as applying Occam's razor (or the law of parsimony).

Exercise 2.2

Describe the general structure of a neutral atom of fluorine. *Answer:* Fluorine has one stable isotope, of mass 19 and nuclear charge +9. It consists of a nucleus somewhat larger than 10^{-13} cm in radius and is assumed to contain 9 protons (each positively charged) and 10 neutrons (each electrically neutral), and each of mass about 1. Outside the nucleus there are 9 electrons (each negatively charged) filling out a total volume of radius about 10^{-8} cm.

NUCLEAR REACTIONS

We may check the applicability of the neutron-proton theory by using it to interpret nuclear reactions. Three types of spontaneous nuclear processes are common: alpha, beta, and gamma ray emission. Alpha particles of mass 4 and positive charge 2 are emitted by many nuclei heavier than mass 208. We interpret this as ejection from a nucleus of a tightly bound packet containing 2 protons (charge 2, mass 2) and 2 neutrons (charge 0, mass 2).

Beta particles (charge −1, mass 0) are emitted by many unstable isotopes. A neutral, massless particle is always emitted simultaneously, thus conserving angular momentum. The particle is called the neutrino ${}_0\nu^0$. We interpret this as a nuclear reaction in which a neutron turns into a proton. Atoms need not be conserved in a nuclear reaction, as they must in a chemical reaction, but note that conservation of charge and of mass number still occurs:

$$ {}_0n^1 = {}_1p^1 + {}_{-1}e^0 + {}_0\nu^0 \tag{2.1} $$

or

$$ {}_0n^1 = {}_1p^1 + {}_{-1}\beta^0 + {}_0\nu^0 $$

It is interesting to note that neutrons outside nuclei undergo this same reaction. Conservation of charge (lower left) and mass (upper right) are usually explicitly indicated in equations for nuclear changes, as shown in equation (2.1).

Gamma rays (charge 0, mass 0) represent energy emitted from a nucleus. Their emission is interpreted as a rearrangement of the nuclear protons and neutrons into a more stable, lower-energy packing. Gamma emission usually accompanies other processes, seldom occurring alone.

Synthetic isotopes, prepared in the laboratory but not found in nature (or very uncommon there), may emit positive electrons (charge +1, mass 0) or neutrons, as well as alpha, beta, and gamma particles. The neutron loss is straightforward in terms of our theory. The positive electron, or positron, emission is interpreted as the following reaction:

$$ {}_1p^1 = {}_0n^1 + {}_1e^0 + {}_0\nu^0 \tag{2.2} $$

When atoms are bombarded with high-energy particles such as neutrons, protons, alpha particles, or others, using energies of up to 10^8 kcal mole^{-1}, many products are noted. Some typical reactions and their interpretation in terms of the neutron-proton theory are listed in Table 2.4. (*Note:* One of the examples of nuclear equations has a numerical error in it. Correct it.) At very high bombardment energies, such as 10^{10} kcal mole^{-1}, high-energy particles (called mesons, baryons, and so on), which cannot be correlated simply with neutron-proton theory, are formed. Since the high-energy particles produced have very short lives (about 10^{-6}

Table 2.4 **Some bombardment reactions in nuclei. The particle most commonly expelled by each bombarding particle is given first.**

Bombarding particle	Expelled particle	Example
n	γ, α, p, $2n$, n, He^3	${}_{48}Cd^{115} + {}_0n^1 = {}_{48}Cd^{116} + {}_0\gamma^0$
d, $(p + n)$	p, α, $2n$, n, γ, $t = (p + 2n)$	${}_{23}V^{51} + {}_1d^2 = {}_{23}V^{52} + {}_1p^1$
p	n, α, p, γ	${}_{25}Mn^{55} + {}_1p^1 = {}_{26}Fe^{55} + {}_0n^1$
α, $(2p + 2n)$	n, α, p, d, $2n$	${}_9F^{19} + {}_2\alpha^3 = {}_{11}Na^{22} + {}_0n^1$
γ	n, p	${}_{35}Br^{81} + \gamma = {}_{35}Br^{80} + {}_0n^1$
$e^- = \beta^-$	$e^- = \beta^-$	${}_{34}Se^{81} + {}_{-1}\beta^0 = {}_{34}Se^{81} + {}_{-1}\beta^0$
He^3, $(2p + n)$	p	${}_{14}Si^{28} + {}_2He^3 = {}_{15}P^{30} + {}_1p^1$

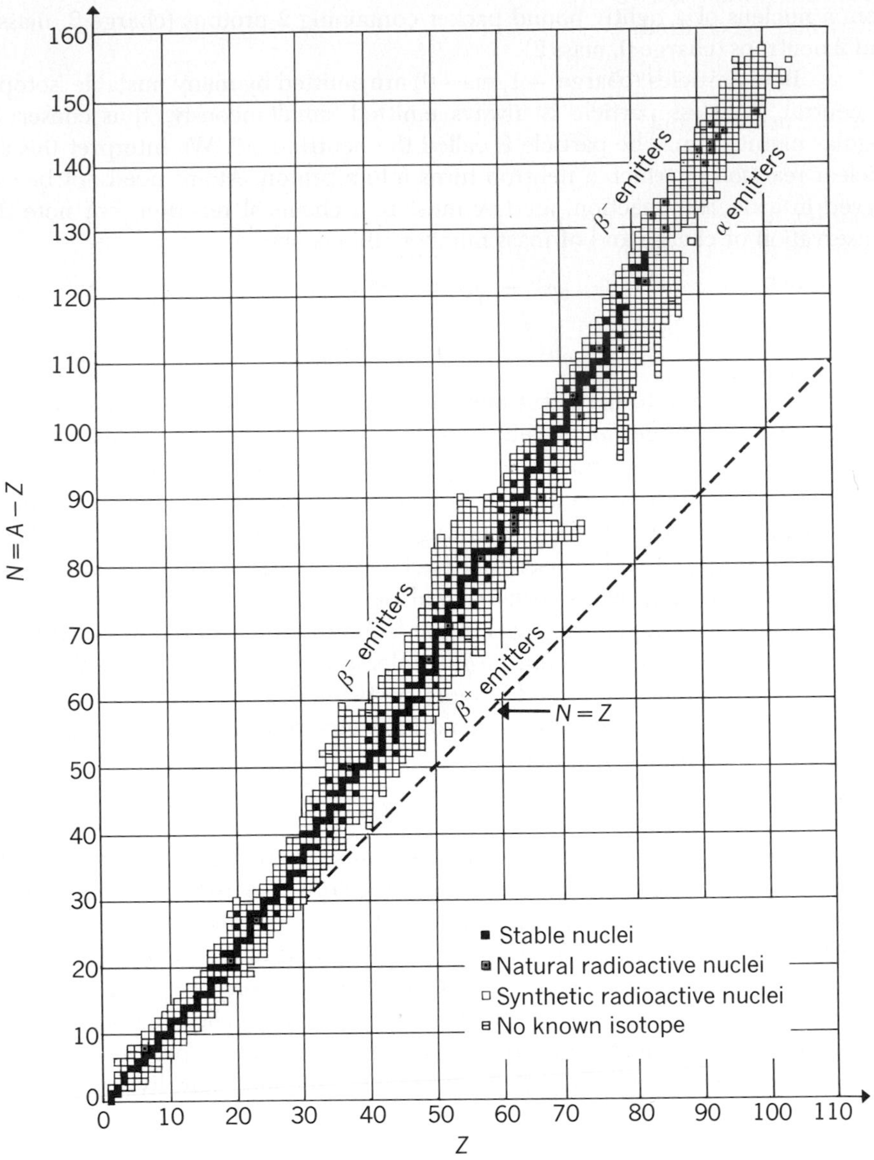

Figure 2.2 Chart of the known nuclei. Number of protons plotted versus number of neutrons. Note that the number of neutrons usually equals or exceeds the number of protons, $N \geq Z$. The regions of N and Z in which β^-, β^+, and α particles are emitted are indicated.

seconds or less) and since such high energies are not met in most chemical experiments, we do not currently find this inadequacy of the neutron-proton theory serious in most chemical work.

Stable nuclei usually contain an equal number of protons and neutrons or a slight excess of neutrons; that is, $N \geq Z$ (see Figure 2.2). If the nuclear mass is heavy compared to the average for any element, the presence of excess neutrons is indicated. If there is a very large excess of neutrons in the nucleus, neutrons themselves may be emitted. Usually, however, such a nucleus emits an electron:

$$\text{within the nucleus } {}_0n^1 = {}_1p^1 + {}_{-1}e^0, \; ({}_{-1}\beta^0 \text{ is emitted})$$

as in the net reaction,

$${}_9\text{F}^{20} = {}_{10}\text{Ne}^{20} + {}_{-1}\beta^0$$

According to our theory, this converts a nuclear neutron into a nuclear proton and moves the nucleus toward stability. Similarly, a nucleus that is lighter than average for any element tends to emit a positive electron:

$$\text{within the nucleus } {}_1p^1 = {}_0n^1 + {}_1e^0, \; ({}_1\beta^0 \text{ is emitted})$$

as in the net reaction,

$${}_9\text{F}^{17} = {}_8\text{O}^{17} + {}_1\beta^0$$

The resulting nuclear conversion of a proton to a neutron makes the nucleus more stable.

Only heavy nuclei emit alpha particles. All heavy nuclei contain more neutrons than protons: $N > Z$. If there are too many protons for stability, an alpha particle may be emitted. Emission of an alpha particle from such a nucleus reduces the number of protons by a greater percentage than it reduces the number of neutrons, and thus the nucleus becomes more stable, as in the net reaction

$${}_{92}\text{U}^{232} = {}_{90}\text{Th}^{228} + {}_2\alpha^4$$

It is worth noting that our previous discussion of $\Delta G = \Delta H - T\Delta S$ applies with equal force to nuclear reactions. Those nuclear reactions will occur for which ΔG is negative. If ΔH is negative (stronger nuclear bonds form than break), or ΔS is positive (increase in freedom of particles occurs, especially at high T), the nuclear reaction tends to occur spontaneously. Thus most spontaneous nuclear reactions are accompanied by the generation of large amounts of heat ($\Delta H = -$), and the emission of a small fragment ($\Delta S = +$). The energy generated is often so large it can be measured as loss of an equivalent amount of mass, as shown in Table 2.5, on the next page.

The experimental evidence appears overwhelming that there are no electrons in any nucleus. Yet electrons appear to emanate from the nuclear reactions indicated above. In a similar way, there are no words in a person, yet he can form them. Nor is there any light in a lamp, yet the lamp emits light. Thus, at least at the subatomic level, it appears to be possible to generate new particles and to effect their emission, even though they were not present before the emission process. We treat electric charge and mass-energy as two of the factors that are conserved in such processes, but we certainly do not fully understand the processes.

HALF-LIFE

Nuclear disintegrations may be characterized in terms of their half-lives—the time required for half of the nuclei present at any instant to disintegrate. Known half-lives vary from about 10^{10} years to 10^{-10} seconds. Longer and shorter half-lives cannot be measured with present instruments. Half the nuclei disappear in the first half-life, half of the remainder (or a quarter of the

Table 2.5 Correlation of mass changes and energy changes in some nuclear reactions. Remember the Einstein equation, $\Delta E = c^2\,\Delta m$. All reactions have negative Δm, so ΔE is negative.

Species	e^-	n	p	H^1	H^2	He^4
Atomic Mass	0.000548597	1.0086654	1.00727663	1.007825	2.01410	4.0026
Species	Li^6	Li^7	C^{12}	C^{13}	Cl^{35}	Cl^{37}
Atomic Mass	6.01513	7.01601	12.00000	13.00335	34.96885	36.96590

Reactions	Δm
$n = e^- + p$ (neutrons are radioactive)	−0.0008402
${}_1H^2 + {}_2Li^7 = 2\,{}_2He^4 + {}_0n^1$ (possible hydrogen bomb reaction)	−0.0162
Bethe chain stellar reaction (presumed to supply much of the stellar energy)	
${}_1H^1 + {}_6C^{12} = {}_7N^{13}$	−0.00210
${}_7N^{13} = {}_6C^{13} + {}_1e^0$	−0.0018
${}_1H^1 + {}_6C^{13} = {}_7N^{14}$	−0.00828
${}_1H^1 + {}_7N^{14} = {}_8O^{15}$	−0.0077
${}_8O^{15} = {}_7N^{15} + {}_1e^0$	−0.00247
${}_1H^1 + {}_7N^{15} = {}_6C^{12} + {}_2He^4$	−0.00515
Net $4\,{}_1H^1 = {}_2He^4 + 2\,{}_1e^0$	−0.02750

original nuclei) disappear in the second half-life, and so forth until the number remaining is too small to follow a statistical prediction.

Half-lives are usually insensitive to external conditions, but they have now been shown to vary: (1) with temperature (they decrease at very high temperatures because of thermal excitation of the nucleus), (2) with the velocity of the nucleus (at high nuclear velocity the half-life in laboratory time increases), and (3) with the chemical environment (the largest known chemical effect is with Nb^{90}, whose half-live in the metallic state is 3.6% shorter than in its fluoride complex). Most chemical effects are undetectable.

NUCLEAR SYNTHESIS

The existence in nature of nuclei that are radioactive suggests that they are either continually being synthesized, or that they are residues of synthetic processes which occurred long ago. Both interpretations are used to account for the observed radioactivities. C^{14} (half-life, 5568 years) is found in all living systems. Its short half-life indicates it must be undergoing continual synthesis, interpreted in terms of the process

$$^{14}_{7}N + ^{1}_{0}n = ^{14}_{6}C + ^{1}_{1}H$$

in the upper reaches of the atmosphere, where cosmic ray reactions provide neutrons. The very longest half-lives observed in naturally occurring radioisotopes are those of elements thought to have been synthesized in the earliest stages of the formation of the earth in its present form, or in the earliest processes which led to the present universe. Study of the present relative abundances of these nuclides and their accumulated decomposition products indicates a probable age of the earth of about 10^9 years; the universe is several times as old. Other observed radioactive isotopes form from the decomposition of these long-lived isotopes or from some of their decomposition products.

SUMMARY

There is as yet no theory which allows quantitative calculation of the known nuclear properties. It is possible there may never be one. All the available evidence is consistent, however, with the idea that each nucleus is concentrated in a small region, about 10^{-12} cm in diameter, that it contains 99% of the mass of the atom, and that is bears a positive charge equal to the atomic number of the element. Electrically neutral atoms contain a number of electrons equal to the positive nuclear charge.

The simplest picture of nuclear constitution is the neutron-proton model. In this model the nucleus is said to contain the same number of protons (each of charge 1+ and mass 1) as the positive charge on the nucleus, and enough neutrons (each of zero charge and mass 1) to give the total nuclear mass. Thus $A = Z + N$; the atomic mass number, A, equals the sum of the number of protons, Z, and the number of neutrons, N.

Nuclear reactions, both those in nature and those occurring during and after bombardment, can be interpreted in terms of the neutron-proton model and the emission or absorbtion of such particles as α, β, γ, positrons, or others.

Perhaps the majority of the exciting findings in nuclear research, as indeed in any other science, have come from pure flights of imagination or experiments carried out from sheer curiosity rather than from calculations dictated by models. Only in this way are completely new frontiers glimpsed and explored.—A. Zucker and D. A. Bromley,
Science, **149,** 1197 (1965).

PROBLEMS

2.1. Write equations for the following nuclear reactions.

(*a*) Os^{192} is bombarded by a neutron and emits an electron (two separate equations).
(*b*) Cs^{142} gives Ba^{142}.
(*c*) Cd bombarded by a proton emits a neutron and gives In^{114}.
(*d*) U^{239} is formed by bombardment with a neutron and emission of a γ ray.
(*e*) Cf^{246} is formed by bombardment with carbon nuclei and emission of 4 neutrons.
(*f*) Tm^{171} is radioactive.
(*g*) Tm^{166} is radioactive.
(*h*) Gaseous neutrons are radioactive.
(*i*) He^{6} is radioactive.
(*j*) U^{227} is radioactive.
(*k*) U^{240} is radioactive.

II

2.2. Assume that α particles and nuclei act as hard spheres of diameter 10^{-13} cm. What percent of the alphas will be deflected by passing through a sheet of metal 10^{-4} cm in thickness? Assume that the nuclei are arranged randomly. List any further assumptions required.

2.3. Complete the following sets with correct values of x, y, and z for the last formula in each set.
(*a*) $ScBr_3$, ScF_3, CBr_4, C_xF_y.
(*b*) Al_2O_3, Cr_2O_3, $NaAl(SO_4)_2 \cdot 12H_2O$, $Na_xCr_y(SO_4)_z \cdot 12H_2O$.
(*c*) SO_3, CrO_3, $K_2Cr_2O_7$, $K_xS_yO_z$.

2.4. A container in which radium has been sealed later proves to contain a highly radioactive gas. The radioactive gas emits alpha particles. Write an equation showing the formation of the gas from radium and another equation showing what is produced when the gas emits alpha rays.

2.5. What factors are responsible for the fact that so many atomic weights are very close to whole numbers? How do you account for the ones that are not whole numbers?

III

2.6. Design a device using a radioactive source which will determine the amount of a liquid solution inside an opaque, vertical, high-pressure storage cylinder. What radiation would you use?

2.7. Fill in the blanks in the accompanying diagram, showing the particles required to cause the indicated changes in Z and N. Indicate the change caused by an n, γ reaction and by an α, n reaction.

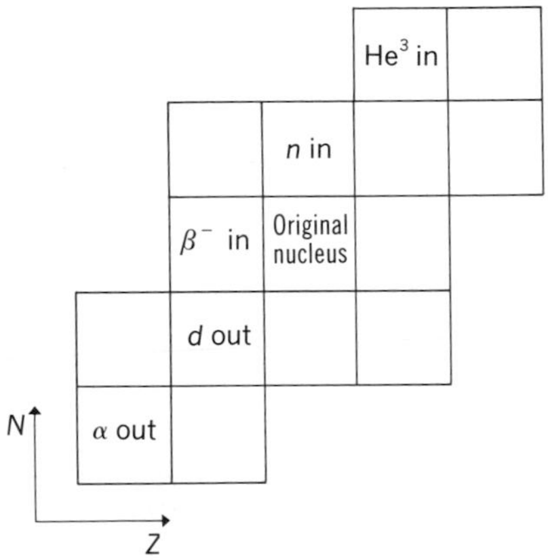

2.8. Is the nuclear reaction $Li^7 = Li^6 + n$ spontaneous?

2.9. Compare the magnitudes of energy obtainable in nuclear and chemical reactions.

2.10. What molecular weights would you expect to find in the mass spectrum of molecular chlorine, Cl_2? What would you predict for the relative abundances of the observed weights?

2.11. Accurate mass spectrometry values are given in NBS Technical Note 277, W. R. Shields, editor (1966) for isotopic abundances for bromine: $[Br^{79}]/[Br^{81}] = 1.028090$, 1.027803 (machine 4); 1.027807, 1.027669 (machine 1); mass $Br^{79} = 78.918348$, mass Br^{81} = 80.916344. Calculate a best value for the atomic weight of bromine. NBS gives 79.90363.

2.12. A mass spectrum of air gives peaks at various intensities at values of m/e listed below; m is expressed in atomic weight units and e in units of electron charge. The pressure of air introduced into the mass spectrometer was $5 \cdot 10^{-5}$ torr. Suggest a possible identification of each peak [Nier, *Am. Scientist,* **54,** 363 (1966)].

m/e	44	40	34	32	29	28	20	18	16	14
Intensity	0.002	0.013	0.001	0.24	0.007	1.000	0.004	0.006	0.019	0.069

2.13. *K*-capture is the name given nuclear reactions in which a *K*-electron, initially in the atom but outside the nucleus, is "swallowed" by the nucleus. Write an equation for this process in terms of the neutron-proton theory. If I^{126} underwent *K*-capture, what atom would be formed?

See page 1090 for a list of references and readings in the recent chemical literature related to the material in this chapter.

CHAPTER 3

Atomic Energy Levels

The occupancy of atomic energy levels is dependent on nuclear charge, number of electrons, and total energy in the atom.

We have seen that electrons can be emitted from nuclei either spontaneously or as a result of bombardment of the nucleus with a high-energy particle. But there are no electrons in the nucleus. Thomson discovered the electron by using energies much lower than those required for nuclear reaction. The electrons he obtained must have come from the region outside the nucleus. Are there electrons in this region?

ELECTRONS FROM ATOMS

No electrically neutral atoms are known which spontaneously emit these atomic (as contrasted to nuclear) electrons, but many methods are known for initiating emission of atomic electrons. Almost any source of energy providing 500 kcal mole^{-1} or more can trigger electron emission. Figure 3.1 illustrates an apparatus for measuring the energy required. Light, electron impact (as shown in Figure 3.1), electric sparks as in neon signs, molecular collisions as in luminous gases, molecular collisions with a hot filament, even strong electric fields as in many X-ray tubes, can all cause atoms to emit electrons. The minimum energy known to cause electron emission from an electrically neutral gaseous atom is 90 kcal mole^{-1}, for gaseous cesium:* the maximum required by any neutral gaseous atom is 567 kcal mole^{-1}, for gaseous helium. All other electrically neutral gaseous elements have

* Francium, element 87, would presumably have a still lower ionization energy.

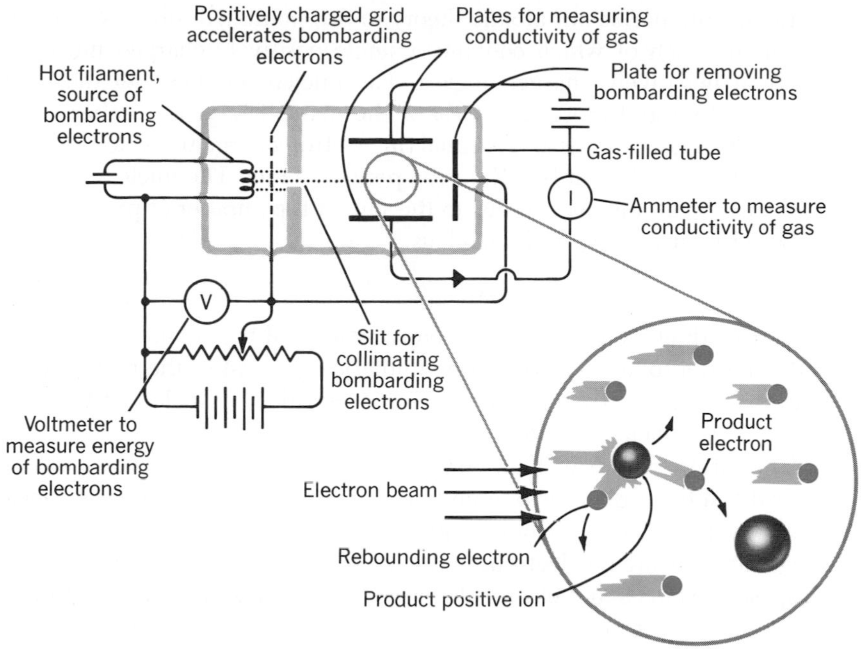

Figure 3.1 Determination of the ionization energy of a gas. Bombarding electrons from a hot filament are accelerated to a known energy and then pass through the gas to be studied. Any ionization of the gas is detected as a current between the two parallel plates in the gas-filled tube (the conductivity of the gas increases rapidly). The lowest voltage at which ionization is observed is the first ionization energy of the gas.

requirements lying between these values. Solids and liquids, both elementary and compound, have energy requirements in the same general range.

The energy required to remove an electron from an isolated gaseous atom is called the ionization energy of the atom. Every neutral atom can lose Z electrons (where Z is the atomic number). Removing a single electron is always easier than removing two; removing a second electron from an atom always requires more energy than removing the first; and the energy rises rapidly as the number of electrons removed increases. Removing the Zth electron requires the most energy of all. These various ionization energies for each atom are known as the first ionization potential (or energy), the second ionization potential, the third ionization potential, up to the Zth ionization potential.

Can you give a conclusive argument—consistent with the picture so far presented of the nuclear atom—as to why the ionization potential of the Zth electron, the last electron, is always greater than that of the Z − 1 (next to the last) electron? Why is the ionization energy of the first electron the lowest ionization energy? Do you need to assume that there are electrons in atoms?

The fact that all atoms can emit electrons and the fact that the energy required to initiate this emission is much less than that found in nuclear processes are both consistent with the idea that the emitted electrons are from a region surrounding the nucleus. The average volume occupied by a nucleus is about 10^{-39} cm^3; that of an atom, about 10^{-23} cm^3. Presumably it is from this larger volume that the electrons are emitted, and all known experiments indicate that this is so. For example, atoms become smaller when they emit atomic electrons.

Let us summarize our atomic theory to this point. All substances are composed of atoms, each of which contains a single positively charged nucleus surrounded by a negatively charged region. The nucleus contains all the positive charge in the atom and more than 99% of the mass. The positive charge of the nucleus is made up of protons and is equal (in electron charge units) to the number of protons or the atomic number, Z, in the periodic table. The nuclear mass number (*A*) is equal (in atomic mass units) to the sum of the number of protons (Z) and the number of neutrons (*N*) in the nucleus:

$$A = Z + N \tag{3.1}$$

Surrounding the nucleus and occupying most of the volume attributable to a neutral atom is a total negative charge numerically equal to the nuclear charge. The atom may emit electrons from this region outside the nucleus if the atom is bombarded with sufficient energy.

The careful reader will note that we have not proved, or even stated, that electrons exist in the region surrounding the nucleus. After all, electrons appear to be emitted by nuclei, but we have said that the experimental evidence is overwhelming that there are no electrons in the nucleus. The nucleus contains the "raw materials," such as mass and electrical charge, needed to synthesize electrons, but does not contain electrons. What is the situation outside the nucleus? Are there electrons there or not? In this chapter we will explore possible answers to this question.

IONIZATION ENERGIES

Table 3.1 lists some experimental ionization energies of the first twenty elements in the periodic table. The ionization energy of the first electron is listed at the extreme right in each row; that of the last or Zth electron (if the table were completed) would be in the column at the extreme left. The numbers are all in kcal mole^{-1} and represent the energy, reading from right to left, required per mole of atoms to remove each successive electron from 1 to Z (where Z is the atomic number) from the atom. Thus 118 kcal/mole are required to strip a single electron per atom from a mole of sodium atoms, 1090 kcal mole^{1} to remove a second electron, and so on up to almost 40,000 kcal mole^{-1} to remove the last electron (the eleventh electron).

Ionization energies (*IE*) are often measured and expressed in terms of electron volts per atom (ev atom^{-1}), or in terms of ergs per atom. First ionization energies in ev/atom range from 3.9 ev atom^{-1} to 24.6 ev atom^{-1}. In ergs atom^{-1} the range is from $6.3 \cdot 10^{-12}$ ergs atom^{-1} to $39.4 \cdot 10^{-12}$ ergs atom^{-1}. The conversion equations are 1 ev atom^{-1} = 23.05 kcal mole^{-1} and 1 ev atom = $1.602 \cdot 10^{-12}$ ergs atom^{-1}. We shall use kcal mole^{-1} as the standard energy unit throughout this book, so that ready comparison is possible between the energies involved in different changes. It will be seen that first ionization energies are roughly the same size as the energies of typical chemical bonds, or about 100 kcal mole^{-1}.

Figure 3.2 shows the ionization energies of Table 3.1, plotted as a function of $Z - a$, where Z is the atomic number of the atom, *a* is an integer, and $Z - a$ is the number of the electron being removed. The curves are remarkedly regular and do not cross. Each curve is made up of short sections where the ionization energy changes rather slowly, with each such region terminating in a sharp break to a new

Table 3.1 Some ionization energies of the first twenty elements (from H, $Z = 1$, to Ca, $Z = 20$) as a function of the number, b, of the electron being ionized ($b = Z - a$, where a is an integer). Values are in kcal mole^{-1}.

Z	Element	Number of electron being ionized (b): Z	Z-1	Z-2	Z-3	Z-4	Z-5	Z-6	Z-7	Z-8	Z-9	Z-10	Z-11	Z-12	Z-13	Z-14	Z-15	Z-16	Z-17	Z-18	Z-19
1	H	314																			
2	He	1260	567																		
3	Li	2820	1750	124																	
4	Be	5020	3540	420	215																
5	B	7850	5980	875	580	191															
6	C	11,300	9050	1490	1100	562	260														
7	N	15,382	12,731	2257	1737	1034	683	335													
8	O	20,094	17,049	3185	2637	1786	1267	810	314												
9	F		21,996	4271	3624	2634	2012	1445	807	402											
10	Ne	31,400				3640	2926	2241	1470	947	497										
11	Na				6100	4300	3970	3190	2280	1660	1090	118									
12	Mg	45,200				6140	5200	4310	3260	2520	1850	347	175								
13	Al						6480	5590	4400	3550	2760	656	434	138							
14	Si	61,500						7000	5680	4730	3840	1040	772	377	188						
15	P								7130	6070	5100	1500	1080	695	453	242					
16	S	80,400							8739	7383	6480	2030	1671	1091	808	540	239				
17	Cl								10,502	9244	8034	2630	2230	1560	1230	920	550	300			
18	Ar											3309	2860	2106	1730	1380	944	637	363		
19	K												3570	2720	2300	—	1400	1060	735	100	
20	Ca	125,600												3390	2970	—	1950	1550	1080	275	142

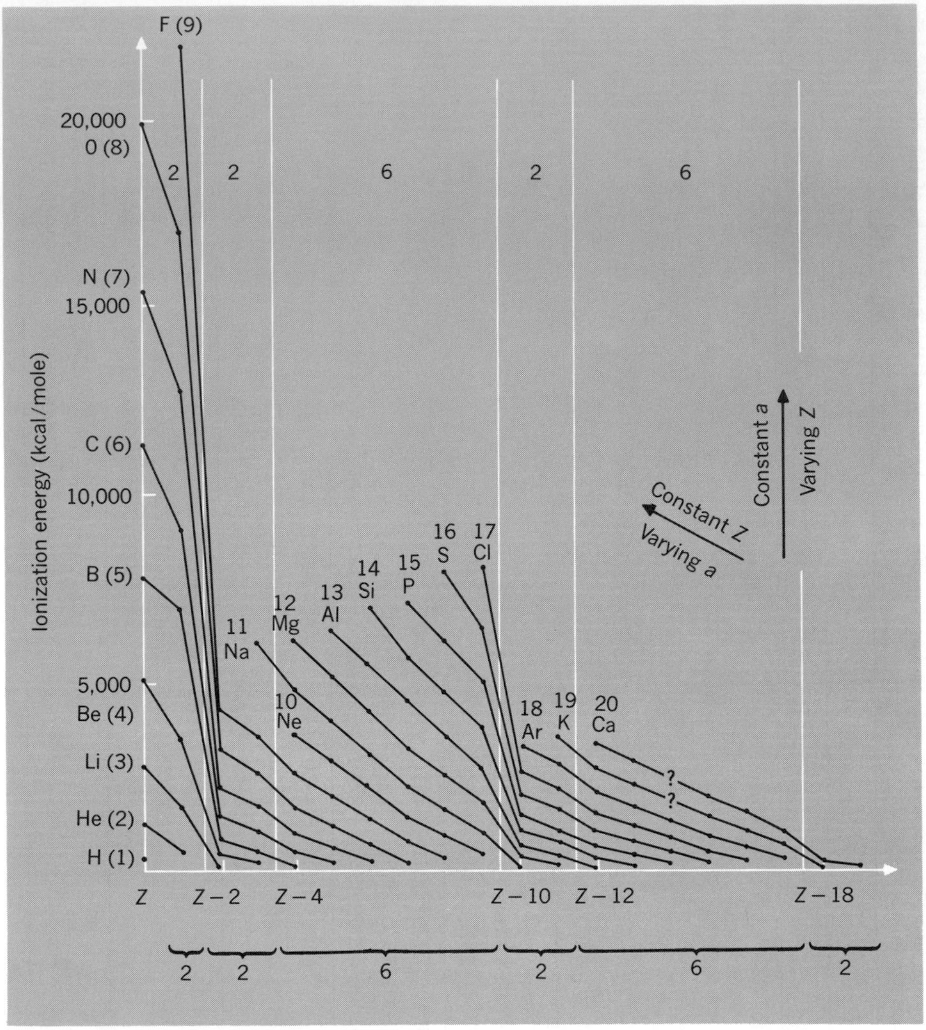

Figure 3.2 Ionization energy versus number of electron being removed, $Z - a$, for the elements H, $Z = 1$, to Ca, $Z = 20$. Note the groups of 2 and 6 electrons, separated by the upward breaks in the curves at $Z - 2$, $Z - 4$, $Z - 10$, $Z - 12$, $Z - 18$. The breaks at $Z - 2$ and $Z - 10$ are especially great.

region of slowly changing energy. Apparently the energies required to remove electrons from atoms are characteristic of the atoms and occur in groups which repeat from one atom to the next. These groups are separated from one another by the vertical lines in Table 3.1 and Figure 3.2. Groups of 2, 2, 6, 2, and 6 electrons are apparent.

It is not possible to measure directly all the ionization energies of all the elements because of the high energies required and the difficulty of obtaining an appreciable concentration of the highly charged atoms whose ionization potentials are desired. Thus the 36th ionization energy of xenon would require us to obtain an appreciable concentration of Xe^{35+} (that is, xenon atoms each of which had already lost 35 electrons) and then to measure accurately the energy required to remove one more. Actually many ionization energy data are obtained from measurements on solar and other stellar atmospheres, where the high temperatures produce a high concentration of some of the ions with large net positive charges.

Fortunately data are available from which we can estimate ionization energies that cannot be measured directly. Figure 3.3 plots these estimated data for some elements of high nuclear charge. Now we find groups of 2, 2, 6, 2, 6, 10, 2, 6, 10, 14, 2, 6, 10. Apparently ionization energies tend to appear in groups of 2, 6, 10, or 14. These numbers bear simple relations to one another. Each differs from its neighbors by 4, or each may be written as 2c, where c = 1, 3, 5, 7, the odd numbers. Perhaps if more elements were known, we could find groups of 18 ionization energies ($2 \cdot 9 = 18$). There is evidence that such a group might exist.

Two possible interpretations of the data on ionization energies are suggested.

1. Every atom contains electrons. The electrons are arranged about the nucleus in groups of 2, 6, 10, or 14. The change in ionization energy in each row of Table 3.1 would then have the following explanation: for a given nuclear charge, Z, the ionization energy increases as the number of electrons in the atom decreases, since each electron is then subject to less repulsion by the other electrons. The trend in ionization energy in each column in Table 3.1 would have the following explanation: for a given number of electrons present, the ionization energy increases as the atomic number, Z, increases, because the nucleus becomes more highly charged.
2. There are shells or clouds of negative charge arranged concentrically around the nucleus, and these shells contain the raw materials needed to synthesize electrons. Each shell can contain a net charge of 2, 6, 10, or 14 electron charges. The distance of a shell from the nucleus depends on the nuclear charge and the number of other shells present. The outer shells, being more distant from the nucleus, can release charge at low ionization energies. As each shell generates and emits electrons, the ionization energy increases. As nuclear charge increases, each shell is drawn nearer the nucleus and the ionization energy increases.

Combinations of models 1 and 2, or different assumptions, can lead to still other interpretations of the experimental data. Model 1 might be called the electron group or "blackberry patch" model. Some "bushes" are easier to pick than others. Model 2 might be called the negative shell or "onion" model. Outer "layers" are peeled more readily than inner layers. Which, if either, model is more nearly correct?

Both models assume that the negative charges are distributed in groups about the nucleus. We shall call the regions of space occupied by the negative charges *orbitals:* that is, an orbital is an extranuclear space which can be occupied by negative charges. The amount of charge per orbital is always an integral number of electron charge units. Orbitals may differ from each other in the energy required to remove a negative charge.

Exercise 3.1

Estimate the ionization energy of the seventh electron from Ne. *Answer:* Z = 10, so we will be ionizing the Z − 3 electron. Table 3.1 shows that, for Na, the difference between Z − 3 and Z − 4 is 6100 − 4800 = 1300 cal mole^{-1}. This would give an

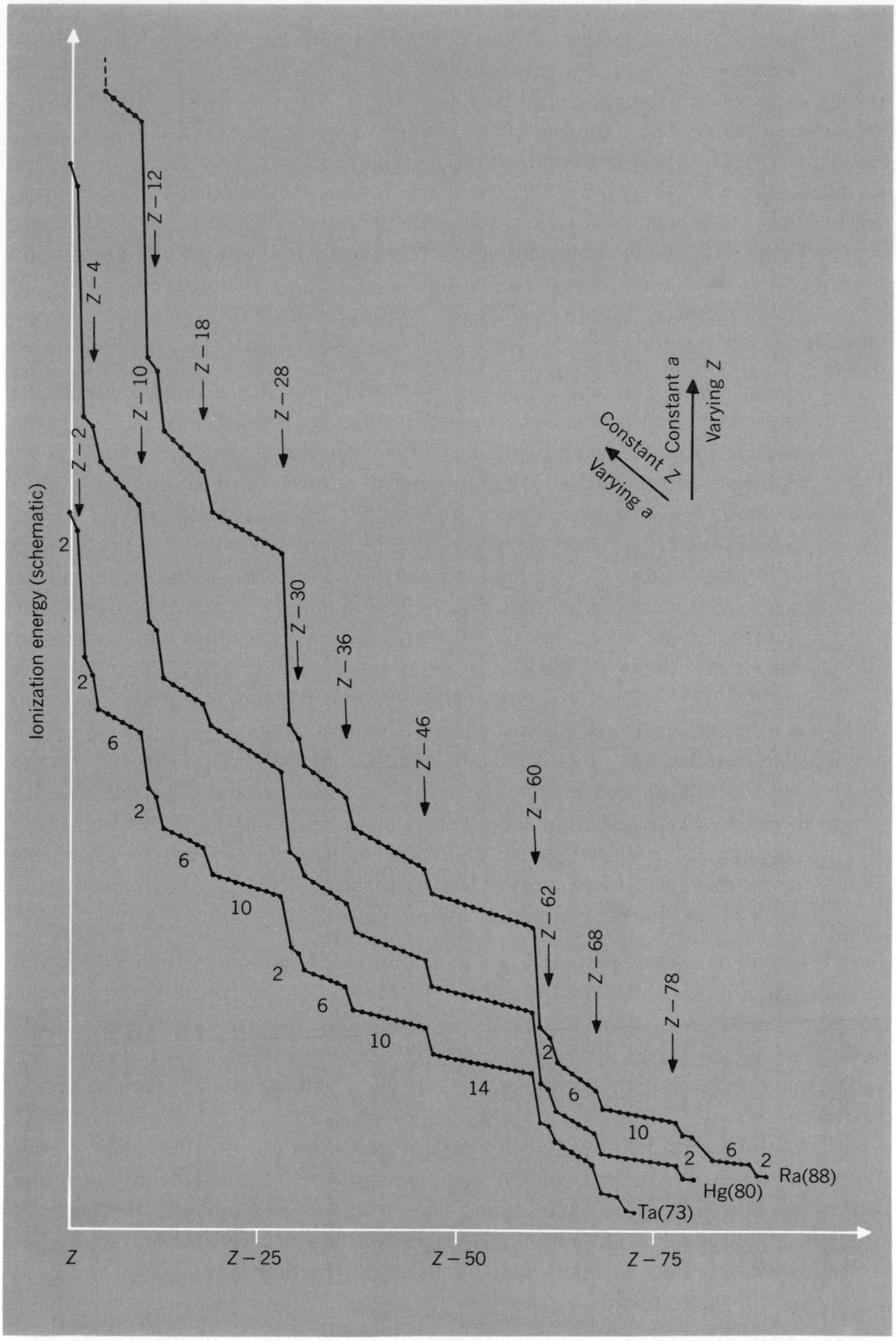

Figure 3.3 Schematic representation of ionization energy versus $Z - a$, where Z = atomic number, $Z - a$ = number of the electron being removed, for some elements of large Z (Ta, $Z = 73$; Hg, $Z = 82$; Ra, $Z = 88$). Note the grouping of electrons into sets of 2, 6, 10, and 14, separated by large breaks in the ionization energy curves.

estimate of 3600 + 1300 = 4900 cal mole^{-1} for the seventh Ne electron. We also see that the Z − 3 electrons from N, O, and F become increasingly hard to ionize by about 1000 cal mole^{-1} for each element. This would give an estimate of 3600 + 1000 = 4600 cal mole^{-1} for the seventh Ne electron. 4600 is probably low and 4900 slightly high. 4800 cal mole^{-1} is a reasonable estimate. Note this agrees with the observation that the Z − 3 electron has an IE very close to that of the Z − 4 electron of the element next higher in atomic number.

EXCITATION ENERGIES

The apparatus shown in Figure 3.1 may be modified as in Figure 3.4 to study the interaction of light, rather than electrons, with gaseous atoms. We now note that certain energies are strongly absorbed by the gaseous sample. One of these energies is the ionization energy, which removes an electron from the atom. But this apparatus also shows absorption of much lower energies—energies too low to lead to ionization. In an apparatus such as that of Figure 3.1, no increase in conductivity of the gas is noted when these lower energies are absorbed.

Atomic hydrogen is the simplest known stable atom. Each hydrogen atom contains a single proton in its nucleus and a single negative charge outside the nucleus. Figure 3.5 shows part of the excitation spectrum of atomic hydrogen—that is, the percent of energy absorbed as a function of the energy of the incident radiation. The pattern consists of a series of absorption maxima, which are very

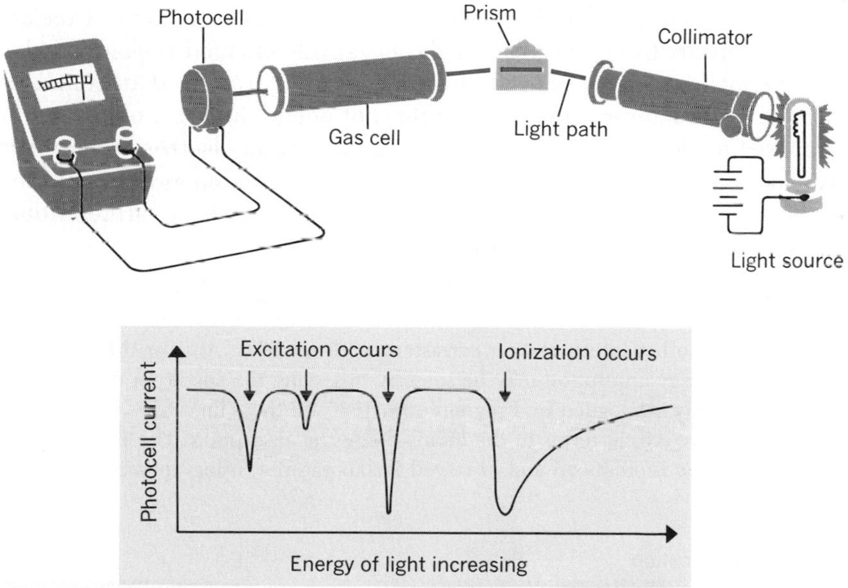

Figure 3.4 Measurement of excitation energy using light. As the energy (frequency) of the light passing through the gas-filled cell is varied by changing the spectrometer setting, the photocell current also varies. Drops in the photocell current at certain, and only certain, values of the light energy indicate that a high percentage of light of these energies is absorbed by the molecules of the gas. One of these absorptions corresponds to the ionization energy—at this condition the energy of the absorbed light exactly equals the ionization energy of the gas.

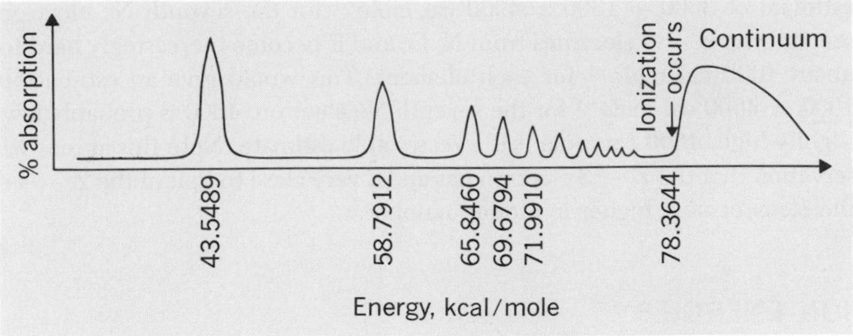

Figure 3.5 Part of the absorption, or excitation, spectrum of atomic hydrogen, H.

narrow in terms of the range of energies each absorption represents. In fact they are so narrow that they are called absorption *lines*. The lines form a regular progression whose energy spacing becomes less and less until the ionization energy is reached. Hydrogen atoms can absorb energies that are not great enough to ionize the atom, but only certain well-defined energies can be absorbed. Since the atom does not decompose or ionize when it absorbs these energies, the energy must be stored in the atom; the atomic energy content is increased a fixed and reproducible amount. We may describe these energy changes either as changes in the level of energy in the atom, or as changes in the atomic energy levels. Since the energy changes (ΔE) that correspond to each spectral line are about 100 kcal mole^{-1} or less, we associate them with the negative charge outside the nucleus, not with the nucleus itself, where changes typically require 10^8 kcal mole^{-1}. Thus these energy changes are also described as changes in the electronic energy levels of the atom. The energy appears to be absorbed in the negatively charged region outside the nucleus, the total energy content of the atom changing by a fixed amount ΔE.

We could interpret these absorptions of energy in terms of either of our two proposed models: (1) the absorbed energy moves an electron from one low-energy cluster into another, incomplete cluster of higher energy, or (2) the absorbed energy excites one of the negative shells and moves it farther from the nucleus. Other interpretations are also possible.

Exercise 3.2

Suggest another interpretation consistent with model 2. *Answer:* Many such lines due to energy absorption may be seen by observing the spectrum of sunlight. Unambiguously catalogued by Fraunhofer in 1820, all these lines have been identified, as in Figure 3.6, in terms of the atoms doing the absorption. The Fraunhofer lines may also be reproduced and observed in laboratories, using apparatus like that in Figure 3.7.

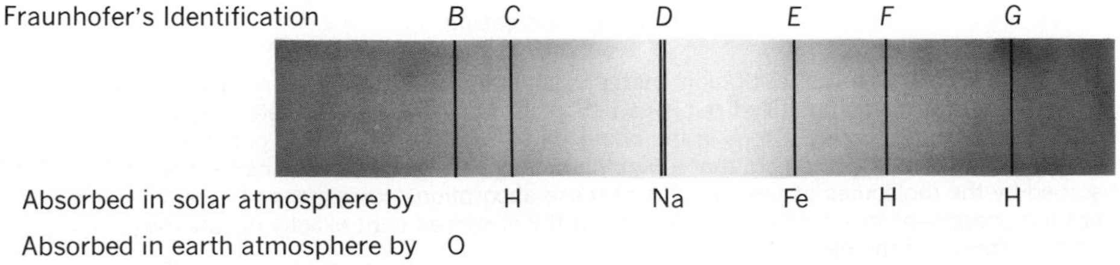

Figure 3.6 Solar spectrum at low resolution, showing some Fraunhofer absorption lines.

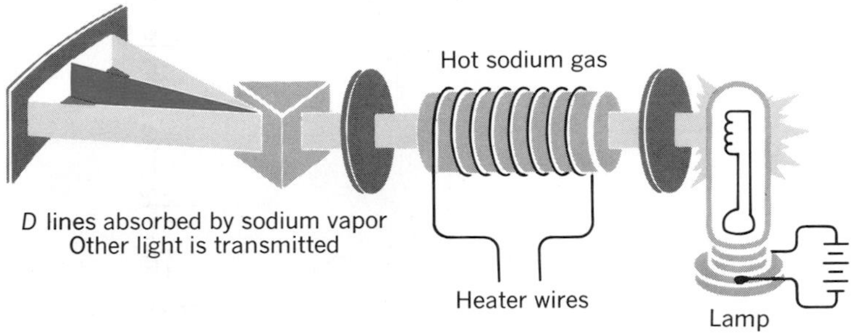

Figure 3.7 Simple laboratory setup for observing the absorption lines of gaseous sodium, the same lines as the Fraunhofer *D* lines.

ATOMIC SPECTRA

When one performs an ionization energy experiment or an excitation energy experiment in the laboratory, an interesting effect is often noticed. Light is emitted from the region in the apparatus where excitation or ionization is occurring. When this light is passed through a prism or a grating, a line spectrum is observed. Apparatus like that shown in Figure 3.8 makes it possible to obtain a great deal of emitted light for analysis.

Atomic hydrogen in the visible light regions emits light which gives the spectrum in Figure 3.9. Only a few lines are observed. It is, however, quite possible to use a wider range of light-detecting devices and thus extend our observations into the ultraviolet and infrared regions beyond the two extremes of the spectrum visible to the human eye. A more complete spectrum of atomic hydrogen is shown in Figure 3.10. [We must emphasize that this is the emission spectrum of atomic hydrogen (symbol H), not molecular hydrogen (symbol H_2). We shall later discuss the spectrum of molecular hydrogen H_2. Would you expect H_2 to form a simpler or more complex spectrum than H? Experimentally, the H_2 spectrum is the more complex one.]

Several groups, or series, or lines are observed. The series first observed

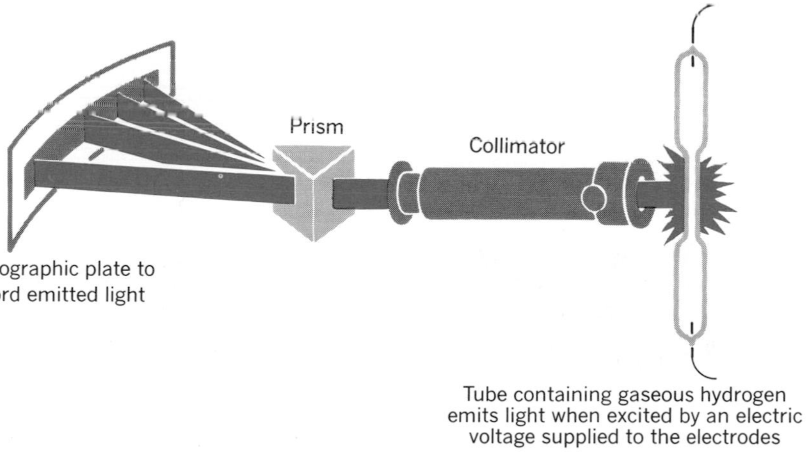

Figure 3.8 Simple spectrometer for observing emission lines from a gas.

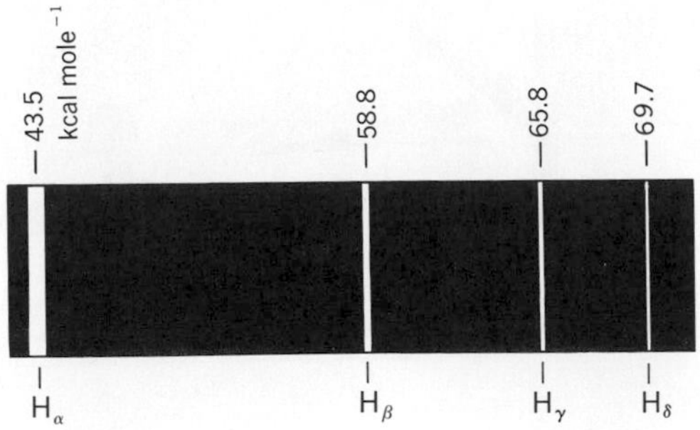

Figure 3.9 Emission spectrum of atomic hydrogen, H, in the visible range.

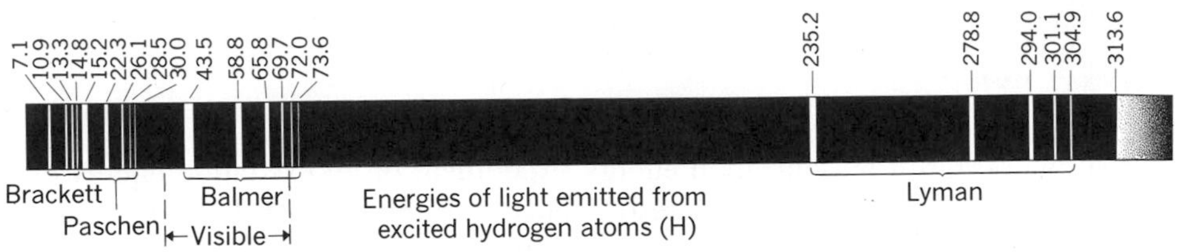

Figure 3.10 Emission spectrum of atomic hydrogen from the infrared through the ultraviolet region. [See "The Spectrum of Atomic Hydrogen—A Freshman Laboratory Experiment." J. L. Hollenberg, *J. Chem. Ed.*, **43,** 216 (1966).]

was the one detected by Balmer in 1884. The other series, about which Balmer speculated but did not have the equipment to detect, are also named in honor of their discoverers. It is interesting to note that enough was known empirically to predict the existence and energies of a further series, which was then found experimentally by Pfund at the predicted energies (3.8, 6.1, 7.7 kcal mole^{-1}, and so on). A more detailed view of the Balmer series is shown in Figure 3.11. Each emission line in the Balmer series corresponds exactly in energy to an absorption line found in the excitation spectrum. The same energy levels are involved in absorption as in emission. Compare Figures 3.5, 3.9, 3.11.

Some emission and absorption spectra of some other much studied elements in the gas state are shown in Figure 3.12. No element has as simple a spectrum as atomic hydrogen, though sodium absorption is similar. Some spectra are very complicated. Again, each absorption line is found among the emission lines of the same element.

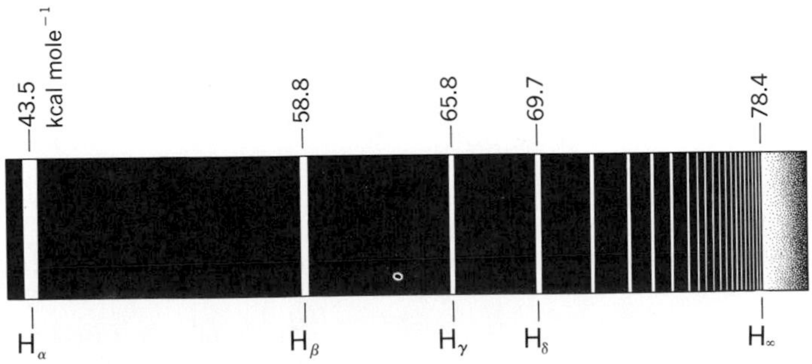

Figure 3.11 The Balmer series of atomic hydrogen, H.

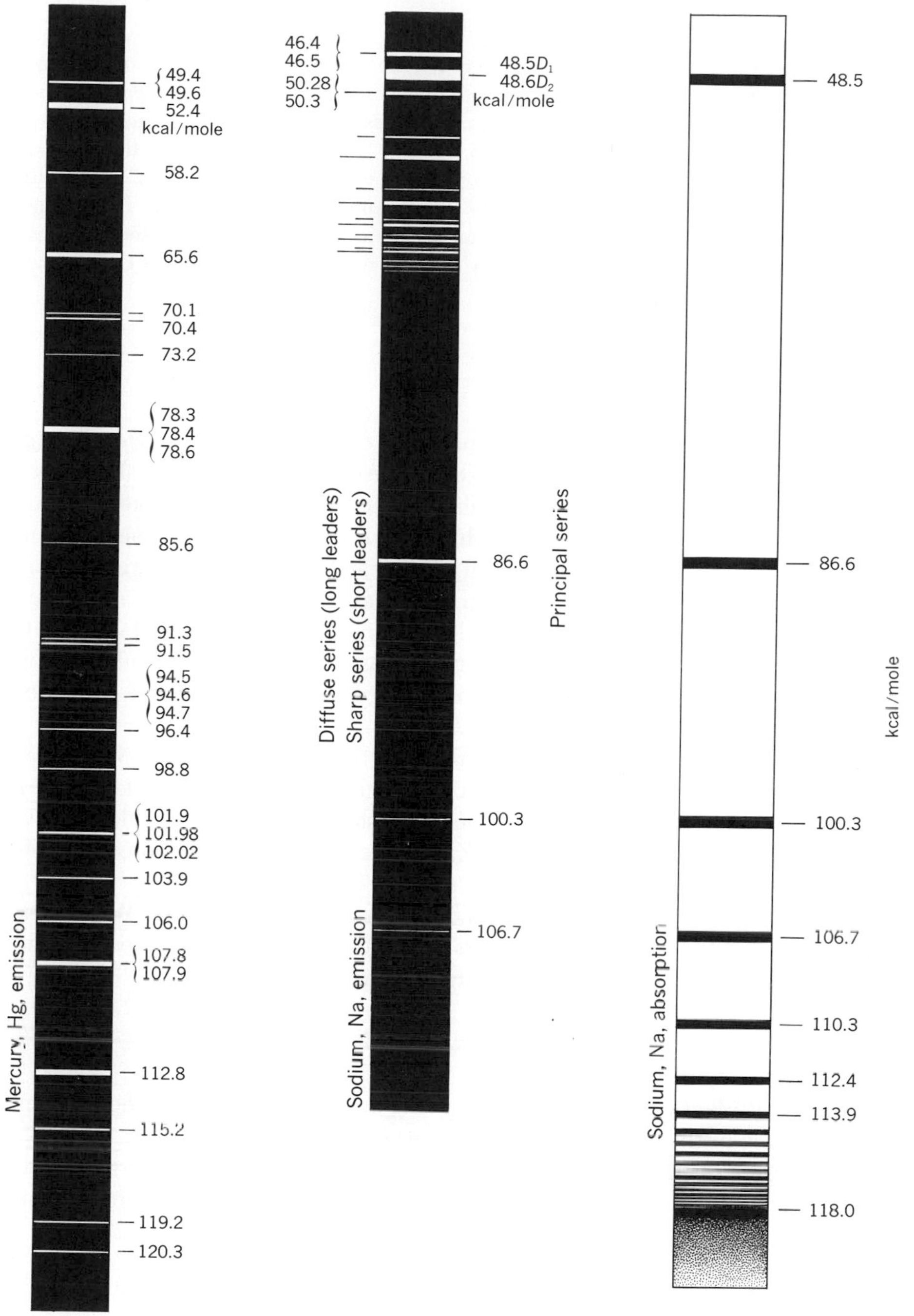

Figure 3.12 Some typical spectra of gaseous elements.

Exercise 3.3

Calculate the difference in energy between the first line in the Lyman series and each other line in that series. Compare with the energies of the lines in the Balmer series. Repeat for the Balmer and the Paschen series. Any comments? *Answer:* 278.8 − 235.2 = 43.6, 294.0 − 235.2 = 58.8, 301.1 − 235.2 = 65.9, etc. gives the energy of the Balmer series lines. Similarly, 58.8 − 43.6 = 15.2, 65.9 − 43.6 = 22.3 gives the Paschen series. This means that the energy differences between the Lyman lines equal the energies found in the Balmer spectra. Perhaps the Balmer series involves transitions between the same energy states as the excited states giving Lyman lines. Similarly for the Paschen series.

HYDROGENLIKE SPECTRA

When emission spectra are carefully analyzed, one sometimes discovers sets of lines very similar to those of atomic hydrogen. Analysis rather easily shows such lines in the helium, lithium, and beryllium spectra; the hydrogenlike lines are caused by He^+, Li^{++}, and Be^{+++}. Each of these atoms contains a nucleus surrounded by a single negative charge. All are isoelectronic with hydrogen; that is, they have the same extranuclear electron charge as does hydrogen. If we compare the spectra of H, He^+, Li^{++}, and Be^{+++}, the spectra all look like that in Figure 3.10, but the lines occur at higher and higher energies as Z increases. Apparently all four atoms have the same pattern of electronic-energy levels, but the energy of each level is influenced by the nuclear charge.

In terms of our two models, either (1) the single electron is held more tightly by the more highly charged nuclei, and higher energy is required to move it to a different energy level, or (2) the negative shell containing a single negative charge is pulled closer to the nucleus as Z increases, thus requiring more energy to excite it to a more distant position.

In fact, the energy shifts are related by simple electrostatics. We find experimentally that the ratio of the energies of any two corresponding lines (n) is the same as the ratio of the two nuclear charges squared:

$$\frac{\Delta E_{n\mathrm{A}}}{\Delta E_{n\mathrm{B}}} = \left(\frac{Z_\mathrm{A}}{Z_\mathrm{B}}\right)^2 \tag{3.2}$$

where A and B identify the nuclei of charge Z_A and Z_A and ΔE_n identifies the corresponding line in the spectrum of A and the spectrum of B.

Further empirical analysis of the energies shows that the energy, ΔE, of any line may be calculated with great accuracy (about five significant figures) from the

RYDBERG EQUATION:

$$\Delta E = KZ^2\left(\frac{1}{n^2} - \frac{1}{n'^2}\right) \tag{3.3}$$

where ΔE is the energy of the line representing the change in energy of the atom, K is a constant (the Rydberg constant), Z is the atomic number, $n = 1$ for Lyman, 2 for Balmer, 3 for Paschen, 4 for Brackett, and 5 for Pfund series lines, and n' is an integer greater than n ($n' = n + 1$, $n + 2$, $n + 3$, and so on). $K = 313.64$ kcal mole^{-1} when Z is in nuclear charge units (H = 1, He = 2, Li = 3, etc.); and E is in kcal mole^{-1}.

Exercise 3.4

Where would you look with a spectroscope for the helium line corresponding to H_α? *Answer:* $\Delta E_{He}/\Delta E_H = (2/1)^2$, $\Delta E_{He} = 43.6 \cdot 4 = 174.4 = 174$ kcal mole^{-1}, which is in the ultraviolet region. Or use Equation (3.3) with $Z = 2$, $n = 2$, $n' = 3$, $K = 313.64$ kcal mole^{-1}. This line is observed in the spectrum of gaseous He^+.

HYDROGENLIKE ENERGY LEVELS

The possible energy changes, ΔE, in an atom isoelectronic with hydrogen are given by the Rydberg equation, which can be written as

$$\Delta E = E_n - E_{n'} = KZ^2\frac{1}{(n)^2} - KZ^2\frac{1}{(n')^2} \tag{3.4}$$

where E_n and $E_{n'}$ represent the total energies of the atom in states n and n'. Such an equation strongly tempts one to identify each of the energies with one of the terms on the right side of the equation. A less radical suggestion is to define the total energies, E_n and $E_{n'}$, of the two possible states, n and n', as

$$\begin{aligned} E_n &= KZ^2\frac{1}{(n)^2} + E' \\ E_{n'} &= KZ^2\frac{1}{(n')^2} + E' \end{aligned} \tag{3.5}$$

These equations assume that the total possible energies of the atom are composed of a part, E', which does not change during these excitation processes, and a part, $KZ^2[1/(n \text{ or } n')^2]$, which does. The nuclear energy, for example, would be included in E'.

Exercise 3.5

Calculate the IE of atomic H. *Answer:* Electron will move from ground state, $n = 1$, to infinity, $n = \infty$, so

$$IE = KZ^2\left(\frac{1}{n^2} - \frac{1}{n'^2}\right) = 313.64 \cdot 1^2\left(\frac{1}{1^2} - \frac{1}{\infty^2}\right) = 313.64 \text{ kcal mole}^{-1}$$

Note that IE of He^+ is $4 \cdot 313.64$, as shown in Table 3.1. That of Ca^{19+} is $400 \cdot 313.64$, and so on.

HYDROGENLIKE ENERGY-LEVEL DIAGRAMS

The suggested definition in Equations (3.5) is remarkably useful. Figure 3.13 is constructed to represent the actual energy levels predicted from our equations. The equations in turn are based on observed energies emitted. Let us use the diagram to predict emission energies and see if our model is adequate. The Lyman lines, as shown, should all be associated with energy changes involving level 1; the Balmer lines, level 2; Paschen, level 3; and Brackett, level 4. The energy differences read from the energy-level diagram agree to five significant figures with those found experimentally in the emission spectra.

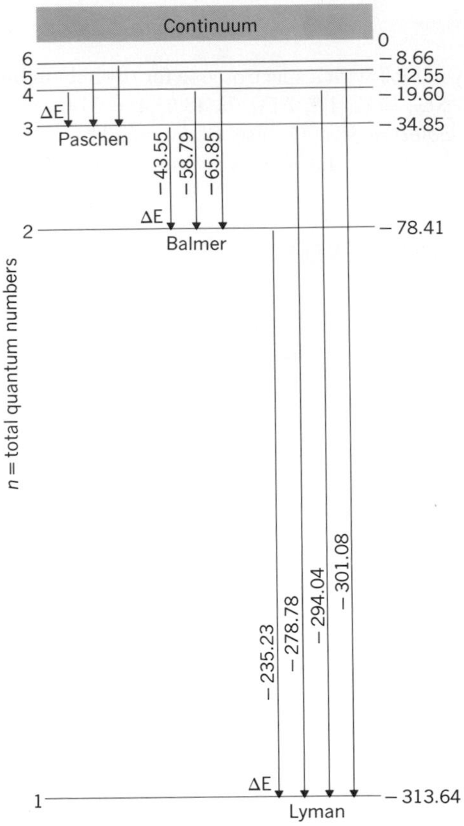

Figure 3.13 Energy levels for atomic hydrogen calculated from the observed spectrum. Compare Δ*E* values with Figure 3.10.

HYDROGENLIKE ATOMS IN ELECTRIC AND MAGNETIC FIELDS

The Rydberg equation correlates all the changes in levels of hydrogenlike (one-electron) atoms observed in simple spectroscopic observations to an accuracy of about 1 part in 100,000. But if one observes the spectral lines very closely, especially in a strong electric or magnetic field, energy changes are observed which do not fit our simple picture. Under very high resolution and the presence of strong electric fields, the lines "split." Several closely spaced lines are observed where only one was seen before. The magnitude of the splitting increases with the magnitude of the applied field. Such splittings are shown in Figure 3.14.

Much work has been done on these splittings, which are called the fine and hyperfine structure of the lines. Some of the effects are due to interactions between the electron energy levels and the nucleus and to the variation of these interactions from one isotope to another. But even when isotopic and other nuclear effects are removed from consideration, splitting due to some other effect (or effects) is still present.

That several energy changes are actually observed under these conditions indicates the presence of several energy levels. That the energy changes are only slightly different (splitting is small) means that the energy levels involved must have almost the same energy. That the splitting is increased by applied electric and magnetic fields indicates that the energy levels must be sensitive to the presence of such fields. The latter is certainly no surprise, since

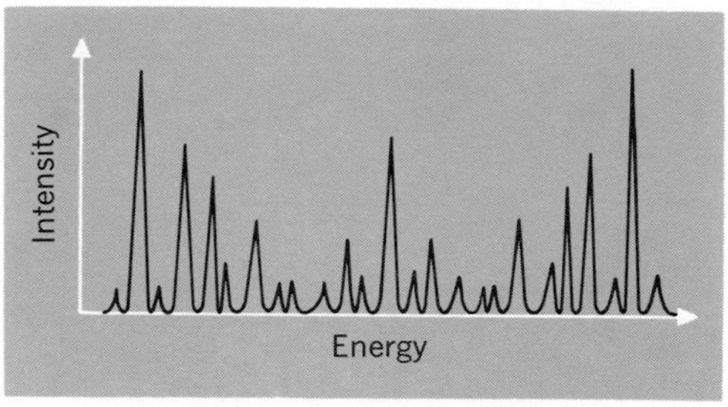

Figure 3.14 Fine structure at very high resolution of the atomic hydrogen line at 65.85 kcal mole^{-1} (H_γ see Figures 3.11 and 3.13) in a strong electric field (Stark effect). The height of each line is proportional to the experimentally observed intensity. Spectral theory can account quantitatively for both the intensities and the energy splittings of this set of lines.

one would expect a negative electric charge in an atomic orbital to interact with both an electric and a magnetic field.

All these effects may be quantitatively correlated if we assume that energy levels with $n > 1$ are actually made up of sets of different energy levels. If only one nucleus and one negative charge are present, these sets of levels have the same energy. But in the presence of a noncentrosymmetric field the levels have slightly different energies. The energy levels split. Careful study shows that the level associated with each value of n is actually composed of n sets of levels.

ENERGY-LEVEL NOTATION

Early study of observed spectral lines grouped them together in terms of line properties. Some lines were very narrow and were called *sharp*. Sets of prominent lines were called *principal* lines; others were broad and were called *diffuse;* still others were listed as *fundamental.* The later discovery of the energy levels associated with these lines led to calling the levels *s, p, d, f* in terms of line characteristics. The energies of the levels in the closely spaced hydrogenlike levels observed in an external field lie in the order *s, p, d, f,* with *s* the most stable (lowest energy) level. This revised picture is presented in Figure 3.15.

The energy levels are identified by two symbols: (1) the value of n (where $n = 1, 2, 3, \ldots$), and (2) a letter *s, p, d, f, g, h, i,* and so on. Since the levels are fixed in terms of the quantity of energy they contain and since they differ from one another by definite quantities of energy, they are often called quantum levels. The light associated with any particular change in electronic energy always contains a fixed, well-defined quantity of energy. These quantities of energy are called quanta.

Electronic energy levels are often described in terms of quantum numbers. A complete set of quantum numbers in modern terms involves four numbers for each negative charge in an orbital about the nucleus: n = the principal quantum number, l = the orbital quantum number ($l = 0, 1, 2, \ldots, n - 1$), m = the magnetic quantum number ($m = 0, \pm1, \pm2, \ldots, \pm l$), s = the spin quantum number ($s = \pm\frac{1}{2}$). For the time being we shall use only n and l. Furthermore, we shall use the orbital notation *s, p, d, f* (instead of l = 0, 1, 2, 3, respectively), since the combination of a number and a letter such as 1*s* or 4*d* is easier to read and write than "$n = 1, l = 0$" or "$n = 4, l = 2$."

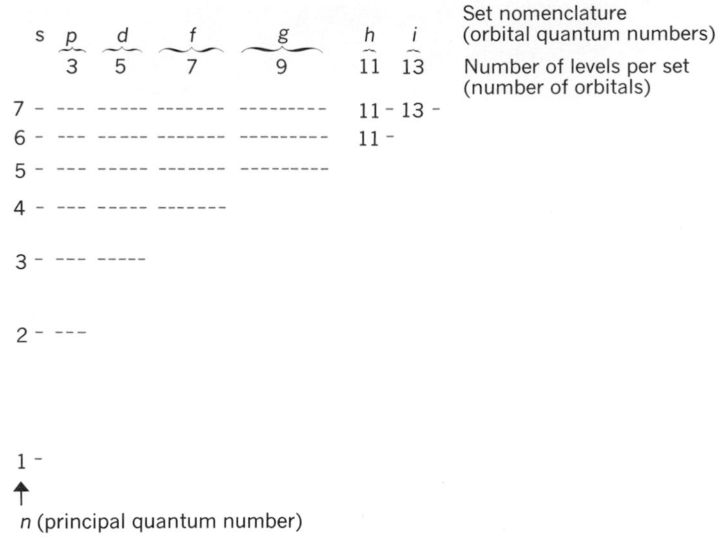

Figure 3.15 Energy-level diagram for hydrogenlike atoms showing number of levels of the same energy. Note that the number of levels per set (number of orbitals = 1, 3, 5, 7, 9) obtained here exactly matches the values of c obtained from ionization energies (see p. 77).

Exercise 3.6

Calculate the energy of the transition in atomic hydrogen from $3p$ to $4d$. Identify the line. *Answer:*

$$\Delta E = KZ^2\left(\frac{1}{n^2} - \frac{1}{n'^2}\right),$$

$K = 313.64$, $Z = 1$, $n = 3$, $n' = 4$ [since all 3 levels (s, p, d) have the same energy, and all 4 levels (s, p, d, f) have the same energy].

$$\Delta E = 313.64 \cdot 1^2\left[\frac{1}{3^2} - \frac{1}{4^2}\right] = 15.2 \text{ kcal mole}^{-1}.$$

This is the first line in the Paschen series (see Figure 3.10).

Hydrogenlike spectra are simple because the negative charge feels a force only in "one direction." Splitting occurs when an external field is applied and the electron is no longer subject only to a central force field. Most atoms, as we have seen, can emit more than one electron; they have more than a single negative charge around the nucleus. It apparently is the interaction of these charges with one another and with the nucleus that leads to the large splittings observed in most atomic spectra. It is reasonable that the splitting should be large, since atoms are small and the charges are close together.

The spectrum and energy-level diagram for lithium (and atoms isoelectronic with lithium) are shown in Figure 3.16. The diagram is directly comparable to that used to describe hydrogenlike atoms in an electric field, and the notation used to describe it is the same. The main difference is that the s, p, d, f splittings are larger. A ready interpretation would be that the electric field caused by several negative charges (3 for lithiumlike atoms) is much greater than that caused by an external field.

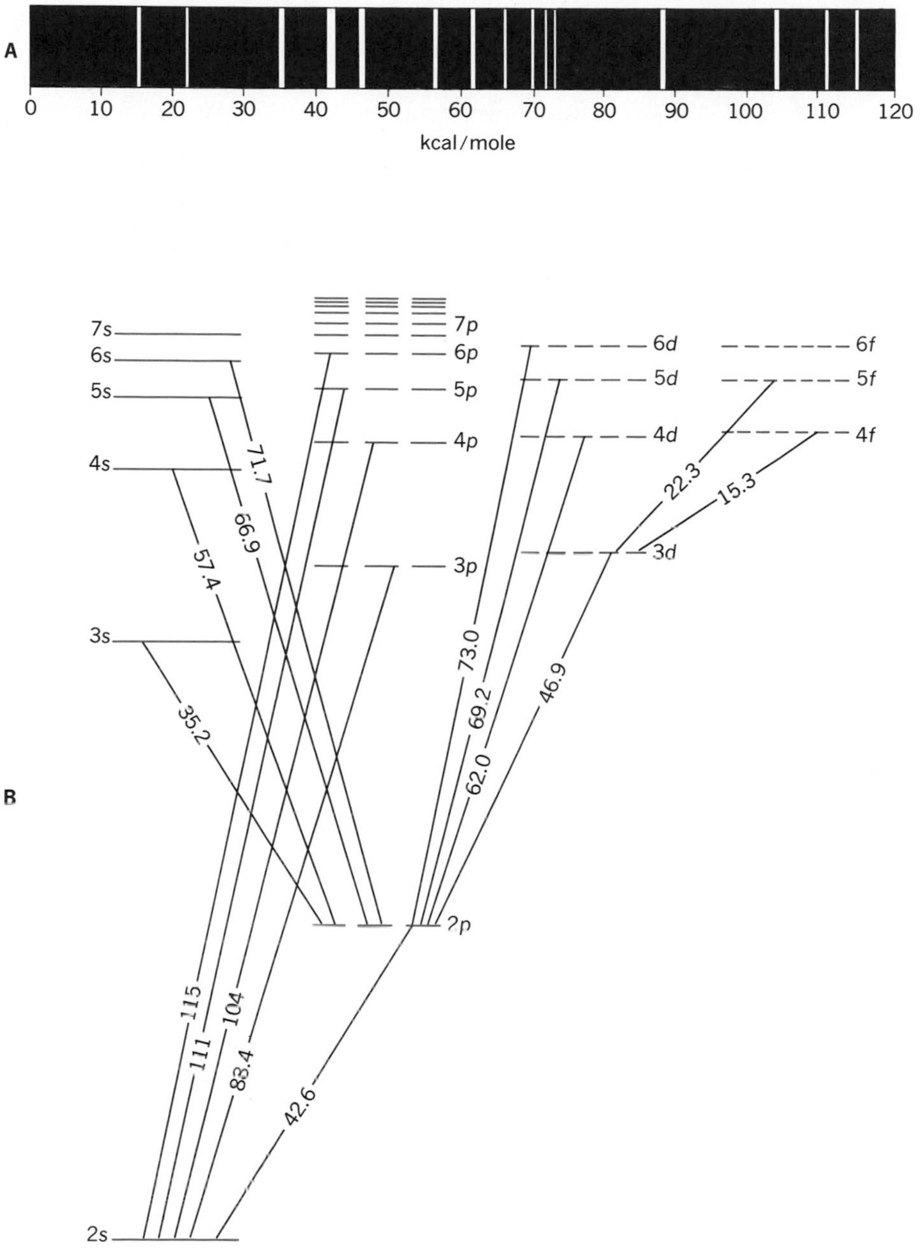

Figure 3.16 Part of the spectrum of gaseous lithium and the energy-level diagram deduced from the spectrum. Note that only certain transitions are observed. Others are said to be "forbidden," such as s-s, or *d*-s.

Examination of all known energy-level diagrams for gaseous atoms indicates similar relationships.

1. As the nuclear charge increases, all energy levels become more stable—they move downward to lower energies in the diagram.

2. If the number of negative charges in the atom exceeds 1, splitting of all levels (except the $n = 1$ level) occurs.
3. The split levels have the same pattern for any set of isoelectronic atoms, but all levels move toward lower energies as the nuclear charge increases.

So much regularity encourages us to search for a single energy-level diagram that will correlate all known atomic energy levels. The occupancy of atomic energy levels is dependent on nuclear charge, number of electrons, and total energy in the atom. A three-dimensional diagram would probably be needed to correlate these three variables. Certainly no two-dimensional diagram is known that can do the whole job. But it is possible to combine two of the variables and obtain a very effective two-dimensional diagram.

We can obtain the two-dimensional diagram in Figure 3.17 by considering spectra of only neutral atoms. That is, we require that the number of electrons in the atom equal the nuclear charge, Z. We then plot relative values of E for the energy levels as a function of Z, and connect the values of E for each set of levels having the same quantum numbers.

Figure 3.17 may be described as a set of lines in which each line represents a single energy level for neutral atoms and shows how the energy of the level (or orbital) varies as Z varies. Each line emanates from a hydrogenlike level ($Z = 1$), splits from the other lines having the same origin as Z increases, and more or less slowly decreases in energy as Z increases. When Z is large, the lines emanating from a single hydrogenlike level (those with the same principal quantum number n) tend to regroup, but not to rejoin. But at intermediate values of Z the lines exhibit considerable crossing and intermingling regardless of their n value. For example, when Z is small, the $3d$ orbital line is at a higher energy than the $4s$ line, but with large Z a $3d$ orbital is at a lower energy level than the $4s$ orbital. The higher the value of Z, the more the lower-lying energy levels tend to group according to principal quantum number. Can you suggest a reason?

Exercise 3.7

For what elements are the following statements most nearly true? (*a*) $4s$ and $4d$ electrons have the same energy. (*b*) $3d$ and $4p$ electrons are about the same energy. (*c*) $2p \longrightarrow 1s$ transition gives maximum energy. *Answer:* See Figure 3.17: (*a*) H (*g*), (*b*) at Ne and again at about Ti (actually should be at about Ca but smoothing causes variation), (*c*) largest possible Z; note logarithmic scales ($2p \longrightarrow 1s$ gives K X-rays).

ORBITAL POPULATION

If we compare Figures 3.3 and 3.17, we note some interesting similarities. Both are plots of energy as a function of nuclear charge and number of electrons. Figure 3.3 shows the energy required to remove electrons sequentially from a range of elements. Figure 3.17 shows the possible electronic energies that the neutral atom can have before the electron is removed. It would not be surprising if ionization energies are related to atomic energy levels. Before we can correlate the two diagrams, however, we must have some idea how the negative charges fill the orbitals.

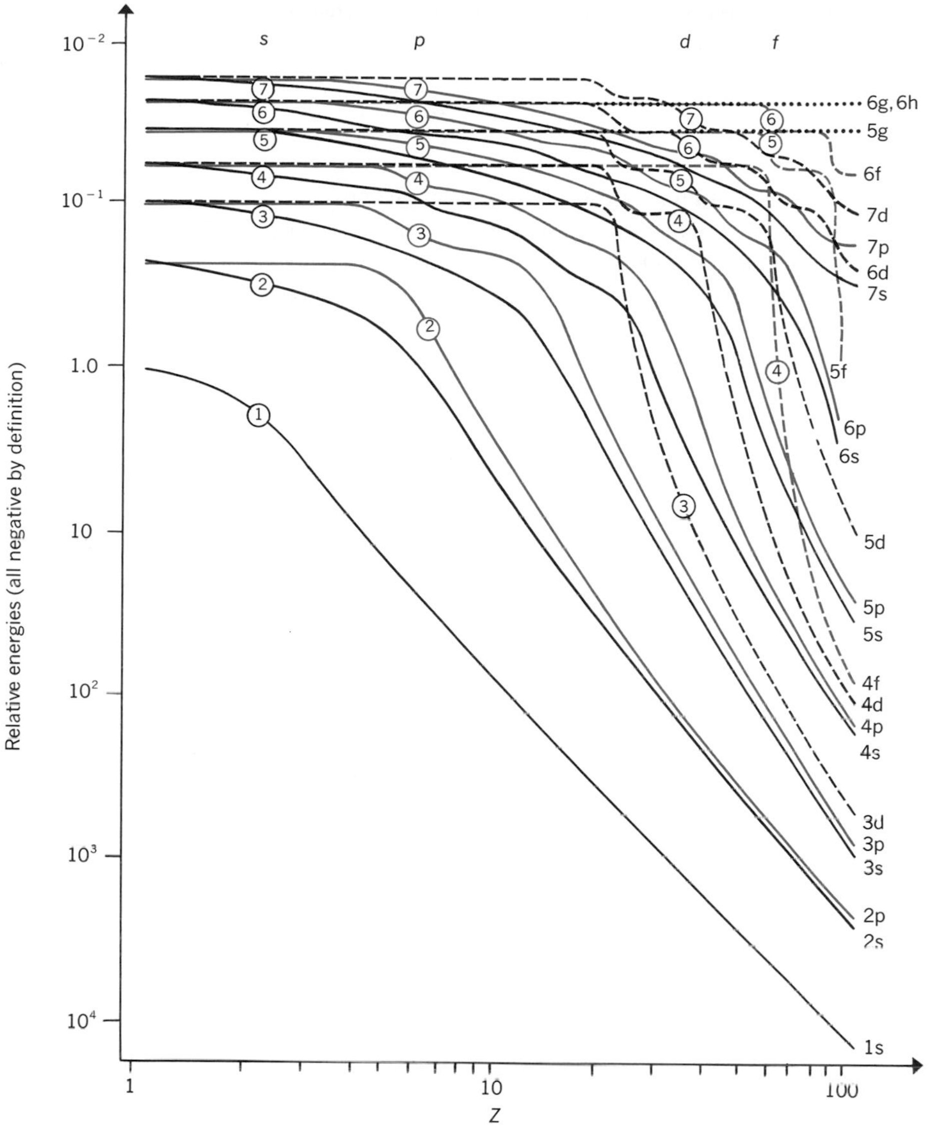

Figure 3.17 Relative energies, E, of atomic orbitals calculated and plotted as a function of nuclear charge, Z (atomic number). Curves are smoothed removing small fluctuations which are actually observed. Note that the scales are linear in the logarithm of each function. [Much of the data is from R. Latter, *Phys. Rev.*, **99**, 510 (1955).]

How many negative charges can there be in a 1s orbital or in 2s, 2p, 4d sets of orbitals?

Figure 3.3 provides valuable clues to this problem. We have already noted that according to ionization energy data, the electron charges cluster in groups of 2, 6, 10, and 14. Perhaps these clusters correspond to the orbitals represented in Figure 3.17.

Consider, for example, the data for a single element, say argon ($Z = 18$). Ionization data from Figure 3.3 show that the five most tightly held charge groups

Table 3.2 Numbers of electron charges in atomic orbitals.

Type of orbital	s	p	d	f	g	h	i	j	...
Maximum number of negative charges	2	6	10	14	18	22	26	30	...

can lose 2, 2, 6, 2, and 6 electrons, respectively. Energy-level data from Figure 3.17 show that the lowest five energy levels are 1*s*, 2*s*, 2*p*, 3*s*, 3*p*. A good possibility would seem to be that *s* orbitals can hold 2 and only 2 negative charges, *p* orbitals 6 and only 6. All available data indicate that this is so. Similarly, from a full examination of spectral data we deduce the maximum negative charge content of each orbital set, as shown in Table 3.2.

The most electrons obtainable from any neutral atom is 104, from Kurchatovium ($Z = 104$). Thus we never, in present-day chemistry, need think of more orbitals than those required to hold about 100 negative charges. Each charge will be strongly attracted to the nucleus, and each will be repelled by all the other negative charges present. What will be the stable equilibrium distribution of the charges among these orbitals?

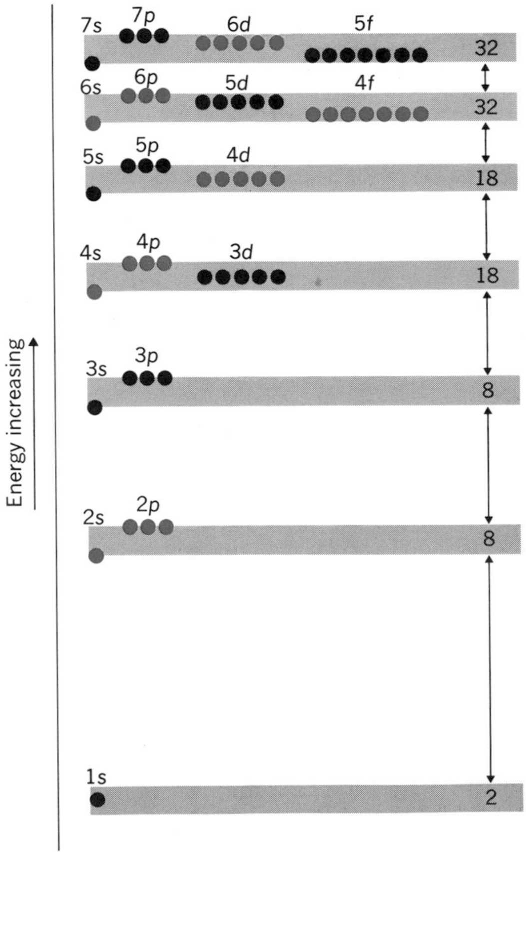

Figure 3.18 Orbital-energy-level chart showing the order of *filling* of atomic orbitals as *Z* increases, when *Z* (nuclear charge) equals the number of extranuclear electrons in a gaseous atom. Each orbital, represented by a circle, can contain 0, 1, or 2 electrons. Low-energy orbitals fill before higher-energy orbitals. In any set of orbitals of equal energy, the electrons "spread out," or unpair, to the maximum extent possible in that set.

Figure 3.18 correlates some of the experimental data for the electrically neutral gaseous atoms. (We discuss some exceptions to Figure 3.18 in Figure 4.6.)

Figure 3.18 is constructed so that one can learn from it the ground state orbital population of most of the electrically neutral gaseous atoms. One first determines the number of electron charges, Z, in the atom. Each charge is then assigned to an orbital, starting with the lowest-energy orbital, 1*s*, and working up the figure in order of increasing orbital energy. Each circle represents an orbital of energy shown on the scale. Each orbital can hold 0, 1, or 2 electron charges—never more than 2 charges in one orbital. The ground state has the charges in the lowest-energy orbitals.

A standard shorthand description of an atom's orbital occupancy lists the orbitals in order of increasing energy, using a superscript to indicate the negative charge content of each orbital. The groups of orbitals that are closely spaced in energy are set apart by semicolons. *Examples:* H ($Z = 1$), $1s^1$; O ($Z = 8$), $1s^2$; $2s^2, 2p^4$; Ca ($Z = 20$), $1s^2$; $2s^2, 2p^6$; $3s^2, 3p^6$; $4s^2$; Fe ($Z = 26$), $1s^2$; $2s^2, 2p^6$; $3s^2, 3p^6$; $4s^2, 3d^7$.

SUMMARY

Measurements of ionization energies, excitation energies, and spectra all lead to the idea that atoms can exist in only certain energy states. Transitions between these states involve the loss and gain of fixed amounts of energy that are characteristic of the atoms, and that correspond to the "lines" found in spectra obtained experimentally from gaseous atoms. These energy levels for atoms having only one electron (hydrogenlike atoms) may be described very simply (as in Figure 3.13) in the absence of external fields. When two or more electrons are present, or in the presence of an external field, the internal field of the atom is no longer centrosymmetric and the spectra become more complicated. Detailed assignment of energy levels then becomes more difficult. Fortunately, most atoms of interest to chemists can be treated in terms of the energy level diagram of Figure 3.18, but it is wise to remember that the actual energy level distribution and resulting electron population is a function of nuclear charge, number of electrons in the atom, total energy in the atom, and the nature of any external field.

Just because you see alpha particles coming out of the nucleus, you should not necessarily conclude that they exist inside it in the same form.—Erwin Schrödinger (1927).

PROBLEMS

3.1. The energy required to remove the first, second, and third electrons from carbon and nitrogen gaseous atoms is, respectively: for carbon, 11.26, 24.38, and 47.87 electron volts; for nitrogen, 14.54, 29.60, and 47.43 electron volts. Account for the fact that it is easier to remove a first and second electron from carbon than from nitrogen, and that it is easier to remove a third electron from nitrogen than from carbon atoms.

3.2. The spectrum of gaseous cesium is quite simple—in fact, very similar to that of gaseous lithium—but the spectrum of gaseous iron is extremely complicated. Interpret this difference qualitatively.

3.3. Arrange the following elements in order of the complexity you would expect in the spectra of their gases and give reasons for your order: H, Rb^+, Rb, U.

3.4. Account for the following experimental observations.

(*a*) Neon signs are red but xenon signs are blue.
(*b*) Sodium vapor lamps emit yellow light, but sodium vapor is blue by transmitted light.
(*c*) Carbon arc lights emit white light, and mercury arc lights emit blue light.
(*d*) Every element may be uniquely identified by its emission spectrum.
(*e*) Most of the elements of Groups 1 and 2 and a few others such as copper may be identified either pure or in their compounds by the color they impart to flames. *Hint:* Flames are good conductors of electricity.
(*f*) Many of the elements emit white light when they burn in oxygen, but even these can often be identified if the flame is observed through a spectroscope.

II

3.5. Predict the ionization energy of each of the following and write the electronic structures for the initial ion and the product ion. (*a*) F^{9+}. (*b*) S^{10+}. (*c*) Sc^+. (*d*) Sc^{++}. (*e*) Sc^{+++}. (*f*) Sc^{4+}. (*g*) Sc^{5+}. (About 11,000 ev in *b*.)

3.6. Compare the absorption spectrum and the emission spectrum of sodium in Figure 3.12. Which is simpler? How do you account for this? Draw an energy-level diagram for sodium like that in Figure 3.16 and identify the lines in Figure 3.12 in terms of transitions in the diagram. What do the lines of the principal series have in common? Those of the sharp series? Those of the diffuse series?

3.7. Design an entirely earth-based experiment (that is, use no rockets) for finding out whether the "B" line in Figure 3.6 is due to terrestrial or to solar oxygen.

See page 1090 for a list of references and readings in the recent chemical literature related to the material in this chapter.

CHAPTER 4

Atomic Models and Chemical Reactions

There are no finite discontinuities in nature.

Thus far we have been able to interpret the cited experimental evidence without committing ourselves to any model except one involving orbitals of fixed and well-defined energy arranged somehow outside a small, positively charged, central nucleus. But what can we say about the actual distribution of the negative charges? Are there individual electrons present—particles having negative charges? Or are there diffuse clouds bearing integral electron charges? Are the orbitals of fixed shape and spatial distribution? Or are the orbitals tenuous, continually shifting and reforming? Or is the situation quite different, or even impossible to describe?

BOHR MODEL

The first, and one of the most exciting, mathematical models was presented by Bohr in 1913, when he was 28. He became intrigued by the simplicity of the hydrogenlike spectra, the simplicity of the Rydberg equation, and the impossibility of interpreting either with the physical theory accepted at that time. He did for atomic theory essentially the same thing that Einstein did for interaction theory—he developed a new postulatory framework.

The contributions of an innovating genius, such as Einstein or Bohr, can be appreciated only by one intimately acquainted with the state of science at the time of the innovation, but let us sketch the usual situation when a new theory is introduced. Typically, a set of theories accounting for most experimental observations is currently accepted. The theories are interrelated and interdependent, with each theory supporting others. The theoretical fabric seems solid, even immutable.

The combination of the theoretical and experimental structure serves as the base of the reputation of all the distinguished scientists of the era, and of many other men from the past. The role of the innovating genius is simply to convince his colleagues that their models are inadequate and that some rather fundamental changes in assumptions must be made. The fact that many scientists who suggest such innovations are twenty to thirty years old does not lighten their task, but it does say something about courage, initiative, and nonconformity. Innovators are aided, of course, by the fact that there are usually enough "exceptions" to long-established theories to make the need for some change apparent.

Sometimes the innovation, like Bohr's, is so simple and accounts so accurately for hitherto unaccountable observations that immediate recognition is obtained. And sometimes the innovator, like Bohr, continues to produce scintillating insights—but not always. And, in the great majority of cases, subsequent innovators provide even more adequate theories. Bohr's own theory of atomic spectra, for example, was replaced within fifteen years by a more inclusive model.

Bohr's essential problem was to find a mathematical model that would lead to the

RYDBERG EQUATION: $$\Delta E = KZ^2\left(\frac{1}{n^2} + \frac{1}{n'^2}\right)$$

Remember that K was known to five significant figures. Any derivation would have to be an accurate one. Let us see some of what Bohr contributed.

Bohr found that he could derive the equation with the following assumptions and procedures. (Actually these steps are a modification due to Sommerfeld.)

1. Hydrogenlike atoms contain a single electron which behaves as a small particle of mass, m, with negative charge e.
2. The electron circles about the nucleus as a center, at radius r and velocity v.
3. The electron experiences a centrifugal force of mv^2/r.
4. The electron is attracted to the nucleus of charge Z by a coulombic force Ze^2/r^2, equaling the centrifugal force; e is the electronic charge.
5. The total energy, E, is the sum of the kinetic energy, $E_K = \frac{1}{2}mv^2$, and the potential energy, $E_P = -Ze^2/r$.
6. The only stable circular paths about the nucleus are those for which the angular momentum of the electron is given by the equation $mvr = n(h/2\pi)$, where n is an integer greater than zero and h is Planck's constant; n is called the principal quantum number. (Assumption 6 is called the quantum condition and is Bohr's great contribution. It is an ad hoc assumption not derivable from simple models, and is justified by the agreement the resulting equation gives with experimental data.)

We may combine these assumptions.

Quantum condition (6):

$$\text{angular momentum} = mvr = n\left(\frac{h}{2\pi}\right); \qquad v^2 = \frac{n^2h^2}{m^2r^24\pi^2} \tag{4.1}$$

Classical conditions (1, 2, 3, 4):

coulombic force = centrifugal force

$$\frac{Ze^2}{r^2} = \frac{mv^2}{r}, \qquad \text{so } v^2 = \frac{Ze^2}{rm}, \qquad \text{or } \frac{1}{2}mv^2 = \frac{Ze^2}{2r} = E_K \tag{4.2}$$

Total energy condition (5):

$$E = E_K + E_P = \frac{1}{2}mv^2 - \frac{Ze^2}{r} = \frac{1}{2}\frac{Ze^2}{r} - \frac{Ze^2}{r} = -\frac{Ze^2}{2r} \tag{4.3}$$

Equating the v^2 terms from the classical and quantum conditions:

$$\frac{n^2h^2}{m^2r^24\pi^2} = \frac{Ze^2}{rm}; \qquad r = \frac{n^2h^2}{Ze^24\pi^2m} \tag{4.4}$$

Substituting in the equation for total energy:

$$E = -\frac{Ze^2}{2r} = -\frac{Z^2e^42\pi^2m}{n^2h^2} = -\frac{2\pi^2me^4}{h^2}Z^2\left(\frac{1}{n^2}\right) \tag{4.5}$$

The difference in energy between two stable states, n and n', is described by the

BOHR EQUATION: $$\Delta E\Big|_{n}^{n'} = E_{n'} - E_n = \frac{2\pi^2me^4}{h^2}Z^2\left(\frac{1}{n^2} - \frac{1}{n'^2}\right) \tag{4.6}$$

where n and n' are integers called the principal quantum numbers of the two states. Using modern values of the physical constants, we get

$$\frac{2\pi^2me^4}{h^2}Z^2 = 2.17853 \cdot 10^{-11}Z^2 \text{ erg/atom}$$

in astounding agreement with the constant $K = 2.1789 \cdot 10^{-11}$ erg atom^{-1}, which is equivalent to the value of $K = 313.64$ kcal mole^{-1} given before as the Rydberg constant. The values available to Bohr gave agreement to about 0.1%. Such excellent agreement between theory and experiment is bound to impress scientists. The difficulty was that one of Bohr's assumptions (6) was contrary to accepted physical theory and another (2) was most unlikely. The solution to this difficulty was to recognize that physical theory designed to describe objects in the macroscopic range might not be adequate to describe atomic phenomena. In this sense Bohr is certainly one of the main founders of contemporary quantum theory, even though his own initial theory describes only hydrogenlike atoms adequately and was replaced within fifteen years. It is clear also that Bohr did not long, if ever, believe that electrons in hydrogenlike atoms circled the nucleus in planar orbits. It was sufficient that the mathematical model correlated the energies accurately without describing all the properties of the "real" atom, and that it opened up fruitful areas of further research.

Exercise 4.1

Are the two values of K, $2.1789 \cdot 10^{-11}$ ergs atom^{-1} and 313.64 kcal mole^{-1}, consistent? *Answer:* See Appendix I:

$$\frac{2.1789 \cdot 10^{-11} \text{ ergs } \cancel{\text{atom}^{-1}} \cdot 6.02252 \cdot 10^{23} \cancel{\text{atoms}} \text{ mole}^{-1}}{4.184000 \cdot 10^{7} \cancel{\text{ergs}}\ \cancel{\text{cal}^{-1}} \cdot 10^{3} \cancel{\text{cal}} \text{ kcal}^{-1}} = 313.64 \text{ kcal mole}^{-1}$$

THE VECTOR MODEL OF THE ATOM

The Bohr model was extended beyond the simple model given above to account for the splittings observed in external electric and magnetic fields, but the number of assumptions and the cumbersomeness of the treatment increased. The vector model was one such attempt to account for these splittings.

The vector model retained Bohr's ideas that particular electrons move around the nucleus with quantization of angular momentum related to $h/2\pi$. But it assumed the angular momentum has only values given by the equation

$$\text{angular momentum} = \sqrt{l(l+1)}\,\frac{h}{2\pi}$$

Only certain values of the orbital quantum number, l, are assumed possible, from 0 for s electrons through 1 for p electrons, 2 for d electrons, and so on up to $n-1$. This assumption, in terms of classical ideas, amounts to considering elliptical as well as spherical electron trajectories.

In a magnetic field the magnetic moment of the orbiting electron will interact with the field. Consider a hydrogenlike atom. Only those energy states are observed in which the projection of the angular momentum vector on the external field takes integral values. Thus each angular momentum vector, of value $l = 0, 1, 2, \ldots, n-1$, can take up $2l+1$ orientations corresponding to $m = 0, \pm 1, \pm 2, \ldots, \pm l$. In the absence of a magnetic field, all orbitals with the same values of n and l have the same energies. But in the presence of a magnetic field, splitting of the energy levels occurs because of the magnetic moment-field interactions, and each orbital of different m has a different energy. Thus every set of energy levels of principal quantum number n (1, 2, 3, . . .) consists of n sets of levels ($s, p, d, \ldots$) and n^2 orbitals.

This model soon incorporated one further feature suggested by Pauli—that two electrons and only two electrons can have the same set of values of n, l, and m. That is, an orbital can hold two and only two electrons. Following Uhlenbeck and Goudsmit, these electrons are said to have spin quantum numbers of $\frac{1}{2}$. When the number of electrons with spin $+\frac{1}{2}$ equals those with spin $-\frac{1}{2}$, and they give a resultant spin of zero, the electrons are said to be completely paired. Two electrons in a single orbital are always paired; their spins are sometimes said to be opposed, or antiparallel.

The vector model is actually an extension of the Bohr model and has to introduce each set of quantum numbers in an ad hoc fashion rather than being able to derive them. It is still used to interpret spectra. The Pauli exclusion principle—that any orbital can hold two and only two electrons, whose spins must be opposed—is the only part of this model we shall use.

Exercise 4.2

The action quantum, $h/2\pi$, recurs in many problems and many types of quantization. Calculate the value of the action quantum in erg sec per molecule and in kcal sec mole^{-1}. *Answer:* $h/2\pi = 6.6256 \cdot 10^{-27}$ erg sec molecule^{-1}/$2 \cdot 3.14159 =$ $1.05450 \cdot 10^{-27}$ erg sec molecule^{-1} $= 1.05450 \cdot 10^{-27}$ ~~erg~~ sec ~~molecule^{-1}~~ $\cdot\, 6.02252 \cdot 10^{23}$ ~~molecule~~ mole^{-1}/$4.18400 \cdot 10^{10}$ ~~erg~~ kcal^{-1} $= 1.51787 \cdot 10^{-14}$ kcal sec mole^{-1}, a very small number.

THE PROBABILITY ATOM

Schrödinger in 1926 put forward the

SCHRÖDINGER EQUATION: $$\frac{-h^2}{8\pi^2 m}\nabla^2(\psi) + V(\psi) = E(\psi) \tag{4.7}$$

which may be worded as "kinetic energy plus potential energy equals total energy." The form of the equation is simple enough, but the ∇ operator and the ψ function are not easy to master. Indeed, only problems related to hydrogenlike atoms can be solved exactly by the Schrödinger equation. But when one carries out the hydrogen solution, the n, l, and m quantum numbers "fall out" from the equation: n can have any positive integral value; $l = 0, 1, 2, \ldots, n-1$; $m = 0, \pm 1, \pm 2, \ldots, \pm l$. The spin quantum numbers must still be added independently as $\pm\frac{1}{2}$.

That only problems concerning the hydrogenlike atom can be solved exactly does not lie in a lack of rigor in the equation, but, rather, in the inability of our current mathematical methods to apply it exactly to more complicated problems. Computers help, as do special simplifying assumptions for certain cases, and with such techniques many molecular problems have been "solved." For such molecules as H_2 and H_2^+, it is easier to get properties from the Schrödinger equation than to measure them in the laboratory. With slightly more complicated molecules, like CH_4, calculation and experiment are about equally difficult. For all other molecules, experiments currently give more satisfactory answers, even though the equation can sometimes give good approximations more quickly. Dirac in 1928 was probably correct when he suggested that all chemistry had been reduced to mathematics, but it seems clear that the laboratory chemist will have plenty to do for a good many years in the future.

It is not certain whether Schrödinger felt that there were individual electrons in atoms or whether he preferred the idea of clouds of negative charge. In any case, the Schrödinger equation gives answers to atomic problems in the form of a probability function relating charge and space. Most chemists interpret the probability as indicating the likelihood of finding an electron in any of the various regions around the nucleus. One of the interesting implications of the probability function is that the probability that electrons will be found at very great distances from the nucleus is finite, although small. Thus every atom "extends" to infinity, at least in the sense that there is a small, but finite, chance of finding its electrons at an infinite distance from the nucleus.

Another interesting feature of the probability atom is that electron trajectories are not included. The Schrödinger equation gives no information on electron paths in atoms.

THE WAVE MODEL

The probability solution of the Schrödinger equation applied to atoms can also be interpreted in terms of a diffuse electron cloud. The probability then indicates the average negative charge density of the cloud in the various orbitals about the nucleus. Each orbital is a region that can hold a diffuse cloud made up of no more than two electrons of opposite spin. Each orbital can and does interpenetrate or overlap other orbitals, but each orbital may be almost independent of the other orbitals in spite of this overlap.

The cloud picture gains some verisimilitude in that even large objects can pulsate in a fashion very similar to that predicted for the hydrogen atom by the Schrödinger equation. Thus steel spheres undergo "s" vibrations, "p" vibrations, and so on, with the symmetry found for electrons in atoms. The steel sphere acts more like a pulsing cloud than it does a wandering particle (see Figure 4.5). Thus it may be that electrons lose many of their particle characteristics when they enter an orbital, though perhaps not to the extent they do upon entering a nucleus.

Both the particle model and the cloud model concur in the conclusion that it is impossible to calculate or measure a path or trajectory for an electron. The Bohr model and the vector model include trajectories, but the trajectory part of these models is seldom interpreted literally.

This belief that the trajectory of high-energy particles can not be determined is supported by our confidence in the Heisenberg uncertainty principle. Heisenberg suggested in 1926 that the mathematical product of the uncertainty in the energy, E, and the uncertainty in the time, τ, of an event, or the mathematical product of the uncertainty in the momentum, p, and the uncertainty in the position, d, of a particle both equal $h/2\pi$. This is stated as the

HEISENBERG UNCERTAINTY PRINCIPLE:

$$\Delta E\,\Delta\tau \cong \frac{h}{2\pi}, \qquad \Delta p \Delta d \cong \frac{h}{2\pi}$$

For example, the spectral lines originating in s orbitals are sharp (have a small uncertainty in energy) since the half-lives of the excited state are long (have a large uncertainty in time), but lines originating in d orbitals are diffuse, or broad, since the half-lives are short. These equations have been experimentally verified for many systems, and no exceptions are known. The Heisenberg principle indicates that it is impossible simultaneously to measure both the position and the momentum (or direction of motion) of a particle accurately; hence it is impossible to determine electron trajectories in atoms.

Fortunately, chemists do not care about the trajectory of electrons in atoms so long as the probability functions are known. Electrons move so much faster than atoms that electron trajectory is not a problem in dealing with atomic and molecular changes. We can use quantum theory, based on the Schrödinger equation, without worrying about trajectories.

We shall use a quantized model throughout this book, sometimes talking of electron clouds, sometimes of individual electrons. In both cases we shall actually be talking of a probability function that indicates the likelihood of finding a negative charge in the various orbital regions about the nucleus.

Exercise 4.3

The uncertainty in energy of the Fraunhofer D lines ($\lambda = 5280$ Å) due to sodium (see Figure 3.6) is about 0.000116 Å. Calculate the lifetime of the excited state. *Answer:* The Heisenberg principle correlates uncertainty in energy and uncertainty in time. If an excited state is very long-lived, the width of the emitted line is very narrow and vice versa, such that $\Delta E \cdot \Delta\tau = h/2\pi$, or $\tau = h/2\pi\Delta E$. Now, from Appendix I, we get $E = hc/\lambda$, so $dE = -hcd\lambda/\lambda^2$; thus

$$\Delta\tau = h/2\pi\Delta E = h/[2\pi(hcd\lambda/\lambda^2)] = \lambda^2/2\pi c d\lambda$$

$$= \frac{(5280\,\cancel{\text{Å}})^2 \cdot 10^{-8}\,\cancel{\text{cm}}\,\cancel{\text{Å}^{-1}}}{2 \cdot 3.14 \cdot 3.00 \cdot 10^{10}\,\cancel{\text{cm}}\,\text{sec}^{-1} \cdot 1.16 \cdot 10^{-4}\,\cancel{\text{Å}}} = 1.27 \cdot 10^{-8}\ \text{sec}$$

This is a short time by our standards but a moderately long time by atomic standards.

DUAL MODELS

You now know at least three systems in which dual models are used. (1) Electrons in atoms are sometimes thought of as clouds and sometimes as particles. (2) Mass and energy appear to be so intimately related as to be two different aspects of the same phenomenon. (3) Light is sometimes treated, as you probably know from former courses, as wave motion and sometimes as moving particles.

If you remember that the words waves, particle, cloud, mass, energy were first invented to describe the behavior of bulk matter, it may be easier to see why they are not easily applied to atomic dimensions. Perhaps eventually we will have a special language to describe atomic behavior and then extend that language to bulk matter. Until then, the reverse will have to do.

You will find that it is possible to accept and use intelligently the dual models. The sooner you are skilled at it, the better.

RADIAL DISTRIBUTION OF CHARGE IN ATOMS

Application of the Schrödinger equation to a hydrogenlike atom gives the curves plotted in Figure 4.1, A and B. Figure 4.1, A shows the radial wave function $[R_{n,l}(r)]$ as a function of the distance r (measured radially) from the nucleus; the square of the radial wave function, $[R_{n,l}(r)]^2$, is related to the negative charge density at any distance, r, from the nucleus. We see that charge tends to accumulate in certain volumes and to avoid others.

Now consider the likelihood of finding an electron charge in the spherical shell of volume $4\pi r^2 dr$ lying between r and $r + dr$.* As r increases, the volume of the shell lying between r and $r + dr$ increases at the same rate as does r^2. If the charge density is proportional to $[R_{n,l}(r)]^2$, then the likelihood of finding an electron charge at distance r from the nucleus must be $4\pi r^2[R_{n,l}(r)]^2$. This result follows because the total charge in the shell at distance r must be proportional to the product of the volume of the shell and the charge density in the shell.

Figure 4.1, B shows the relative probability of finding an electron charge along the y axis defined in Figure 4.3. The probability is high in certain volumes and low in others; sometimes it is higher far from the nucleus than it is close to the nucleus. Thus it is quite likely that electron charges will be far from the nucleus, even though the charge density at these great distances is small. Note that this gives an atom a diffuse character. Its size is not defined; its edges just "fade away." This is consistent with the general observation that there are no finite discontinuities in nature. Atoms do not "end" or have radial boundaries, they extend indefinitely, overlap, and merge with one another. But the extent of overlap is very small indeed beyond 10 or 20 Å, as indicated in Figure 4.1, B. The measured "size" of an atom depends greatly on how the measurement is made.

You will recall that the Schrödinger equation essentially stated that the

---

* We shall use the differential operator, d, to mean "infinitesimally small change in," thus:

$$\lim_{\Delta r \to 0} \Delta r = dr$$

sum of the kinetic energy and the potential energy is a constant. We may partially rationalize Figure 4.1, B in these terms. The nuclear charge tends to pull the negative electrons toward the nucleus, thus decreasing the potential energy. Since the total energy does not change, the kinetic energy of the electrons must increase. The increase in kinetic energy tends to move the charge into larger volumes—that is, away from the nucleus. But the process of receding from the nucleus increases the potential energy, and hence decreases the kinetic energy. Some relative probabilities which result from keeping the sum of the potential energy and kinetic energy constant (and the corresponding values of n and l) are shown in Figure 4.1, B.

Exercise 4.4

Arrange the 1*s*, 2*s*, 2*p*, 3*s*, 3*p*, 3*d* H atom orbitals in terms of the distance from the nucleus for the maximum probability of finding an electron. *Answer:* See Figure 4.1,B. 1*s*, 2*p*, 2*s*, 3*d*, 3*p*, 3*s*. Note that *s* electrons tend to be on the "outside" of each principal quantum level.

ANGULAR DISTRIBUTION OF CHARGE IN ATOMS

Solving the Schrödinger equation not only gives the radial distribution, as in Figure 4.1, A and B, it also gives angular distributions for the orbitals. These results are usually expressed in terms of three quantum numbers. It should not surprise you that three quantum numbers are required to describe each orbital—after all, orbitals are regions of space, and space is usually described in terms of three dimensions. A common and very succinct form of expressing the quantum numbers is in terms of n $(1, 2, 3, \ldots)$, l $(0, 1, 2, \ldots, n-1)$ and m $(0, \pm 1, \pm 2, \ldots, \pm l)$. For our purposes it will be simpler to use a different set of symbols: n; *s*, *p*, *d*, *f*, *g*, *h*, . . . ; and functions of x, y, and z. A partial correlation is shown in Table 4.1.

OVER-ALL ORBITAL SYMMETRY

Let us now look at the results obtained from the Schrödinger equation for the shapes and orientations, or the symmetries, of the orbitals. We know from probability calculations like those summarized in Figure 4.1, A and B, that every orbital extends indefinitely in space. Each electron *could be* almost anywhere. But each electron charge spends most of its time relatively close to a nucleus (see Figure 4.1, B). Figure 4.2 shows "electron cloud" representations for the H atom in various quantum states. The fuzziness is again apparent.

Table 4.1 Correlation of quantum numbers and quantum symbols.

	Principal	Orbital	Magnetic	Spin
Mathematical quantum numbers	$n = 1, 2, 3, 4, 5$	$l = 0, 1, 2, 3, \ldots n-1$	$m = 0, \pm 1, \pm 2, \pm 3, \ldots, \pm l$	$+\frac{1}{2}, -\frac{1}{2}$
Textual quantum symbols	$n = 1, 2, 3, 4, 5$	*s, p, d, f*	functions of *x, y, z*	α β

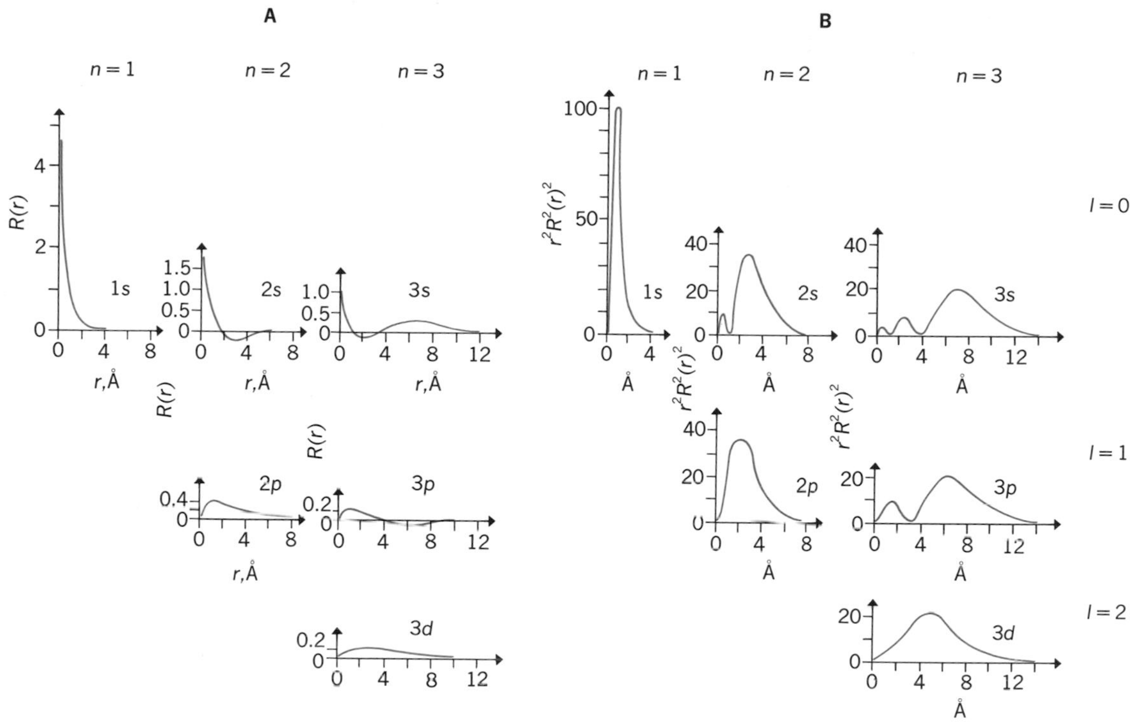

Figure 4.1 (**A**) Radial wave functions as a function of distance, *r*, from the nucleus for various orbitals. $[R(r)]^2$ is related to relative charge density. (**B**) Relative probability of finding an electron as a function of distance, *r*, from the nucleus for various orbitals all measured along the *y* axis of Figure 4.3.

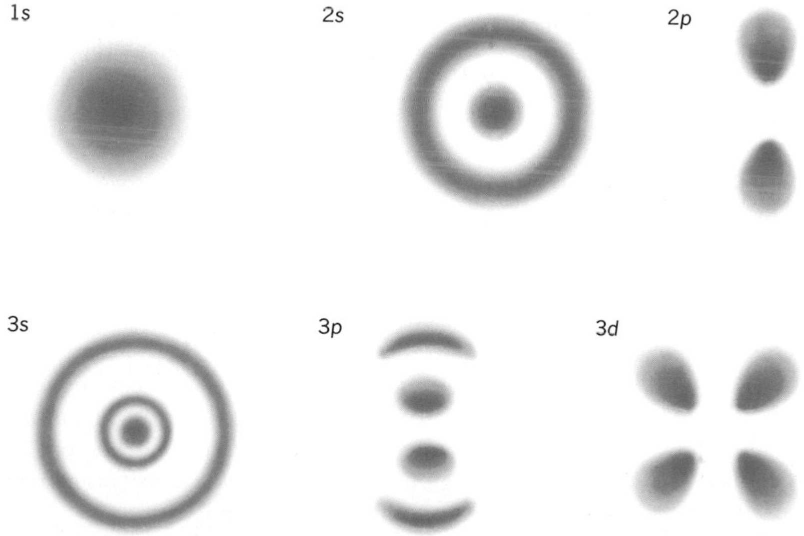

Figure 4.2 Electron cloud representations for hydrogen atoms in various quantum states. Each representation is of the distribution of a single unit of negative electricity around a hydrogen nucleus. The energies of orbitals of identical *n* (such as 3*s*, 3*p*, 3*d*) are identical, but differ from the energies of orbitals of different *n*.

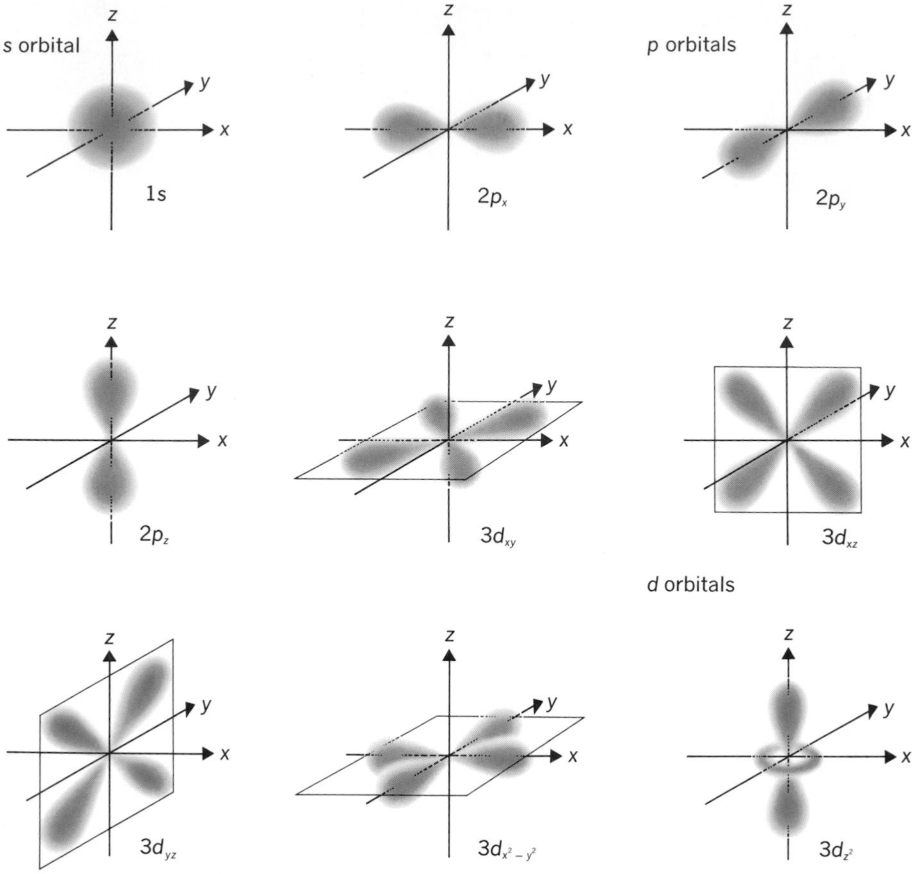

Figure 4.3 Schematic representations of the shapes of some s, p, and d orbitals. Nodal surfaces are not shown but the following types should be clear from the figures: (1) radial spherical nodes (at infinity for all orbitals), (2) axial planes acting as angular nodes (in all p's, and in d_{xy}, d_{yz}, d_{xz}), (3) interaxial planes as angular nodes in $d_{x^2-y^2}$, and (4) interaxial cones as angular nodes in d_{z^2}.

Figure 4.3 shows the general shape of *s*, *p*, and *d* orbitals. We shall not discuss orbitals of larger orbital quantum numbers, *f*, *g*, *h*, *i*, . . . , since they seldom are intimately concerned with chemical reactions. The single *s* orbitals are always *spherically* symmetrical about the nucleus. The three *p* orbitals (p_x, p_y, p_z) are always *perpendicular* to one another and directed along the three axes *x*, *y*, and *z*. Three of the *d* orbitals (d_{xz}, d_{yz}, d_{xy}) are *diagonally* positioned between the *x*, *y*, and *z* axes. The other two ($d_{x^2-y^2}$, d_{z^2}) are directed along the axes. The mnemonic may be helpful: *s* = spherical, *p* = perpendicular, *d* = diagonal. The orbital patterns of Figures 4.2 and 4.3 show regions of high electron density separated by nodal surfaces where the probability of finding an electron is zero.

The shapes and energies of these orbitals are not only used in interpreting properties of single atoms, they are also useful in interpreting interatomic forces and bonding between atoms.

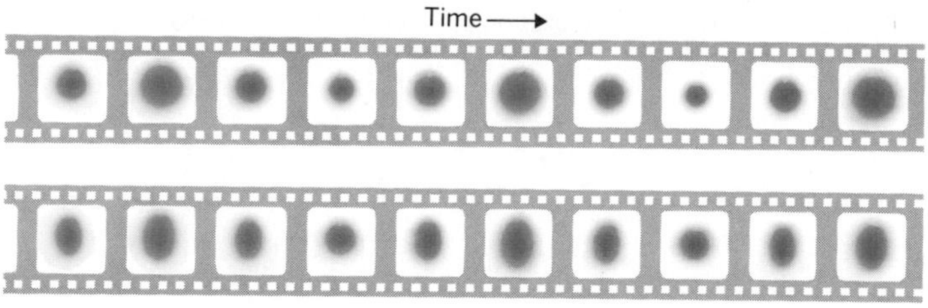

Figure 4.4 Some possible vibrational patterns of a homogeneous sphere, such as a gas-filled balloon.

THE PULSING ATOM—NODES

In the section on the wave model we mentioned that the atom may be considered as a diffuse cloud of negative electric charge, which pulsates in patterns similar to those observed in macroscopic objects. We then discussed the experimentally observed changes in terms of radial and angular distribution of charge, utilizing the ostensibly static models of Figures 4.1, A and B, 4.2, and 4.3. The electrons are, of course, not static; they move in such a way as to give the probability distributions. But perhaps the distributions can be further clarified if we consider Figures 4.2 and 4.3 in terms of pulsating electron clouds separated by nodal surfaces.

Figures 4.4 and 4.5 show some patterns observed when homogeneous spherical objects (gases, liquids, or isotropic solids) vibrate. They may be classified in terms of the number of nodes observed. (A node is a surface in which the amplitude of vibration is zero.) We see that there are *s* vibrations (no angular nodes), *p* vibrations (one angular node), and *d* vibrations (two angular nodes). Vibrations with larger numbers of angular nodes can also be observed (3 nodes for, *f*, 4 nodes for *g*, and so on).

Figure 4.5 shows some vibrational patterns in cross section, using data obtained by applying the equations describing spherical vibrations. We obtain the same symmetries and nodal patterns as previously. The total number of nodes corresponds to the principal quantum number: for $n = 1$, there is one radial node, at infinity; for $n = 2$, two nodes; for $n = 3$, three nodes; and so on. For *s* states, the number of angular nodes is zero; for *p* states, there is one angular node; for *d* states, two angular nodes; and so forth. The maximum number of angular nodes is always $n - 1$, since the total number of nodes $= n$, and there is always one radial node at infinity.

Exercise 4.5

Convert the 3*p* diagram of Figure 4.2 into the type of diagram found in Figure 4.3. *Answer:* There will be three 3*p* orbitals each concentrated along one of the axes *x*, *y*, and *z*. Along each axis there will be a node at the nucleus, a node at infinity, and (unlike the 2*p* orbital) a node a few angstroms from the nucleus (as in Figures 4.1 and 4.2).

ATOMIC MODELS

The Schrödinger equation provides, in principle, a mathematical device for calculating many atomic properties, for example energy levels. But it may be useful to have a "physical picture" for correlating experimental observations. Such models are always oversimplified, but it is often convenient to visualize atoms as com-

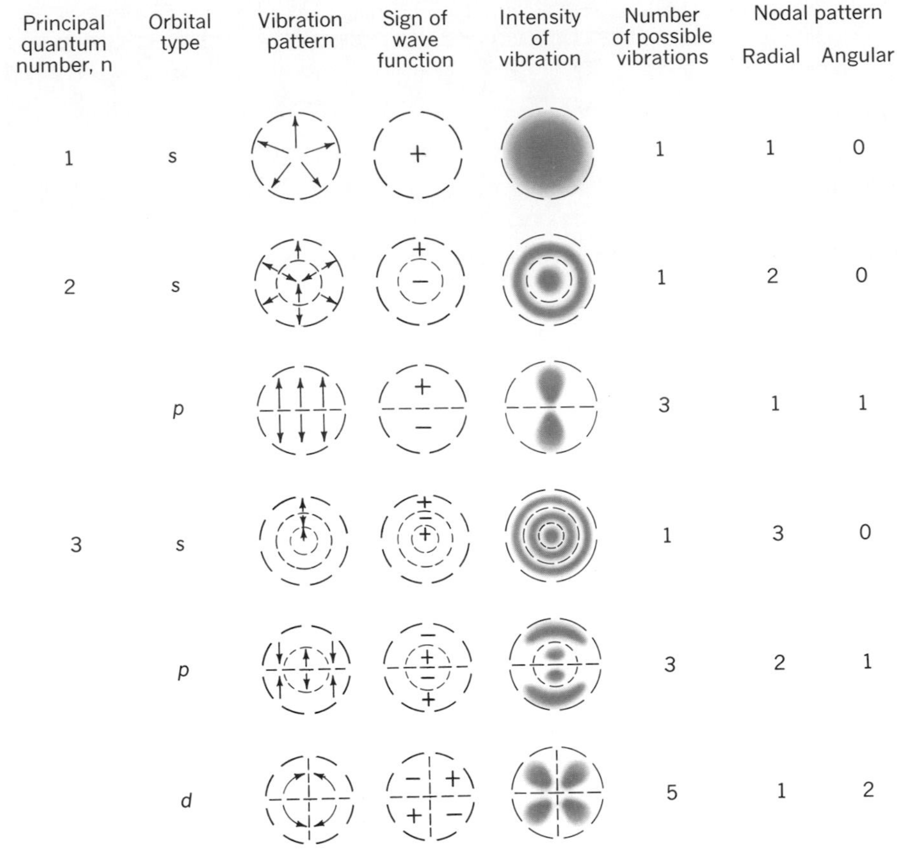

Principal quantum number, n
Orbital type
Vibration pattern
Sign of wave function
Intensity of vibration
Number of possible vibrations
Nodal pattern
Radial
Angular
1
s
+
1
1
0
2
s
+
−
1
2
0
p
+
−
3
1
1
3
s
+
−
+
1
3
0
p
−
+
−
+
3
2
1
d
−
+
+
−
5
1
2

Figure 4.5 Cross sections through some possible vibrational patterns of a homogeneous sphere. Compare with Figure 4.2. These vibrational patterns correspond to the quantum states observed in hydrogen atoms. Nodes are indicated by dotted lines. The radial node at infinity is indicated by the outer circle.

posed of a positively charged nucleus surrounded by a nebulous region of negative electric charge. This region extends to infinity for every atom (there is a node at infinity). The atom is made up of subregions of space called orbitals, each of which has a definite radial and angular symmetry defined by radial and angular nodes. Each orbital can hold 0, 1, or 2 negative charges, or electrons. The trajectory of the electron in the orbital cannot be specified (consistent with the uncertainty principle). The distribution of negative charge within each orbital can be described either in terms of the probability of finding an electron at each point in the orbital, or in terms of the average density of a cloud of negative charge. Some properties may be interpreted in terms of pulsing of this cloud in the pattern of the orbital symmetry. The problem of energy, or electrons, passing through a node (plane of zero probability) is relaxed in relativistic quantum mechanics, in which the idea of a node of strictly zero probability does not appear.

Exercise 4.6

List the number of electrons, the relative energies, and the relative symmetries of the

$3p$ and $3d$ orbitals. *Answer:* Number of electrons, $3p^6$, $3d^{10}$; energies, $3p$ lower than $3d$; symmetries, $3p$ (see Exercise 4.5), $3d$ (see Figure 4.3).

ATOMIC ORBITALS

Let us set down the results of quantum mechanics of most immediate interest to us.

1. The space around each nucleus can be described in terms of regions called orbitals. Each orbital can hold zero, one, or two, but no more, electrons.
2. These orbitals may be described in terms of three quantum numbers: principal quantum number n (1, 2, 3, 4, . . .); orbital quantum numbers $s, p, d, f, \ldots$ (instead of l); and axial quantum numbers x, y, z (instead of m). The electron(s) in each orbital will be described in terms of the spin quantum numbers α, β (instead of $\pm\frac{1}{2}$). [You may previously have used K, L, M, N to describe electron energies. The correlations are $K, n = 1$; $L, n = 2$; $M, n = 3$; $N, n = 4$.]
3. Every principal quantum level, n, is made up of n sets of s, p, d, f orbitals. The s, p, d, f orbitals corresponding to a given value of n have different energies except in hydrogenlike atoms.
4. A set of s orbitals can hold 2 electrons; p orbitals, 6 electrons; d orbitals, 10 electrons; and f orbitals, 14 electrons. Thus, there can be only a single s orbital, but there may be as many as three p orbitals, five d orbitals, and seven f orbitals (each orbital capable of holding 0, 1, or 2 electrons) in any given set. In the presence of external fields the energies of the orbitals in any set may become different. Thus, for example, it could be that not all d orbitals would have the same energy.
5. The symmetries of the orbitals may be described in terms of n; s, p, d, f; and functions of x, y and z, as in Figure 4.3.
6. No orbital can hold more than two electrons (Pauli exclusion principle).

Exercise 4.7

A neutral gaseous atom has the following set of orbitals fully occupied: $1s$; $2s$, $2p$; $3s$, $3p$, $3d$; $4s$. What element is it? *Answer:* There are a total of four s orbitals, six p orbitals, and five d orbitals, or 15 orbitals in all. Each orbital holds two electrons for a total of 30 electrons. The atom is electrically neutral, so $Z = 30$. The element is zinc.

ELECTRON STRUCTURE AND THE PERIODIC TABLE

Table 4.2 gives the currently accepted electron configuration of each neutral gaseous atom in its lowest energy, or ground, state. As the table develops, more and more levels are grouped together as inert gas "kernels" or "cores" in order to concentrate on the levels that change. There are, of course, exceptions, but the general order of fillings of orbitals is s; s, p; s, p; s, d, p; s, d, p; s, f, d, p; s, f, d, p. Each group set off by the semicolons shows those energy levels that are much closer together in energy than the orbitals separated by semicolons. The levels are found to occur in

Table 4.2 Probable electron configurations of gaseous atoms in their ground states. The "exceptions" to Figure 4.6 are given in color: 11 of these are due to *s*–*d* orbital interchange and 16 are due to *f*–*d* orbital interchange. Note that all but three of the exceptions are due to having one rather than the expected two *s* electrons or to having one rather than the expected zero *d* electrons.

Atomic Number	Element	1*s*	2*s*	2*p*	3*s*	3*p*	3*d*	4*s*	4*p*	4*d*	4*f*	5*s*	5*p*	5*d*	5*f*	6*s*	6*p*	6*d*	7*s*
1	H	1																	
2	He	2																	
3	Li	2	1																
4	Be	2	2																
5	B	2	2	1															
6	C	2	2	2															
7	N	2	2	3															
8	O	2	2	4															
9	F	2	2	5															
10	Ne	2	2	6															
11	Na	2	2	6	1														
12	Mg				2														
13	Al				2	1													
14	Si		Neon		2	2													
15	P		core		2	3													
16	S				2	4													
17	Cl				2	5													
18	Ar				2	6													
19	K	2	2	6	2	6		1											
20	Ca							2											
21	Sc						1	2											
22	Ti						2	2											
23	V						3	2											
24	Cr						5	1											
25	Mn						5	2											
26	Fe						6	2											
27	Co						7	2											
28	Ni			Argon core			8	2											
29	Cu						10	1											
30	Zn						10	2											
31	Ga						10	2	1										
32	Ge						10	2	2										
33	As						10	2	3										
34	Se						10	2	4										
35	Br						10	2	5										
36	Kr						10	2	6										
37	Rb	2	2	6	2	6	10	2	6			1							
38	Sr											2							
39	Y									1		2							
40	Zr									2		2							
41	Nb									4		1							
42	Mo									5		1							
43	Tc									5		2							
44	Ru					Krypton core				7		1							
45	Rh									8		1							
46	Pd									10		0							
47	Ag									10		1							
48	Cd									10		2							
49	In									10		2	1						
50	Sn									10		2	2						
51	Sb									10		2	3						
52	Te									10		2	4						
53	I									10		2	5						
54	Xe									10		2	6						

Atomic Number	Element	1s	2s	2p	3s	3p	3d	4s	4p	4d	4f	5s	5p	5d	5f	6s	6p	6d	7s
55	Cs	2	2	6	2	6	10	2	6	10		2	6			1			
56	Ba															2			
57	La													1		2			
58	Ce										1			1		2			
59	Pr										2			1		2			
60	Nd										4					2			
61	Pm										5					2			
62	Sm										6					2			
63	Eu										7					2			
64	Gd										7			1		2			
65	Tb										8			1		2			
66	Dy										10					2			
67	Ho										11					2			
68	Er										12					2			
69	Tm										13					2			
70	Yb										14					2			
71	Lu										14			1		2			
72	Hf					Xenon core					14			2		2			
73	Ta										14			3		2			
74	W										14			4		2			
75	Re										14			5		2			
76	Os										14			6		2			
77	Ir										14			9		0			
78	Pt										14			9		1			
79	Au										14			10		1			
80	Hg										14			10		2			
81	Tl										14			10		2	1		
82	Pb										14			10		2	2		
83	Bi										14			10		2	3		
84	Po										14			10		2	4		
85	At										14			10		2	5		
86	Rn										14			10		2	6		
87	Fr	2	2	6	2	6	10	2	6	10	14	2	6	10		2	6		1
88	Ra																		2
89	Ac																	1	2
90	Th																	2	2
91	Pa														2			1	2
92	U														3			1	2
93	Np														5				2
94	Pu														6				2
95	Am														7				2
96	Cm							Radon core							7			1	2
97	Bk														8			1	2
98	Cf														9			1	2
99	Es														10			1	2
100	Fm														11			1	2
101	Md														12			1	2
102	No														13			1	2
103	Lw														14			1	2
104	Ku(?)														14			2	2

energy groups as they fill. This sequence is easy to remember—and you will find remembering it very useful. Note that each sequence (except the original *s*) repeats itself. And in each new set, the added new orbital immediately follows the *s* orbital of that set. A somewhat fuller listing of the energy sequence in which orbitals add electrons as the nuclear size increases one unit at a time is 1*s*; 2*s*, 2*p*; 3*s*, 3*p*; 4*s*, 3*d*, 4*p*; 5*s*, 4*d*, 5*p*; 6*s*, 4*f*, 5*d*, 6*p*; 7*s*, 5*f*, 6*d*, 7*p*. The principal quantum numbers are not worth remembering, since they may be assigned so easily.

The number of electrons in each energy group increases in the order 2, 8, 8, 18, 18, 32, 32. The total possible electron content of the listed orbitals is 118, whereas the element 104, having more electrons than any other currently known element, has only 104 electrons. Thus the 6*d* level is not filled, and the 7*p* level is not actually occupied by any of the known elements in their ground state.

The sequence 2, 8, 8, 18, 18, 32, 32 has an exact correlation with the number of elements in each row of the periodic table: 2, 8, 8, 18, 18, 32, 32. The last row of the table may be actually incomplete, of course, but we can predict with some confidence the electron structures of the as yet unknown elements. The periodic table is labeled in terms of the orbitals that are filled in each of its sections as the nuclear charge increases. In each row the general order of filling is *s*, *f*, *d*, *p*, though some rows do not contain all these orbitals.

The periodic table was initially based on bulk properties of the elements and their compounds. Quantum theory indicates that there are very similar regularities in the orbital patterns of the gaseous atoms. Electrons have an intimate relation with chemistry.

ORBITAL CHART FOR ELECTRON STRUCTURES IN THE GROUND STATE

The data in Table 4.2 may be presented more succinctly using a slight modification of Figure 3.1. This modification is presented in Figure 4.6.

We have seen that it is impossible to construct a two-dimensional energy-level diagram that will correlate all electron structures. This is because the relative energies of the levels vary greatly as Z and the number of electrons in the atom vary. See Figure 3.17. Figure 3.18 was our initial attempt to describe electron structures in neutral atoms by using a two-dimensional figure in which electrons are assigned to the lowest available levels in an unchanging diagram.

Figure 4.6 shows the general order as well as the exceptions which must be made to account for the experimental electron structures listed in Table 4.2. It is used in the following way.

1. Determine the total number of electrons, Z, in the neutral atom.
2. Assume that all the orbital sets lower in energy than the one that would contain the Zth electron are completely full.
3. Subtract the number of electrons in the full levels from Z to obtain the number of electrons which must still be assigned orbitals.
4. Assign these electrons to the orbital set which would be expected to contain the Zth electron. Use Hund's rule of maximum spreading out of electrons in partially empty orbitals and the arrows in Figure 4.6 which indi-

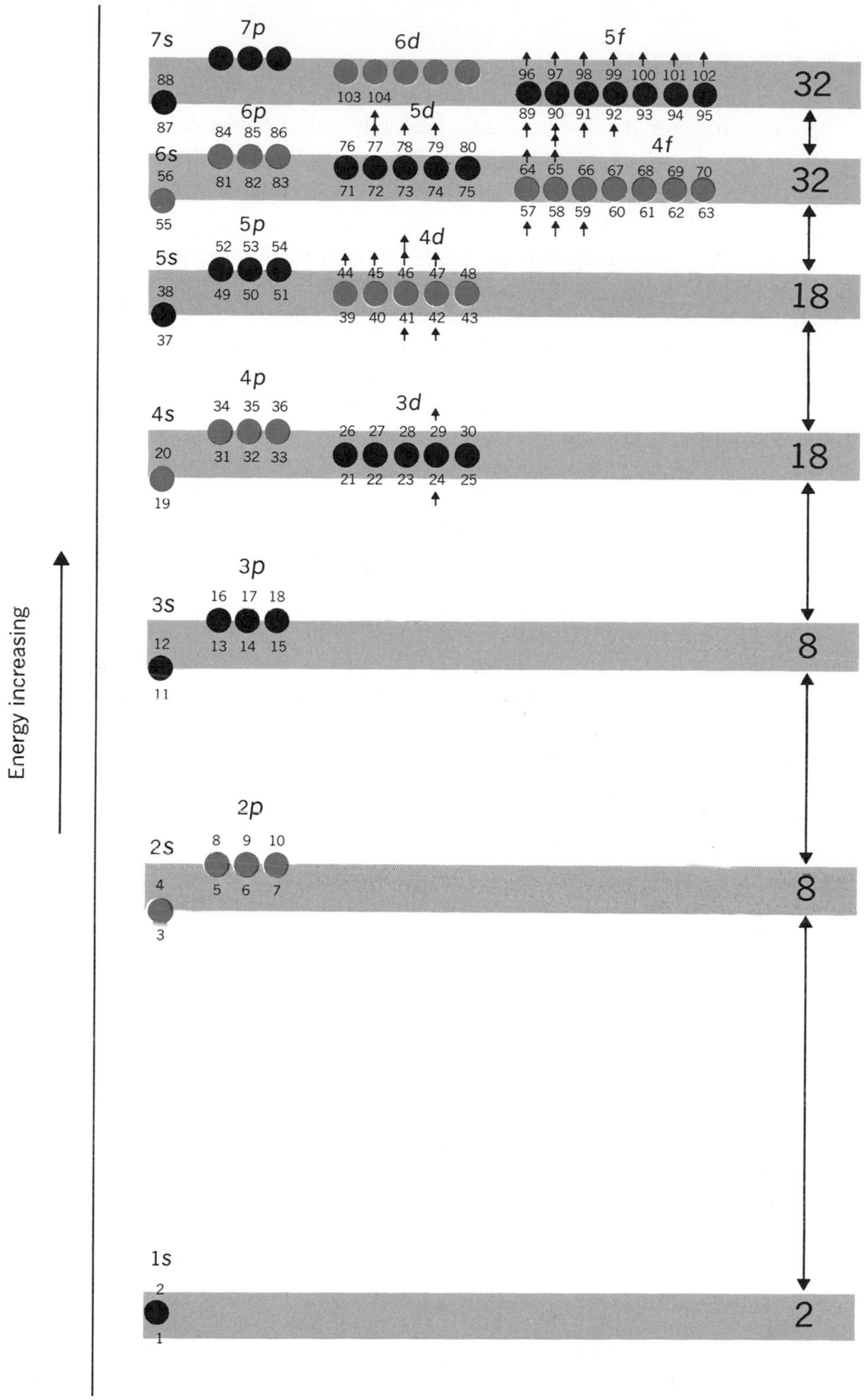

Figure 4.6 Orbital energy level chart for neutral gaseous atoms showing the order of *filling* of atomic orbitals as *Z* increases. The exceptions to the experimental values of Table 4.2 are indicated by arrows. Arrows on *d* orbitals indicate that an s electron (or 2) enters the *d* orbital at the value of *Z* corresponding to that orbital filling. Arrows on *f* orbitals indicate that the electron (or 2) expected in that *f* orbital actually enters the next higher *d* orbital. Correlate these arrows with the circled numbers in Table 4.2.

cate transfer of *s* electrons into *d* orbitals and of *f* electrons into *d* orbitals at certain values of Z. It is convenient to use a diagonal stroke in a circle to represent one electron per orbital and crossed diagonal strokes to represent two electrons.

Note that the exceptions to simple filling of the lowest orbitals in Figure 4.6 occur when *d* or *f* levels are almost full or half full [as in Cr(24), Cu(29), Nb(41), Gd(64), and others], or when the 5*d*–4*f* or 6*d*–5*f* orbitals are very close to the same energy (as in the 4*f* and 5*f* elements). Remember from our previous discussion that the energies of orbitals are lowered as the nuclear charge increases (see Figure 3.17) and that orbitals of lower *n* quantum numbers are lowered faster than those of higher *n* quantum numbers, for example $4f > 5d > 6s$ or $5f > 6d > 7s$.

Figure 4.6 is designed to give the sequence in which electrons *enter* the orbitals as Z increases. Of even greater interest to chemists, it also tells how further electrons can be added—to form negative ions, for example. Only empty orbitals can be used to add further electrons, and the diagram shows which orbitals are still empty, together with their relative energies. Furthermore, the tendency to add electrons will drop as the number of added electrons increases, because of increasing electron repulsion.

Figure 4.6 can also help to decide the order in which electrons may be lost —to form positive ions, for example. To make such a prediction successful we must remember (see Figure 3.17) that all energy levels decrease in energy as Z increases, and that the decrease in energy for orbitals of lower quantum numbers occurs more rapidly than with levels of higher *n*. This is an important effect in any set of closely spaced levels. Consider the set 4*s*, 3*d*, 4*p*. The orbitals fill in the order 4*s*, 3*d*, 4*p* as Z increases, but the orbitals empty in the order 4*p*, 4*s*, 3*d* if Z remains constant. As the 4*p* electrons are removed, the 3*d* level begins to decrease in energy faster than the 4*s*, because of the decrease in the number of total electrons as Z remains constant. The net effect is that the 4*s* electrons are lost before the 3*d*. In the same way, in the energy set 6*s*, 4*f*, 5*d*, 6*p*, the electrons are lost in the order 6*p*, 6*s*, 5*d*, 4*f*.

In general, electrons are lost from any set of closely spaced levels in order of decreasing principal quantum number, *n* (and in order *f*, *d*, *p*, *s* when *n* is constant).

The careful reader will have noted that the ionization and excitation energies and the resulting energy-level diagrams discussed here apply only to gaseous atoms. Fortunately the diagrams, and especially Figure 4.6, give reasonably accurate information on the energy-level population in condensed systems as well. Thus many of the properties of liquid and solid elements and of molecules can be correlated with this diagram.

Exercise 4.8

What is the quantum description of the electrons which distinguish Fe from Mn? Fe^0 from Fe^{++}? *Answer:* Fe has a 3*d* electron not present in Mn; Fe^{++} is formed when Fe^0 loses two 4*s* electrons (not 3*d* electrons).

Exercise 4.9

Are there any "breaks" in the expected monotonic sequence of orbital filling in the first 38 elements? *Answer:* Cr(24) and Cu(29) appear "out of line," for each has a single 4*s* electron whereas the neighbors all have two 4*s* electrons. This could possibly be connected with half-full and completely full 3*d* levels, since similar effects occur with the 4*d* level.

ATOMIC KERNELS AND VALENCE ELECTRONS

A principal reason for studying atomic models and determining electron structures is to correlate and predict chemical reactions and chemical formulas. When atoms interact, it will be the electrons and orbitals of the higher energy levels which are most apt to be involved since they are on the outside of the atoms and have the lowest energy requirements for orbital changes. These outer electrons are called valence electrons and the orbitals valence orbitals. The rest of the electrons and orbitals are called the atomic kernel.

Certain electron structures are relatively inert. The Group 0 elements of the periodic table are especially unreactive. They also have high ionization energies. In fact, the group is often identified as the "inert gases." Apparently their electron structures are especially resistant to change. Other atoms (such as Na^+, F^-, Ca^{++}) that are isoelectronic with the inert gases are also relatively unreactive.

The most common atomic kernels correspond to noble gas structures with the indicated number of electrons: He(2), Ne(10), Ar(18), Kr(36), Xe(54), Rn(86). A first approximation to the number of valence (or reactive) electrons may be obtained by finding how many electrons an atom has beyond the noble gas kernel. See Table 4.3 for some examples.

A second type of kernel is found when, as in Cu in Table 4.3, additional full *d* (or *f*) orbital sets are found beyond the noble gas structure. These full *d* (and *f*) sets are generally quite inert toward change. Thus Cu has only 1 valence electron since all of its other electrons are in full orbitals. The kernel for Cu is the noble gas structure of Ar plus a complete $3d^{10}$ set.

For many elements, the actual number of valence electrons involved in any chemical change can vary depending on the other atoms present. This variation leads to much of the variety found in chemical compounds.

Exercise 4.10

Is there any relation between the number of valence electrons listed in Table 4.3 and the periodic table? *Answer:* In most cases the number of valence electrons corresponds to the family number in the periodic table; exceptions are Pt and U.

Exercise 4.11

Suppose that the orbital energies were given by Figure 4.6 and that the Pauli exclusion principle permitted four (but no more than four) electrons per orbital. How many valence electrons in strontium then? *Answer:* Strontium has 38 electrons, requiring nine and one half orbitals in this system (1*s*, 2*s*, $2p^3$, 3*s*, $3p^3$, 4*s*/2) and leaving 2 valence electrons (half filling the 4*s* orbital).

Exercise 4.12

Cobalt and nickel are often said to have 2 valence electrons. Is this consistent with their electron structure? *Answer:* The gaseous atoms each have a pair of 4*s* electrons, consistent with saying there are two valence electrons.

Table 4.3 Further data on determination of valence electrons.

Element	No. of electrons	Kernel	Outer electrons (valence electrons colored)	Shorthand (valence electrons colored)	Number of valence electrons	Group in periodic table	Comments
Li	3	He^2	2s ⦸	He^2 $2s^1$	1	IA	
S	16	Ne^{10}	3s ⊗ 3p ⊗⦸⦸	Ne^{10} $3s^2, 3p^4$	6	VIA	
Cr	24	Ar^{18}	4s ⦸ 3d ⦸⦸⦸⦸⦸	Ar^{18} $4s^1, 3d^5$	6	VIB	4s and 3*d* both half-full
Cu	29	Ar^{18}	4s ⦸ 3d ⊗⊗⊗⊗⊗	Ar^{18} $4s^1, 3d^{10}$	1	IB	4s half-full, 3*d* full
I	53	Kr^{36}	5s ⊗ 4d ⊗⊗⊗⊗⊗ 5p ⊗⊗⦸	Kr^{36} $5s^2, 4d^{10}, 5p^5$	7	VIIA	
Pt	78	Xe^{54}	6s ⦸ 4f ⊗⊗⊗⊗⊗⊗⊗ 5d ⊗⊗⊗⊗⦸	Xe^{54} $6s^1, 4f^{14}, 5d^9$	10	VIII	6s half-full, 4*f* full
Pb	82	Xe^{54}	6s ⊗ 4f ⊗⊗⊗⊗⊗⊗⊗ 5d ⊗⊗⊗⊗⊗ 6p ⦸⦸○	Xe^{54} $6s^2, 4f^{14}, 5d^{10}, 6p^2$	4	IVA	
U	92	Rn^{86}	7s ⊗ 5f ⦸⦸⦸○○○○ 6d ⦸○○○○	Rn^{86} $7s^2, 5f^3, 6d^1$	6	Actinide	

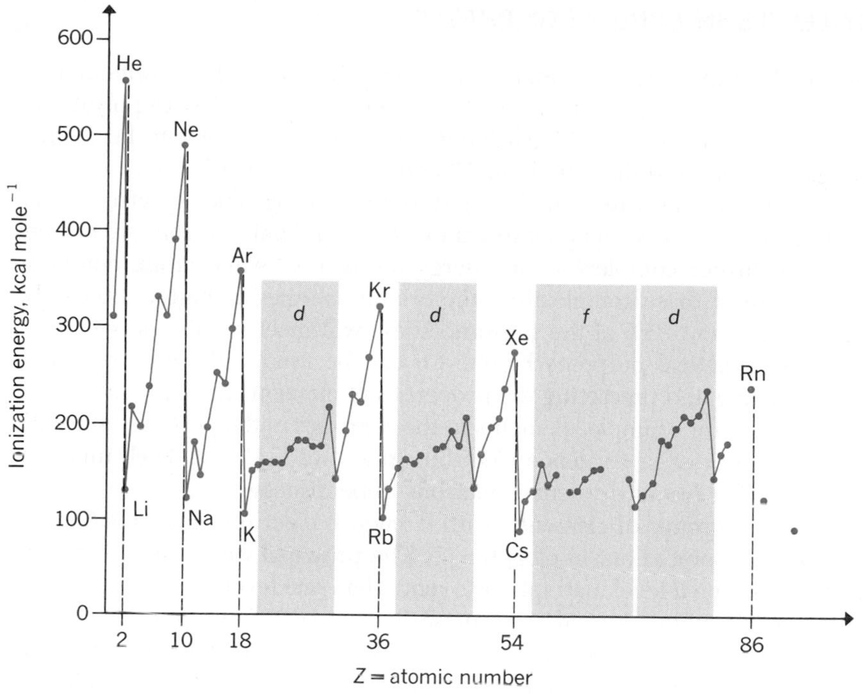

Figure 4.7 First ionization energies of the monatomic gaseous elements. Table 3.1 gives actual values for the first 20 elements. Note maxima at noble gases (s^2p^6 valence electrons), minima at alkali metals (s^1 valence electron).

FIRST IONIZATION ENERGIES

Figure 4.7 shows a plot of the first ionization energies of most of the elements as gaseous atoms. These are the ionization energies of the most easily removed electron when the gaseous monatomic element is initially in its ground state. The first *IE* represents the difference in energy between the monatomic gaseous atom and its gaseous ion plus a free electron:

$$IE + M(g) = M^+(g) + e^-(g)$$

There should be a strong correlation between the magnitude of these first ionization energies and the chemical reactivity of the gaseous atoms. It is left as an exercise for you to discover these correlations and to interpret any "irregularities" you find. Note, for example, the great similarity in the breaks in the curve between Z = 2 and Z = 10, compared to the breaks between Z = 10 and Z = 18. Can you account for these breaks in terms of orbital populations of the atomic ground states?

Exercise 4.13

Elements of which family have the highest ionization energy for their row in the periodic table? Which the lowest? *Answer:* The noble gas family 0 has only full orbitals and shows the highest ionization energy. The alkalies of family I have single *s* electrons and have the lowest ionization energy.

ENERGY LEVELS IN CONDENSED PHASES

Thus far, all the experimental evidence on energy levels has been obtained for monatomic gaseous species. Is it possible to extend these models to polyatomic molecules, liquids, and crystals? We shall only touch on these problems here, since we investigate them more thoroughly in Chapters 14 through 17.

It should not surprise you that, just as the hydrogenlike spectra of one-electron atoms shift to more complex spectra when additional electrons are present to interact, so further complexities in energy levels arise when atoms condense together. In spite of these complexities, the orbital energies of Figure 4.6 can be used to interpret about 95% of the substances you will meet in this course.

For all practical purposes Figure 4.6 can be used with complete confidence in correlating and predicting the properties of elements having only *s* and *p* valence electrons—for example, elements in the A groups in the periodic table. We shall have little interest in *f* valence electrons, since we shall not dwell much on these elements. This leaves *d* valence electrons to be discussed.

For the B groups of elements, with *d* valence electrons, Figure 4.6 needs modification, as is pointed out in Chapter 17. The principal variation is that in an unsymmetric field the *d* level may split into more than one level. The unexpectedly large value for the atomic size of manganese [Mn, Z = 25] in Figure 4.9 is consistent with this splitting. The intense color and rapid and powerful oxidizing ability of MnO_4^- ions are also connected to splitting of the *d* level in condensed species.

For the present we shall study mainly elements of the A groups that have only *s* and *p* valence electrons. For them, Figure 4.6 is adequate.

VALENCE ELECTRONS AND OXIDATION STATES

It should be clear from our discussion of ionization energies, spectra, and electronic energy levels that elements differ greatly in the ease with which electrons may be lost or gained by an atom. Figure 4.7 illustrates this for loss of one electron, and Figures 3.2 and 3.3 illustrate the trends for additional loss of electrons.

When elements are mixed, the outer, or valence, orbitals of the atoms come in contact and electron orbital interactions occur. These may lead to formation of ions (if the elements differ greatly in their ability to hold electrons—for example, differ in *IE*) or to sharing of electrons by orbital overlap between neighboring atoms (if, for example, the *IE*'s are similar). The extent of interchange or overlap will vary with the elements involved, their atomic ratio in the reacting system, the temperature, and other factors that we will explore later.

When two elements combine, we say that the element that has the greater attraction for electrons (and so acquires net negative electric charge) is reduced. The element that appears to undergo a net loss of electrons is said to be oxidized; its net charge becomes more positive.

Assignment of oxidation numbers, related to apparent loss and gain of electrons, is accomplished through a set of rules outlined on pages 000–000. For the present we shall merely point out that the maximum oxidation state of an element corresponds to its group number in the periodic table and represents the maximum number of electrons apparently lost in chemical reactions. The minimum oxidation state is normally either zero (as in the pure element, which has neither lost nor gained electrons) or is equal to the group number minus eight, as shown in Figure 4.8. There are no simple rules for the number of valence electrons of the *d* elements lumped together as group VIII. Their usual oxidation states are +2, +3, or +4.

Using these simple rules we may predict or correlate the formulas of many compounds. For example, sodium and the rest of the elements in group IA have a single valence electron and rather low IE values. Thus they tend to appear in their compounds as ions of charge plus one, M^+. Similarly, group IIA and IIIA elements tend to be found as M^{++} and M^{+++} ions, respectively, in their compounds.

The halogen atoms lack one electron of achieving inert gas structures and have high values of IE. This is consistent with their common existence in compounds, especially with IA, IIA, and IIIA elements, as negative ions of charge minus one, X^-. Similarly, the group VIA elements are often found as $X^=$ ions.

Oxidation states higher than 2 are usually achieved by sharing of electrons. Thus chromium with 6 valence electrons can share them with three oxygens each needing 2 electrons to achieve the stable noble gas structure, to give CrO_3, chromium trioxide. Examination of the most common oxidation states in Figure 4.8 shows that the oxidation number most commonly equals the group number or equals 8 minus the group number, consistent with the above discussion of numbers of valence electrons and valence orbitals.

Please note, however, that most elements show various oxidation states. We shall discuss these variations in later chapters, but most of them can be interpreted in terms of the general ideas so far presented. You may want to anticipate the discussions and try your own hand at generalizing.

ATOMIC SIZE

One of the effects of varying nuclear charge, gain and loss of electrons, and orbital overlap is a variation in the internuclear distance of closest approach of two atoms, often identified as atomic size. Figure 4.9 illustrates the variation in this property of internuclear distance. The values used for the radii of the spheres in Figure 4.9 are usually half the shortest internuclear distance in the crystalline elements. In a few cases, where unexpectedly short distances are found in the crystals (as in O_2 or N_2), we have used half the internuclear distance in compounds (HO—OH for O, $H_2N—NH_2$ for nitrogen, etc.). The spheres below and to the right of the elements indicate the relative sizes calculated for the ions of the charges shown.

Note that internuclear distance generally increases with Z in each family of elements, and decreases with Z in each row of the periodic table. It is also clear that beginning a new *s* or *p* energy level tends to increase the internuclear distance. All these trends are consistent with the ideas that (1) orbitals occupy space but decrease in size as Z increases, (2) higher energy sets of orbitals are more voluminous than lower energy sets, and (3) *s* and *p* electrons are more shielded from the nucleus by *d* electrons than vice versa (occupancy of new *s* or *p* orbitals tends to increase internuclear distance more than occupancy of new *d* levels).

Note the general correlation of atomic size with *IE* and with oxidation states.

PERIODIC TABLE OF THE ELEMENTS

Key: Symbol and atomic number at upper left.
Electronic structure along diagonal.
Common oxidation states at lower right.
(Most stable at bottom, least at top.)

Period (Row)		IA	IIA	IIIB	IVB	VB	VIB	VIIB	VIII	VIII	VIII	IB	IIB	IIIA	IVA	VA	VIA	VIIA	O
I		H 1; 1; −1 +1																H 1; 1; −1 +1	He 2; 2; 0
II		Li 3; 2,1; +1	Be 4; 2,2; +2											B 5; 2,3; +3	C 6; 2,4; ±2 ±4	N 7; 2,5; +4 +3 −3 +5	O 8; 2,6; −1 −2	F 9; 2,7; −1	Ne 10; 2,8; 0
III		Na 11; 2,8,1; +1	Mg 12; 2,8,2; +2											Al 13; 2,8,3; +3	Si 14; 2,8,4; ±2 ±4	P 15; 2,8,5; −3 +3 +5	S 16; 2,8,6; +4 −2 +6	Cl 17; 2,8,7; +1 +7 +5 −1	A 18; 2,8,8; 0
IV	2	K 19; 8,8,1; +1	Ca 20; 8,8,2; +2	Sc 21; 8,9,2; +3	Ti 22; 8,10,2; +2 +3 +4	V 23; 8,11,2; +2 +3 +4 +5	Cr 24; 8,13,1; +2 +6 +3	Mn 25; 8,13,2; +4 +3 +7 +2	Fe 26; 8,14,2; +2 +3	Co 27; 8,15,2; +3 +2	Ni 28; 8,16,2; +2	Cu 29; 8,18,1; +1 +2	Zn 30; 8,18,2; +2	Ga 31; 8,18,3; +3	Ge 32; 8,18,4; ±4	As 33; 8,18,5; −3 +3 +5	Se 34; 8,18,6; −2 +4 +6	Br 35; 8,18,7; +1 +5 −1	Kr 36; 8,18,8; 0
V	2,8	Rb 37; 18,8,1; +1	Sr 38; 18,8,2; +2	Y 39; 18,9,2; +3	Zr 40; 18,10,2; +4	Nb 41; 18,12,1; +3 +5	Mo 42; 18,13,1; +6	Tc 43; 18,13,2	Ru 44; 18,15,1; +4 +3	Rh 45; 18,16,1; +3	Pd 46; 18,18; +4 +2	Ag 47; 18,18,1; +1	Cd 48; 18,18,2; +2	In 49; 18,18,3; +3	Sn 50; 18,18,4; +2 +4	Sb 51; 18,18,5; −3 +5 +3	Te 52; 18,18,6; +6 +4	I 53; 18,18,7; +7 +1 +5 −1	Xe 54; 18,18,8; 0
VI	2,8,18	Cs 55; 18,8,1; +1	Ba 56; 18,8,2; +2	Lanthanides 57–71; 18,9,2 to 32,9,2; +3	Hf 72; 32,10,2; +4	Ta 73; 32,11,2; +5	W 74; 32,12,2; +6	Re 75; 32,13,2; +7	Os 76; 32,14,2; +4 +3	Ir 77; 32,17; +4 +3	Pt 78; 32,17,1; +2 +4	Au 79; 32,18,1; +1 +3	Hg 80; 32,18,2; +1 +2	Tl 81; 32,18,3; +3 +1	Pb 82; 32,18,4; +4 +2	Bi 83; 32,18,5; +3	Po 84; 32,18,6; +2	At 85; 32,18,7	Rn 86; 32,18,8; 0
VII	2,8,18,32	Fr 87; 18,8,1; +1	Ra 88; 18,8,2; +2	Actinides 89–103; 18,9,2 to 32,9,2; +3 to +6	Kh 104 (?); 32,10,2; +4(?)														

s elements (IA–IIA); Lanthanide elements (f elements) (IIIB); d elements (IIIB–IIB); p elements (IIIA–O)

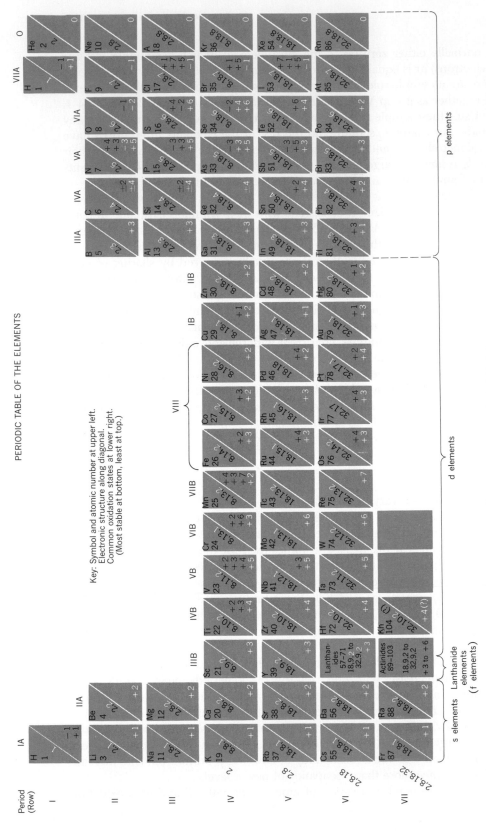

Figure 4.8 Periodic table showing ground state electron structures and common oxidation states. Note that (1) the maximum positive oxidation state seldom exceeds the family, or column, number, (2) the minimum oxidation state never exceeds the family number minus eight, (3) the most common oxidation states are 1, 2, 3, and 4—especially 2 and 3.

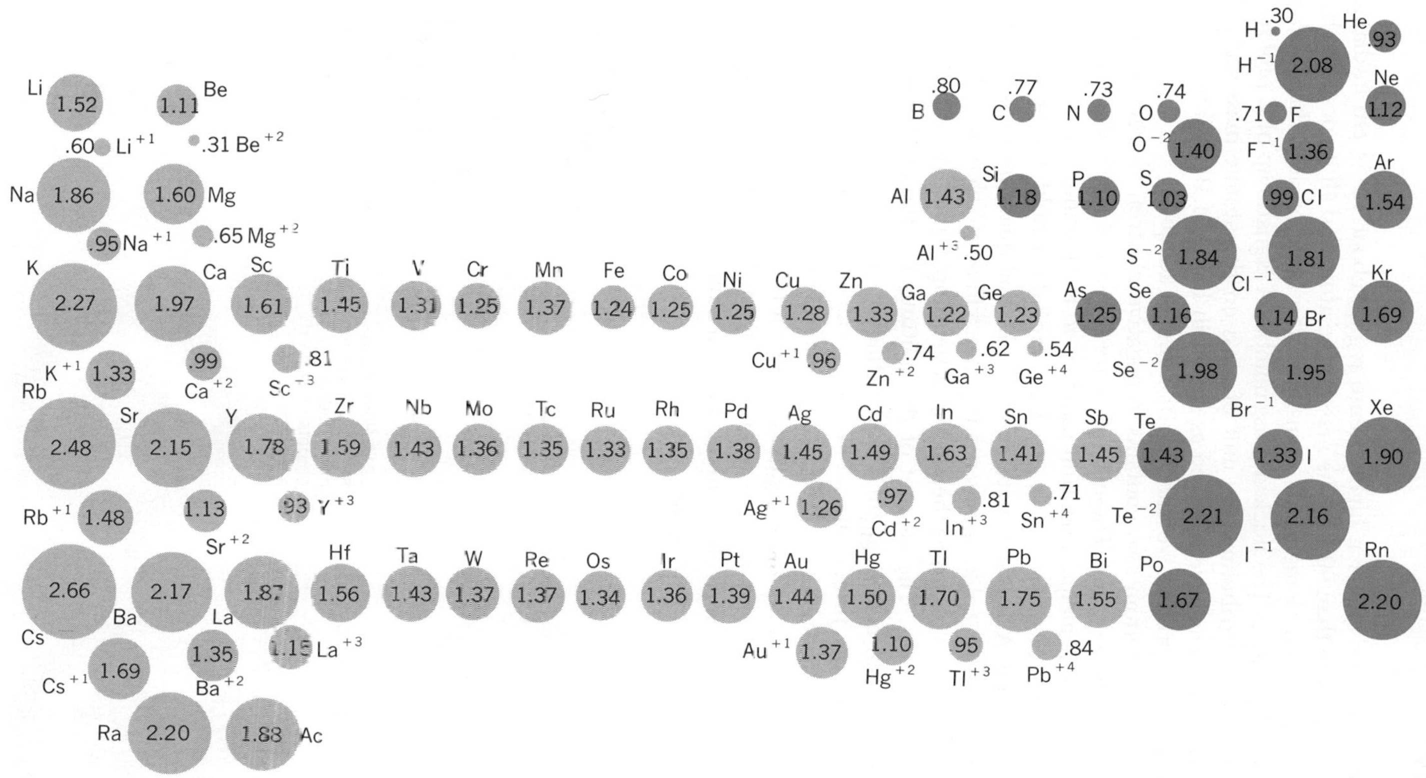

Figure 4.9 Relative sizes of atoms and ions. Metallic elements unshaded.

SUMMARY

Each atom has at its center a highly dense region about 10^{-13} cm in diameter, which contains more than 99% of the mass of the atom and all its positive electric charge. For any given element, all atoms have the same nuclear charge, Z, considered to be Z protons. The nuclear mass number A is made up of Z protons and N neutrons, each contributing one unit of mass on the atomic mass scale: $A = Z + N$. Atomic models have changed as shown in Figure 4.10, and will continue to change. For the present we find the 1932 model adequate.

The neutral atom also contains Z negative electron charges arranged in orbitals outside the nucleus. These orbitals are regions of space that may be defined in terms of a principal quantum number, n, their symmetry ($s, p, d, f, \ldots$), and their directions in space ($x, y, z, \ldots$). Each orbital can hold 0, 1, or 2 (α, β) electrons, and no more. All orbitals with a given principal quantum number have the same energy in hydrogenlike atoms not in an unsymmetric electric field. Splitting of the orbital energies occurs as the field loses the simple spherical symmetry found in hydrogenlike atoms. The amount of the splitting and the energy of the levels depends on the total field strength acting in that atom.

Chemists are principally interested in valence (or outer) electrons, since these are the ones mainly involved in interactions between atoms. The valence electron structure of an atom of a gaseous element (and to a first approximation of the atom in any state) may be correlated with Figure 4.6, which also correlates the way in which additional electrons may add to an atom, or ways in which electrons may be lost or shared by an atom.

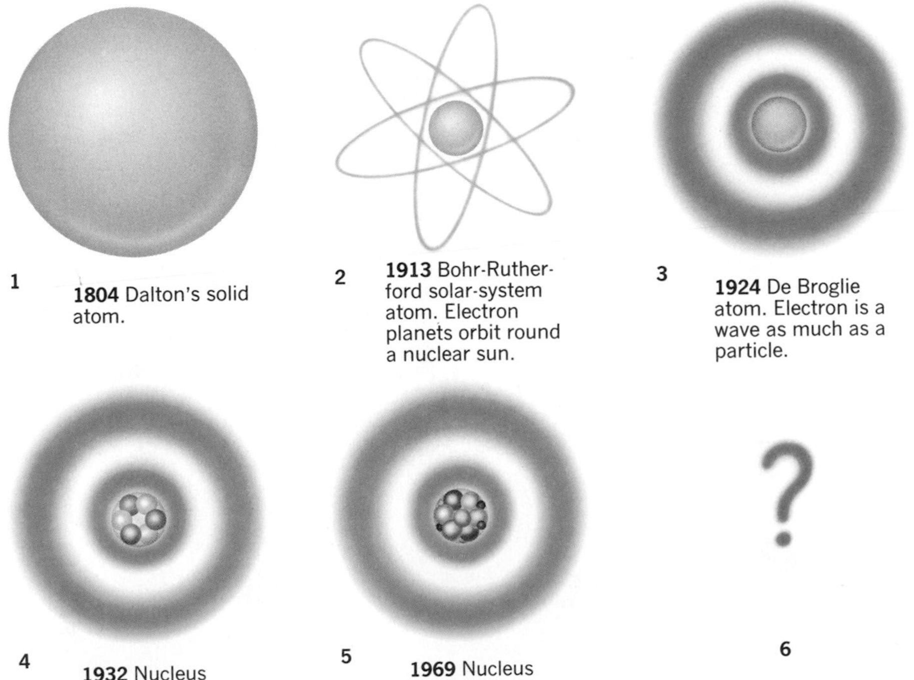

1 **1804** Dalton's solid atom.

2 **1913** Bohr-Rutherford solar-system atom. Electron planets orbit round a nuclear sun.

3 **1924** De Broglie atom. Electron is a wave as much as a particle.

4 **1932** Nucleus formed from neutrons and protons.

5 **1969** Nucleus formed from many kinds of particles.

6

Figure 4.10 Some atomic models.

Thus, chemistry is concerned with the behavior and interactions of electrons and nuclei and with the energy changes associated with such interactions.

One of the unhappy facts of our time is that while the new-generation scientist has made great gains in technical competence he has lost ground in philosophical understanding of his subject.—I. I. Rabi, Scientific Research (Sept. 1967).

PROBLEMS

4.1. Sketch the orbitals in space (and show the electrons in each one) for the following gaseous atoms. (*a*) H. (*b*) Be. (*c*) B^+. (*d*) O. (*e*) F^{++}. (*f*) Ne. Use three-dimensional drawings wherever possible, adding cross sections to show otherwise hidden features.

4.2. Write orbital occupancy (electron structure) descriptions for each of the following neutral atoms and determine the number of valence electrons per atom: K, O, As, W, Fe, Cu, Ag, Ir, I, La, Ti.

4.3. Sketch the nodal pattern (as in Figure 4.5) for the 4*s* and 4*p* orbitals. Sketch the $4p_x$ orbital in the style of Figure 4.3.

4.4. How can an experimental value for the *IE* of the twentieth electron in calcium be listed in Table 3.1 when the value for the nineteenth electron is much less well established?

4.5. Use Figure 4.9 to decide which crystalline element probably has the lowest density, and which probably has the highest density. List your assumptions.

4.6. Cite some experimental evidence that all the electrons in a given atom are not identical.

4.7. The ionization potential of atomic hydrogen is 13.6 ev. What is the longest wavelength of light that could ionize hydrogen atoms? (About 900 Å.) The Balmer series of spectral lines of atomic hydrogen are given in Figure 3.11. How can you reconcile your calculated wavelength with those given there?

II

4.8. Use the data in Table 3.1 to plot Z versus first ionization energy, from $Z = 1$ to $Z = 11$. Interpret each rise or fall in *IE* as Z increases one unit at a time in terms of the orbital occupancy in the gaseous element and the resulting ion. Remember that *IE* represents the *difference* in energy between the electrically neutral atom and the ion.

4.9. Compare a plot, as in Figure 4.7, for Z versus *IE* (with $Z = 1$ to $Z = 11$) with another plot of Z versus *IE* (with $Z = 9$ to $Z = 19$).

4.10. Discuss the variation of ionization energy with Z from Z = 18 to Z = 36. Compare with that from Z = 36 to Z = 54.

4.11. Estimate the pair repulsion energy, *P*, of two electrons in a single $2p$ orbital by plotting the first *IE* values for O, F, and Ne versus Z and comparing with those expected from an extrapolation of the first *IE* values for B, C, and N versus Z. (About 100 kcal mole^{-1}.) Repeat for $3p$ electrons and comment on the two values of *P*.

4.12. The density of crystalline sodium and iodine are 0.97 and 4.93 g cm^{-3} respectively. That of sodium iodide (what is the formula?) is 3.667 g cm^{-3}. Discuss, in terms of atomic behavior, the change in volume when sodium iodide forms from the elements. Repeat for magnesium oxide for which the densities (metal, oxygen, oxide) are 1.74, 1.43, 3.58 g cm^{-3}. Account for the apparent contribution by the magnesium atoms to the volume of the oxide.

4.13. Light of wavelength 4280 Å interacts with a motionless hydrogen atom in the stationary state $n = 3$. What is the velocity of the resulting photoelectron when it is no longer associated with the hydrogen atom (that is, at ∞)? (About 5.10^7 cm sec^{-1}.)

4.14. Approximate calculations can be made of the fraction of time (probability) that the valence electron of lithium spends within the electron cloud formed by the $1s$ electrons. For the $2s$ state of the valence electron the probability is small, for the $2p$ state the probability is almost zero. Thus the ionization potential of Li in the $2p$ state should be nearly identical with the ionization energy of hydrogen (atomic) in the $n = 2$ state. From the following data calculate the ionization energy of Li in the $2p$ state and compare to that of hydrogen. (About 80 kcal mole^{-1}.) Explain why these numbers are the same (or why they are not, if they are grossly different). The transition from $2s$ to $2p$ for lithium occurs at 6708 Å (absorption spectroscopy). The ionization potential of Li is 5.39 ev.

4.15. The nuclear reaction $Nb^{90} + e^- = Zr^{90}$ proceeds by capture of a $1s$ electron by the nucleus. The rate of this reaction is 3.6% higher in metallic niobium than in the fluoride complex of niobium. Rationalize this fact.

III

4.16. Compare Table 4.2 with Figure 4.6 and identify each of the neutral gaseous atoms whose ground state is not correctly described by Figure 4.6, such as $Cu_{(g)}$. List the electron structure of all these atoms in terms of kernals and other electrons. Discuss the factors in each case which lead to the experimental ground state rather than the one predicted by Figure 4.6. Can you reduce these factors to two or three generalizations?

4.17. The K_α X-ray line of an element is emitted when an electron falls from the *L* shell into a vacancy in the *K* shell of an atom. Write down the electronic configuration of an ion before and after the emission of a K_α photon. Assume that the Rydberg formula holds for the energy levels in a complex atom, with an effective nuclear charge Z' equal to the atomic number minus the number of electrons in shells between the given electron and the nucleus. On this basis estimate the wavelength of the K_α line of iron. (About 10^5 kcal mole^{-1}.) Compare your value with the observed value of 1.936 Å.

See page 1090 for a list of references and readings in the recent chemical literature related to the material in this chapter.

CHAPTER 5

The Chemical Elements

A chemical element is made up of a collection of atoms each having the same nuclear charge, Z. When one asks, for example, "How much sodium does a substance contain?" he means, "For what fraction of the nuclei is Z = 11?"

In most cases the identification of a chemical element has involved isolating it and showing that it has properties different from those of any other element. However, a great deal has been known about many elements before samples of them were prepared. Pure fluorine, for example, was not prepared until 1886, but its existence had been postulated for almost eighty years and many of its properties predicted. The existence and properties of scandium, gallium, and germanium were predicted before there was any experimental proof that these elements existed. Visible quantities of the elements with atomic numbers higher than 98 have never been made, and perhaps never will be. Yet the properties of such elements were so accurately predicted that identifications based on samples containing less than ten atoms were possible. The principal guide in making predictions and correlations of elements and their properties is the periodic table.

CHEMICAL ELEMENTS

History records many attempts to analyze the world into a simple set of elements or components. One school of Greek philosophers suggested earth, water, air, and fire as a possible set. The alchemists prepared lists of elements and essences, and included many of our present chemical elements in the list (see Table 5.1 and Figure 1.8). They also included many substances now listed as compounds and many

Table 5.1 Discovery of the Elements. Time Chart.

Ancients:	Au Ag Cu Fe Pb Sn Hg S C
Alchemists:	As Sb Bi P Zn
Eighteenth Century	
1735–1745:	Co Pt
1745–1755:	Ni
1755–1765:	
1765–1775:	H N O Cl Mn F
1775–1785:	Mo W Te
1785–1795:	U Sr Ti Y
1795–1805:	V Cr Be Nb Ta Ce Pd Rh Os Ir
Nineteenth Century	
1805–1815:	Na K Ba Ca Mg B I
1815–1825:	Li Cd Se Si Zr
1825–1835:	Al Br Th
1835–1845:	La Tb Er Ru
1845–1855:	
1855–1865:	Cs Rb Tl In
1865–1875:	
1875–1885:	Ga Yb Sm Sc Ho Tm
1885–1895:	Pr Nd Gd Dy Ge Ar
1895–1905:	He Eu Kr Ne Xe Po Ra Ac Rn
Twentieth Century	
1905–1915:	Lu
1915–1925:	Hf Pa
1925–1935:	Re
1935–1945:	Tc Fr At Np Pu Cm
1945–1955:	Am Pm Bk Cf Es Fm
1955–1965:	Md No Lw
1965–	Ku(?)

essences no longer thought to be useful in interpreting experimental results. But their cut-and-try methods, guided by a minimum of quantitative theory, provided enough increase in knowledge to lead to real interest in experimentation from the seventeenth century onward.

Modern chemistry is usually dated from the late eighteenth century. Many qualitative experiments concerning changes in matter were performed then, and Lavoisier's introduction of the analytical balance about 1770 provided quantitative mass measurements for the first time. This led to the idea of a chemical element as a substance which could not be decomposed into two or more different substances of less weight. This, in turn, led to Dalton's ideas of indivisible atoms as characterizing the elements. Problems still arose, however, with substances that could not be decomposed or could be decomposed only into gases. Thus the quicklime obtained by heating limestone was long thought to be an element, since it could not be further decomposed. We now identify it as calcium oxide, CaO.

Exercise 5.1

At about what time, and why, did it probably become clear that CaO was not an element? *Answer:* Metallic calcium was identified in about 1810, so the oxide could hardly be thought an element much beyond that date.

APPROXIMATE ATOMIC WEIGHTS

The first generalization to bring some theory into the determination of atomic weights was that of Dulong and Petit in 1819. They noted that for all the elements then known, except carbon, the mathematical product of the specific heat of the element (the number of calories required to heat one gram of the element one degree centigrade) and its atomic weight was equal to about 6 ($\pm$15%). We would phrase this as the

LAW OF DULONG AND PETIT:

$$\text{the molar heat capacity of an element} = 6 \text{ cal mole}^{-1}\ {}^\circ\text{K}^{-1}$$

This rule worked quite well, except for carbon, as shown in Table 5.2.

One major problem was that both hydrogen and oxygen were gases that no one could liquefy or solidify. Thus the law of Dulong and Petit offered no assistance whatever in determining their atomic weights. As a result, a major error was made: the atomic weights of hydrogen and oxygen were assumed to be in the ratio of 1 to 8 (rather than 1 to 16, as is now known). The accepted formula for water was HO. This formula was still in use as late as 1880.

Exercise 5.2

In the last quarter of the nineteenth century a metallic element was discovered with a specific heat of 0.08 cal $^\circ\text{K}^{-1}$ gm^{-1}. The chloride contained about 40% of the metallic element. What is the modern name and atomic weight of the element? *Answer:* At. wt. $\cong 6.0/0.08 \cong 70$–80. Weight combined with 35.5 g Cl =

Table 5.2 **Molar heat capacities. The law of Dulong and Petit assumes that the molar heat capacity $\cong$ 6 cal mole^{-1} deg^{-1}.**

Element		Actual specific heat c = cal $^\circ\text{K}^{-1}$ g^{-1}	Molar weight from law of Dulong and Petit	Actual molar weight M = g mole^{-1}	Actual molar heat capacity $c \cdot M$ = cal $^\circ\text{K}^{-1}$ mole^{-1}
Carbon (graphite)	C	0.165	36	12.0	2.06
Magnesium	Mg	0.235	25	24.3	5.71
Sulfur	S	0.175	35	32.0	5.60
Potassium	K	0.178	34	39.1	6.97
Iron	Fe	0.109	55	55.8	6.03
Copper	Cu	0.0921	65	63.5	5.85
Tin (white)	Sn	0.0531	110	118.7	6.30
Platinum	Pt	0.0325	180	195.1	6.35
Lead	Pb	0.0314	190	207.2	6.51

$(0.40/0.60) \cdot 35.5 \simeq 24$ g X. This is one-third of the atomic weight, suggesting 3 valence electrons or periodic table family III and atomic weight 72, which is gallium. The modern atomic weight of gallium, Ga, is 69.72.

ACCURATE ATOMIC WEIGHTS

The suggestions that probably were most instrumental in removing the confusion over relative atomic weights were those of Avogadro in 1811 and Cannizzaro in 1860. Avogadro suggested that equal volumes of all gases when measured at the same temperature and pressure contain equal numbers of moles. Thus, the density ratio of any two gases at the same temperature and pressure immediately gives the ratio of their molar weights. The density ratios for hydrogen, oxygen, chlorine, and methane, for example, are 1.0/16/35/8.0, which must also be the ratios of the molar weights of these gases and also of their molecular weights, since all moles contain the same number of molecules. Avogadro's suggestion attracted little support, probably largely because of the difficulty of making accurate measurements of gases.

But techniques of handling gas improved, and Cannizzaro provided the final key to clarity when he pointed out that the weights of any element in one molecular weight of its compounds must always be divisible by the atomic weight of the element. The largest common divisor of all the known weights of an element in a molecular weight of its gaseous compounds would be the atomic weight of the element. Thus one could combine the molecular weights calculated from Avogadro's suggestion with analytical data to gain accurate and unambiguous atomic weights for the first time. Table 5.3 gives some examples of atomic weight determinations derived from the Avogadro-Cannizzaro approach.

The accurate atomic weights obtained from work on gases could then be combined with accurate analytical work on solid compounds and the approximate atomic weights obtained from the law of Dulong and Petit to give accurate atomic weights for all known elements. This was done within a few years of the publication of Cannizzaro's suggestion in 1860.

Table 5.3 Determination of atomic weight following Avogadro–Cannizzaro.

Compound	$r = \frac{\text{density gas}}{\text{density } O_2}$	Molar wt. of gas $M = \frac{\text{g compound}}{\text{mole compound}} = 32 \cdot r$	Wt. fraction of nitrogen in compound $f = \frac{\text{g N}}{\text{g compound}}$ (from wt. analysis)	Wt. of nitrogen/mole of compound $M \cdot f = \frac{\text{g N}}{\text{mole compound}}$
Ammonia	.53	17	0.82	14
Nitric oxide	.94	30	0.47	14
Nitrous oxide	1.3	44	0.64	28
Ethyl amine	1.4	45	0.31	14
Ethylene diamine	1.8	60	0.47	28
Nitrobenzene	3.8	123	0.11	14
Nitrogen	.87	28	1.00	28

Exercise 5.3

Molecular weights from gas densities and accurate analytical data gave the following data respectively for compounds of element X: 87.0, 81.6%; 67.5, 52.6%; 154, 92.2%. What is the atomic weight and what element is X? *Answer:* $87.0 \cdot 0.816 = 71.1$ g X $mole^{-1}$ of compound, $67.5 \cdot 0.526 = 35.5$ g X $mole^{-1}$ of compound, $154 \cdot 0.922 = 142$ g X $mole^{-1}$ of compound. We thus get the grams of X per each mole. Probable atomic weight is 35.5, the probable element is Cl. The compounds probably are Cl_2O, ClO_2, CCl_4. Show this.

THE PERIODIC TABLE

Within ten years of the publication of Cannizzaro's idea, Mendeleev in Russia and Meyer in Germany independently arrived at the periodic table in essentially its present form.

Each man noted that elements could be arranged into families with similar properties and that the recurrence of these properties was a periodic function of the atomic weight of the element. Problems of purity and scarcity of compounds made some of the atomic weights uncertain, but the regularities were so striking that the correlating power of the periodic table was not seriously questioned. Table 5.4 reproduces a table first presented by Mendeleev. Mendeleev must be given credit for appreciating the experimental uncertainties in the atomic weights, and must also be given credit for showing that many properties were functions correlated by his table: formulas of oxide and many other compounds, acidic and basic properties, density, boiling point, melting point, crystal structure, chemical reactivity, gram atomic volume. In addition, Mendeleev had such confidence in his table that he left spaces for undiscovered elements and actually predicted their properties—predictions that proved to be accurate.

Shortly after the periodic table was presented, the convention of identifying each element by its order number in the table—its atomic number—was introduced. Two main types of trends are correlated in the periodic table: (1) column or group trends, (2) row or atomic number trends. There are also, of course, two diagonal trends involving both column and row. Thus any element in the periodic table may be expected to have properties intermediate between those of any two neighbors in its column, row, or diagonal. Combining all four trends offers a comparison of an element with up to eight other elements and can give a great deal of correlation of the properties and behavior of neighboring elements and their compounds.

The researches of Rutherford and many others show that the periodic table was based only accidentally on atomic weights. It is not mass, but electrical properties, that lead to periodicity. Thus a correct modern statement would be that the properties and behaviors of the chemical elements and their compounds is a periodic function of the nuclear charge (atomic number) of the element.

Exercise 5.4

Mendeleev is sometimes credited with predicting scandium, element 21, and sometimes not. Can you suggest reasons for the divided opinion? *Answer:* Mendeleev did

Table 5.4 **The form of the periodic table suggested by Mendeleev in 1869. Modern symbols are used (Mendeleev used different symbols for Er, Tb, U, and Dy). Asterisks indicate those elements whose positions as assigned by Mendeleev differ appreciably from those in present tables. Parentheses include modern values for atomic weights differing by one unit or more from those of Mendeleev. Note the remarkable improvement in atomic weight values over those used before Mendeleev, as shown in Tables 2.1 and 2.2. Mendeleev had a perfect batting average on new elements—predicting four, marked by question marks (?) and the lack of a symbol—all of which were later discovered. He missed only two "families"—the scandium group (which he got partly right) and the noble gases.**

			Ti = 50(48)	Zr = 90(91)	? = 180(179)
			V = 51	Nb = 94(93)	Ta = 182(181)
			Cr = 52	Mo = 96	W = 186(184)
			Mn = 55	Rh = 104.4(103)	Pt = 197.4(195)
			Fe = 56	Ru = 104.4(101)	Ir = 198(192)
			Ni = Co = 59	Pd = 106.6	Os = 199(190)
H = 1			Cu = 63.4	Ag = 108	Hg* = 200
	Be = 9.4	Mg = 24	Zn = 65.2	Cd = 112	
	B = 11	Al = 27.4	? = 68(70)	U* = 116(238)	Au* = 197?
	C = 12	Si = 28	? = 70(73)	Sn = 118	
	N = 14	P = 31	As = 75	Sb = 122	Bi = 210(209)
	O = 16	S = 32	Se = 79.4	Te = 128?	
	F = 19	Cl = 35.5	Br = 80	I = 127	
Li = 7	Na = 23	K = 39	Rb = 85.4	Cs = 133	Tl* = 204
		Ca = 40	Sr = 87.6	Ba = 137	Pb* = 207
		? = 45	Ce* = 92(140)		
		?Er* = 56(167)	La* = 94(139)		
		?Tb* = 60(159)	Dy* = 95(163)		
		?In* = 75.6(115)	Th* = 118?(232)		

indeed predict an element of atomic weight about 45 just after calcium, element 20. But, in terms of later tables, he misplaced the next three elements, Er, Tb, In, and the corresponding ones in the next row (Ce, La, Dy, Th). Thus he left a space at the proper point but used fallacious reasoning.

IDENTIFICATION OF CHEMICAL ELEMENTS

Elements may be identified whether they are in the pure state, in mixtures, or in compounds. The methods of identification that involve treating a substance with other substances and noting the changes are called chemical methods. Methods that identify a substance without involving a reaction with another substance or a change to another substance are called physical methods. Compounds whose properties are known from past measurements may usually be identified most rapidly by physical methods, which include the determination of density, refractive index, boiling point, melting point, absorption or emission spectrum (infrared, visible, ultraviolet, X-ray), heat capacity, viscosity, hardness, electrical or thermal conductivity. A typical set of properties sufficient for identification are boiling and melting points, and density. These may often be determined with simple apparatus, and extensive tables of these properties exist to aid in ready identification. Refractive index is especially useful for identifying previously known compounds. Even quicker identification is possible with spectroscopic techniques, but the instruments are expensive. With modern spectrometers, it is possible to determine the elements present in a sample, and obtain the percentage of each, in less than an hour.

CHARACTERISTIC X-RAYS

The most conclusive proof of the presence of an element is the detection of its spectrum, especially its X-ray spectrum. Moseley* showed in 1913 that the X-ray spectrum of each element was simple and almost unchanged, whether the element was pure, in a mixture, or in a compound. This was especially true of the most energetic X-rays from any element, the so-called *K* X-rays. (Other, less energetic X-rays are called *L*, *M*, *N*, and so on.) A plot of the square root of the energy of the *K* X-rays versus the atomic number gives an almost straight line (see Figure 5.1). The X-ray spectrum showed unambiguously that the periodic table order for cobalt and nickel should not follow atomic weight, but atomic number. Furthermore, the determination of X-ray spectra established unquestionably the identity of the elements discovered in the years between 1914 and 1950 (see Table 5.1).

The interpretation of the curve in Figure 5.1 is particularly simple in terms of our nuclear atomic model. The fact that the square root of the energy of the emitted X-ray is linearly related to the atomic number may remind you of the Rydberg equation, which gives the same linear relationship. The Rydberg equation gives the energy absorbed or emitted by an atom having a single electron around its nucleus in terms of an exactly linear relation between $E^{1/2}$ and Z (at constant n and n'). The Moseley relationship gives the energy emitted, for example, when an electron from a higher quantum level drops into an empty 1*s* orbital (*K* X-rays are emitted). Since the energy levels for principal quantum number $n = 1$ are strongly influenced only by the nuclear charge, Z, rather than by other electrons (see Figure 3.17), the straight left-hand curves of Figure 5.1 are obtained. Because changes in the valence electrons due to chemical interactions have almost no effect on the $n = 1$ orbital (except for elements of low Z) the *K* X-rays of an element are almost independent of the surrounding atoms. Nor are there appreciable isotope effects, since the interaction of orbitals and nuclei depends mainly on nuclear charge, not nuclear mass.

Thus a chemical element is made up of a collection of atoms, each having the same nuclear charge, Z. When one asks, "How much sodium does a substance contain?" he means, "For what fraction of the nuclei is $Z = 11$?"

Exercise 5.5

The X-ray spectrum of an element shows an emission line corresponding to $E = 1.48 \cdot 10^5$ kcal mole^{-1}, $E^{1/2} = 385$ (kcal mole^{-1})$^{1/2}$. What is the element? *Answer:* A

* "Moseley and the Numbering of the Elements," W. A. Smeaton, *Chemistry in Britain,* **1,** 353 (1965). H. G. J. Moseley, *Phil. Mag.,* **26,** 1024 (1913); **27,** 703 (1914).

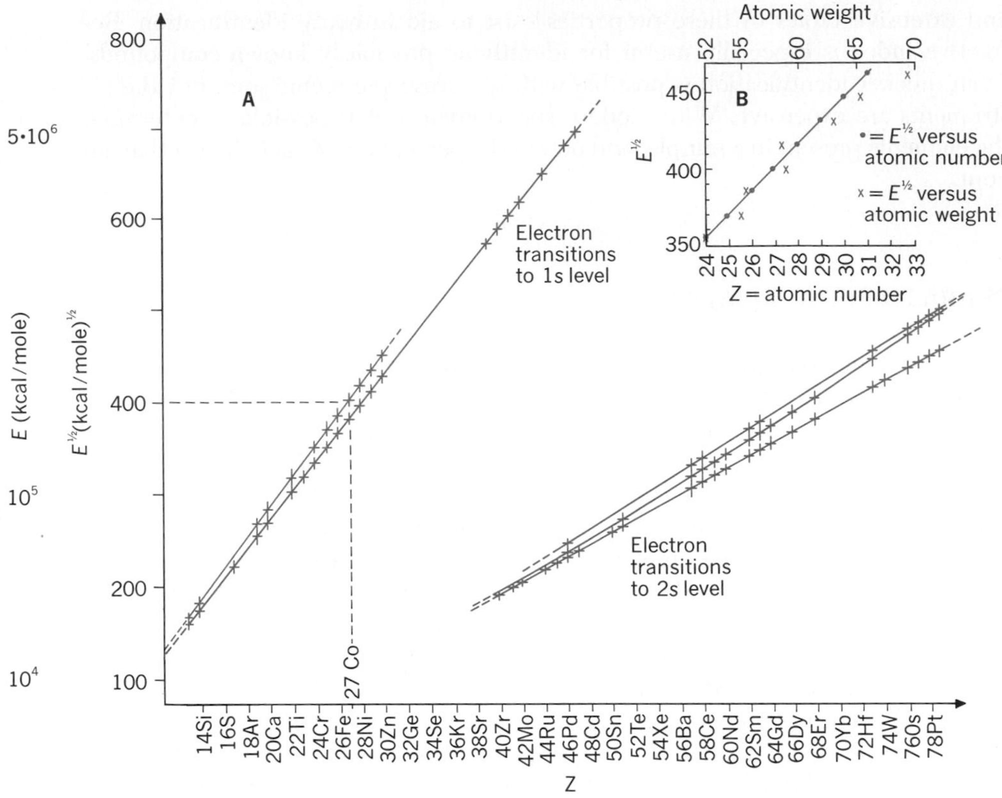

Figure 5.1 (**A**) A Moseley plot. Note that cobalt and nickel must have atomic numbers of 27 and 28 respectively: not the reverse, which would be indicated by using atomic-weight data alone. (**B**) Plots of both atomic weight and atomic number, Z, versus $E^{1/2}$ (for K X-rays) are shown for the elements Cr (24) through Ga (31). Note the linearity of Z versus $E^{1/2}$ and the scattering when atomic weight is used.

single line does not give an unambiguous answer (see Figure 5.1). Several lines are needed. Thus the 385 line could be Fe (line in Figure 5.1 farthest to left), element 63 (third line from left), or element 65 (fourth line from left), or element 68 (last line at right). More lines would be needed for definite identification.

CHEMICAL ANALYSIS BY X-RAYS

The K X-rays are excited by bombarding an element with X-rays or electrons, so that one of the 1s electrons is emitted. An electron from a higher level, say the $n = 2$ level, then falls into the half-empty 1s orbital and a K X-ray is emitted. Note that the "K X-ray" of hydrogen is identical with the first line in the Lyman series.

Though costly, the X-ray method of identifying elements is so straightforward and so powerful that it is the preferred method in critical cases such as the identification of new elements or the analysis of substances whose chemical elements are difficult to separate or test for in other ways. It is especially useful if many samples are to be analyzed for the same elements. The spectrometer may then be preset to detect radiation from the desired elements and the signal fed into a computer. The computer then determines the intensity of emission of each element and prints out a complete quantitative analysis of the substance. For example, silicates containing Si, O, Cl, Na, Ca, K, Mg, and many other elements are among the most common substances in the world. Yet the listed elements are very difficult to separate and identify. A single silicate analysis using separation techniques might take a skilled chemist a full month, and even then find him disagreeing with an analysis done in another laboratory. The X-ray technique is very fast, it is reproducible, and it requires little training to perform. It gives excellent direct values for Si and for the ions of the metals. The oxygen is obtained, if desired, by difference—just as in the previous methods. It is now possible for a single person to perform as many silicate analyses in one year as had been done by all chemists working on the problem during the whole period before 1962. The resulting insights into the geological history of silicates and their chemistry are very great indeed. See Figure 5.2 for a diagram of the apparatus used in this silicate analysis.

ANALYSIS BY NUCLEAR PROPERTIES

The elements of very high atomic number have so far been prepared in quantities of a few thousand atoms or less—too few atoms to give a detectable X-ray spectrum. Some of these elements were identified in terms of their nuclear reactions. Relations are known, especially for alpha-particle emission, between the energy of the emitted particle and the atomic number of the nucleus. Detection of an alpha particle of the predicted energy indicates the presence of the element. Other nuclear properties may also be used. But, even with a few hundred atoms, it is possible to do chemical separations and to compare the properties of the separated atoms with those predicted from the periodic table. If a new set of properties is observed, our confidence that a new element has been identified is reinforced if the set is that predicted for a new element. Methods involving only a small number of atoms were initially used to identify all the synthetic elements so far made: atomic numbers 43, 61, 85, 87, and all those greater than 92. Later work (including X-ray work) with larger samples has confirmed the identifications made by chemical methods.

ANALYSIS BY CHEMICAL REACTION

Most chemists would be delighted if all identification of elements could be done by X-ray spectroscopy and similar techniques. Unfortunately the great majority of chemical compounds contain C, O, H, and other elements of low atomic number.

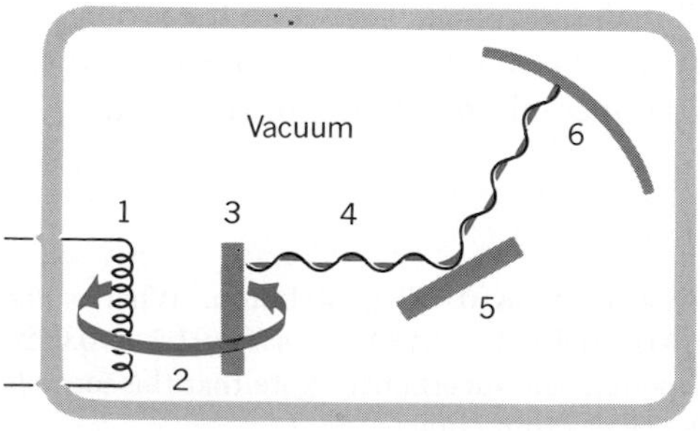

Figure 5.2 Use of X-ray in quantitative analysis for elements of low atomic number. A vacuum chamber contains (1) a source of electrons of high to moderate energy. The electrons are bent (2) by a controlled electric field and strike the sample (3), generating characteristic X-rays (4), which are deflected by the crystalline analyzer (5) and strike a detector (6). Each angle of deflection, or point on the detector, corresponds to a particular X-ray energy, and hence to a particular element. Thus a signal at a point characteristic of calcium X-rays indicates the presence of calcium in the sample. The intensity of the signal is proportional to the amount of calcium. Thus a quantitative analysis is achieved.

Present spectroscopic methods are not ideal for the quantitative determination of these elements. Nor does every lab have spectroscopic setups suitable for the determination of the heavier elements.

For these reasons, methods for converting an unknown substance into known substances that can be identified by known reactions are still an important part of chemistry. Typical chemical methods are: separation by ion exchange, using synthetic resins; conversion to H_2O, CO_2, and so on, and determination of the products; purification by distillation, filtration, crystallization, and/or chemical reaction, followed by spectroscopic tests (infrared, visible, ultraviolet) of the products; specific reagent tests for substances suspected to be present.

A typical chemical approach is (1) to carry out preliminary qualitative tests to determine the general composition of the unknown; (2) to separate the unknown substance into sets of fragments—sets in which each fragment can be analyzed in the presence of the other fragments in its set; (3) to test quantitatively for the fragments; (4) to make allowance for any changes that might have occurred during the separation and analysis, such as the conversion of a carbon-hydrogen compound to H_2O and CO_2, or of a sulfide to a sulfate; (5) to calculate the composition of the original unknown. A favorable analysis will be reported in terms of the pure substances actually present in the unknown: other analyses can be given only in terms of the percentage of each element present (that is, the percentage of nuclei of identical Z).

It should be kept in mind that analyses are reported in terms of the elements present, even when the atoms are not actually in their elementary state. Thus water is said to be, by weight, 88.81% oxygen and 11.19% hydrogen; and, by atoms, 33.33% oxygen and 66.67% hydrogen, even though no atoms of oxygen and hydrogen are present as such. Calcium carbonate is reported as 40% calcium, 12% carbon, and 48% oxygen by weight; and 20% calcium, 20% carbon, and 60% oxygen by atoms, even though there are no atoms of elementary calcium, carbon, or oxygen present. An elementary analysis, of itself, does not tell us the state of the atoms. It merely indicates the percentage of nuclei of each atomic number, without describing the electronic structure about each nucleus. Determination of the electronic structures requires more than data on elementary composition.

A common problem in chemistry is to convert weight analyses into atomic analyses. This is readily done by applying the idea that a mole of any kind of atoms contains the same number of atoms, $6 \cdot 10^{23}$; thus the ratio of the number of moles of atoms in any substance also gives the atomic ratio. If a sample of copper sulfide is found to contain 3.17 g of copper (atomic weight 63.5) and 1.60 g of sulfur (atomic weight 32.0), it must have contained (3.17 g)/63.5 g mole^{-1} = 0.0500 moles of copper, and 1.60/32.0 = 0.0500 moles of sulfur. Therefore the mole ratio is one-to-one, and the atomic ratio must also be one-to-one. The formula of the original compound is CuS, within the experimental uncertainty of the data.

Exercise 5.6

A 2.480-g sample of zirconium boride contains 0.476 g of boron. What is the formula? *Answer:* 0.476/10.8 = 0.0441 moles B; (2.480 − 0.476)/91.2 = 0.0220 moles Zr. Formula = ZrB_2 within experimental uncertainty. Note that this formula does not match predictions from valence electron number.

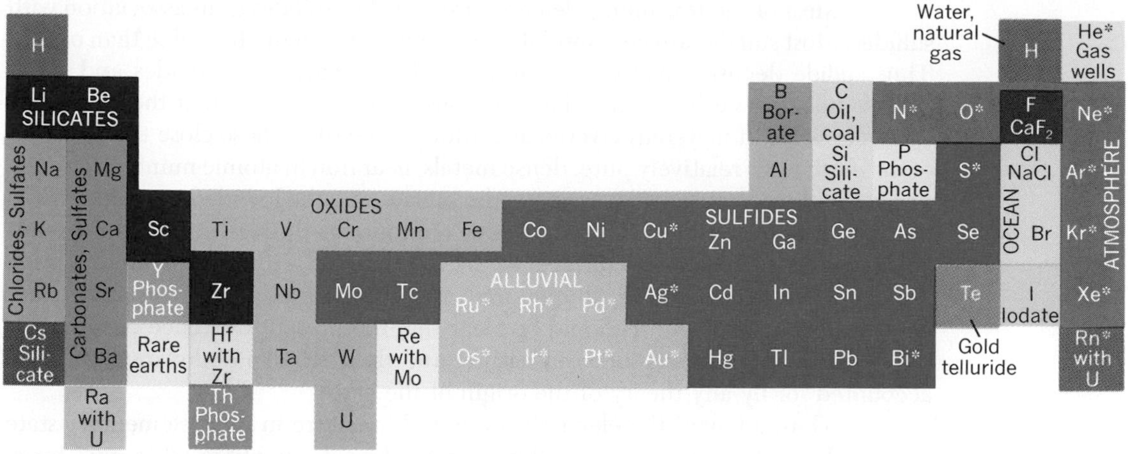

Figure 5.3 Some natural sources of the elements in terms of the periodic table. Elements that commonly occur uncombined in nature are indicated by an asterisk.

OCCURRENCE OF THE ELEMENTS

The periodic table in Figure 5.3 shows the most common form in which the elements are found on earth. The inert gases and the metals near platinum (precious metals) are commonly found in the pure elementary state. This is no doubt related to the fact that atoms of the inert gases have outer p orbitals which are exactly filled and that atoms of the platinum metals have outer d orbitals which are full or almost full. (See the periodic table inside the front cover.) In crystalline platinum, it is likely that electrons actually do fill these d orbitals, even though in the gaseous atoms they do not. The electric fields in crystals are high, and we have ample experimental evidence (see Chapter 3) that such fields can lead to energy-level shifts compared to the isolated gaseous atom.

The earth's oceans, or the deposits left by the evaporation of former oceans, hold most of the elements of groups I and VII, usually in the form of ionic compounds such as NaCl. These ions tend to be isoelectronic to inert gas atoms, and thus are relatively unreactive themselves except as they interact coulombically with other ions. Similar deposits are the main sources of group II elements, most often found as carbonates—for example, $CaCO_3$ as limestone. That these elements are found in oceanic sites shows that many, if not most, of their compounds must be soluble in water and so must have been carried to the ocean over geologic time. It is, in fact, possible to estimate a lower limit for the age of the earth in terms of the amount of salt in oceanic deposits.

By far the greatest number of elements are found in nature in the form of their oxides, mostly solid. A notable liquid oxide is hydrogen oxide, or water. So stable are most oxides with respect to decomposition into their elements that it is unlikely that the primordial earth had any free oxygen in its atmosphere—carbon dioxide, water, methane, and ammonia (plus the noble gases) are far more likely constituents of the primitive atmosphere. It is probable that most of our atmospheric oxygen is biogenic, which is consistent with the belief that the earliest forms of living matter generated oxygen and only later forms required it.

Most of the remaining elements are found as sulfides or in association with sulfides. Most sulfides are very insoluble in water—even more insoluble than oxides. Thus sulfide deposits may be the result of the interactions of oxides and sulfur compounds over geologic time. There is considerable evidence that the primordial earth consisted of materials layered according to density. Those close to the center of the earth were relatively pure, dense metals, near iron in atomic number. The less dense sulfides composed a layer above the metals, and the low-density oxides made up most of the outer layer. Later, volcanic outpourings through cracks in the outer layer brought sulfides to the surface, where they reacted with oxides, often through the catalytic effect of water, to give the present sulfide ores. We will not further develop this subject, but it should be clear that the present existence of relatively pure bodies of chemicals (ores) in nature, and their relative abundance, must be accounted for by any theory of the origin of the earth.

Thus, a few of the elements are found in nature in their elementary state and need only be separated from their surroundings to be obtained in pure form. The rest must be extracted from compounds—usually oxides, sulfides, or oceanic deposits of carbonates or halides.

Exercise 5.7

What property in addition to inertness accounts for the occurrence of platinum and its neighboring elements in alluvial sands? *Answer:* These metals occur in veins in rocks and are exposed by weathering. They are then carried downstream until the gradient of the stream becomes so small that the high density of the elements makes it more likely they will stay on the streambed rather than be carried along with the sand or mud of lower densities. See Figure 5.19 for information on density trends.

EXTRACTION OF PURE ELEMENTS

Although the technical details of preparing the chemical elements vary greatly and, in some cases quite different methods are used to prepare a single element, there is a good degree of regularity among the methods. This is, of course, inevitable, since many of the elements are found in nature in similar compounds.

The elements that exist in the elementary state in nature are seldom found in large pure chunks that can be directly marketed. The precious metals, for instance, owe their preciousness not only to scarcity but to the fact that a great deal of work is required to obtain appreciable quantities. They usually occur in veins in hard silicate rock, which must be mined, or in alluvial deposits where water has carried them as the silicate veins weathered away. In either case the concentration of the precious metal is normally 0.1% or less by weight. Two general methods are used for extracting the desired element.

First method—The ore body is finely divided (by crushing, if necessary) and is suspended as slurry in running water. The high-density metals (tightly compressed, nearly filled *d* orbitals and high nuclear mass) settle quickly to the bottom, and the low-density silicates are washed away. The miner's pan is a primitive but effective device for accomplishing this. The mining dredge effects the same operation, but it processes hundreds of tons of material per day, thus paying for its large initial cost and upkeep. Special methods may also be used—wetting the bottom of the sluice with mercury, to which the metal sticks, or adding chemicals to the water to cause a larger difference in settling rates.

Second method—The metal is dissolved by using an oxidizing agent (usually oxygen from the air) and a solvent (an aqueous solution of a chemical that will form a complex ion of the metal and increase its tendency to go into solution). Later the ion is reduced back to the metal by adding a cheaper metal such as iron (scrap iron) or zinc to the solution. The cyanide process for recovering gold and silver operates in this way:

$$4Ag_{(c)} + O_{2(g)} + 8CN^-{}_{(aq)} + 2H_2O = 4Ag(CN)_2{}^-{}_{(aq)} + 4OH^-{}_{(aq)} \quad (5.1)$$

followed by

$$2Ag(CN)_2{}^-{}_{(aq)} + Zn_{(c)} = 2Ag_{(c)} + Zn(CN)_4{}^{2-}{}_{(aq)} \quad (5.2)$$

(Note that these equations can be balanced by inspection once the correct formulas are known. Try it. Note also that the oxidation states are those predicted by the family number in the periodic table.) Gold behaves similarly but forms the complex $Au(CN)_4{}^-$. Platinum could form $Pt(CN)_6{}^{2-}$ or $Pt(CN)_4{}^{2-}$, depending on the conditions. Which would be preferable for the recovery of pure platinum? Estimate the relative ΔH^0 and ΔS^0 effects in the above processes.

Sulfur is obtained from its ore bodies by melting it. The process must be controlled carefully because the S_8 rings of solid sulfur break open when the temperature of the liquid goes much higher than its melting point, and the resulting changes give a very viscous liquid. The temperature is therefore maintained just above the melting point of the sulfur so that S_8 rings preponderate and the liquid is fluid. When sulfur is found on the surface of the earth, it is melted merely by setting fire to the ore. The combustion of some of the sulfur melts the rest, which runs off into collecting bins. This method is rather annoying to the neighbors.

Most sulfur deposits are, however, deep underground—especially in the Louisiana area. These underground deposits are mined in a very clever fashion, originally engineered by Frasch. The method involves drilling a single hole into the sulfur deposit and then introducing three concentric pipes into the hole. Hot water is piped down one pipe (How hot should the water be?), and air is pumped down through another. The hot water melts the sulfur, the air forms a foamy liquid of low density with the mixture of water and sulfur, and the low-density foamy liquid rises through the third pipe. At the surface the air escapes from the foam, the water runs off, and the liquid sulfur is run into enormous bins to solidify. Later it is dynamited and loaded into freight cars for shipping.

Exercise 5.8

Draw a picture of the top and bottom of a sulfur well, showing the arrangement of pipes that would produce the desired effect. Give thought to which pipe (inner, middle, or outer) should be used for pumping each of the three fluids.

The earth's atmosphere is the source of most of the other elements that are found "free" in nature. Table 5.5 gives an average composition of dried air. (The

Table 5.5 Average composition of dry air and the boiling and melting points of the constituents. Traces (less than 0.0002% by volume) of formaldehyde, oxides of nitrogen, hydrogen peroxide, ozone, carbon monoxide, methane, ammonia, iodine, and radon are also known to be present in the atmosphere as gases.

Substance	Volume (%)	Weight (%)	B.P. (°C)	B.P. (°K)	M.P. (°K)
Nitrogen	78.09	75.51	−195.8	77.3	63.2
Oxygen	20.95	23.15	−183.0	90.1	54.3
Argon	0.93	1.28	−185.8	87.2	83.7
Neon	0.0018	0.0013	−245.9	27.2	24.5
Krypton	0.0001	0.0003	−152.	121.	115.9
Xenon	0.0000087	0.00004	−108.0	165.0	161.2
Helium	0.00052	0.00007	−268.9	4.2	—[a]
Hydrogen	0.00005	0.000003	−252.8	20.3	13.9
Carbon Dioxide	0.03	0.05	—	—	—[a]

[a] Helium will not crystallize at atmospheric pressure. At 35 atm pressure the melting point is 1.7°K. Carbon dioxide, on the other hand, cannot be liquid at 1 atm. The vapor pressure of the solid is 1 atm at −79°C (194°K).

water content varies from almost zero to about 5%, depending on locale and temperature.) Note that gases are usually measured in percent by volume, not weight. Gaseous volume is easier to measure than gaseous weight and percent by volume in gases is the same as the mole percent, consistent with Avogadro's law. The mole (or volume) percent is also the same as the pressure percent, a fact that is sometimes stated as Dalton's law. Thus column two of Table 5.5 gives the volume percent, the mole percent, and the pressure percent composition of this sample of the atmosphere. Clearly there are relatively few molecules of most of the inert gases present.

Table 5.5 also lists the boiling points of the major components of the atmosphere. They are not widely different, but they do differ enough that modern distillation equipment can separate all of them. Oxygen of better than 99% purity is made routinely at the rate of hundreds of tons per day by distilling liquefied air; nitrogen and inert gases of similar purity are also produced. The purity can be increased to better than 99.99%, if desired, by very careful distillations. Some factories producing materials sensitive to oxygen or nitrogen are made air-tight and filled with argon and the personnel wear gas-tight suits with a built-in oxygen supply; it is cheaper to do this than to put the sensitive product in a small space, control its atmosphere, and have the personnel operate in an open room.

Exercise 5.9

Copper is commonly found as its sulfide, CuS, in friable silicate rocks. Suggest a method for concentrating the copper ore. *Answer:* CuS is much more dense than most silicates (high atomic weights versus low atomic weights and small differences in atomic volumes), so sedimentation should work. A more frequently used scheme is flotation, in which a detergent and bubble system produce a froth to which the CuS adheres while the silicate sinks. The froth containing the CuS is skimmed off and the CuS is allowed to settle out to give concentrated ore.

PURE ELEMENTS FROM SULFIDES

Most sulfides when heated in air undergo one of three reactions.

1. They decompose into the elements: $HgS_{(c)} = Hg_{(g)} + \frac{1}{8}S_{8(g)}$. The sulfur may then burn in the air.
2. They form the metallic element and sulfur dioxide: $CuS_{(c)} + O_{2(g)} = Cu_{(c)} + SO_{2(g)}$.
3. They form the metallic oxide and sulfur dioxide: $2FeS_{2(c)} + \frac{11}{2}O_{2(g)} = Fe_2O_{3(c)} + 4SO_{2(g)}$.

(Again, all these equations can be balanced by inspection once the correct formulas are known. Try it.) In the usual commercial practice, mercury, copper, silver, and lead can be produced directly as metals merely by heating their naturally occurring sulfides. Other elements normally emerge as oxides. Consider the relative effects of ΔH^0 and ΔS^0 in the above processes. Note also the oxidation states. Are they all equal to the family number in the periodic table?

Exercise 5.10

Suggest a method for getting silver from a silver sulfide ore. *Answer:* Try heating the ore, since silver is a rather noble metal and might release the sulfur easily (small positive ΔH, large ΔS to form gaseous sulfur). If this does not work (it doesn't), heat in a limited supply of air. Now ΔH^0 will probably be minus, since sulfur goes to SO_2; ΔS^0 is still favorable at high T, so metallic silver should result if Ag_2O does not form. (It doesn't at high T, because of small ΔH and large ΔS effects.)

PURE ELEMENTS FROM OXIDES—CARBON AS A REDUCING AGENT

A typical process is used to obtain iron, the metal produced in largest tonnage. Clearly the problem is to "take the oxygen away from the iron." Usually this is done by mixing the oxide with another element that forms an even more stable compound under the industrial conditions than does iron. Clearly, too, this reducing agent must be cheaper than iron. The cheapest available reducing agents are coal, which is 80% ± 10% carbon, and natural gas, which is mainly CH_4 (80%) and C_2H_6 (15%). Which of these two is cheaper depends on the location. Some typical coal compositions are listed in Table 5.6. But neither coal nor natural gas is used industrially to prepare iron, because no known process using either one is easy to control. Instead, the coal is heated in the absence of air to produce coke, which is almost 100% carbon. The coking process almost pays for itself by producing large quantities of valuable chemicals: coal tar, benzene, coal gas, and ammonia, among others.

Coke is a good reducing agent. It will "take oxygen away" from all the elements except those in groups IA, IIA, and IIIA, and a few others, but coke alone is a very slow reducing agent. After all, it is a solid and the metallic oxides are solids, and solids make poor contact and so react slowly. The problem, surprisingly enough, is solved by admitting atmospheric oxygen into the reaction chamber. Can

Table 5.6 Chemical composition of some coals and coal precursors.

Material	Weight (%)				Atoms (%)			
	Carbon	Hydrogen	Oxygen	Nitrogen	Carbon	Hydrogen	Oxygen	Nitrogen
Wood fiber	50	6	43	1	32	46	22	0.5
Peat	59	6	33	2	37	46	16	1
Brown coal (lignite)	69	5.5	25	0.8	45	43	12	0.5
Bituminous coal	82	5	13	0.8	54	39	6.5	0.5
Anthracite	95	2.5	2.5	trace	75	24	1	trace

you deduce why? With atmospheric oxygen present, the rate of reaction becomes high, and net reduction of the metallic oxide occurs. But the high rate and net reduction occur only if the relative amounts of oxide, coke, and oxygen are carefully controlled. The products of the blast furnace (the name for the reaction chamber in which iron oxide is reduced) are liquid iron, liquid slag (mainly calcium silicate), gaseous carbon dioxide, gaseous carbon monoxide, and, of course, the nitrogen originally present in the air. The reaction might be presumed to proceed through steps such as the following [sometimes we shall use subscript (*s*) to indicate a solid state that is not highly crystalline].

	ΔH^0_{298} (kcal)	ΔS^0_{298} (cal °K^{-1})	
$C_{(s)} + O_{2(g)} = CO_{2(g)} + \text{energy}$	-94.05	-0.69	(5.3)
$\text{energy} + CO_{2(g)} + C_{(s)} = 2CO_{(g)}$	$+41.21$	$+42.01$	(5.4)
$3CO_{(g)} + Fe_2O_{3(c)} = 3CO_{2(g)} + 2Fe_{(l)}$	-6.09	$+3.0$	(5.5)

Reactions (5.3) and (5.4) are well known and certainly can occur in the indicated steps. Reaction (5.5) is a very unlikely single step. The simultaneous collision of 3 molecules with a single site on a solid is a rare event indeed. Thus the following steps are much more likely on an a priori basis. (Experiments indicate that they are more likely in the blast furnace as well.)

	ΔH^0_{298} (kcal)	ΔS^0_{298} (cal °K^{-1})	
$CO_{(g)} + 3Fe_2O_{3(c)} = CO_{2(g)} + 2Fe_3O_{4(c)}$	-12.83	$+9.4$	(5.6)
$CO_{(g)} + Fe_3O_{4(c)} = CO_{2(g)} + 3FeO_{(c)}$	$+8.67$	$+10.10$	(5.7)
$CO_{(g)} + FeO_{(c)} = CO_{2(g)} + Fe_{(l)}$	-3.83	-3.41	(5.8)

Reaction (5.6) may look as unlikely to you as reaction (5.5), since each appears to involve 4 molecules of reactants. But there is an important difference. Reaction (5.5) requires the collision of 3 gaseous molecules at a single site on the surface, whereas reaction (5.6) requires only a single molecule of gas to strike the surface and remove a single atom of oxygen. The surface composition then changes from Fe_2O_3 to Fe_3O_4. But it is only the surface that changes. There are no molecules of Fe_2O_3 (or Fe_3O_4 or FeO). The iron oxide formulas merely give the composition of the solid surface. They do not suggest that small molecules exist there. Thus reactions (5.3), (5.4), (5.6), (5.7), and (5.8) are consistent with our assumption that collisions must involve only one gaseous molecule. They are also consistent with the observed increase in rate when oxygen is added (to form some initial CO_2, then CO, which reacts with Fe_2O_3 faster than solid coke does). The reactions also have values of ΔH^0 and ΔS^0 that indicate (if ΔH and ΔS do not change much with T) that ΔG^0 values will be negative at high temperatures.

There are silicate impurities in most iron ores that form a highly viscous mass unless some limestone ($CaCO_3$) is added to the oxide ore and the coke. The $CaCO_3$ decomposes to CaO and CO_2, and the CaO then reacts with the silicates (SiO_2 will do as a formula) to form a fluid slag (such as $CaSiO_3$):

$$CaCO_{3(c)} = CaO_{(c)} + CO_{2(g)} \qquad (5.9)$$

$$CaO_{(c)} + SiO_{2(l)} = CaSiO_{3(l)} \qquad (5.10)$$

Since all CO_2 molecules are alike, those produced in reactions (5.6), (5.7), (5.8), and (5.9) can react further as in reaction (5.4). Thus any given carbon atom may pass back and forth between CO and CO_2 many times as it passes up the blast furnace before escaping at the top.

Analysis of the gas at the top of the furnace shows about 26% CO and 13% CO_2 (most of the rest is N_2). Clearly a great deal of the reducing ability is escaping in the form of CO, thus lowering the efficiency of the operation. When this was noted in early blast furnaces, it was surmised that the gases did not remain in the furnace long enough to react. So, at considerable cost, bigger and bigger furnaces were built—but the percent of escaping CO remained constant. The discovery of chemical equilibrium constants and their application to the blast furnace provided the needed corrections in technique.

The equation for the over-all reaction for the reduction of Fe_2O_3 by C is

	ΔH^0_{298} (kcal)	ΔS^0_{298} (cal °K^{-1})	
$Fe_2O_{3(c)} + \frac{3}{2}C_{(c)} = \frac{3}{2}CO_{2(g)} + 2Fe_{(l)}$	+55.73	+66.1	(5.11)

Note that this reaction is thermodynamically unlikely at 298°K, but it occurs in the hot blast furnace where one must also consider the reaction

$C_{(c)} + CO_{2(g)} = 2CO_{(g)}$	+41.21	+42.01	(5.12)

whose equilibrium constant is

$$K = \frac{p_{CO}{}^2}{p_{CO_2}} \qquad (5.13)$$

Assuming that our exit gases are in equilibrium, we get $K = 0.26^2/0.13 = 0.52$. The measurements of Rhead and Wheele* show that this is the actual value of K at 580°C. Average temperatures in the reaction zone in the blast furnace are 550–600°C. Thus there is no point in enlarging the furnace. The amount of CO could be reduced if reaction temperatures were lower, but the rates of reaction would then be too low for economic feasibility.

* *J. Chem. Soc.*, **97**, 2178 (1910).

Figure 5.4 shows a modern blast furnace and its chemistry. Because of increasing cost of coke, many blast furnaces now operate on air enriched with oxygen (to about 25%) plus the addition of powdered coal and/or fuel oil to the air blast, all of which reduce the coke requirement. The exhaust gas is mixed with more air and the CO burned on brick checkerwork which, after the gas flow has been shifted, is then used to preheat air entering the blast furnace.

The confusion between rate effects and equilibrium effects that resulted in attempts to make the early blast furnaces operate beyond their possible level of performance provides a good example of the desirability of calculating equilibrium concentrations for all industrial processes. The methods used in these calculations are those of chemical thermodynamics, and methods of calculating thermodynamically possible changes constitute a major part of this book. When a process can be shown to be thermodynamically unprofitable, there is no point in trying it. One should, instead, find a thermodynamically profitable procedure.

Exercise 5.11

ΔG^0 for reaction (5.11) is negative at high T because of the ΔS term, but where does the energy come from to satisfy its endothermic nature? *Answer:* Some of the coke, or other reducing agent, burns with oxygen [as in Equation (5.3)]. Note from the relative sizes of the energy terms that less than two-thirds of the carbon can be used in reducing the iron.

Carbon is not a strong enough reducing agent to convert all of the oxides of groups IA through VIIA to the elements. Better reducing agents such as sodium, magnesium, or aluminum can be used, the reducing agent being converted to its oxide in the process. These oxides are solid and remain in the reaction as possible contaminants, unlike CO_2 and CO, which escape as gases. But the oxides and metal that are produced are usually insoluble in one another and differ in density, and so may be separated. The thermite or Goldschmidt process, which uses metallic aluminum as a reducing agent, is an especially handy method of preparing small quantities of the metals of groups IVB through VIIIB from their oxides:

$$Al_{(l)} + Cr_2O_{3(c)} \longrightarrow Cr_{(l)} + Al_2O_{3(c)} + \text{energy} \qquad \text{(not balanced)}$$

The reactions are so exothermic, once started, that the aluminum melts (thus increasing its contact with the oxide to be reduced) and produces molten metal (which can flow away from the solid oxides and so purify itself). Since ΔS is small and ΔH is highly negative, ΔG is negative and the reaction is highly probable. If pure manganese were desired, which would be preferable—an excess of aluminum or an excess of manganese dioxide?

Exercise 5.12

Discuss the Goldschmidt process from the standpoint of the effect of ΔH^0, ΔS^0, and T on the likelihood of reaction. *Answer:* $\Delta S^0 \cong 0$, since there are few structural changes. Thus reaction must rely on large negative ΔH^0 to give negative ΔG^0 as well as to produce enough heat to give liquid metals and an appreciable rate of reaction. Reaction will probably only occur if Al has a much lower ionization energy than the metal to be prepared, since the net reaction might be oversimplified, for this argument, to: $Al + X^{+++} \longrightarrow Al^{+++} + X$, a simple exchange of electrons.

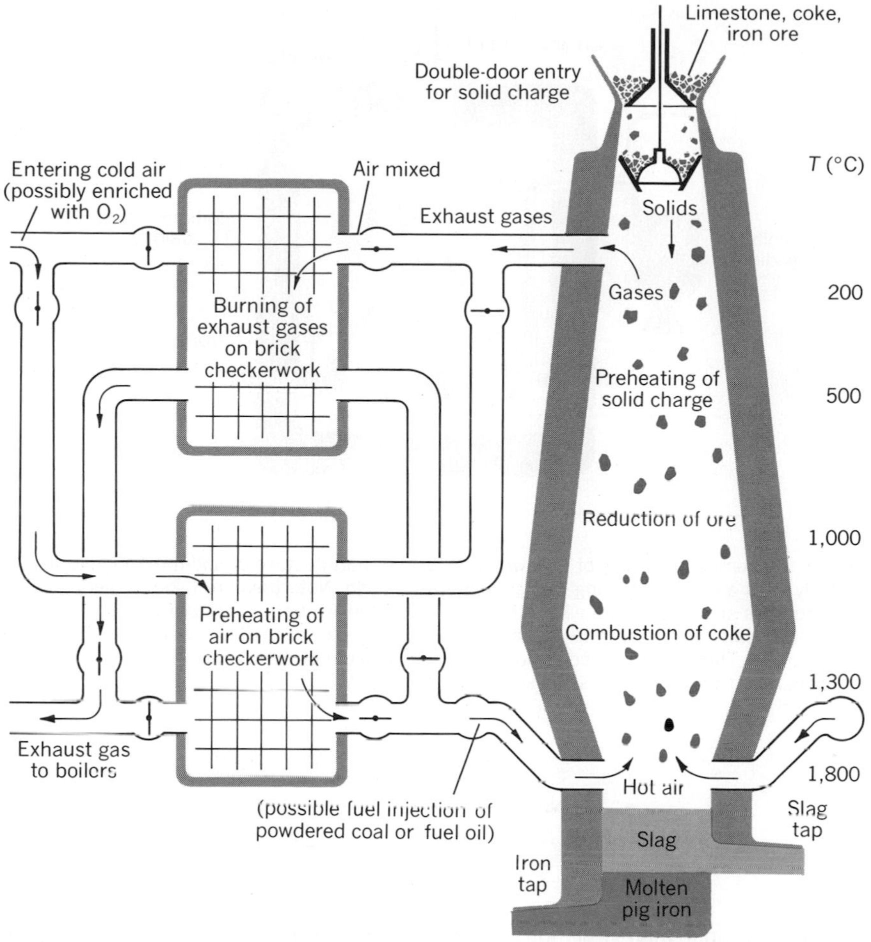

Figure 5.4 Schematic representation of a blast furnace for the production of iron. Try to correlate reactions (5.3), (5.4), (5.5), (5.6), (5.7), (5.8), (5.9), and (5.10) with the figure, so you can see what principal chemical reactions are occurring in each region of the blast furnace.

ELEMENTS BY ELECTROLYSIS

But how are the sodium, magnesium, and aluminum produced? There are no good industrial methods for producing them by using chemical reducing agents. All such methods that have been suggested are either very expensive or thermodynamically impossible.

The fundamental problem may be looked at in terms of the atomic changes required. We wish to produce atoms of sodium, magnesium, and aluminum, which are electrically neutral, but the starting materials we have are compounds containing positive ions of sodium, magnesium, or aluminum. The problem may be considered as one of supplying electrons in these half-equations:

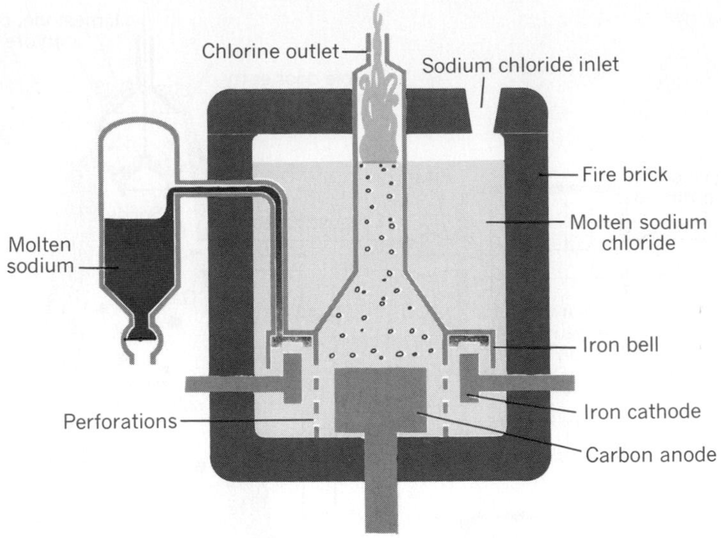

Figure 5.5 Schematic diagram of a Downs cell for the manufacture of sodium and chlorine by electrolysis of a bath containing molten sodium chloride. Note the care taken to keep the two products separated from each other. Why? The molten bath is not pure sodium chloride. Other salts are present to give a solution having a lower melting point than pure sodium chloride. This minimizes corrosion (always a problem at high temperatures) and power costs. What properties must these other salts have?

	$\mathcal{E}^0$ (volts)*
$e^- + Na^+ = Na$	-2.714
$2e^- + Mg^{++} = Mg$	-2.375
$3e^- + Al^{+++} = Al$	-1.66

All these elements have low ionization energies and their $\mathcal{E}^0$ values in aqueous solution are negative, indicating relatively small tendencies to acquire or hold electrons. The above half-reactions are probably endothermic $\Delta H^0 = +$, and have $\Delta S^0 = -$. They are improbable spontaneous reactions, $\Delta G^0 = +$. The generally cheapest solution is to electrolyze a liquefied compound of the desired element. Electrolysis is a method by which electrons are removed from one substance at the anode and supplied to another substance at the cathode. The liquid bath supplies the fluid through which ions can move toward the electrodes. Nonaqueous solutions must be used for these three metals since any water present would be reduced to $H_{2(g)}$ more easily than these ions would be reduced to the metals. An electric generator provides a high concentration of electrons on a cathode, and the fluid bath allows the ions of the metals to migrate to the cathode, where they acquire

* $\mathcal{E}^0$ is given in units of volts and represents the tendency of the half-reaction to occur in the standard state in aqueous solutions. Positive values of $\mathcal{E}^0$ characterize those more likely to occur; negative values, those less likely to occur. Just as two half-reactions may be added to give a full reaction, so $\mathcal{E}^0$ values for half-reactions may be added to give $\mathcal{E}^0$ values for full reactions. Each $\mathcal{E}^0$ is associated with a particular half-reaction. If the half-reaction is reversed (left to right) the sign of $\mathcal{E}^0$ changes from $-$ to $+$ or vice versa. Thus $e^- + Na^+ = Na\ (c)$, $\mathcal{E}^0 = -2.714$, but $Na\ (c) = Na^+ + e^-$, $\mathcal{E}^0 = +2.714$. The relationship between $\mathcal{E}^0$ and ΔG^0 is $\Delta G^0 = -n\mathcal{F}\mathcal{E}^0$. A table of $\mathcal{E}^0$ values is given in Table 20.2. For the moment, merely remember that the more positive $\mathcal{E}^0$ is, the more likely it is that the reaction will occur.

electrons and are reduced to metal. The generator supplies the necessary free energy to "make the electrolysis occur." The negative ion of the compound is usually oxidized to the corresponding element at the anode, giving up electrons to the external circuit. The electrons are then pumped by the generator to the cathode, where the metal is formed.

Figures 5.5 and 5.6 show typical industrial designs for the manufacture of sodium and aluminum.

It will be noted that the production of sodium also produces chlorine, which is formed by the oxidation reaction at the anode:

$$Cl^- = \tfrac{1}{2}Cl_{2(g)} + e^-, \qquad \mathcal{E}^0 = -1.3583 \text{ volts}$$

There is no chemical oxidizing agent now industrially available to remove electrons from Cl^- and produce chlorine. Remember the high *IE* of chlorine and note the large negative value of $\mathcal{E}^0$. Chloride ions, Cl^-, also have a high *IE*. Thus industrial chlorine is usually produced by electrolysis. The same is true of fluorine. Remember that oxidation means apparent loss of electrons, as in $Cl^- = \tfrac{1}{2}Cl_{2(g)} + e^-$, and reduction means apparent gain of electrons, as in $Na^+ + e^- = Na$. Thus species with very high *IE* values are usually formed by electrolysis, as are species with very low *IE* values. Species of intermediate *IE* values can lose and gain electrons to one another as in the Goldschmidt process, and hence can be formed by treatment with chemicals.

Exercise 5.13

Figures 5.5 and 5.6 show that sodium floats on liquid sodium chloride, but aluminum sinks in molten aluminum oxide. Account for this in terms of atomic electronic energy levels. *Answer:* The reactions are $Na^+ + e^- = Na_{(l)}$ and $Al^{+++} + 3e^- = Al_{(l)}$. One might guess that the aluminum, when it gains three electrons, would become larger than the sodium. But the higher nuclear charge in Al pulls in all the electrons more tightly and, since both atoms have valence shells of $3p$ and/or $3s$ electrons, the atomic size drops as nuclear charge rises. Thus Al is more dense than sodium. Furthermore, Cl^- ions are more dense (more mass per unit volume) than $O^{=}$, so $NaCl_{(l)}$

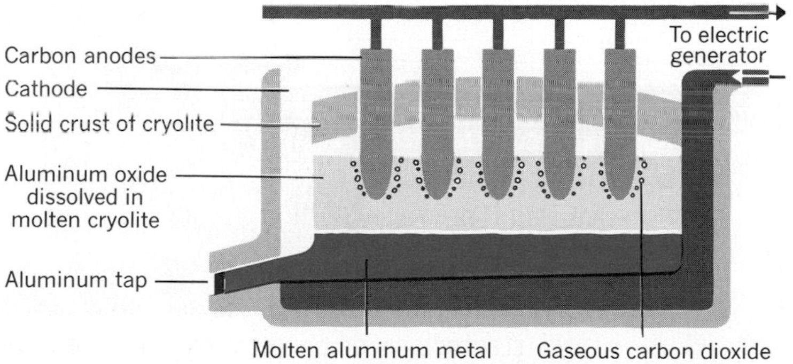

Figure 5.6 Schematic diagram of a Hall cell for the manufacture of aluminum by electrolysis of bath containing molten aluminum oxide. The comments in the legend for Figure 5.5 apply here as well. Why are there fewer mechanical precautions (such as metal baffles) to keep the products separated here than in Figure 5.5?

tends to be more dense than Al_2O_3. Both effects contribute to the observed results. See Figure 4.9 for data from which the relative densities of Na and NaCl and Al and Al_2O_3 can be estimated.

CHEMICAL OXIDIZING AGENTS

Bromine and iodine may be, and are, produced by treating bromides or iodides with chlorine:

$$\tfrac{1}{2}Cl_{2(g)} + Br^-_{(aq)} = \tfrac{1}{2}Br_{2(l)} + Cl^-_{(aq)}, \qquad \mathcal{E}^0 = 0.271 \text{ volts}$$
$$\tfrac{1}{2}Cl_{2(g)} + I^-_{(aq)} = \tfrac{1}{2}I_{2(c)} + Cl^-_{(aq)}, \qquad \mathcal{E}^0 = 0.823 \text{ volts}$$

Here both $\mathcal{E}^0$ values are positive, consistent with the great tendency of these reactions to occur as written. Chlorine is a good oxidizing agent (high *IE* value—tends to hold or acquire electrons); it is both rapid and powerful, quickly and vigorously removing electrons from other atoms. Oxygen is much cheaper, but it is usually slower and is less powerful. Thus, when an oxidizing agent is needed, oxygen is always tried first because of its availability from the atmosphere and its low cost. When oxygen will not work, either because of a slow rate or an unfavorable equilibrium, chlorine is normally the second choice. Other oxidizing agents exist, of course, for processes in which chlorine would be unsuitable. You might try correlating ionization energies (as in Figure 4.7) with oxidizing and reducing power. Does such a correlation seem likely?

Figure 5.7 summarizes the usual industrial methods of preparing some of the chemical elements. Note that each type of process tends to be used in a restricted region of the periodic table.

Exercise 5.14

Is there any correlation between Figure 5.7 and ionization energies? *Answer:* Compounds containing elements of high or low *IE* are usually electrolyzed to obtain the

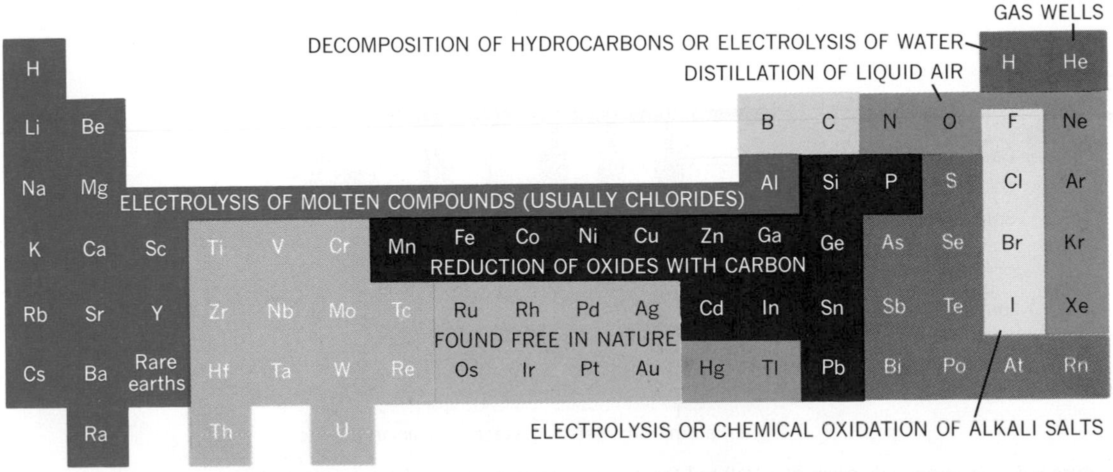

Figure 5.7 Some common industrial methods of preparing the elements. Special methods are also used, especially for obtaining pure samples and for the elements not included in any shaded area.

free elements due to the high $\Delta H(+)$ associated with decomposition of the compounds. Elements of intermediate *IE* may have their oxides reduced by carbon because of the likelihood of ΔH^0 being negative and ΔS^0 being positive, due to the formation of strongly bonded, gaseous CO_2. Elements of very high *IE* are found free in nature. The occurrence of pure elementary substances (such as Pt, Au, Ag, of intermediate *IE*) has a more complicated interpretation in terms of small ΔH^0 values and large entropy effects associated with the decompositions of their compounds.

Exercise 5.15

What is $\mathcal{E}^0$ for the half-reaction $Br^- = \frac{1}{2}Br_2 + e^-$? *Answer:*

	$\mathcal{E}^0$
$\frac{1}{2}Cl_2 + Br^- = \frac{1}{2}Br_2 + Cl^-$	0.271
$-[\frac{1}{2}Cl_2 + e^- = Cl^-]$	$+1.3583]$
$Br^- = \frac{1}{2}Br_2 + e^-$	-1.087

Thus, subtracting the chlorine half-reaction (and its $\mathcal{E}^0$) gives the bromide half-reaction (and its $\mathcal{E}^0$).

METALS AND NONMETALS

Figure 5.8, A shows samples of all but the rarest of the elements arranged as a periodic table. One of the most striking observations is that most of the elements are metals. Almost all of the elements except those at the extreme right have a highly reflective, silvery luster. Even copper, gold, and bismuth, though colored, have a similar luster. These metallic elements also have higher electrical and thermal conductivities and ductility than the elements at the extreme right of the table.

The nonmetallic elements are clustered at the extreme right, and toward the top, of the table. They are, by contrast, nonreflective, poor electrical and thermal conductors, and nonductile (brittle) in the crystalline state.

If we examine the electron structures of the elements as gaseous atoms, we find that the nonmetals (except hydrogen and helium) have six, or nearly six, *p* electrons in their highest energy levels. The inert gas elements have exactly six *p* electrons. All the monatomic nonmetals have very few empty orbitals in their outer set of energy levels. Either they have the inert gas structure or they lack only a few electrons of achieving one. The monatomic metals, on the other hand, have few filled orbitals in their outermost energy set. Most of their orbitals are empty or only half filled in the gaseous atoms.

Exercise 5.16

Suggest why metallic properties in the condensed phases may result when there are many empty orbitals in the gaseous atoms. Is there any correlation with ionization energies? *Answer:* If there are few empty orbitals, few interatomic bonds can form. If there are many empty orbitals, there are many ways the electrons can fit into them, leading to mobile, or loosely held, electrons and metallic properties. Low *IE* further frees the electrons, increasing the likelihood of metallic properties.

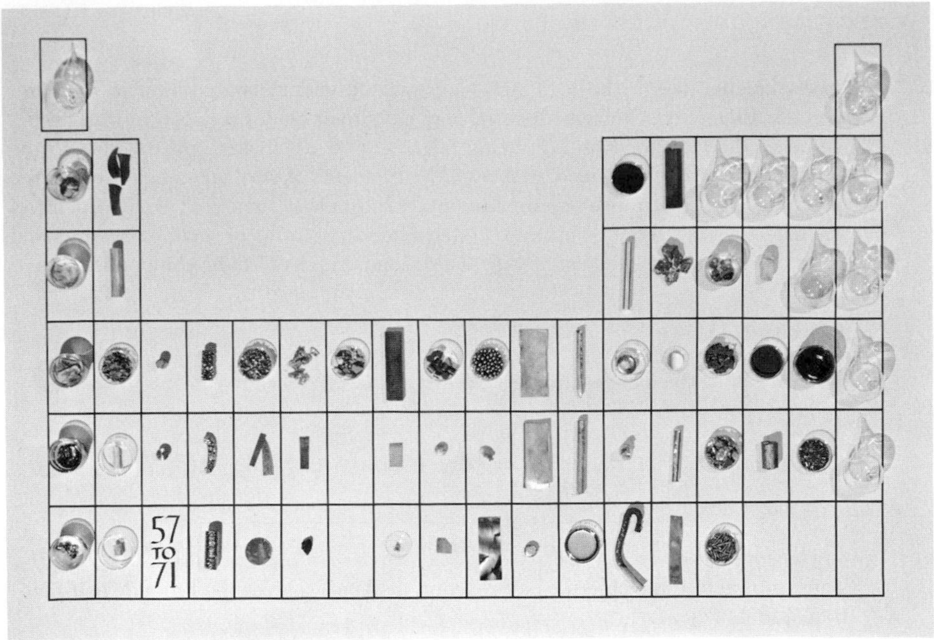

Figure 5.8, A Samples of all but the rarest of the elements. Note the regions of the periodic table in which elements are gaseous at room temperature. Note also the regions containing the metallic elements. [Chemical Education Material Study, *Chemistry, An Experimental Science*, San Francisco, W. H. Freeman and Company, 1963.]

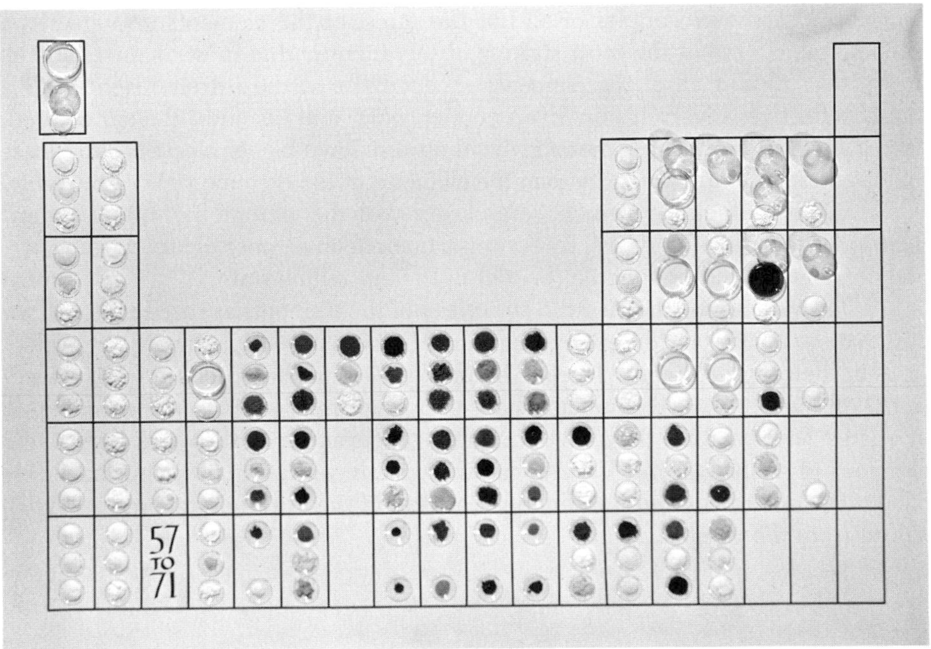

Figure 5.8, B Samples of typical oxides (*top*), chlorides (*middle*), and some other compound (*bottom*), of all but the rarest of the elements. Note the regions of the periodic table in which compounds (1) are colored, (2) are gaseous at room temperature, and (3) are liquid at room temperature. [Chemical Education Material Study, *Chemistry, An Experimental Science*, San Francisco, W. H. Freeman and Company, 1963.]

Table 5.7 Periodic table showing melting points (first figure) and boiling points (second figure) of the elements in °K. (Where crystal modifications occur, data are for the substance with the lower values.)

He	Ne	Ar	Kr	Xe	Rn	
——, 4.2	24.5, 27.2	83.7, 87.2	115.9, 121	161.2, 165.0	202, 211.3	
H	F	Cl	Br	I	At	
13.9, 20.3	53.5, 85.2	172, 239.1	265.9, 331.3	386.1, 456.6		
	O	S	Se	Te	Po	
	54.3, 90.1	392.3, 717.7	490.5, 961	726, 1360.3	527, 1235	
	N	P	As	Sb	Bi	
	63.0, 77.3	317.3, 553	1090, 886 (sublimes)	903.6, 1713	544.4, 1832	
	C	Si	Ge	Sn	Pb	
	4100, —— (triple pt = 3900; p = 100 atm)	1683, 2950	1232, 3103	505.0, 2960	600.5, 2024	
	B	Al	Ga	In	Tl	
	2300, 4200	932, 2600	302.9, 2500	429.3, 2320	575.6, 1730	
			Zn	Cd	Hg	
			692.6, 1181	594.0, 1038	234.2, 629.6	
			Cu	Ag	Au	
			1356, 2855	1233.9, 2485	1336, 2980	
			Ni	Pd	Pt	
			1725, 3073	1823, 3400	2042.4, 4100	
			Co	Rh	Ir	
			1763, 3373	2239, 4000	2727, 4403	
			Fe	Ru	Os	
			1803, 3008	2700, 4000	3000, 4503	
			Mn	Tc	Re	
			1517, 2368	2400, ——	3453, 5903	
			Cr	Mo	W	U
			2173, 2915	2883, 5077	3650, 5950	1405, 3800
			V	Cb	Ta	
			2190, 3650	2770, 5400	3269, 5700	
			Ti	Zr	Hf	Th
			1998, 3550	2125, 4653	2488, 5500	
			Sc	Y	La	
			1700, 2753	1773, 3500	1193, 4515	
	Be	Mg	Ca	Sr	Ba	Ra
	1556, 3243	923, 1393	1124, 1760	1043, 1657	983, 1911	
H	Li	Na	K	Rb	Cs	
13.9, 20.3	453.6, 1604	371, 1162	336.7, 1030	311.9, 952	301.7, 963	

Figure 5.8, B shows some typical compounds of all but the rarest elements. Most compounds shown are solid and colorless, but elements in the middle of the table normally have colored compounds. We will discuss this and the occurrence of gaseous compounds shortly.

THE ELEMENTS AS CRYSTALS, LIQUIDS, AND GASES

It is easy to concentrate too much on the properties of an element at room temperature. These properties are important to society, of course, since man happens to survive best in a narrow temperature range of 290°K ± 20°. Outside this range, only special measures keep him alive. But we can learn a great deal about the elements, including an understanding of their properties at room temperature, if we study the elements over a range of temperature.

Table 5.7 and Figure 5.9 show the known melting points and boiling points of the elements as a function of atomic number Z. The periodicity of the two temperatures with Z is marked, but is not completely regular. However, all the nonmetals have relatively low melting and boiling points. The elements of highest melting and boiling points are generally in groups IVB to VIB. If we note the orbital occupancy of these substances of high boiling points, we see that the number of valence electrons always approximately equals the number of orbital vacancies in the same energy set. The boiling point tends to fall when there are few orbital vacancies compared to the number of valence electrons or when there are few electrons compared to the number of orbital vacancies.

The melting points are not so regular. Perhaps this is because melting breaks up the regular crystal structure but does not greatly change the interatomic distance. Boiling separates

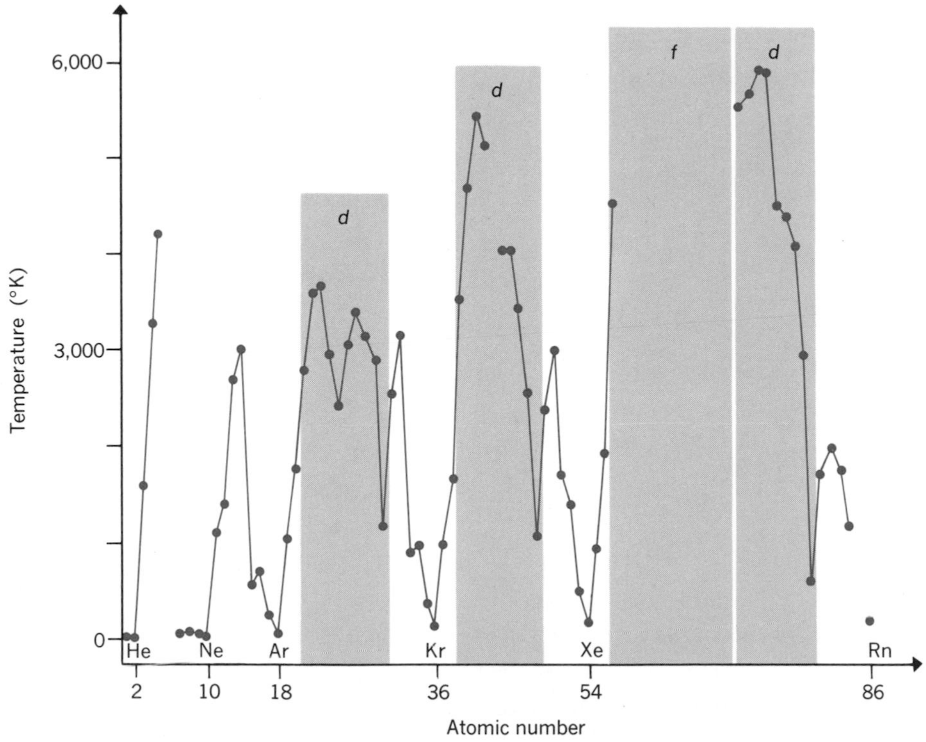

Figure 5.9 Boiling points of the elements (in °K) versus atomic number. Compare this figure with Figure 4.7. Are there any regularities? Can you correlate them?

H_2 104									H_2 104	He
Li(Li_2) 25.8	Be 16(?)				B 66	C_3 (other odd) 144	N_2 226	O_2 118	F_2 37	Ne
Na (Na_2 16%) 17.5	Mg 7.2				Al 39	Si 75	P_4 116	S_8 101	Cl_2 57	Ar
K 11.9	Ca	Ni 54	Cu 46	Zn 6	Ga 33(?)	Ge 64	As_4 91	Se_6 73	Br_2 45	Kr
Rb 11.3			Ag 38	Cd 1	In 22	Sn 46	Sb_4 70	Te_2 54	I_2 36	Xe
Cs 10.4			Au 52	Hg 1	Tl 14(?)	Pb 23	Bi 47			Rn

Figure 5.10 Formulas of the principal species present for some elements in the gaseous state near the boiling point. (Some species, present to only a few percent, are given in parentheses.) Substances not listed are assumed to be mainly monatomic as gases at the boiling point. The numbers give the bond energies (in kcal $mole^{-1}$) measured for some of the elements as diatomic gases. Note that the bond strength, and hence the tendency to dimerize, generally decreases with increasing atomic number in any family. [Mostly from B. Siegel, *Quarterly Reviews*, **19**, 77(1965).]

the atoms widely from one another. If chemical bonding is effected by the simultaneous attraction of one or more electrons to one or more nuclei, bonding will probably be much less altered in the transition from solid to liquid than in that from liquid to gas. After all, in the solid-liquid transition, the average internuclear distance increases only slightly. Thus effects other than the strength of the bonding may be important in determining melting points.

MOLECULES OF THE ELEMENTS

Application of Cannizzaro's law and Avogadro's law allows the determination of the molecular weights of the gaseous elements. Our standard of weight is a carbon isotope ($Z = 6$, $N = 6$, $A = 12$, equals exactly 12 mass units), but a more convenient standard for using Avogadro's law is oxygen gas. The mass spectrum of carbon dioxide and of oxygen readily shows that the average atomic weight of oxygen compared to C^{12} is about 16 (exactly 15.9994), and that the molecule of gaseous oxygen contains two atoms, formula O_2. Using gaseous elementary oxygen (mass 31.9988) as our standard allows the determination of the molecular weights of all other gases merely by determining the relative weights of a sample of the unknown and of oxygen at the same temperature and pressure. Avogadro's law then states the ratio of the average molecular weights. Or, of course, the unknown gases could be run through a mass spectrometer.

Comparison of the molecular weight of the gas with the atomic weight of the element immediately gives the formula of the gaseous molecule. Figure 5.10 gives the formula of the most abundant gaseous molecules for some elements that have been measured at temperatures just above their boiling points. The high-temperature data are obtained from rates of effusion, spectroscopy, and mass spec-

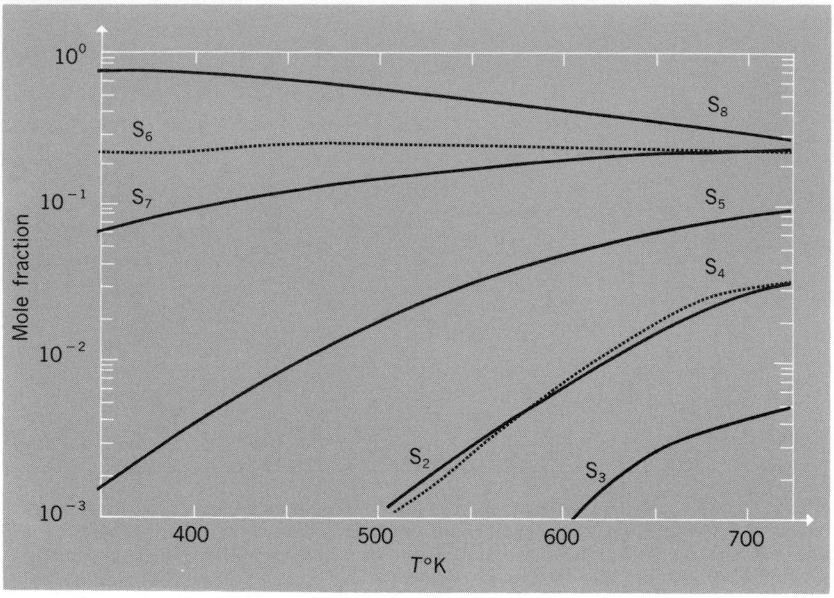

Figure 5.11 Varying composition of saturated sulfur vapor. Note ever-increasing proportion of "simpler" molecules, and the decrease in S_8 as *T* increases. [J. Berkowitz and J. R. Marquart, *J. Chem. Phys.*, **39,** 275 (1963).]

trometry, whereas most of the low-temperature data come from application of Avogadro's law and measurements of gas density.

An example of the complexity of elementary gases and their varying composition with temperature is illustrated in Figure 5.11. Few elementary gases, you will be pleased to know, are this complex in their behavior.

Most of the elements are monatomic in the gas phase but groups IVA, VA, VIA, and VIIA (nonmetals) have polyatomic molecules in the gas phase; some are diatomic and some contain more than two atoms per molecule. Many of the energies required to dissociate the diatomic molecules into atoms (the bond energies of the diatomic molecules) are given in Figure 5.10. Although the figure does not show it, all the elements tend to become monatomic gases at high temperatures.

Exercise 5.17

Suggest an interpretation of the tendency of all elements to become monatomic gases at high temperatures. *Answer:* The dissociation of molecules into atoms requires energy, always more available at high *T*; the $T\,\Delta S^0$ term becomes more and more positive as *T* increases, since ΔS^0 is generally positive for dissociation processes.

MOLECULES IN LIQUIDS AND CRYSTALS

There is, at present, no technique as unambiguous as mass spectrometry, or as simple as gas density, for determining molecular formulas in liquids and crystals. Diffraction techniques (Chapter 31) and solution effects (Chapter 34) do give insights, however, into aggregates in these condensed phases. In many cases the molecules in condensed phases are very large indeed. They may be long chains (as in selenium or tellurium), extended planes (as with red phosphorus and graphite), or essentially infinite three-dimensional structures (most metals and diamond).

Some condensed phases do contain small molecules, for example, F_2, S_8, P_4. Molecular and crystal structures are often correlated in terms of the coordination number—the number of nearest neighbors each atom has. As Figure 5.12 shows, a coordination number of two ($CN = 2$) indicates strong bonding to two adjacent atoms and a chain or ring structure. A $CN = 3$ indicates strong bonding to three neighbors, usually in a planar arrangement. A *CN* of 4, 6, 8, or 12 or more indicates strong bonding to the corresponding number of atoms in a three-dimensional array. A *CN* of 5, 7, 9, and 11 is rare in crystalline elements; these involve unsymmetrical three-dimensional structures. Mn is the only pure element forming more than 12 bonds ($CN = 12$) to neighboring atoms. Figure 5.13 lists the *CN* found in the crystal and liquid just below and above the melting point for some of the elements. When small molecules are found, their formulas are given: compare these with the formulas of the gases when they are just above the boiling point (Figure 5.10). Only a few elements consistently have the same molecules (or *CN*) in all three phases—gas, liquid, crystal. They are H_2, N_2, O_2, F_2, Cl_2, Br_2, I_2. We might stretch a point and include the inert gases, since the forces in their crystals and liquids are very weak. (Note the low melting points and short liquid ranges.) The inert gases are essentially monatomic at all conditions. Their formulas are He, Ne, Ar, Kr, Xe, Rn. But the other monatomic gases condense to give very stable (high boiling point) liquids and tightly bonded (hard) crystals.

Exercise 5.18

Why are all the elements that have constant molecular formulas in all phases in one region of the periodic table? *Answer:* There is only one way of achieving $CN = 1$, a diatomic molecule. Other *CN*'s may be achieved in several ways (see Figure 5.12). The common diatomic molecules form when all low lying orbitals can be filled by sharing electrons with a single neighboring atom. The halogens are the best example,

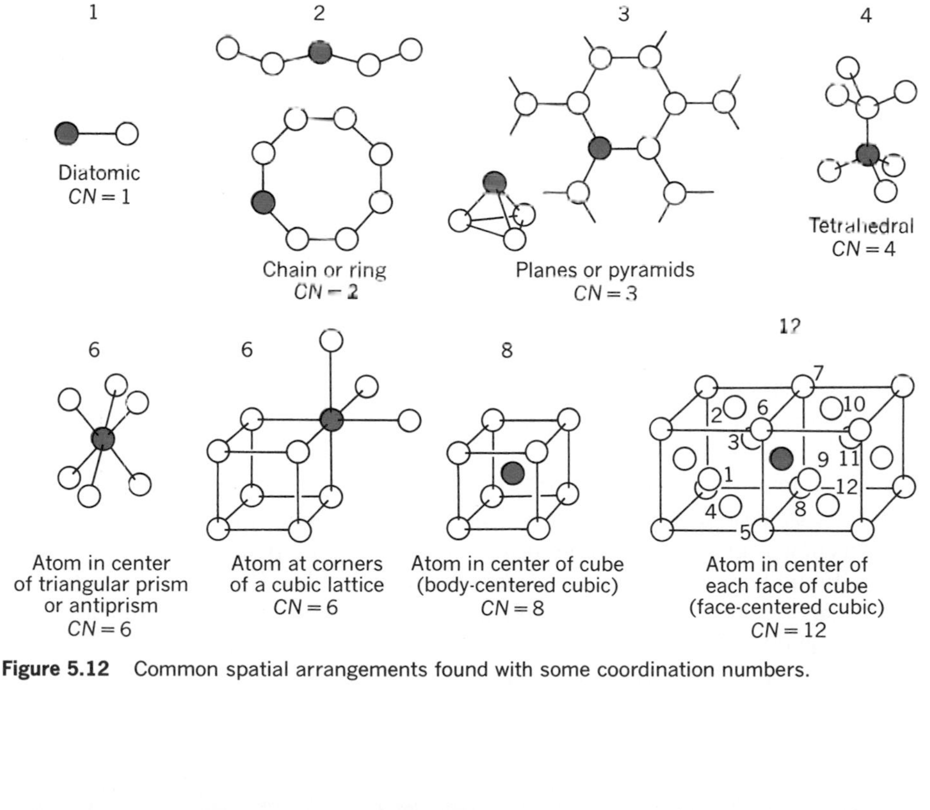

Figure 5.12 Common spatial arrangements found with some coordination numbers.

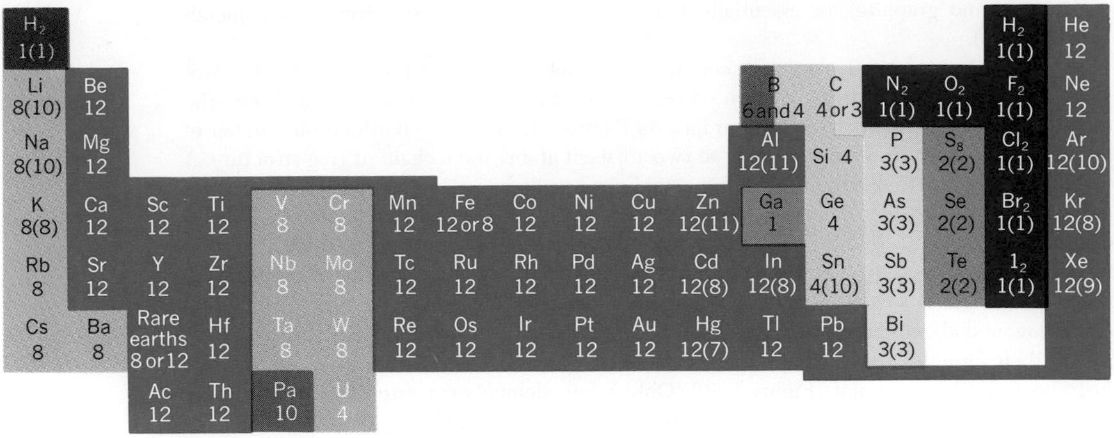

Figure 5.13 Coordination numbers, *CN*, of elements in the crystal and, in some cases (given in parenthesis), liquid phases at the melting point. The *CN* gives the number of nuclei within ±5% of the average distance of closest approach of the nearest neighbor nuclei. Note that crystal *CN*'s of 12 are most common, followed by 8, 1, 4, 3, and 2, in that order. Other values are found only for isolated elements. Note also that the *CN* of almost every liquid is equal to or less than that of the same substance as a crystal. When the *CN* is the same for liquid and crystal, the presence of well-defined small molecules is indicated in both phases. What does the decrease or increase in *CN* from crystal to liquid indicate?

but the other stable diatomics indicate that further possibilities exist, but only with atoms of rather high *IE*, perhaps because of their large tendency to hold on to electrons.

CRYSTAL AND MOLECULAR MODIFICATIONS

In addition to melting and boiling, many elements change from one structural arrangement to another when temperature, pressure, and/or energy content vary. These modifications—formerly called allotropes, before their structures were known—are now described as crystals or molecular modifications. Many such modifications are due to changes in *CN*.

We have already mentioned that the viscosity of liquid sulfur increases remarkably when the liquid is heated much beyond the melting point. Most liquids get less viscous when heated. The anomalous behavior of sulfur is easily interpreted in terms of molecular modifications. Crystalline sulfur exists in two common crystal forms (rhombic and monoclinic structures). Each crystal is made up of molecules of formula S_8, but the two packings differ. At the melting point the liquid is mainly S_8 molecules. Further heating ruptures the rings to give linear segments that join in long chains. The viscosity becomes very high, for the chains tangle and cannot easily flow past one another. Further heating continues the bond rupture and the chain segments become shorter. Near the boiling point the chains are short and at the boiling point the vapor is largely S_8 molecules. Figure 5.14 charts pressure versus temperature to show regions in which these various modifications of sulfur are stable. The figure also shows the variation of viscosity with temperature: see also Figure 5.11 for gaseous forms.

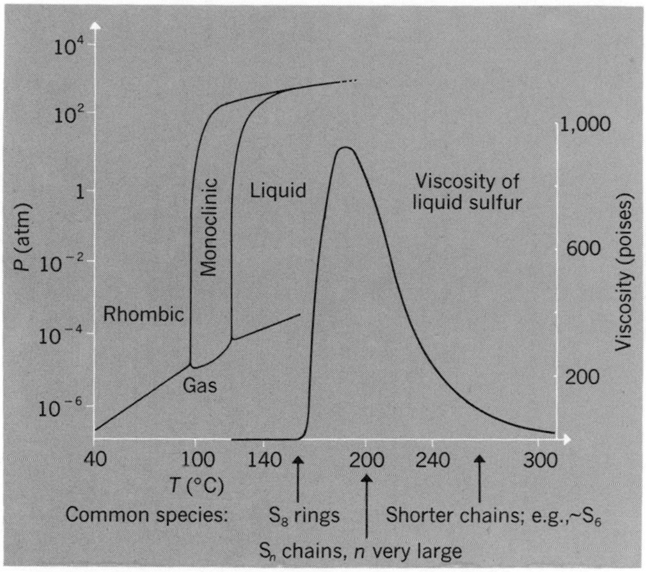

Figure 5.14 Pressure-temperature (phase) diagram for elementary sulfur and the viscosity of liquid sulfur as a function of temperature. The regions of pressure and temperature in which the monoclinic crystal modification of sulfur is stable are indicated, as well as part of the liquid, gaseous, and crystalline rhombic ranges. Note the unusual peak at about 190°C in the viscosity versus temperature curve for liquid sulfur. This peak is due to the general disintegration of the ring form of liquid sulfur into the open-chain form followed by a gradual shortening of the resulting chains.

Ozone, O_3, which may be formed by passing O_2 through an electric discharge, is well known. Less well known is O_4.

The four known crystal modifications of iron are diagramed in Figure 5.15. The transition temperatures are sharp. Only the α form can be magnetized. Thus any iron magnet heated above 1039°K loses its magnetization. Magnetization is not regained upon cooling, but the iron is again susceptible of being magnetized.

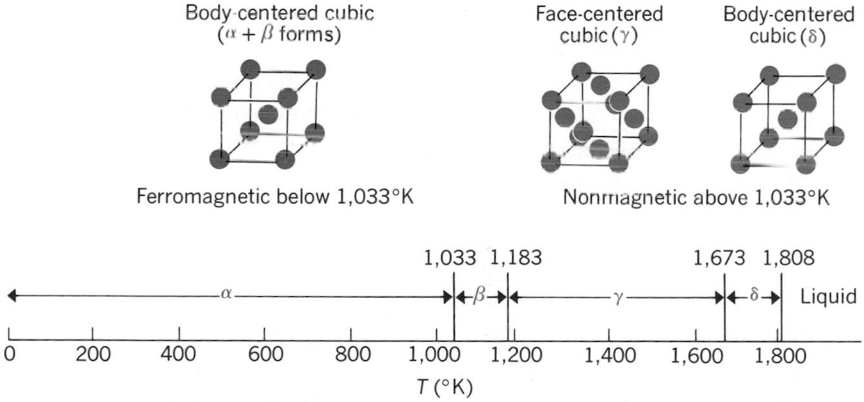

Figure 5.15 Temperature ranges for the stabilities of the four crystal modifications of iron. Note that though four ranges are given, there are only two different crystal structures—body-centered cubic and face-centered cubic. [ϵ iron is stable at very high pressures (greater than $1.3 \cdot 10^5$ atm) at room temperature. It has hexagonal closest packing with $CN = 12$.]

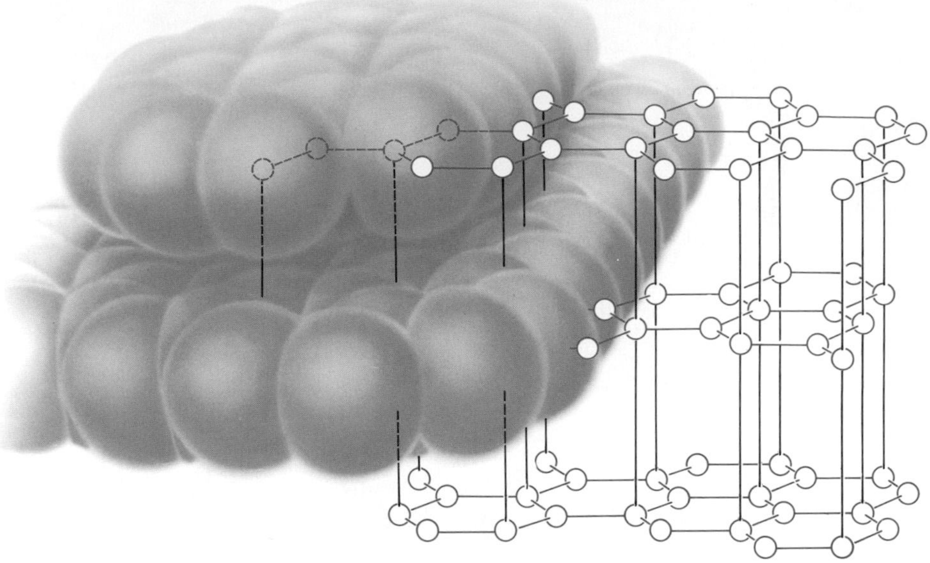

Figure 5.16 The crystal structure of carbon as graphite. Note the *CN* of 3 in planar structures of regular hexagons. Forces between the hexagonal layers are much weaker (and so the internuclear distances are much longer) than within the layers.

Diamond and graphite, both pure carbon, are other noteworthy examples of crystal modifications. The three-dimensional diamond lattice creates one of the hardest substances known. Graphite, with weak bonds between the layers, is soft. Graphite is made even softer when other molecules, such as those of air, get between the layers. The slippery quality of graphite is the result of the tightly bound layers of carbon sliding over one another. The slipperiness is increased greatly if a film of air is adsorbed between the sliding graphite layers (see Figure 5.16).

BONDING IN THE GASEOUS ELEMENTS

Most of the gaseous elements are monatomic, as shown in Figure 5.10. Little bonding force is acting between the atoms of these elements when they are near their boiling points. The group VIIA elements, on the other hand, form only diatomic molecules, regardless of their phase. Why?

If we examine the electron structure of the group VIIA atoms, we find that they contain p^5 electrons in their outer energy level. This leaves a p orbital half empty, and each atom could hold one more electron in this orbital. If an electron from another atom paired up with the electron already present the resulting pair would be attracted by both nuclei simultaneously and bond them together. This is what happens in F_2, Cl_2, Br_2, and I_2. By the cooperative process of sharing or overlapping their orbitals (remember that orbitals are regions in space), these atoms achieve inert gas electron structures of p^6 for the outer set of orbitals. Similar inert gas structures are found in many molecules.

Perhaps the ability of electrons to overcome their pairing repulsion when they can be attracted simultaneously by more than one nucleus, and of orbitals to overlap, accounts for the fact that almost all the polyatomic molecules in Figure 5.10 contain an even number of atoms, and hence an even number of electrons. (C_3 is a possible exception, the number of atoms is odd, of electrons even.) Figure 5.17 uses a simplified representation to indicate bonding. A pair of valence electrons is indicated by a bar or single stroke. Electrons in overlapping orbitals and, therefore, strongly attracted to two nuclei, are indicated by a bar, or bond, placed between the atomic symbols and parallel to the internuclear axis, as H—H. Electrons in orbitals belonging to a single atom are indicated by a bar placed around the atomic symbol: for example, |F—F| for a fluorine molecule bonded by sharing of two electrons, each atom having its other three electron pairs in nonoverlapping orbitals. An unpaired electron is indicated by a dot: for example, |F· for a fluorine atom.

Sometimes atoms share a single pair of electrons and have only one orbital shared between the atoms: H—H, |F—F|, Na—Na, and others. Sometimes atoms share two, or even three, pairs of electrons by overlapping two or three orbitals: |N≡N|, S—S. No substances are known in which more than six electrons appear to be shared in overlapping orbitals. We shall find that molecules of most compounds also contain an even number of electrons arranged in pairs.

It is not possible to draw a simple picture like the above with full sp^3 orbitals to account for C_3 molecules, and we shall find later that the ground state of oxygen is not correctly represented by O=O. There are other molecules presenting similar problems. The remarkable fact, however, is that such a high percentage of molecules can be described in terms of overlapping atomic orbitals containing pairs of electrons, especially when we might expect (and do find experimentally) great splitting and energy shifts among the atomic orbitals when nuclei are close together.

We have already suggested that all chemical forces, or bonds, can be interpreted as the effect of the simultaneous attraction of one or more electrons by more than one nucleus. Note the variations in strength shown in Figure 5.10. Strong bonds can form only when atoms get close together, and when their orbitals can

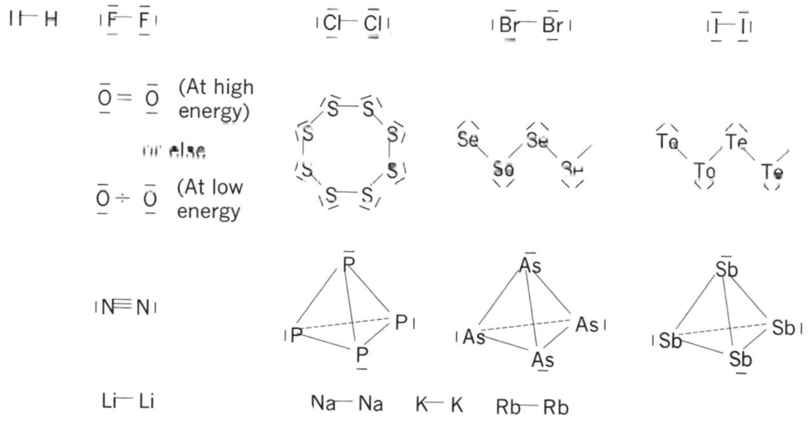

Figure 5.17 Shorthand electron structure representations of molecules of the elements. — indicates a pair of electrons, · indicates a single, unpaired electron in an orbital. Kernels are indicated by symbols for the elements. Such structural representations are called "valence electron structures."

interpenetrate, or overlap, because they are not yet full. Hence the noble gases, with all orbitals full, form weak bonds to one another, whereas C and N can overlap several partly full orbitals and form strong bonds. The number of electrons in the bond also influences bond strength—for example, N_2 (6 electrons) 225 kcal mole^{-1}, H_2 (2 electrons) 104, H_2^+ (1 electron) 62. Most two-electron bond strengths lie between 30 and 140 kcal mole^{-1}.

Exercise 5.19

The valence electron structure of acetylene is often given as H—C≡C—H. How many valence electrons does this indicate? Does this number seem reasonable? Which bond is probably the stronger, the H—C or the C≡C bond? *Answer:* Five bonds are indicated; that is, 10 valence electrons (4 from each C, 1 from each H) as predicted from the periodic table. The triple bond should be much the stronger because it involves more electrons than the single bond.

BONDING IN CONDENSED STATES OF THE ELEMENTS

Most of the elements in their condensed states, especially the metals, have a quite different coordination number than they have in their gaseous state. Compare Figures 5.10 and 5.13. Most also are quite hard as crystals and are good conductors of electricity both as liquids and crystals. These attributes suggest at least three differences between the bonding in the condensed phase and the gas: (1) many bonds can form in the condensed phases; (2) the bonding in the condensed phase must be strong if the solids are hard and the liquids are stable over a long temperature range; (3) electrons must be able to move readily through those condensed phases that exhibit electrical conductivity.

Atoms of metals are characterized by the presence of many empty or partly empty orbitals. Extending the model developed for gases, we might presume that orbitals of metallic atoms could overlap in the condensed phase. But in many metals there are not enough electrons available to fill all the orbitals. This is consistent with the observed high electron mobility: electrons move readily from one orbital to another and conduct electricity. Furthermore, with so many orbitals available, many bonds can form to neighboring atoms. Remember that $CN = 12$ is the most common. No one bond may be extremely strong, since so few electrons are available to undergo simultaneous attraction to the two nuclei, but many somewhat weaker bonds make the phase as a whole strongly bonded to give hard crystals and liquids of high boiling point. This theory is lent further credence by the fact that the hardest substances and those of highest boiling points are those in which the number of valence electrons approximately equals the number of empty half-orbitals (see Table 5.8 and Figure 5.9). This condition gives maximum electron-nucleus interactions since it coincides with maximum possible pairing of electrons in the available orbitals to give the maximum number of strong bonds.

Additional evidence on bonding in condensed phases is obtained by studying the molar volumes and effective atomic radii of the elements (see Figures 5.18, 5.19, and 5.20). Low molar volumes (small internuclear distances) occur, as do high melting and boiling points, when the number of valence electrons approximately equals the number of empty half-orbitals.

Table 5.8 Correlation of number of valence electrons, available bonding orbitals, and boiling point for the first row elements. Note the three maximum boiling points when the number of valence electrons approximately equals the number necessary to fill the available orbitals by sharing.

Element	K	Ca	Sc	Ti	V	Cr	Mn	Fe	Co
Number of valence electrons	1	2	3	4	5	6	7	8	9
Number of empty half-orbitals	11	10	9	8	7	6	5	10	9
Boiling point (°K)	1030	1760	2753	3550	3650	2915	2368	3008	3373
Element	**Ni**	**Cu**	**Zn**	**Ga**	**Ge**	**As**	**Se**	**Br**	**Kr**
Number of valence electrons	10	1	2	3	4	5	6	7	0
Number of empty half-orbitals	8	7	6	5	4	3	2	1	0
Boiling point (°K)	3073	2855	1181	2500	3103	886	961	331	121

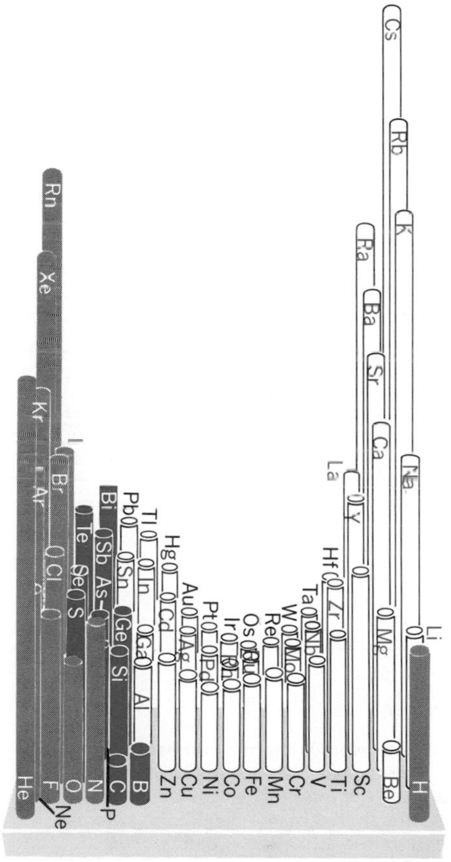

Figure 5.18 Relative molar volumes of the crystallized elements as a function of position in the periodic table. Note the regular increase in molar volume with increasing atomic number in each family (helium and nitrogen are exceptions). Note also the minimum in molar volume in each row near the center of the periodic table. Compare with Figures 4.7, 5.9, and 5.19. Are there any regularities? Can you correlate them?

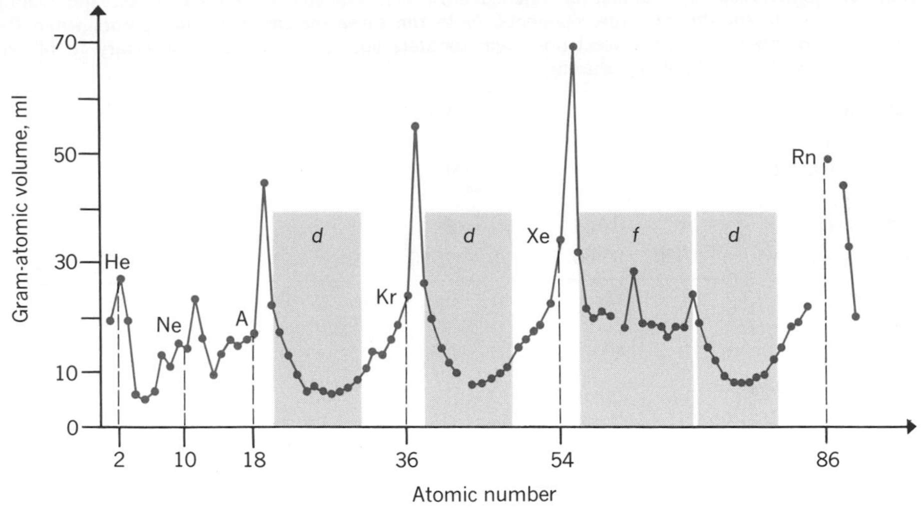

Figure 5.19 Molar volume versus atomic number for the elements. Compare Figures 4.7, 5.9, and 5.18 and look for correlations.

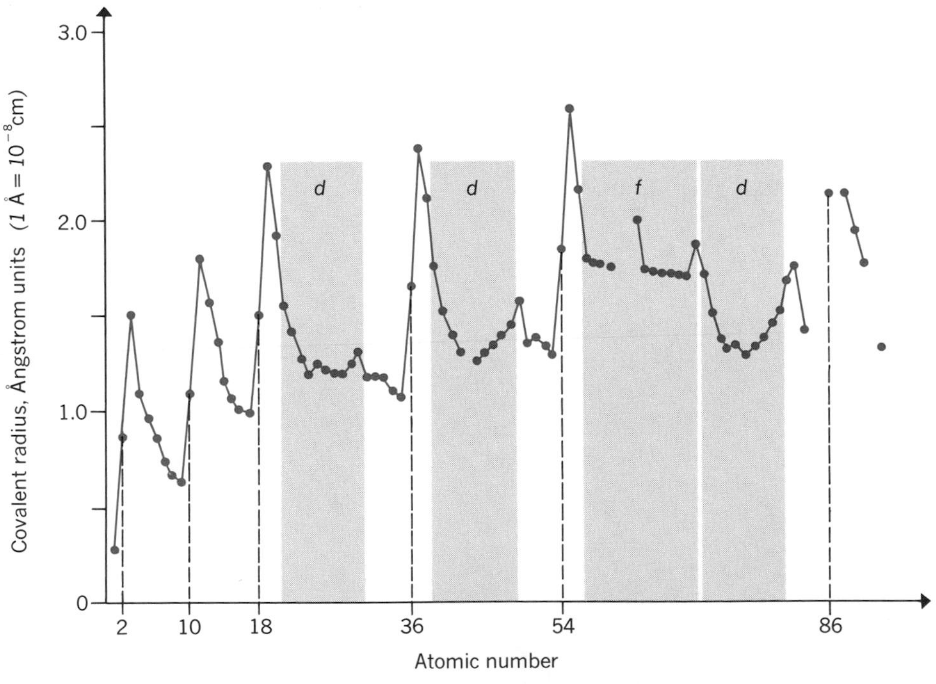

Figure 5.20 Internuclear distance for singly bonded atoms versus atomic number. This internuclear distance is usually equal to the shortest internuclear distance in the crystalline element. In molecules such as O_2 and N_2 (see Figure 5.17) the internuclear distances in the elements are small, since more than two electrons are shared by the neighboring atoms. The single-bond distances are then obtained from internuclear distances in compounds such as HO—OH or $H_2N—NH_2$, where only single pairs of electrons seem to be shared.

Exercise 5.20

How do you account for the general tendency of molar volume to increase with greater atomic number in every column of the periodic table? *Answer:* Moving down in any column of the periodic table means adding at least one more full energy level underlying the valence electrons. This more than overcomes the increased Z, and so the nuclei become more and more shielded and the atoms become larger. Variation in atomic packing tends to be of lesser importance.

FORMATION OF COMPOUNDS

Atoms react not only with their own kind but also with atoms of other elements. Some 95% of all known substances can be reasonably described by slight extensions of the simple orbital overlap just discussed. Figure 5.21 gives some possible electronic structures of molecular compounds, or substances in which small groups of atoms remain bonded together (act as molecules) over appreciable periods of time. In every case there is an even number of electrons, all orbitals of a given energy level set are filled, and each atom has achieved an inert gas electron structure of eight valence electrons. We shall find that eight valence electrons, arranged as four pairs, constitute the stable arrangement in the great majority of known substances.

THEORIES OF MOLECULAR BONDING

We have now deduced a single theoretical picture that works for the elements and simple compounds. It correlates the experimental data mentioned so far. But this theory is not the only theory that could, or indeed will, be presented. We introduced and shall use this theory because we have been able, with a minimum of assumptions beyond those explored in Chapter 4, to tie together the simplest and most obvious experimental observations. Other observations are not so easy to fit

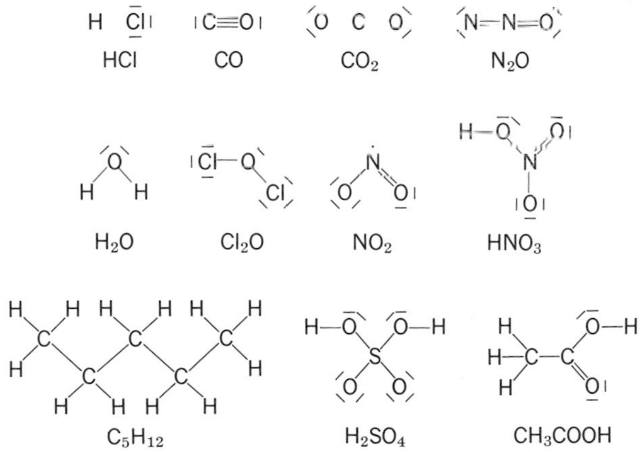

Figure 5.21 Valence electron structures for some simple molecules. In these molecules, and in more than 95% of all known molecules, there are an even number of electrons, all the electrons are paired, and each atom has a valence structure of eight electrons. Later we shall study molecules that do not follow these three generalizations.

to the simple theory now at hand, and other theories will be explored that may interpret even the above experimental data more clearly (see Chapters 14 through 17).

SUMMARY

Most of the known elements are metallic in the condensed phase. The nonmetallic elements are positioned toward the right and top of the periodic table we are using (do not forget hydrogen). Bonding and properties and their variation with temperature may be interpreted in terms of orbital overlap, allowing one or more electrons to be attracted simultaneously to more than one nucleus.

Molecular weights are the sum of the weights of the atoms in the molecule. Molar weights are the sum of the weights of moles of atoms. Analytical weight data can be readily converted to analyses in terms of relative numbers of moles by dividing the weight by the molar weight. The relative numbers of moles of atoms are the same as the relative numbers of atoms; thus one obtains chemical formulas.

Application of Avogadro's law to gases allows the determination of the molecular formulas of gases.

The periodic table is the most useful single device available for correlating properties of elements and their compounds. The periodicity itself is a result of the cyclical recurrence of similar outer electron structures as the nuclear charge increases linearly. Most chemical bonds can be interpreted in terms of overlapping orbitals containing paired electrons.

We have to remember here that scientific problems are no definite tasks. The scientist knows his aim only in broad terms and must rely on his intuition of deepening coherence to guide him to discovery. He must keep his imagination fixed on these growing points and force his way to what lies hidden beyond them. We must see how this is done.
—*Michael Polanyi,* Chem. and Engin. (1966).

PROBLEMS

5.1. You will note in Table 5.1 three time periods during which most of the chemical elements were discovered. Each of these periods of discovery was triggered by a single scientific discovery or theory. What three discoveries do you think were involved?

5.2. What property is shared by the elements known to the ancients? Are there any other elements whose absence from this list surprises you? Comment on your conclusion.

5.3. The plot of Z versus $E^{1/2}$ is not quite linear over all Z in Figure 5.1. How do you account for this lack of linearity?

5.4. Where in Figure 5.7 (or the periodic table) are the elements that are commercially prepared by electrolysis? Where are those prepared by reduction with coke? Where are those prepared by oxidation by air? Where are those found pure in nature? Account for any regularities in terms of ionization energies.

5.5. Draw shorthand electron structures, like those in Figure 5.17 or 5.21, for ozone, hydrogen sulfide, iodine monochloride, sulfur dioxide, S_2, graphite.

5.6. Draw simple bonding diagrams for the following molecules: I_2, P_4, S_8, K_2, HCN, CH_4, HCCH, HOCl, LiH.

5.7. Would you select an oxidizing agent or a reducing agent to accomplish each of the following?
(*a*) Preparation of hydrogen from water.
(*b*) Preparation of chlorine from sodium chloride.
(*c*) Preparation of sulfur from hydrogen sulfide.
(*d*) Preparation of sulfur from sulfur dioxide.
(*e*) Preparation of gold from $Au(CN)_4^-$.

5.8. In Figure 5.18 the molar volume of carbon is less than that of boron, in Figure 5.19 the molar volume of carbon is greater. Rationalize this difference.

5.9. When 1.0000 g of AgCl is completely converted to AgI, the weight of the silver iodide is 1.6381 g. From the atomic weights of silver and chlorine calculate the atomic weight of I.

5.10. The periodic table gives some data on beryllium. What can you deduce concerning the structure of a beryllium atom? Concerning its chemical behavior?

5.11. Analysis of a series of compounds of element X gives the following data. From these data, what is the most probable atomic weight of X? [About 10.]

Mole wt of compound	30.0	92.0	58.0
X (%)	80.0	65.2	82.8

What other possibilities are there for the atomic weight? What independent experiments could be performed to prove the atomic weight?

5.12. Aluminum minerals are much more common than iron minerals. Why is aluminum metal more expensive than iron metal?

5.13. Give the electronic structures of elementary sodium, elementary xenon, elementary chlorine, bromide ions, and hydroxide ions. Which of these would be (*a*) the best reducing agent, (*b*) the best oxidizing agent. Give reasons for your answers in terms of the electronic structures.

5.14. (*a*) What natural source would you use and (*b*) what commercial method would you use to prepare industrial amounts of each of the following? H_2, O_2, Cl_2, N_2, Ni, Hg, W, Y.

5.15. Write an equation to represent the extraction of gold from its ores by treatment with aqueous potassium cyanide in the presence of air.

5.16. Pure tin metal has been used to make organ pipes. Occasionally such pipes crumble, or develop weak spots, if exposed to cold weather. Analysis of the crumbled pipe shows it still is pure tin. Suggest an explanation of the change and a means of preventing it.

5.17. Diamonds sometimes contain flecks of graphite, but graphite is not known to contain flecks of diamond. Suggest a reason.

II

5.18. Calculate the empirical formulas (simplest relative number of atoms) for the sets of analytical data in (*a*) and (*b*).

(*a*) 1.35 g of carbon react exactly with 1.20 g of oxygen to form a gaseous oxide.

(*b*) A colorless liquid decomposes to give 0.540 g of water and 0.480 g of oxygen.

5.19. How many tons of sulfur are required to produce 172 tons of an aqueous solution of sulfuric acid containing 90% sulfuric acid, the rest being water? (About 50 tons.)

5.20. Helium is found in certain natural gas wells at a concentration of about 10%, the balance being mainly methane, CH_4, and ethane, C_2H_6. Design a method of producing 99% helium.

5.21. Would it be possible to obtain pure helium by burning the gas described in Problem 5.28 in a carefully regulated supply of air, then removing the combustion products of CO_2 and H_2O by passing the exhaust gases over CaO to give a mixture of solid $Ca(OH)_2$ and $CaCO_3$? CaO is very cheap compared to helium.

5.22. In the blast furnace, what effect makes it impossible to use gas with more than 25% oxygen?

5.23. The elements R, X, Y, and Z have outer electron shells respectively of 8,1; 18,2; 8,7; and 18,8. Their atomic numbers increase in the order Y, Z, X, R. Which elements are metallic and which nonmetallic? Which has the largest atomic radius? Which is the best oxidizing agent? Which element is most apt to be naturally radioactive? Give the formulas of any combinations of atoms they form among themselves, tell whether the combinations are ionically or covalently bonded, and estimate whether the substances would melt below 0°C, above 100°C but below 1000°C, or above 1000°C.

5.24. The edge of a unit cube of a metal is found by X-rays to be 3.160 Å long, with two atoms to each cube. The experimentally determined density is 19.35 g/cm^3. Calculate from these data the atomic weight (about 200) and the identity of the metal.

5.25. Assume that the earth is a sphere 8000 miles in diameter, $\frac{2}{3}$ covered by oceans of average depth 1 mile, with waters averaging 3% sodium chloride ions by weight. Salt is being added to the oceans at the rate of about $2 \cdot 10^{16}$ g per year through the rivers. If this rate has been constant, what is the approximate age of the oceans? Comment.

5.26. A metallic element is discovered, 0.462 g of which combines with oxygen to give 0.542 g of oxide. The heat capacity of the 0.462-g sample of the element is 0.020 cal/0.462 g °C. Calculate the atomic weight of the metal. (Slightly below 150.)

5.27. X-ray fluorescence analysis of a red crystalline material gave 31.3% Cu, 17.8% Zn, 16.9% Ge, and the balance was assumed to be sulfur. The experimental uncertainties are about ±1% in each percentage figure. Calculate an empirical formula for the substance. [R. Mitsche et al., *J. Cryst. Growth,* **1,** 52 (1967).]

III

5.28. 254 ml of a gaseous oxide of an unidentified element, symbol Q, form when 127 ml of the gaseous element reacts with 128 ml of gaseous oxygen known to be O_2. All pressures and temperatures are the same. From these data alone what can you deduce about the formula of the gaseous oxide? about the formula of the gaseous element? Write a chemical equation which would interpret the data and show how the equation accounts for the experimental observations. The 254 ml of gaseous oxide will react with an additional 127 ml of gaseous oxygen to give 253 ml of a second gaseous oxide. All temperatures and pressures are the same. Write a chemical equation which accounts for this second reaction.

5.29. 0.222 g of a purified rare earth fluoride known to have the formula XF_3 reacts with excess oxygen to form 0.189 g of the oxide X_2O_3. What is the atomic weight of X? (Slightly more than 150.) Which one of the rare earths is X?

5.30. A careless chemist analyzed a series of binary gaseous compounds of element X as to molecular weight and composition. Unfortunately, he recorded the data on separate pieces of paper and lost his key to their identity. The molecular weights were 20, 54, 68, and 71. The analyses (not necessarily in the same order) were 29.6% O, 19.6% N, 16.1% B, and 5.0% H; balance X in each instance. Show that he can calculate a likely atomic weight for X without his key to the data. Being a venturesome sort, he proceeded deliberately to lose track of the data on his next experiment with element Q. They were: molecular weights, 52, 58, 68, 138; percentages, 17.2%, 47.1%, 53.9%, and 82.5%. How did he get along with these data, knowing only that he had binary compounds of element Q with F, O, N, and H? (Both atomic weights can be found.)

5.31. If a well driller discovered a deep underground deposit of metallic cesium, estimated size 10^9 tons, would it be worthwhile trying to obtain the metal? Be specific as to possible uses. Design a method of obtaining the metal and delivering it in tank cars.

5.32. Design a concentric pipe arrangement for both the bottom and top of a Frasch sulfur well.

See page 1091 for a list of references and readings in the recent chemical literature related to the material in this chapter.

CHAPTER 6

Gases—Equations of State

The behavior of real systems can be described accurately only with actual experimental data, but equations and graphs often provide good approximations.

The gaseous state of matter, as we have indicated in our discussion of Avogadro's law, follows some especially simple patterns. It is commonly said that all gases increase in volume when their pressure decreases, when their temperature increases, or when their number of moles increases. Actually none of these statements, widely accepted though they may be, is literally correct. Each statement assumes that one is noting the volume change when only *one* other variable is being adjusted—in the order of pressure, temperature, and number of moles. Thus each statement, to be correct, must be modified.

1. All gases, if kept at the same temperature and the same number of moles, increase in volume when the applied external pressure decreases.
2. All gases, if kept at the same number of moles and the same total pressure, increase in volume when their temperature increases.
3. All gases, if kept at the same temperature and pressure, increase in volume when the number of moles increases.

In each of these three aspects, gases behave in a more regular fashion than liquids or crystals. This is true even though statements 1 and 3 apply with equal force to liquids and crystals, and statement 2 is true for most solids and liquids. However, the most impressive regularity is not that which follows from the three qualitative statements given, but from the quantitative relationships found among the variables—pressure, volume, temperature, and number of moles—when one is dealing with gaseous systems. Before we attempt to describe such systems, we need to investigate what we mean by a system and something of the conditions under which chemists usually deal with systems.

CHEMICAL SYSTEMS

Any region of space we care to investigate may be called a system. A vacuum system may contain no molecules at all. Most systems, however, do contain atoms and molecules and are bounded by surfaces which are usually, but not always, identifiable. Figure 6.1 illustrates three types of systems.

When the surfaces bounding the system of interest are impervious to all types of energy and all types of matter (mass), the system is said to be *isolated* (Figure 6.1, A). Isolated systems neither gain nor lose matter or energy. We say that mass-energy is conserved in the universe—meaning that mass-energy can neither be lost nor gained. Note that we may define the universe as isolated even though we know nothing of the bounding surfaces.

When the surfaces bounding a system are permeable to energy, but impermeable to matter, we say the system is *closed* (Figure 6.1, B). A closed system may gain or lose energy but cannot gain or lose matter. In chemistry this means that atoms and molecules cannot escape or enter but that light, heat, and other forms of energy may be both lost and gained. A reaction occurring in a sealed, heat-conducting steel bomb would be occurring in a closed system.

When the surfaces bounding a system are permeable to both energy and matter, we say the system is *open* (Figure 6.1, C). An open system may gain or lose both energy and atoms. A reaction occurring in an uncovered container in a laboratory illustrates an open system.

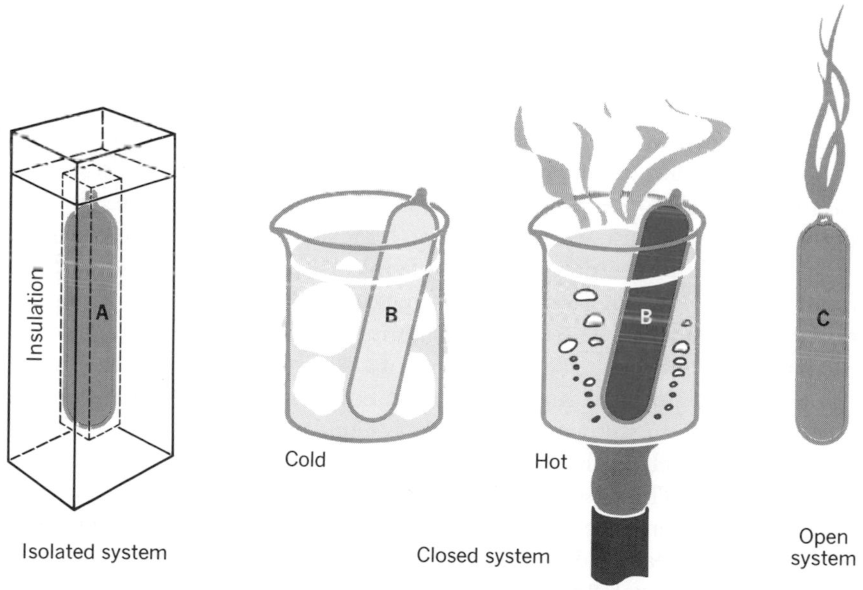

Figure 6.1 Possible classification of chemical systems. **(A)** Isolated—constant mass and constant energy. **(B)** Closed—constant mass, variable energy. **(C)** Open—variable mass and energy. In each case only the capsule and its contents are included in the "system." In **B**, for example, neither the beaker, nor the ice, nor the burner is part of the system.

We find it convenient to define *three* types of systems in order to emphasize *two* conservation laws—of atoms and of energy. Isolated systems conserve both, closed systems conserve one, open systems conserve neither. Charge is conserved in all cases.

Exercise 6.1

What kind of systems are hot-water bottles and thermos bottles? *Answer:* Hot-water bottles are designed to supply heat without their contents leaking—they are closed systems. Thermos bottles are designed to retain both their material contents and to keep their energy content constant—they approximate isolated system.

EQUILIBRIUM STATES

Equilibrium is often defined as a state experiencing no net change. Equilibrium is also defined as a condition which, if subjected to a differential change, will return to the original condition.

If no net changes are occurring at equilibrium, all gradients must be zero and all changes must be exactly balanced by simultaneous changes in the reverse direction. No net transfer or flow of atoms or energy is possible. Hence an equilibrium system is, to all intents and purposes, an isolated system. An equilibrium system must be bounded by surfaces through which there is no net flow of either energy or atoms. If net flow begins, the equilibrium state will be changed.

Equilibrium is not the same as steady state. A steady-state system does not change with time, but its constancy is maintained by net flow of some substances in and net flow of other substances out, exactly balancing. An adult human is roughly at steady state, but is not at equilibrium; food comes in, waste products leave, there is little net change in the human. A river or an industrial assembly line is roughly at steady state, but not at equilibrium. Gradients can, in fact must, exist in steady-state systems, but not in systems at equilibrium.

If an equilibrium state is one which, when differentially disturbed, will return to its original condition, there must be a function which is at a minimum or maximum in the equilibrium state. The search for such maximizing and minimizing functions to apply to the description of chemical equilibrium is a central task of thermodynamics. Two such very useful functions were introduced in Chapter 1—entropy and free energy. The entropy of an *isolated* system of constant volume is a maximum at equilibrium. The free energy of a *closed* system of constant temperature and constant pressure is a minimum at equilibrium. You should continually apply these criteria in studying changes in systems.

A great deal of chemistry concerns itself with describing and studying equilibrium states. The absence of transients (here variables changing with time) simplifies the mathematics. Furthermore, and fortunately, study of equilibrium states provides a great deal of insight into nonequilibrium or changing systems.

Let us investigate the general description of equilibrium systems. We shall do this by comparing the number of variables in the system to the number of mathematical conditions which must be satisfied at equilibrium.

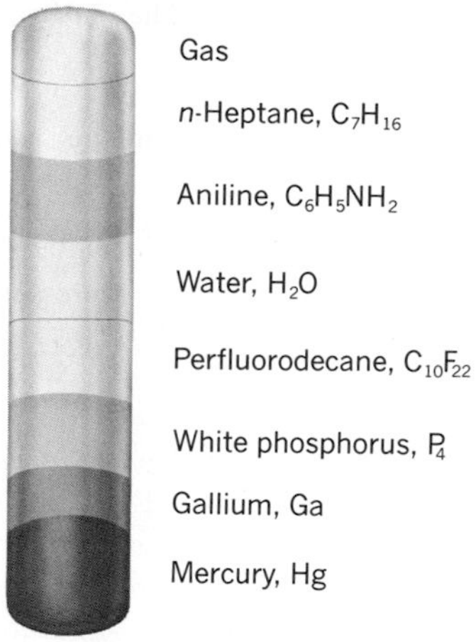

Figure 6.2 Seven stable liquid layers plus a gaseous layer, each saturated with respect to all the others. Vigorous shaking causes emulsions which take a long time to separate, but the eight phases will again form, given sufficient time.

An equilibrium system may consist of a number of phases.* The three most common phases are crystal, liquid, and gas. A sealed container may hold ice, water, and water vapor. Figure 6.2 shows a system made up of seven liquid layers and a gaseous layer—eight phases, all in equilibrium. Each phase at equilibrium is a region of uniform composition. The mole fraction of each type of molecule is constant throughout the phase. At equilibrium there is no net flow of energy or atoms into or out of any phase. How can these conditions be described mathematically?

ALGEBRAIC DESCRIPTION OF EQUILIBRIUM SYSTEMS

Consider first the number of independent variables. In each phase there will exist molecules of various kinds. We call these various kinds of molecules constituents or species, and the number of species we designate as S. Since every phase is in equilibrium with every other phase, molecules of each species will be present in each phase. The composition of any phase may be expressed in terms of the mole fraction, X; X_i represents the fraction of the total molecules which are of species i, or

$$\sum_i X_i = X_1 + X_2 + X_3 + \cdots + X_S = 1$$

Therefore, in each phase containing S species, there are $S - 1$ independent compositions or concentrations. The number of phases is P, and in P phases there will be a total of $P(S - 1)$ independent concentration terms.

We can also treat as independent variables the intensive properties of each phase in terms of the "fields" acting—temperature, pressure, electric and gravitational fields, and

* A phase is a body of matter of uniform properties throughout. All bodies with the same properties are part of the same phase, even though separated from one another in space. All chunks of ice are ice phase, all drops of water are liquid phase, and so on.

others. Let the number of these "field" terms be L. Then in P phases there will be $P \cdot L$ "field" variables.

Thus the total number of variables is $P(S-1) + PL = P(S-1+L)$.

But at equilibrium, since there can be no gradients, each field variable must have the same value in every phase. For example,

$$T_1 = T_2 = T_3 = T_4 = \cdots = T_P \quad \text{(temperature)} \tag{6.1}$$

$$P_1 = P_2 = P_3 = P_4 = \cdots = P_P \quad \text{(pressure)} \tag{6.2}$$

$$\mathcal{E}_1 = \mathcal{E}_2 = \mathcal{E}_3 = \mathcal{E}_4 = \cdots = \mathcal{E}_P \quad \text{(electric potential)} \tag{6.3}$$

$$g_1 = g_2 = g_3 = g_4 = \cdots = g_P \quad \text{(gravitational field)} \tag{6.4}$$

and so on for L fields. These give $L(P-1)$ restrictive equations.

The set of temperature equations above [Equation (6.1)] states the zeroth law of thermodynamics: If state 1 is in temperature equilibrium with state 2 and state 2 is in temperature equilibrium with state 3, then state 1 is also in temperature equilibrium with state 3. No exceptions are known to this observation, and it may be generalized from temperature to all other "field" properties. Measurements of temperature and pressure are so commonly used largely because (*a*) these variables are constant throughout any system at equilibrium, and (*b*) they are quite easy to measure with considerable precision and accuracy.

A special type of equilibrium exists to which Equations (6.1) to (6.4) do not apply. For example, a column of fluid, like air, can quickly come to equilibrium in a gravitational field. At equilibrium there are no net flows and the system will return to the same state if differentially disturbed. Yet the pressure is not constant. It is a function of height (see p. 185). Equilibria in which fields vary are said to be constrained equilibria. However, we shall seldom have to deal with constrained equilibria in this book.

Likewise, at equilibrium, the chemical reactivity of each species, as represented by its tendency to undergo reaction, must be the same in every phase. We shall call this the chemical potential of the species and identify it as μ. Thus for species 1 the chemical potential ${}_1\mu_P$ in each phase is the same.

$$\text{Species 1:} \quad {}_1\mu_1 = {}_1\mu_2 = {}_1\mu_3 = \cdots = {}_1\mu_P \tag{6.5}$$

$$\text{Species 2:} \quad {}_2\mu_1 = {}_2\mu_2 = {}_2\mu_3 = \cdots = {}_2\mu_P \tag{6.6}$$

$$\vdots \qquad \vdots$$

$$\text{Species S:} \quad {}_S\mu_1 = {}_S\mu_2 = {}_S\mu_3 = \cdots = {}_S\mu_P \tag{6.7}$$

This set gives $S(P-1)$ restricting equations.

In addition, it may be possible for some of the constituents to react with one another, and these reactions will also come to equilibrium if the whole system is at equilibrium. The resulting equilibria may be described by R linearly independent equilibrium constant expressions. The equilibrium constant expressions of the R possible independent reactions will give R restrictive equations.

$$\text{Total number of restrictions} = L(P-1) + S(P-1) + R = (L+S)(P-1) + R \tag{6.8}$$

$$\text{Total number of variables} = P(S-1+L) \tag{6.9}$$

The number of undetermined or "free" variables (also called "degrees of freedom," F) is the difference between the number of variables and the number of restrictions, or

$$F = [P(S-1+L)] - [(L+S)(P-1)+R]$$
$$= PS - P + LP - LP + L - SP + S - R$$

GENERAL PHASE RULE:

$$F = S - R - P + L \tag{6.10}$$

The general phase rule applies to all equilibrium systems. It states that the maximum number of degrees of freedom, or independent variables, F, that may be changed without destroying the equilibrium always equals the number of kinds of molecules (species) present, minus the number of independent chemical equilibria occurring, minus the number of phases present, plus the number of variable fields. If more than F variables are changed, one or more of the phases will disappear and/or one or more of the species and of the chemical equilibria will disappear in order that Equation (6.10) may still be satisfied. Since, in general, no reactions go to completion, and therefore no reactants are completely removed in a closed system, phases are what usually disappear.

Equation (6.10) may be considerably simplified for immediate use by applying it to typical chemical problems instead of to the more general situations considered in its derivation. For instance, the only two "field" properties of concern in most chemical problems are pressure and temperature. Keeping constant all other fields (electric, magnetic, gravitational, and so on), we have $L = 2$, or

$$F = S - R - P + 2 \tag{6.11}$$

It is also common to introduce the concept of chemical component. The number, C, of chemical components in a system is: $C = S - R$. That is, the number of components, C, may be less than the number of types of molecules, S, present at equilibrium, and their difference, $S - C$, equals the number of independent reactions, R, that occur at equilibrium.

We shall apply Equation (6.11) mainly to nonreacting systems where $R = 0$. In such systems the number of components, C, equals the number of kinds of molecules (species) present. A pure substance is a one-component system, a binary solution is a two-component system, and so forth.

THE PHASE RULE

A very common form of the mathematical relation describing equilibria is the

PHASE RULE:
$$F = C - P + 2 \tag{6.12}$$

Equation (6.12) applies very simply to systems if no reactions are occurring and if only temperature, pressure, and concentration can be varied. Then C equals the number of kinds of (nonreacting) molecules present and the 2 refers to the variables of temperature and pressure; P is the number of phases and F is the number of variables (temperature, pressure, and concentrations) that may be changed without destroying the equilibrium—that is, without changing the number of phases or the number of kinds of molecules present. If $F \geq 1$, the relative amounts of the phases and the relative numbers of the kinds of molecules present in each phase may, and usually will, change if temperature, pressure, or concentrations change; however, where the changes are small, no kinds of molecules or phases form or disappear. Where $F = 0$, any change in T, P, or concentration will lead to the formation or disappearance of at least one kind of molecule or phase.

We thus arrive at the conclusion that an equilibrium system may be completely described in terms of field properties such as temperature and pressure and in concentration terms such as chemical potentials. Indeed, one may profitably think of the chemical potential as a field term very similar to temperature and pressure. Temperature fields determine the tendency of heat to flow from one region to another; pressure fields determine the tendency of mass (actually momentum) to flow from one region to another; chemical potential determines the tendency of atoms to move from one combination to another.

Suppose we apply the equation $F = C - P + 2$ to a pure gas. With

$P = 1$ (only gas phase present), and $C = 1$ (gas is pure), we get $F = 2$. There are two and only two independent variables at equilibrium. The usual variables are concentration, n/V, temperature, T, and pressure, P. If we fix two of them arbitrarily, the third is automatically fixed also; $F = 0$.

In a mixture of gases, $P = 1$, with the number of components equal to C:

$$F = C - P + 2 = C - 1 + 2 = C + 1$$

If $C = 2$, all the properties become fixed if we fix any three of the four variables (temperature, pressure, two concentrations). The mathematical equations describing the relationships among these variables are called equations of state.

Exercise 6.2

In which of the following equilibrium systems can one vary the temperature at constant pressure without changing the number of phases: (*a*) a glass of ice and water, (*b*) a closed closet containing mothballs, (*c*) a balloon of helium gas? *Answer:* (*a*) $F = 1 - 2 + 2 = 1$, so if P is fixed, so is T. (*b*) $F = 1 - 2 + 2$, so if P is fixed, so is T. (*c*) $F = 1 - 1 + 2 = 2$, so T can be varied at constant P.

EQUATION OF STATE FOR IDEAL GASES

All crystals and liquids at sufficiently high temperatures and low pressures turn to gases. And gases at temperatures well above the boiling points of their liquids and/or pressures less than one atmosphere (760 torr)* usually obey or follow the same equation of state with an error of less than 5%. When gases follow this equation of state within the experimental uncertainty, they are said to be perfect or ideal gases. The equation relating the concentration (n/V), absolute temperature (T), and absolute pressure (P) of an ideal gas is

$$\left(\frac{n}{V}\right)\frac{T}{P} = \frac{1}{R} = \text{a constant}$$

This is more commonly written as the

IDEAL GAS EQUATION: $$PV = nRT \qquad (6.13)$$

where R is the gas constant, which is the same for all ideal gases.

When any two of the variables in Equation (6.13) are held constant, only one independent variable is left. Any variation in it causes a calculable change in the fourth variable, as shown in Figure 6.3.

Equation (6.13), like all mathematical equations, must satisfy certain mathematical conditions. If one side contains an extensive property (for example, a property such as V, which depends on the amount of matter), so must the other side, here n. The dimensions of the two sides must also be the same. Here PV has the dimensions of

$$\frac{\text{force}}{\text{area}}\,\text{volume} = \frac{MLT^{-2}}{L^2}\,L^3 = ML^2T^{-2} = \text{energy}$$

* 1 torr = pressure due to a column of mercury 1 mm tall when the temperature of the mercury is 0°C and the value of the acceleration due to gravity is $g = 980.665$ cm sec^{-2}. 1 standard atm = 760 torr.

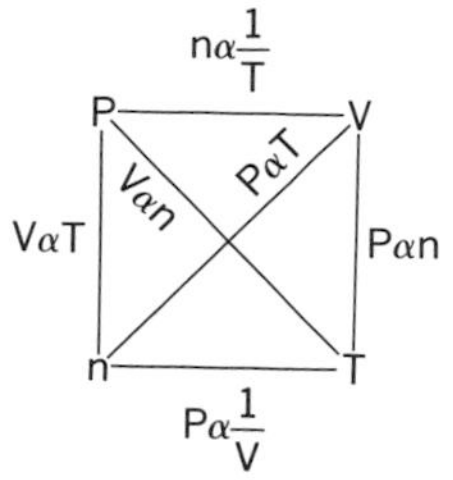

Figure 6.3 Binary relationships in PV = nRT. When any two of the variables represented at the corners of the square are held constant, the remaining two variables are related as shown along the connecting line.

The dimensions of nRT must be those of energy. The units of PV are usually atmospheres · liters = liter atmospheres, and so the units of nRT must also be liter atmospheres. These two conditions can only be satisfied if R has the dimensions of energy · mole^{-1} · degrees Kelvin^{-1} and the units of liter · atmospheres · mole^{-1} · degrees Kelvin^{-1}. When R is expressed in these units, it has the value of 0.082053 liter atm mole^{-1} °K^{-1}.

Gases that follow the equation of state, which is known as the

IDEAL GAS EQUATION: $$PV = 0.082053\ nT$$

are said to behave as ideal gases. Practically speaking, any gas that follows this equation within a deviation of ±1% is usually considered as ideal. Under these conditions, most of the common gases at laboratory conditions behave "ideally," with $PV = 0.082\ nT$. No gases are known which always behave ideally. That is, no gases follow this equation at all concentrations, temperatures, and pressures.

Exercise 6.3

Calculate the molar volume of air at 27°C and 730 torr pressure. *Answer:* $PV = nRT$, $\overline{V} = V/n = RT/P$. $\overline{V} = 0.0821\ l$ atm °K^{-1} · (273 + 27°K)/(730/760) atm = 25.6 l, assuming air acts ideally under these conditions. (It does.)

DALTON'S LAW OF PARTIAL PRESSURES

Most pure gases closely follow the ideal gas equation of state at low pressures and high temperatures (including usual laboratory conditions); so also do most gases in gaseous solutions. This is summarized in a most useful relationship known as

DALTON'S LAW: $$P_{tot} = p_a + p_b + \cdots + p_i \quad \text{and} \quad p_i = X_i P_{tot}$$

where the p's indicate the partial pressures, $p_i = n_i RT/V$, and the X's represent the mole fractions of each of the gaseous species present.

REAL GASES

Table 6.1 gives some values of PV/nT for common gases at 1 atm pressure and 273.16°K (0°C). The table also gives the molar volume, $\overline{V} = V/n$, of the gases under the same conditions. The maximum deviation from the ideal gas value is ±2% at 0°C and 1 atm pressure.

Table 6.1 Molar volume, $\overline{V}$, and gas "constant," R, of some gases. (In liters at 0°C and 1 standard atmospheric pressure. The molar volume of an ideal gas is 22.4136 liters under these conditions. Ideal $R = 0.082053$ liter atm mole^{-1} °K^{-1}.)

Gas	Formula	Molar volume, $\overline{V}$	$R = PV/nT = P\overline{V}/T$	
Hydrogen	H_2	22.428	0.082109	"Ideal" to ± 1% when P ≤ 1 atm, T ≥ 273°K. (Hydrogen through Acetylene)
Helium	He	22.426	.082101	
Neon	Ne	22.425	.082098	
Nitrogen	N_2	22.404	.082021	
Carbon monoxide	CO	22.403	.082017	
Oxygen	O_2	22.394	.081984	
Argon	Ar	22.393	.081981	
Nitric oxide	NO	22.389	.081966	
Methane	CH_4	22.360	.081860	
Carbon dioxide	CO_2	22.256	.081845	
Hydrogen chloride	HCl	22.249	.081453	
Ethylene	C_2H_4	22.241	.081424	
Acetylene	C_2H_2	22.19	.08124	
Ammonia	NH_3	22.094	.08087	
Chlorine	Cl_2	22.063	.08076	

Figure 6.4 shows for a few gases the quantity PV/nRT, called the compressibility factor (z), as a function of P and T. The behavior shown is typical of every real gas.

Exercise 6.4

Which has the higher pressure at 0°C, a mole of O_2 or a mole of CO_2 in a container of the same volume? *Answer:* Under all conditions covered in Figure 6.4, the compressibility factor, $z = PV/nRT$, is less for CO_2 than for O_2 at approximately equal pressures. Thus if $\overline{V}$ and T are the same, P for CO_2 will be less than P for O_2.

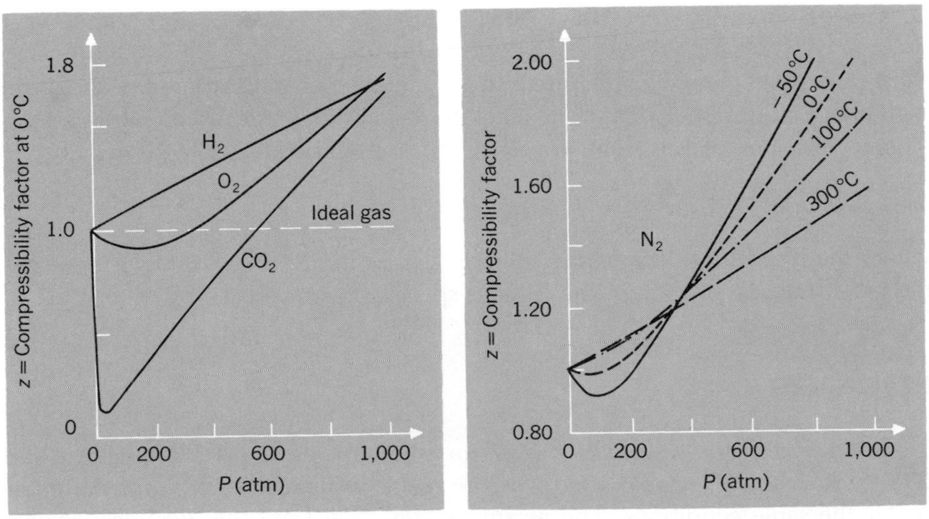

Figure 6.4 Compressibility factor, $z = PV/nRT$, as a function of P and T for a few gases.

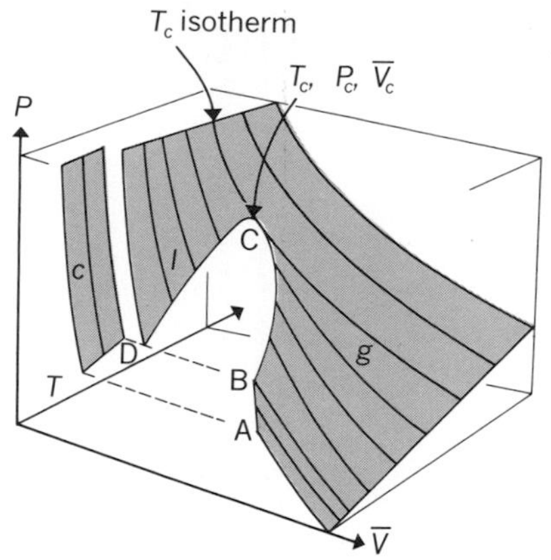

Figure 6.5 P, $\overline{V}$, T surface for a pure substance, CO_2. There are two three-dimensional surfaces in the diagram. One (labeled c) at low values of $\overline{V}$, low T, and extending to high values of P, represents the values of P, $\overline{V}$, and T at which crystals are stable. The other, at higher values of T and $\overline{V}$, but extending over most of the pressure range, represents the locus of all values of P, $\overline{V}$, and T where liquid or gaseous (that is, fluid) material is at equilibrium.

For each gas there is a temperature, called the Boyle temperature (T_B), at which the gas behaves ideally over a range of small pressures; that is, $PV/nRT_B = 1$ when P is small. As the pressure increases at the Boyle temperature, the compressibility factor increases. At these higher pressures the molar volume is always larger than that of an ideal gas at the same P and T.

At temperatures above the Boyle temperature, the molar volume is always greater than that of an ideal gas at the same conditions of P and T. This is true for all gases.

At temperatures below the Boyle temperature, the PV/nRT function goes through a minimum as a function of P for all gases. At low pressures the molar volume of the gas is less than that of an ideal gas, but, eventually, at high pressures the molar volume exceeds what an ideal gas would have at the same conditions of P and T.

These curves are so similar for all gases that one is tempted to look for a small number of variables and constants that will describe all gases. No such set has been found, but considerable simplification is found in terms of the theory of corresponding states which we shall now develop.

EQUILIBRIUM PHASE DIAGRAMS

Figures 6.5 and 6.6 show the relationship between T, P, $\overline{V}$, and the three phases—crystal, liquid, and gas—for a typical pure substance. Figure 6.7 contains only two completely bounded or separated regions—one crystal (c) and the other fluid (l and g). The crystal region contains all values of T, P, and $\overline{V}$ for which the crystal is stable. The fluid region contains all values of T, P, and $\overline{V}$ in which either gas or

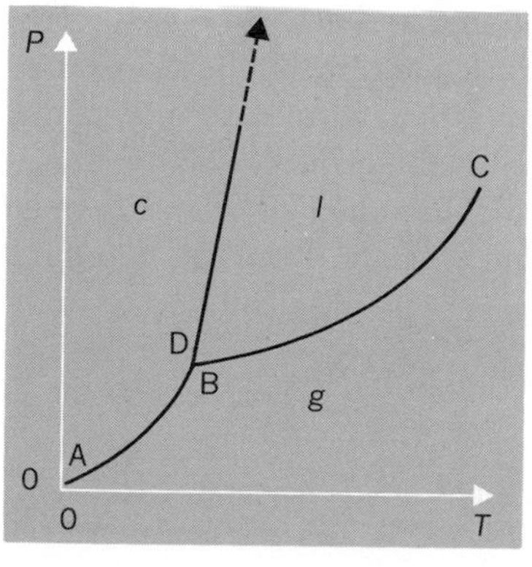

Figure 6.6 Projection of Figure 6.5 along the $\overline{V}$-axis onto the T-P plane. Points A, B, C, D and phases c, l, and g are identified here just as in Figure 6.5.

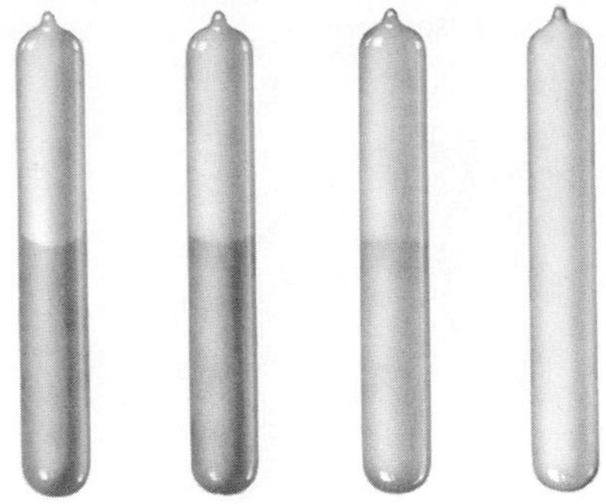

Figure 6.7 Appearance of a sealed tube containing carbon dioxide as its temperature is increased from about 220°K to $T_C = 304$°K (31°C). The meniscus slowly becomes less curved. As the system approaches T_C the meniscus becomes very faint. At T_C the meniscus disappears completely, and only one phase is present at temperatures above T_C.

liquid are stable. Point D or B (they now coincide) represents a unique situation in which g, *l*, and *c* have the same *T* and *P* and thus are all in equilibrium. There are three phases present. Since $F = C - P + 2$ for a one-component system, under these conditions we have $F = 1 - 3 + 2 = 0$. Thus point D (or B) is completely fixed if *c*, *l*, and g are merely mixed and allowed to equilibrate in a one-component system. The corresponding temperature, called the triple-point temperature, is very stable. The triple-point temperature cannot vary so long as all three phases are present.

The loop line, BCD, in Figure 6.5 has projected as a single curve in Figure 6.7, since BC and CD now lie on top of one another. Only along this line on the *T-P* diagram can one observe gas and liquid in equilibrium. And only if the system crosses this line does a phase boundary appear and an observable phase change occur between the gas and the liquid. We shall discuss this in considerable detail later, but note again here that gases and liquids are not fundamentally different and are only distinguishable when the *T-P* values happen to lie along BCD. Figure 6.7 shows the changes in a carbon dioxide system as it changes along the BCD loop from near B and D to C.

CRITICAL CONDITIONS

Point C in Figure 6.6 is known as the critical point. It is the high *T* and *P* terminal point of the line on the *T-P* projection along which liquid and gas can coexist. The critical point coordinates are the highest temperature, T_c, and the highest pressure, P_c, at which a liquid-gas interface can exist; T_c is the critical temperature, P_c is the critical pressure. The volume, $\overline{V}_c$, at the critical point is the critical molar volume.

All known gases have a critical point. At higher values of *T* and *P*, only one fluid phase can exist. Below it, along a single line of *T* and *P* values, two fluid phases can coexist.

CORRESPONDING STATES

We have already noted that gases approach ideal behavior more and more closely as the temperature rises and the pressure falls, and that the function PV/nRT varies in a similar manner

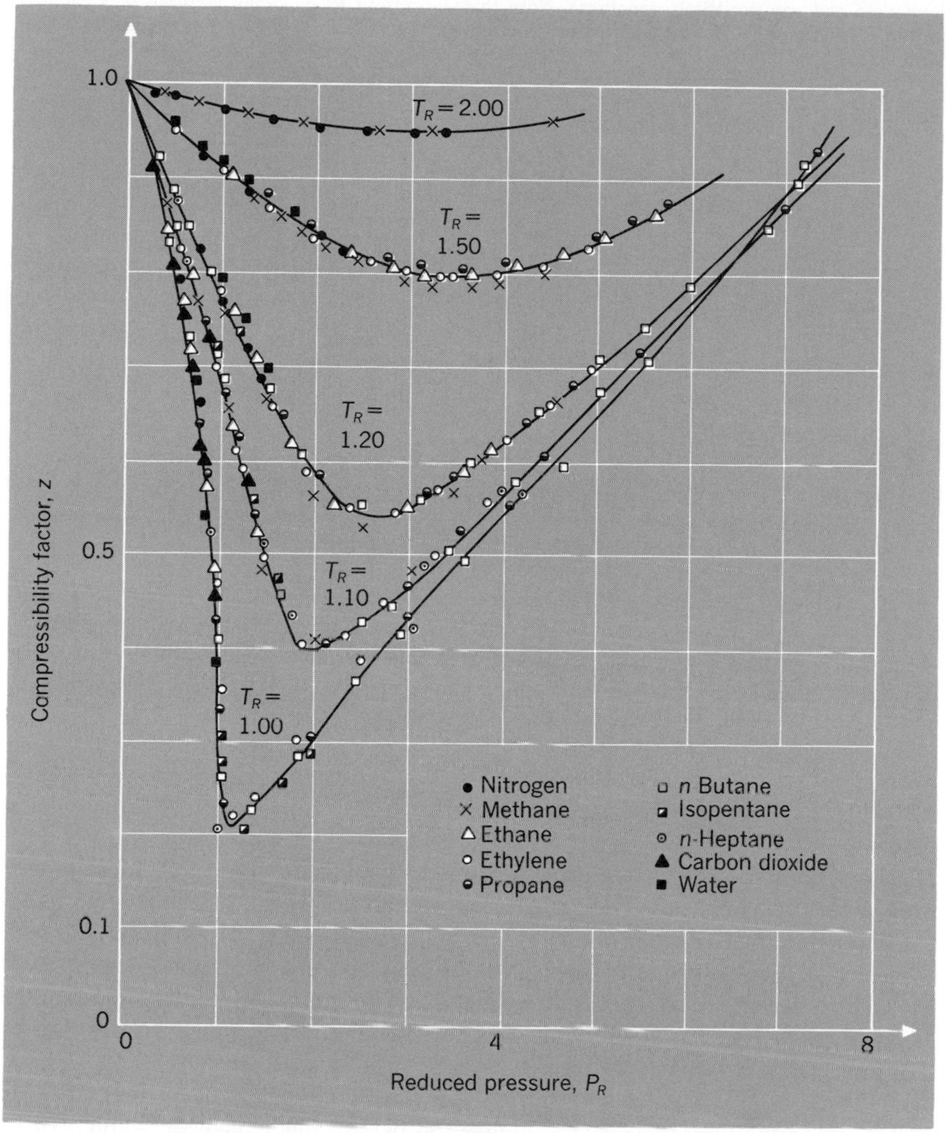

Figure 6.8 Compressibility factor as a function of reduced variables for some common gases. Note the relative independence of z with respect to the formula of the gas. [Gouq-Jen Su, *Ind. Eng. Chem.*, **38**, 803 (1946). © 1946 by the American Chemical Society.]

for most gases (see Figure 6.4). One of the most successful efforts to further simplify the description of gaseous behavior expresses all pressures relative to the critical pressure, all temperatures relative to the critical temperature, and all volumes relative to the critical volume. These relative values are known as reduced values, P_r, T_r, and $\overline{V}_r$:

$$P_r = \frac{P}{P_c}, \; T_r = \frac{T}{T_c}, \; \overline{V}_r = \frac{\overline{V}}{\overline{V}_c}$$

Figure 6.8 shows for some common gases the compressibility factor, $z = PV/nRT$, plotted as a function of the reduced temperature and pressure. The degree of regularity is highly satisfying. Substances with the same reduced values are said to be in corresponding states, and tend to exhibit similar properties.

Table 6.2 Critical point data and van der Waals constants. Note that T_c, a, and P_c generally increase in a roughly parallel pattern. $\overline{V}_c$ and b show less variation, and generally parallel one another (see Equations (6.14) and (6.15)). Note also the remarkable constancy of $P_c\overline{V}_c/T_c$ over a long range in T_c.

Formula	T_c (°K)	P_c (atm)	$\overline{V}_c$ (cc/mole)	a(l^2 atm/mole^2)	b(cc/mole)	$\overline{V}_c/b$	$P_c\overline{V}_c/T_c$ (l atm/mole °K)
He	5.23	2.26	57.6	0.0341	23.6	2.44	0.0249
H_2	33.3	12.8	65.0	0.245	26.7	2.44	0.0250
N_2	126.1	33.5	90.0	1.39	39.4	2.28	0.0249
CO	133.0	34.53	90.0	1.49	39.9	2.33	0.0232
Ar	150.8	48.0	75.5	1.35	32.2	2.34	0.0241
O_2	154.4	49.7	74.4	1.36	31.8	2.34	0.0240
C_2H_4	282.9	50.9	127.5	4.47	57.1	2.23	0.0229
CO_2	304.2	73.0	95.7	3.59	42.7	2.23	0.0230
NH_3	405.6	112.0	72.4	4.17	37.0	1.95	0.0200
H_2O	647.2	218.5	56.0	5.46	30.5	1.84	0.0190
Hg	1823.0	200.0	45.0	8.09	17.0	2.64	0.000492

Table 6.2 gives critical data for some compounds; data for hundreds more are available in the standard compendia and handbooks. When working at pressures and temperatures at which the ideal gas laws will not apply and where one does not have actual P, $\overline{V}$, T data for gases, application of the principle of corresponding states and use of Figure 6.8 give results within about 5% of the experimental values.

ABSOLUTE TEMPERATURE

No gas is ideal in every state, but all gases become more and more ideal as the pressure approaches zero. This means that we can define the behavior of an ideal gas in terms of the behavior of all gases at low pressures. Thus a gas becomes ideal when its behavior is the same as a group of other gases at the same low pressure. Most gases become ideal (that is, like other gases within experimental uncertainty) at pressures of 100 mm or so. Others become ideal only at lower pressures. Gases that have large intermolecular forces become ideal only at very low pressures indeed. The pressure at which any gas becomes ideal is a function of the temperature —the higher the temperature, the higher the pressure at which ideal behavior is found.

We are in danger here of engaging in circular reasoning. We earlier defined an ideal gas as one having the equation of state $P\overline{V} = RT$. The P, $\overline{V}$, and R were defined, but T was merely identified as the temperature. Yet we now observe that ideality is a function of T. How do we get out of this circle? We do so by relying on the preceding paragraph and the zeroth law of thermodynamics.

According to the zeroth law of thermodynamics, any two gases in thermal equilibrium with one another will have the *same* temperature, even though we may not be able to measure T. According to the first paragraph in this section, all gases become ideal at low pressures. Thus we define ideal gases as those which have the same $P\overline{V}$ products at each temperature over a range of temperatures (defined by the zeroth law only). We can then use the full ideal gas equation, $P\overline{V} =$

RT, to define T rather than to define ideal gases. This is the present basis of all temperature scales; it is called the ideal gas temperature scale.

As the temperature of an ideal gas is lowered, the $P\overline{V}$ product decreases linearly according to our definition $P\overline{V} = RT$. Experimental observation on many gases at low pressures shows that the $P\overline{V}$ product extrapolates to zero at a temperature slightly lower than $-273°C$. Other experiments also indicate that there is a temperature of about $-273°C$ which is unique. One of its unique features is that it seems to be the lower limit of the temperature scale—there is no lower temperature. Just as the absence of volume is called zero absolute volume, and the absence of pressure zero absolute pressure, so we call this extremity of the temperature scale—absence of temperature—zero absolute temperature. To avoid confusion with 0°C (an arbitrary zero related to the properties of water), we call this lower limit of all temperature scales absolute zero, meaning there is no lower temperature than 0° absolute.

Unfortunately absolute zero is not very useful in defining T, since absolute zero has never been attained and our best theories say it never will be. Thus, following a suggestion by W. F. Giauque, the absolute temperature scale is not defined in terms of absolute zero. Instead, a readily available, highly reproducible temperature is chosen—that represented by point B in Figure 6.6 in the phase diagram for water. (see Figure 34.17).

Water is a one-component system. At point B three phases (gas, liquid, and crystal) coexist; thus $F = C - P + 2 = 1 - 3 + 2 = 0$, and both T and P are fixed. Therefore any system containing only water will automatically come to this fixed temperature if liquid, gas, and crystal are all present. This temperature is called the triple-point temperature, since three phases are present. The triple-point temperature of water, T_t, is defined as 273.16°K (degrees Kelvin). (This fractional value retains the equality $1°K = 1°C$.) It is reproducible to at least one millionth of a degree. Figure 6.9 shows a triple-point bath of the water system.

By measuring the $P\overline{V}$ product in many gases at 273.16°K and applying the

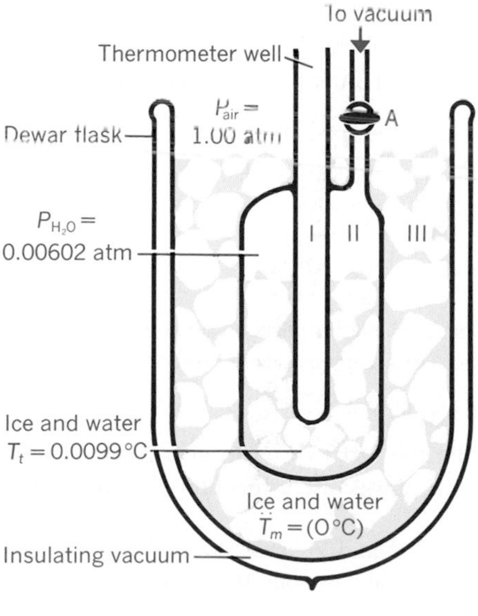

Figure 6.9 Triple-point bath for water system. Carefully distilled liquid water is placed in chamber II and the system evacuated. The water boils at low pressure and all dissolved gases are swept out leaving pure water. Stopcock A is closed and most of the water in II frozen slowly to ice. II is then immersed in an ice-water slush held in Dewar flask III. II is again evacuated to remove any last traces of foreign gases and stopcock A closed. A thermometric device to be calibrated is immersed in the central well I. When the entire system comes to equilibrium (atmospheric pressure being 1 atm and the ice bath in III being saturated with air), the following conditions hold: $T_{II} = T_t = 273.1600°K$ (by definition) $=$ 0.0099°C, $P_{II} = 0.00602$ atm of pressure due to gaseous water, $T_{III} = T_m = 0°C$ by definition, $P_{III} = 1$ atm of pressure due to normal atmosphere. Thus $T_{III} = 273.15°K = 0°C$.

ideal gas equation, $P\overline{V} = RT$, we obtain the value of $R = 0.082053$. Once R is evaluated, the measurement of the $P\overline{V}$ product for any equilibrium ideal gas immediately gives the corresponding value of T, the ideal gas temperature. From the legend to Figure 6.11 we see that Kelvin temperatures may be converted to °C by subtracting 273.15° from the Kelvin value. Conversely, °C may be converted to °K by adding 273.15° to the Centigrade, or Celsius, value.

EQUATIONS OF STATE FOR REAL GASES

Figure 6.8 and the principle of corresponding states can give quite good values of P, $\overline{V}$, and T over a wide range of conditions when the critical constants are known, but a mathematical equation would be more succinct and perhaps simpler to use. Various such equations have been suggested.

Van der Waals reasoned that gas volumes could be less than ideal because of attractive forces between the molecules, and that gas volumes could be larger than ideal because two molecules could not completely overlap. He surmised that the attractive force, a, would vary with $(n/V)^2$, since the force would be related both to the number of molecules near a given one (proportional to n/V) and inversely to their distance apart (also proportional to n/V). The total effective pressure then becomes $(P + n^2a/V^2)$. He also surmised that the excluded volume would vary with the number of moles present. He called the total excluded volume nb, giving a total effective free volume of $(V - nb)$. He thus arrived at the

VAN DER WAALS EQUATION: $$\left(P + \frac{a}{\overline{V}^2}\right)(\overline{V} - b) = RT$$

or

$$\left(P + \frac{n^2}{V^2}a\right)(V - nb) = nRT \tag{6.14}$$

Exercise 6.5

Is van der Waals equation more useful at calculating V, knowing P and T; or P, knowing V and T? *Answer:* The equation is third order in V, but first order in P and T; thus it is much simpler to use if V is known.

Berthelot found that allowing the attractive force to vary with T often improved the agreement, and he suggested the equation

$$\left(P + \frac{n^2}{V^2}\frac{A}{T}\right)(V - nB) = nRT$$

More general equations, containing terms sufficient to describe gaseous behavior to any desired accuracy, are also used. Typical is the virial equation suggested by Holborn:

$$P\overline{V} = RT + AP + BP^2 + CP^3 + \cdots$$

The higher terms are needed at high pressures, but the first two terms give good values at lower pressures. Each of the virial coefficients—A, B, C—is also a function of T, their value varying from gas to gas.

Each of these equations purports to relate P, T, and $\overline{V}$ (or V) for real gases. Figure 6.10 shows a projection of the P, T, $\overline{V}$ surface for a typical gas along the T-axis onto the P-$\overline{V}$

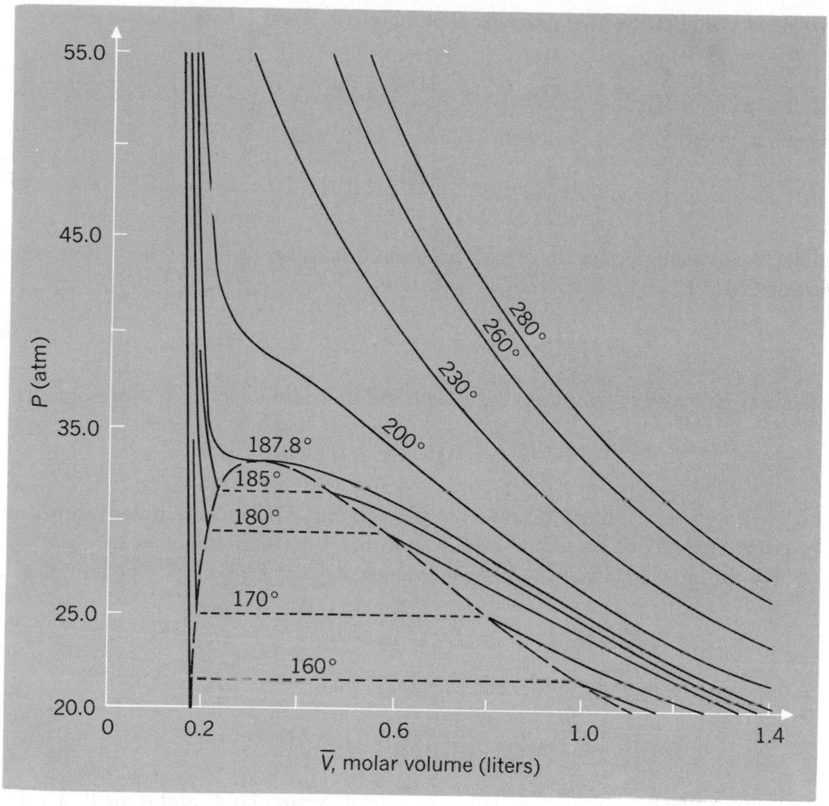

Figure 6.10 Projection of Figure 6.7 along the T-axis onto the P-$\overline{V}$ plane. Various isotherms are indicated, including the critical isotherm, $T_c = 187.8°C$. The substance is isopentane, $(CH_3)_2CHCH_2CH_3$.

plane. Lines of constant temperature (experimental isothermals) are drawn. Any exact equation of state should describe these isothermals. Let us check this idea against the van der Waals equation and correlate it with the principle of corresponding states:

$$\left(P + \frac{n^2}{V^2}a\right)(V - nb) = nRT$$

$$P = \frac{nRT}{V - nb} - \frac{n^2}{V^2}a$$

Consider 1 mole of gas, for $n = 1$:

$$P = \frac{RT}{\overline{V} - b} - \frac{a}{\overline{V}^2}$$

For the T_c isothermal,

$$P = \frac{RT_c}{\overline{V} - b} - \frac{a}{\overline{V}^2}$$

But the T_c isothermal is flat and has a point of inflection in the P-$\overline{V}$ plane at $(P_c, \overline{V}_c)$. Therefore, at (P_c, $\overline{V}_c$, for this isothermal):

$$\frac{dP}{d\overline{V}} = 0 = \frac{-RT_c}{(\overline{V}_c - b)^2} + \frac{2a}{\overline{V}_c^3}$$

the zero slope condition for the critical isothermal at P_c. We also have

$$\frac{d^2P}{d\overline{V}^2} = 0 = \frac{2RT_c}{(\overline{V}_c - b)^3} - \frac{6a}{\overline{V}_c^4}$$

the inflection condition for the critical isothermal at P_c, and

$$P_c = \frac{RT_c}{\overline{V}_c - b} - \frac{a}{\overline{V}_c^2}$$

the van der Waals condition for the critical isothermal at P_c. We can solve these three equations simultaneously for P_c, T_c, and $\overline{V}_c$, to get

$$P_c = \frac{a}{27b^2}, \qquad \overline{V}_c = 3b, \qquad T_c = \frac{8a}{27bR} \tag{6.15}$$

Assuming that R is really a constant and $R = 0.082$ liter atm mole^{-1} °K^{-1}, we obtain

$$\frac{P_c\overline{V}_c}{T_c} = \frac{3R}{8} = 0.031 \text{ liter atm mole}^{-1}\ °\text{K}^{-1}$$

The last two columns of Table 6.2 show that the van der Waals equation does approximately describe critical conditions for many systems, but that it is certainly not exact.

We can now calculate the reduced values, $P_r = P/P_c$, $\overline{V}_r = \overline{V}/\overline{V}_c$, and $T_r = T/T_c$:

$$P_r = \frac{27b^2}{a}P, \qquad \overline{V}_r = \frac{\overline{V}}{3b}, \qquad T_r = \frac{27Rb}{8a}T \tag{6.16}$$

The van der Waals equation in reduced variables is then

$$\left(P_r + \frac{3}{\overline{V}_r^2}\right)(\overline{V}_r - \tfrac{1}{3}) = \tfrac{8}{3}T_r \tag{6.17}$$

Thus the van der Waals equation may either be used in terms of a, b, and R, or P_r, $\overline{V}_r$, T_r. Similarly, a and b can be calculated from experimental values of the critical constants (the usual method), or critical constants can be estimated from experimentally derived values of a and b.

KINETIC THEORY OF IDEAL GASES

Consider now the interpretation of the bulk properties of gases in terms of molecular behavior. What molecular behavior leads to such regularity as is indicated by the simple relation $PV = nRT$? Once we have a molecular model that interprets ideal behavior, we can test it be seeing if it also can interpret the experimentally observed behavior of real gases.

We can, in fact, get some clues from looking at the van der Waals equation. It closely resembles the ideal gas equation except for an added term involving intermolecular attractive forces, plus a second term involving repulsions due to molecular volumes. No such terms are present in the ideal gas equation. Let us then assume as our ideal model a set of molecules which have mass but no size ($b = 0$), and which collide but have no intermolecular attractive or repulsive forces ($a = 0$). Thus the collisions are all elastic; no translational kinetic energy, $\frac{1}{2}mv^2$, is gained or lost.

If the molecules do collide, they must have a velocity. Let the average velocity be v. Then the velocity components along the three coordinate axes are $\vec{v}_x$, $\vec{v}_y$, and $\vec{v}_z$.

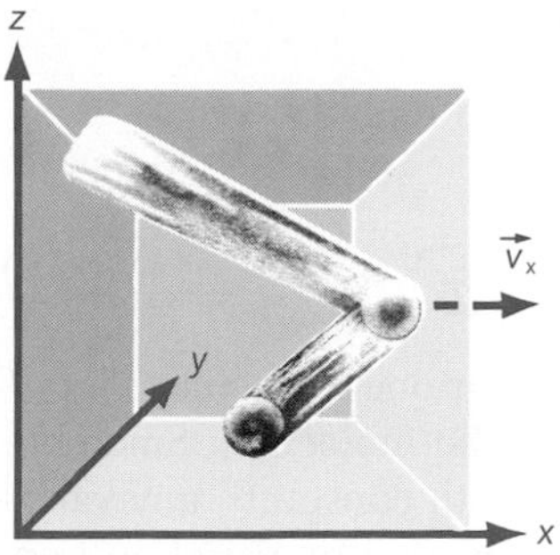

Figure 6.11 Particle in a cubical box showing the x vector of the momentum. General proofs relating the kinetic energy of the particle to pressure are available which make no assumptions about the shape of the container.

Consider motion along the x coordinate. Pressure on the wall perpendicular to the x coordinate will arise from momentum changes in the molecules striking the wall with momentum vectors of $m\vec{v}_x$ (see Figure 6.11). Assuming that each collision is elastic, the molecule will leave with the x coordinate of the momentum unchanged in magnitude but reversed in direction; thus the net change in momentum per average molecular collision is $2m\vec{v}_x$. There are N molecules in the box of volume V and half of these have a $\vec{v}_x$ vector directed toward each yz wall. The number hitting each wall per second is given by the product of the concentration of molecules moving toward that wall, $(N/2)/V$, and their velocity $\vec{v}_x$, or $N\vec{v}_x/2V$.

Thus the pressure on the wall is $P = 2m\vec{v}_x(N\vec{v}_x/2V) = Nm\vec{v}_x^{\,2}/V$. But the actual velocity vector is related to the x, y, and z vectors by the equation $\vec{v}^{\,2} = \vec{v}_x^{\,2} + \vec{v}_y^{\,2} + \vec{v}_z^{\,2} = 3\vec{v}_x^{\,2}$, since the three velocity vectors will on the average be identical. Thus $\vec{v}_x^{\,2} = \vec{v}^{\,2}/3$, which, upon dropping the vector sign, gives

$$P = \frac{Nmv^2}{3V},$$

But

$$\frac{N}{V} = \frac{N_0}{\overline{V}}$$

and therefore

$$P\overline{V} = \frac{N_0 mv^2}{3} = \frac{2N_0}{3}\,\frac{mv^2}{2} = \frac{2N_0}{3}\epsilon_{\text{trans}} = \tfrac{2}{3}N_0\epsilon_{\text{trans}} = \tfrac{2}{3}\overline{E}_{\text{trans}}$$

This model of an ideal gas gives the

KINETIC PRESSURE EQUATION $$P = \frac{1}{3}\,\frac{N_0 mv^2}{\overline{V}} = \frac{2}{3}\,\frac{\overline{E}_{\text{trans}}}{\overline{V}} \tag{6.18}$$

where ϵ_{trans} = average translational kinetic energy of each molecule, and $E_{\text{trans}} = \frac{1}{2}Nmv^2$ = total kinetic or translational energy of all the molecules. Thus the pressure of an ideal gas is two-thirds of its translational energy density.

We know experimentally that $P\overline{V} = RT$ for an ideal gas. Since our theoretical treatment in terms of gas collisions gives $P\overline{V} = 2\overline{E}_{\text{trans}}/3$, then

$$RT = \frac{2\bar{E}_{\text{trans}}}{3} = \frac{2N_0(\frac{1}{2}mv^2)}{3}$$

or the

KINETIC TEMPERATURE EQUATION:

$$T = \frac{mv^2}{3k} = \frac{2}{3}\frac{\bar{E}_{\text{trans}}}{R} \qquad (6.19)$$

where $k = R/N_0$ = Boltzmann constant or gas constant for one molecule. Thus T is linearly related to the average translational energy of the molecules. Since the molecular mass for any one gas is fixed and 3 and R are both constants, any variation in T, the Kelvin temperature, must always be accompanied by variation in v, the average molecular velocity. The ratio T/v^2 must be constant at all values of T or v for any one gas. Furthermore, the product mv^2 must be the same for all gases at the same temperature. Experiments bear out all these predictions for ideal gases. For example, (1) in a gas the velocity of sound (carried by molecular collisions) is inversely proportional to the square root of the molecular mass of the gas at constant temperature; with any particular gas the velocity of sound is proportional to the square root of the Kelvin temperature of the gas; (2) the rate of effusion of gaseous molecules through a small orifice is directly proportional to the square root of the Kelvin temperature for any one gas and varies inversely as the square root of the molecular mass from gas to gas.

Thus the average velocity of gaseous molecules increases with the Kelvin temperature and decreases with increase in molecular mass. The mean free path (the average distance between molecular collisions) is given by

$$l = \frac{V}{(2^{1/2}\pi N d^2)}$$

where d is the molecular diameter. Table 6.3 gives some typical values of molecular constants for gases. The collision frequency equals the average number of collisions any one molecule experiences per second.

Table 6.3 Molecular constants for gases.

Gas	Molecular diameter, d (Å)	Average Velocity, v (cm/sec) 0°C	20°C	Collision frequency, z (sec^{-1}) (20°C, 750 mm)	Mean free path, l (cm) (20°C, 750 mm)
Air	—	$4.47 \cdot 10^4$	$4.63 \cdot 10^4$	—	—
Argon	2.9	$3.81 \cdot 10^4$	$3.95 \cdot 10^4$	$4 \cdot 10^9$	$9.88 \cdot 10^{-6}$
Carbon dioxide	3.3	$3.62 \cdot 10^4$	$3.76 \cdot 10^4$	$6.1 \cdot 10^9$	$6.15 \cdot 10^{-6}$
Hydrogen	2.4	$16.96 \cdot 10^4$	$17.55 \cdot 10^4$	$10.0 \cdot 10^9$	$17.44 \cdot 10^{-6}$
Neon	2.6	$5.38 \cdot 10^4$	$5.57 \cdot 10^4$	—	—
Nitrogen	2.8	$4.54 \cdot 10^4$	$4.71 \cdot 10^4$	$5.07 \cdot 10^9$	$9.29 \cdot 10^{-6}$
Oxygen	2.9	$4.25 \cdot 10^4$	$4.44 \cdot 10^4$	$4.43 \cdot 10^9$	$9.93 \cdot 10^{-6}$
Water	—	$5.66 \cdot 10^4$	$5.87 \cdot 10^4$	—	—
Xenon	3.5	$2.10 \cdot 10^4$	$2.18 \cdot 10^4$	—	—
Krypton	3.1	$2.63 \cdot 10^4$	$2.72 \cdot 10^4$	—	—

Exercise 6.6

Calculate the relative average velocities of hydrogen molecules and UF_6 molecules at $T = 100°C$.

Answer:

$$T = \left(\frac{mv^2}{3k}\right)_{H_2} = \left(\frac{mv^2}{3k}\right)_{UF_6}, \qquad v_{H_2}/v_{UF_6} = \sqrt{m_{UF_6}/m_{H_2}} = \sqrt{352/2.02} = 13.2.$$

DEVIATIONS FROM IDEAL GAS BEHAVIOR

The behavior of ideal gases may be interpreted in terms of elastic collisions between molecules having no size, but only mass and velocity. Deviations from ideal behavior may be interpreted in terms of deviations from these two ideal properties.

Actual molecules do have size. Their orbitals extend in space around the nuclei. When the molecules are close together a large fraction of the time (as at high pressures, where molecular crowding occurs) the volume from which each molecule is excluded by the orbitals of other molecules constitutes an appreciable fraction of the total available volume. Van der Waals' nb becomes appreciable compared to V, and the actual volume is appreciably larger than the ideal volume. (See the upper right section of Figures 6.5 and 6.10.)

At low pressures the value of nb is small compared to V, and the gas approximates ideality. But at low temperatures the molecular velocity falls. Molecular collisions become "sticky" because each molecule remains in the vicinity of each collision partner for a longer time as is true also at high pressures. The electrons in the outer orbitals can be simultaneously attracted to both nuclei, there is actually time for "lining up" the orbitals to increase this tendency, and the actual volume becomes less than that predicted from the ideal gas equation. At sufficiently low temperatures, especially if the pressure is not exceptionally low, these "sticky" collisions may lead to liquid or crystal formation and the gas phase may tend to disappear. The attractive forces at the close distances found in liquids and crystals are great enough that the thermal kinetic energy, $\bar{E}_{trans} = 3RT/2$, is insufficient to tear the molecules apart. Condensation then occurs.

The minima in the curves of Figures 6.4 and 6.8 occur because the effects of a and b are in opposite directions as pressure rises; a tends to decrease the compressibility factor, and b tends to increase it.

COMPLETE DEFINITION OF AN IDEAL GAS

For an ideal gas there are no intermolecular forces acting, and so the internal energy, E, is not a function of the distances between the molecules. Thus, we get a further*

IDEAL GAS EQUATION: $$(\partial E/\partial V)_T = 0 \qquad (6.20)$$

* We shall use the partial differential operator, ∂, to mean "infinitesimal change when some specified variables are held constant." Thus $(\partial E/\partial V)_T$ is read, "the partial of E with respect to V at constant T," and means the rate of change in E as V varies while T is held constant.

This condition can be added to the first

IDEAL GAS EQUATION: $$PV = nRT \qquad (6.13)$$

to give a complete description of an ideal gas. Any gas that obeys these two equations is acting as an ideal gas.

DIFFUSION OF GASES

Direct evidence for molecular motion may be obtained by observing two pure substances next to one another. As time passes they may interpenetrate one another. One can often observe this diffusion in veined rocks that have been in contact for a long time; with crystals placed in contact with liquid (potassium permanganate in water); but especially easily and rapidly with a colored gas placed in contact with a colorless one (see Figure 6.12). The volume, pressure, temperature, and number of moles in the system remain essentially constant; no new molecules form, yet the gases intermix, driven by the difference in chemical potential. We see this intermixing of substances occurring so commonly that we seldom wonder about the process, yet it may be mildly surprising to note that no energy change need be involved when such mixing occurs.

Interpretation of mixing processes in terms of the random motions of gaseous molecules is straightforward. The molecules have randomly oriented velocity vectors, there is considerable "open" space (not occupied by the concentrated portion of any orbitals), and the molecules move around much as one wanders through a crowd at a fair, until the chemical potential is the same everywhere.

It is easy to see that a diffusing system, which might be treated as an isolated system of constant volume, has changed to an equilibrium condition in which no further net changes are occurring. Furthermore, we do not expect to see and indeed do not see the gases spontaneously separating from one another again. In fact, if the system is disturbed slightly, forcing such a separation, the system will return spontaneously to the equilibrium condition of uniform distribution. The mixed system meets both the criteria we have set for equilibrium.

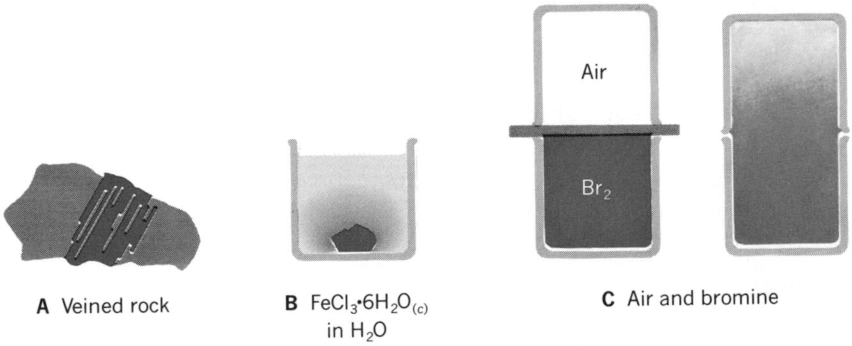

Figure 6.12 Examples of diffusion. (**A**) Diffusion of solids into solids is generally slowest. (**B**) Diffusion into liquids is slow, but much faster than into solids. (**C**) Diffusion of gases into gases is generally most rapid.

We have already decided to use the term entropy, S, for the function which increases to a maximum in an isolated system of constant volume. Thus, in this intermixing system, the entropy must have increased to the maximum possible in the system. The intermixing or randomness of the system also increased. Thus increases in entropy seem related to increases in randomness, a conclusion we shall reach again and again.

THE BAROMETRIC FORMULA

A variation on the diffusion problem is posed by the diffusion of gases up and down in the earth's gravitational field. What is the "equilibrium" state here? We put equilibrium in quotes because we have previously defined equilibrium states as those in which the pressure is constant throughout. This zero gradient condition does not hold in a vertical section of the atmosphere, since the effect of the variation due to gravity is appreciable. This is a constrained equilibrium.

The pressure in the atmosphere will vary with height if the number of molecules varies with height. We shall assume constant temperature in a vertical section of the atmosphere in our solution. Let P = pressure, ρ = density = $wt/V = PM/RT$, M = molar weight, g = gravitational constant, and h = height. The change in air pressure with height in a gravitational field is proportional to the density (mass/volume) of the air and the gravitational constant:*

$$-dP = \rho g\, dh$$

$$-dP = \frac{PM}{RT} g\, dh$$

$$\frac{-dP}{P} = \frac{gM}{RT} dh$$

Integrating, we obtain (assuming constant T and g):**

$$\int_{P_0}^{P} \frac{dP}{P} = -\frac{gM}{RT} \int_0^h dh$$

$$\ln \frac{P}{P_0} = -\frac{gMh}{RT} = \frac{-\Delta \bar{E}_P}{RT}$$

where $\Delta \bar{E}_P$ = change in potential energy of a mole of molecules from $h = 0$ to $h = h$, as the pressure changes from P_0 to P. By rearranging terms,

$$P = P_0 e^{-\Delta \bar{E}_P/RT} = P_0 e^{-(\epsilon - \epsilon_0)/kT}$$

where ϵ = average potential energy of a single molecule at height $h = \bar{E}_P/N_0$, and k = Boltzmann's constant = R/N_0, or

$$\frac{N}{V} = \frac{N_0}{V_0} e^{-(\epsilon - \epsilon_0)/kT}$$

*The calculus operator d, as in dP and dh, indicates an infinitesimal change in the variable, here pressure and height.

**The calculus operator, $\int$, indicates that an integration is to be performed; $\int_{P_0}^{P}$ means to integrate between the two limits P_0 and P.

where N/V = number of molecules per unit volume at height h, since $P/P_0 = (N/V)/(N_0/V_0)$ at constant T. At constant unit volume this becomes the

BOLTZMANN EQUATION: $$N = N_0 e^{-(\epsilon - \epsilon_0)/kT} \tag{6.21}$$

Thus the number of molecules per unit volume at any height is exponentially related to the change of the potential energy in rising to that height divided by the Kelvin temperature. Net diffusion will occur until this distribution is achieved. Here we have the tendency to diffuse outward (increase in spatial entropy) counterbalanced by the tendency of gravity to return the molecules to $h = 0$ (decrease in potential energy). A constrained equilibrium is reached, involving a balance of the two tendencies.

Equation (6.21) is a special form of the Boltzmann equation—an equation we shall use a great deal. The general equation (see p. 211) gives the probable energy distribution in a great variety of systems.

Exercise 6.7

Calculate the atmospheric pressure at 20,000 feet, then compare with Figure 22.14. *Answer:* $P_{20,000} = \exp - (mgh/kT)$, $P_{20,000}$ in atm, $m = (29/6.02 \cdot 10^{23})$ g molecule^{-1}, g = 980 cm sec^{-1}, $T = 300°$K (assume constant), $k = 1.38 \cdot 10^{-16}$ (g cm^2 sec^{-2} molecules^{-1} °K^{-1}). So convert 20,000 feet to cm = $6.1 \cdot 10^5$ cm. $P_{20,000} = \exp - (29 \cdot 980 \cdot 6.1 \cdot 10^5/6 \cdot 10^{23} \cdot 1.4 \cdot 10^{-16} \cdot 300) = e^{-0.69} = 0.50$ atm. Figure 22.14 gives about 300 mm, which agrees within the uncertainty of reading the figure.

DETERMINATION OF ACCURATE MOLECULAR WEIGHTS

We have already used Avogadro's principle to obtain molecular weights. It should be clear, however, that Avogadro's principle—equal volumes of gases contain equal numbers of molecules (temperature and pressure being the same)—is strictly true only when the gases are behaving ideally. Under other conditions, application of the principle can give only approximate molecular weights. However, as P approaches zero, the compressibility factor (PV/nRT) approaches 1, and all gases tend to become ideal (see Figure 6.8). Figure 6.13 shows some molecular weight data for methyl chloride, CH_3Cl, and argon, Ar, as a function of pressure. At low pressure straight lines are obtained, which can be readily extrapolated to zero

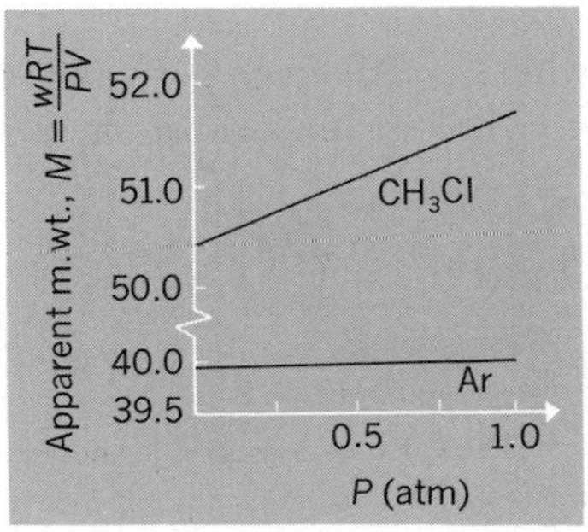

Figure 6.13 Apparent molecular weights of argon and of methyl chloride, CH_3Cl (calculated from gas density data and the ideal gas law), as a function of pressure of the gas. The smaller the slope of the line the more ideal is the gas. Note that Ar is more nearly ideal than is CH_3Cl. The intercept of the line with the $P = 0$ axis is the ideal gas limiting value of the molecular weight.

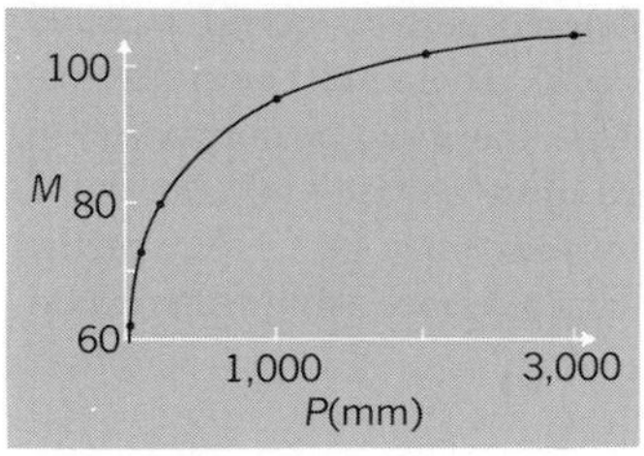

Figure 6.14 Apparent molecular weight of gaseous acetic acid as a function of pressure of the gas. Applying the criteria of Figure 6.16, the gas seems to become more ideal at higher pressures as the molecular weight increases. The limiting molecular weight as P approaches zero corresponds to the formula CH_3COOH. [M. Taylor, *J. Am. Chem. Soc.*, **73,** 315 (1951). © 1951 by the American Chemical Society.]

pressure, giving accurate values for the molecular weights under ideal gas conditions. Figure 6.14 shows similar data for gaseous acetic acid. Again the data at low pressures approach a limiting value, which allows an accurate calculation of the molecular weight under ideal conditions. But at higher pressures another limit is approached. These data at higher pressures indicate a molecular weight of over 100, about twice the value at zero pressure. This is accepted as excellent evidence that gaseous acetic acid (often abbreviated as HOAc) at moderate pressures consists largely of dimerized molecules, $(HOAc)_2$. For a discussion of the forces that hold the dimer together see Figure 15.19.

The molecular weight of the noble gases can also be obtained from their gas density at low pressures, as in Figure 6.13. The question then arises as to how many atoms there are in a molecule. We now accept the answer of 1, but this was not always known. When the noble gases were discovered, it was not sure where they "fitted" into the periodic table. (See Chapter 11.) It was impossible to apply the law of Dulong and Petit, since the gases could not readily be condensed to crystals with the methods then available. True, the gases could not be decomposed into smaller molecules, which gave credence to the idea that there was only one atom per molecule, but the evidence was not conclusive. A determination of the atomic number by Rutherford's scattering technique or by Moseley's X-ray method would have been definitive. However, neither method was known when the gases were discovered. (Even had they been known, these methods would not have been readily applicable at that time. Why? Look up the melting and boiling points of these substances in Table 5.5 and suggest an answer.)

Proofs of the atomic weights of the noble gases were actually obtained with a calorimeter, which should remind us of the Dulong and Petit method, but this calorimeter measured the heat capacity of the gas, not of the crystal. Chapters 7 and 8 will discuss some of the relationships between molecular composition and heat capacities.

Exercise 6.8

A compound of carbon, hydrogen, and chlorine is observed to have the following gas densities (g/l) at 27°C and the pressures (in atm) listed in the following: 2.1043 (1.0000), 1.0382 (0.5000), 0.5154 (0.2500). Calculate the molar weight of the gas and its probable molecular formula. *Answer:* Either plot density versus pressure and extrapolate to 0 pressure or calculate

$$M = \frac{w}{V} \cdot \frac{RT}{P} = \frac{\rho RT}{P}$$

for each set of data, plot M versus ρ and extrapolate to zero to get $M = 50.49$. Atomic weight of H = 1.008, of C = 12.00, of Cl = 35.45. There must be at least one atom of Cl per molecule and, from the molecular weight, there can be only one atom of Cl. This leaves 15.01 g for C and H. Again there must be one and only one C atom, which leaves three H atoms. The molecular formula must be CH_3Cl, methyl chloride, with an accepted formula weight 50.47, which agrees within the experimental uncertainty.

SUMMARY

Equilibrium in any system—isolated, closed, or open—is characterized by a state of no net flows. Thus an equilibrium system may be interchanging energy or atoms with its surroundings, but since there is no net flow, the equilibrium system is an isolated one for all practical purposes.

The number of independent variables at equilibrium is given by the general equation $F = S - R - P + L$, often written $F = C - P + L$. If the only field variables are T and P, we can apply a more restricted equation, $F = C - P + 2$, and from this see that a one-component, one-phase system has two independent variables. We normally describe such systems by an equation of state using P, $\overline{V}$, and T as the variables, only two of the three being independent variables.

Although there are no gases that behave "ideally" over the whole range of pressure, volume, and temperature, many gases, over part of their range, do follow the equations

$$PV = nRT, \qquad (\partial E/\partial V)_T = 0 \qquad (6.13,\ 6.20)$$

These two equations define ideal gas behavior.

For an ideal gas, using simple kinetic theory, P and T may be identified with molecular properties through the equations

$$P = \frac{2}{3}\frac{\overline{E}_{\text{trans}}}{\overline{V}} = \frac{1}{3}\frac{N_0 m v^2}{\overline{V}} \qquad (6.18)$$

$$\overline{E}_{\text{trans}} = \tfrac{3}{2}RT = \tfrac{1}{2}N_0 m v^2 \qquad (6.19)$$

Real gases deviate more and more from ideal behavior as the temperature decreases or the pressure increases. These deviations can be qualitatively interpreted in terms of an increase in the magnitude of intermolecular attractive and repulsive forces as the molecules get closer together, and/or a decrease in the average kinetic energies of the individual molecules. Thus the ratio of the kinetic energy (which tends to give ideal behavior) and the intermolecular energy (which tends to give nonideal behavior) decreases rapidly as P increases and/or T decreases. The gas deviates more and more from ideality. Intermolecular interactions become more and more important.

The behavior of real gases, like that of all real systems, can be described accurately only with actual experimental data, but various equations and graphs have been discovered which correlate the experimental data to a good approximation. The simplest, and one of the most widely used, is the van der Waals equation

$$\left(P + \frac{a}{\overline{V}^2}\right)(\overline{V} - b) = RT \qquad (6.14)$$

The kinetic theory of ideal gases is based on certain assumptions: (1) gases consist of stable atomic aggregates—molecules; (2) only the translational motion of the molecules affects their P, V, T, n relationship (the molecules act as mathematical point masses); (3) the molecules occupy negligible volume (compared to the volume of the gas); (4) the molecules are moving in random paths; (5) no attractive or repulsive forces are exerted between the molecules except at the instant of collision; (6) collisions are elastic.

Comparison of the results of these assumptions with the behavior of real gases gives the following generalizations: (1) most real gases behave ideally within $\pm 5\%$ at high temperatures (generally defined as above the boiling point) and low pressures (generally defined as below 1 atm); (2) T is proportional to the average translational kinetic energy of the molecules, $T = (2/3R)\overline{KE}_{trans}$, where $\overline{KE}_{trans} = \frac{1}{2}Nm\overline{v^2}$; (3) P is proportional to the average translational kinetic energy per unit of volume—the energy density; $P = \frac{2}{3}(KE_{trans}/V) = \frac{2}{3}(\frac{1}{2}nm\overline{v^2}/V)$; (4) the actual molecular velocities (or translational kinetic energies), as we shall soon see, vary and are described by the Maxwell-Boltzmann equation (see p. 223).

> *The air-fuel ratio for complete combustion [of gasoline] should be 15:1. For practical reasons, to give maximum flame propagation, ratios of 12:1 are used, leaving part of the fuel unburned. In addition, there are large losses of fuel through leakage around piston rings and from the carburetor. In Los Angeles alone these emissions—through tailpipes and leakage—amount to about 2000 tons of hydrocarbons plus 10,000 tons of carbon monoxide per day. To this is added 500 tons of oxides of nitrogen formed at high temperatures during combustion.—A. J. Haagen-Smit,* Chem. Eng. News, **89,** 99–105 (1965).

PROBLEMS

6.1. Comment on the phrase, "The molar volume of a gas is 22.4 liters." Write a more accurate statement about molar volumes of gases.

6.2. In Table 6.1, why are some of the values of R greater than the ideal value, and why are others less? Do you see any correlation with the properties of the molecules?

6.3. An adiabatic system is one that is thermally insulated; that is, no heat can enter or leave.

(*a*) Is every isolated system adiabatic?

(*b*) Is every adiabatic system isolated? If not, how can the energy of an adiabatic system change?

(*c*) Is every adiabatic system closed?

6.4. What is the temperature of 2.5 g of hydrogen in a 10.0-liter container at 30 cm of mercury pressure? (About 40°K.)

6.5. In which of the two 1.0-liter containers is the average molecular velocity the higher? (1) Ethane, formula C_2H_6, at 200 mm of mercury pressure and 127°C, or (2) neon, formula Ne, at 100 mm of mercury pressure and 27°C.

6.6. Interpret, in terms of the gas laws, the fact that a falling barometric pressure indicates the onset of high winds and storms.

6.7. How many steel cylinders containing compressed helium must be used to fill a blimp with a capacity of exactly one million cubic feet? The cylinders each contain helium at 230 atm pressure and are 30.0 cubic feet in volume. (Less than 150.)

6.8. Fill in the blanks. 1.12 liters of CH_4 will burn with ______ liters of oxygen to produce ______ g of carbon dioxide, all gases being measured at standard conditions. This 1.12 liters of CH_4 will contain ______ moles of CH_4, and ______ atoms of carbon may be made from it.

6.9. You have a very well-thermostatted bath of constant temperature and all the chemical reagents and glassware you wish but no thermometer and no barometer. How could you determine the molecular weight of an unknown gas?

6.10. (*a*) Which occupies the larger volume, 2 g of hydrogen or 14 g of nitrogen at the same temperature and pressure?

(*b*) Which is at the higher temperature, 4 g of oxygen in a 2-liter container or 4 g of carbon dioxide in a 2-liter container at the same pressure?

(*c*) A measured volume of pure oxygen is bubbled through alcohol and the volume is again measured at the original total pressure and temperature. Is this volume larger than, smaller than, or unchanged from the earlier volume?

6.11. Calculate the molar volume of gaseous water at its boiling temperature at 730 torr pressure. (About 30 l.)

6.12. The rate of diffusion of gases in a system such as that of Figure 6.16, at 300°K and 1 atm, is about 1 meter/hr. How can an odorous gas spread as rapidly as it does throughout a chemistry laboratory?

6.13. Two identical cylinders contain gases at the same pressure and at 20°C. In one cylinder is H_2, in the other O_2. (*a*) How does the rate of molecular collision with the wall compare in the two cylinders. (*b*) The gases are now mixed, react as completely as possible to form water, and all the products are put in one of the cylinders at 20°C. How does the pressure in this cylinder now compare with the original pressure?

II

6.14. Is it necessary to assume randomly moving molecules to account for the ideal gas laws? Show that Boyle's law (PV = constant at constant T and n) may be interpreted on the assumption that the particles are stationary and mutually repelling one another with a force proportional to the inverse of the internuclear distance. (You will be in good company—Isaac Newton developed this theory prior to 1686 and almost all scientists used it until 1845.)

6.15. In 1845 Joule tried to detect temperature changes when an ideal gas, expanded from one container into another, evacuated one. He could detect no change in temperature of the ideal gas, and used this argument to demolish the Newtonian theory of problem 6.14. Can you suggest his line of reasoning?

6.16. Very precise work by Joule showed that the expansion of an ideal gas into a vacuum did result in a state in which the final temperature in the initial flask was very slightly lower than it was originally, and the temperature of the gas that entered the initially evacuated flask became very slightly higher than it was at the start of the experiment. Interpret this result. Compare problem 6.15.

6.17. If gaseous ammonia, initially at 300°K, escapes rapidly from high to low pressure, its temperature drops. If hydrogen is used under the same conditions, the temperature of the expanded gas is higher than it was originally. Interpret the two effects and the difference between ammonia and hydrogen. Cite other gases that would probably behave like ammonia or hydrogen, and justify your statements.

6.18. Assume that only two types of molecules, monomers and dimers, of acetic acid (CH_3COOH) exist in the gas phase at 394.2°K. Calculate the ratio of these two types of molecules at P = 10.0 mm, 100 mm, 1000 mm, and 3000 mm. Why does this ratio change even though T is constant? (About 0.4 monomer at 1000 mm.)

6.19. The density of some gaseous substances are given below. Calculate an accurate value for the atomic weight of each element listed, assuming that of H is known. The gas density measurements were made with the samples immersed in an ice bath.

	Gas	P (atm)	ρ (g/l)
(*a*)	H_xBr	1.0000	3.6444
		0.6667	2.4220
		0.3333	1.2074
(*b*)	CH_x	0.2500	0.17893
		0.5000	0.35808
		0.7500	0.53745
		1.0000	0.71707
		P (torr)	ρ (g/l)
(*c*)	N_x	253.30	0.41667
		506.70	0.83348
		760.00	1.25036

6.20. Estimate the percentage of the air in the 0-to-100-foot layer over Los Angeles that passes through automobile engines each day. The Los Angeles basin, an area of 10^4 square miles, contains half the cars in California. About 10^{11} gallons of gasoline (octane, C_8H_{18}) are consumed in the United States each year, 10% of it in California. List other assumptions.

6.21. In a laboratory experiment a student placed 4.2 g of iron (Fe) into 60 ml of 9.5 *M* HCl solution. Hydrogen gas was evolved and was collected over water in an inverted graduate. What volume of gas was collected in this way if the temperature was 30°C and the barometric pressure was 800 torr? (About 2 l. The reaction is: $Fe + 2H^+ + 6Cl^- = FeCl_6{}^{4-} + H_{2(g)}$.)

6.22. A gaseous substance containing no oxygen was burned in oxygen to give 2.2 g of carbon dioxide, 2.25 g of water, and 1.26 liters of nitrogen dioxide (NO_2), measured at 735 mm of Hg pressure and 25°C. What is the simplest formula of this substance?

6.23. The density of $HF_{(g)}$ at 28°C and 1.00 atm is 2.30 grams liter^{-1}. Interpret this figure.

6.24. Given initial and final conditions as listed, indicate the questioned relationships by =, >, <, or (if no decision is possible) by a question mark.

(*a*) $T_1 = T_2$, $v_1 > v_2$, m_1 ? m_2.

(*b*) $m_1 = m_2$, $T_1 = T_2$, $v_1 = v_2$, $n_1 > n_2$, P_1 ? P_2.

(*c*) $P_1 = P_2$, $T_1 = T_2$, $m_1 = m_2$, Z_1 ? Z_2 (number of molecular collisions/sec).

6.25. Calculate the molar volume of carbon dioxide at 150 atm and 335°C, using (*a*) the ideal gas law, (*b*) van der Waals equation (about 0.3 l), (*c*) reduced values of *T* and *P*. Calculate the volumes at 1 atm and at 10 atm.

6.26. From the following experimental data for methane, CH_4, in the gaseous state, calculate a value for the volume of the methane molecule (in Å^3). Compare the value calculated with that obtained from molecular structure studies, which suggest that methane is approximately spherical with a van der Waals radius of 1.9 Å. $T_c = -82.5°C$, $P_c = 45.8$ atm (critical constant), $\rho_c = 0.162$ grams cc^{-1}.

III

6.27. A deep-sea diver or underwater worker sometimes breathes a gaseous mixture of oxygen and helium, rather than air. There are two serious problems as a result: (1) the pitch of his voice rises, making vocal communication rather irritating to the hearer, and (2) the worker has trouble staying warm. Account for these phenomena in terms of atomic behavior.

6.28. Calculate the volume of a spherical tank designed to hold one ton of carbon dioxide at 50°C and 10 atm pressure. [About 2 meters radius.] What would be the principal design changes in the container if it were to be used to store a ton of carbon dioxide at its sublimation T, 193°K? Which type of storage would you recommend?

6.29. An average person breathes about 35 pounds of air per day and exhales gas containing about 1% carbon dioxide. Design a rebreather system for an astronaut on a ten-day mission based on the reaction: $CO_{2(g)} + 2KO_{2(c)} = K_2CO_{3(c)} + \frac{3}{2}O_{2(g)}$. What other lung exhalants would you control, and how?

See page 1091 for a list of references and readings in the recent chemical literature related to the material in this chapter.

CHAPTER 7

Molecular Energies—Classical Theory

The total energy of a system can be calculated by summing the translational, rotational, vibrational, electronic, and nuclear energies of its constituent molecules.

The behavior of gases is interpreted by the kinetic theory in terms of random translational motions. Any change in temperature is accompanied by a concomitant change in translational molecular velocities. In this chapter we shall study some of the relationships between molecular motions and the energy content of a gas.

HEAT

The phlogiston theory of combustion, current in the 18th century, assumed an entity—phlogiston—which escaped from a burning system. The caloric theory, a little later, discussed heat effects in terms of flow of "caloric." We still talk of heat flow, but we no longer consider heat a substance. Rather, we associate heat with processes. When the temperature of a system rises, we say it is hotter, or that its heat content has increased. Objects may become hotter or increase in temperature when exposed to flames or other high temperature systems, or to electric sparks or light or similar sources of energy. We define heat, q, in terms of temperature change, which, in turn, is related to molecular motions. Many units are used; we shall find the calorie and kilocalorie (1000 calories) most useful. A calorie is now defined in terms of the heating produced by a given electric current, voltage, and resistance, but you will have a more practical feel for the calorie if you remember that, to a good approximation, one calorie is the heat required to raise the temperature of one gram of water, at room temperature, one degree Centigrade.

Heat effects in systems are, then, measured in terms of calories. And, though calories are not substances, we shall use the terminology of "heat flow" and "gain and loss of heat" in a way remarkably reminiscent of the phlogiston and caloric theories.

Heat content is an extensive property related to the vigor of molecular motions. The heat content is proportional to the total mass of the system and to the intensity of the molecular agitation. We shall also find that all forms of energy tend finally to appear as heat; that is, finally they all produce random molecular motions.

HEAT CAPACITIES

The heat capacity of an object may be defined as the ratio of the heat supplied to the temperature change observed—$C = q/\Delta T$—but this definition can be refined considerably.

Consider the total internal energy, E, in a system. This internal energy can be changed in two ways: by adding or removing heat, q, or by work, w.* We shall define the algebraic signs of these functions by the

FIRST LAW OF THERMODYNAMICS: $$E_2 - E_1 = \Delta E = q - w \tag{7.1}$$

for a change from state 1 to state 2. If the system gains heat or has work done on it, ΔE is positive. Thus q is positive if the system gains heat from the surroundings, and w is positive if the system does work on the surroundings. Note that the algebraic sign of each variable is defined in terms of its effect on the system. This statement is another form of the law of conservation of mass-energy. It is so widely accepted that any threats to its generality are met by postulating new types of energy or work rather than suggesting that the law is wrong. There are no known exceptions to it.

We shall assume that you have an intuitive understanding of heat for the moment, an understanding we shall expect you to increase and deepen as we further investigate changes involving heat. You have learned for example, that heat is transferred by three processes—radiation, conduction, and convection.

There are many forms of work, but one of the most commonly met forms in chemistry is that associated with a change in volume, especially of a gas. Such work is known as pressure-volume (or $P\,dV$) work and is given the equation

$$\text{pressure-volume } (P\,dV) \text{ work} = w = \int P_{ext}\,dV \tag{7.2}$$

where P_{ext} is the external pressure acting on the system and dV is the volume change. P here must be the *external*, or surrounding, pressure since w is defined as being done on the surroundings, and it is the work done that is needed for calculations using Equation (7.1). In a system where all the work is $P\,dV$ work, we may substitute for w to get the

CHANGE IN INTERNAL ENERGY: $$\Delta E = q - w = q - \int P_{ext}\,dV$$

*It is easy to generalize energy flow to include effects of electrical, magnetic, gravitational, and other fields. But we shall limit ourselves almost entirely to thermal and pressure fields. Thus changes in energy in a system will be related to heat flow caused by thermal fields and to work associated with pressure, $P\,dV$ work.

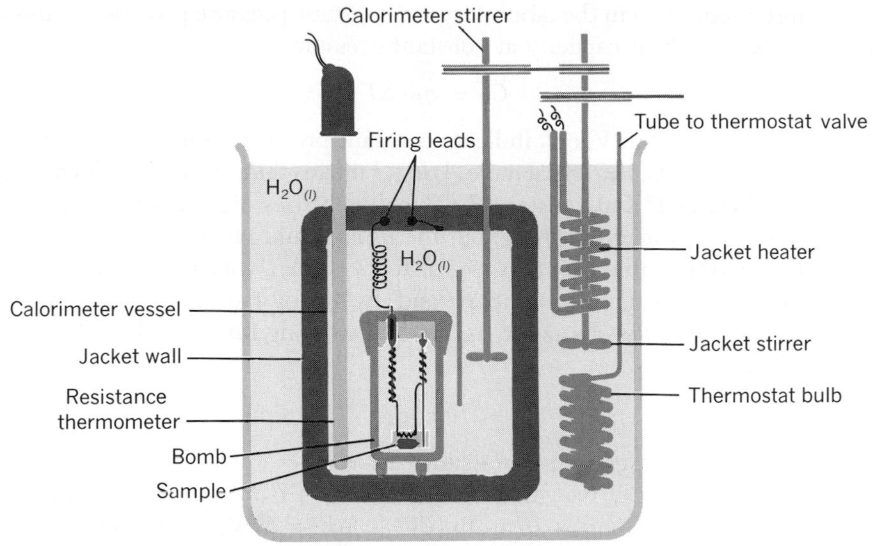

Figure 7.1 Schematic diagram of a bomb calorimeter and its surrounding equipment. High pressure gas (usually oxygen, hydrogen, or fluorine) is contained in the bomb. Reaction is initiated by passing electric current through the firing leads. The resulting change in internal energy, ΔE, is determined from the temperature change and the known heat capacity of the calorimeter.

If we consider a system at constant volume, where $dV = 0$ and $\int P_{\text{ext}}\, dV = 0$, then $\Delta E = q - \int P_{\text{ext}}\, dV = q_V - 0 = q_V$, or

AT CONSTANT VOLUME: $$\Delta E = q_V \tag{7.3}$$

Thus, for a system at constant volume, the change in internal energy is equal to the heat absorbed. Figure 7.1 illustrates a constant-volume (steel bomb) calorimeter.

Since the heat capacity is related to q, we may define the heat capacity at constant volume as

$$C_V = \frac{q_V}{\Delta T} = \frac{\Delta E}{\Delta T}$$

or in the limit as ΔT approaches zero,

$$C_V = \frac{dE}{dT}$$

This definition may be made more explicit by using the notation of partial derivatives, allowing us specifically to mention what is being held constant. Then we write*

HEAT CAPACITY AT CONSTANT VOLUME: $$C_V = \left(\frac{\partial E}{\partial T}\right)_V \tag{7.4}$$

The equation $C_V = q_V/\Delta T$ and the others stemming from it are very handy for constant-volume processes.

* See footnote on p. 183.

Just as common in the laboratory are constant-pressure processes. Thus we also use the idea of heat capacity at constant pressure:

$$C_P = q_P/\Delta T$$

(Note that the sub P, sub V, etc. indicate constant pressure, constant volume, etc.) For example, $\overline{C}_P(H_2O_{(l)}) = 18$ cal mole^{-1} deg^{-1} means that 18 calories will heat one mole of liquid water 1°K at constant P. (This value varies slightly with temperature but is a good approximation throughout the usual liquid range.)

In much the same way that we related q_V to ΔE, we can establish a similar function related to q_P. Let us call it ΔH and, by analogy, evaluate it by "working backward" through a development, as we did "working forward" for ΔE.

Then

$$\Delta H = q_P \tag{7.5}$$

Adding $\int V\,dP = 0$ at constant pressure, $\Delta H = q + \int V\,dP$. Then, subtracting and adding $w = \int P\,dV$, we get $\Delta H = q - w + \int P\,dV + \int V\,dP$. Combining differentials gives $\Delta H = q - w + \int d(PV) = \Delta E + \Delta PV$, since $\Delta E = q - w$. Expanding the Δ terms, $H_2 - H_1 = E_2 - E_1 + P_2V_2 - P_1V_1$, or

$$H_2 - H_1 = (E_2 + P_2V_2) - (E_1 + P_1V_1)$$

We therefore arrive at a definition of

ENTHALPY: $$H = E + PV \tag{7.6}$$

Apparently if we define $H = E + PV$, we also get $\Delta H = q_P$, our desired relation.

The function H is extremely useful, especially for constant-pressure processes; H is called the heat content or enthalpy. (Unfortunately this sounds much like entropy—a quite different function. You will have to be careful not to confuse the two terms.)

Just as we defined

HEAT CAPACITY AT CONSTANT VOLUME: $$C_V = \left(\frac{\partial E}{\partial T}\right)_V$$

in Equation (7.4), so we define

HEAT CAPACITY AT CONSTANT PRESSURE: $$C_P = \left(\frac{\partial H}{\partial T}\right)_P \tag{7.7}$$

Thus the heat capacity at constant volume is the rate of change of the internal energy with temperature at constant volume. The heat capacity at constant pressure is the rate of change of the enthalpy with temperature at constant pressure. Figure 7.2 illustrates a constant-pressure calorimeter.

Exercise 7.1

Calculate ΔE for a process inside a steel bomb which raised the temperature of 1092 g of surrounding water 1.12°C. The bomb itself is equivalent in thermal behavior to 682 g of water. *Answer:* Assume heat capacity of water = 1.000 cal °C^{-1} g^{-1}. Then $\Delta E = q_V = \int C\,dT = C(T_2 - T_1)$, if C = constant. $\Delta E = 1.000$ cal °C^{-1} g$^{-1}\cdot$ (1092 + 682) g $\cdot$ 1.12°C = 1990 cal. Since energy is evolved from bomb, $\Delta E_{\text{process in bomb}} = -1990$ cal.

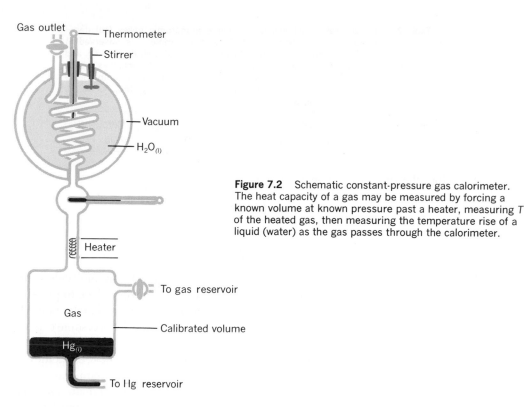

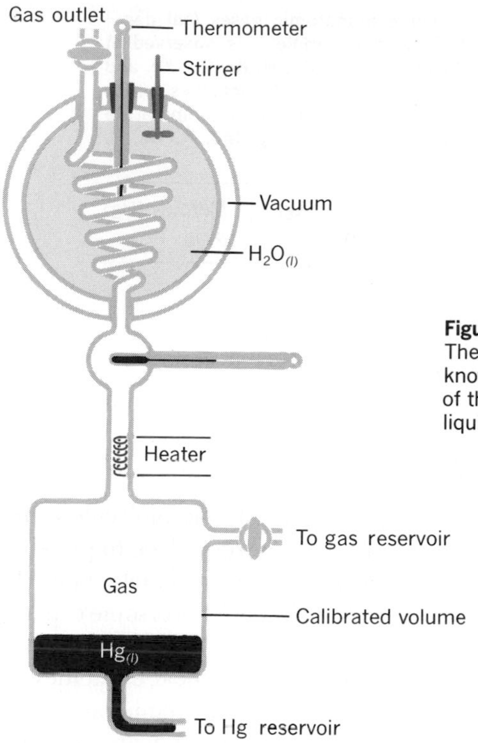

Figure 7.2 Schematic constant-pressure gas calorimeter. The heat capacity of a gas may be measured by forcing a known volume at known pressure past a heater, measuring T of the heated gas, then measuring the temperature rise of a liquid (water) as the gas passes through the calorimeter.

$C_P - C_V$ FOR AN IDEAL GAS

For all systems $H = E + PV$, and, differentiating with respect to T:

$$\frac{dH}{dT} = \frac{dE}{dT} + \frac{d(PV)}{dT}, \text{ or } C_P = C_V + \frac{d(PV)}{dT}$$

For an ideal gas $PV = nRT$ and $d(PV)/dT = nR$, or, for one mole of any

IDEAL GAS:
$$\overline{C}_P - \overline{C}_V = R \tag{7.8}$$

Here $\overline{C}_P$ and $\overline{C}_V$ are molar heat capacities. Note that $\overline{C}_P$ is always larger than $\overline{C}_V$ (since both must be positive). The "extra" heat required to heat a gas at constant pressure equals the work of pushing back the surroundings of the gas as the volume increases. At constant volume there is no such work, so that all the heat is used up in changing the energies of the gaseous molecules in the system. Let us see what these changes are.

MONATOMIC GASES AND TRANSLATIONAL HEAT CAPACITY

In our discussion of the kinetic theory of ideal gases, we found that the kinetic energy of translation, $\overline{E}_{\text{trans}}$, as given by Equation (6.19), is

$$\overline{E}_{\text{trans}} = \frac{3RT}{2}$$

Table 7.1 Molar heat capacities, $\overline{C}_V$, of some monatomic gases (cal deg^{-1} mole^{-1}). The same value, 2.98 cal deg^{-1} mole^{-1}, is observed at all temperatures up to 3000°K for gaseous Cd, H, Kr, Ru, Xe, and Zn. The following monatomic gases have heat capacities which are similar, but higher by a few percent in the high-temperature range: As, Au, Ba, Be, Bi, Ca, Cs, Cu, K, Li, Mg, Mo, N, Na, P, Pb, Rb, Re, Sb, Sr, Tl, and Yb.

Helium (He)	Neon (Ne)	Argon (Ar)	Silver (Ag)	Mercury (Hg)
2.98	2.98	2.98	2.98	2.98

Therefore the translational heat capacity is given by

$$(\overline{C}_V)_{\text{trans}} = \left(\frac{\partial \overline{E}_{\text{trans}}}{\partial T}\right)_V = \frac{3R}{2} \tag{7.9}$$

or

$$(\overline{C}_V)_{\text{trans}} = 3 \text{ cal mole}^{-1} \text{ °K}^{-1}$$

It seems reasonable to assume that all the energy of a monatomic molecule is involved in its translational kinetic energy—that is, its motion from place to place in the system. Thus $\overline{C}_V$ for a monatomic gas should equal $3R/2 = 3$ cal mole^{-1} deg^{-1}, since the value of R used here is 1.9871 cal mole^{-1} °K^{-1}. Table 7.1 lists some experimental molar heat capacities, $\overline{C}_V$, for gaseous elements known to be monatomic, as well as the molar heat capacities of some of the noble gases. The heat capacities of these substances as gases are constant from the lowest attainable temperatures to temperatures greater than 2000°K, indicating that the gases are monatomic over the whole range and that they absorb energy only by increasing their translational energy and not in any other way. If they did absorb energy in some other way, the heat capacity would be higher, the additional heat going into the other ways of increasing the energy of the molecules.

Table 7.1 gives us excellent confirmation of our kinetic theory of gases, of our interpretation of heat capacity, and of our belief that these substances are indeed monatomic in the gaseous state. Such experimental agreements, that involve the interdependence of several ideas, are especially valuable in evaluating theories.

The translational heat capacity of all gases is constant at $\overline{C}_V = 3$ cal mole^{-1} °K^{-1}. We know that $(\partial E/\partial T)_V = C_V$ or $\int_0^T dE = C_V \int_0^T dT$. But $E_{\text{trans}} = 0$ at 0°K so $E_{\text{trans}} = C_V T$ at any temperature T. We also derived this as Equation (6.19), $E_{\text{trans}} = \frac{3}{2}RT$.

Exercise 7.2

Calculate ΔH for the process of heating 162 g of Ar (g) from 135°C to 412°C. *Answer:* $\Delta H = n \int \overline{C}_P \, dT = n\overline{C}_P(T_2 - T_1)$, if $\overline{C}_P$ is constant. Since $\overline{C}_P = \overline{C}_V + R$ for an ideal gas, $\Delta H = n(C_V + R)(T_2 - T_1) = (162/40.0)(2.98 + 1.99)(412 - 350) = 1250$ cal.

HEAT CAPACITIES OF DIATOMIC AND POLYATOMIC GASES

Table 7.2 gives the heat capacities, $\overline{C}_V$, of several gases at 298°K. All the new values are greater than the 3 cal mole^{-1} found for monatomic gases. This reinforces our

Table 7.2 **Molar heat capacities, $\bar{C}_V$, of some gases (cal deg^{-1} mole^{-1} at 25°C). In general, the more complex (larger number of atoms in) the molecule, the higher the value of $\bar{C}_V$. Also, but much less dramatically, the more massive the atoms, the higher the heat capacity when the molecular complexity is unchanged.**

Gas	Formula	Mol. wt.	$\bar{C}_V$
Monatomic			
Argon	Ar	40	2.98
Helium	He	4	2.98
Mercury	Hg	201	2.98
Diatomic			
Hydrogen	H_2	2	4.91
Nitrogen	N_2	28	4.95
Carbon monoxide	CO	28	4.97
Hydrogen chloride	HCl	36	5.01
Oxygen	O_2	32	5.05
Nitric oxide	NO	30	5.11
Chlorine	Cl_2	71	6.14
Triatomic			
Carbon dioxide	CO_2	44	6.92
Nitrous oxide	N_2O	44	7.29
Sulfur dioxide	SO_2	64	7.3
Polyatomic			
Ammonia	NH_3	17	6.57
Methane	CH_4	16	6.59
Ethane	C_2H_6	30	10.65
Dimethyl ether	C_2H_6O	42	13.75

belief that these gases contain more than one atom per molecule, as deduced previously from Avogadro's and Cannizzaro's principles. Figures 7.3 and 7.4 show the heat capacities of several gases as a function of the temperature. There is a marked variation of heat capacity with temperature in contrast to the constant heat capacity of the monatomic gases over a very wide temperature range. But it is interesting to note that all the heat capacities increase as the temperature increases. How do we interpret the generally higher values, their variation with temperature, and the fact that some gaseous heat capacities (that of H_2, for example) approach that of a monatomic gas even though the molecules are not monatomic?

Consider the heat capacity of elementary hydrogen, H_2. At low temperatures $\bar{C}_V = 3$ cal mole^{-1} °K^{-1}, or $\bar{C}_P = 5$ cal mole^{-1} °K^{-1}. Around 70°K the heat capacity begins to increase, then almost levels off again at about $\bar{C}_V = 5$ cal mole^{-1} °K^{-1}, rising slowly thereafter as the temperature increases. Examination shows that all the diatomic gases have heat capacities that behave in this way. Diatomic substances must have ways of absorbing energy not available to monatomic substances, and the availability of these ways of absorbing energy must vary with temperature.

Our derivation of the heat capacity of a monatomic gas actually contained no assumptions about the atomic content of the gas; it merely assumed that all heat went into translational kinetic energy. Presumably it is the translational heat ca-

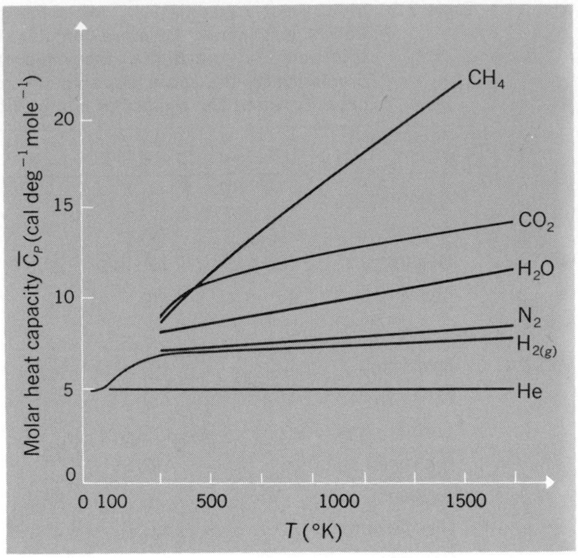

Figure 7.3 Heat capacities of several gases as a function of the temperature. *Note* $C_P = \overline{C}_V + R$ is plotted.

pacity which is responsible for the limiting value of $\overline{C}_V = 3$ cal mole^{-1} °K^{-1} for gases at low temperatures. But this means that diatomic hydrogen molecules are not changing their rotational or vibrational energy or their electronic or nuclear energy below about 70°K. It may be easy to believe that their electronic states and nuclear energy states are not changing, but it probably comes as a surprise that neither their rotational nor vibrational motions are absorbing energy at low temperatures. A workable theory, however, may be based on the idea that only their translational motions are absorbing energy. We also include in the theory the idea that energy can be used in causing the molecules to rotate increasingly as the temperature rises, and that still further rise in temperature begins to change the vibrations, then the electronic and finally the nuclear energy states of the molecules. Let us develop these ideas.

CLASSICAL TOTAL HEAT CAPACITIES

Figure 7.5 illustrates three classical forms of motion. In a gas the various motions are almost independent of one another and the total energy can be calculated by summing the translational, rotational, vibrational, electronic, and nuclear energies of the gas:

$$\Delta E = q_V = q_{\text{trans}} + q_{\text{rot}} + q_{\text{vib}} + q_{\text{elect}} + q_{\text{nuc}}$$

Similarly, for the heat capacities:

$$C_V = C_{\text{trans}} + C_{\text{rot}} + C_{\text{vib}} + C_{\text{elect}} + C_{\text{nuc}}$$

We shall assume that the last two terms are zero at readily attainable temperatures —say less than 2000°K. Now classical theory gives a heat capacity of $(R/2)$ for each translation and each rotation, and a value of $(2R/2)$ for each vibration. For diatomic

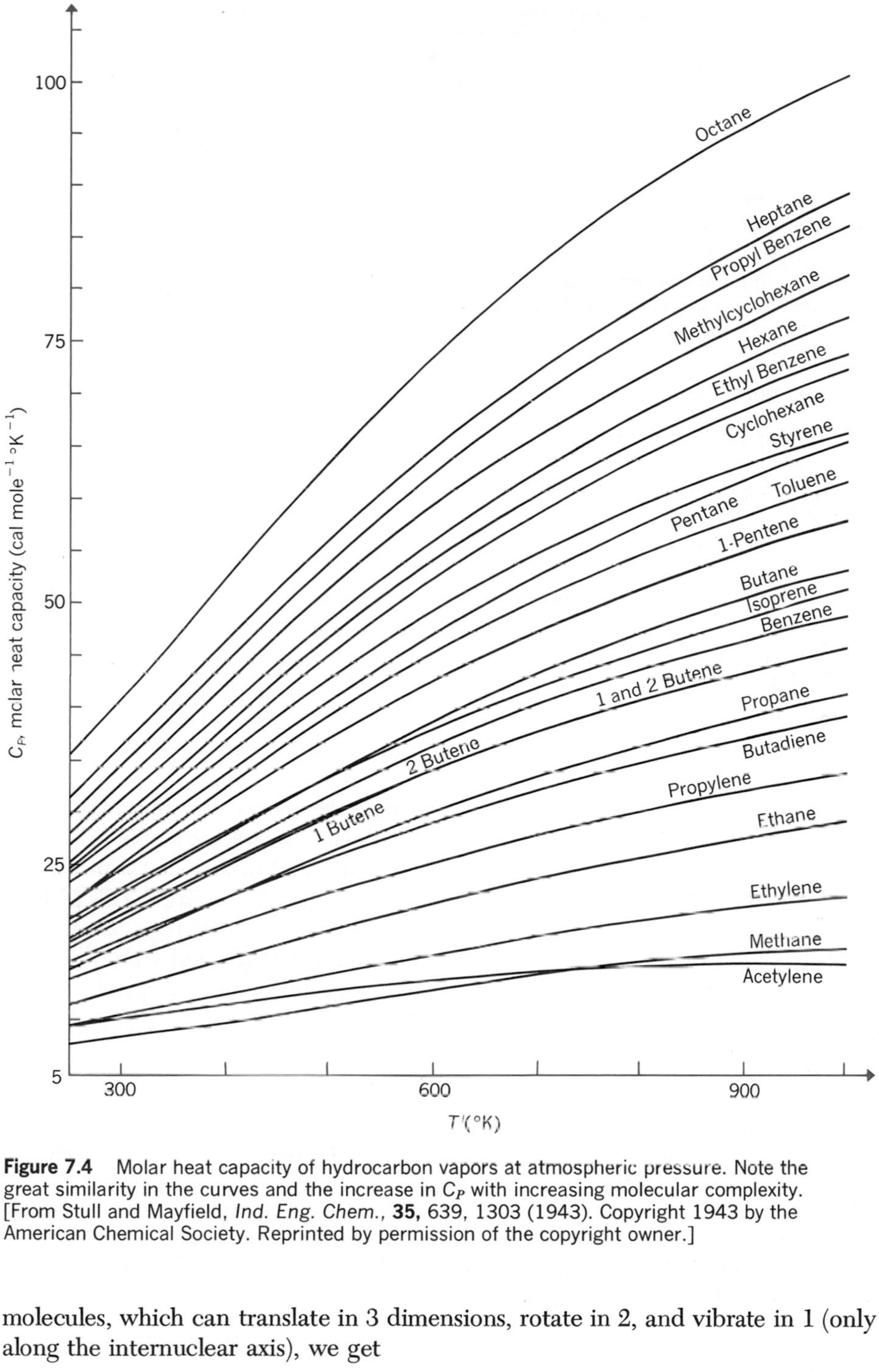

Figure 7.4 Molar heat capacity of hydrocarbon vapors at atmospheric pressure. Note the great similarity in the curves and the increase in C_P with increasing molecular complexity. [From Stull and Mayfield, *Ind. Eng. Chem.*, **35,** 639, 1303 (1943). Copyright 1943 by the American Chemical Society. Reprinted by permission of the copyright owner.]

molecules, which can translate in 3 dimensions, rotate in 2, and vibrate in 1 (only along the internuclear axis), we get

$$\overline{C}_V = \overline{C}_{\text{trans}} + \overline{C}_{\text{rot}} + \overline{C}_{\text{vib}}$$

which becomes, for a classical

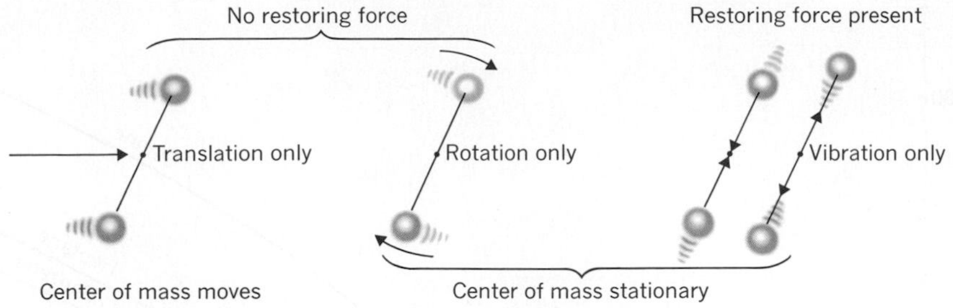

Figure 7.5 Translational, rotational, and vibrational motions of a diatomic molecule. The center of mass is indicated by a dot at the center of the bond.

DIATOMIC MOLECULE:

$$\overline{C}_V = 3R/2 + 2R/2 + 2R/2 = 7R/2 \cong 7 \text{ cal mole}^{-1} \text{ °K}^{-1} \qquad (7.10)$$

and $\overline{C}_P = \overline{C}_V + R = 9$ cal mole^{-1} °K^{-1} for any ideal diatomic gas. Calculation of E gives

$$E = E_{\text{trans}} + E_{\text{rot}} + E_{\text{vib}} = 3RT/2 + RT + RT$$

Unfortunately for classical theory, not all diatomic gases have a heat capacity of $\overline{C}_V = 7$ cal mole^{-1} °K^{-1} even at 2000°K, and all have much lower values at low temperatures (see Figure 7.3 and Table 7.2). Classical theory also predicts heat capacities independent of T for all gases. Actually, only monatomic gases show this behavior experimentally. Clearly classical theory, which treats all molecules alike (except as they differ in number of atoms and are linear or nonlinear), is not adequate.

We obtained great assistance in decoding the energy distribution in atoms by using spectral evidence. On the basis of that evidence we were able to deduce the possible energy contents of the electronic states and to arrive at a picture of orbitals, each of which could hold two electrons of specified energy. This picture accounted quantitatively for the experimental evidence. Perhaps absorption spectra could give similar evidence concerning the rotational and vibrational energies of molecules. But in what region of the spectrum should we search for this evidence? Chapter 8 will explore this problem.

Exercise 7.3

Estimate the classical heat capacity, $\overline{C}_V$, of Cl_2. Compare this to the experimental value of $\overline{C}_V$ in Table 7.2 and comment on the differences. *Answer:* Classically, for a diatomic molecule, $\overline{C}_V = 3(R/2)_{\text{trans}} + 2(R/2)_{\text{rot}} + 1 \cdot (2R/2)_{\text{vib}} = 7(R/2) = 7$ cal mole^{-1} °K^{-1}. The experimental value is 6.14 at 298°K. Apparently Cl_2 molecules are translating and rotating freely at 298°K but vibration is contributing only about 1 calorie to the heat capacity rather than the 2 calories expected from the classical model. Chapter 8 will explore this problem.

SUMMARY

The first law of thermodynamics, $\Delta E = q - w$ (when restricted to work of the type $w = \int P_{\text{ext}}dV$), gives the relation $\Delta E = q_V$. Similarly, the definition of enthalpy, $H = E + PV$, gives the relation $\Delta H = q_P$. A common form of heat effect is the actual heating of a substance from T_1 to T_2 with no phase changes or changes in chemical substances. This leads to the definition of heat capacities as $C_V = (\partial E/\partial T)_V$ and $C_P = (\partial H/\partial T)_P$. For an ideal gas the relationship $C_P - C_V = R$ holds rigorously.

It proves interesting to consider the heat capacity (and the internal energy and enthalpy) as made up of contributions due to various types of molecular changes—translational, rotational, vibrational, electronic, nuclear. Thus

$$C_V = C_{\text{trans}} + C_{\text{rot}} + C_{\text{vib}} + C_{\text{elect}} + C_{\text{nuc}}$$

Classical theory predicts that each degree of freedom, or each way of absorbing energy, accounts for $R/2$ units in the heat capacity. Thus $C_{\text{trans}} = 3(R/2)$, $C_{\text{rot}} = 2(R/2)$ for a linear molecule or $C_{\text{rot}} = 3(R/2)$ for a nonlinear molecule, and $C_{\text{vib}} = (2R/2)$ for each possible vibration. Calculations based on these simple classical formulas agree well with experimental data at high temperatures but the agreement becomes poorer and poorer as T decreases. No substances give experimental values for heat capacity at room temperature in agreement with classical excitation of nuclear, electronic, or vibrational energies. But all, except for H_2, agree on rotation and translation. Below 70°K, H_2 has no observable rotational contribution to the heat capacity, but only at temperatures too low to make experimental measurements on gases would the translational contribution differ from the classical prediction.

Thus, the classical formulas are actually violated by all systems at sufficiently low T, a fact we shall try to account for in the next chapter.

From the earliest times man's apprehension of the causes and connections of natural phenomena has been rendered uncertain and imperfect by his willfully ignoring the great fact that Natural Philosophy is an experimental, and not an intuitive, science. No a priori reasoning can conduct us demonstratively to a single physical truth; we must endeavour to discover what is, not speculate on what might have been, or presumptuously decide what ought to have been. Hence it matters not to us what Aristotle or Bacon may have laid down, or Locke and Descartes imagined, with regard to the nature of heat.—P. G. Tait, Sketch of Thermodynamics, *Edinburgh* (1877)

PROBLEMS

7.1. Suggest a theoretical rationalization of the Law of Dulong and Petit in terms of atomic properties. Why is the constant equal to 6 cal mole^{-1} deg^{-1}? Why does diamond not follow the law?

7.2. Calculate ΔH for heating 200 g of $C_2H_{6(g)}$ from 300 to 600°K. (About 25 kcal.)

7.3. The temperature rise in a bomb calorimeter is 0.148°C. The bomb plus its water jacket is equivalent to 1738 g of H_2O. The sample weight is 0.2094 g. Calculate ΔE per gram of sample. (About 1 kcal g^{-1}.)

7.4. Calculate the difference between $\Delta\overline{H}$ and $\Delta\overline{E}$ for methane, CH_4, burning in oxygen at 1000°K.

II

7.5. Estimate, and justify, the heat capacities of the following gases at 400°K: Ar, O_2, Br_2, H—C≡C—H, SiH_4, SO_2. Estimate, and justify, uncertainties for each of the heat capacities you select.

7.6. The heat capacity of oxygen as a function of T is given by the equation $\overline{C}_P = 7.16 + 1.00 \cdot 10^{-3}T - 0.40 \cdot 10^5 T^{-2}$. How much heat is required to increase T for a ton of O_2 to the maximum temperature in a blast furnace making iron? (About $4 \cdot 10^5$ kcals.)

III

7.7. Design a constant pressure gas calorimeter which is an improvement over that in Figure 7.2. Describe the improvements.

7.8. Design an apparatus based on the determination of heat capacities to detect firedamp (CH_4 gas) in coal mines. Design a device more sensitive at low concentrations based on some other property of CH_4. Estimate the upper and lower limits of sensitivity of each device. Any reason to use both of them?

See page 1091 for a list of references and readings in the recent chemical literature related to the material in this chapter.

CHAPTER 8

Molecular Energy Levels—Quantum Theory

Classical mechanics applies when kT is much greater than ϵ; quantum mechanics must be used when kT approaches or is less than ϵ, where ϵ is the energy gap between two quantum states.

Chapter 7 related H, E, q, w, C_P, and C_V to macroscopic changes. It explored some of their interrelationships and introduced the notion of their dependence on the molecular motions of translation, rotation, and vibration. In this chapter we shall explore further the relationships between molecular behavior and energy.

The partial success, but detailed failure, of the classical theory of heat capacities, internal energies, and enthalpies of gases provides encouragement that an adequate theory may be found. A similar problem with respect to electronic levels was solved by the introduction of quantized states. We shall explore that possibility here with respect to vibrations, rotations, and translations.

Figure 8.1, for example, is the absorption spectrum of air at sea level. Clearly many processes occur which absorb energy. Figure 8.1 should remind you of the spectra of the monatomic gases explored in Chapter 3. But air is not monatomic, nor is it a single component system; let us look at a simpler system for possible interpretations.

SPECTRAL EVIDENCE FOR MOLECULAR ROTATION AND VIBRATION

If there is any merit in the idea of interpreting the variation of heat capacity of diatomic and polyatomic molecules with temperature in terms of variations in the rotation and vibrational energy, we might use this idea as a start in deciding which spectral region should be promising. Consider molecular hydrogen.

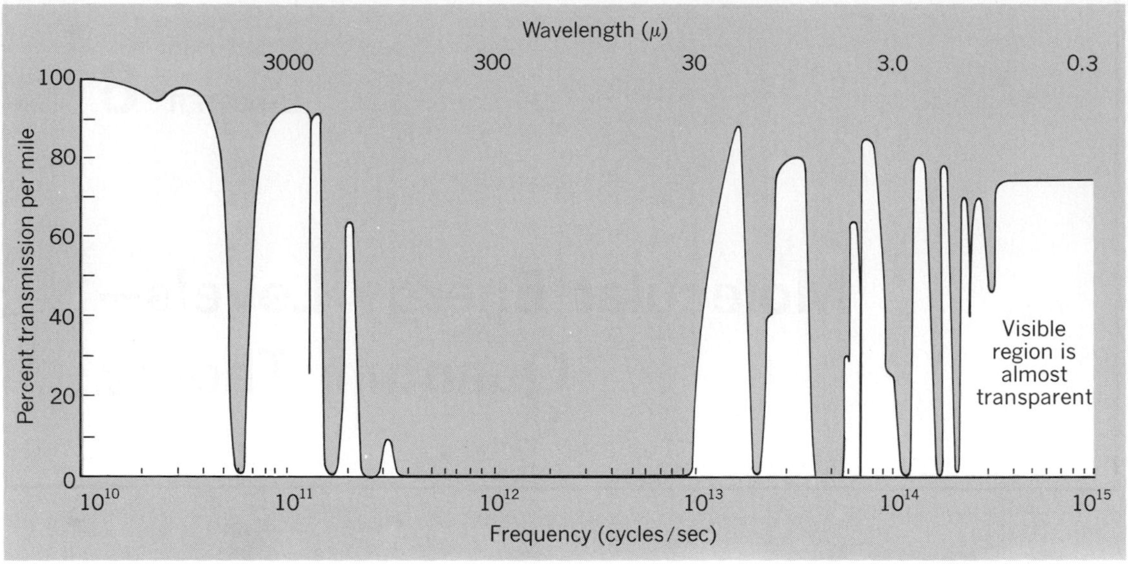

Figure 8.1 Electromagnetic spectrum of air at sea level. [R. Kompfner, *Science*, **150,** 149 (1965). Copyright 1965 by the American Association for the Advancement of Science.]

We have seen in Figure 7.3 that molecular hydrogen has the same heat capacity as a monatomic gas at temperatures below 70°K. Its rotational energy, we have surmised, is not changing until the temperature rises above that value. Any change in rotations must be the result of collisions with other molecules, collisions which result in transferring some translational energy (since that is the only kind of energy the hydrogen molecules appear to have below 70°K) into rotational energy. From Equation (6.19) we see that the average translational kinetic energy of a mole of hydrogen molecules is $\overline{E} = 3RT/2 = 3 \cdot 70 = 210$ cal mole^{-1}. This is a very small amount of energy per mole but it is all the average molecule has to transfer in a collision, so that rotational excitation probably involves less than this much energy in hydrogen. Using the relation*

$$\overline{E}/N_0 = \epsilon = h\nu$$

we find that 210 cal mole^{-1} corresponds to a frequency of $2.2 \cdot 10^{12}$ sec^{-1}. This frequency is found in the infrared region of the spectrum, as shown in Figure 8.2.

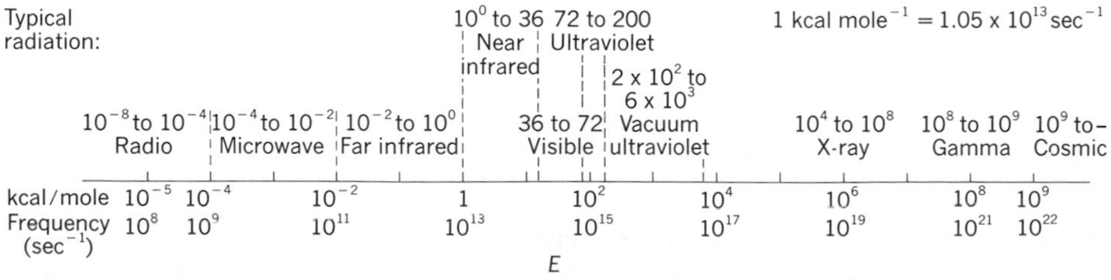

Figure 8.2 Part of the electromagnetic spectrum.

*We shall use E for macroscopic energies (such as $\overline{E}$ = molar internal energy) and ϵ for energies per molecule (such as ϵ_{trans} = translational energy of a single molecule).

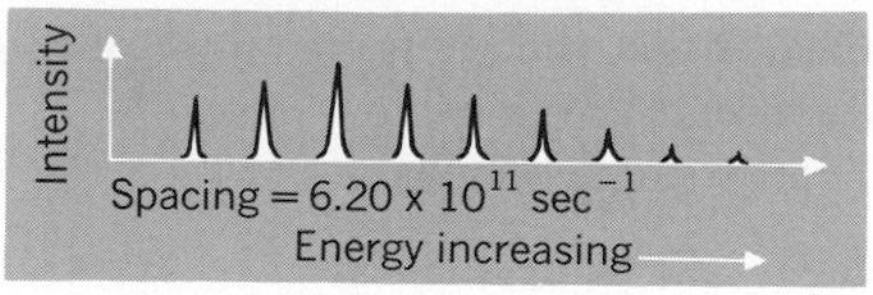

Figure 8.3 A schematic diagram of the far infrared spectrum of gaseous hydrogen chloride near 100 cal mole^{-1} or a frequency of 10^{12} sec^{-1}.

But if we examine the absorption spectrum of gaseous hydrogen, H_2, we find no absorption of energy anywhere near this region. Molecular hydrogen absorbs no infrared frequencies.

Radiant energy, as we have seen, can be pictured as an alternating electromagnetic field of frequency ν, and energy $\epsilon = h\nu$, moving past the molecule. In a molecule like hydrogen the two ends of the molecule are electrically identical. There is no asymmetric field to interact with the alternating electric field of the light. What happens if we try an asymmetric diatomic molecule such as hydrogen chloride? Figure 8.3 shows the results. Infrared light is absorbed by the electrically unsymmetric hydrogen chloride, HCl, molecule. Other unsymmetric (polar) molecules also absorb in the infrared, and we are suddenly presented with a great wealth of information concerning possible energy states of these molecules.

Just as we interpreted the sharp visible and ultraviolet absorption lines in terms of only certain allowable electronic energy levels, so here we interpret sharp infrared absorption lines as indicating that only certain energy changes are possible in this energy region. Do these absorptions really result from changes in rotational or vibrational energy contents?

If so, how do we account for the following three observations? (1) The spectrum of Figure 8.3 consists of a set of almost equally spaced absorption lines occurring in the general frequency region of 100 cal mole^{-1} or a frequency of 10^{12} sec^{-1} (slightly less energy than we predicted for hydrogen). (2) The line spacing is $6.20 \cdot 10^{11}$ sec^{-1}. (3) The lines vary in intensity. Further experimentation shows that the intensity of the lines is a function of temperature but that the position and spacings of the lines are not. Increasing the temperature increases the relative intensity of the lines of higher energy, and the maximum line intensity slowly shifts toward lines of higher energy.

Exercise 8.1

Calculate the energy difference associated with a line spacing of $6.2 \cdot 10^{11}$ sec^{-1} as in the HCl spectrum. *Answer:* $\Delta E = h\nu = 6.63 \cdot 10^{-27}$ erg sec molecule$^{-1} \cdot 6.2 \cdot 10^{11}$ sec^{-1} $= 4.1 \cdot 10^{-15}$ erg molecule^{-1}, or $\Delta E = 4.1 \cdot 10^{-15}$ erg molecule$^{-1} \cdot 6.02 \cdot 10^{23}$ molecule mole^{-1} $= 2.5 \cdot 10^{9}$ ergs mole^{-1}, or $\Delta E = 6.2 \cdot 10^{11}$ sec$^{-1} \cdot$ (kcal mole^{-1}/ $1.05 \cdot 10^{13}$ sec^{-1}) $= 0.059$ kcal mole^{-1} (from Appendix I).

A ROTATIONAL MODEL FOR GASEOUS HYDROGEN CHLORIDE

Let us assume that these lines result from changes in the rotational energy of hydrogen chloride, HCl, molecules. This is consistent with the decrease in its heat capacity at low temperatures and with our rough calculations of the energies required to account for the heat capacity changes noted in gases at low temperatures. The existence of sharp lines in the spectrum indicates that the energy content of the molecules is quantized; only certain energy contents are possible.

Energy of rotation, ϵ_{rot}, may be shown by simple mechanics to be

$$\epsilon_{rot} = \tfrac{1}{2}I\omega^2$$

with ω = angular velocity and the amount of inertia $I = \mu d^2$, and, for a diatomic molecule,

$$\mu = \frac{m_1 m_2}{m_1 + m_2}$$

where m_1 and m_2 are the atomic masses separated by distance d. In the quantization of electronic energies we assumed that momentum was quantized in units of $h/2\pi$ [see Equation (4.1)]. We will try a similar assumption here.

A particularly simple assumption is similar to Bohr's famous one, Equation (4.1):

$$\text{Angular momentum} = I\omega = j\frac{h}{2\pi}$$

where $j = 0, 1, 2, 3, \ldots$; therefore

$$\omega = \frac{jh}{2\pi I}, \qquad \omega^2 = \frac{j^2h^2}{4\pi^2 I^2}, \qquad \epsilon_{rot} = \frac{j^2h^2}{8\pi^2 I}$$

For simplicity, let

$$\frac{h}{8\pi^2 I} = B = \frac{\text{gm cm}^2\ \text{sec}^{-1}}{\text{gm cm}^2} = \text{sec}^{-1}$$

Then

$$\frac{\epsilon_{rot}}{h} = j^2B = \text{the possible rotational energies of a rotating molecule divided by } h.$$

Now suppose that, when the molecule absorbs energy, its rotational energy, ϵ_{rot}, can change by an amount $\Delta\epsilon_{rot}$ in going from state j to state $j + 1$. Then

$$\frac{\Delta\epsilon}{h} = \frac{\epsilon_{rot(j+1)}}{h} - \frac{\epsilon_{rot(j)}}{h} = B[(j+1)^2 - j^2]$$
$$= B(2j + 1)$$

the possible energy changes if $\Delta j = 1$. Table 8.1 gives, as a function of j, the values of $\epsilon_{rot(j)}$ and $\Delta\epsilon$.

Our model seems successful, but we can also check the positions, $\Delta\epsilon/h$, of the spectral lines. Our theory puts them at B, $3B$, $5B$, $7B$, etc. or 3.1, 9.3, 15.5, and 21.7, each times 10^{11} sec^{-1}. The experimentally observed positions in Figure 8.3 are at 6.2, 12.4, 18.6, and 24.8, each times 10^{11} sec^{-1}. The predicted lines are at odd multiples of B, but the actual lines are at even multiples of B. Something is wrong; apparently our quantization is close but not correct. We must try another set of assumptions. By either trial and error or direct derivation from the Schrödinger equation, we find that the following model is in better agreement with experiment.

Assume that the angular momentum quantizes in the same manner used in the vector model of electronic states. If we assume that

$$I\omega = \sqrt{J(J+1)}\,\frac{h}{2\pi} \tag{8.1}$$

Table 8.1 An "almost adequate" model of molecular rotation.

	j = 0	1	2	3	4	5	6
$\frac{\epsilon_{rot}}{h} = j^2B$	0	B	4B	9B	16B	25B	36B
$\frac{\Delta\epsilon_j{}^{j+1}}{h} = B(2j + 1)$	B	3B	5B	7B	9B	11B	
Predicted spectrum (intensities unknown)							
Line spacing (sec^{-1})		2B	2B	2B	2B	2B	

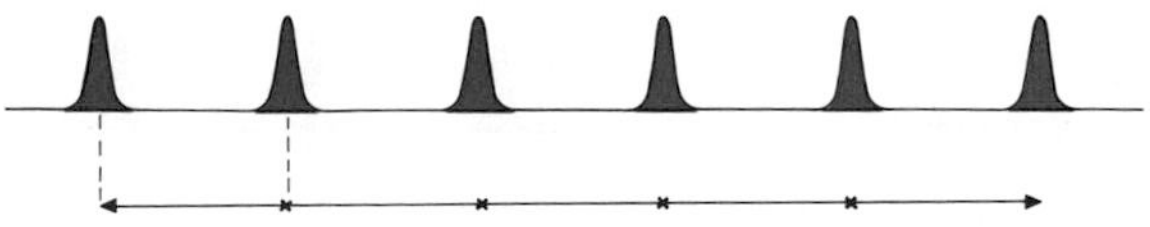

where $J = 0, 1, 2, 3, 4, \ldots$, then

$$\omega^2 = J(J + 1)\frac{h^2}{4\pi^2I^2}$$

and

$$\frac{\epsilon_{rot}}{h} = J(J + 1)\frac{h}{8\pi^2I} = J(J + 1)B \tag{8.2}$$

where

$$B = \frac{h}{8\pi^2I} = \frac{\text{g cm}^2\ \text{sec}^{-1}}{\text{g cm}^2} = \text{sec}^{-1}$$

Note that B has the units of sec^{-1} and is related to the rotational frequency. For the change in energy from J to $J + 1$, we get

$$\frac{\Delta\epsilon}{h} = B[(J + 1)(J + 2) - J(J + 1)]$$
$$= B[J^2 + 3J + 2 - J^2 - J] = 2B[J + 1]$$

or

$$\frac{\Delta\epsilon}{h} = 2B[J + 1] = 2BJ' \tag{8.3}$$

where J' is the quantum number of the upper rotational energy level involved in the change.

Again we tabulate values for ϵ/h and $\Delta\epsilon/h$ as a function of the quantum number J (see Table 8.2). These give the rotational frequencies for each value of J.

This model gives a set of equally spaced lines at the experimentally observed positions. The spacing is

$$2B = \frac{2h}{8\pi^2I} = \frac{h}{4\pi^2\mu d^2} = \frac{h(m_1 + m_2)}{4\pi^2m_1m_2d^2} \tag{8.4}$$

The observed frequency spacing is $6.2 \cdot 10^{11}\ \text{sec}^{-1} = 2B$, so that

$$d = \left(\frac{h(m_1 + m_2)}{4\pi^2m_1m_22B}\right)^{1/2} = \left(\frac{h(m_1 + m_2)}{4\pi^2m_1m_26.2 \cdot 10^{11}}\right)^{1/2}$$

Table 8.2 **An adequate model of molecular rotation.**

	Quantum number, J						
	0	1	2	3	4	5	6
Energy level, $\frac{\epsilon_{rot}}{h} = J(J+1)B$	0	2B	6B	12B	20B	30B	42B
Line position, $\frac{\Delta\epsilon_J{}^{J+1}}{h} = 2B(J+1) = 2BJ'$	2B	4B	6B	8B	10B	12B	
ΔJ	0–1	1–2	2–3	3–4	4–5	5–6	
Spectrum (intensities unknown)	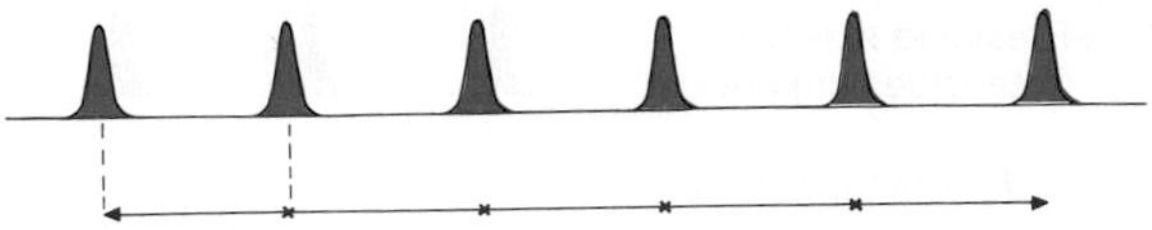						
Line spacing (sec^{-1})	2B	2B	2B	2B	2B		

But $m = M/N_0$, where M is the molar weight in grams, and N_0 is Avogadro's number. Thus, for HCl,

$$d = \left(\frac{h(M_1 + M_2)N_0}{4\pi^2 M_1 M_2 2B}\right)^{1/2} = \left(\frac{6.625 \cdot 10^{-27}(1.01 + 35.5)6.03 \cdot 10^{23}}{4\pi^2 1.01 \cdot 35.5 \cdot 2 \cdot 6.2 \cdot 10^{11}}\right)^{1/2} = 1.3 \cdot 10^{-8} \text{ cm}$$

This is the same figure obtained from other measurements of the internuclear distance in HCl. Furthermore, the line positions are at even multiples of B, also in agreement with experiment.

Figure 8.4 presents this model in terms of a rotational molecular energy level diagram in a manner exactly analogous to that used in presenting the electronic energy level in Figure 4.6. The rotational energy level diagram is the simpler of the two since the energy levels (ϵ), energy differences ($\Delta\epsilon$), and the spectrum may all be represented as a function of $B = h/8\pi^2 I$ and J. Note that $\Delta J = 1$ only.

What about the line intensities? The intensity should be proportional to the number of molecules in the lower energy level corresponding to each line, since these are the molecules which absorb the energy. Thus the intensity of the first line ($J = 0$ to $J = 1$) should be directly proportional to the number of molecules in state $J = 0$. The intensity of the next line ($J = 1$ to $J = 2$) should be proportional to the number of molecules in state $J = 1$, and so on. Thus we need to calculate the number of molecules in each level. The ratios of these numbers may give us the ratios of the corresponding line intensities.

Since the experimentally measured line intensity goes through a maximum as J increases (see Figure 8.3), we probably need at least two terms in our intensity equation: one intensity term to increase with J (especially at small J), the other intensity term to decrease as J increases (especially at large J). At least one of the terms must also depend on temperature, since line intensities are found to vary with changing T.

Exercise 8.2

Use the data in Exercise 7.3 (p. 202) to calculate the rotational spacing in Br_2 (*g*). Would lines of this spacing be observed in the *IR* spectrum?

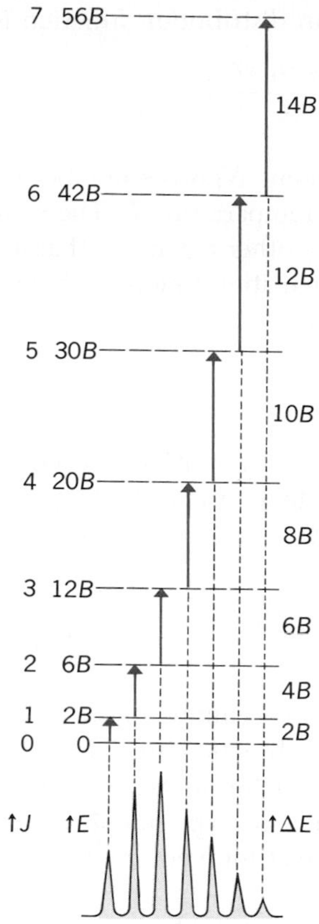

Figure 8.4 Origin of rotational absorption lines in a diatomic molecule in terms of levels of energy, $\epsilon_J = J(J + 1)B$.

Answer: Spacing $= 2B = \dfrac{h}{4\pi^2\mu d^2} = \dfrac{6.63 \cdot 10^{-27}}{4\pi^2 \cdot 3.2 \cdot 10^{-40}} = 5.2 \cdot 10^{11}\ \text{sec}^{-1}$

No lines corresponding to this spacing will be found in the *IR*, since Br_2 has a symmetrical electron field that does not absorb *IR* radiation.

THE BOLTZMANN EQUATION

Interestingly enough, the barometric formula, Equation (6.22), gives us some guidance here. It says that the ratio, N/N_0, of number of molecules of energy ϵ to those of energy 0 is given by

$$\frac{N}{N_0} = e^{-\epsilon/kT}$$

The barometric formula is a special case of a most useful expression, the

BOLTZMANN EQUATION:
$$\frac{N_2}{N_1} = \frac{g_2}{g_1} e^{-(\epsilon_2 - \epsilon_1)/kT} \tag{8.5}$$

Here N_2/N_1 gives the equilibrium ratio of numbers of particles having energies ϵ_2 and ϵ_1 at temperature T, where there are g_2 ways for the particle to have energy ϵ_2 and g_1 ways for the particle to have energy ϵ_1; g is called the a priori probability, or statistical weight, of an energy level; k is Boltzmann's constant.

The most general form of the Boltzmann distribution function is

$$\frac{N_i}{N} = \frac{g_i e^{-\epsilon_i/kT}}{\sum_i g_i e^{-\epsilon_i/kT}} = \frac{g_i e^{-\epsilon_i/kT}}{Z} \tag{8.6}$$

where N is the total number of particles in the system, N_i is the number in the ith state of energy ϵ_i and of statistical weight g_i at temperature T. The summation term in the Boltzmann equation occurs in so many other equations that it is given a special symbol, Z, and is called the molecular partition function of the system, defined as

$$Z = \sum_i g_i e^{-\epsilon_i/kT}$$

Note that Equation (8.5) is readily derived by writing two equations of the form of (8.6)—one for state 2 and one for state 1—then dividing the first by the second. In this case, Z need not be evaluated.

ROTATIONAL LINE INTENSITIES

The relative likelihood that any molecule will have energy $\epsilon_{\text{rot}} = J(J+1)hB$ is given by the Boltzmann factor as $e^{-J(J+1)hB/kT}$. This function involves T, increasing as T increases and decreasing as J increases. The g factor or statistical weight must then increase with J if we are to get agreement with experiment. Agreement is obtained if $g = 2J + 1$. (It will be helpful to recall the vector electronic model again, page 98.)

Thus, intensity of absorption, I, by state J is given by

$$I = K(2J+1)e^{-J(J+1)hB/kT} \tag{8.7}$$

where K is a constant to give the appropriate units and J is a pure number.

Maximum intensity occurs when $dI/dJ = 0$:

$$\frac{dI}{dJ} = 0 = K2e^{-J(J+1)hB/kT} - K(2J+1)(2J+1)\frac{hB}{kT}e^{-J(J+1)hB/kT}$$

$$= Ke^{-J(J+1)hB/kT}\left[2 - \frac{(2J+1)^2 hB}{kT}\right]$$

At $J_{\max}$ the bracketed term must equal 0, since $Ke^{-J(J+1)hB/kT} \neq 0$; then

$$2 - \frac{(2J_{\max}+1)^2 hB}{kT} = 0$$

$$2J_{\max} + 1 = \left(\frac{2kT}{hB}\right)^{1/2}$$

$$J_{\max} = \left(\frac{kT}{2hB}\right)^{1/2} - \frac{1}{2} \tag{8.8}$$

An experimental check of $J_{\max}$ as a function of T shows that the theory gives good agreement, correlating the regular line spacing ($2B$), the positions of the lines (nB, where n is even), and the line intensity variation as J and T vary.

Our theory of rotational spectra involves three major points: (1) rotational angular momentum is quantized: $I\omega = [J(J+1)]^{1/2}\ h/2\pi$, $J = 0, 1, 2, 3, \ldots$, (2) only changes of $J = +1$ occur in absorption (and of $J = -1$ in emission), and (3) $g = 2J + 1$.

Exercise 8.3

Calculate the relative number of molecules in the $J = 1$ and $J = 2$ rotational states of HCl at 27°C. *Answer:* $N_2/N_1 = (g_2/g_1)e^{-\Delta\epsilon/kT} = (2 \cdot 2 + 1)/(2 \cdot 1 + 1)$ exp $(2 \cdot 6.63 \cdot 10^{27}$ erg sec $\cdot\ 6.2 \cdot 10^{11}$ sec$^{-1}/1.38 \cdot 10^{-16}$ ergs °K$^{-1} \cdot 300$°K$) = (5/3)e^{-0.20}$ $= 1.37$ times as many in $J = 2$ as in $J = 1$.

Equation (8.7) allows a simple correlation of rotational energy states with T. Consider any rotational line whose intensity is determined at two different temperatures. Then, since the values of J and the other constants are independent of T,

$$\frac{I_2}{I_1} = \frac{[K(2J+1)e^{-J(J+1)hB/kT}]_2}{[K(2J+1)e^{-J(J+1)hB/kT}]_1} = \exp\{[-J(J+1)hB/k][(1/T_2) - (1/T_1)]\}$$

Thus a measurement of the relative line intensities plus a knowledge of J, B, and one of the two temperatures allows calculation of the other value of T. This approach is actually used in determining the temperatures of hot gases, in stars for example.

ROTATIONAL STRETCHING

Close examination discloses that the spacing of rotational lines actually varies. This can be accounted for by assuming that the bond stretches at higher angular momenta—increasing d and hence decreasing B—so that the spacing $2B$ decreases. Measurement of this effect gives evidence as to the springiness of the bond (the force constant, k) and further confirms our belief in the general validity of the model proposed.

ROTATIONAL HEAT CAPACITY

Hydrogen is the substance in which the falling off in heat capacity at low temperatures (as in Figure 7.3), arising from cessation of molecular rotation, can be most easily seen experimentally. The fact that B is inversely proportional to μ [see Equation (8.4)] pushes this transition to such low temperatures for other gases that the vapor pressure is too low to allow experimental measurements. At experimentally feasible temperatures the quantum levels are so closely spaced that the molecules behave classically. To a very good approximation, all gases at all temperatures (except H_2 below 300°K) act as classical rotors and all diatomic and other linear molecules have a rotational molar heat capacity of $2(R/2) = 2$ cal mole^{-1} °K^{-1}. Nonlinear gases have $\bar{C}_V = 3(R/2)$. Exact equations for rotational contributions to heat capacity, enthalpy, and entropy will be discussed again in Chapter 28. But, for all practical purposes, molecules act as classical rotors since, for all conditions, $\bar{E}_{\text{trans}}/N_0 \gg \epsilon_{\text{rot}}$.

VIBRATIONS IN MOLECULES

If molecules can rotate and if such rotation stretches the bonds, it seems quite reasonable to believe that molecules might also vibrate. Let us construct a model and then look for experimental evidence against which to test it.

Three coordinates are needed to define completely the position of an atom in three-dimensional space. For a molecule containing N atoms, we would need a total of $3N$ coordinates. Many coordinate systems could be used. Translation can be readily defined in terms of the three Cartesian coordinates of the center of mass of the molecule, leaving $3N - 3$ coordinates to be defined in some other way.

If the atoms maintain fixed distances and angles with respect to one another, the whole molecule can still rotate about three axes through its center of mass, requiring three rotational coordinates (or two axes requiring two rotational coordinates if it is a linear molecule). Diatomic molecules are, of course, linear. Since every molecule is characterized by the existence of bonds holding the atoms together as an aggregate, it seems feasible to use additional internal coordinates, related to the molecule, to define the distribution of atoms about the center of mass. The other internal coordinates can be thought of as bond lengths and bond angles sufficient to describe the molecule completely. These last coordinates can be considered the vibrational coordinates, of number U. Some will involve mainly bond stretching, some mainly bond bending, some both stretching and bending.

Thus, for

LINEAR MOLECULES: $U = 3N - 5$ (5 represents 3 translational and 2 rotational coordinates) (8.9)

For

NONLINEAR MOLECULES: $U = 3N - 6$ (6 represents 3 translational and 3 rotational coordinates) (8.10)

For

DIATOMIC MOLECULES: $U = (3)(2) - 5 = 1$ vibrational coordinate (8.11)

There is only one possible way in which a diatomic molecule can vibrate. This vibration consists of an in-phase motion of the two atoms toward and away from the center of mass along the internuclear axis. Such motions along bond axes are called stretching motions (see Figure 7.5).

The frequency, ν, of a vibration is related inversely to the reduced mass of the vibrating particles and directly to the force constant, k, associated with the restoring force:

$$\nu = \frac{1}{2\pi}\sqrt{k/\mu} \qquad \text{or} \qquad k = 4\pi^2\nu^2\mu \tag{8.12}$$

We shall customarily express ν in sec^{-1}, or number of vibrations per second.

Exercise 8.4

Calculate the number of vibrational degrees of freedom for the following gaseous molecules: (*a*) I_2, (*b*) H—C≡C—H, (*c*) H—S—H, (*d*) NH_3, (*e*) C_6H_6. *Answer:* Linear molecules [(*a*) and (*b*)], $U = 3N - 5$; (*a*) $U = 1$, (*b*) $U = 7$. Nonlinear molecules [(*c*), (*d*), and (*e*)], $U = 3N - 6$; (*c*) $U = 3$, (*d*) $U = 6$, (*e*) $U = 30$. Note that U increases rapidly as N increases.

A MODEL OF QUANTIZED MOLECULAR VIBRATIONS

We shall assume that molecular vibrations are simple harmonic motions and that only certain energy states of spacing, $\epsilon = h\nu$, are possible. This means that the possible energy states will differ from one another by a constant amount ϵ. Thus the first excited vibrational state will have an energy $\epsilon_1 = \epsilon$, the second an energy $\epsilon_2 = 2\epsilon$, the third $\epsilon_3 = 3\epsilon$, the fourth $\epsilon_4 = 4\epsilon$, etc., above their ground state of energy ϵ_0. The total vibrational energy, ϵ_{vib}, of the Vth state is

$$\epsilon_{vib} = V\epsilon + \epsilon_0$$

Consider a system of diatomic molecules which can differ in energy content but are identical in all other respects. We can calculate the total vibrational energy above the ground state, $(E - E_0)_{vib}$. This energy difference, $(E - E_0)_{vib}$, will be the sum of the energies of the separate molecules, each possible energy, ϵ_V being multiplied by the number of molecules, n_V, having that energy. Then ϵ_V is the energy difference between the ground state and the Vth excited state. We may summarize this in the quantum condition $\epsilon_{vib} - \epsilon_0 = V\epsilon = \epsilon_V$, where the vibrational quantum number, $V = 0, 1, 2, 3, 4, \ldots$.*

Then $(E - E_0)_{vib} = n_1\epsilon_1 + n_2\epsilon_2 + n_3\epsilon_3 + \cdots$, where n_V = number of particles of energy ϵ_V. But $n_V = n_0e^{-\epsilon_V/kT}$ from the Boltzmann equation, assuming $g_V = 1$. Hence

$$(E - E_0)_{vib} = n_0\epsilon_1e^{-\epsilon_1/kT} + n_0\epsilon_2e^{-\epsilon_2/kT} + n_0\epsilon_3e^{-\epsilon_3/kT} + \cdots$$

For our quantized oscillator, $\epsilon_1 = \epsilon$, $\epsilon_2 = 2\epsilon$, $\epsilon_3 = 3\epsilon$, etc. For simplicity let $x = \epsilon/kT$. Then $(E - E_0)_{vib} = n_0\epsilon e^{-x}[1 + 2e^{-x} + 3e^{-2x} + \cdots]$.

Now let us evaluate n_0. First, let

$$\begin{aligned} N = \text{total number of moles in system} &= n_0 + n_1 + n_2 + n_3 + \cdots \\ &= n_0 + n_0e^{-\epsilon/kT} + n_0e^{-2\epsilon/kT} + n_0e^{-3\epsilon/kT} + \cdots \\ &= n_0[1 + e^{-x} + e^{-2x} + e^{-3x} + \cdots] = n_0z \end{aligned}$$

where

$$z = 1 + e^{-x} + e^{-2x} + e^{-3x} + \cdots$$

Then $ze^{-x} = e^{-x} + e^{-2x} + e^{-3x} + e^{-4x} + \cdots$ and $z - ze^{-x} = 1$

or

$$z = \frac{1}{1 - e^{-x}} = 1 + e^{-x} + e^{-2x} + e^{-3x} + \cdots$$

But $N = n_0z = n_0/(1 - e^{-x})$, so $n_0 = N(1 - e^{-x})$.

Thus

$$\begin{aligned} (E - E_0)_{vib} &= N(1 - e^{-x})\epsilon e^{-x}[1 + 2e^{-x} + 3e^{-2x} + \cdots] \\ &= N(1 - e^{-x})\epsilon e^{-x}y \end{aligned}$$

where $y = 1 + 2e^{-x} + 3e^{-2x} + \cdots$. Then, since $ye^{-x} = e^{-x} + 2e^{-2x} + 3e^{-3x} + \cdots$,

$$y - ye^{-x} = 1 + e^{-x} + e^{-2x} + \cdots = z = \frac{1}{1 - e^{-x}}$$

*It is common to use v as the vibrational quantum number; V is used here to avoid confusion with ν or with velocity.

Therefore

$$y(1 - e^{-x}) = z = \frac{1}{(1 - e^{-x})}$$

$$y = \frac{1}{(1 - e^{-x})^2}$$

Finally,

$$[E - E_0]_{\text{vib}} = \frac{N(1 - e^{-x})\epsilon e^{-x}}{(1 - e^{-x})^2} = \frac{N\epsilon e^{-x}}{(1 - e^{-x})}$$

$$= \frac{N\epsilon}{e^x - 1} = \frac{NkT(\epsilon/kT)}{e^x - 1}$$

The series expression reduces to

$$[\overline{E} - \overline{E}_0]_{\text{vib}} = \frac{RT(\epsilon/kT)}{e^{\epsilon/kT} - 1} = \frac{RTx}{e^x - 1} \tag{8.13}$$

where $\overline{E}$ = molar vibrational energy in a system of quantized harmonic oscillators, $\overline{E}_0$ = molar energy of the ground state (the zero-point energy contribution), T = Kelvin temperature, R = gas constant, and $x = \epsilon/kT$, with ϵ the energy difference of two adjacent vibrational states. See Table 28.4 for easy evaluation of Equation (8.13).

Consider $[\overline{E} - \overline{E}_0]_{\text{vib}}$ at very low temperatures ($T \longrightarrow 0°K$):

$$\lim_{T \to 0} [\overline{E} - \overline{E}_0]_{\text{vib}} = \frac{RTx}{e^x - 1} = \frac{RT\epsilon/kT}{e^{\epsilon/kT} - 1} = \frac{N_0\epsilon}{e^{\infty} - 1} = 0 \tag{8.14}$$

Thus $\overline{E} \longrightarrow \overline{E}_0$ as $T \longrightarrow 0°K$. All the molecules would be in the ground state at 0°K, and

$$[\overline{E} - \overline{E}_0]_{\text{vib}} = 0$$

at low temperatures. At high temperatures, Equation (8.13) reduces to

$$[\overline{E} - \overline{E}_0]_{\text{vib}} = RT - N_0 \frac{\epsilon}{2} \tag{8.15}$$

We can equate this on a term by term basis, since we recognize $\overline{E} = RT$ [from Equation (7.11)] as the classical equation for the energy of a diatomic molecule at temperature T.

At very low temperatures $\overline{E}_0 = N_0(\epsilon/2)$ or $\overline{E}_0/N_0 = \epsilon/2$ = average energy of each oscillator in the ground state. But we have already showed by Equation (8.14) that all the molecules are in the ground state at 0°K; thus this value, $\epsilon/2$, is the zero point or residual energy of a harmonic oscillator molecule at 0°K. Hence each vibration is occurring at the absolute zero of temperature, with one-half unit of vibrational energy. Thus the energy of state V is given by $\epsilon_V = Vh\nu + \frac{1}{2}h\nu = h\nu(V + \frac{1}{2})$.

Note that residual vibration at 0°K is consistent with the Heisenberg uncertainty principle, which implies that the atoms cannot be at rest since one cannot know both the position and momentum of a particle at the same instant. The fact that our simple harmonic oscillator model agrees with experiment both as $T \longrightarrow 0°K$ and as $T \longrightarrow \infty$ augurs well for its general success.

Figure 8.5 illustrates our vibrational model in a plot of potential energy (vibrational only) versus internuclear distance, d. For a simple harmonic vibrator the vibrational energy levels are equally spaced and only one line of energy $\epsilon = h\nu$ would appear in the purely vibrational spectrum.

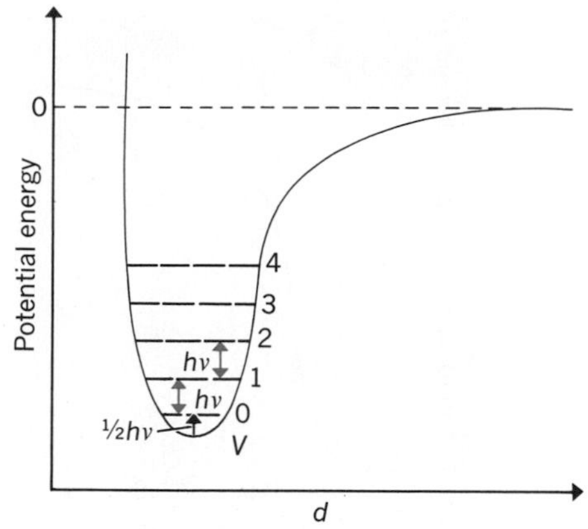

Figure 8.5 Origin of the single vibrational absorption line, $\Delta\epsilon = h\nu$, in a diatomic harmonic oscillator in terms of levels of energy, $\epsilon_V = h\nu(V + \frac{1}{2})$.

QUANTIZED VIBRATIONAL HEAT CAPACITY

Heat capacity data gave valuable clues to molecular rotation. Perhaps similar insights on vibration are possible. Let us use our quantized model to calculate some vibrational heat capacities,

$$C_{V(\text{vib})} = \left(\frac{\partial E_{\text{vib}}}{\partial T}\right)_V$$

and check them with experiment.

We know that E_0 can never make any contribution to the heat capacity, since it represents only the energy in the ground state. Thus $(\partial[E - E_0]_{\text{vib}}/\partial T)_V = (\partial E_{\text{vib}}/\partial T)_V$, or

$$C_{V(\text{vib})} = \left(\frac{\partial E_{\text{vib}}}{\partial T}\right)_V = \left(\frac{\partial[E - E_0]_{\text{vib}}}{\partial T}\right)_V = \left[\frac{\partial}{\partial T}\left(\frac{N\epsilon}{e^{\epsilon/kT} - 1}\right)\right]_V$$

$$C_{V(\text{vib})} = \frac{Rx^2e^x}{(e^x - 1)^2} \tag{8.16}$$

where $x = \epsilon/kT = h\nu/kT$. This equation is known as the Einstein heat capacity equation for one degree of vibration. See Table 28.4 for its easy evaluation.

As we did with energy, we will check the value of $C_{V(\text{vib})}$ as $T \longrightarrow 0$ and as $T \longrightarrow \infty$. As $T \longrightarrow 0$, $x \longrightarrow \infty$, $e^x - 1 \longrightarrow e^x$, and

$$\overline{C}_{V(\text{vib})} \longrightarrow R\frac{\infty^2}{e^\infty} \longrightarrow 0$$

As $T \longrightarrow \infty$, $x \longrightarrow 0$, and, for each vibration,

$$\overline{C}_{V(\text{vib})} \longrightarrow \frac{Rx^2\left(1 + x + \dfrac{x^2}{2} + \cdots\right)}{\left(1 + x + \dfrac{x^2}{2} + \cdots - 1\right)^2} \longrightarrow \frac{Rx^2}{x^2} \longrightarrow R = 2\left(\frac{R}{2}\right)$$

These two limits are certainly consistent with the experimental data and theoretical calculations already given for H_2 and other diatomic gases in Chapter 7.

Figure 8.6 shows C_{vib} as a function of $1/x = kT/h\nu = cT$—that is, as a

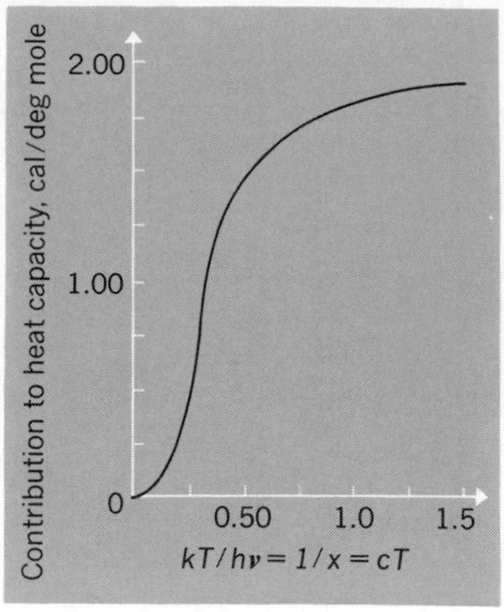

Figure 8.6 Vibrational heat-capacity contribution of a quantized harmonic oscillator.

function of T at constant ν. The agreement with the shapes of the curves in Figure 7.4 is most encouraging.

Unfortunately we have no clue to ϵ, the quantum of vibrational energy of a molecule, so cannot use the formula $\overline{C}_{V(\text{vib})} = Rx^2e^x/(e^x - 1)^2$ to calculate values of $\overline{C}_V$ for comparison with experimental values. But we could work backward and estimate $\overline{C}_{V(\text{vib})}$, x, and hence ϵ, from experimental heat capacities.

The experimental heat capacity, $\overline{C}_V$, of hydrogen chloride gas, HCl, at 298°K is 5.01 cal mole^{-1} °K^{-1}. We assume that this total heat capacity is the sum of the translational, rotational, and vibrational contributions, with translations and rotations contributing their full "classical" amount (Figure 7.3) and vibrations accounting for the rest. Let us see if this is true.

If so,

$$\overline{C}_{\text{vib}} = \overline{C}_V - \overline{C}_{\text{trans}} - \overline{C}_{\text{rot}} \qquad \text{(all at constant volume)}$$
$$= 5.01 - (\tfrac{3}{2}\,1.987) - (\tfrac{2}{2}\,1.987) = 5.01 - (\tfrac{5}{2}\,1.987)$$
$$= 5.01 - 4.967 \cong 0.04$$

The difference, 0.04 cal mole^{-1} deg^{-1}, is too small for accurate evaluation but is in the right direction. Let us try a higher temperature.

If we try 1000°K, $\overline{C}_V$ is then 5.550. Under our same assumptions, which should hold better at this higher value of T,

Table 8.3 Calculation of vibrational frequency in HCl from gas heat capacity, $\overline{C}_V$.

	T			
	1000	1200	1400	1500
$\overline{C}_{V(\text{expt})}$	5.550	5.800	6.080	6.229
$\overline{C}_{V(\text{vib})}$	0.583	0.833	1.113	1.262
x	4.1	3.37	2.73	2.40
$\epsilon_{(\text{ergs})}$	$5.66 \cdot 10^{-13}$	$5.61 \cdot 10^{-13}$	$5.28 \cdot 10^{-13}$	$4.96 \cdot 10^{-13}$
$\nu_{(\text{theor})}(\text{sec}^{-1})$	$8.6 \cdot 10^{13}$	$8.5 \cdot 10^{13}$	$8.0 \cdot 10^{13}$	$7.5 \cdot 10^{13} \cong 8 \cdot 10^{13}\ \text{sec}^{-1}$

$$\overline{C}_{\text{vib}} = 5.550 - 4.967 = 0.583 \text{ cal mole}^{-1} \text{ deg}^{-1} = \frac{Rx^2e^x}{(e^x - 1)^2}$$

Solving for x gives $x = 4.1 = \epsilon/kT$ (see Table 28.4 for handy data), and $\epsilon = 5.7 \cdot 10^{-13}$ ergs $= h\nu$. Then $\nu = 8.6 \cdot 10^{13}$ sec^{-1}. This frequency is in the near infrared.

Table 8.3 repeats the calculation at 1200, 1400, and 1500°K. The small variation in ν is gratifying in view of the rough calculation. We predict that the vibration frequency of HCl is about $8 \cdot 10^{13}$ sec^{-1} and should be observable spectroscopically in the near infrared frequencies near that value.

Exercise 8.5

Estimate the zero-point vibrational energy of HCl. *Answer:* $\epsilon_0 = \frac{1}{2}h\nu$. $\epsilon_0 = \frac{1}{2} \cdot 6.63 \cdot 10^{-27}$ ergs sec molecules$^{-1} \cdot 8 \cdot 10^{13}$ sec$^{-1} \cong 3 \cdot 10^{-13}$ ergs molecules^{-1}. $N_0\epsilon_0 = \overline{E}_0 = 4$ kcal mole^{-1}.

VIBRATION SPECTRA

Figure 8.7 shows the near infrared spectrum of gaseous HCl from 10^{13} to 10^{15} sec^{-1}. An absorption peak is observed at about $8 \cdot 10^{13}$ sec^{-1}. [Note the remarkable agreement with the prediction from our model in the previous section.] Furthermore, another peak is observed at $16 \cdot 10^{13}$. We can attribute this to a double jump in vibrational energy, $h\nu = 2\epsilon$. Such a jump, for example, might be from the ground state to the second vibrational state. The double jump is much less intense than the single, indicating that a "double" transition is less likely than a single one under these conditions.

Close examination under moderate resolution of the region around $8 \cdot 10^{13}$ sec^{-1} gives the spectrum of Figure 8.8. Many lines are observed; the spacing is quite constant but the intensities vary. This is reminiscent of the experimental results in the region of 10^{11} sec^{-1}, where only rotation was occurring. Measurement of the spacing shows it to be about $6 \cdot 10^{11}$ sec^{-1}, just as was the rotational spacing previously discussed. Again the spacing varies slightly, perhaps again indicating that the molecule stretches as rotation increases. All these predictions are borne out by detailed calculations using the spectral data. Thus vibrational changes are accompanied by simultaneous rotational changes ($\Delta J = +1$ or -1) as shown in Figure 8.9.

For the moment we shall be satisfied that our model interprets the total energy, the heat capacity, and the absorption spectrum of gases in terms of translation, rotation, and vibration of the quantized molecules. The model is simple.

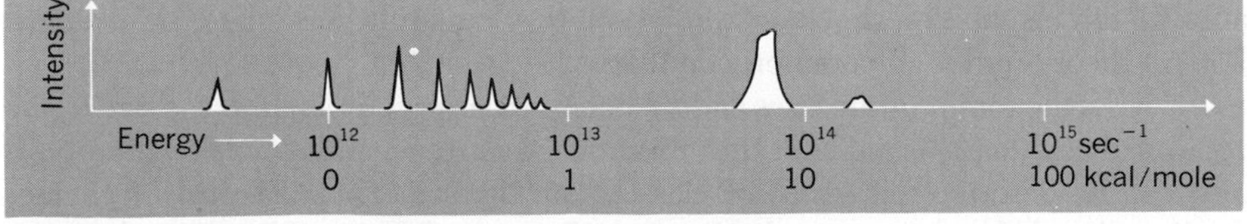

Figure 8.7 Schematic diagram of the near infrared spectrum of gaseous hydrogen chloride at low resolution. Rotational transitions are near 10^{12} sec^{-1}. Simultaneous vibration-rotation transitions near 10^{14} sec^{-1}.

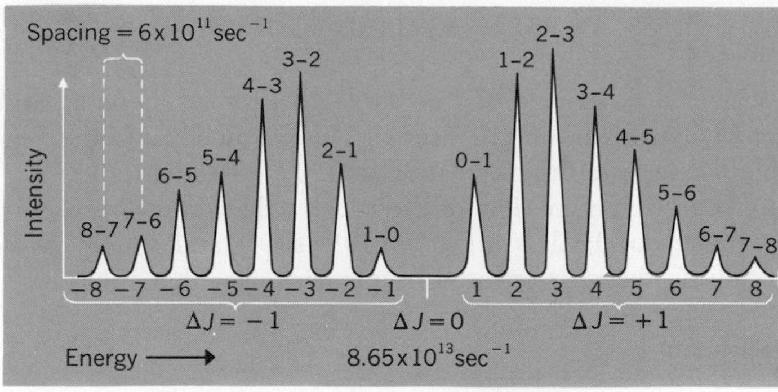

Figure 8.8 Near infrared spectrum of gaseous hydrogen chloride at moderate resolution, $\Delta V = +1$, $\Delta J = +1$ or -1 (schematic). The center of the band, $8.65 \cdot 10^{13}$ sec^{-1}, corresponds to the vibrational frequency of the molecules, but note that no energy corresponding to change in vibration only is absorbed. Each of the observed lines corresponds to a change in both vibrational *and* rotational energy, thus giving sets of lines each separated by $6 \cdot 10^{11}$ sec^{-1} in energy. The lines to the right of center correspond to one unit of change in vibrational energy, $8.65 \cdot 10^{13}$ sec^{-1}, plus an increase in rotational energy. The lines to the left correspond to one unit of change in vibrational energy, accompanied by a loss in rotational energy. This type of spectrum is consequently known as a vibration-rotation band. Note that the transition in which vibration would change without change in rotation is not observed—such transitions are observed to be forbidden in harmonic oscillators. See also Figure 3.16.

It merely assumes that rotation is so quantized that only certain values of the angular momentum are possible—that is, $I\omega = [J(J+1)]^{1/2}h/2\pi$, for $J = 0, 1, 2, 3, 4, \ldots$—and that the only possible energy changes are those in which $\Delta J = 1$. The model also assumes that vibration is so quantized that $\epsilon_V - \epsilon_0 = V\epsilon$. Since $\epsilon_0 = \epsilon/2$, we may rewrite the quantum condition for

VIBRATIONAL ENERGY:
$$\epsilon_V = (V + \tfrac{1}{2})\epsilon \tag{8.17}$$

where ϵ_V is the total vibrational energy of the state of vibrational quantum number $V = 0, 1, 2, 3, \ldots$, and ϵ is the energy of one quantum of vibrational energy.

We have seen that rotational quanta have a frequency of about 10^{11} sec^{-1} for HCl and vibrational quanta a frequency of about 10^{13} sec^{-1}. These are typical of the spectral range in which each type of absorption can be observed for many molecules. Usually the rotational frequency is lower by a factor of 100 cycles per second.

So far as we have been able to detect in the above discussion, translational motions do not show quantum effects. Careful study indicates that translational motions *are* quantized, but that the quantum spacing is so small as to be undetectable in any usual experiment. Translation is adequately described by classical kinetic theory under all common conditions.

As the temperature rises and kT becomes large compared to the size of the rotational quanta ($2B$), and later the vibrational quanta (ϵ), these molecular motions also can be described in terms of classical mechanics. Thus classical mechanics applies when $kT \gg h\nu$, or as $e^{-h\nu/kT} = e^{-\epsilon/kT}$ approaches unity. Rotational quanta are so small that they are classical at room temperature. Vibrational quanta are larger, and most molecular vibrations become classical only at elevated temperatures. Recall the case of hydrogen chloride calculated above. Figure 8.10 shows

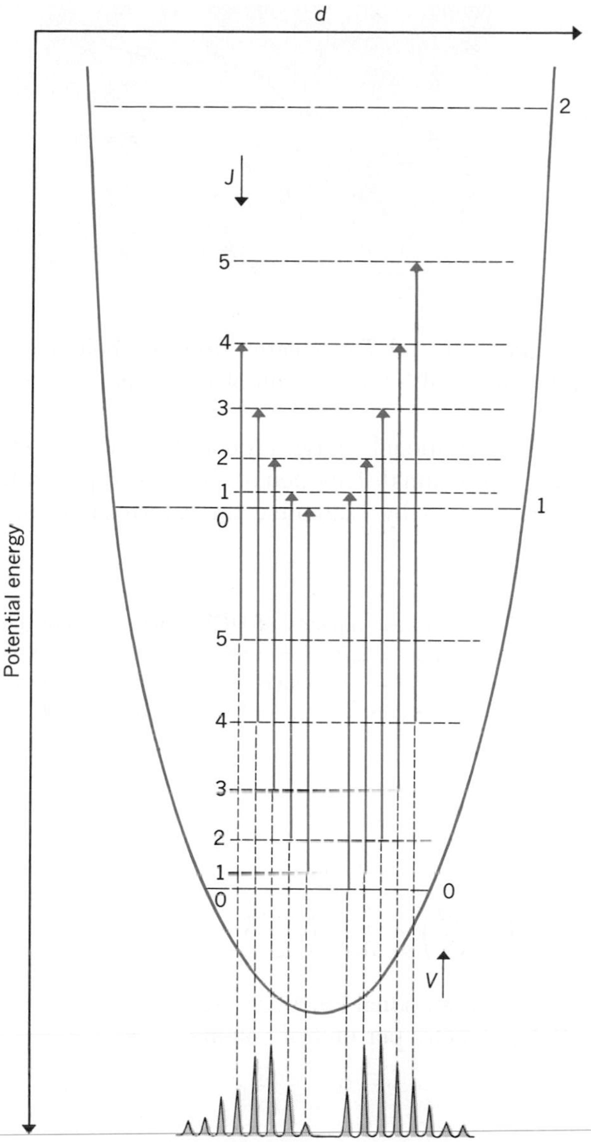

Figure 8.9 Origin of observed vibration-rotation spectral lines in a diatomic molecule: $\Delta V = +1$, $\Delta J = \pm 1$ as in Figure 8.8.

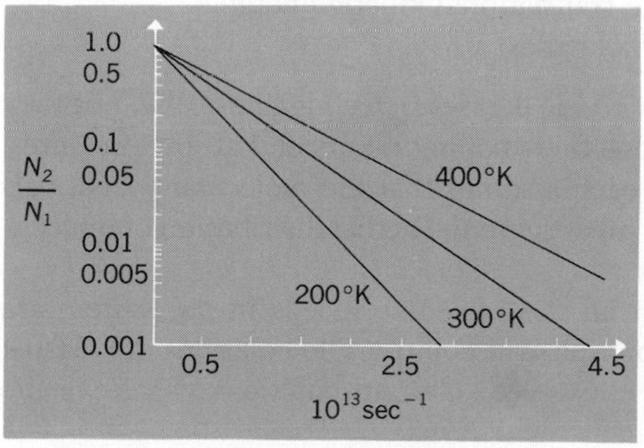

Figure 8.10 The relative population N_2/N_1, Equation (8.5), for vibrational levels of a harmonic diatomic molecule at 200, 300, and 400°K. Note that the HCl vibration, $8.65 \cdot 10^{13}$ sec^{-1}, will have very little excitation at these temperatures as already noted.

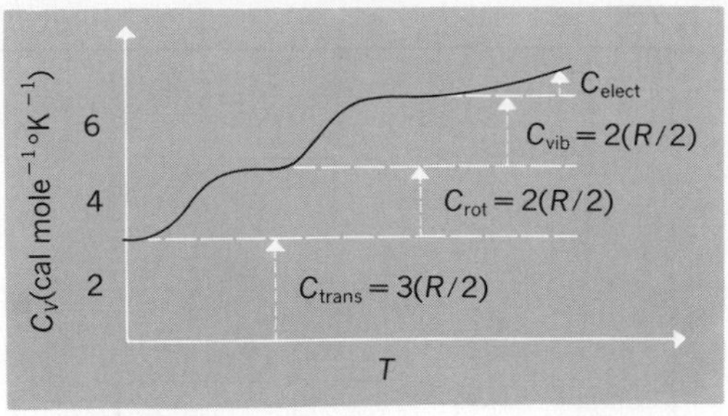

Figure 8.11 Schematic variation of C_V with T for a diatomic molecule. Only with H_2 is it possible to detect calorimetrically the variation in C_{rot}.

the variation of N_2/N_1 as a function of $h\nu$ and T calculated from the Boltzmann equations. Figure 8.11 summarizes the total interpretation of the variation of C_V with T.

Though the quantization of translational energies is not observable in our usual experiments, the effect of the Boltzmann distribution of energies is apparent. We shall round out our discussion of gases by examining this interrelationship.

Exercise 8.6

Calculate the T at which the vibrational heat capacity of HCl achieves 99% of the classical value. *Answer:* Classical value $= 2(R/2) = 1.9871$ cal mole^{-1}. $0.99 \cdot 1.9871 = 1.97$ cal mole^{-1}, $1.97 = Rx^2/(e^x - 1)^2$, where $x = h\nu/kT = 0.35$ from Table 28.4. $T = h\nu/kx = 6.63 \cdot 10^{-27} \cdot 8.65 \cdot 10^{13}/1.38 \cdot 10^{-16} \cdot 0.35 = 12{,}000$°K.

TRANSLATIONAL ENERGIES IN GASES

We have already shown (p. 181) that

$$P = \frac{Nmv^2}{3V} = \left(\frac{2}{3}\right)\left(\frac{Nmv^2}{2V}\right) = \frac{2}{3}\left[N\left(\frac{mv^2}{2}\right)/V\right]$$

$$= \frac{2}{3} \cdot \text{(average translational kinetic energy of the molecules per unit of volume)}$$

and that

$$T = \left(\frac{2}{3k}\right)\left(\frac{mv^2}{2}\right)$$

$$= \frac{2}{3k} \cdot \text{(average translational kinetic energy of the molecules)}$$

These equations apply rigorously only to ideal gases behaving classically, but they apply reasonably well to all gases above their boiling points and at low pressures. They give only average values, since each assumes that the molecular speed, v, is an average for the system. Let us now investigate the actual distribution of molecular translational speeds.

Assume that at some instant all the molcular speeds in the system are identical. The molecules are in motion and will collide. The collisions are elastic, and momentum and energy will be conserved. Certain collisions will leave the speeds unchanged, but most collisions will result in a redistribution of the energy. A given collision may result in one of the two molecules slowing down and the other gaining speed, but each molecule will shortly undergo another collision and can again change its speed. Although the system starts with all molecules at the same speed and energy, it soon contains molecules of many different speeds or translational energies. [Since all changes in an isolated system lead to an increase in entropy, you should not be surprised here.] We may then ask as to the equilibrium distribution of molecular speeds and, hence, of translational kinetic energies. Once more the Boltzmann factor $e^{-\Delta E/RT} = e^{-\epsilon/kT}$ appears in the solution.

A complete derivation and treatment of this problem is given in many books on physical chemistry or the kinetic theory of gases. The result is the

MAXWELL-BOLTZMANN EQUATION:
$$\frac{dN}{N} = 4\pi v^2\left(\frac{m}{2\pi kT}\right)^{3/2} e^{-mv^2/2kT}\,dv \tag{8.18}$$

where dN/N = fraction of molecules having speed between v and $v + dv$. Note the occurrence of the Boltzmann function, $e^{-mv^2/2kT}$. The Maxwell-Boltzmann equation is often plotted as $(1/N)(dN/dv)$ versus v or versus $E_{\text{trans}} = \frac{1}{2}mv^2$.

Figure 8.12 shows such a plot for several temperatures. In any gas the molecular velocities and energies vary over a wide range. Differentiation will show that the most probable speed, v_p, is

$$v_p = \left(\frac{2kT}{m}\right)^{1/2} = \left(\frac{2RT}{M}\right)^{1/2}$$

A molecule with a molecular weight of 50 will have a most probable speed, v_p, of about 30,000 cm sec^{-1} at 25°C. Most molecular speeds in gases at room temperature are within a factor of 3 of this figure; that is, gaseous molecular speeds are in the range of 10,000 to 100,000 cm sec^{-1} at 25°C.

The mean speed is $\bar{v} = (8RT/\pi M)^{1/2} = 0.921\sqrt{\bar{v}^2}$, where $\sqrt{\bar{v}^2}$ is the root-mean-square speed, and $v_p = 0.885\bar{v} = 0.816\sqrt{\bar{v}^2}$. Thus the translational speed (and energy) varies from molecule to molecule; the average values depending on molecular mass, m and bulk temperature, T.

We shall next consider how the total energy of the system is distributed among the molecules, and investigate the relation of these distributions to changes in the system. It should not surprise you to discover that the equilibrium distribution of energy in molecular systems may be described in terms of a Boltzmann distribution among the quantized electronic, vibrational, rotational, and translational states.

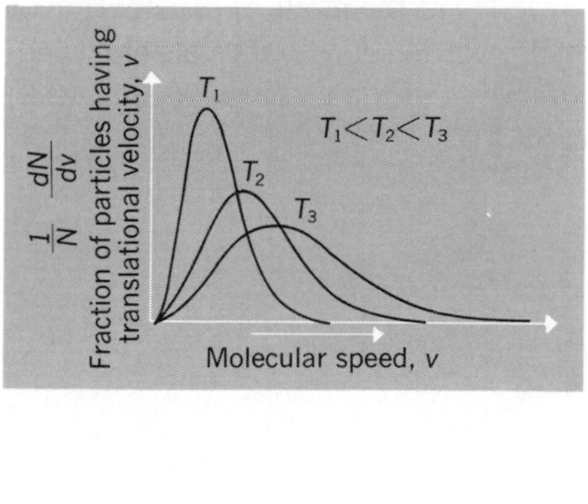

Figure 8.12 Distribution of molecular speeds at various temperatures.

Translation, as with rotation and vibration, is quantized, but the quantum levels are so close together that the effects on heat capacity are unobservable even at the lowest temperatures at which measurements are possible. Effects attributable to translational quantization are, however, observable in calculations of translational entropy.

EFFECT OF MASS ON QUANTUM LEVELS

For rotational states we find

$$\Delta E = 2(J + 1)h^2/4\pi^2 d^2 \mu$$

and for vibrational states

$$\Delta E = h\nu = (h/2\pi)(k/\mu)^{1/2}$$

In both instances a larger value of reduced mass gives a smaller quantum spacing. Thus quantum effects are not noticeable in systems of large mass and at high temperatures where $\epsilon \ll kT$; at lower temperatures, they vary with the mass of the system.

Though we shall not develop the equations, translational quantum effects are also a function of mass. Thus, heavy molecules are classical translators at lower temperatures than are lighter molecules, just as heavy molecules are classical rotors and vibrators at lower temperatures than is H_2 (see Figure 7.3).

SUMMARY

Molecules rotate and vibrate. The occurrence of sharp lines in the infrared spectrum of most substances gives rather direct measurement of these molecular motions. The total energy content (E), the heat capacity (C), and the infrared spectrum of a gas all can be interpreted in terms of quantized rotational frequencies of about 10^{11} sec^{-1} and quantized vibrational frequencies of about 10^{13} sec^{-1}. The angular momenta of rotation, $I\omega$, are quantized such that $I\omega = \sqrt{J(J+1)}(h/2\pi)$, $J = 0, 1, 2, 3, \ldots$. Vibrational frequencies are quantized such that $\epsilon_V = (V + \frac{1}{2})\epsilon$, where $V = 0, 1, 2, 3, \ldots$. Quantum effects are most noticeable at low temperatures and with particles of small mass, with spectra giving some of the most directly observable evidence for quantum effects.

Thus experimental values for heat capacity, energy ($\Delta E = q - w$), enthalpy ($H = E + PV$), and other molar properties can be considered as composed of contributions due to translational, rotational, vibrational, and electronic effects at the molecular level. Thus $C_{\text{tot}} = C_{\text{trans}} + C_{\text{rot}} + C_{\text{vib}} + C_{\text{elec}}$. Since $\Delta H = \int C_P \, dT = q_P$ and $\Delta E = \int C_V \, dT = q_V$, a knowledge of the mode of distribution of the molecules among the various translational, rotational, vibrational, and electronic states allows the calculation and interpretation of the molar heat capacities, energies, entropies, and other properties.

The scientist escapes lightly—instead of ten commandments only four: to avoid self-aggrandizement at the expense of one's fellow-scientist; fearlessly to defend the freedom of scientific inquiry and opinion; fully to communicate one's findings through primary publication, synthesis and instruction; and to demand of the people, and of their leaders too, a discussion and consideration of all those impending problems that grow out of scientific discovery and the amplification of human power.
—*Bently Glass*, Science, **150**, 1254–1261 (1965).

PROBLEMS

8.1. It seems reasonable that the likelihood of a bond-breaking reaction would depend on the amount of energy in colliding molecules. Use Figure 8.12 and discuss the effect of increasing temperature on the likelihood of such bond-breaking reactions. What would be the effect of increasing temperature on bond-forming reactions?

8.2. Suggest an interpretation of the experimental observation that only polar molecules can have their rotational energy changed by a photon, and nonpolar molecules cannot.

8.3. Consider a mole of gaseous diatomic molecules, Cl_2 for example, at 298°K, under a total pressure of one atmosphere. The molecules possess energy in various forms, chemical bonds, rotation, vibration, and translation. Rank the foregoing in terms of decreasing contribution to the total energy of the system of molecules (largest first, smallest last).

8.4. Would you expect molecular energy transfers of electronic, vibrational, and rotational energy into rotational energy of a second molecule to have a high or low probability per collision?

II

8.5. What is the relative probability that a gaseous hydrogen chloride molecule at 27°C will be in its ground vibrational state and (*a*) the first excited vibrational state, $v = 1$, (about 10^{-6}) (*b*) the second vibrational state, $v = 2$? (See Figure 8.1 for some useful data.)

8.6. Which would have the higher capacity due only to the rotational contribution, H_2O^{16} or H_2O^{18}? The temperature is assumed constant and below that at which the rotations are completely excited. How would the rotational heat capacities compare were the temperature to be above that at which the rotations are completely excited?

8.7. In dealing with vibrations, rotations, and other processes in physical chemistry we are continually making a comparison of energy changes with the kT term of the Maxwell-Boltzmann distribution equation. Evaluate kT at 300°K in the following "energy" units: (*a*) ergs, (*b*) electron volts, (*c*) cm^{-1}, (*d*) g, (*e*) kcal/mole.

8.8. The following data have been obtained for the carbon monoxide molecule. (*a*) Fundamental vibration frequency $6.50 \cdot 10^{13}$ sec^{-1}. (*b*) $B = 1.743 \cdot 10^{11}$ sec^{-1}. Find the rotational quantum number for which the CO molecule will have the same energy as it would have in its first vibration state with no rotational energy. (About 10.)

8.9. Calculate and check the C—H internuclear distances in HCN, using the fact that the rotational spacing in HCN is $11.95 \cdot 10^{10}$ sec^{-1} and in DCN is $7.23 \cdot 10^{10}$ sec^{-1}. [See R. Little, *J. Chem. Ed.*, **43**, 2 (1966).] Independent data give C≡N equal to 1.1553 Å in HCN. (About 1 Å.)

III

8.10. The interatomic distance in gaseous hydrogen bromide is 1.414 Å. (*a*) Calculate the rotational spectrum of gaseous hydrogen bromide. (*b*) Estimate the lowest temperature at which the rotational heat capacity of gaseous hydrogen bromide would first be noticeable.

8.11. Estimate the values of I for the following molecules—1, 2, or 3 values, as the case may be. Covalent bond distances are available in Chapter 14.

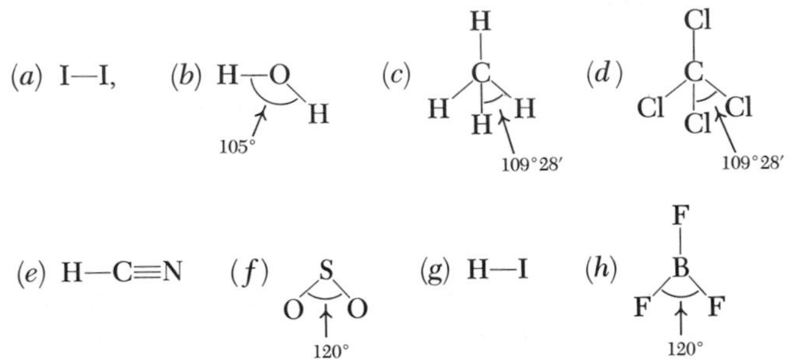

8.12. Sketch a figure like Figure 8.8 for each of the following molecules as you would actually expect to find it in the IR spectrum at 400°K: HI, CO, I_2, N_2. Covalent bond distances are in Chapter 14.

8.13. The isotopic molecules listed have IR absorption bands like those in Figure 8.8. Calculate the force constant and the internuclear distance for H^1—Cl^{35} and compare it with the value for one of the other molecules. Comment on the comparison. Units are cm^{-1}.

Species	H^1Cl^{35}	H^1Cl^{37}	H^2Cl^{35}	H^2Cl^{37}
Band center (cm^{-1})	2885.67	2883.58	2090.63	2087.59
Line spacing (cm^{-1}) (at band center)	20.58	20.58	10.65	10.65

8.14. The spectrum below is a vibration-rotation band obtained from a gas phase sample of HCl. It corresponds to transitions $\Delta V = +2$ and $\Delta J = \pm 1$.

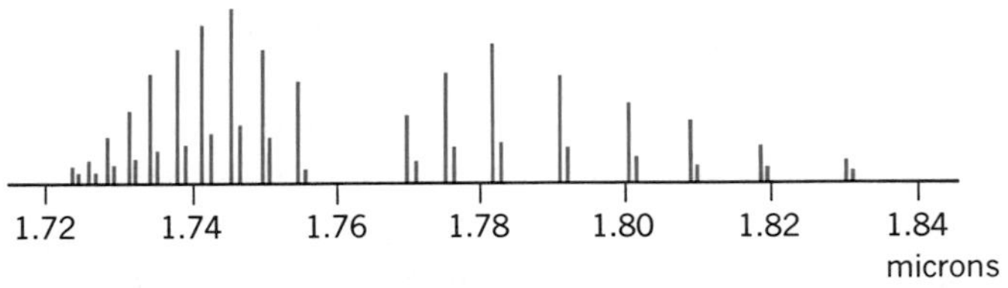

(*a*) Explain why each absorption peak is split into a "doublet."
(*b*) What kinds of transitions give rise to the peaks which occur to the long-wavelength side of the band's center at about 1.765 μ? (Answer this by giving the actual changes of *J* corresponding to these peaks.)
(*c*) Explain why each peak on the long-wavelength side of the band is less intense than the corresponding peak on the short-wavelength side of the band.

8.15. Here are the absorption rotation-vibration lines for some isotopic HCl molecules in wave numbers, cm^{-1}. Calculate the interatomic distance in one of the isotopic species.

$\Delta V \rightarrow$	H^1Cl^{35} 0–1	H^1Cl^{35} 0–2	H^1Cl^{37} 0–1	H^2Cl^{35} (obs.) 0–1	H^2Cl^{35} (calc.) 0–1	H^2Cl^{37} 0–1	$\Delta J \downarrow$
−10	2651.97		2650.36				
−9	2677.73		2675.90	1986.07	1986.11	1983.31	9 → 8
−8	2703.06	5468.55	2701.29	1998.53	1998.56		8 → 7
−7	27.75	96.97	26.01	2010.76	2010.82	2007.72	7 → 6
−6	52.03	5525.04	50.31	22.85	22.87	19.94	6 → 5
−5	75.79	51.68	73.77	34.73	34.72	31.85	5 → 4
−4	98.78	77.25	96.88	46.38	46.36		4 → 3
−3	2821.49	5602.05	2819.51	57.79	57.78	54.86	3 → 2
−2	43.56	24.81	41.59	68.95	69.00	65.82	2 → 1
−1	65.09	47.03	62.99	79.98	80.00	76.94	1 → 0
1	2906.25	87.81	2904.16	2101.28	2101.33	98.24	0 → 1
2	25.78	5706.21	23.69	11.69	11.65	2108.63	1 → 2
3	44.81	23.29	42.71	21.81	21.75	18.71	2 → 3
4	63.24	39.29	61.08	31.62	31.62	28.50	3 → 4
5	80.90	53.88	78.68	41.29	41.24	38.14	4 → 5
6	97.78	67.50	95.66	50.64	60.63	47.45	5 → 6
7	3014.29	79.54	3012.16	59.81	59.78	56.59	6 → 7
8	29.96	90.54	27.69	68.66	68.67	65.37	7 → 8
9	44.88	99.94	42.62	77.34	77.32	74.15	8 → 9
10	59.07		56.84	85.74	85.72	82.50	9 → 10

The second column of H^2Cl^{35} values are calculated from the values observed for H^1Cl^{35}. Note the excellent agreement. All other values are observed. [See F. E. Stafford, C. W. Holt, and G. L. Paulson, "Vibration-rotation Spectrum of HCl," *J. Chem. Ed.*, **40**, 245 (1965); L. W. Richard, "The Infrared Spectra of Four Isotopes of HCl," *J. Chem. Educ.* **43**, 552 (1966).]

See page 1091 for a list of references and readings in the recent chemical literature related to the material in this chapter.

CHAPTER 9

Entropy, Probability and Change

Energy tends to spread out among all the available states in such a way that the equilibrium state is the one that can be achieved in the largest possible number of ways.

The properties of individual molecules in a gas are relatively independent of neighboring molecules since the molecules are, on the average, so far apart. It is thus possible to describe the states of the individual molecules with some accuracy and to clarify our past discussions of order, disorder, entropy, and criteria for change and equilibrium in terms of the attainable spatial and energy states of individual molecules.

ENERGY AND ITS DISTRIBUTION—PRESSURE AS A VARIABLE

Consider our methods of describing physical systems. At equilibrium in a gas (consistent with the zeroth law of thermodynamics), we find that pressure and temperature are constant throughout the system. For any change (consistent with the first law of thermodynamics) we find that the energy of the universe remains constant—energy is conserved in all known changes. But note that the zeroth law merely describes an equilibrium system, and the first law puts limits on a changing system. Neither one specifies what changes will occur.

Yet experience tells us that systems do change. Perhaps there is another law which gives guidance in describing this observation and allows us to decide which changes may occur and which cannot. We might tentatively suggest such a law: all systems tend to change toward equilibrium as time passes. Perhaps we can apply this idea to some of the systems we have studied.

One of the criteria of equilibrium is constancy of pressure throughout the system. (We will neglect the effects of gravitational, electrical, magnetic, and similar fields in our discussion.)

We have already shown (p. 163) that

$$P = \frac{2}{3}\frac{(Nmv^2/2)}{V} = \frac{2}{3}\frac{\text{average translational kinetic energy}}{\text{volume}}$$

$$= \tfrac{2}{3} \text{ translational kinetic energy density}$$

Thus pressure is proportional to the translational kinetic energy density in a system. At equilibrium the pressure (translational energy density) is constant in a gaseous system; therefore the translational kinetic energy must be uniformly distributed throughout the volume of the system.

In an ideal gas all positions have equal energy, since there are no attractive or repulsive forces acting. Thus there is no variation of energy with volume: $(\partial E/\partial V)_T = 0$. So far as total energy goes, any arrangement of the molecules is the same as any other arrangement of the molecules at constant T. But experimentally we observe that the system tends toward an equilibrium state in which the molecules are uniformly distributed; the translational kinetic energy density becomes the same everywhere.

Even in real gases we observe experimentally that the system moves, as time passes, toward an equilibrium state in which the pressure is constant throughout the gas. In a real gas, as in an ideal gas, the energy density becomes constant at equilibrium. Thus any full description of a system must not only describe its total energy, it must also describe the distribution of the energy throughout the system. Work is possible when there is net flow of energy. Since we are very often interested in obtaining work from a system, there will be many occasions when the distribution of the energy proves of even more interest than the energy content.

ENERGY AND ITS DISTRIBUTION—TEMPERATURE AS A VARIABLE

Prior to the end of the nineteenth century it was believed that all energy states were possible and that the energy of each particle was directly proportional to T (classical theory). A rise in temperature was thought to increase the energy of every particle equally. Under these conditions (called the equipartition of energy) the heat capacity, for example, would be constant at all temperatures, and the total energy would be equally distributed among all the particles present. Experimental observations show that neither of these ideas is valid. Quantum theory and the Boltzmann equation provide a model more in agreement with the experimental evidence.

Not only can energy be distributed through ordinary three-dimensional space (translational energy density proportional to pressure), it can also be distributed among the various internal energy levels—rotational, vibrational, electronic, and nuclear. Spectra, as we have shown, give direct evidence for the existence of these quantum levels, evidence which is confirmed by our study of heat capacities, and, indeed, by all available experimental observations.

The distribution of the total energy among the available quantum levels is given by the

BOLTZMANN EQUATION:

$$\frac{N_i}{N} = \frac{g_i e^{-\epsilon_i/kT}}{\sum_i g_i e^{-\epsilon_i/kT}}$$

where N is the total number of particles in the system, N_i is number in the ith energy level of energy ϵ_i and statistical weight g_i at temperature T; k is the Boltzmann constant. The energy contained in the ith level is $N_i\epsilon_i$.

Unlike the spatial distribution among equally probable levels, discussed with pressure as a variable, the thermal distribution of energy is exponential among the available energy levels. The low-energy levels contain more molecules, at least if the a priori weights of the levels are equal. Again, knowledge of the total energy is not sufficient to describe the system; we must also know the distribution of the energy among the available levels.

Consider a system of three possible energy levels of identical g value, with $\epsilon_0 = 0$, $\epsilon_1 = 1$, and $\epsilon_2 = 2$. The system contains twenty particles and their total energy is ten units. There are six, and only six, possible distributions of the ten units of energy among the three levels (as shown in Table 9.1). These six states are known as the microstates, or complexions, of the system. Over a period of time the system will exhibit all the microstates, occupying each one for a fraction of the total time proportional to the number of ways, W, each microstate can be achieved. W is called the thermodynamic probability of the microstate. The entire collection of microstates is called the ensemble of the system. Which Roman numeral in Table 9.1 represents the most probable microstate? There are certainly many ways the particles themselves could distribute within each of these six possible energy distributions or microstates. The number of ways to achieve each microstate in Table 9.1 is given by the formula

$$W = \frac{N!}{\prod_i N_i!} = \frac{20!}{N_0!N_1!N_2!}$$

This formula gives the number of ways N distinguishable things can distribute themselves among i levels, N_i identical things being in the ith level. The results for this system are listed in the last column of Table 9.1. Microstate IV is most probable.

If we apply the Boltzmann equation to the problem in Table 9.1, we get

Table 9.1 Most probable microstate.

Microstate	Number of particles, N_i, of energy $\epsilon = 0$	$\epsilon = 1$	$\epsilon = 2$	Total energy $\Sigma N_i\epsilon_i = 10$	Number of ways, W, to achieve distribution	
I	15	0	5	10	1.6×10^4	
II	14	2	4	10	5.8×10^5	
III	13	4	3	10	2.7×10^6	Most probable state
IV	12	6	2	10	3.5×10^6	Most probable state
V	11	8	1	10	1.5×10^6	Most probable state
VI	10	10	0	10	1.9×10^5	

$N_{i+1}/N_i = e^{-\Delta\epsilon/kT}$ = constant at any given T, since $\Delta\epsilon$ is constant. Thus $N_1/N_0 = N_2/N_1$. Further, $N_0 + N_1 + N_2 = N = 20$ and the total energy $= \Sigma N_i\epsilon_i = N_0 \cdot 0 + N_1 \cdot 1 + N_2 \cdot 2 = 10$. Thus we have three equations in three unknowns, N_0, N_1, N_2. The algebraic solution is $N_0 = 11.5$, $N_1 = 5.7$, $N_2 = 2.8$, or, to the closest set of integers, $N_0 = 12$, $N_1 = 6$, $N_2 = 2$, the result already calculated from probability theory in Table 9.1. (Remember there are only 20 particles, too small a number for an accurate statistical prediction.) Thus, examination of the Boltzmann equation allows us quickly to select the most probable microstate for an ensemble like 9.1, since (1) $N_{i+1} < N_i$ (eliminating I and II), (2) N_{i+1}/N_i = constant (eliminating all but IV which is closest). In the limit of infinite T, all microstates become equally populated, $N_{i+1}/N_i = 1$.*

Chemical systems can and do distribute the energy available to them in many ways. At equilibrium they will spend most of their time in the microstate that can be achieved in the maximum number of ways. The time average over all the possible microstates gives the same equilibrium state, which is described by the Boltzmann equation. Table 9.1 uses only a small number of particles, so the most probable state (IV) is not the same as the average state, which would have a population between those of III and IV. For systems of large numbers of particles, such as we meet in chemistry, the most probable microstate provides a good approximation to the equilibrium system and it is seldom necessary to consider any other microstates in describing the macroscopic properties of the system.

ENERGY AND WORK

Thus we find that the rotational, vibrational, electronic, and nuclear energy distributes itself as widely as possible among the available energy levels just as the translational kinetic energy distributed itself throughout the available volume as expressed by pressure. The energy tends to spread out among all the available energy states in such a way that the equilibrium state is the one that can be achieved in the largest number of possible ways. The tendency toward equilibrium can be described in terms of this tendency toward the most probable distribution of the energy. The total energy of the universe remains constant, but it gradually becomes degraded; that is, energy distributes itself more and more widely among the available quantum states and becomes less and less available for useful work. While the energy is distributing itself, it may be said to be flowing from one part of the system to another. Under these conditions we may be able to get work as the energy flows. But once the most probable state is achieved, the net flow of energy ceases, and so work is impossible.

Exercise 9.1

What is the most probable distribution of 12 atoms over three states of energy, 0, 1, and 2, if there are 5 units of energy in the system? *Answer:* There are only three possible microstates: 7, 5, 0; 8, 3, 1; and 9, 1, 2. Assume all g's are the same. If Boltz-

* We shall discuss only Boltzmann statistics in this book. Actually, many particles should be treated with Bose-Einstein or Fermi-Dirac statistics. Fortunately for us, all three treatments become equivalent at the temperatures (high) and pressures (low) with which we shall normally deal.

mann statistics is followed, the 9, 1, 2 state is not the most probable, since no most probable Boltzmann distribution with equal g's has a higher level more populous than a lower one. Furthermore, 8, 3, 1 is more probable than 7, 5, 0 since N_2/N_1 must be constant if $(\epsilon_2 - \epsilon_1)$ is a constant in a Boltzmann distribution.

SOME PROBABILITY IDEAS

Probability theory can be of great use in correlating and/or predicting the behavior of chemical systems. You may have applied such ideas to the chance of getting heads when tossing coins, or getting thirteen spades when playing bridge. We shall find three probability generalizations especially useful in discussing spatial distribution and/or energy distribution.

1. If n independent, equally likely states of a system can exist and m of them involve a particular condition or state, the probability of that condition or state is $m/n = p$. If $p = 0$, that state will not occur; if $p = 1$, only that state will occur. The sum of the probabilities in any given system equals 1, $\Sigma m = n$. (For any ensemble of microstates, the relation between probability, p, and thermodynamic probability, W, is $p_i = W_i/\Sigma W_i$.) *Example:* The probability of a particular molecule of an ideal gas being in the total volume of the system is 1, the probability of it being in one particular half of the system is $\frac{1}{2}$.
2. The probability of two independent conditions or states, i and j, of independent systems 1 and 2 both occurring simultaneously is the product of the separate probabilities of the individual states, $p_{ij} = p_i p_j$. *Example:* The probability that two molecules will enter a given volume element at the same time (that they will collide, for example) is the product of the probabilities that each molecule will be there (proportional to the product of their concentrations in the system).
3. Small fluctuations from the condition or state having the maximum probability are more probable than large fluctuations, but both occur. In spite of fluctuations, the most probable microstate provides a good approximation of the observed macroscopic properties. *Example:* The most probable condition in Table 9.1 is IV, but each of the other states occurs, decreasing in probability as its difference from the most probable state increases.

PROBABILITY AND ENERGY DISTRIBUTION—ENTROPY

Consider the problem of an ideal gas at constant pressure. What is the probability that the gas will spontaneously concentrate into one-third the total available volume? This sounds like a rhetorical mathematical question, but actually the answer that is based on probability alone matches what one observes in the laboratory.

The probability of finding any one of the N molecules in the total volume is p. The probability of finding a molecule in the smaller volume is $\frac{1}{3}$, since the smaller volume is $\frac{1}{3}$ of the total volume (rule 1). The probability of finding all N

molecules simultaneously in the smaller volume (and none elsewhere) is the product over all N molecules of finding any one of them there (rule 2):

$$\prod_N \frac{1}{3} = \left(\frac{1}{3}\right)^N$$

We can compare this possible "collected" state with the state in which the molecules are uniformly distributed throughout the total volume. The probability of finding any given molecule in the total volume is p; the probability of finding all N molecules is the product of the individual probabilities (rule 2):

$$\prod_N p = 1^N$$

We see that this distribution is much more probable than the one above.

The ratio of the two probability products is $1^N/(\frac{1}{3})^N$. This ratio favors the uniform distribution throughout the whole volume by 3^N. The uniform distribution is favored for any value of N, but if N is large (say Avogadro's number), the uniform distribution is highly favored.

Thus the distribution of translational kinetic energy as represented by the tendency of pressures to become uniform at equilibrium is consistent with the fact that this state is the most probable microstate. It can be achieved in more ways than any other microstate.

The probability cannot only be expressed as a product, it can also be expressed in terms of the sums of the logarithms. If the gas is initially (state 1) concentrated in one-third of the volume, we have

$$p_1 = \prod_N \frac{1}{3}$$

$$\ln p_1 = \sum_N \ln \frac{1}{3} = N \ln \frac{1}{3}$$

If the gas is later (state 2) uniformly distributed in the whole volume, we have

$$\ln p_2 = \sum_N \ln 1 = N \ln 1$$

The difference in these two terms, in favor of the uniform state, is

$$N \ln 1 - N \ln \frac{1}{3} = N \ln 3 = \ln \frac{p_2}{p_1} = \ln \frac{W_2}{W_1}$$

since $p_i = W_i/\Sigma_i W_i$. Here p_1 and p_2 (and W_1 and W_2) are the probabilities (and thermodynamic probabilities) of the initial state, 1, and the uniform state, 2, respectively. Their ratio is a dimensionless number dependent only on the number of particles involved.

We find such a ratio of probabilities coming into many descriptions of equilibrium, and always as the logarithm of the ratio. To simplify the terminology we introduce a new variable, the entropy, and define it so that the entropy always increases in any isolated constant-volume system that is changing toward equilibrium. It was Boltzmann who first defined entropy change, ΔS, in the statistical form of the

SECOND LAW OF THERMODYNAMICS:

$$\Delta S = S_2 - S_1 = k \ln \frac{W_2}{W_1} \qquad (9.1)$$

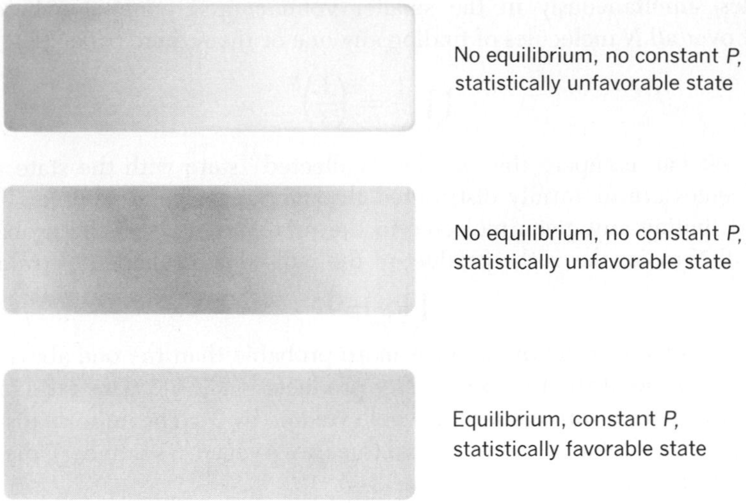

Figure 9.1 Statistically unfavorable and favorable states. The most probable state is the one in which the particles are most evenly distributed among the sites of identical energy.

where W_1 and W_2 represent the thermodynamic probabilities of (or numbers of ways of achieving) the two states between which the change is occurring; and k is the Boltzmann constant. Note that if $W_2 > W_1$, indicating a likely change, ΔS is positive. (For other statements of the second law see Appendix III.)

We thus reach the conclusion that the drive toward constant pressure at equilibrium can be interpreted in terms of the tendency to attain the most probable distribution of energy in space (see Figure 9.1). The drive toward constant temperature at equilibrium can be similarly interpreted in terms of the tendency to attain the most probable distribution of energy in the available quantum levels. In every shift toward equilibrium in a constant-energy and constant-volume system, the change in probability may be described in terms of the logarithm of the ratio of the final to the initial probability. This ratio is always greater than unity, and so the logarithm is always positive. The entropy function is introduced to aid in the description of these changes. Though we have not proved it for every case, it is well established that the *entropy always increases in any spontaneous change in an isolated system.*

Since the universe is defined as an isolated system, we can infer that any change toward equilibrium in the universe will involve an increase in entropy. The amount of energy stays constant, but it tends to redistribute in more and more random ways. Entropy is, thus, a powerful function, for it provides a means of predicting what changes may occur spontaneously and what cannot. It gives a means of deciding the direction of change and a means of controlling that direction.

ENTROPY AT LOW TEMPERATURES— THE THIRD LAW OF THERMODYNAMICS

We were able to test our earlier models for interpreting heat capacities by extrapolating them to 0°K. What happens if we try the same thing for entropy?

Consider the defining equation for the statistical

SECOND LAW OF THERMODYNAMICS: $$\Delta S = k \ln \frac{W_2}{W_1} \tag{9.1}$$

where W represents the thermodynamic probability of a state. This might also be written

$$\Delta S = S_2 - S_1 = k \ln W_2 - k \ln W_1$$

One can then write, on a term-by-term comparison,

$$\begin{aligned} S_1 &= k \ln W_1 + \text{constant} \\ S_2 &= k \ln W_2 + \text{constant} \end{aligned} \tag{9.2}$$

where the two constants must be the same.

We have already shown [Equations (8.14) and (8.15)] that at absolute zero, 0°K, the zero point energy of a system includes one-half unit of vibrational energy, and that all the molecules of any one kind have the same amount of zero point vibrational energy. They are all in the same vibrational energy state. It is possible to show that all these molecules will also be in the same electronic energy state and that the nuclear energy states will also be identical.

Every substance but helium forms a stable crystal when cooled to near 0°K. (Helium will form its crystals only at high pressures, even near 0°K.) In crystals near 0°K there is no translational motion and no rotational motion, since the magnitude of the crystal forces is too great. Thus all the molecules in a crystal of a pure substance at 0°K would be in the *same* energy state: zero translation, zero rotation, and $h\nu/2$ for each vibration. Since there is only one possible energy state, there is only one possible way for the energy to distribute. It is equally divided among all the molecules.

Similarly, the arrangement of molecules in an ideal crystal is uniquely defined. There is only one way in which the molecules can pack to form the crystal structure if it is to repeat itself over and over again indefinitely. Thus the ideal crystal at 0°K is completely described, and there is only one way it can be constructed, so far as position and energy distribution are concerned. For such a system, $W = 1$ and $\ln W = 0$. Then, designating the crystal at 0°K as state 2, at 0°K we obtain

$$\begin{aligned} S_2 &= k \ln W_2 + \text{constant} = k \ln 1 + \text{constant} \\ S_{0^\circ\text{K}} &= \text{constant} \end{aligned}$$

We cannot establish the value of this constant from our present arguments, but it is conventional to say that the entropy of a pure, perfect crystal at 0°K equals zero. Practically all tabulated values of entropy are based on this definition, which is called the

THIRD LAW OF THERMODYNAMICS: $$S_{0^\circ\text{K}} = 0 \tag{9.3}$$

Combining Equations (9.2) and (9.3) gives the form Planck first suggested for the second law

$$S = k \ln W \tag{9.4}$$

From this definition we see that the entropy of any system is zero if all of the molecules are in the same quantum state and the same geometrical state, $W = 1$. For

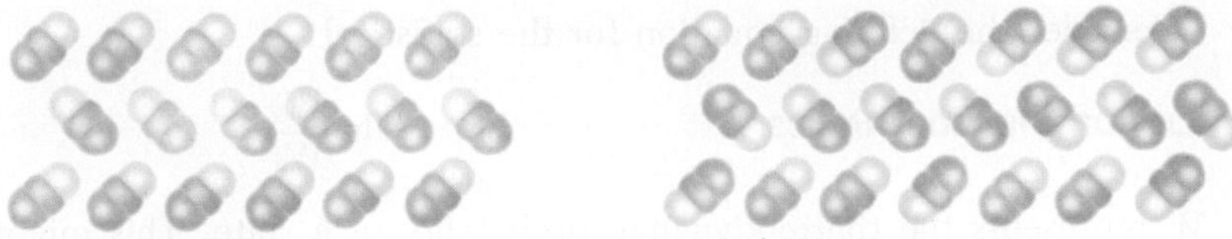

Entropy = 0 at 0°K

Entropy = R ln 2 = 1.38 cal mole^{-1} K^{-1} at 0°K

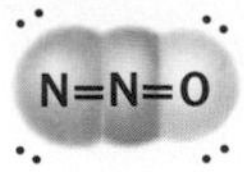

Probable election distribution in NNO, N_2O

Figure 9.2 Repeating and random packing possibilities for symmetrically shaped molecules which are unsymmetric in atomic content, using NNO as an example.

example, the entropy of a perfect crystal would be zero as long as all the molecules were in the same quantum state, whether it was the ground state or some excited electronic state, as in a laser.

"EXCEPTIONS" TO THE THIRD LAW

It is interesting to note that there are a few crystals in which the molecules have shapes such that they can pack into their crystal structure in more than one way without appreciably altering the energy of the crystal. In such cases the entropies turn out to be greater than zero near 0°K and to be calculable in terms of probability. This gives us further confidence in our use of the probability definition of entropy. It not only fits the perfect crystals, it also fits the imperfect ones for which it was not originally intended.

For example, the entropy of crystalline nitrous oxide, N_2O, can be shown experimentally to equal 1.14 ± 0.25 cal mole^{-1} °K^{-1} near 0°K. Figure 9.2 indicates that each molecule might pack in one of two ways in the crystal. The entropy of such a system (involving for each of N molecules two and only two distinguishable ways of packing) is $k \ln 2^N = R \ln 2 = 1.38$ cal mole^{-1} °K^{-1}, agreeing with the experimental value within the experimental uncertainties.

Exercise 9.2

Would crystalline HD have zero entropy near 0°K? *Answer:* HD would show end-for-end randomness in the crystalline state, which would probably remain even near 0°K. If so, its molar entropy would then be $R \ln 2$.

SUMMARY

The zeroth law of thermodynamics summarizes our experience that temperature is constant throughout a system at equilibrium. The first law summarizes our experience that the energy content of an isolated system is constant, and that energy is conserved in any change. The second law summarizes our experience that the tendency to equilibrium parallels energy redistributions which give the most probable energy density (uniform pressure) and the most probable distribution of the energy among the available quantum levels (uniform temperature). The third law of thermodynamics summarizes our experience that pure, ideal crystals at 0°K contain molecules with identical energies and a single type of packing, which is repeated throughout the crystal; the entropy of such crystals is zero.

The equilibrium state of an isolated system is the most probable state. It is the state which can be achieved in the largest number of ways. The equilibrium state is both (1) the most likely state at any instant, and (2) the time average of all the possible states.

Science is not primarily concerned with the uniqueness of events but with what they have in common with other events, so that it can explain their uniqueness in terms of general principles. Literature, art, and history, on the other hand, are chiefly concerned with unique human experiences and events, and even though they use public terms in their attempts to communicate those experiences, or general principles to try to explain them, there is always a unique element in their subject matter which is irreducible and inescapable. It is when science studies man himself that the tension between these two modes of understanding become acute.—*Walter R. Brain,* Science, 148, 192 (1965).

PROBLEMS

9.1. All processes tend to increase the entropy of the universe. Will there be a time in the future when the universe loses all capacity to do work? Justify your answer.

9.2. Which of the following substances would probably not have zero entropy in the crystalline state near 0°K: O_2, OCS, CO, IBr (Table 4.2 and Figure 5.21 may be helpful).

9.3. Can you suggest a reason why the experimental value of S_0 for N_2O is 1.14 rather than the theoretical value of 1.38 cal mole^{-1} °K^{-1}?

II

9.4. Estimate the entropy of vaporization of a liquid whose boiling point is 70°C, using only the change in volume of the system. Is this estimate apt to be high or low? Justify your decision.

9.5. Which would have the higher entropy in the gas phase at the same temperature—neon or methane? Give your reasons.

9.6. Which of the following changes would involve an increase in entropy (*i*) of the universe, (*ii*) of the closed system discussed? Draw the system and write an equation for the reaction in each case.

(*a*) Vaporization of benzene, C_6H_6, into a vacuum at 60°C.
(*b*) Solution of barium nitrate in water at 40°C.
(*c*) Precipitation of cadmium sulfide by hydrogen sulfide gas from aqueous cadmium nitrate at 27°C.
(*d*) Explosion of a gaseous solution of ethane, C_2H_6, and oxygen in a steel bomb at 110°C.
(*e*) Condensation of steam in a heat exchanger at 120°C.
(*f*) The precipitation of barium sulfate (exothermic) at 20°C upon mixing aqueous solutions of barium hydroxide and sulfuric acid.
(*g*) The gas phase reaction $C_6H_{6(g)} + 3H_{2(g)} = C_6H_{12(g)}$ at 140°C (exothermic).
(*h*) The gas phase reaction $C_2H_{6(g)} = C_2H_{2(g)} + 2H_{2(g)}$ at 30°C (endothermic).

9.7. Calculate the relative numbers of molecules with vibrational quantum numbers of $V = 0$, $V = 1$, and $V = 2$ for N_2 as $T \longrightarrow 0$.

9.8. Discuss the increasing entropy of gaseous Ar with increasing T, (*a*) arguing from $\Delta S = q_{rev}/T$, (*b*) arguing from $\Delta S = k \ln W_2/W_1$, (*c*) arguing from Figure 8.12.

9.9. Design a device (for a lecture experiment) to illustrate the entropy principle in terms of a statistical distribution.

9.10. Estimate the entropy of CH_3D at 0°K.

See page 1091 for a list of references and readings in the recent chemical literature related to the material in this chapter.

CHAPTER 10

Entropy and Gases

A general tendency in changing systems is to convert all forms of energy into heat.

The total energy of an isolated system remains constant, but the total energy does not adequately characterize the system. We need also to know how the energy is distributed among the available quantum states. At equilibrium the energy level (temperature) and the translational energy density (pressure) are the same throughout any system. It is the shifts in energy distribution toward these equilibrium conditions that characterize the changes in isolated systems, and often in closed and open systems as well. We shall now investigate possible relationships between the amount of energy which redistributes as heat, q, and the change in entropy, ΔS.

ENTROPY AND GASES AT CONSTANT TEMPERATURE

The Boltzmann statistical definition of ΔS is

$$\Delta S = k \ln (W_2/W_1)$$

For an ideal gas (point molecules with no intermolecular forces) every volume element accessible to the gas is just like any other volume element.

We considered in Chapter 9 the relative probabilities, p_2/p_1, of a system of N ideal gas molecules being in two different volume elements, V_2 and V_1, and arrived at a relationship which we can generalize as

$$N \ln \frac{V_2}{V_1} = \ln \frac{P_2}{P_1} = \ln \frac{W_2}{W_1}$$

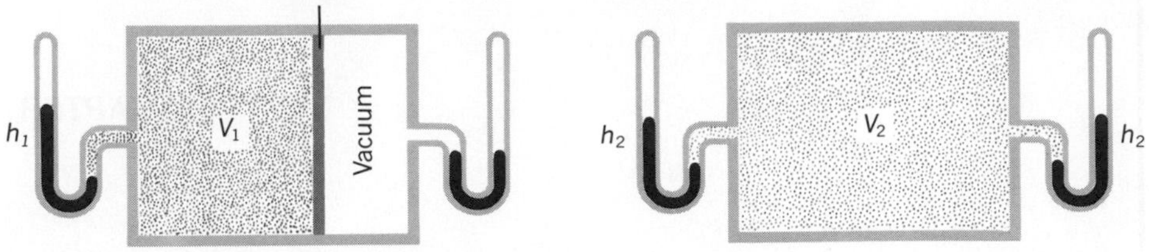

Figure 10.1 Expansion of an ideal gas into a vacuum at constant T: $\Delta\bar{S} = R \ln (V_2/V_1)$.

For the volume change of n moles of an ideal gas from V_1 to V_2, (remembering that $N = nN_0$ and $N_0k = R$) we get

$$\Delta S = k \ln \frac{W_2}{W_1} = nR \ln \frac{V_2}{V_1}$$

Consider the expansion of an ideal gas into a vacuum at constant T as illustrated in Figure 10.1. For an ideal gas, $(\partial E/\partial V)_T = 0$. Thus, for the process shown in Figure 10.1, $\Delta E = 0 = q - w$ and $q = w$. For an expansion of an ideal gas into a vacuum, however, there is no work, so $w = 0 = q$. Since $q = 0$, but $\Delta S = nR \ln (V_2/V_1)$, a positive value, we do not find any obvious relationship.

Although ΔS depends only on V_1 and V_2, the initial and final conditions, q can vary depending on how the change is accomplished or on what path is followed during the change. Figure 10.2 shows a path different from that of Figure 10.1. In this process we accomplish the same transition from the same initial V_1 to final V_2 for the gas at the same constant T. Thus ΔS and ΔE are the same here as they were in the expansion into a vacuum (Figure 10.1). But look at q and w. They are still equal (since $\Delta E = 0 = q - w$) but they might no longer be zero, since work might be done on the piston and the atmosphere behind it. The amount of work could be zero (if the piston is frictionless, and has a vacuum behind it) or positive (if one or both of these qualifications is not met). Let us assume that the piston is frictionless and that the pressure behind the piston is so adjusted that piston movement is very slow. Under these conditions the pressure behind the piston must be essentially the same as that inside the cylinder, $P_{\text{internal}} = P_{\text{external}} - dP$. Since a slight increase in the external pressure would reverse the piston's movement, these slow processes under almost zero driving force are called reversible processes. Let us calculate w, and hence q, for the reversible process.

We have seen that

$$\text{work} = \int f\,dl = \int (f/A)A\,dl = \int P\,dV$$

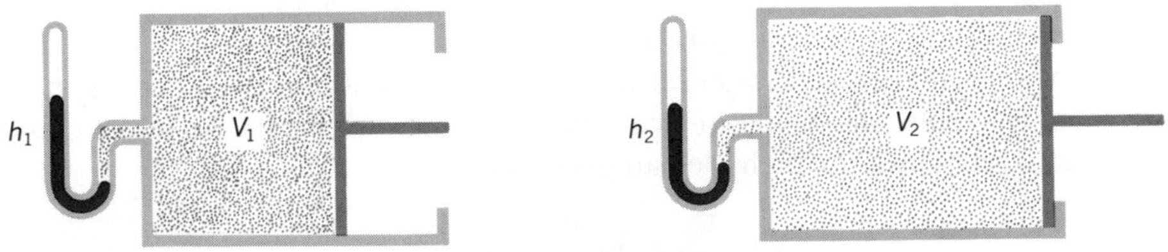

Figure 10.2 Expansion of an ideal gas against a piston at constant T: $\Delta S = R \ln (V_2/V_1) = q_{\text{rev}}/T$.

For our reversible process, $q_{rev} = w_{rev} = \int_1^2 P_{ext}\, dV$, because all work is pressure-volume work. Since the gas is ideal, $P = nRT/V$. Thus

$$q_{rev} = w_{rev} = \int_1^2 \frac{nRT}{V}\, dV = nRT \int_1^2 \frac{dV}{V} = nRT \ln \frac{V_2}{V_1} \qquad (10.1)$$

but

$$\Delta S = nR \ln \frac{V_2}{V_1} \qquad (10.2)$$

Therefore

$$q_{rev} = T\, \Delta S \qquad (10.3)$$

our sought-for relationship. The heat necessary to carry on the isothermal expansion of an ideal gas reversibly, q_{rev}, equals the Kelvin temperature times the change in entropy, $T\,\Delta S$.

Exercise 10.1

Would ΔS be $+$, $-$, or 0 for the expansion of an ideal gas from a high-pressure cylinder (230 atm) into an evacuated space chamber? Calculate ΔS and q_{rev} if the final pressure is 1.00 atm. *Answer:* ΔS should be $+$, since the volume increases, $\Delta S = nR \ln (V_2/V_1)$, but at constant T and n, $(V_2/V_1) = (P_1/P_2)$, so $\Delta S = nR \ln (P_1/P_2) = nR$ 2.303 log (230/1.00), $\Delta \overline{S} = 4.575 \log 230 = 10.82$ cal mole^{-1} °K^{-1}; $q_{rev} = T\,\Delta S$. The value of q_{rev} depends on T, but the value of ΔS does not in this case.

ENTROPY OF MIXING

Now consider a slightly different process—mixing two ideal gases. Since the gases are ideal, they will act independently of one another. Thus each will change from its initial volume to the final total volume, V_2 at constant T and P.

For gas A, from Equation (10.1),

$$\Delta S_A = n_A R \ln \frac{V_2}{V_A}$$

where V_A is the initial volume of A.

For gas B,

$$\Delta S_B = n_B R \ln \frac{V_2}{V_B}$$

where V_B is the initial volume of B.

For two gases, A and B,

$$\Delta S_{total} = \Delta S_A + \Delta S_B = n_A R \ln \frac{V_2}{V_A} + n_B R \ln \frac{V_2}{V_B}$$

$$= R \ln\left(\frac{V_2}{V_A}\right)^{n_A} + R \ln\left(\frac{V_2}{V_B}\right)^{n_B} = R \ln\left[\left(\frac{1}{V_A/V_2}\right)^{n_A}\left(\frac{1}{V_B/V_2}\right)^{n_B}\right]$$

Suppose we limit the mixing process so that P and T are constant, and $V_2 = V_A + V_B$; that is, the mixing occurs isothermally at constant total volume and constant

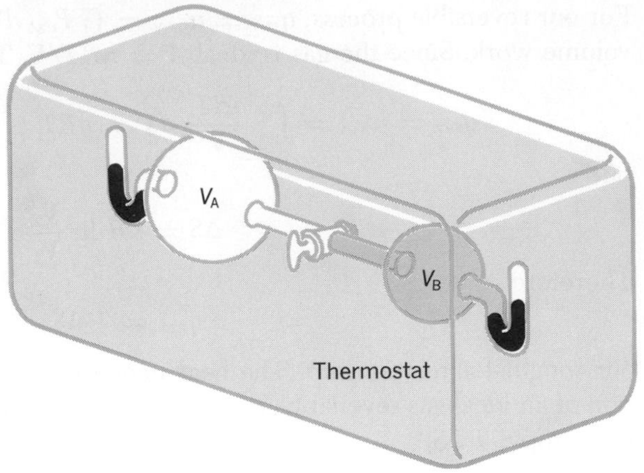

Figure 10.3 Mixing at constant total V, P, and T: $\Delta\bar{S}_{tot} = -R[X_A \ln X_A + X_B \ln X_B] = q_{rev}/T$.

pressure as in Figure 10.3. Under these conditions the volume ratio and the mole ratio or mole fraction ratio are the same. Thus

$$\frac{V_A}{V_A + V_B} = \frac{V_A}{V_2} = X_A = \frac{n_A}{n_A + n_B}$$

the mole fraction of substance A in the final mixture, and

$$\frac{V_B}{V_A + V_B} = \frac{V_B}{V_2} = X_B = \frac{n_B}{n_A + n_B}$$

the mole fraction of substance B in the final mixture.

Since we have

$$X_A = \frac{n_A}{n_A + n_B}, \; n_A = X_A(n_A + n_B)$$

then

$$\Delta S_{tot} = R \ln \left[\left(\frac{1}{X_A}\right)^{X_A(n_A+n_B)}\left(\frac{1}{X_B}\right)^{n_B}\right] = R(n_A + n_B) \ln \left[\left(\frac{1}{X_A}\right)^{X_A}\left(\frac{1}{X_B}\right)^{n_B/n_A+n_B}\right]$$

$$= Rn_{tot} \ln \left[\left(\frac{1}{X_A}\right)^{X_A}\left(\frac{1}{X_B}\right)^{X_B}\right] = -Rn_{tot}[X_A \ln X_A + X_B \ln X_B]$$

If $n_{tot} = 1$, then $\Delta\bar{S}_{tot} = -RX_A \ln X_A - RX_B \ln X_B$. Or, for i number of noninteracting species mixed isothermally at constant pressure and constant total volume,

$$\Delta\bar{S}_{mixing} = -R\sum_i X_i \ln X_i \tag{10.4}$$

where X_i is the mole fraction of the ith species in the final mixture. Thus the entropy of isothermal, isobaric (constant pressure) mixing at constant total volume of two noninteracting species is a function only of the mole fraction of the species in the final mix. For ideal gases, $X_i = V_i/V_2$. Thus, remembering $n_{tot} = 1$,

$$\Delta\bar{S}_{mixing} = -R\sum_i X_i \ln \frac{V_i}{V_2} = R\sum_i X_i \ln \frac{V_2}{V_i} = R\sum_i n_i \ln \frac{V_{tot}}{V_i}$$

But since each gas is quite independent of the others, the process of mixing is just like the change of each gas from its initial volume, V_i, into a final total volume of V_2. We have already calculated q_{rev} for this process in Equation (10.1):

$$\frac{(q_i)_{\text{rev}}}{T} = n_i R \ln \frac{V_{\text{tot}}}{V_i}$$

Therefore

$$\Delta \bar{S}_{\text{mixing}} = \sum_i \frac{(q_i)_{\text{rev}}/T}{n_{\text{tot}}}$$

If $n_{\text{tot}} = 1$, then

$$\Delta \bar{S}_{\text{mixing}} = \frac{\sum_i (q_i)_{\text{rev}}}{n_{\text{tot}}\, T} = \frac{\bar{q}_{\text{rev}}}{T} \qquad (10.5)$$

Once again the entropy change equals the total reversible heat, q_{rev}, divided by the Kelvin temperature, T.

Equation (10.4) was derived for an ideal gas but actually the only assumption involved is that $X_i = V_i/V_{\text{tot}}$: that is, that the mole fraction of component i equals the initial volume of component i divided by the final total volume. This assumption holds well for many liquid and solid solutions (though not all). Thus Equation (10.4) can be used to calculate the entropy of mixing for many solutions—gas, liquid, and solid.

ENTROPY CHANGE AND REVERSIBLE HEAT FLOW

We obtain the same result, $T\,\Delta S = q_{\text{rev}}$, for two different processes: (1) isothermal change in volume of a single ideal gas [Equation (10.3)], and (2) mixing ideal gases isothermally and isobarically at constant total volume [Equation (10.5)]. Identical results are obtained for *all* isothermal processes which are now known.

At constant temperature we can write the general equation

$$\Delta S = \frac{q_{\text{rev}}}{T} \qquad (10.6)$$

If temperature varies, we must write

$$dS = \frac{dq_{\text{rev}}}{T} \qquad \text{or} \qquad \Delta S = \int_1^2 \frac{dq_{\text{rev}}}{T} \qquad (10.7)$$

Note in Appendix III that this equation is sometimes used to define entropy, S, or its change. What we have really shown here (though only in two cases) is that the statistical definition of entropy change

$$\Delta S = k \ln \frac{W_2}{W_1} \qquad (10.8)$$

and the classical thermal definition of entropy change

$$\Delta S = \frac{q_{\text{rev}}}{T} \qquad \text{or} \qquad dS = \frac{dq_{\text{rev}}}{T} \qquad (10.9)$$

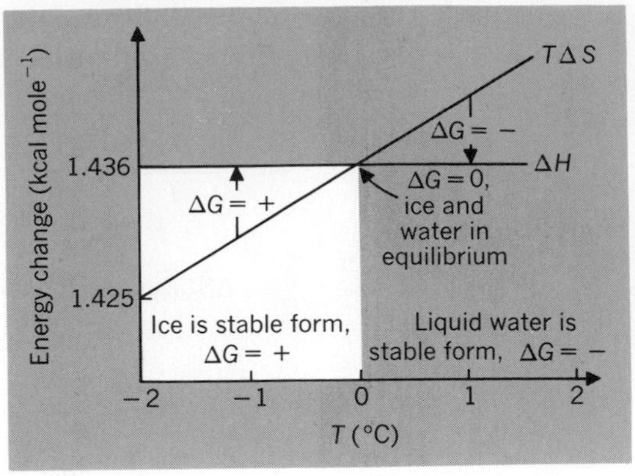

Figure 10.4 Thermodynamic quantities for the melting of ice: $H_2O_{(c)} \longrightarrow H_2O_{(l)}$. $\Delta\bar{S}_{pc}$ (5.25 eu) and $\Delta\bar{H}_{pc}$ (1436 cal) are essentially constant in this range so: $\Delta\bar{G}_{pc} = \Delta\bar{H}_{pc} - T\Delta\bar{S}_{pc} \cong [1436 - T \cdot 5.25]$ cal mole^{-1}.

are equivalent. We shall sometimes use one, sometimes the other, depending on whether statistical or thermal data are more readily available.

ENTROPY CHANGES AND PHASE EQUILIBRIA

A particularly simple form of calculation can be done to determine the entropy of a phase change. Reversible phase changes occur at constant T and P; hence $q_{rev} = q_{pc} = \Delta H_{pc}$, and

$$\Delta S_{pc} = \frac{q_{rev}}{T} = \frac{\Delta H_{pc}}{T}$$

If ΔH_{pc} is $+$, ΔS must be $+$. If ΔH is $-$, ΔS must be $-$. Similarly, since $\Delta G = \Delta H - T\Delta S$, we get $\Delta G_{pc} = \Delta H_{pc} - T(\Delta H_{pc}/T) = 0$ at equilibrium.

Now consider the effect on the equilibrium if T varies. In many instances ΔH_{pc} and ΔS_{pc} are almost constant as T varies. Thus only ΔG varies rapidly with T in the equation $\Delta G = \Delta H - T\Delta S$. If ΔH (and ΔS) are positive, ΔG will become negative as T rises above the equilibrium value and the phase of lower entropy will disappear. Conversely, a decrease in T favors the phase of lower entropy. Thus we may interpret melting, boiling, and sublimation as the disappearance of phases of low entropy, and freezing and condensation as the disappearance of phases of high entropy. The former (all having ΔH and ΔS positive) may be brought about by increasing T, which favors states of greater randomness. The latter (all having ΔH and ΔS negative) may be brought about by decreasing T, which favors states of lesser randomness. See Figure 10.4 for a treatment of the melting of ice.

Exercise 10.2

Calculate ΔH, ΔS, and ΔG for the melting of 100 g of ice at 0°C. *Answer:* $\Delta H = q_P$, $\Delta S = q_P/T$, $\Delta G = 0$ for any equilibrium phase change. $\bar{q}_P = 1.436$ kcal mole^{-1} for $H_2O_{(c)} = H_2O_{(l)}$. For 100 g, $q_P = \frac{100}{18}\,\bar{q}_P$. $\Delta H = \frac{100}{18}\,1.436$, $\Delta S = \frac{100}{18} \cdot 1.436/273$, $\Delta G = 0$. (Watch the units.)

Exercise 10.3

Calculate the relative numbers of distinguishable states in ice and in water at 0°C. *Answer:* $\Delta\bar{S} = k \ln W_2/W_1 = 1436/273$. (Watch units.)

$$\log \frac{W_2}{W_1} = \frac{1436 \text{ cal mole}^{-1} \cdot 4.18 \cdot 10^7 \text{ erg cal}^{-1}}{1.38 \cdot 10^{-16} \text{ erg } ^\circ\text{K}^{-1} \cdot 2.303 \cdot 273^\circ\text{K}} = 6.9 \cdot 10^{23} \text{ per mole}$$

$$\frac{W_2}{W_1} = 10^{6.9 \cdot 10^{23}}$$

Thus there are roughly 10^{24} times as many ways to arrange a mole of water molecules in liquid as in ice at 0°C. If the state of each molecule could be considered as independent of all other molecules (actually they cannot) there would be $W_2/W_1 = 10^{6.9 \cdot 10^{23}/6.02 \cdot 10^{23}} = 14$ times as many ways to arrange an individual molecule in the liquid compared to the crystal.

CONFIGURATIONAL AND THERMAL ENTROPY

Entropy and changes in entropy may be conveniently classed under two types: (1) entropy attributable to configurational arrangements and their changes, and (2) entropy due to quantum levels and their relative populations. The tendency of a gas to assume equal pressures throughout the available volume in an equilibrium system is interpretable in terms of spatial, or configurational, entropy alone. Consistent with the third probability rule in Chapter 9, the most probable system (highest entropy) is that in which the probability of finding a molecule is the same in every volume element of the container.

But, in general, all probabilities are not equal. Quantum levels exist and their relative populations in many systems may be described by Boltzmann statistics. Three factors are important: (1) the energy difference, ϵ, of the states, (2) the statistical weights, g, of the states, and (3) the equilibrium temperature, T.

Thus the effect of changing T on entropy is to change the relative populations of the energy states, and so affect the entropy of mixing of the states. Examination of the Boltzmann equation in the form

$$\frac{N_2}{N_1} = e^{-(\epsilon_2 - \epsilon_1)/kT}$$

shows that $N_2/N_1 \longrightarrow 1$ as $T \longrightarrow \infty$ when all values of g are identical. All states tend to become equally populated at high temperatures. In the presence of unlimited energy, all states would be equally probable and the entropy of the system would be a maximum consistent with the third probability rule. This interprets an observed general tendency in changing systems to convert all forms of energy into heat. Conversion of all forms of energy into heat tends to make the occupation of all quantum levels similar in probability and thus tends toward the mathematically most probable system.

Exercise 10.4

Calculate the temperature at which there would be as many molecules of HI in the first vibrational state as in the ground state. All g's equal one. *Answer:* $n_1/n_0 =$

$e^{-\Delta\overline{E}/RT} = 1$, but $\Delta\overline{E}/R$ is positive, so $T \longrightarrow \infty$ as $n_1/n_0 \longrightarrow 1$. Only at infinite T would the two states be equally populous. At all attainable values of T the ground state is the more populous state.

ENTROPY CHANGES IN CLOSED SYSTEMS

Our discussion so far has dealt mainly with specialized systems. Consider the more general problem of a closed system. For a closed system we have actually two systems to consider: (1) the closed system itself, and (2) the surroundings. The closed system plus the surroundings constitute the universe. According to the second law of thermodynamics, any change in the universe must be such that S_{universe} increases. Symbolically,

$$\Delta S_{\text{universe}} = \Delta S_{\text{surroundings}} + \Delta S_{\text{system}} \qquad (10.10)$$

or

$$\Delta S_{\text{univ}} = \Delta S_{\text{sur}} + \Delta S_{\text{sys}}$$
$$= \int \left(\frac{dq_{\text{rev}}}{T}\right)_{\text{sur}} + \Delta S_{\text{sys}} \qquad (10.11)$$

In many actual cases the surroundings are at constant temperature and the system operates at constant pressure with no work other than PdV work. Then

$$\Delta H_{\text{sys}} = -(dq_{\text{rev}})_{\text{sur}}$$

since ΔH represents the heat gained by the system from its surroundings [see Equation (7.5)]. Making this substitution and assuming that T is a constant in the surroundings, we obtain

$$\Delta S_{\text{univ}} = -\frac{\Delta H_{\text{sys}}}{T_{\text{sur}}} + \Delta S_{\text{sys}}$$

This expresses the total change in the universe solely in terms of changes in the closed system and the temperature of the surroundings. If we extend the constant temperature to the system as well (a common laboratory occurrence), we get

$$\Delta S_{\text{univ}} = \left[-\frac{\Delta H}{T} + \Delta S\right]_{\text{sys}} = -\frac{[\Delta H - T\,\Delta S]_{\text{sys}}}{T_{\text{sys}}} \qquad (10.12)$$

which contains only properties of the system.

The function $[\Delta H - T\,\Delta S]_{\text{sys}}$ occurs so commonly in thermodynamic equations and calculations that it is given its own symbol and name. It is called the change in the Gibbs free energy of the closed system at constant temperature and constant pressure.

We define this function in a completely general way as the

GIBBS FREE ENERGY: $$G = H - TS \qquad (10.13)$$

The total differential form is

$$dG = dH - T\,dS - S\,dT$$

The increment form is

$$\Delta G = \Delta H - T\,\Delta S - S\,\Delta T$$

which, at constant temperature, becomes

$$\Delta G = \Delta H - T\,\Delta S \qquad (10.14)$$

the form we found in Equation (10.12).

The G and ΔG are variables much used by scientists, since they combine in a single term the effects of enthalpy and entropy changes in the system.

Note that for a closed system at constant T and P, from Equations (10.12) and (10.14), with no work other than PdV work,

$$\Delta G_{sys} = -T\,\Delta S_{univ} \qquad (10.15)$$

Since ΔS_{univ} is positive for *all* changes, ΔG must be negative for *all* changes in such a system at constant temperature and constant pressure. Any net changes that would produce a positive value of ΔG under conditions of constant T and P in a closed system cannot occur (this means they have never been observed). The actual changes that do occur in such systems are the opposite of those for which calculations were made—the system will run "backward" from the predicted direction. The wide generality of Equation (10.15) makes it very useful.

If ΔG is zero for some possible change, the two states involved are at equilibrium—no net change is occurring. Remember our discussion of equilibrium phase changes, for all of which $\Delta G = 0$ in a closed system at constant T and P. These statements are summarized in Table 10.1.

Table 10.1 Some criteria for change and equilibrium.

System	For spontaneous change	At equilibrium
Isolated	$\Delta S = +$	$\Delta S = 0$
(constant E and V)		$S =$ maximum
Closed	$\Delta G = -$	$\Delta G = 0$
(constant T and P)		$G =$ minimum

ENTROPY OF VIBRATION

As an example of entropy evaluation, consider the entropy associated with molecular vibration in the same manner that we considered the energy and heat capacity associated with vibration in Chapter 8.

In general,

$$\Delta S = \frac{q_{rev}}{T}$$

For a heating process,

$$q_{rev} = \int C\,dT$$

$$\Delta S = \int \frac{C}{T}\,dT$$

Now consider only the changes in vibration that occur on heating. Then $C = C_{\text{vib}}$ and, from Equation (8.16), we have

$$\overline{C}_{\text{vib}} = \frac{Rx^2e^x}{(e^x - 1)^2}$$

for each possible vibration.

Thus for $\overline{S}_{\text{vib}}$ we get

$$\overline{S}_{\text{vib}} = \int_0^T \frac{\overline{C}_{\text{vib}}\, dT}{T} = \int \frac{Rx^2e^x\, dT}{(e^x - 1)^2 T}$$

Since $x = h\nu/kT$,

$$\frac{dx}{dT} = -\frac{h\nu}{kT^2} = -\frac{x}{T}, \qquad \frac{dx}{x} = -\frac{dT}{T}$$

$$\overline{S}_{\text{vib}} = -R\int \frac{xe^x\, dx}{(e^x - 1)^2} = -R\int \frac{x}{(e^x - 1)^2}\, d(e^x - 1)$$

$$\int u\, dv = uv - \int v\, du$$

Let $u = x$; then

$$dv = \frac{d(e^x - 1)}{(e^x - 1)^2}, \qquad v = -\frac{1}{e^x - 1}$$

$$\overline{S}_{\text{vib}} = -R\frac{-x}{e^x - 1} + R\int\left[-\frac{dx}{e^x - 1}\right] = \frac{Rx}{e^x - 1} - R\int \frac{dx}{e^x - 1}$$

$$= \frac{Rx}{e^x - 1} - R\int \frac{e^{-x}\, dx}{1 - e^{-x}} = \frac{Rx}{e^x - 1} - R\int \frac{-d(e^{-x})}{1 - e^{-x}}$$

$$= \frac{Rx}{e^x - 1} - R\int \frac{d(1 - e^{-x})}{1 - e^{-x}}$$

$$\overline{S}_{\text{vib}} = \frac{Rx}{e^x - 1} - R\ln(1 - e^{-x}) + \text{constant}$$

As $T \longrightarrow 0$,

$$\overline{S} \longrightarrow \frac{R\infty}{e^{\infty} - 1} - R\ln(1 - e^{-\infty}) + \text{constant} = 0 - 0 + \text{constant}$$

Thus, as $T \longrightarrow 0$, $\overline{S} \longrightarrow$ constant; and from the third law, $\overline{S} \longrightarrow 0$, so the constant $= 0$, and, for each vibration,

$$\overline{S}_{\text{vib}} = \frac{Rx}{e^x - 1} - R\ln(1 - e^{-x}) \qquad (10.16)$$

CALCULATION OF THERMODYNAMIC FUNCTIONS

We shall devote much time in Chapters 26 through 29 to calculations involving thermodynamic functions, but you already have the fundamental knowledge to use them in many ways. Table 10.2 lists the most commonly useful formulas we have already derived.

We have also derived some special equations—for example, those for calculating ΔE, C_V, and ΔS for vibrators as a function of temperature. But, for the present, these special equations should be used to give you insight into the relationships between thermodynamic functions and molecular behavior rather than as actual calculational tools.

Table 10.2 **Some previously derived thermodynamic equations. Note that, for heating processes (no chemical reactions or phase changes), a knowledge of heat capacity, *C*, as a function of *T* allows the calculation of ΔH, ΔE, and/or ΔS.**

$\Delta E = q - w; = q_V$, if $w = \int P_{\text{ext}}\, dV$

$\Delta H = \Delta E + \Delta PV; = q_P$, if $w = \int P_{\text{ext}}\, dV$

$$C_P = \left(\frac{\partial H}{\partial T}\right)_P; \text{ for heating, } \Delta H = \int_{T_1}^{T_2} C_P\, dT = q_P$$

$$C_V = \left(\frac{\partial E}{\partial T}\right)_V; \text{ for heating, } \Delta E = \int_{T_1}^{T_2} C_V\, dT = q_V$$

$C_p - C_V = R$, for ideal gas

$$\Delta S = \frac{q_{\text{rev}}}{T}\,[= 0 \text{ at equilibrium (at constant } E \text{ and } V)]$$

$$\text{for heating at constant } P,\ \Delta S = \int_{T_1}^{T_2} \frac{C_P}{T}\, dT$$

$$\text{for heating at constant } V,\ \Delta S = \int_{T_1}^{T_2} \frac{C_V}{T}\, dT$$

$$\text{for ideal gas at constant } T,\ \Delta S = nR \ln \frac{V_2}{V_1} = nR \ln \frac{P_1}{P_2}$$

for phase change, $\Delta S = \Delta H_{\text{pc}}/T$

$$\Delta S = k \ln \frac{W_2}{W_1}$$

$\Delta G = \Delta H - T\,\Delta S$ (closed system at constant T and P) $= 0$ at equilibrium

Note that all the equations in Table 10.2 express thermodynamic functions in terms of experimentally measured values of q—the heat absorbed by the system—and its variation with temperature. Thus thermodynamics describes changes in terms of energy and its flow—as heat and work—from place to place.

SUMMARY

The entropy changes of a system may be described either in terms of statistical ideas or in terms of heat flow. In statistical terms the entropy of any system may be calculated as the entropy due to mixing of the configurational and quantum states actually present in the system. Thus, when any system contains only molecules having the same configuration and the same energy, the entropy of the system is zero. Or entropy changes may be calculated in terms of the reversible heat divided by the absolute temperature. These two methods of calculation give identical results.

In general, all naturally occurring processes in the universe as we know it are accompanied by an increase in the entropy of the universe. The universe is continually moving toward a more mixed, or less ordered, equilibrium state. Equilibrium will be attained when the entropy of the universe reaches a maximum value. The total energy of the universe will then be distributed in the most random way possible.

The criterion for equilibrium in a closed system of constant temperature and constant pressure is that the Gibbs free energy of the system be a minimum. Because many systems of interest to chemists are of this type, the Gibbs free energy is a function of great usefulness to chemists.

I would like to draw an analogy between science and basketball. Our high school basketball coach used to say, "In setting up a good shot at the basket, by all means keep the ball moving. It doesn't matter so much where the ball moves as long as it does not remain in one place; only in this way are openings created."—Alvin M. Weinberg, Science, **154,** 619 (1966).

PROBLEMS

10.1. Calculate the entropy of HD, hydrogen deuteride, near 0°K. (About 1 cal mole^{-1} °K^{-1}.)

10.2. The statement was made on page 187 that the atomic weights of the noble gases were determined with a calorimeter. Outline the experimental evidence.

10.3. Ice is more voluminous than the same weight of liquid water at 0°C. What changes will occur in an ice-water system which is reversibly freezing at almost 0°C and 1 atm pressure if the pressure is raised differentially without changing the temperature.

II

10.4. Calculate the entropy of crystalline chlorine near 0°K. There are two isotopes—mass 35 and 37.

10.5. Calculate ΔH for the process $H_2O_{(l)25°C} \longrightarrow H_2O_{(l)60°C}$. (About 600 cal mole^{-1}.) Calculate ΔS. (About 2 eu.)

10.6. (*a*) Calculate the entropy change when 1 mole of hydrogen at 1 atm pressure and 1 mole of chlorine at 1 atm pressure intermix at 25°C to give a gaseous solution in which the partial pressures of hydrogen and chlorine are each 1 atm. (About 1 eu.) (*b*) Reaction then is brought about at 25°C. The vessel is kept at 25°C. ΔS^0 for the reaction is +4.8 cal mole^{-1} °K^{-1} (see p. 30). Calculate the relative number of distinguishable, accessible states after and before the reaction. (*c*) Discuss this ratio in terms of translation, rotation, and vibrational quantum states. (The entropies of the gases at 1 atm and 25°C are H_2, 31.208; Cl_2, 53.289; HCl, 44.645 cal mole^{-1} °K^{-1}).

10.7. The heat of fusion of sulfur, S_8, is 0.392 kcal mole^{-1}. Compare the entropy of fusion of sulfur with that of ice and interpret any differences in terms of possible structural relations.

III

10.8. Use the data in Table 27.1 to calculate the heat required (about 10^5 kcal) and the entropy change (about 10^5 eu) in raising the temperature of 1000 pounds of aluminum from room temperature to 900°K.

10.9. Use the data in Table 27.1 to calculate the heat required (about 30 kcal) and the entropy change (about 30 eu) when 2 moles of gaseous water are heated from 400°K to 2000°K at 1 atm pressure.

10.10. Calculate the vibrational entropies of gaseous HCN (about 0.1 eu) and DCN (about 0.2 eu) at 300°K from the following data after predicting which gas has the higher vibrational entropy. The vibrational frequencies are given below. Note that ν_2 is a double frequency (molecules can vibrate in two ways at this frequency) and must be counted twice. Tables 28.2 and 28.4 will be useful.

	ν_1 (cm^{-1})	ν_2 (2)(cm^{-1})	ν_3 (cm^{-1})
HCN	2089	712	3317
DCN	1906	569	2629

See page 1091 for a list of references and readings in the recent chemical literature related to the material in this chapter.

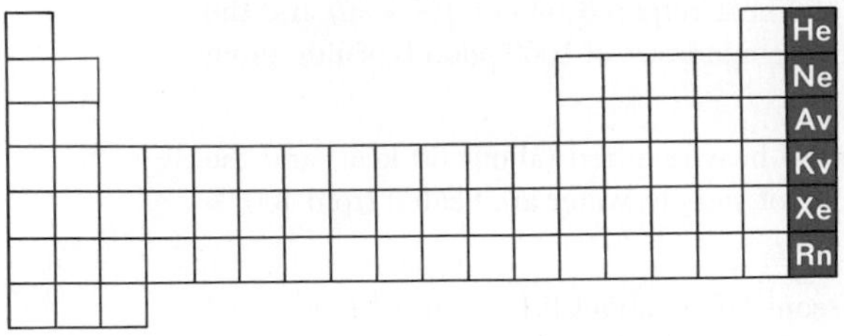

CHAPTER 11

The Noble Gases—Group 0

Probably well over 99% of the atoms in the earth's crust are isoelectronic with a noble-gas atom.

Examination of the periodic table in Figure 5.8, A, shows that the elements gaseous at room temperatures are found at the top of that table and, especially, near the right ends of these rows. Compounds gaseous near room temperature are known for many elements, but the majority of common gaseous compounds contain elements that are also gaseous at room temperature. These elements, and some of their compounds, exist as molecules with especially small intermolecular forces—forces so small that the kinetic energies available at room temperature ($RT =$ about 600 cal mole^{-1}) are sufficient to keep the molecules in the gaseous state at 300°K. The methods of Avogadro and Cannizzaro and measurements of heat capacity allow us to determine the molecular weights and formulas of these gaseous compounds, and the spectroscopic data give considerable insights into their molecular motions, interatomic distances, and the quantization of their energies. We will use these experimental methods to look systematically into the behavior of some of these elements and a few of their compounds.

Figures 5.3, 5.7, 5.9, 5.13, 5.18, 5.19, 5.20 and Tables 5.5, 5.7 have already listed many of the properties of these elements. You should review these figures and tables.

THE NOBLE GASES

Compounds of all the elements in the periodic table are known, but not all elements are equally reactive; nor are all compounds equally easy to store and keep. The most unreactive element, in terms of the number of its known compounds and the stability of those compounds, is probably helium. Its best-known compound is HeH^+ *(g)*. This compound is known only in the gaseous state, but some of its properties are as well known as those of many other gases. Its bond length, bond strength, and bond force constant are remarkably similar to those of molecular hydrogen, H_2, with which it is isoelectronic. Interestingly, HeH_2^+ *(g)* is also a stable molecule with respect to decomposition.*

The other elements in the helium column of the periodic table also form compounds, some of which we shall discuss later. But the number of known compounds is small, many of them decompose readily into the elements, and others, like HeH^+ and XeC_2^+, exist only as gaseous ions. For many years it was thought these elements—helium, neon, argon, krypton, xenon, and radon—should be called the noble or inert gases. Since they are not really inert, "noble gas" is the currently preferred term. All of them are relatively uncommon on earth (see Table 5.5 for their concentration in air) and so are also called the rare gases.

Helium was the first of the noble gases to be "discovered." Lockyer in 1868 noticed a line very near the sodium *D* lines in the solar spectrum not attributable to any known element or compound—hence the name helium, from the Greek *helios* for sun.

Prior to this, Cavendish in 1785 in England had passed electric sparks through air to cause the reaction $N_{2(g)} + 2O_{2(g)} = 2NO_{2(g)}$. He then dissolved the NO_2 in aqueous sodium hydroxide:

$$2NO_{2(g)} + 2OH^-_{(aq)} = NO_3{}^-_{(aq)} + NO_2{}^-_{(aq)} + H_2O$$

The resulting gas seemed to be pure nitrogen. Cavendish then added excess oxygen, resumed the sparking, and again removed the nitrogen dioxide. Passing the resulting gas over hot copper removed the remaining oxygen and left a residual gas corresponding to about 1% of the original volume of the air sample. Cavendish did not comment on the composition of this gas, perhaps assuming it was unreacted nitrogen.

Not until 1894, over a hundred years later, were the noble gases "rediscovered." Lord Rayleigh, another Englishman, prepared nitrogen in three ways: (1) by removing oxygen from air: $2Cu_{(c)} + O_{2(g)} = 2CuO_{(c)}$; (2) by heating ammonium nitrite: $NH_4NO_{2(c)} = N_{2(g)} + 2H_2O_{(g)}$; and (3) by burning ammonia in air: $4NH_{3(g)} + 3O_{2(g)} = 2N_{2(g)} + 6H_2O_{(g)}$. The three resulting samples were carefully dried and their densities at 25°C and 1 atm determined to be as follows: sample 1, 1.2572 g/liter; sample 2, 1.2505 g/liter; and sample 3, 1.2564 g/liter. The last figure varied with changes in the relative amounts of ammonia and air, and many experimenters would have neglected the variations as due to experimental uncertainty. Instead, Rayleigh and Ramsay repeated and modified the Cavendish experiment and so obtained an inert gas which they called argon. Spectroscopic evidence convinced them the gas was not a single element, and their continued work—spread over several years, and including careful distillation of the liquefied gas—finally gave relatively pure samples of argon, neon, krypton, and xenon. Spectral data showed that these were new elements, and heat capacity data showed that they were monatomic. A new family was added to

*S. E. Kuprianov, *Zhur. eksp. teor. Fiz.*, **48**, 467 (1965).

Mendeleev's periodic table to hold these elements. Ramsay also found helium, Lockyer's solar element, in uranium ores (from alpha particles trapped in the course of geologic time). In 1900 the family was completed by the discovery of radon, from radium ores. The discovery was first announced by Dorn, but Ramsay and others made almost simultaneous observations.

One of Ramsay's earliest problems with argon resulted from the discovery that its atomic weight was about 40. This placed it between potassium and calcium in the periodic table, destroying, to his consternation, the very nice order put forward by Mendeleev. The atomic weights of the other gases soon indicated that the correct position of the noble gases in the periodic table was between the halogens and the alkalies, but the atomic weight of argon remained a problem until isotopes and their relative stabilities were discovered and interpreted.

Radon is still obtained from radium ores, and neon, argon, krypton, and xenon are still obtained from the distillation of liquid air. Helium is obtained from certain gas wells. The only known wells are in North America, some producing as much as 16% helium, the balance being nitrogen or natural gas. One well in Arizona produces 8.5% He, 90% N_2, 1% CO_2, and 0.5% Ar with hydrocarbons less than 0.1%. This gas is liquefied, giving residual gaseous He of about 99% purity. This cold gas is then passed over activated carbon to give He of purity higher than 99.999%. (Gas percentages indicate volume or mole percent.)

Most of the current large-scale uses of the noble gases are based on their high degree of inertness. Some 30% of the helium is used in space programs as a pressurizing agent to expel liquid oxygen and liquid hydrogen in rockets. About 20% is used in AEC programs as heat transfer gas, because the helium is inert both chemically and nuclearly, and has a high thermal conductivity and low viscosity and density. About 18% of the helium is used in shielded arc welding, about 12% in balloons, and the balance in breathing atmospheres. Again the low viscosity and molecular weight allow an appreciable increase in the work rate, since respiration is easier and the worker is kept cooler. Helium is far less soluble in aqueous solutions, such as blood, than nitrogen (remember helium's low intermolecular forces), and so it need not be removed from the blood when a worker moves from high pressure to atmospheric pressure. This lessens the time and danger of the decompression period.

Argon is used in tungsten incandescent bulbs to lower the rate of evaporation of the tungsten filament, and to carry by convection the tungsten which does evaporate to a small segment of the bulb's area. (Hence the restricted black area inside burned-out bulbs.) Argon is also used to shield welding arcs to prevent air contamination of the weld, and even to fill whole factories with an inert atmosphere to protect highly reactive products.

Radon is sometimes used as a powerful source of alpha radiation, but it is being replaced by other isotopes produced synthetically.

Neon's use in electric signs is based on a fortuitous match between its electronic quantum levels and a frequency range to which the human eye actively responds. The light emitted by electronically excited krypton matches the response curve of photographic films and thus is much used in flash guns. Xenon acts as an anesthetic, but this only gives an interesting insight into the physiology of anesthetics, since xenon is not used in hospitals because other anesthetics are far cheaper.

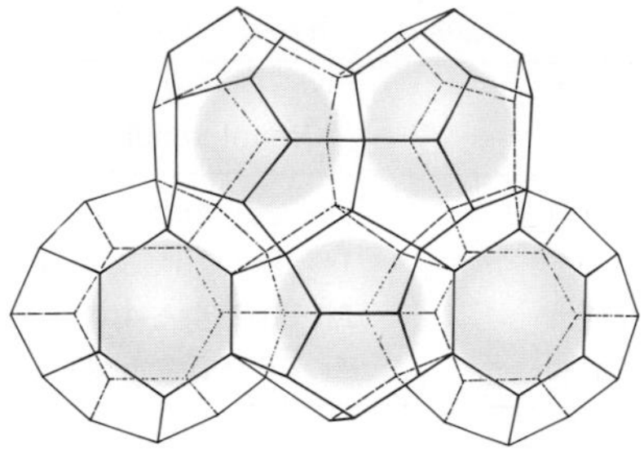

Figure 11.1 Structure of a noble gas hydrate or clathrate. 5 of the 8 polyhedra in each unit cell are shown. A xenon atom is located within each polyhedron. An oxygen atom is located at each apex and a hydrogen-bonded hydrogen along each edge. A count shows that 46 water molecules make up the polyhedra per unit cell. Thus the formula is $Xe_8 \cdot 46H_2O$ or $Xe \cdot 5\frac{3}{4}H_2O$.

CLATHRATES

We shall return to the compounds of the noble gases with fluorine and oxygen after discussing the halogen family, but first let us note a most interesting set of compounds known as clathrates. When water is saturated with argon, krypton, or xenon at high pressure and then cooled, white crystals form. Their formula is typified by $Xe \cdot 5\frac{3}{4}H_2O$ (see Figure 11.1). Crystal structure analysis shows that the water has crystallized around polyhedral "holes" that contain the inert gas atoms. The water molecules connected by hydrogen bonds form a continuous three-dimensional network and the inert gas atoms take up positions in the interstices of the network. Other small molecules (such as Cl_2, SO_2, CH_4) can fit into the same holes. Other water structures ($8\,M \cdot 136H_2O$) are also known which can hold larger molecules (CH_3I, C_3H_8), and molecules other than water (quinol, formula HOC_6H_4OH) are known to form similar clathrates, in which hydrogen-bonded structures surround small embedded molecules. It is possible that the anesthetic action of xenon (and of many other anesthetics) may be due to aqueous clathrate formation in physiologically strategic spots. When the anesthetic is no longer administered, the clathrate equilibrium is destroyed, the clathrates decompose, and consciousness returns.

It is interesting to note* that the compound Na_8Si_{46} has a structure identical to that of the xenon clathrate in water. The silicon atoms are bonded to four neighboring silicons in a distorted tetrahedral packing just as are the waters, and the sodium atoms occupy the "holes" just as do the xenons.

THE INERTNESS OF THE NOBLE GASES

The noble gases are very nearly ideal in gas behavior over a long range of conditions. The equation of state, $PV = nRT$, comes close to describing their behavior in the gaseous state. This is consistent with their general inertness, as are their low melting points and boiling points. Their constant value of C_V over a long gaseous range is further evidence that the orbital population of the noble gases is a stable one.

Not only are the noble gases inert, but so are many ions with the same number of electrons—that is, atoms which are isoelectronic with the noble gases. Table 11.1 lists some ions that are isoelectronic with some of the noble gases. Each of the ions listed is found commonly in nature and must therefore be relatively unreactive, since it has existed in this form throughout geologic time. Similarly, we find that most of the substances most common in nature are composed of atoms that have surrounded themselves with a number of electrons equal to the number found in one of the inert gases, often by a process of sharing electrons between pairs

* *Science*, **150**, 1713 (1965).

Table 11.1 Some ions isoelectronic with a noble gas.

Inert gas	Number of electrons	Isoelectronic ions	Orbital population
Ne	10	$O^=$, F^-, Na^+, Mg^{++}, Al^{+++}	$1s^2$; $2s^2$, $2p^6$
Ar	18	$S^=$, Cl^-, K^+, Ca^{++}, Sc^{+++}	$1s^2$; $2s^2$, $2p^2$; $3s^2$, $3p^6$
Kr	36	$Se^=$, Br^-, Rb^+, Sr^{++}, Y^{+++}	Ar, $3d^{10}$; $4s^2$, $4p^6$
Xe	54	$Te^=$, I^-, Cs^+, Ba^{++}, La^{+++}	Kr, $4d^{10}$; $5s^2$, $5p^6$

of atoms. Probably the most common atomic aggregate in the world is a silicon atom tetrahedrally surrounded by four oxygens, each of which is sharing electrons with another silicon. Or consider water molecules (composed of two hydrogen nuclei, an oxygen nucleus, and ten electrons each) or nitrogen molecules (composed of two nitrogen nuclei and fourteen electrons). All of these, and many other common (and hence rather unreactive) substances, can be pictured as made up of nuclear and electronic arrangements that allow each nucleus to be surrounded by a number of electrons equal to that of a noble gas, as shown in Figure 11.2. Note that any given pair of neighboring atoms may simultaneously share (or attract) one, two, or three pairs of electrons in achieving the noble gas number, each pair of electrons being represented by a single bar. Many substances are known in which the atoms are not isoelectronic with noble gas atoms, but probably well over 99% of all the atoms in the earth's crust are isoelectronic with a noble gas atom. And probably over 95% of the substances you will discuss in elementary chemistry courses contain atoms isoelectronic with inert gas atoms.

Such statistics are most impressive and suggest that much can be learned about chemical interactions by studying the electronic structures of the noble

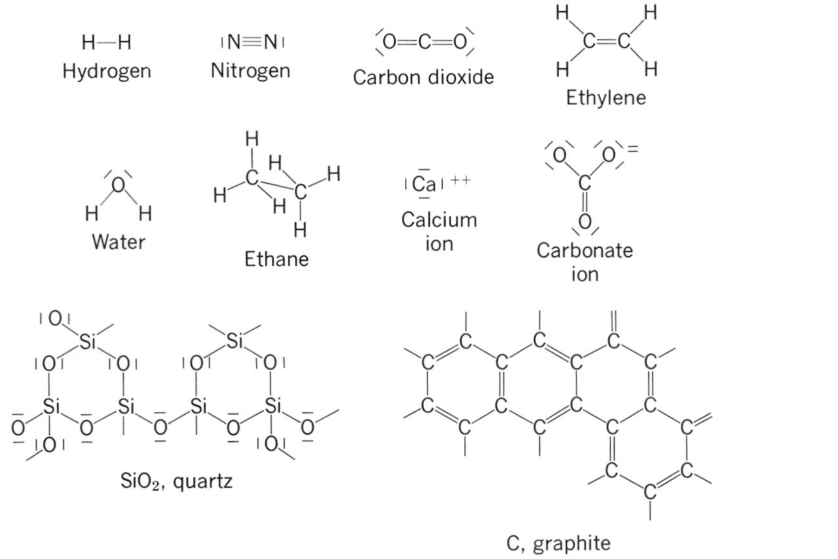

Figure 11.2 Some common substances in which each atom has a noble gas electron structure. Each bar (—) indicates a pair of valence electrons. Ca^{++} and silicon have the argon structure of 18 electrons. H holds only 2 electrons (helium structure). The other atoms shown here have a total of 10 electrons (neon structure).

Table 11.2 Some properties of the inert gases. (Heats and free energies of formation at 298°K = 0.)

Gas	M.P. (°K)	B.P. (°K)	Ionization energy (kcal mole^{-1})	Electron structure	S^0_{298} (cal mole^{-1} °K^{-1})
He	—	4.2	569	$1s^2$	30.1244
Ne	24.5	27.2	499	$1s^2$; $2s^2$, $2p^6$	34.9471
Ar	83.7	87.3	365	$1s^2$; $2s^2$, $2p^6$; $3s^2$, $3p^6$	36.9822
Kr	115.7	121	323	$1s^2$; $2s^2$, $2p^6$; $3s^2$, $3p^6$; $4s^2$, $3d^{10}$, $4p^6$	39.1905
Xe	161.1	165	280	$1s^2$; $2s^2$, $2p^6$; $3s^2$, $3p^6$; $4s^2$, $3d^{10}$, $4p^6$; $5s^2$, $4d^{10}$, $5p^6$	40.5290
Rn	—	211	248	$1s^2$; $2s^2$, $2p^6$; $3s^2$, $3p^6$; $4s^2$, $3d^{10}$, $4p^6$; $5s^2$, $4d^{10}$, $5p^6$; $6s^2$, $4f^{14}$, $5d^{10}$, $6p^6$	42.09
Trend(↓)	up	up	down		up

gases. The data of Table 11.2 give some quantum mechanical and experimental support for the stability of these electronic structures. The noble gases all have low melting points and boiling points (indicating weak interatomic forces) and high ionization energies (indicating high attraction for their own atomic electrons). They also have outer electronic energy levels that are completely full (indicating little tendency to add electrons), and they all have next-higher energy levels that are energetically distant from the ground state (again indicating it might be difficult to alter the electronic arrangement). The inertness of the noble gases results from this combination of full levels and energetically distant empty levels.

The same arguments apply to the atoms isoelectronic with the noble gas atoms. However, we must remember that the energy levels and their relative positions are functions of the ratio of nuclear charge to number of electrons (see Figures 3.3 and 3.17). Thus, though we expect the atoms isoelectronic with the noble gases to have some degree of inertness, certainly some of the isoelectronic atoms will accept electrons with less energy change than would a noble gas, and others will lose electrons with less energy change. Reactivity is not solely a function of the number of electrons and the electronic quantum numbers; it is also a function of the nuclear charge.

THERMODYNAMIC HEATS AND FREE ENERGIES OF FORMATION

Table 11.2 lists the entropies of the inert gases and also gives their standard heats and free energies of formation at 298°K as 0. Heats of free energy and formation are defined as the enthalpy and free energy changes when a substance is formed in its standard state (pure at 1 atm and 298°K) from the elements in their standard states. Thus, by this definition, the heats and free energies of all pure elements at one atmosphere pressure and 298°K are zero. Since we measure and are interested only in differences, we can define an arbitrary zero (as is also done in the usual thermometer) for enthalpy and free energies. Entropy, however, has a real value of zero for a perfect crystal at absolute zero (similar to 0°K, being an absolute value) and thus entropies are based on these zero values. Note that the entropies of the inert gases increase monotonically with increasing molecular weight. They also increase with T.

THE REACTIVITY OF THE NOBLE GASES

Just as we do not expect all atoms isoelectronic with the noble gases to be equally inert, so we would not expect all the noble gases themselves to be equally inert. Figures 3.17 and 3.18 indicate that the energy-level spacings are not identical, and Table 11.2 shows that the ionization energies vary from one inert gas to another. Note that—in the order He, Ne, Ar, Kr, Xe, Rn—it becomes increasingly easy for the noble gases to lose electrons. It is reasonable to believe that the reactivity of these elements toward substances that could attract electrons might increase in the same order. This line of reasoning has been known for at least fifty years and has led to many experimental efforts to produce compounds of the noble gases. All, except those producing clathrates or gaseous ions, failed until 1962.

In 1962 N. Bartlett found that platinum hexafluoride formed a compound with oxygen—formula $(O_2^+)(PtF_6^-)$—a most unusual crystal in that it contained the O_2^+ ion. Apparently the ion was made stable by the nature of the crystal and the electron-attracting properties of PtF_6. Bartlett remembered that the ionization energy of xenon (280 kcal mole^{-1}) is approximately the same as that of O_2 (282 kcal mole^{-1}) and that the molecular diameters are also similar (Xe $\cong$ 4.0 Å, $O_2 \cong$ 4 Å). He immediately proceeded to mix xenon and platinum hexafluoride (both gases) at room temperature, and obtained on his first attempt a crystalline substance of formula $XePtF_6$, as he had predicted. Predictions based on knowledge can pay off!

Since that time a growing number of compounds of xenon and of krypton with fluorine and oxygen have been discovered. Among them are: XeF_2, XeF_4, XeF_6, $XeOF_2$, $XeOF_4$, XeO_3, and XeO_4. The xenon fluorides may be synthesized by passing gaseous xenon and fluorine, in the proper mixture, through a heated nickel tube. The oxygen compounds result when XeF_6 reacts with water; HF is produced simultaneously. Cs_2XeF_8 and Rb_2XeF_8 are the most thermally stable xenon compounds known to date. They do not decompose appreciably until $T > 400°C$.

The xenon fluorides are stable with respect to decomposition into the elements at room temperature, but crystalline XeO_3 is highly unstable, exploding with considerable violence if a small amount of activation energy is supplied. Aqueous solutions of XeO_3 are safe, however, and can serve as potent oxidizing agents. Depending on the pH and the extent of disproportionation occurring, the following species are known to exist: XeO_3, $HXeO_4^-$, $H_2XeO_6^=$, $HXeO_6^{\equiv}$, XeO_6^{-4} (in order of increasingly basic solutions). The solutions also have the great advantage of producing only xenon as a by-product, which, being inert toward most substances, causes no chemical complications in the preparation and ensuing purification of the desired product.

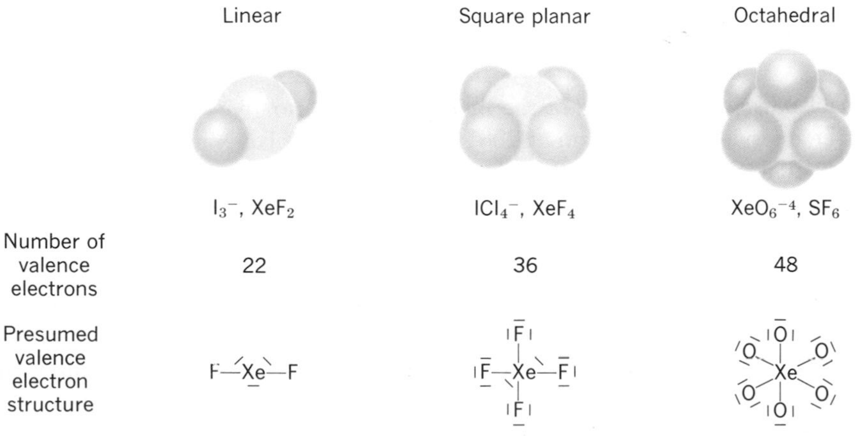

Figure 11.3 Schematic shapes of some isoelectronic molecules.

Just as the inert gas atoms have some properties similar to the atoms and ions isoelectronic with them, so the inert gas compounds have properties similar to some substances isoelectronic (so far as valence electrons go) with them. For example, I_3^- is isoelectronic with XeF_2 and both are linear molecules; ICl_4^- is isoelectronic with XeF_4 and both are symmetrical, square planar molecules with the halogens at the corners of the square surrounding the central atom; the XeO_6^{-4} ion (found in crystalline $Na_4XeO_6 \cdot 8H_2O$) is isoelectronic with hexafluorides such as SF_6 and, like them, consists of a regular octahedron of atoms surrounding a central one (see Figure 11.3).

Current theories of bonding do not give unambiguous pictures of the interatomic forces in these compounds, as we shall see in following chapters, but the bonds do not seem to differ from those found in isoelectronic substances.*

SUMMARY

On at least three occasions in the history of chemistry the noble gases have played a decisive role. The first, which followed their "rediscovery", was their fitting into the periodic table, thus providing an outstanding example of its great ability to coordinate chemical information. The second is connected with the interpretation of electronic energy levels: the inertness associated with noble gas electron structures provides a guide to some of the strongest driving forces that determine the direction of chemical reactions. Third and most recently, the discovery of compounds of the noble gases has provided additional and dramatic examples of bonding systems that can be used to test and extend theories of the nature of chemical bonds.

Scientists, far from wanting to impose their ideas upon other people, are often too little interested in the social implications of their work, and in any case too much occupied with it to have time for political activities.—W. R. Brain, Science, **148**, 192–198 (1965).

PROBLEMS

11.1. How can gaseous heat capacities distinguish monatomic from polyatomic elements? Do monatomic gaseous elements have infrared absorption spectra? Do diatomic gaseous elements have infrared absorption spectra? Would you expect gaseous ozone, O_3 (write its valence electron structure), to have an infrared absorption spectrum?

11.2. Write formulas of one or two stable gaseous molecules which are isoelectronic with each of the following: (*a*) H_2O, (*b*) LiF, (*c*) H—C≡C—H, (*d*) N=N=O.

* H. A. Bent, "Isoelectronic systems," *J. Chem. Ed.*, **43**, 170 (1966).

11.3. Sketch the inside of an incandescent light bulb and show the mechanisms (*a*) by which argon minimizes the rate of evaporation of the tungsten filament, and (*b*) by which argon concentrates the tungsten which does vaporize onto a small area of the glass envelope.

11.4. Which would have the higher gaseous heat capacity at 298°K, He or Xe? At 100,000°K?

11.5. Ar and Kr atoms are about the same size. Which would form the more stable clathrates?

II

11.6. Compare the following gaseous molecules (isoelectronic so far as valence electrons are concerned) as to dipole moment, infrared absorption spectra, boiling point of the liquid containing only that substance, bond strength, and bond length: (*a*) I_3^-, XeF_2, (*b*) HeH^+, H_2, (*c*) H_2O, HF, (*d*) HF, HI.

11.7. Gaseous xenon costs about $50 per liter at 1 atm and 25°C. XeF_4 is formed when Xe and F_2 are passed through a hot nickel tube. The resulting XeF_4 dissolves in H_2O to give a stable solution of XeO_3. What is the minimum cost of preparing 1 liter of 0.400 *F* XeO_3 in water? (About $500.)

11.8. How do you account for the fact that the entropy of He is about 30 and that of Ne is about 35 cal mole^{-1} °K^{-1} at 298.15°K, but each increases at exactly the same rate at higher temperatures so that $\bar{S}_{8000°K} - \bar{S}_{298.15°K} = 16.35$ for both of them.

11.9. XeO_4 is tetrahedral, XeO_6^{-4} octahedral, $XeCl_4$ and XeF_4 are apparently planar, and XeF_2 is linear. Suggest valence electron structures for each of these substances.

III

11.10. To explore further the properties of the noble gas family of elements, plot boiling point versus (*a*) atomic number, (*b*) number of valence electrons, (*c*) ionization energy, (*d*) molar volume. Which relation seems simplest? Discuss possible reasons for the result in each plot. What other variable might influence the boiling point? Try a plot and comment on the result.

11.11. Design a distillation method and a chemical reaction method for separating Kr and Xe. Discuss the relative merits and demerits of each method.

11.12. You have been asked to investigate synthesis of a fluoride of radon. How would you proceed? [See C. L. Chernick et al., *Science*, **138**, 136 (1962).]

See page 1091 for a list of references and readings in the recent chemical literature related to the material in this chapter.

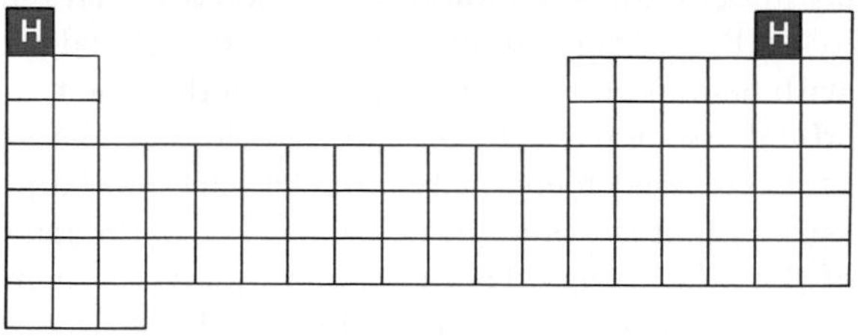

CHAPTER 12

Hydrogen

In terms of entropy, the proton will move in a random fashion among the available orbitals. In terms of energy, it will spend most of its time in the orbitals to which it is most strongly attracted.

The substance exhibiting the smallest intermolecular forces, with the exception of helium, is hydrogen. Note the low melting and boiling points in Table 5.5 and the close approximation to an ideal gas in Table 6.1. Heat capacity data, combining volumes, and Cannizzaro's method all indicate—as does all other available evidence—that hydrogen at laboratory conditions consists of diatomic molecules (formula, H_2). At high temperatures, H atoms form; at very high temperatures, protons and electrons form. Hydrogen and its compounds are more apt to show molecular quantum effects than any other substances, since the small mass of hydrogen leads to large spacings of the quantum levels, as indicated in Chapter 8.

MOLECULAR HYDROGEN

Since each atom is thought to consist of a single proton and a single electron, the H_2 molecule should consist of two electrons and two protons. The massive protons must be separated in space to give the moment of inertia and the rotational heat capacity found in gaseous hydrogen. The molecule is quite stable with respect to decomposition into monatomic hydrogen: 103 kcal mole^{-1} are required to cause the decomposition. Only above 35,000°K is the average translational kinetic energy, $\frac{3}{2}RT$, sufficient to dissociate most of the molecules. The ionization energy of the molecule is even higher: 356 kcal mole^{-1}. Thus molecular hydrogen holds on to its electrons with considerable avidity. Nor does hydrogen gain electrons readily. The molecule H_2^- forms only under unusual conditions and then dissociates into H and H^-. Some of the stability of the hydrogen molecule may be correlated with the fact that it is isoelectronic with helium atoms. One difference is that the two electrons in helium are in an orbital associated with only one nucleus of charge +2, but in hydrogen the two electrons bond together two nuclei each of charge +1.

Yet, in spite of the strength of the bond in molecular H_2, hydrogen reacts exothermically with most of the other elements but seldom rapidly at room temperature. Many of the resulting compounds (especially those with the nonmetallic elements in the upper right corner of the periodic table) are gaseous at room temperature, but most of the compounds with the metals are crystalline at room temperature. The former have relatively weak intermolecular forces compared to the latter. The formulas of the most common binary compounds of hydrogen are shown in Figure 12.1. The hydrogen is probably present primarily as hydride ion, H^-, in compounds with the most metallic elements; as atomic hydrogen, H, with some of the metals; and covalently bonded, as in H—O—H, with most nonmetals.

Though hydrogen reacts exothermically with many of the other elements, it is not highly reactive toward most compounds. When it does react, the reaction is often slow at room temperatures because of a high activation energy (often due to the strong H—H bond). Hydrogen is odorless and tasteless (unreactive with the sensory apparatus in nose and mouth), is colorless (has no energy-level spacings corresponding to visible light), has little solubility in water and other polar solvents (indicating that its bonds to polar molecules are less strong than the bonds between the polar solvent molecules themselves), but is soluble in nonpolar solvents (indicating that its interactions with nonpolar substances must be similar to the interactions between the nonpolar molecules themselves).

One of the commonest reactions of hydrogen is with unsaturated molecules (see Chapter 21). A particularly common reaction is its addition to two carbon atoms originally joined by a double bond (sharing of four electrons):

$$H_2 + R_2C{=}CR_2 = R_2CHCHR_2$$

or

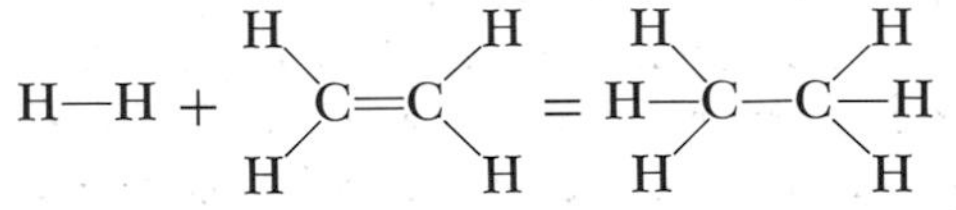

				$\Delta(\ )_{reac\ 298°}$	$T\,\Delta S_{298°}$
ΔH^0_{form}(kcal mole^{-1})	0	12.556	−20.191	−32.747	
S^0(cal mole^{-1} °K^{-1})	31.211	52.45	54.85	−28.81	−8.605 (kcal mole^{-1})
ΔG^0_{form}(kcal mole^{-1})	0	16.282	−7.860	−24.142	

See Table 12.1 for a discussion of ΔH^0_{form}.

Unsaturated vegetable oils, which are often liquid, may be converted into materials solid at room temperature by such hydrogenation. Unsaturated carbon-hydrogen compounds from a petroleum refinery may be converted into fuels of higher octane number by hydrogenation, especially when hydrogenation is coupled

H_2																H_2	—
LiH	BeH_2											B_2H_6	C_nH_{2n+2} C_nH_m	NH_3	$H_2O_{(l)}$	HF	—
NaH	MgH_2											AlH_3	SiH_4	PH_3	H_2S	HCl	—
KH	CaH_2	$ScH_{<3}$	$TiH_{<2}$	$VH_{<1}$	$CrH_{<2}$	—	FeH_2	CoH_2	NiH_2	CuH	ZnH_2	Ga_2H_6	GeH_4	AsH_3	H_2Se	HBr	—
RbH	SrH_2	$YH_{<3}$	$ZrH_{<2}$	$NbH_{<1}$	—	—	?	?	$PdH_{<1}$	AgH	CdH_2	InH_3	SnH_4	SbH_3	H_2Te	HI	—
CsH	BaH_2		$HfH_{<2}$	$TaH_{<1}$	—	—	—	—	?	AuH	HgH_2	TlH_3	PbH_4	BiH_3	H_2Po	—	—
				Binary substances containing hydrogen; solid at room temperature.									Binary hydrogen compounds gaseous at room temperature.				

Figure 12.1 Some binary substances containing hydrogen. Not all these substances are well-defined compounds, as is indicated by the nonstoichiometric formulas (for example, $ScH_{<3}$, $VH_{<1}$). Thousands of compounds of carbon and hydrogen are known (see Chapter 21). The most common set, including CH_4, C_2H_6, C_3H_8, and so on, have the general formula C_nH_{2n+2}. Other "series" are also known. Some of the other elements also have extensive numbers of binary compounds with hydrogen. The elements for which no hydride formula is given have no known stable binary compounds with hydrogen.

with other processes that rearrange the atoms in the hydrocarbon molecules. Note that these reactions proceed even though ΔS^0 is negative (1 mole of gas disappears). Thus ΔH must have a rather large negative value. The experimental data, as given on page 262, show this to be so.

Since many of the reactions of hydrogen (and of its compounds) are strongly exothermic—as in its reaction with oxygen—hydrogen (and compounds containing hydrogen) may often be used as fuel. Hydrogen itself has the drawback of usually being gaseous, thus requiring bulky storage facilities. It is solid or liquid only at the lowest temperatures (m.p. 13.9°K, b.p. 20.3°K), requiring extensive refrigeration facilities if it is to be stored as liquid or crystal. Hence its major fuel use as an element is in hydrogen-oxygen torches, run from high-pressure gas storage cylinders, and used where very high flame temperatures (of the order of 2000°K) are required. These high-pressure steel cylinders are extremely dangerous. If one falls and breaks off its exit valve, the escaping hydrogen will quickly convert the tank into a rocket-powered missile with a great flaming tail as the escaping hydrogen burns in the air. Such missiles have sufficient power to penetrate as much as six inches of concrete. *Moral:* Fasten high-pressure cylinders securely and never transport them with their protective caps removed.

Although hydrogen and its compounds react with many substances, the initial rate of reaction is often slow. Hydrogen and oxygen gas, or hydrogen and chlorine gas, may be mixed at room temperature, and then kept for very long periods of time with no apparent reaction. However, introduction of a localized energy source—spark, flame, flash of light—will often initiate an explosion. The activation energy for reaction with hydrogen and many of its compounds must be relatively high, and the apparent inertness of the gas is often only a reflection of a low rate of reaction. As a result, many reactions with hydrogen are carried on in the presence of a catalyst that may lower the activation energy even to the point at which the kinetic energy of the molecules at room temperature is sufficient to provide the energy. (Introduction of finely divided platinum into a gaseous solution of hydrogen and oxygen initiates an explosion. Thus the activation energy for this catalyzed reaction is probably about 1 kcal mole^{-1}, since $RT = 1.99 \cdot 298 \cong 600$ cal mole^{-1} at room temperature.) Some of these hydrogenation catalysts, such as Ni, Fe, Pt (see Figure 12.1), seem to operate by forming an intermediate hydride, or by adsorbing the hydrogen on the metal as atomic hydrogen, as the first step in the catalytic reaction (see Figure 12.2).

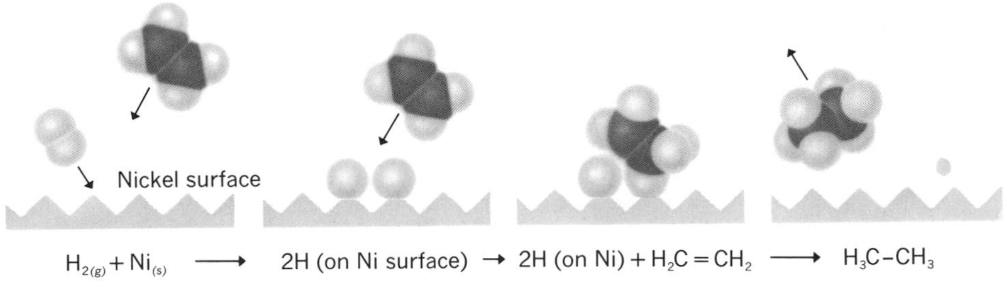

Figure 12.2 Schematic representation of the catalytic action of nickel metal on the hydrogenation of ethylene, C_2H_4, to ethane, C_2H_6.

THERMODYNAMIC PROPERTIES OF SOME HYDROGEN COMPOUNDS

Table 12.1 gives values of ΔH^0_{form}, ΔG^0_{form}, and S^0_{298} for some hydrogen-containing species. We shall find these useful in discussing the chemistry of hydrogen and its compounds. Remember that $\Delta G^0 = \Delta H^0 - T\,\Delta S^0$, and that standard heats and free energies of formation of elements are zero for the pure element at 1 atm and 298°K. All other heats and free energies of formation are referred to elements in their standard states, except for $H^+_{(aq)}$, for which ΔH^0_{form}, ΔG^0_{form}, and S^0_{form} are zero by definition.

Exercise 12.1

Note that ΔG^0_{form} of the hydrogen halide gases decreases monotonically from HF to HI. Is this primarily an entropy or enthalpy effect? *Answer:* The entropies of the halogens and the hydrogen halides do not vary greatly from one to another, but

Table 12.1 Thermodynamic constants of some hydrogen compounds at 298.15°K.

Substance	State[a]	$\Delta \bar{H}^0_{form,298.15°K}$[b] (kcal mole^{-1})	$\Delta \bar{G}^0_{form,298.15°K}$[c] (kcal mole^{-1})	$\bar{S}_{298.15°K}$[d] (cal mole^{-1} °K^{-1})
H_2	*g*	0	0	31.208
H	*g*	52.095	48.580	27.391
H_2O	*g*	−57.796	−54.635	45.104
	l	−68.315	−56.688	16.71
NH_3	*g*	−11.02	−3.94	45.97
CH_4	*g*	−17.88	−12.13	44.492
C_2H_4	*g*	12.556	16.282	52.45
C_2H_6	*g*	−20.191	−7.860	54.85
HF	*g*	−64.8	−65.3	41.508
	1 *F* un-ionized	−76.50	−70.95	21.2
	1 *F* ionized	−79.50	−66.64	−3.3
HCl	*g*	−22.062	−22.774	44.646
	1 *F* ionized	−39.952	−31.372	13.5
HBr	*g*	−8.70	−12.77	47.463
	1 *F* ionized	−29.05	−24.85	19.7
HI	*g*	6.33	0.51	49.351
	1 *F* ionized	−13.19	−12.33	26.6
$H^+_{(aq)}$[e]	1 *F*	0	0	0

[a] Standard state: pure substance at 1 atm pressure, $T = 298.15$°K; solutions at 1 *F* in water, ionized, or unionized as indicated, at 1 atm, 298.15°K.

[b] $\Delta \bar{H}^0_{form}$ = heat (q_P) gained by system when substance is formed in its standard state from elements in their standard states; solutions are referred to formation from pure H_2O and elements of solute in their standard states.

[c] $\Delta \bar{G}^0_{form}$ = free energy gained by system when substance is formed in its standard state from elements in their standard states; solutions are referred to formation from pure H_2O, and elements of solute in their standard states. *Remember:* $\Delta G^0 = \Delta H^0 - T\,\Delta S^0$.

[d] $\bar{S}^0_{298.15°K}$ = entropy of the substance in its standard state.

[e] $\Delta H^0 = \Delta G^0 = S^0 = 0$ at 298°K for 1 *M* H^+ by definition and is used as the basis of comparison of all other aqueous ionic species.

ΔH^0_{form} of the halides does vary and in just the fashion necessary to lead to the observed trends in ΔG^0. Thus it is the small ΔH^0 for HI compared to HF which accounts for the overall trend. At higher T the entropy effects are greater and at very high T they are determining.

Exercise 12.2

Calculate ΔG^0 for the process $HF_{(aq)} = H^+{}_{(aq)} + F^-{}_{(aq)}$. *Answer:* $\Delta G^0 = -66.64 + 0 - (-70.95) = +4.31$ kcal mole^{-1}. Thus HF is mainly un-ionized in aqueous solution.

Exercise 12.3

Calculate ΔG^0 for the reaction $2CH_{4(g)} = C_2H_{6(g)} + H_{2(g)}$. Is this a likely reaction? *Answer:* $\Delta G^0 = -7.860 + 0 - (2 \cdot 12.13) = -7.86 + 24.26 = 16.4$ kcal, a highly unlikely reaction. The reverse reaction should occur.

THE HABER PROCESS

One of the major uses of hydrogen is in the synthesis of ammonia. The net reaction is

	$N_{2(g)}$	$+\ 3H_{2(g)}$	$=\ 2NH_{3(g)}$	$\Delta(\ )_{reac\ 298°}$	$T\,\Delta_{298°}$
H^0_{298}	0	0	2(−11.0)	−22.0 kcal	
S^0_{298}	45.8	3 · 31.2	2 · 46.0	−47.4 cal °K^{-1}	−14.1 kcal
G^0_{298}	0	0	2(−3.94)	−7.9 kcal	

Again the entropy change is negative and unfavorable, but ΔH is negative and favorable to reaction. Application of Le Châtelier's principle* indicates that the formation of ammonia would be favored by operating at high pressures. This follows from the equation, which indicates that 4 moles of gaseous reactants unite to form 2 moles of gaseous product. The formation of additional ammonia minimizes the pressure rise (by decreasing the number of moles of gas present). But even at high pressures the reaction is slow.

Raising the temperature increases the rate, but calorimetric studies show that the reaction as written is still exothermic:

$$N_{2(g)} + 3H_{2(g)} = 2NH_{3(g)} + 22 \text{ kcal (at 298°K)}$$
$$N_{2(g)} + 3H_{2(g)} = 2NH_{3(g)} + 27 \text{ kcal (at 725°K)}$$

Not only is the reaction exothermic; it becomes increasingly exothermic as the temperature is raised. Le Châtelier's principle again points out that the yield of ammonia will be decreased at the higher temperatures. (Temperatures are raised by adding heat to the system, but the equilibrium will shift in such a direction as to use up some of the added heat. Remember also the effect of T if ΔS is negative.) Furthermore, the reaction is still slow even at 700°K and high pressures.

* Le Châtelier's principle states that a system at equilibrium will react to any imposed change in such a manner as to minimize the effect of the change. Thus adding heat to a system encourages endothermic changes which minimize the temperature rise. Compressing a system encourages reactions which decrease the pressure. Adding more of one component to an equilibrium system encourages those reactions which use up the added component and so minimize the increase in its concentration.

One might guess that the apparent activation energy* for the synthesis of ammonia must be very high. But the uncatalyzed reaction is so difficult to study that we don't know its rate, its activation energy, or its possible mechanism; that is, the detailed path by which reaction proceeds. The catalyzed reaction, however, has been extensively studied. On a typical industrial iron catalyst, the apparent activation energy is 42 kcal** and the rate-determining step appears to be the adsorption of atomic nitrogen, N, on the catalyst. If the uncatalyzed reaction also has to go through a slow step involving atomic nitrogen, we can readily account for the very slow rate. The energy of dissociation of molecular nitrogen is 226 kcal, a very large amount of energy:

$$226 \text{ kcal} + N_{2(g)} = 2N_{(g)}$$

A reaction of the degree of complication of the ammonia synthesis, which had an activation energy of 226 kcal, should be very slow indeed.

Although the ammonia synthesis reaction has been used industrially for more than fifty years and has been studied by hundreds of chemists and engineers, the mechanism is still not understood. A detailed knowledge of the kinetics of chemical reactions is still difficult to work out, though computers are giving great promise of more satisfactory analysis of data, and data are becoming easier to obtain. One of the greatest needs is a usable theory to apply to chemical kinetics. If we could calculate the rates of all the reactions possible in a given system, we could save thousands of hours and millions of dollars, and we could, at the same time, successfully predict conditions for synthesizing countless compounds, both those known at present and those not yet discovered. The field of reaction kinetics is probably as full of potential discoveries as any field in chemistry.

Though the mechanism is not known, even beginning students can predict (with the help of Le Châtelier's principle and the relationship $\Delta G = \Delta H - T\,\Delta S$) that ammonia synthesis should be carried out at high pressures and low temperatures in order to attain as high a yield of ammonia as possible. It is also easy to predict that a catalyst and as high a temperature as possible (and probably high pressure) should be used in order to achieve a favorable rate of reaction. Industrial conditions, found by trial and error as well as systematic research, commonly range from 300 to 1000 atm pressure and 600 to 900°K, using a catalyst such as iron containing small quantities of fused oxides (K_2O, CaO, Al_2O_3). Figure 12.3 gives some data on the relationships between *P*, *T*, and yield of NH_3 at equilibrium.

A suitable reaction mixture can be obtained by passing a mixture of natural gas, mainly CH_4, and steam over a catalyst. The product is called synthesis gas. The principal reactions are

$$CH_{4(g)} + 2H_2O_{(g)} = 4H_{2(g)} + CO_{2(g)} \tag{12.1}$$

$$CH_{4(g)} + H_2O_{(g)} = 3H_{(g)} + CO_{(g)} \tag{12.2}$$

At the same time air is introduced to give the necessary nitrogen. The principal reaction is

---

* Activation energy is the minimum energy which must be available during a molecular collision to allow a reaction, other than simple rebound, to occur. It may be thought of as representing the energy necessary to loosen up the original bonds to the place where the reaction proceeds "down hill energetically" from that state to the final products.

** A. Nielson et al., *J. Catalysis*, **3**, 68 (1964).

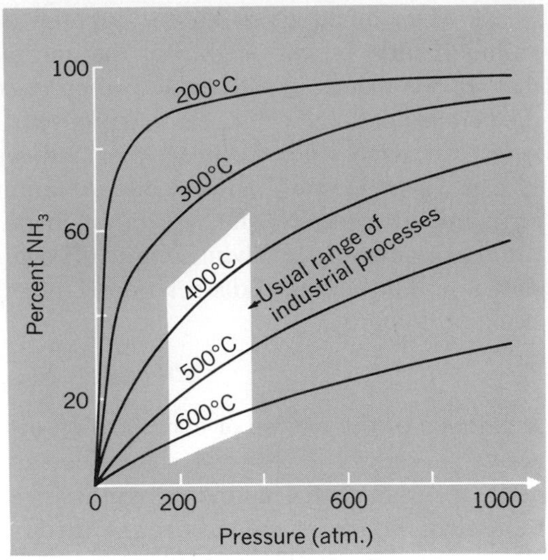

Figure 12.3 Percentage ammonia in equilibrium with $3H_2:1N_2$ mixture. [J. T. Gallagher and F. M. Taylor, *Ed. Chem.*, **4**, 30 (1967).]

$$CH_{4(g)} + O_{2(g)} = CO_{2(g)} + 2H_{2(g)} \qquad (12.3)$$

The resulting gases, mainly H_2, N_2, CO_2, and CO plus a small excess of H_2O, are passed over another catalyst to convert most of the CO to CO_2:

$$CO_{(g)} + H_2O_{(g)} = H_{2(g)} + CO_{2(g)} \qquad (12.4)$$

The CO_2 and residual H_2O and CO may then be removed in absorption towers. The resulting gas contains primarily H_2 and N_2, about 1% noble gases (Ar and others) and traces of methane. The desired H_2/N_2 ratio is 3/1. Why? What ratio of steam and oxygen should be introduced into the first reaction chamber to give this ratio?

The H_2, N_2 mix is then passed through a catalytic reactor at high pressures (why?) and moderately high temperatures (why?) to give the equilibrium H_2, N_2, NH_3 system. The extent of reaction is further enhanced by cooling the products to condense out the ammonia, and then recycling the gases over the catalyst bed. A small fraction of the gas is continually bled off to prevent the concentration of noble gases and methane from rising high enough to interfere with the desired reaction (see Figure 12.4).

Ammonia, NH_3, finds its main use in fertilizers, since all living things require some source of the amine group, $—NH_2$, in order to survive. It is not surprising that NH_3 can serve as a good source of the $—NH_2$ group.

Exercise 12.4

How many tons of NH_3 could be made from the nitrogen in a cubic mile of air? *Answer:* Assume likely values. $2x$ moles $NH_3 = x$ moles $N_2 = PV/RT =$ $[0.80(730/760) \cdot 5.280^3 \cdot 10^9 \text{ ft}^3 \cdot 12^3 \text{ in}^3/\text{ft}^3 \cdot 2.54^3 \text{ cm}^3/\text{in}^3 \cdot 10^{-3} \text{ l/cm}^3]/[0.0820 \cdot 300] = 1.3 \cdot 10^{11}$ moles. Tons NH_3 (100% yield) $= 2 \cdot 1.3 \cdot 10^{11}$ moles $\cdot$ 17 g mole^{-1}/454 g lb$^{-1} \cdot 2000$ lbs ton$^{-1} = 4.8 \cdot 10^6$ tons.

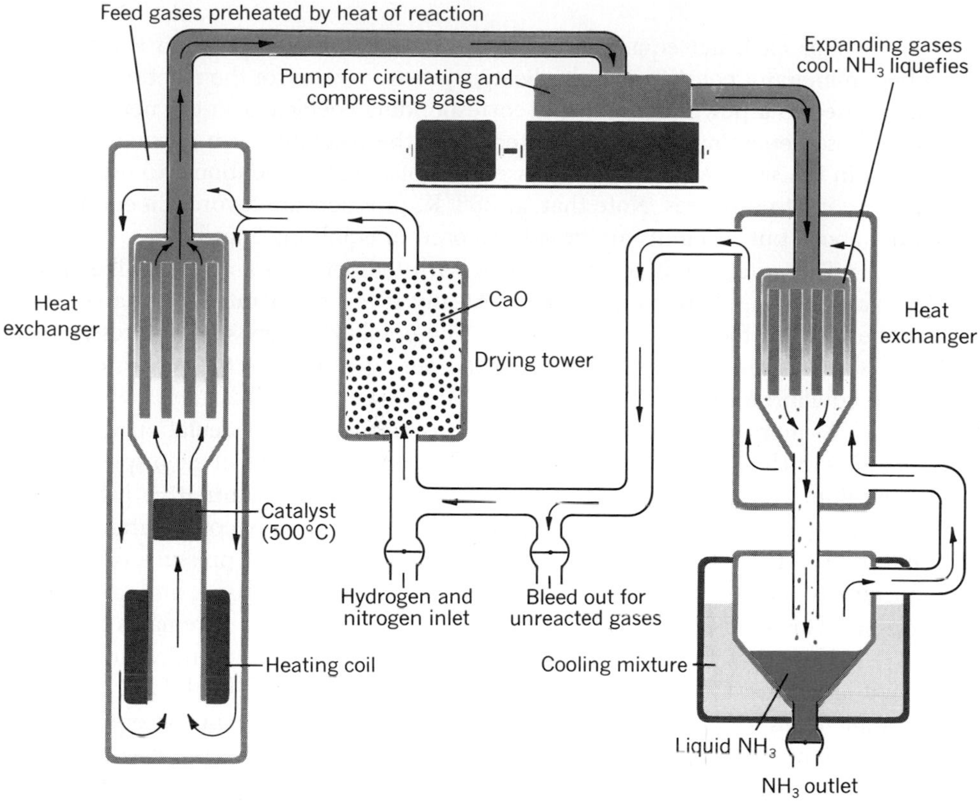

Figure 12.4 Schematic flow diagram for the synthesis of ammonia from the elements.

EQUILIBRIUM CONSTANTS, LE CHÂTELIER'S PRINCIPLE, AND ΔG°

Chemical systems and their equilibria can also be viewed in terms of the equilibrium constant for the net reaction. We shall develop this idea fully in Chapters 19 and 29 and rely here on a semiempirical approach plus your previous studies in science.

For any net equation one can, by inspection of the equation, write an equilibrium constant expression for the system. Consider a few of the reactions discussed above:

$$N_{2(g)} + 3H_{2(g)} = 2NH_{3(g)},\ K_{eq_1} = \frac{p_{NH_3}{}^2}{p_{N_2}p_{H_2}{}^3} = 7.96 \cdot 10^2 \text{ at } 298°K$$

$$CH_{4(g)} + 2H_2O_{(g)} = 4H_{2(g)} + CO_{2(g)},\ K_{eq_2} = \frac{p_{H_2}{}^4 p_{CO_2}}{p_{CH_4}p_{H_2O}{}^2} = 7.4 \cdot 10^{-20} \text{ at } 298°K$$

$$CH_{4(g)} + H_2O_{(g)} = 3H_{2(g)} + CO_{(g)},\ K_{eq_3} = \frac{p_{H_2}{}^3 p_{CO}}{p_{CH_4}p_{H_2O}} = 7.1 \cdot 10^{-25} \text{ at } 298°K$$

$$CO_{(g)} + H_2O_{(g)} = H_{2(g)} + CO_{2(g)},\ K_{eq_4} = \frac{p_{H_2}p_{CO_2}}{p_{CO}p_{H_2O}} = 1.04 \cdot 10^5 \text{ at } 298°K$$

For each net equation the equilibrium constant expression is a fraction whose numerator consists of multiplicative pressure terms for the reaction products each raised to a power equal to the corresponding coefficient in the net equation, and whose denominator consists of terms for the reactants with exponents determined in the same way. For gas phase reactions, it is conventional to express the pressure in atmospheres. Note that, at 298°K, products are favored in equilibria 1 and 4 above but reactants are greatly favored in equilibria 2 and 3.

The equilibrium constant varies with temperature and we shall consider this variation in Chapters 27 and 29. At any given temperature it is a constant independent of the pressure or volume. The equilibrium constant expression can always be written from examination of the net equation, but the numerical value of the equilibrium constant must be measured experimentally.

Numerical values of equilibrium constants assist the calculation of numerical values of the equilibrium pressures and/or concentrations of each species. The equilibrium constant expression above allows excellent quantitative predictions concerning the effects on all concentrations of changing any combination of concentrations. Thus K_{eq_1} indicates that increasing the partial pressure of N_2 in a constant volume equilibrium system will lead to a decrease in p_{H_2} and an increase in p_{NH_3}. This follows because K_{eq} will not change as long as T remains constant.

Note that the conclusion from reasoning with K_{eq} is identical to that obtained using Le Châtelier's principle, as must be true. Use of Le Châtelier's principle leads to the prediction that adding N_2 (in a fixed volume at equilibrium) causes the net reaction that uses up part of the added N_2 to occur, thus decreasing p_{H_2} and increasing p_{NH_3}. The use of K_{eq} has the advantage over Le Châtelier's principle of allowing quantitative estimates of the extent of change and even exact calculations if the numerical value of K_{eq} is known.

Note also that values of K_{eq} are interrelated. For example, equation 2 minus 3 gives equation 4, and $K_2/K_3 = K_4$. You should be able to show rigorously that the K_{eq} for an equation which is the sum of other equations always equals the product of the equilibrium constants for the individual equations. Consider a further example from the gas-phase air oxidation of NH_3 to NO_2:

$$2NH_{3(g)} + \tfrac{5}{2}O_{2(g)} = 2NO_{(g)} + 3H_2O_{(g)}, \qquad K_{eq_5} = p_{NO}{}^2 p_{H_2O}{}^3 / p_{NH_3}{}^2 p_{O_2}{}^{5/2}$$

$$2NO_{(g)} + O_{2(g)} = 2NO_{2(g)}, \qquad K_{eq_6} = p_{NO_2}{}^2 / p_{NO}{}^2 p_{O_2}$$

$$2NH_{3(g)} + \tfrac{7}{2}O_{2(g)} = 2NO_{2(g)} + 3H_2O_{(g)}, \qquad K_{eq_7} = p_{NO_2}{}^2 p_{H_2O}{}^3 / p_{NH_3}{}^2 p_{O_2}{}^{7/2} = K_{eq_5} K_{eq_6}$$

In every case of addition of chemical equations, the equilibrium constant for the total equation is the product of the equilibrium constants of the individual steps.

You will find the use of the equilibrium constant expression and numerical values of K valuable additions to Le Châtelier's principle in correlating shifts in equilibrium systems. It should be clear that, since both ΔG^0 and equilibrium constants, K, are a measure of equilibrium concentrations, the two must be related. The relationship, given before in Chapter 1, is

$$\Delta G^0 = -RT \ln K_{eq}$$

Even though we have not derived this relationship (we will do this in Chapter 29), you will find it most useful in converting ΔG^0 to K_{eq} and vice versa.

NUCLEAR SPIN AND NUCLEAR MAGNETIC RESONANCE

The property of spin is not only associated with electrons. Since Pauli's suggestion in 1925, we have assumed spin to be associated with many particles, including neutrons and protons and atomic nuclei. An ordinary hydrogen nucleus should be a particularly simple case, since it contains only a proton. This proton could have either an α spin or a β spin. In an isolated atom in space there might be no frame of reference that would allow us to differentiate these spins, but when a hydrogen atom is in an unsymmetrical electric field, the field could supply a frame of reference and the spins might be experimentally differentiable. Such an unsymmetrical field could be generated when a hydrogen atom is bonded to another atom or when a hydrogen atom is placed in an external magnetic or electric field.

Consider a hydrogen atom bonded to another atom. The 1*s* orbital of the hydrogen surrounds the nucleus of the hydrogen and is surely distorted by the other atom. Thus the interaction between the hydrogen proton and the 1*s* electrons will depend on the extent to which the other atom is also affecting the 1*s* electrons. Since the field surrounding the proton is now asymmetric, the interaction between the proton and the electrons will be different if there are various possible proton spin states. In the presence of a magnetic field two nuclear spin states are possible. Let us call them α and β and assume that the α state will result in a lower energy level for the system. Energy would be required to change the spin state of the nucleus to β. The amount of energy required to change the α spin to β will depend on the field created by the 1*s* electrons and on the strength of any additional external field placed around the system. The larger the additional external field, the larger the energy difference between the α and β spin state for the hydrogen proton. All of these ideas had been suggested by spectroscopic experiments and from applications of quantum theory by about 1940, but the actual observations on hydrogen compounds were not made until 1945.

Calculations indicated that magnetic field strengths of about 15,000 gauss should lead to a proton spin energy difference of $\alpha - \beta$ for typical hydrogen-containing compounds of about 10^{-6} kcal mole^{-1}. This is a very small amount of energy and corresponds to the photon energy of a radio frequency source of about 10^8 cycles per second. From Figure 8.2 we see this is near the lower end of the experimentally accessible electromagnetic spectrum.

Ethyl alcohol (ethanol) was one of the first small molecules to be tried out in a nuclear magnetic resonance (NMR) spectrometer, like that of Figure 12.5. After much effort an absorption spectrum like that shown in Figure 12.6 was obtained. The positions of the peaks were sensitive to the strength of the magnetic field, just as predicted, but at constant field strength the absorbed energies were constant and the relative amounts of energy absorbed at the three peaks were in the ratio of 3 to 2 to 1. The existence of three peaks indicated three different electron environments around the protons in the ethanol, just as had been predicted for a substance of formula CH_3CH_2OH. The relative intensities of the peaks indicated that there were three of one kind of proton-electron interaction, two of another, and one of a third—again consistent with the previously accepted structural formula, shown as a space-filling model in Figure 12.6.

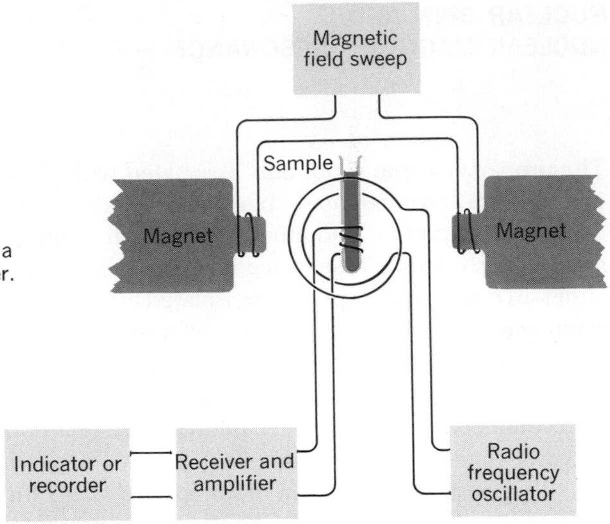

Figure 12.5 Schematic arrangement of a nuclear magnetic resonance spectrometer.

The discovery of nuclear magnetic resonance produced an extremely powerful tool for structural determinations. It also greatly enhanced our belief in wave mechanics and our theories of the nuclear atom. Previous spectroscopic and thermodynamic evidence and theoretical inference were supported in every detail. The existence of two forms of hydrogen molecules (called ortho- and para-hydrogen and deducible from heat capacity data), the existence of the astronomically observed hydrogen atom emission line at $7.3 \cdot 10^{-5}$ kcal mole^{-1}, and the NMR spectra of every hydrogen-containing substance studied, all fit the idea that the proton in a hydrogen nucleus has spin and that the difference in energy between the α and β states is a function of the strength of the surrounding fields.

NMR can be applied to any nuclei having net spin, but the effects are most readily observed with hydrogen. Some other isotopes whose surroundings can currently be effectively studied with NMR are B^{11}, C^{13}, N^{14}, O^{17}, F^{19}, and P^{31}.

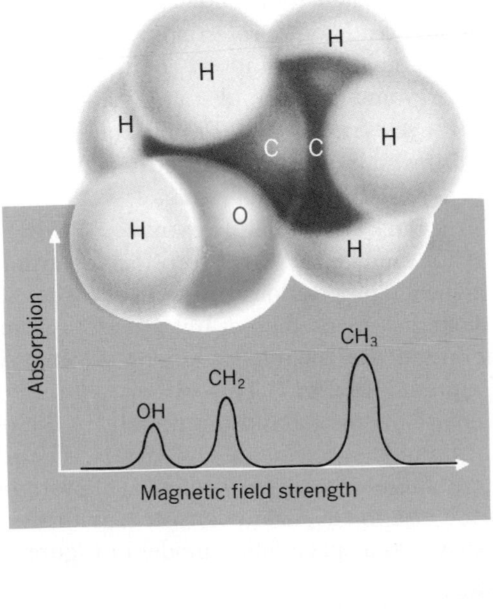

Figure 12.6 NMR spectrum of ethanol, CH_3CH_2OH, at low resolution.

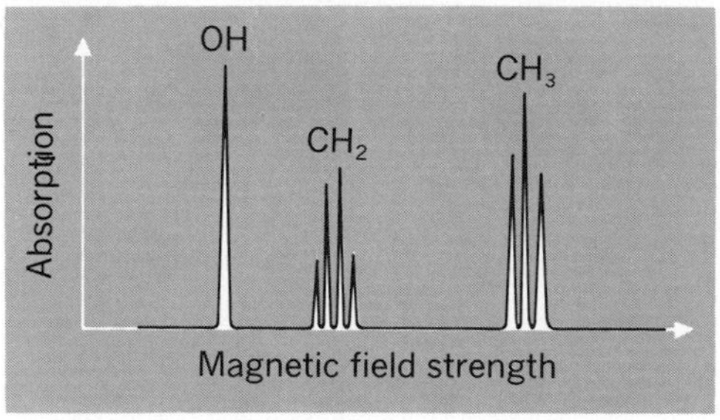

Figure 12.7 NMR spectrum of ethanol, CH_3CH_2OH, at moderate resolution.

Many of the main NMR peaks can exhibit fine structure, as shown by two of the three peaks in ethanol in Figure 12.7. We shall limit our discussion at this point, however, to the number of main peaks (corresponding to the number of kinds of hydrogen atoms present) and the relative intensities of the peaks (corresponding to the relative number of hydrogen atoms of that kind). The fine structures give additional confirmation of these two numbers and also allow considerable insight into the nature of the bonds holding the hydrogen atom to the neighboring nuclei.

NMR is particularly useful, and it was discovered at an especially fortuitous time, since other structural determination methods, such as X-ray diffraction, are relatively unable to detect hydrogen atoms. (The intensity of diffraction of X-rays varies with the square of the atomic number of the atom, so that hydrogen of atomic number 1 diffracts only weakly.) The existence and availability of deuterium, and the hydrogen isotope of mass 2 that comprises 0.015% of natural hydrogen considerably extends the applicability of NMR. Deuterium has a nuclear spin twice that of the proton, since the nucleus contains one proton and one neutron and the two spins add. Thus substitution of deuterium for hydrogen of mass 1 in a compound shifts the NMR signal corresponding to that bond in the molecule to a different spectral region but does not otherwise change the structure or behavior of the molecule appreciably. Disappearance of some of the proton peaks upon deuterium substitution gives strong confirmation of structural assignments. Figure 12.8 shows some NMR curves for a few molecules that all contain the same atoms, but arranged differently (they are isomers). The power of the method should be apparent.

The concomitant support of our model of the nuclear atom is also pleasing. We feel more confident than ever that atoms can be treated as deformable electromagnetic fields surrounding a central nucleus, and that the interactions of the fields with the nucleus, and vice versa, depend on the symmetry and strength of the fields.

In particular, we shall continue to treat hydrogen atoms as composed of a central proton interacting with the field of the 1*s* valence electrons.

WATER

Water is so common on earth that discussions of it and its properties pervade any chemistry course. Table 12.2 lists some of these properties. No laboratory is complete without a supply of distilled water, no industrial plant could operate without access to water, and no living system can survive in its absence. In fact, from 50–99% of the weight of most living systems is made up of water. Since the molar

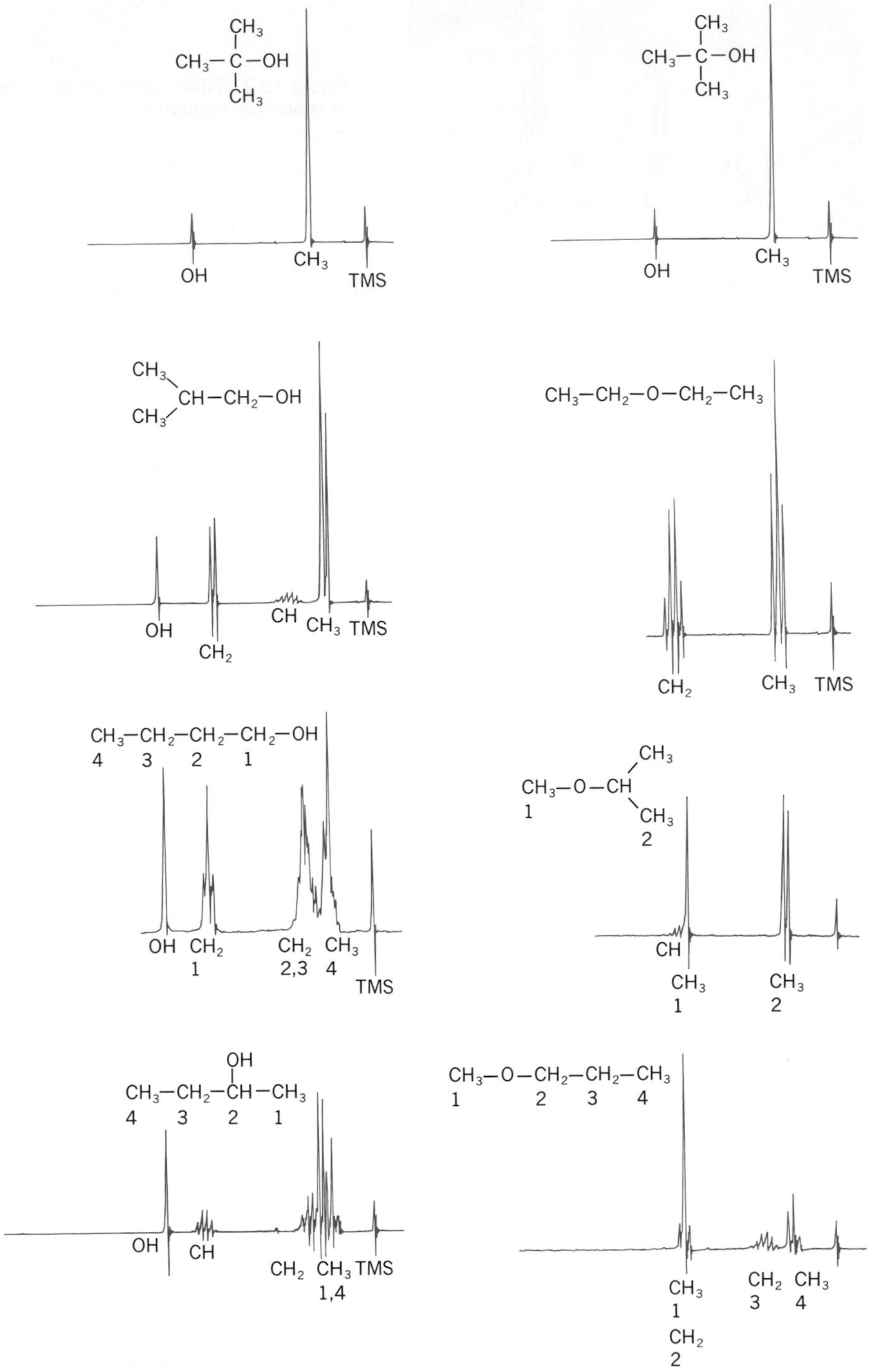

Figure 12.8 NMR spectra of some isomeric molecules. TMS indicates the peaks due to hydrogens in tetramethyl silane, $(CH_3)_4Si$, used as a standard. [Spectra by P. Myhre and Linda James.]

Table 12.2 Some properties of water (see also Table 6.2).

$\Delta H^0_{form\,(l)}$ (kcal mole^{-1})	M.p. (°K)	B.p. (°K)	$\Delta H_{fus(m.p.)}$ (kcal mole^{-1})	$\Delta H_{vap(b.p.)}$ (kcal mole^{-1})	$S^0_{298(l)}$ (cal mole^{-1} °K^{-1})	$S^0_{298(g)}$ (cal mole^{-1} °K^{-1})
−68.315	273.15	373.15	1.436	9.770	16.75	45.104

Vapor pressure									
°C	0	10	20	25	30	40	50	60	80
torr	4.58	9.21	17.54	23.76	31.82	55.32	92.51	149.38	355.1
°C	90	96	98	99	100	120			
torr	525.8	633.9	707.3	733.2	760.00	1489			

weight of water is only 18, whereas most molar weights are 100 or more, considerably more than 90% of all the molecules in most living things are water molecules. Many a man has spent his whole professional life studying water and its reactions, and much remains to be unraveled about it even yet. At this point we shall only consider, and briefly at that, the reactions between water and the binary compounds of hydrogen.

Water is a bent molecule and deviates appreciably from an ideal gas at its boiling point. It has a high melting point and a high boiling point for its size. All these effects indicate that the water molecule can form relatively strong attractions to other water molecules and probably to many other molecules as well.

Exercise 12.5

ΔH^0_{vap} of water at 25°C is 10,500 calories mole^{-1}. Calculate ΔG^0 for the vaporization of water at 25°C. Comment on the sign and magnitude of ΔG^0. *Answer:* We expect ΔG^0_{vap} to be + at 25°C, since the equilibrium pressure is less than 1 atm. $\Delta G^0 = \Delta H^0 - T\,\Delta S^0$. $\Delta G^0 = 10{,}500 - 300(45.1 - 16.8) = 2000$ cal mole^{-1}. The small positive value of ΔG^0 indicates an appreciable vapor pressure over liquid H_2O at 25°C but less than 1 atm. [In fact, assuming an ideal gas during the process of changing the pressure of H_2O from 1 atm to equilibrium pressure, P, we get $\Delta G = 2000 = \Delta H - T\,\Delta S = 0 - T\,\Delta S = -RT\ \ln\ (P/P^0)$. $-\log P = 2000/4.575 \cdot 298$. $P = 0.034$ atm $= 26$ mm. Direct measurement (see Table 12.2) gives 24 mm, well within the uncertainty of our calculation here.]

THE REACTION OF WATER WITH OTHER BINARY HYDROGEN COMPOUNDS

When most of the metallic hydrides of Figure 12.1 are placed in water, gaseous hydrogen is rapidly evolved. Very little of the hydrogen gas remains in the water. This low solubility of hydrogen in water is consistent with our past experience that hydrogen is almost an ideal gas and so has very small intermolecular forces toward itself and toward many other molecules. The low solubility is also consistent with the nonpolar nature of hydrogen and the polar nature of water.

Gaseous water is far from an ideal gas. Strong intermolecular forces exist even in the gas. At the much closer intermolecular distances found in liquid water, these forces are quite strong. In order for the H_2 to dissolve in H_2O, the water molecules (which attract one another) must be pushed apart, but the H_2 does not form similarly strong attractions to the water. Thus ΔH is positive, ΔS is not favorable, and H_2 does not dissolve appreciably in H_2O.

Many binary hydrogen compounds dissolve in water and often react to form new species. Analysis of the systems shows that the following equations describe many of the reactions of the metallic hydrides with water. For the alkali metal hydrides (LiH, NaH, KH, RbH, CsH—all containing H^- ions),

$$LiH_{(c)} + H_2O_{(l)} = H_{2(g)} + Li^+{}_{(aq)} + OH^-{}_{(aq)}$$

The reactions of CaH_2, SrH_2, and BaH_2 are similar:

$$CaH_{2(c)} + 2H_2O_{(l)} = 2H_{2(g)} + Ca^{++}{}_{(aq)} + 2OH^-{}_{(aq)}$$

The interactions of the ionic products with water tend to make ΔH negative, and the formation of $H_{2(g)}$ tends to make ΔS positive. So the reactions occur. Most of the metals, however, form rather insoluble hydroxides, and this minimizes the amount of metal present as aqueous ions after the reaction:

$$BeH_{2(c)} + 2H_2O_{(l)} = 2H_{2(g)} + Be(OH)_{2(c)}$$
$$ZnH_{2(c)} + 2H_2O_{(l)} = 2H_{2(g)} + Zn(OH)_{2(c)}$$

Some of the metallic hydrides—for example, TiH_2, CuH, SnH_4, PbH_4—are unreactive with water. The principal effect here must be a large negative ΔH^0_{form} of the metallic hydrides, since ΔS^0 would certainly favor formation of $H_{2(g)}$.

The only hydrides of a nonmetal that react vigorously with water to give hydrogen are those of boron:

$$B_2H_{6(g)} + 6H_2O_{(l)} = 6H_{2(g)} + 2H_3BO_{3(aq)}$$

The carbon hydrides, which like H_2 are relatively perfect gases with low intermolecular forces, do not dissolve appreciably in water nor do they react with it at low temperatures.

The hydrides of the nonmetals in the upper right portion of the periodic table are generally appreciably soluble in water, as one might guess from the data on gas imperfections in Table 6.1. But the solubility goes considerably beyond what would be expected in terms of intermolecular forces alone. These binary hydrogen compounds react appreciably with the water, but not to produce hydrogen.

Ammonia, NH_3, is highly soluble, increases the electrical conductivity of the liquid, and makes the solution basic (see Figure 12.9). The hydrogen halides are equally soluble, make the solution much more conductive than does ammonia, and produce acidic solutions in water. Hydrogen sulfide is intermediate in all these properties. It is not highly soluble, increases the electrical conductivity somewhat, and gives a weakly acidic solution. Electrolysis of each of these solutions gives hydrogen gas at the *cathode* (contrast the molten hydrides of the alkali metals), indicating that the hydrogen is probably being produced from a positive ion in these aqueous solutions, rather than from a negative ion as in the metal hydrides.

The nature of these positive hydrogen-containing ions has been a puzzle ever since their existence was first suggested toward the close of the nineteenth century, and the full story is still not known. In modern terms, it seems extremely

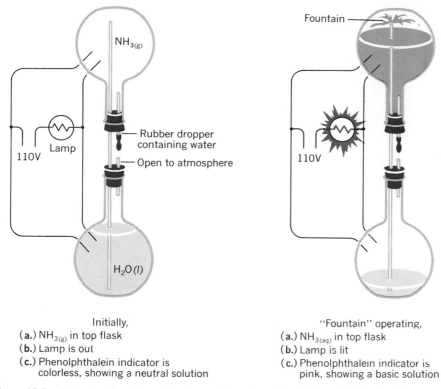

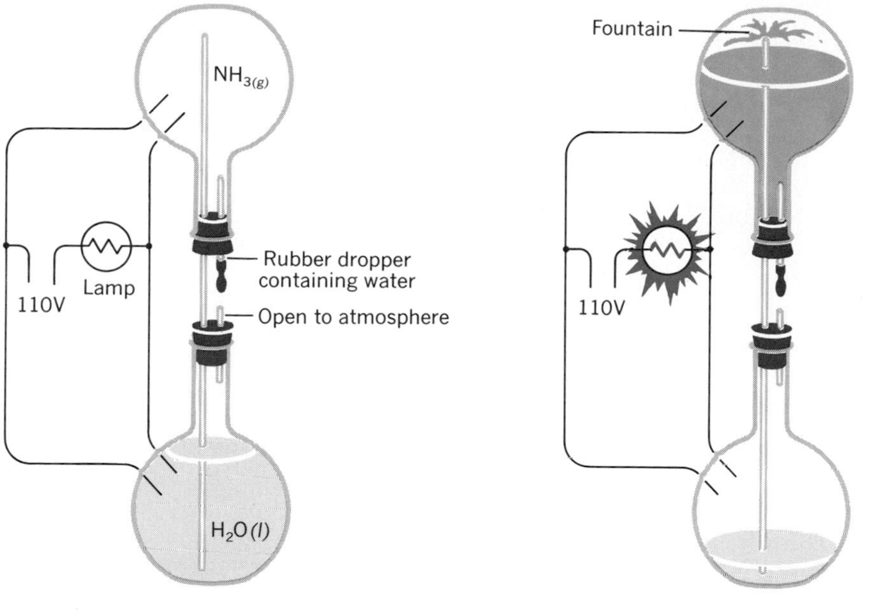

Initially,
(**a.**) $NH_{3(g)}$ in top flask
(**b.**) Lamp is out
(**c.**) Phenolphthalein indicator is colorless, showing a neutral solution

"Fountain" operating,
(**a.**) $NH_{3(aq)}$ in top flask
(**b.**) Lamp is lit
(**c.**) Phenolphthalein indicator is pink, showing a basic solution

Figure 12.9 Apparatus for determining some effects associated with the solution of gases (such as ammonia) in water. The experimental changes are initiated by injecting a few drops of water into the top flask by squeezing the dropper bulb. The top flask will finally fill with water because of the high solubility of ammonia. The resulting solution conducts electricity, and so must contain ions.

unlikely that simple, monatomic, positive hydrogen ions of formula H^+ could exist in aqueous solution. After all, such an ion would consist only of a proton. The radius usually given for a proton is about 10^{-12} cm and the intensity of its electric field is enormous. The likelihood that it would remain independent of the surrounding water molecules is essentially zero. Similar problems exist in attempting to describe any ion in solution, but the electric field of the proton is much more intense than that of any other ion, and hence the problem is more severe with hydrogen.

Present evidence, based on NMR, infrared spectroscopy, kinetic studies of reaction rates, equilibrium data on the distribution of the positive ions between various phases, and inference from the behavior of other ions and of hydrogen-containing ions in other phases (for example, crystals) suggests that H^+ ions in solution are normally associated with several other molecules. These molecules cluster about the H^+ center and distribute the positive charge among themselves. The mechanism may be such that the proton distorts the orbital electron clouds of the surrounding molecules toward itself, but the electrons do not leave the solvent molecules. The result will be to polarize the molecules, making the side toward the H^+ more negative and the side away from it more positive, and so diffusing the positive charge over a larger volume and decreasing the charge density (see Figure

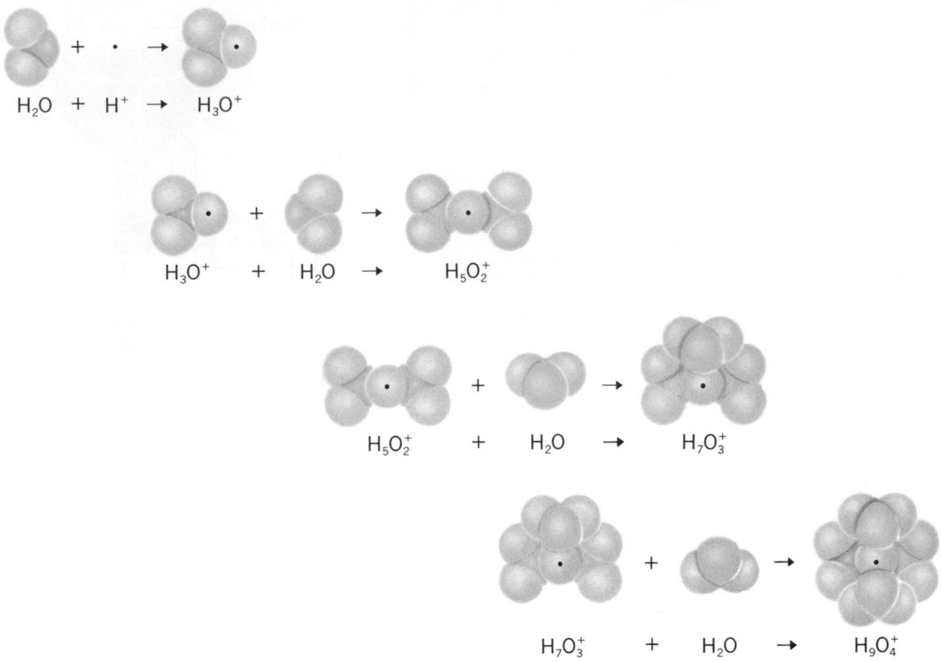

Figure 12.10 Possible steps in the hydration of a proton.

12.10). The nature of these hydrated protons is not known and may not even be well defined. Perhaps they are continually forming and disintegrating with various numbers of solvent molecules surrounding the proton at different times. We shall, therefore, adopt the convention of writing the hydrated proton as H_3O^+, or as $H^+{}_{(aq)}$. Each of these symbols indicates that the proton is not alone, but is interacting with the water. The H_3O^+ symbol does *not* indicate that the proton is adhering to only one water molecule, though it might be more tightly held to one water than to the other surrounding molecules. By convention, $[H_3O^+] = [H^+]$ = concentration of aqueous hydrogen ion in moles per liter. Also by convention, the heat of formation, free energy of formation, and entropy of formation of $H^+{}_{(aq)}$ is zero, as shown in Table 12.1.

We may then write equations to indicate the solution and reaction of the hydrogen halides with water, where X indicates F, Cl, Br, or I:

$$HX_{(g)} + H_2O_{(l)} \longrightarrow HX_{(aq)}$$

$$HX_{(aq)} = H^+{}_{(aq)} + X^-{}_{(aq)}$$

or

$$HX_{(aq)} + H_2O_{(l)} = H_3O^+{}_{(aq)} + X^-{}_{(aq)}, \qquad K_{eq} = \frac{[H_3O^+][X^-]}{[HX]}$$

This set of equations accounts for the experimental observations. The high solubility is due primarily to the large negative values of ΔH that result from the high hydration energy of the proton:

$$H^+{}_{(g)} + H_2O_{(l)} \longrightarrow H^+{}_{(aq)}, \qquad \Delta H^0 = -367 \text{ kcal}$$

Note that the change in entropy would not seem to favor high solubility. The increase in electrical conductivity is represented in terms of formation of new ions.

The acidity is interpreted in terms of the existence of aqueous hydrogen ions or of labile protons which can move from molecule to molecule.

The interpretation of the reaction of hydrogen sulfide is similar:

$$H_2S_{(g)} + H_2O_{(l)} \longrightarrow H_2S_{(aq)}, \qquad K = \frac{[H_2S_{(aq)}]}{p_{H_2S}} = 0.013$$

$$H_2S_{(aq)} = H^+{}_{(aq)} + HS^-{}_{(aq)}, \qquad K = \frac{[H^+][HS^-]}{[H_2S]} = 1.0 \cdot 10^{-7}$$

or

$$H_2S_{(aq)} + H_2O_{(l)} = H_3O^+{}_{(aq)} + HS^-{}_{(aq)}$$

$$\left(HS^-{}_{(aq)} = H^+{}_{(aq)} + S^={}_{(aq)} \text{ is a very slight reaction, } K = \frac{[H^+][S^=]}{[HS^-]} = 1.3 \cdot 10^{-13}\right)$$

The decreased solubility, conductivity, and acidity with hydrogen sulfide are consistent with one another and indicate that $HS^-{}_{(aq)}$ competes with water for the protons more successfully than any of the halide ions do; H_2S is a more stable molecule with respect to ionization in water than are the hydrogen halides. Thus there is less hydration energy and less negative ΔH, and hence lower solubility.

We mentioned above that when these binary hydrides dissolved in water its electrical conductivity increased and the acidity changed. Water itself conducts an electric current slightly; it also has acidic and basic properties. These properties can be interpreted in terms of the self-ionization of water:

$$H_2O_{(l)} = H^+{}_{(aq)} + OH^-{}_{(aq)}, \qquad K_{H_2O} = [H^+][OH^-] = 10^{-14} \text{ (at 25°C)}$$

$$OH^-{}_{(aq)} = H^+{}_{(aq)} + O^={}_{(aq)}, \qquad K_{OH^-} = \frac{[H^+][O^=]}{[OH^-]} \cong 10^{-36} \text{ (at 25°C)}$$

The equilibrium constants for these two reactions are normally written as indicated. Note that the second ionization is so small—$[O^=] \cong 10^{-36}\ F$ in pure water—as to be negligible.

Exercise 12.6

What is the most probable reaction of each of the following with water: (*a*) NaH, (*b*) CdH_2, (*c*) C_2H_6, (*d*) H_2Se, (*e*) HI? *Answer:* Metallic hydrides (*a* and *b*) tend to give hydrogen and a soluble ($Na^+ + OH^-$) or insoluble [$Cd(OH)_2$] hydroxide, following the general reaction: $H^- + H_2O = OH^- + H_2$. Nonmetallic hydrides tend to ionize H^+ more or less strongly depending on the negative charge density of the nonmetal. (*c*) Hydrocarbons are inert to water. Apparently the peripheral H's keep the carbon free from any attack by water at room *T*. At high *T* expect $C_2H_{6(g)} + 2H_2O_{(g)} = 2CO_{(g)} + 5H_{2(g)}$ due to favorable ΔS. (*d* and *e*) A higher negative charge density (H_2Se, moderate size, -2 oxidation number) = weaker acid. A lower negative charge density (HI, larger size, -1 oxidation number) = more highly acidic.

AMMONIA AND HYDROCARBONS IN WATER

Ammonia and similar compounds also dissolve in water to give a solution of increased electrical conductivity. But compared to water these solutions are basic, not acidic, as shown in Figure 12.10. Extension of our previous argument concerning the effect of charge density shows that this experimental observation can be correlated with the results observed with the hydrogen

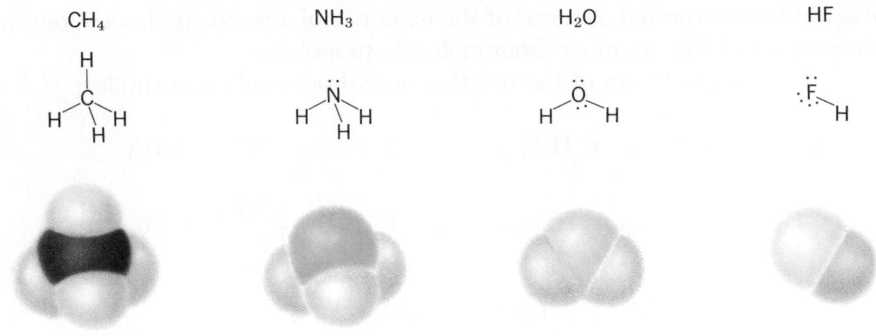

Figure 12.11 Schematic representation of some isoelectronic molecules showing the relative availability of electron-filled orbitals for further bonding.

halides and substances like H_2S. The negative charge density around the nitrogen in NH_3 (oxidation state -3 on N) should be *higher* than that around the isoelectronic oxygen in H_2O (oxidation state -2 on O), since the nuclear charge of the nitrogen is one unit less positive. Thus hydrated ammonia can gain a proton from water:

$$NH_{3(g)} = NH_{3(aq)}$$

$$H_2O_{(l)} + NH_{3(aq)} = NH_4{}^+{}_{(aq)} + OH^-{}_{(aq)}$$

$$K_{eq} \equiv \frac{[NH_4{}^+][OH^-]}{[NH_3]} = 1.8 \cdot 10^{-5} \text{ (at 25°C)}$$

The rather small value of the equilibrium constant indicates that the production of $NH_4{}^+{}_{(aq)}$ and $OH^-{}_{(aq)}$ does not proceed to any great extent, suggesting that the proton bonding forces are not greatly different in water and in ammonia. If the forces are not greatly different, we can ascribe most of the tendency to react to the entropy effect—that is, to the tendency of the atoms to move at random between the various atomic combinations available to them. Although aqueous ammonia is often written as NH_4OH, the current evidence suggests that few such identifiable molecules are present. Thus $NH_4{}^+{}_{(aq)}$ is the preferred symbolism. See the discussion on $H^+{}_{(aq)}$.

The binary carbon-hydrogen compounds are almost inert toward water. Unlike the hydrides of groups VA, VIA, and VIIA of the periodic tables, the entire surface of the carbon is surrounded tetrahedrally by hydrogens. The electron cloud of the carbon is not exposed to attack, for instance, as is that of N, O, or the halogens, which have only three, two, or one of their tetrahedral apices "covered" by hydrogens (see Figure 12.11). There are no carbon orbitals which can interact strongly with additional hydrogen atoms. There are at least two effects acting: (1) the lack of "exposed" electrons decreases the rate of any possible reaction, and (2) the four bonds to each carbon tend to make the molecules thermodynamically stable. They undergo few reactions at ordinary temperatures.

ACID-BASE THEORY

We may generalize the above discussion of hydrogen reactions. The proton is unique among atoms in being only a nucleus and thus having an enormous positive charge density. Protons will be actively attracted to the negative electron clouds in exposed electron orbitals of other atoms. The attraction will vary from orbital to orbital but will certainly depend on the exposure of the orbital and the charge density in it. When several different orbitals are present, there will be competition

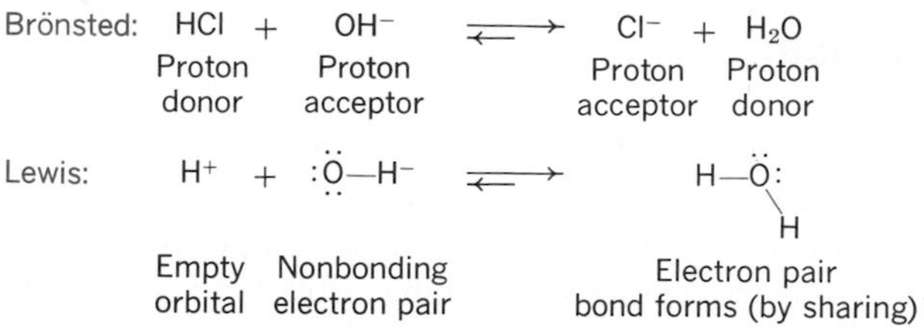

Figure 12.12 Schematic comparison of the Brönsted and Lewis theories.

among them for the proton. In terms of entropy, the proton will move in a random fashion among the available orbitals. In terms of energy, it will spend most of its time associated with the orbitals to which it is most strongly attracted.

This competition and the resulting distribution of protons are readily observed in water solutions. But similar effects occur in other solutions. If liquid HF and HI are mixed, they dissolve, the conductivity increases, and the species $H_{(HF)}{}^+$ and $I_{(HF)}{}^-$ are found. In effect, some of the protons have transferred from the HI to HF. The extent of transfer is not as great as in water, but neither this fact nor the occurrence of the transfer should be any surprise in terms of the ideas presented above.

Proton transfer reactions are so common—partly because of our great use of water as a solvent—that they are often treated in terms of a specialized theory: acid-base theory. Experimentally an acid may be defined as a chemical that changes the color of certain indicator dyes (as bromthymol blue from yellow to blue), whereas a base reverses the color change. Theoretically, following the Brönsted concept, acids may be defined as proton donors and bases as proton acceptors. Somewhat more generally, following the Lewis theory (which we will use most of the time), acids are chemicals that can provide an empty valence orbital—that is, they lack a valence electron pair—and bases are chemicals having a full orbital which is not engaged in bonding—that is, they have an extra, nonbonding electron pair. Figure 12.12 compares these two theories. It is quite possible for a single compound, such as water, both to donate and accept protons or electrons, and so to act sometimes as an acid and sometimes as a base, as we have already indicated. Which way a given compound will act depends not only on its own properties but also on its properties compared to the properties of other substances in the system. Acid-base reactions, and chemical reactions in general, occur because there are various possible combinations of atoms. These various combinations may differ in energy, but the random motions of the atoms ensure that all the combinations will exist. The relative concentrations of the various possible combinations will be determined by the energy levels and the spatial likelihood of each combination.

Exercise 12.7

Classify the following as Lewis acids or bases: Cr^{+++}, Cl^-, H^+, NH_3, SO_3.

Answer: Acids: Cr^{+++} (empty 3*d*), H^+ (empty 1*s*), 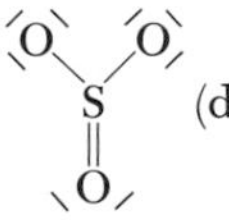 (double bond indicates lack of electrons). Bases: $[|\overline{\underline{Cl}}|]^-$, 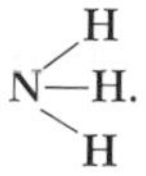.

OXIDATION STATES OF HYDROGEN

Three different oxidation states are known: H^- (a proton surrounded by a single orbital holding two electrons), H_2 (two protons sharing two electrons in some sort of a common orbital), and H^+ (a bare proton that has such a high positive charge density that it is strongly attracted to electron-containing orbitals of other substances, such as H_2O). The H^- ions (as in melts*) and H_2 molecules can exist relatively independently of other molecules, but H^+ "ions" are only found closely associated with other atoms (except in the gas phase).

It has become customary to treat the chemistry of hydrogen in terms of these three oxidation states:

- -1: H^-, as in the metal hydrides
- 0: H or H_2, as in the atomic or molecular element
- $+1$: hydrogen, as in all other compounds of the element

We have already shown, in our discussion of acid-base theory, that the interaction of H^+ with an electron-filled orbital depends on the orbital properties. But it is still conventional to describe all hydrogen atoms in hydrides of the nonmetals, such as the boron hydrides or compounds containing elements of periodic table groups IVA, VA, VIA, and VIIA, as being in the $+1$ oxidation state. More than 99% of the known hydrogen compounds (all of them except the binary metal hydrides) are normally treated as having hydrogen in an oxidation state of $+1$.

We shall discuss the bonding forces and nature of the bonds found with hydrogen in Chapters 14 through 17. It is sufficient here to point out that (*a*) hydride ions in oxidation state -1 have two electrons in their 1*s* orbital; (*b*) elementary hydrogen atoms of oxidation state zero have one electron in their 1*s* orbital; and (*c*) hydrogen atoms of $+1$ oxidation state have an average of less than one electron in their 1*s* orbital. The bare proton, of course, has no electrons in its 1*s* orbital.

SUMMARY

Hydrogen forms binary compounds with most of the elements and forms an indefinitely large number of compounds with carbon. The general role of hydrogen is to cover the periphery of a molecule. Each hydrogen atom normally forms strong bonds to only one other atom. Simple hydrogen ions, H^+, exist only in the gas phase and at high temperatures. At other conditions the enormously concentrated electric field of the bare proton ensures that it will interact strongly with other atoms in the vicinity and adhere to these other molecules. The competition among all the possible sites for the hydrogen ions can be treated in terms of acid-base theory. Hydrogen can exist as the -1 ion, H^-, but this ion is a strong reducing agent.

Well over 95% of all known compounds contain hydrogen, so that its

---

*Melts are liquid salts, metals, and their solutions obtained by melting the appropriate materials—usually well above room temperature.

detection by such techniques as NMR and infrared spectroscopy gives very valuable information concerning molecular structure and the nature of chemical bonds. We shall take up the nature of chemical bonds in later chapters.

We must cease to give the impression that we don't have time to talk to the public—and even worse that if we did talk to them, they couldn't grasp our meaning anyway. We must abandon the idea that some sort of taint attaches to the scientist who explains his endeavors to outsiders.
—*Ivan L. Bennett,* Science, **154,** 619 (1966).

PROBLEMS

12.1. Estimate the temperature at which heated hydrogen will be appreciably dissociated into protons and electrons. (About 10^5 °K.)

12.2. Platinum catalyzes the reaction of hydrogen and oxygen gases. Iron does not. Use Figure 12.1 and suggest a possible mechanism for the platinum catalysis.

12.3. Which in each pair is ionized to the greater extent in 0.1 *F* aqueous solution: (*a*) H_2S, H_2Se; (*b*) H_2S, HCl; (*c*) H_2Se, HI; (*d*) HBr, HF?

12.4. It is necessary to remove the trace of hydrogen (about 0.1%) in a 2-liter sample of gaseous oxygen prepared by the electrolysis of water. What process do you recommend?

12.5. Hydrogen and chlorine burn vigorously together but reaction does not begin without ignition, or supply of energy from an outside source. Write the equation for the reaction and interpret the necessity of ignition in terms of a possible mechanism of the reaction.

12.6. There is ten times as much hydrogen (by volume) in the air as neon. Why is hydrogen never reclaimed from the air whereas neon is?

12.7. Lithium aluminum hydride, $LiAlH_4$, reacts vigorously with water to give a gas and a white precipitate. Write an equation to represent these experimental observations. Use the equation to predict another experimental observation that would allow you to check the validity of the equation.

II

12.8. Calculate the weight which could be lifted by a balloon filled with 10^6 liters of gaseous hydrogen; 10^6 liters of gaseous helium; 10^6 liters of gaseous methane.

12.9. How is it that hydrogen was thought to be diatomic well before any diffraction techniques or heat capacity data were available?

12.10. Ordinary hydrogen gas consists of two kinds of molecules—ortho-hydrogen, in which the nuclear spins add to give a net spin of one, and para-hydrogen, in which the nuclear spins are opposed to give a net spin of zero. At room temperature the ratio of ortho to para molecules is 3 to 1. All rotational J values for para-hydrogen are even ($J = 0, 2, 4, 6, \ldots$). All rotational J values for ortho-hydrogen are odd ($J = 1, 3, 5, 7, \ldots$). Which form, ortho or para, will constitute the equilibrium state in liquid hydrogen?

12.11. H_2 molecules are thought to absorb on αAl_2O_3 with the internuclear axis of H_2 perpendicular to the surface. Ortho- and para-hydrogen (in the 3:1 mix) can be quantitatively separated by passing H_2 gas over αAl_2O_3 below 70°K. Which molecules, ortho or para (see Problem 12.10), are more strongly adsorbed? Why must T be below 70°K?

12.12. Assume that a low temperature catalytic process is discovered to "fix" nitrogen by the reaction

$$N_2 + CH_4 + O_2 = CH_3C\begin{matrix} \diagup O \\ \\ \diagdown NH_2 \end{matrix} + H_2O$$

$\Delta\overline{H}^0_{\text{form}}$ of CH_3CONH_2 (c) is known to be -76.60 kcal, but its S^0 is unknown. Is the process thermodynamically feasible? ($\Delta G^0 \cong -100$ kcal mole^{-1})

12.13. The manufacturers of a chemical (a mixture of metallic aluminum and sodium hydroxide) commonly used in cleaning household drains paid almost a million dollars in damages in 1967 after several cans of their product exploded. They had recently changed from a pry-top closure to a screw closure for the can. Write an equation for the net reaction and suggest the reason for the explosions with the new containers.

12.14. On combustion, 2.000 g of a compound containing only carbon and hydrogen gave 3.269 g of H_2O and 5.989 g of CO_2. What is the empirical formula of the compound?

12.15. Calculate K_{eq} for the system $2NO_2$ (g) = N_2O_4 (g) when the partial pressure of NO_2 is 0.2 atm and that of N_2O_4 is 0.4 atm at equilibrium. What would the partial pressure of NO_2 be if the N_2O_4 pressure were 1 atm at equilibrium? [$p_{NO_2} \cong 0.3$ atm]

12.16. The energy difference between nuclear spin quantum states is not constant but depends on the product of the nuclear magnetic moment (μ) and the strength of the applied magnetic field H_0). Splitting of energy levels for nuclei with allowed spin states α and β is shown.

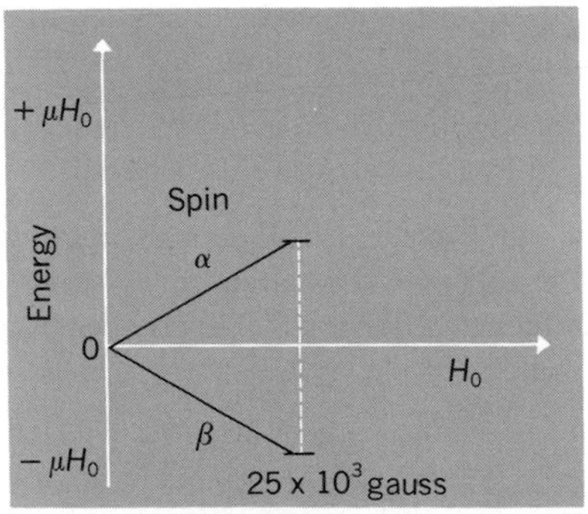

(a) Calculate the frequency that would be required to induce a transition, $\beta \longrightarrow \alpha$, if an assembly of protons, say the protons in sulfuric acid, is placed in a magnetic field of 25,000 gauss. $\mu_H = 1.42 \cdot 10^{-23}$ erg gauss^{-1} = magnetic moment of hydrogen. (About 10^7 sec^{-1}.) (b) What is the difference in population of the two spin states α and β at a field strength of 25,000 gauss? (About 0.98.) (c) On the basis of your calculation comment on the inherent sensitivity of nuclear magnetic resonance spectroscopy.

12.17. Why are the two heat exchangers in Figure 12.4 run so that the two gases flow countercurrent to one another in each case?

12.18. Sketch possible low-resolution NMR spectra for the molecular formulas listed: C_2H_6, $CH_3CH_2CH_3$, $(CH_3)_2CHCHCl_2$, $CH_2{=}CHCH_3$.

12.19. When gaseous atomic hydrogen is passed over platinum gauze, the gauze becomes red hot. Write a possible net equation and a possible mechanism to account for this experimental observation. Include the energy term in the net equation.

III

12.20. Which would you predict would have the higher ionization energy—H or H_2? Look up the values and discuss them.

12.21. A hydrogen balloon of capacity 10^6 liters is to be launched in Antarctica. Design three methods of obtaining the hydrogen in Antarctica and compare the relative merits of the methods.

12.22. A student titrating 25.00-ml portions of a carefully prepared standard acid with some base he had prepared obtained the following buret readings.

Initial	0.57	23.82	4.65
Final	23.82	46.92	27.44

What should the student do next? Comment on the precision and accuracy of his work according to the above data. Calculate the relative concentration of acid and base to three significant figures.

See page 1091 for a list of references and readings in the recent chemical literature related to the material in this chapter.

PART 2

Chemical Bonds

WHAT HOLDS MOLECULES TOGETHER?

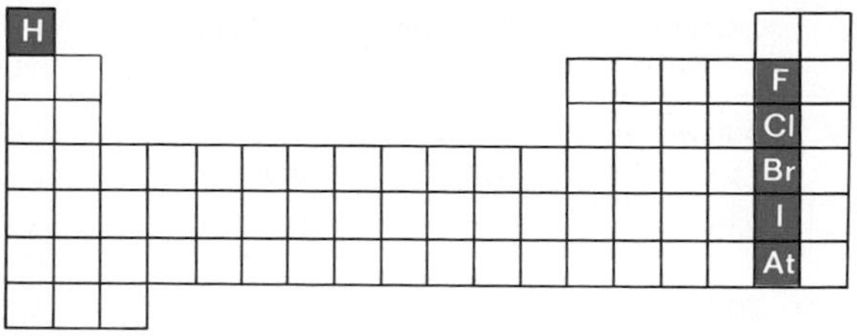

CHAPTER 13

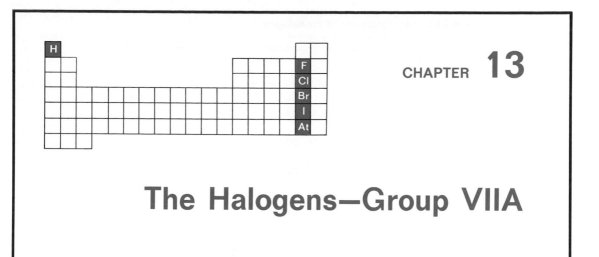

The Halogens—Group VIIA

Halogen reactions with most other elements generally proceed rapidly, even violently, and go almost to completion.

The only family other than the noble gases whose elements can all readily exist in the gaseous state at usual laboratory conditions is the halogens. (We shall neglect astatine here, since it has no stable isotopes.) Combining volumes, Cannizzaro's principle, heat capacity data, and all other evidence indicate that under these conditions the elements fluorine, chlorine, bromine, and iodine are diatomic molecules: F_2, Cl_2, Br_2, I_2. The same diatomic molecules are found in the liquid and crystalline states for these elements. At high temperatures the diatomic gaseous molecules dissociate into atoms. The extent of dissociation at constant T decreases from iodine to bromine to chlorine, but fluorine is dissociated about as much as iodine. The bond energy between two fluorine atoms is weaker than would be expected, if we assume uniform trends in properties as the atomic number varies. This contrasts with the regular trends in the other properties listed in Table 13.1.

Table 6.1 indicated that chlorine deviated considerably from being an ideal gas near room T and P. With bromine the deviation is larger and with iodine still larger, as indicated by their existence in the liquid and solid states respectively at room conditions. Fluorine approaches ideality more closely than chlorine. We thus see that there is not a direct correlation between the forces holding the atoms together in the diatomic molecules (greatest attraction between chlorine atoms) and those acting between the diatomic molecules themselves (greatest attraction with iodine). It is also worth noting, however, that the anomaly is minimized if we neglect fluorine for the moment: we then find that the intramolecular forces get stronger from iodine to chlorine but the intermolecular forces get stronger in the reverse direction. With this in mind it is interesting to compare in Table 13.2 the

Table 13.1 Some properties of the halogens.

Property	Fluorine (F_2)	Chlorine (Cl_2)	Bromine (Br_2)	Iodine (I_2)	Trend (⟶)
Color	light yellow	yellow-green	red-brown	violet	deepens
Melting point (°K)	50	172	266	387	increases
Boiling point (°K)	85	239	332	460	increases
Ionization energy (kcal mole^{-1})	402	300	273	241	decreases
X—X bond energy (kcal mole^{-1})	37.8	58.2	46.1	36.1	maximum at Cl
Electron structure (gaseous atom)	2, 7	2, 8, 7	2, 8, 18, 7	2, 8, 18, 18, 7	
S^0_{298}	$48.44_{(g)}$	$53.29_{(g)}$	$58.65_{(g)}$ $36.38_{(l)}$	$62.28_{(g)}$ $27.76_{(c)}$	increases

Table 13.2 ΔH (kcal mole^{-1}) for the reactions indicated at 298°K and 1 atm.

Reaction	ΔH^0_{298}	ΔS^0_{298}	ΔG^0_{298}
$F_{2(g)} = 2F_{(g)}$	37.76	27.39	29.44
$Cl_{2(g)} = 2Cl_{(g)}$	58.16	25.62	50.524
$Br_{2(l)} = 2Br_{(g)}$	53.48	47.23	39.400
$I_{2(c)} = 2I_{(g)}$	51.07	58.61	33.596

total energy, ΔH^0_{298}, necessary to obtain monatomic gaseous atoms, starting with each element in the form in which it is stable at room temperature, with the X—X bond energy in Table 13.1. It is apparent that the total interaction of a given halogen atom with all of its neighbors at room temperature is roughly constant, again except for fluorine. When we discuss the nature of chemical bonding in more detail in Chapters 14 through 17 we shall need to account for this difference, and, of course, for the similarities. It will also be interesting to account for the difference from the bond energy of 103 kcal mole^{-1} found in hydrogen molecules, H_2.

THE REACTIVITY OF THE HALOGENS

Though differing from the noble gases by only one unit of nuclear charge or one electron per atom, the halogens are enormously different from the noble gases in reactivity, being one of the most rapidly and completely reactive set of elements. Indeed, none of the halogens is found free in nature. As we have already seen (Figure 5.3), the halogens are most commonly found in the ocean (as chloride or bromide ion), in former ocean deposits including those that have been oxidized by the air (as iodate ions), or as calcium fluoride, which has a very limited solubility in water. We also have pointed out in Chapter 5 that fluorine and chlorine compounds are so stable that the elements are prepared from them by electrolysis, whereas bromine and iodine can be generated from their naturally occurring minerals with chemical reactants.

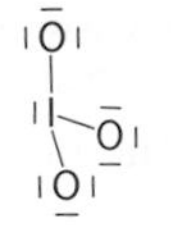

Figure 13.1 Valence electron structure of IO_3^-.

That three of the halogens are customarily found in nature as ions isoelectronic with noble gas atoms—F^-, Cl^-, and Br^-—underlines again the stability of this structure. Iodine is commonly found in nature as I^-, isoelectronic with Xe, but it is also found as IO_3^-. This last species may well have resulted from the air oxidation of I^- that had originally been deposited from the sea:

$$I^- \, (aq) + \tfrac{3}{2}O_2 \, (g) = IO_3^- \, (aq) \qquad \Delta G^0 = -18.3 \text{ kcal,}$$

Even with the IO_3^- it is possible to write an electronic structure in which every atom has a noble gas set of valence electrons. Thus an iodine atom has seven valence electrons, each oxygen atom has six, and one additional electron accounts for the net negative charge—a total of 26 electrons. If we follow our past conventions (as in Figures 5.17 or 5.21), we can obtain Figure 13.1, which uses 26 electrons (13 pairs) to give each atom a noble gas set of eight valence electrons.

Table 13.3 lists some common species containing halogen atoms, in terms of the oxidation state of the halogen, and gives a possible assignment of the electrons, assuming that each atom ends up isoelectronic with a noble gas. ΔG^0_{form} is also listed. Can you see from ΔG^0 values that Br_2 is most soluble in H_2O and that Cl_2 reduces Br^- to Br_2 while forming Cl^-?

Table 13.3 **Some stable halogen-containing species with suggested noble gas electron structures, and (in parentheses) their ΔG^0_{form} for 1 *M* aqueous solutions in kcal mole^{-1} at 298°K.**

Oxidation state	Name (Prefix and suffix)	Fluorine	Chlorine	Bromine	Iodine
-1	(—ide)	F^-, $\vert\overline{\underline{F}}\vert$ (−66.64)	Cl^-, $\vert\overline{\underline{Cl}}\vert$ (−31.372) Chloride	Br^-, $\vert\overline{\underline{Br}}\vert$ (−24.85)	I^-, $\vert\overline{\underline{I}}\vert$ (− 12.33)
0	(—ine)	F_2, $\vert\overline{\underline{F}}-\overline{\underline{F}}\vert$ (large +)	Cl_2, $\vert\overline{\underline{Cl}}-\overline{\underline{Cl}}\vert$ (1.65) Chlorine	Br_2, $\vert\overline{\underline{Br}}-\overline{\underline{Br}}\vert$ (0.94)	I_2, $\vert\overline{\underline{I}}-\overline{\underline{I}}\vert$ (3.92)
$+1$	(hypo—ite)	Not known	OCl^-, 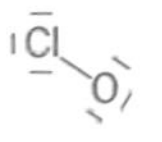 (−8.8) Hypochlorite	HOBr, 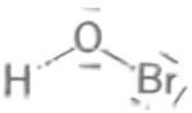 (−19.7)	HOI, 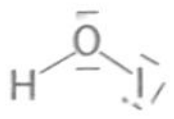 (−23.7)
$+5$	(—ate)	Not known	ClO_3^-, 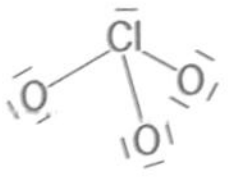 (−0.8) Chlorate	BrO_3^-, 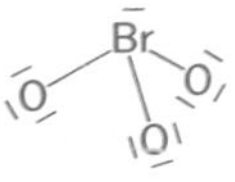 (0.4)	IO_3^-, 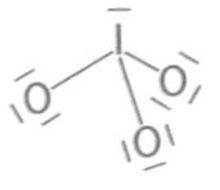 (−30.6)
$+7$	(per—ate)	Not known	ClO_4^-, 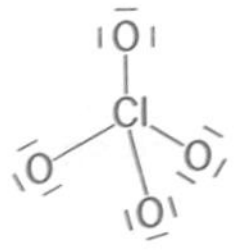 (−2.06) Perchlorate	BrO_4^- (probably tetrahedral, first reported in 1968)	IO_4^-, 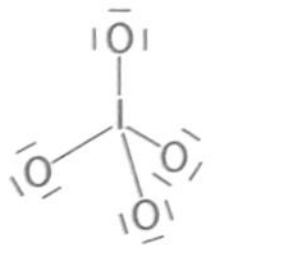 (?)

Other oxidation states, especially of chlorine, are also known, but we shall neglect them here. The possibility that all of the species listed in Table 13.3 do contain atoms isoelectronic with the noble gases is enhanced by the fact that all these species can exist as aqueous ions and as ions in crystalline salts. In many of these cases the interactions with neighboring molecules seem primarily coulombic in nature—that is, arising from the net charge on the halogen-containing species rather than from any special orbital interaction or overlap.

We might repeat here that probably 90% of all known substances can be represented by electron structures involving noble gas arrangements, and that probably 95% of the substances studied in beginning courses fall into this category. Thus the "rule of 8" based on filling sets of sp^3 valence orbitals is a highly useful generalization.

That the noble gas set of electrons does not always give a complete picture is well illustrated by the existence of a large set of interhalogen molecules, both neutral and negative ions, as indicated in Table 13.4. Note their generally negative ΔG^0_{form}, indicating considerable thermodynamic stability with respect to the elements. In each molecule the halogen atom of highest atomic number is known to be surrounded by the other atoms. Only the diatomic molecules can be considered to be possibly isoelectronic to noble gas structures. Other halogen-containing species, such as H_5IO_6 and the compounds discussed in connection with Figure 11.3, attest further to the inadequacy of the noble gas picture as a general interpretation. From the formulas in Table 13.4, however, we may get a clue to a possible solution if we note that fluorine does not occur as the central atom; fluorine atoms are found only on the periphery of molecules, consistent with their tendency to form only one covalent bond per atom. Reference to Figure 3.18 suggests that the lack of 3*d* orbitals in fluorine may be a factor; *d* orbitals are present only for higher values of the principal quantum number. The presence of *d* orbitals, especially in I and Br, should allow the formation of a larger number of bonds and might be useful in accounting for cases in which there are too many valence elec-

Table 13.4 Some halogen molecules, and (in parentheses) some of their ΔG^0_{form} (gases, or 1 *F* solution of ions) at 298°K in kcal mole^{-1}.

Coordination number	Electrically neutral (even number of atoms)	Ions (odd number of atoms, except $I_8^{=}$)
1	ClF (−12.28), BrF, $BrCl$, ICl, (−1.30), IBr (0.89)	
2		Br_3^-, (−25.59), Br_5^-, (−24.8), I_3^-, (−12.3), ICl_2^-, (−38.5), IBr_2^-, (−29.4), $BrICl^-$ (−35.0), I_5^-, $I_8^{=}$
3	ClF_3 (−28.4), BrF_3 (−54.83)	
4	I_2Cl_6	BrF_4^-, ICl_4^-
5	BrF_5 (−83.8), IF_5 (−179.68)	
7	IF_7 (−195.6)	

trons about some atoms to allow them to be isoelectronic with the noble gases. We must also remember, however, that such molecules contain many atoms crowded together. This may lead to large electric fields of rather low symmetry, which will result in further splitting of the atomic orbitals, similar to that already observed in the polyelectronic (as opposed to the hydrogenlike) gaseous atoms. Or the fact that fluorine usually has a $CN = 1$ may be due to the larger energy gap between the $2s$ and $2p$ levels that results from the lower Z in fluorine (see Figure 3.17). Only the half-empty $2p$ orbital may be energetically available for bonding, not the s and p^3 as in the other halogens.

In any case it is clear that the halogens have many more oxidation states than hydrogen and that the halogens much more commonly serve as "central atoms" in molecules than does hydrogen, which generally has a peripheral role. However, note the similarity here between fluorine and hydrogen. It is largely the peripheral role that both have which justifies comparing hydrogen with fluorine and has led some chemists to place hydrogen in the halogen family in the periodic table.

Exercise 13.1

How do you interpret the observation that all neutral interhalogen compounds contain an even number of atoms and all ions (except $I_8^{=}$) contain an odd number of atoms (Table 13.4)? *Answer:* All neutral halogen atoms have seven valence electrons. They must combine to give an even number of atoms per molecule if all electrons are to be paired, as is usual in molecules. Likewise the presence of an "extra" electron giving a negative ionic charge means there must be an odd number of atoms so that the total electron count is even. $I_8^{=}$ is seen to have a double negative charge, so it must have an even number of atoms.

METALLIC HALIDES

Binary compounds of the halogens and the metals are called halides. Note the—ide suffix. The halogen is considered to be in the -1 oxidation state. Many of these metallic halides dissolve in water to give ionic solutions, and many of the halides have crystal structures in which the coordination number of halogens about the metal is larger than the coefficient in the chemical formula. Thus the coordination numbers in the halides of the group IA elements (such as NaCl, RbI, LiBr) is either 6 or 8. Many of the molten halides are conductors of an electric current. These and other data indicate that many of the metallic halides contain ions in the crystalline, liquid, and dissolved states. This is consistent with our earlier assumption that halogen atoms in the -1 state would be isoelectronic with noble gas atoms. Each halide ion has one more electron than the corresponding halogen atom, and so has the noble gas number of electrons. The reaction of halogens with metals might then be generalized in these equations:

$$M + a(\tfrac{1}{2}X_2) = MX_a = (M^{a+})(X^-)_a$$

or

$$e^- + \tfrac{1}{2}X_2 = X^-, \qquad M = M^{+a} + ae^-$$

These reactions generally proceed vigorously, even violently, and go practically to completion—that is, until one of the reactants is completely consumed.

Figure 13.2 Structure of Al_2Cl_6.

Most of the metallic halides have high melting and boiling points, and low vapor pressures at usual temperatures. All of the group IA and group IIA halides have these properties, as do most of the halides of the metals in the middle of the periodic table.

There is an appreciable number of metallic halides, however, that are rather volatile—for example, the halides of aluminum, titanium, ferric iron, tin, plus a large group of fluorides having the formula MF_6. Almost all of the volatile halides show a coordination number of either four or six halogen atoms around each central atom. Examples are gaseous $TiCl_4$, $SnCl_4$, UF_6, and the chlorides of aluminum and ferric iron. The first three examples seem straightforward and consistent with the position of the metals in groups IV and VI of the periodic table. The chlorides of aluminum and iron, however, have the empirical formulas $AlCl_3$ and $FeCl_3$. By applying the method of gas density (see Figure 6.13) to these compounds, we find that the molecules present in the gas near the boiling point are Al_2Cl_6 and Fe_2Cl_6, respectively. These molecules can achieve a coordination number of four halides about the metal if two of the halides act as bridge atoms between the two metal atoms while the other four chlorides are on the periphery of the molecule. All available data indicate that this gives the correct structure of the molecules, which we can write as in Figure 13.2.

The metal atoms are situated on the line of intersection of two perpendicular planes. One of these planes contains the two bridge chlorines, the other plane contains the four peripheral chlorines. The coordination number of chlorines about the metal atoms is four.

The hexafluorides have a structure in which the six fluorines are octahedrally coordinated to the central atom. Known hexafluorides include those of Mo, Tc, Ru, Rh, W, Re, Os, Ir, Pt, U, Np, Pu. We have already mentioned XeF_6 and SF_6. The list is completed with the elements Se, Te, and Po. The volatility of the first group of fluorides above is remarkably constant. Their boiling points range only from 290°K for WF_6 to about 350°K for RhF_6. Interestingly enough, the most nonvolatile hexafluoride is XeF_6, the only hexafluoride whose central element is highly volatile.

Exercise 13.2

How would you prepare pure NaCl? Pure Ga_2Cl_6? *Answer:* NaCl by recrystallization from aqueous solution. Ga_2Cl_6 by cautiously passing $Cl_{2(g)}$ (perhaps at low pressure to control reaction) over metallic gallium. Let cool. Pump off excess Cl_2. Distill Ga_2Cl_6 (low boiling point) away from excess Ga (high boiling point).

NONMETALLIC HALIDES

In contrast to the metallic halides (but like the nonmetallic hydrides) the nonmetallic halides are generally volatile, indicating that they consist of well-defined molecules in the crystalline, liquid, and gaseous states. It is customary to assign an oxidation state of -1 to the halogen in these compounds, but the evidence is strong that simple halide ions are not present. Like the metallic halides, the nonmetallic halides may usually be made by direct combination of the two elements: most reactions are vigorous and essentially complete. The halogens are reactive toward most of the chemical elements.

We have already discussed the noble gas fluorides in Chapter 11. They appear to owe their existence to the great tendency of fluorine to attract an electron. The element having the next greatest tendency to attract electrons is oxygen. Chlorine is next, but the lack of compounds so far found between chlorine and the noble gases suggests that the interaction with chlorine is too small to lead to stable compounds.

The most commonly encountered nonmetallic halides, by far, are those of hydrogen: HF, HCl, HBr, and HI. These may be prepared from the elements or by treating an appropriate metallic halide with nonvolatile, strong acid, as in the reaction

$$H_2SO_{4(l)} + NaCl_{(c)} = HCl_{(g)} + NaHSO_{4(c)}$$

or, in general,

$$HY_{(l)} + MX_{(c)} = HX_{(g)} + MY_{(c)}$$

All the hydrogen halides are readily volatile, and so can be distilled out of the reaction mixtures as gases. The success of this distillation depends on a lack of volatility in the other ingredients, and therefore a nonvolatile acid such as sulfuric or phosphoric acid is used. Pure hydrogen halides will be obtained only if no other volatile products are formed. The most likely contaminants are the elementary halogens themselves, which are formed if the halide ions are oxidized. Sulfuric acid is a strong enough oxidizing agent to convert bromide to bromine and iodide to iodine, so phosphoric acid (which is a poor oxidizing agent) is the reagent of choice in preparing HBr and HI. Sulfuric acid is ordinarily used for HF and HCl, since it is more readily available, cheaper, and reacts more rapidly.

Hydrogen halides are often formed when nonmetallic halides react with water. The following are standard methods of preparing HBr and HI, using red phosphorus, the halogen, and water as starting materials.

HBr: $$P + \tfrac{3}{2}Br_2 = PBr_3$$
$$PBr_3 + 3H_2O = H_3PO_3 + 3HBr_{(g)}$$

HI: $$2P + 3I_2 + 6H_2O = 2H_3PO_3 + 6HI_{(g)}$$

An alternate method of preparation, if an aqueous solution of HBr or HI is desired, is to mix the halogen and hydrogen sulfide in the presence of water and filter off the sulfur:

$$X_2 + H_2S + H_2O \longrightarrow 2H^+_{(aq)} + 2X^-_{(aq)} + S_{(s)}$$

OXYGEN-HALOGEN COMPOUNDS: NOMENCLATURE

Table 13.3 shows that there are many halogen compounds containing oxygen. Some other binary compounds are—Cl_2O, ClO_2, Cl_2O_6, Cl_2O_7. The only halogen oxides stable with respect to decomposition into the elements are F_2O and I_2O_5. The rest decompose, often with explosive violence. Several of these oxides are interesting for having an odd number of electrons. ClO_2, BrO_2, and BrO_3 are all odd molecules; that is, they contain an odd number of electrons. Clearly there must be atoms in an odd molecule which are not isoelectronic with noble gas atoms, all of which contain even numbers of electrons. The names of these binary compounds usually have prefixes indicating the number of atoms per molecule: chlorine dioxide, dichlorine monoxide, dichlorine heptoxide, bromine trioxide. Absence of a prefix indicates one atom per molecule.

Of much wider interest and use are the oxygen-containing species listed in Table 13.3. These hypo—ite, -ite, -ate, and per—ate compounds are much used in chemical laboratories and have varied commercial applications. It may be wise here to note the systematics of naming such oxygen-containing species. The prefix hypo- means "beneath" or "less than." The prefix per- means "above" or "beyond." The suffix -ite refers to the less positive of two oxidation numbers for an atom, and the suffix -ate to the more positive. The nomenclature system for negative ions in chlorine-oxygen and similar compounds is described in Table 13.5. The corresponding electrically neutral hydrogen compounds (the electrically neutral acids) are characterized by changing the suffix -ite to -ous (sulfite ion, $SO_3^{=}$, to sulfurous acid, H_2SO_3), and changing the suffix -ate to -ic (perchlorate ion, ClO_4^-, to perchloric acid, $HClO_4$). The -ous and -ic suffixes are also used on positive ions to distinguish the less positive (-ous, as in ferrous, Fe^{++}) from the more positive (-ic, as in ferric, Fe^{++}) oxidation state. Nothing but memory will serve to keep these clear, but continual use will help.

The distinctions inherent in this nomenclature are important and must be learned. A number of unfortunate hospital patients have died because those in charge did not distinguish between mercurous chloride (Hg_2Cl_2, insoluble in body fluids, therefore nonpoisonous) and mercuric chloride ($HgCl_2$, highly poisonous), and explosions have occurred because of a failure to distinguish between ammonium nitrite (NH_4NO_2) and ammonium nitrate (NH_4NO_3).

A more recent system of nomenclature, based on oxidation numbers, is rapidly being adopted. Here are some examples: $HgCl_2$, mercury (II) chloride; Hg_2Cl_2, dimercury (I) dichloride; Fe_2Cl_6, diiron (III) hexachloride. Note that pre-

Table 13.5 Some nomenclature for ions.

Prefix-suffix[a]	Chlorine-oxygen			Other		
	Formula	Oxidation state	Name	Formula	Oxidation state	Name
hypo—ite	OCl^-	+1	hypochlorite	$H_2PO_2^-$	+1	hypophosphite
—ite	ClO_2^-	+3	chlorite	$HPO_3^{=}$	+3	phosphite
				$SO_3^{=}$	+4	sulfite
—ate	ClO_3^-	+5	chlorate	$PO_4^{\equiv}$	+5	phosphate
				$SO_4^{=}$	+6	sulfate
per—ate	ClO_4^-	+7	perchlorate			

[a] Note that the prefixes and suffixes do not represent the same oxidation state or stoichiometry of the ion when used with different elements. +5 phosphorus and +6 sulfur are both—ate ions, and ClO_2^- and SO_3 are both—ite ions, for example.

fixes are used only when necessary to remove ambiguity, and the -ous and -ic suffixes are replaced by indicators of oxidation states.

Exercise 13.3

Name the following compounds, in two ways when feasible: CuCl, $CuCl_2$; $CrSO_4$, $Cr_2(SO_4)_3$; Na_2SO_3, Na_2SO_4; $KClO_3$, KCl, $KClO_4$. *Answer:* Cuprous and cupric chloride or copper (I) and copper (II) chloride; chromous and chromic sulfate or chromium (II) and chromium (III) sulfate; sodium sulfite, sodium sulfate; potassium chlorate, chloride, and perchlorate.

REACTIONS OF OXYGEN-HALOGEN COMPOUNDS

The binary compounds of oxygen with the halogens are so unstable as to have little use except insofar as their properties shed light on the nature of forces holding atoms together. Chlorine monoxide, Cl_2O, can serve as a powerful oxidizing agent ($Cl_2O + 2H^+ + 4e^- = 2Cl^- + H_2O$). Cl_2O is the anhydride of hypochlorous acid, HOCl, and may be prepared by distilling aqueous solutions of the acid at reduced pressure ($2HOCl = H_2O + Cl_2O$). It may also be prepared by passing chlorine gas over freshly prepared mercuric oxide:

$$2Cl_{2(g)} + HgO_{(c)} = HgCl_{2(c)} + Cl_2O_{(g)}$$

Note that chlorine is both oxidized and reduced in this reaction. Such a change, in which a single element oxidizes and reduces itself, is known as an auto-oxidation.

All of the oxygen-halogen acids are strong oxidizing agents, themselves being reduced in the process to the halide ions or to the elementary halogens. The oxygen-halogen ions are much slower and poorer oxidizing agents at room temperature than the acids, so that the crystalline salts and their aqueous solutions are normally more stable than the pure acids. If you write a half-equation for any of these ions acting as an oxidizing agent, you will see why this is so. At higher temperatures both the acids and the crystalline salts become very powerful oxidizing agents. Thus, many fireworks and flares are based on the strong oxidizing power of hot potassium perchlorate, $KClO_4$. Hot (above about 60°C) concentrated perchloric acid, $HClO_4$, is an extremely dangerous chemical. A 100 gallon vat of it, in use as an electroplating bath, once blew up in Los Angeles, and the explosion leveled a large part of two city blocks. A possible series of reactions is an initial dehydration to the anhydride, Cl_2O_7, followed by decomposition into the elements:

$$2HClO_4 = H_2O + Cl_2O_7$$
$$Cl_2O_7 = Cl_{2(g)} + \tfrac{7}{2}O_{2(g)}$$

As with many substances, so here the concentrated solutions are unstable but the dilute solutions are stable. Thus, 70% $HClO_4$ in H_2O has an over-all ΔG^0 for decomposition of -7 kcal mole^{-1} whereas 1 F $HClO_4$ has a corresponding ΔG^0 of $+7$. *Moral:* Use dilute reagents when possible and when in doubt of their stability.

The hypo—ite state can be formed merely by dissolving the appropriate halogen in a basic aqueous solution. Auto-oxidation occurs to form the halide ion and the hypohalite. In an acid solution the hypohalous acid forms

$$X_2 + 2OH^- = X^- + OX^- + H_2O \text{ (in basic solutions)}$$

or

$$X_2 + H_2O = H^+ + X^- + HOX \text{ (in neutral or acid solutions)}$$

The halate states may be formed by further reaction, especially if the solution is heated to increase the rate. Auto-oxidation continues, forming halide and halate ions:

$$3OX^- = 2X^- + XO_3^-$$

Perchlorate may be formed by an additional auto-oxidation if potassium chlorate is heated just above its melting point:

$$4ClO_3^-{}_{(l)} = Cl^-{}_{(l)} + 3ClO_4^-{}_{(l)} \text{ (in molten salts)}$$

However, a cheaper and more useful method of preparing the halate and perhalate compounds is through electrolysis of aqueous solutions of the chloride or iodide. (Perbromates are not known.) Electrolyses are easier to regulate and the syntheses can be carried out at room temperature. The net reactions are

$$Cl^-{}_{(aq)} + 3H_2O_{(l)} = ClO_3^-{}_{(aq)} + 3H_{2(g)} \text{ (upon electrolysis)}$$
$$Cl^-{}_{(aq)} + 4H_2O_{(l)} = ClO_4^-{}_{(aq)} + 4H_{2(g)} \text{ (upon electrolysis)}$$

ASTATINE

The longest lived astatine nuclide is At^{210}, with a half-life of 8 hours. Its chemistry has been studied both on the purified element and by tracer techniques. It is more metallic than iodine, but still forms compounds such as HAt, CH_3At, and interhalogen compounds. It also is like iodine in that it concentrates in the thyroid gland and may be useful in radiating diseased thyroid glands.

SOME ANALYTICAL METHODS

It is all very well to write chemical equations for the many species we have been discussing and to outline methods of preparation and reactions of many compounds. But how do we know the formulas for these compounds and the products of their reactions? So far we have indicated how one might approach the problem if the substances were gaseous—by combining Avogadro's and Cannizzaro's methods. We have also pointed out that X-ray excitation (see Figure 5.2) is a powerful analytical method. But other methods, in many cases more powerful and easier to use, are also available. We shall briefly mention a few here.

ANALYSIS FOR NOBLE GASES

Analysis of the noble gases is carried out most easily by observing the visible and ultraviolet spectrum of the gaseous sample (see Figure 3.12). These spectra are characteristic of the electron structures of the atoms and are a rapid and accurate way of determining whether the elements are present (qualitative analysis) and in what amount (quantitative analysis). The amounts of the elements can also be determined by measuring the pressure, volume, and temperature of the purified element and calculating the number of moles of gas present. This method will be very accurate, since the noble gases behave almost ideally under laboratory conditions, but it does involve initial purification of the gases by fractional distillation.

ANALYSIS FOR HYDROGEN

Hydrogen may also be determined spectroscopically, but the situation is complicated by its tendency to form compounds and by the complexity of the spectra of these compounds. A much more common method is to rely upon the great stability of water. When most hydrogen-containing compounds are heated in the presence of oxygen (especially in the presence of suitable catalysts and oxides such as cupric oxide, CuO) the hydrogen is quantitatively converted into gaseous water. This gas may then be swept out of the reaction zone with a stream of carrier gas, and the water absorbed on a suitable, weighed amount of solid such as calcium sulfate (commercially sold as Drierite) or magnesium perchlorate (commercially sold as Anhydrone). These anhydrous solids absorb the water to form very stable hydrates whose water vapor pressure is low. The solid plus the absorbed water may be weighed. The weight of water absorbed is equal to the gain in weight of the solid, for these solids absorb only water under the conditions of the experiment. The amount of hydrogen in the sample may then be calculated in a direct fashion.

For example, the products of combustion of an 0.0862-g piece of polyethylene in oxygen increased the weight of a tube containing calcium sulfate from 5.6394 g to 5.7499 g. We conclude that 5.7499 g − 5.6394 g = 0.1105 g of water formed and that the water contained 0.1105 · 2.016/18.02 = 0.0124 g of hydrogen. This represents 0.0124 g/1.008 g mole^{-1} H = 0.0123 moles of hydrogen (H). Polyethylene contains only carbon and hydrogen, so that the initial sample, 0.0862 g, must have contained 0.0862 g − 0.0124 g = 0.0738 g of carbon or 0.0738 g/12.00 g mole^{-1} C = 0.00615 moles of carbon. The ratio of number of moles of hydrogen (H), 0.0123, to number of moles of carbon (C) 0.00615, is 2.00, indicating that the empirical formula of polyethylene is $(CH_2)_n$. From many such analyses and a large number of other data we find that polyethylene is made of long chains of linked carbon atoms, with each carbon also holding onto two hydrogen atoms, consistent with the above analysis, $(CH_2)_n$.

ANALYSIS FOR HALOGENS

The variety of chemical compounds of the halogens in terms of oxidation states is greater than with the noble gases or with hydrogen (though the number of hydrogen compounds is far greater). Thus the analysis for halogens is often considerably more complicated than for the noble gases and hydrogen. The analytical problem is somewhat simplified by the fact that the most highly reduced forms of the halogens, the halide ions, are relatively easy to form from most halogen compounds. A common first step, then, is to treat the compound suspected of containing halogens with a powerful reducing agent. Metallic sodium is sometimes used in qualitative work.

Under appropriate circumstances, any halogen present will be converted to the -1 oxidation state, the halide ion.

Qualitative analysis for halide ions may be very complicated if other materials are present, for these materials may have many properties similar to those of the halide ions and so interfere with the interpretation of the analytical results. For simplicity at this stage, we will assume that the only possible negative ions present are F^-, Cl^-, Br^-, or I^-, and that the problem is to find which are there and in what quantity. We shall also assume that the sample can be dissolved in water to give the aqueous halide ions. Since all of them are colorless, their presence is not indicated by visual observation.

You may remember, however, that fluorides occur naturally as the calcium salt because of its high insolubility. Thus the presence of fluoride would be indicated if a precipitate formed upon addition of a solution of calcium nitrate. (Nitrate is used in order not to add any halide ions, as we would if we used calcium chloride, for instance.) The calcium fluoride could be filtered off an weighed to obtain a quantitative measure of the fluoride present. Much better methods are available for analyzing for fluoride, but we will not investigate them here.

The other halide ions—Cl^-, Br^-, and I^-—all form insoluble silver compounds when a solution of silver nitrate is added to their aqueous solutions. Silver chloride is white, silver bromide is light yellow, and silver iodide is bright yellow. (But note that all appear white if the particles are small.) The total weight of the precipitate allows calculation of the total weight of halide ions present. If the precipitate is pure white, only chloride is present and the qualitative analysis is complete. Yellow tinges indicate the presence of bromide and/or iodide, and small amounts of these could be covered by large amounts of white silver chloride, so supplementary tests are needed for an unambiguous solution to the analysis. One possible method is to add 3 *M* aqueous ammonia to the mixed precipitates. The silver chloride is most soluble, as shown by the *K* values in Table 13.6, so only AgCl dissolves in 3 *M* NH_3, forming a silver ammonia complex ion. The resulting solution may be separated from any residual precipitate, and the chloride ion reprecipitated by adding dilute nitric acid. This separation is not completely quantitative (precision may be poorer than $\pm 0.1\%$), but from the weight of the carefully dried precipitate, the chloride content of the unknown can be estimated. Here are the net equations:

Table 13.6 Some equilibrium constants. Note that the concentrations of solid phases, being themselves constant, are included in *K* rather than in the concentration terms (see Table 19.3).

$AgCl_{(c)} = Ag^+_{(aq)} + Cl^-_{(aq)}$	$K_{sp} = 1.8 \cdot 10^{-10}$	$= [Ag^+][Cl^-]$
$AgBr_{(c)} = Ag^+_{(aq)} + Br^-_{(aq)}$	$= 5.0 \cdot 10^{-13}$	$= [Ag^+][Br^-]$
$AgI_{(c)} = Ag^+_{(aq)} + I^-_{(aq)}$	$= 8.5 \cdot 10^{-17}$	$= [Ag^+][I^-]$
$Ag(NH_3)_2{}^+_{(aq)} = Ag^+_{(aq)} + 2NH_{3(aq)}$	$K = 5.9 \cdot 10^{-8}$	$= [Ag^+][NH_3]^2/[Ag(NH_3)_2{}^+]$
$AgCl_{(c)} + 2NH_{3(aq)} = Ag(NH_3)_2{}^+_{(aq)} + Cl^-_{(aq)}$	$= 4.7 \cdot 10^{-3}$	$= [Ag(NH_3)_2{}^+][Cl^-]/[NH_3]^2$
$AgBr_{(c)} + 2NH_{3(aq)} = Ag(NH_3)_2{}^+_{(aq)} + Br^-_{(aq)}$	$= 8.5 \cdot 10^{-6}$	$= [Ag(NH_3)_2{}^+][Br^-]/[NH_3]^2$
$AgI_{(c)} + 2NH_{3(aq)} = Ag(NH_3)_2{}^+_{(aq)} + I^-_{(aq)}$	$= 1.4 \cdot 10^{-9}$	$= [Ag(NH_3)_2{}^+][I^-]/[NH_3]^2$

	K_{eq}
$Cl^-_{(aq)} + Ag^+_{(aq)} = AgCl_{(c)}$	$5.6 \cdot 10^9$
$AgCl_{(c)} + 2NH_{3(aq)} = Ag(NH_3)_2{}^+_{(aq)} + Cl^-_{(aq)}$	$4.7 \cdot 10^{-3}$
$Ag(NH_3)_2{}^+_{(aq)} + Cl^-_{(aq)} + 2H^+_{(aq)} = AgCl_{(c)} + 2NH_4{}^+_{(aq)}$	$4.8 \cdot 10^{20}$

The residual precipitate will contain any bromide or iodide, which may be separated by treatment with 7 *M* aqueous ammonia. The bromide dissolves, leaving any iodide as a residual precipitate. Note that this behavior is consistent with the values for K_{eq} in Table 13.6. Weighing of each of these precipitates would, of course, allow an approximate (±1%) analysis for the amounts of halogens present.

Weighing methods have the great advantage of high accuracy because of the sensitivity of the modern analytical balance. They have the disadvantage of requiring considerable time, a good deal of transferring of material from one container to another (with consequent possibility of loss in transfer), and considerable care in carrying out the required separations. It would be desirable to have methods that could be performed in a single solution, and would use the unique properties of each species being sought so that each could be analyzed for in the presence of all the others. No such system is available for analyzing for each of the 104 elements in the presence of all the rest, but great strides in this direction are continually being taken. We shall discuss some general methods in Chapter 36.

A qualitative analysis for bromide and iodide in the presence of chloride and fluoride may be carried out very quickly in a single solution by relying on the fact that slow addition of aqueous chlorine to such a solution will first oxidize colorless iodide ions to colored iodine. Further addition of aqueous chlorine will oxidize the colored iodine to colorless iodate, and still further addition will oxidize colorless bromide to colored bromine. It is even possible to get a rough quantitative analysis by noting the quantities of chlorine water used. The net reactions are

$$I^-_{(aq)} + \tfrac{1}{2}Cl_{2(aq)} = \tfrac{1}{2}I_{2(aq)} + Cl^-_{(aq)} \qquad \text{(color appears)}$$

$$\tfrac{1}{2}I_{2(aq)} + \tfrac{5}{2}Cl_{2(aq)} + 3H_2O_{(l)} = IO_3{}^-_{(aq)} + 5Cl^-_{(aq)} + 6H^+_{(aq)} \qquad \text{(color disappears)}$$

$$Br^-_{(aq)} + \tfrac{1}{2}Cl_{2(aq)} = \tfrac{1}{2}Br_{2(aq)} + Cl^-_{(aq)} \qquad \text{(color appears)}$$

You may calculate from the data in Table 13.3 that ΔG^0 for each of the above is negative.

The sensitivity of the chlorine water test for bromide and iodide can be appreciably increased by adding a small quantity of carbon tetrachloride to the reaction vessel and shaking vigorously as the chlorine water is added. Both iodine and bromine are far more soluble in carbon tetrachloride than in water, yet the carbon tetrachloride and water are not appreciably soluble in one another. Thus two liquid layers form, the lower one being the carbon tetrachloride because it is more dense than water. As iodine forms, it concentrates in the carbon tetrachloride layer, giving a deep violet color. This color disappears as the iodine is later oxidized to iodate and returns to the aqueous layer. Further addition of chlorine water will oxidize any bromide to bromine. The bromine then concentrates in the carbon tetrachloride layer, giving it a brown color. The colors in carbon tetrachloride are easier to identify than those in water (both iodine and bromine are brown in aqueous solutions), and the higher solubility of the halogens in the carbon tetrachloride allows the detection of small quantities because of the intensification of the color upon concentration there.

Exercise 13.4

An aqueous solution suspected of containing F^-, Cl^-, Br^-, or I^-, and no other ions except alkali metals, gives a brown color upon addition of a little chlorine water. The brown color extracts readily into a CCl_4 layer. What conclusions can you draw? *Answer:* Definitely no I^-, or CCl_4 would be colored violet by I_2 formed. Must be Br^- to give brown Br_2. No evidence concerning F^- or Cl^-. Confirm with silver nitrate and ammonia tests.

SUMMARY

The noble gases and the halogens constitute two of the families of elements in the periodic table. The properties of the elements are generally a regular function of their atomic weights within each family, but notable exceptions occur. (Remember the bond strength in fluorine.) The halogen family and hydrogen exist in the crystalline, liquid, and gaseous states as diatomic molecules, which decompose more and more as the temperature is raised. The noble gases exist as monatomic molecules under almost all conditions, though a few compounds have been formed. Hydrogen and the halogens, on the other hand, form very large numbers of compounds. The formation of many, but not all, of those compounds can be interpreted in terms of the tendency of hydrogen and halogen atoms to achieve a noble gas electron structure. Indeed the existence of these elements as diatomic molecules is similarly interpreted.

The halogens form simple negative ions (the halide ions) as well as polyatomic negative ions, mainly with oxygen. The halogens also form binary, and more complicated, compounds with almost all the elements. Some of these compounds—for example, those with the metallic elements—contain simple negative halide ions. Other halogen compounds are composed of discrete electrically neutral molecules, many of which are volatile. Redox is an important factor in halogen chemistry, since so many oxidation states exist.

Substances introduced by scientists, who are accustomed to accurate measurements, have to be used and distributed by workers, most of whom have no knowledge of science and who may not adequately appreciate the importance of accuracy in calculating the amounts of these powerful substances to be used. This illustrates the fact that a scientific culture demands some scientific virtues in a large part of the population.
—*W. R. Brain,* Science, **148,** 192–198 (1965).

PROBLEMS

13.1. Suggest an interpretation for the trend in bond energy in the elementary diatomic gaseous halogens.

13.2. Suggest a possible geologic history of calcium fluoride deposits. (*Hint:* Many of the deposits contain large crystals of CaF_2.)

13.3. Show that the H_5IO_6 molecule cannot be interpreted in terms of noble gas electron structures. What assumptions did you use?

13.4. The following constitute a complete set of acids containing nitrogen $(HON)_2$, HNO_2, and nitric acid (HNO_3). Name the first two acids.

13.5. Which is aurous chloride and which is auric chloride—AuCl, $AuCl_3$? Why are the names gold(I) chloride, and gold(III) chloride currently preferred? Name the following compounds by each system: $FeSO_4$, $Fe_2(SO_4)_3$; $TiCl_4$, $TiCl_3$; CuI_2, CuI.

13.6. Write electron structures for the species present in the following substances. Which contain only atoms isoelectronic with noble gas atoms? (*a*) Ca^{++}, (*b*) $S^{=}$, (*c*) H_2O, (*d*) $HClO_3$, (*e*) Cl_2, (*f*) CCl_4, (*g*) $ZnCl_4^{=}$, (*h*) $Cd(H_2O)_4^{++}$, (*i*) HOCl, (*j*) $La(ClO_4)_3$, (*k*) H_3PO_4. Give two or three other examples of species containing only atoms isoelectronic with noble gas atoms.

13.7. The length of a sulfur-chlorine bond is 2.0 Å. The closest distance between Cl nuclei in neighboring Cl_2 molecules in solid chlorine is 3.6 Å. Solid chlorine is nearly incompressible. Explain the fact that, although the octahedral molecule SF_6 is well known, the corresponding Cl, Br, and I compounds cannot be prepared.

13.8. Some iodine has been spilled on a dirty floor. How do you recommend that it be repurified?

13.9. You are given some hydrogen bromide gas. How could you (*a*) prove that the compound forms ions in water solution, (*b*) identify the ions formed in *a*, and (*c*) prepare a molar water solution of the compound?

13.10. Addition of chlorine water to a colorless solution of unknown composition resulted in the formation of a light brown solution. This was thought to indicate presence of either Br^- or I^- in the original solution. How could a decision be made between these two possibilities if no more unknown was available? Write equations showing the possible reactions.

13.11. A mixture of phosphorus and potassium chlorate is very dangerous. Why? Write a possible equation. Would it be safe to mix sulfur and potassium chlorate? Reasons!

13.12. A certain white solid might be either sodium chloride or sodium chlorate. What different tests could you perform that would distinguish between a chloride salt and a chlorate salt.

II

13.13. Suggest methods of synthesizing: (*a*) Al_2Br_6, knowing the reaction is highly exothermic; (*b*) Al_2S_3, knowing the product decomposes in the presence of water; (*c*) ICI "free of" I_2; (*d*) $I_3^{-}{}_{(aq)}$.

13.14. Account for the fact that all the neutral interhalogen molecules in Table 13.4 contain an even number of atoms; most of the interhalogen ions contain an odd number of atoms.

13.15. What products would you predict if gaseous chlorine were passed over lead monoxide, lead(II) oxide. Figure 4.8 may help. List at least two possible reactions and describe how you would determine experimentally the actual reaction products.

13.16. The following data give the composition of seawater in milligrams of various substances per kilogram of solution.

Cl	$1.898 \cdot 10^4$ mg/kg
I	0.05 mg/kg
Ag	$3 \cdot 10^{-4}$ mg/kg

Assuming that the density of seawater is 1.03 and that the above species are present entirely as monovalent ions, calculate the concentrations (moles per liter) of all of them ($[Cl^-] \cong 0.6\ M$). With these assumptions, is seawater saturated with respect to the indicated silver halides?

13.17. Calculate ΔG^0 and K_{eq} for the reaction $I_{2(g)} + Cl_{2(g)} = 2ICl_{(g)}$. ($K \cong 80$.)

13.18. A mixture known to contain only NaCl and KCl weighs 1.9872 g. The mixture is dissolved in water and all of the chloride is precipitated as AgCl, which weighs 4.2941 g. What fraction of the mixture is NaCl? (About 0.4 by weight.)

13.19. Manganese dioxide, MnO_2, is a good catalyst for the release of oxygen from molten potassium chlorate. Observation shows that addition of the catalyst leads to a rapid exothermic reaction (the mixture can become red hot) followed by a slower endothermic reaction. Suggest a possible mechanism. Is it reasonable from the equation you write that your second step should be endothermic?

See page 1091 for a list of references and readings in the recent chemical literature related to the material in this chapter.

CHAPTER **14**

Chemical Bonds—Angles, Frequencies, Distances, Energies, Polarities

Bond angles, distances, frequencies, energies, and electrical polarities tend to be characteristic of the pair of atoms involved in the bond and only moderately changed by changes in the rest of the molecule.

Dirac may well have been right in 1928 when he suggested that the Schrödinger equation had reduced all of chemistry to mathematics. It is generally accepted that the methods of wave mechanics can lead to exact solutions of the nature and magnitude of the forces acting between particles, and that the resulting properties of chemical systems can be calculated without recourse to experiment. But the mathematics of wave mechanics are as yet both too complicated and too time-consuming to offer a valid substitute for experimentation or for the use of simpler, but less exact, mathematical models. We shall, therefore, leave the methods of wave mechanics to more-advanced texts and concentrate here on less exact, but more immediately useful, methods.

THE EXISTENCE OF MOLECULES AND OF CONDENSED PHASES

Let us begin by looking at some experimental data on the nature of chemical bonds. The work of Cannizzaro and data from gas density, from heat capacity, from spectroscopy, and from many other sources indicate that atomic clusters, or molecules, do exist—even in the gaseous phase. They also indicate that many of these molecules remain essentially undissociated until the temperature exceeds 2000°K or more. At low temperatures the molecules cluster to form liquids and solids.

This evidence leads us to believe that strong attractive forces, or bonds, can exist between atoms. These bonds can be disrupted by forceful collisions. Since such collisions become more likely with increasing temperature (translational kinetic energy of the system), condensed phases and molecules tend to disintegrate into smaller and smaller atomic aggregates as the temperature rises (see Figure 5.11).

We shall first investigate the attractive forces that tend to hold atoms together, starting with a system made up of only two interacting atoms—that is, a gaseous diatomic molecule.

THE HYDROGEN CHLORIDE MOLECULE

Consider some of the things we now believe about the molecules in gaseous hydrogen chloride, HCl.

Bond Angle—Since the molecule contains only two nuclei, which must by definition be in a straight line, we say that HCl is linear. The molecule must consist of two nuclei—one of mass 1 and the other mass of 35, if we consider the most common isotope—plus 1 electron from the hydrogen and 17 from the chlorine. There are 18 electrons in all.

Bond Frequency—We have already found in Chapter 8 that HCl nuclei vibrate along the internuclear axis with a frequency of $8.65 \cdot 10^{13}$ cycles sec^{-1}, and that the molecule can rotate with frequencies on the order of $6.2 \cdot 10^{11}$ cycles sec^{-1}.

Bond Distance—The internuclear distance has been measured many times. Three careful, independent checks give 1.2746, 1.2744, and $1.274_4 \cdot 10^{-8}$ cm, with a suggested best value of $1.274_5 \cdot 10^{-8}$ cm (1.274_5 Å).

Bond Energy—The minimum energy, D, required to dissociate a hydrogen chloride molecule into a hydrogen atom and a chlorine atom is 103.22 kcal $mole^{-1}$.

Bond Polarity—If gaseous HCl is placed between two oppositely charged plates, the molecules tend to orient between the plates. The "H ends" are attracted to the negative plate, the "Cl ends" toward the positive plate. HCl is electrically polar, and the magnitude of the polarity is measured as a dipole moment. The dipole moment of gaseous HCl is $\mu = 1.07 \cdot 10^{-18}$ esu · cm; the dipole moment has the dimensions of an electric charge times a distance:

DIPOLE MOMENT: $$\mu = Q_{\text{eff}} \cdot d$$

The equilibrium internuclear distance is $d = 1.274 \cdot 10^{-18}$ cm. Thus the HCl molecule seems to be acting like a linear dipole (containing a + end and a − end), each end having a charge of

$$\frac{1.07 \cdot 10^{-18} \text{ esu} \cdot \text{cm}}{1.274 \cdot 10^{-8} \text{ cm}} = 0.84 \cdot 10^{-10} \text{ esu}$$

The electronic charge (−1) equals $4.8029 \cdot 10^{-10}$ esu. Thus HCl acts electrically somewhat like a rod $1.274 \cdot 10^{-8}$ cm (1.274 Å) long with a charge equal to $0.84 \cdot 10^{-10}/4.80 \cdot 10^{-10} = 0.176$ electron charges on each end, the hydrogen end being positive and the chlorine negative. These partial charges, or effective atomic charges, are called Q_{eff}. Thus $Q_{\text{eff}} = 0.176$ for HCl.

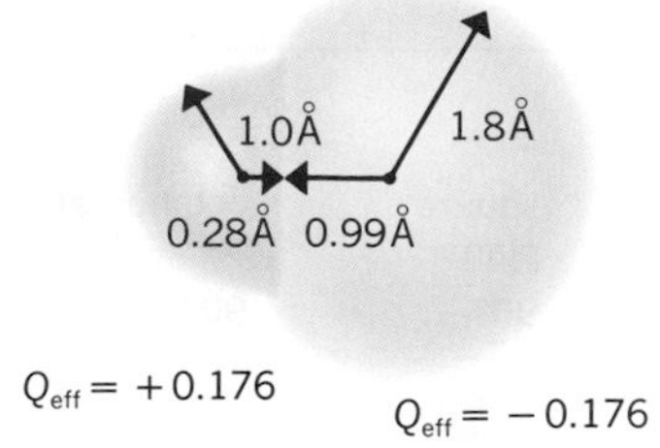

Figure 14.1 A representation of the HCl molecule.

d_{eq} = 1.274$_5$Å

D = bond energy = 103.22 kcal mole^{-1}

ν = bond vibrational frequency = 8.65·10^{13} cycles sec^{-1}

μ = dipole moment = 1.07·10^{-18} esu·cm

Q_{eff} = effective charges separated by 1.27Å = 0.176 electron charges

Molecular Shape—Collision experiments in the gas phase and studies of packing in crystalline phases indicate that HCl is not really rodlike. The HCl molecule is three-dimensional, not merely one-dimensional. These shape measurements are only accurate to about ±0.1 Å (±0.1 · 10^{-8} cm) but they indicate that the electron cloud around the hydrogen extends less into the space around its nucleus than does the electron cloud at the chlorine end of the molecule. These "nonbonded" radii are known as van der Waals radii. They are largely responsible for determining the value of the constant b in van der Waals equation.

Many other properties of the hydrogen chloride molecule have been measured, and many of these properties are most useful in understanding the behavior of the molecule. For our purposes, however, the above set is adequate. Indeed, we shall find that the properties of bond angle, bond distance, bond energy, bond polarity, and molecular shape are the ones we shall use the most. Any model we use for molecules should contain as much of this information as possible. Figure 14.1 shows such a model for hydrogen chloride. Note the relative precisions with which the various properties are given.

Clearly, also, any theory of chemical bonding should include interpretations of all these properties in terms of as few fundamental ideas as possible. Before exploring some current theories let us briefly explore each of the properties over a wider range of molecules.

BOND ANGLES

Bond angles are known over the whole range from about 60° to 180°, but certain values are found much more commonly than others. The most common values cluster around the angles 90°, 109°, 120°, and 180°. It does not appear to be coincidental that these angles correspond to those found in certain rather symmetrical structures. We might be led to assume, even at this early stage, that there is a close connection between the mathematical concept of symmetry and the structures one actually finds in nature. Such an assumption is borne out by the experimental

Table 14.1 The most common molecular symmetries.

Coordination number	2	2	3	4	4	6
Symmetry	linear	bent	planar triangle	tetrahedral	square planar	octahedral
Common bond angles	180°	60–180°	120°	109°28′	90°	90°
Example	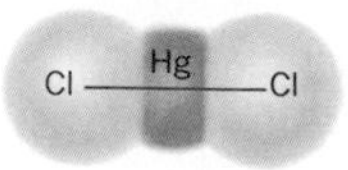	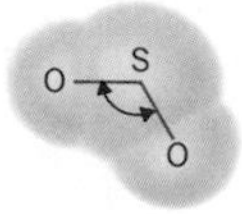	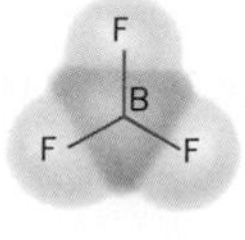	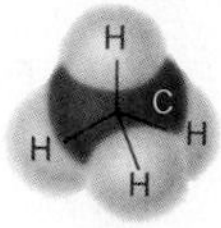	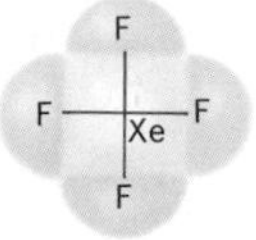	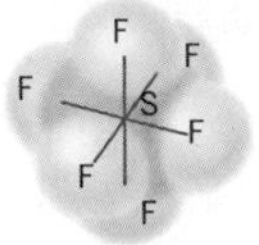

observations. Symmetry theory gives valuable insights into the understanding of the properties of matter.

Some common structures were introduced in Figure 5.12. Table 14.1 correlates some of the most common symmetries with the corresponding bond angles.

Bond angles are determined primarily from spectroscopic data or from diffraction data. Spectroscopic measurements on rotational spectra in the microwave, infrared, and ultraviolet-visible regions can often give the moments of inertia of the molecules, from which it may be possible to calculate internuclear distances and bond angles. You have already seen in Chapter 8 how the bond distance in a diatomic molecule can be calculated in this way. Diffraction of X-rays, electrons, and neutrons also gives data on internuclear distances and bond angles, as we shall see later in Chapter 30. Symmetries can also be ascertained from the optical properties of substances, from the number of isomers of a given formula, and from the chemical reactivity of the molecules. We shall discuss all these techniques later, primarily in Chapters 21 and 24.

One of the most pleasant discoveries in connection with bond angles is that they tend to remain nearly the same ($\pm 5°$) around any given nucleus, regardless of the other nuclei in the molecule. Thus the great majority of carbon atoms have bond angles of about 109° or 120°, depending only on whether the coordination number about the atom is four or three. Table 14.2 gives a very small percentage of the currently known data, and only for simple compounds of carbon. The angles about four-coordinated carbon are about $109 \pm 3°$ and those about three-coordinated carbon are $120 \pm 3°$. A similar range would hold for most carbon compounds whose structure is comparable to those in Table 14.2. The constancy of bond angles is similar around other atoms. Two-coordinated oxygen shows bond angles of about 105°, as does three-coordinated nitrogen. Two-coordinated sulfur has angles near 95°, and so it goes. The degree of reproducibility is highly gratifying both in aiding remembrance of structures and in encouraging one to look for a relatively simple theoretical interpretation, since the theory need consider only the "central atom" in each coordination sphere and not the atoms to which it is connected (at least to a first approximation).

Exercise 14.1

Estimate the bond angles in C_2H_6. *Answer:* H's will be peripheral, carbons connected as in $H_3C—CH_3$. All bond angles are H—C—C and should be about 109°, since carbon has $CN = 4$.

Table 14.2 Angles and distances in some simple carbon compounds.

Substance	CN	Angles (°) (±3° or less)			Distances (Å) (±0.03 or less)				
		∠HCH	Others		C—H	C—F	C—Cl	Others	
CCl_2F_2	4		109.5	FCF		1.34	1.78		
			108.5	ClCCl					
CF_3I	4		108.4	FCF		1.340		C—I	2.135
$CHCl_3$	4		110.9	ClCCl			1.762		
CHFO	3		121.1	FCO	1.093	1.345		C—O	1.190
			118.2	FCH					
CH_2O	3	118			1.12			C—O	1.21
CHO*(OH)	3		124.3	OCO*	1.085			C—O*	1.245
								C—OH	1.312
CH_3I	4	111°50′	106°58′	HCI	1.0958			C—I	2.1387
CH_3Br	4	111°38′	107°14′	HCBr	1.0954			C—Br	1.9388
CH_3Cl	4	110°52′	108°0′	HCCl	1.0959		1.78123		
CH_3F	4	110	109	HCF	1.105	1.38527			
CH_4	4	109°28′			1.093				
CH_3OH	4	Probably tetrahedral about C			1.095			C—O	1.428
								O—H	0.960
CH_3SH	4	109.8			1.091			C—S	1.819
								S—H	1.336
C_6H_6	3		120	CCC	1.084			C—C	1.397
			120	HCC					
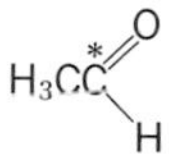	3		123.9	CC*O	1.114 (C*—H)			C*—O	1.2155
			117.5	CC*H				C—C*	1.5005
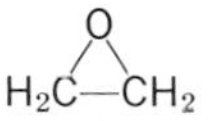					1.083			C—O	1.435
								C—C	1.470

SOURCE: Data from *Interatomic Distances; Supplement*, (Special publication 18), London, The Chemical Society (1965).

BOND VIBRATIONAL FREQUENCIES

We shall discuss frequencies of bond vibration further in Chapters 10, 23, and 30. It is enough here to show Figure 14.2, which indicates that bond frequencies, like bond angles, are relatively constant from one molecule to another as long as each molecule contains the same bonding pair. Note the general trend of frequencies as one moves through a family of elements or along a row in the periodic table.

If we consider a chemical bond to be analogous to a coil spring, we can see a possible interpretation of these variances. Just as a strong spring has a higher vibrational frequency than a weak spring, so a strong chemical bond has a higher vibrational frequency than does a weak chemical bond, so long as the bond is between the same two atoms. When the atoms vary in weight, we have a situation similar to that when weights of various magnitude are suspended from the same

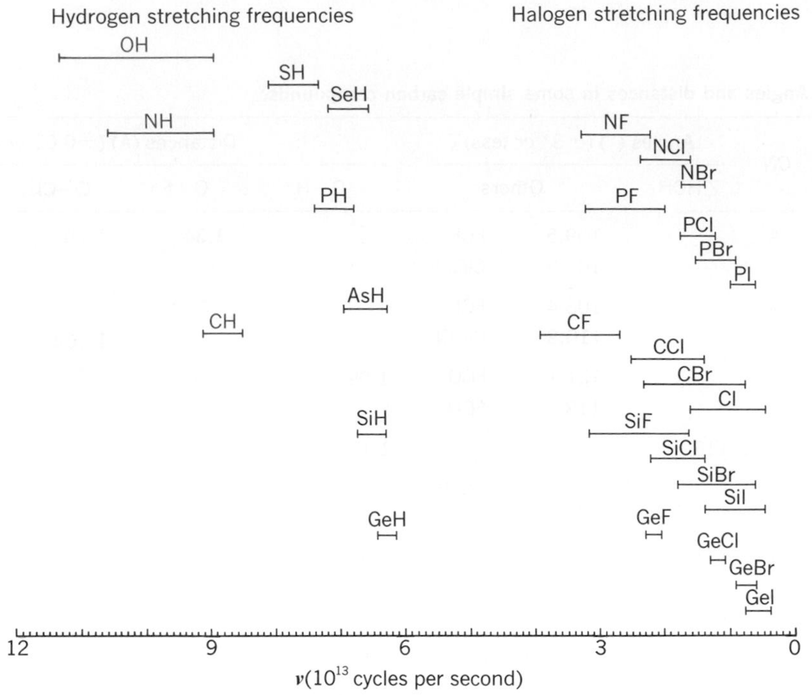

Figure 14.2 Some stretching frequencies. Note that frequency decreases as atomic mass increases in each family of elements (for example, O—H, S—H, Se—H, Te—H) and that frequency decreases as nuclear charge decreases in each row of elements (for example, O—H, N—H, C—H).

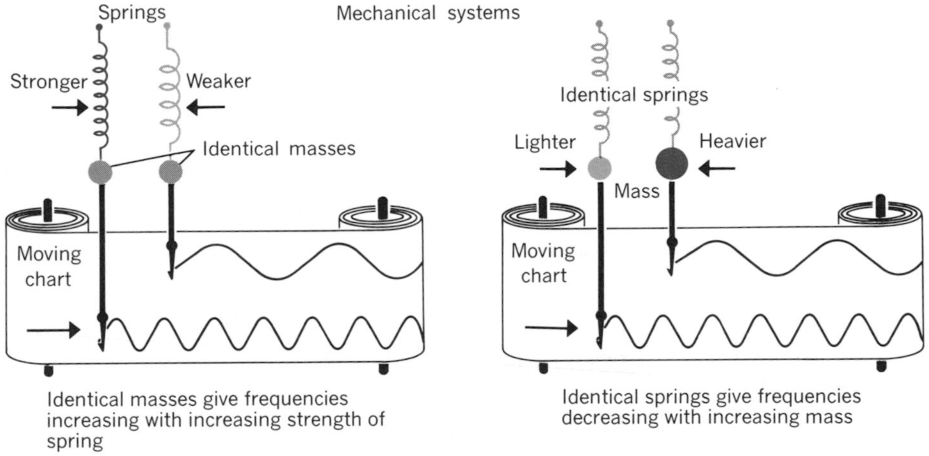

Chemical examples:

R—O—R, ether C—O frequency $= 3 \cdot 10^{13}$ cycles sec^{-1} = weaker bond

$R_2C{=}O$, ketone C—O frequency $= 5 \cdot 10^{13}$ cycles sec^{-1} = stronger bond

$R_2C{=}S$, C—S frequency $= 3 \cdot 10^{13}$ cycles sec^{-1} = larger mass (bond is also somewhat weaker)

$R_2C{=}O$, C—O frequency $= 5 \cdot 10^{13}$ cycles sec^{-1} = smaller mass

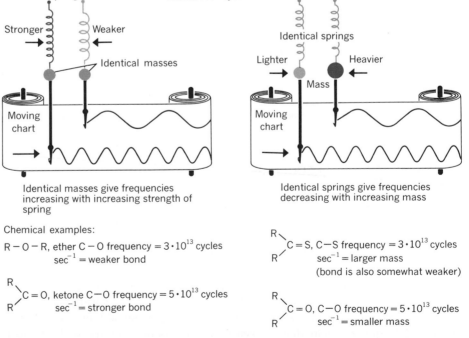

Figure 14.3 Effect of springiness (bond strength) and mass on vibrational frequency. R refers to a group (like CH_3) made up only of carbon and hydrogen. See also Equation (8.12).

spring. A light weight hung from a given spring will vibrate with a higher frequency than a heavy weight hung on the same spring. In the same way, light atoms connected by a bond of the same strength as that connecting a pair of heavy atoms will vibrate with a higher frequency than will the corresponding heavy atoms (see Figure 14.3). We have already given a relationship between bond force constant and frequency in Equation (8.12).

Exercise 14.2

A liquid is known to be either $CHCl_3$, chloroform, or CCl_4, carbon tetrachloride. Would *IR* spectra distinguish the possibilities? *Answer:* Probably $CHCl_3$ should have an absorption at about $9 \cdot 10^{13}\ sec^{-1}$, but CCl_4 should not.

BOND DISTANCE

Bond distance is defined as the equilibrium internuclear distance in a substance. Like bond angles, distances are determined primarily from spectroscopic and diffraction data (discussed in Chapters 8 and 31, respectively), and, like bond angles and bond frequencies, they are delightfully constant so long as the same two atoms are involved in similar compounds. But bond distances are more closely correlated with bond frequencies than with angles. Just as the bond frequency depends on the strength of the bond, so too does the bond distance. Strong bonds mean that strong attractive forces are acting; hence the bond distance tends to be short and the frequency high. Weak bonds mean longer bond distances and smaller bond frequencies. Thus bond distances give us valuable information concerning the relative strengths of bonds.

If, for the moment, we compare only similar compounds, we see that the distances are remarkably constant, as shown by Table 14.2. All the values for the C—H bond are 1.10 ± 0.02 Å, all the C—Cl bonds are 1.77 ± 0.01 Å. The C—O bonds are not as constant, but there is a group which seems to center around 1.23 Å and another set about 1.43 Å. There are too few examples of the other bonds listed to generalize further.

It is interesting to note that the short C—O bonds are usually to an oxygen that is not connected to any atom but the one carbon, whereas the longer C—O bonds are found when the oxygen is connected to a third atom. This may even seem reasonable to you: perhaps if the oxygen concentrates all its "bonding strength" on one atom, the resulting bond is stronger and shorter than when the oxygen is simultaneously bonded to two atoms.

The constancy of bond values tempts one to try some arithmetic on the observed distances. Could it, for example, be possible that these internuclear distances might be divided between the two bonded atoms, so that the total internuclear distance might be considered the sum of two distances, where each of the shorter distances is characteristic of one of the atoms? Such shorter distances, if they existed, might be called the bonding radii (or covalent radii) of the atoms. Such an idea proves very productive. But how do we apportion the internuclear distance into "radii" for the two atoms?

One way is to consider bonds between identical atoms, so that we can call the radii half of the internuclear distance. For example, the equilibrium internuclear distance in molecular hydrogen is 0.74130 Å, giving a bonding radius, or covalent radius, for hydrogen of 0.37065 Å. But we have already seen that radii between the same pairs of atoms may vary by ± 0.02 Å or more, so we will round off our radii to the closest 0.01 Å. Tentatively, the covalent radius of hydrogen is 0.37 Å. Since the carbon hydrogen bond has a rather constant distance of 1.10 Å, we would predict a covalent radius for carbon of $1.10 - 0.37 = 0.73$ Å. How can we check this?

There are two forms of elementary carbon—diamond and graphite. The shortest internuclear distances are, respectively, 1.54452 and 1.4210 Å. The covalent radii in diamond and graphite would be, respectively, 0.77 and 0.71 Å. The rough agreement may be fortuitous, but the track seems worth following. (Actually we interpret the difference in bond lengths in diamond and graphite as caused by an appreciable variation in bond character.)

The internuclear distance in molecular chlorine is 1.988 Å, giving a covalent radius of 0.99 Å. Using 0.77 Å (from diamond) as the covalent radius of carbon leads us to predict that the C—Cl bond should have a length of 1.76 Å. The values in Table 14.2 are about 1.77 Å. The agreement is still encouraging to our arithmetical efforts. Many scientists have followed this path and have produced extensive tables of bond radii. Table 14.3 is one such table; most of the values shown are merely half the shortest internuclear distance in the pure element at 25°C. As in many other properties, so here, H is an exception. The best average value is 0.30, although the "radius" in H_2 is 0.37 Å.

It is no longer possible to blame lack of additivity of the values in the table on inaccurately known internuclear distances, for too many thousands of distances have been accurately measured. We have to be thankful that many of the tabulated distances, when added, agree with experiment to about $\pm 5\%$, and find reasons for the deviations from additivity. Table 14.4 compares bond distances in some typical compounds with the values obtained by adding the covalent radii in Table 14.3. The general agreement over a very wide range of elements is satisfying, but note carefully the discrepancies, especially in some fluorine compounds and in compounds between elements widely separated in the periodic table.

Any theory of bonding will have to interpret both the general constancy and detailed variation in "bond radii."

Exercise 14.3

Estimate bond distances in C_2H_6. *Answer:* Structure H_3C—CH_3. C—C bond about $2 \cdot 0.77 = 1.54$ Å, all C—H bonds about $0.77 + 0.30 = 1.07$ Å.

IONIC RADII

The covalent radii in Table 14.3 are obtained by dividing the internuclear distance in the element in half, since the nuclei at each end of the bond are identical. In ionic substances this may not be justified, since the nuclei differ. Furthermore, Table 14.4 indicates that ionic effects give shorter bonds than predicted from covalent radii. One can measure internuclear distances in any compound; the question is how to divide the distance to give useful radii.

Table 14.3 Single-bond "covalent" radii of the elements, usually half the smallest internuclear distance observed in the pure element at 25°C. All values should be rounded off to the closest 0.01 Å before being added to obtain internuclear bond distances. Uncertainty in additive figure is about ±0.05 Å. An asterisk (*) indicates values obtained from compounds containing "single" bonds. For C, N, O, P, and S, double-bond and triple-bond radii are also given in parentheses, with double-bond radii first.)

H 0.37065 (0.30 av)	F 0.709	Cl 0.994	Br 1.142	I 1.333	At ?		Lu 1.717	Lw
	O 0.74* (0.62,—)	S 1.03 (0.94,—)	Se 1.161	Te 1.432	Po 1.67		Yb 1.940	102
	N 0.726* (0.62, 0.55)	P 1.10 (1.00,—)	As 1.25	Sb 1.45	Bi 1.55		Tm	Mv
	C 0.77226 (0.67, 0.60)	Si 1.176	Ge 1.225	Sn 1.405	Pb 1.750		Er 1.734	Fm
	B 0.795	Al 1.432	Ga 1.221	In 1.626	Tl 1.704		Ho 1.743	Es
			Zn 1.333	Cd 1.489	Hg 1.503		Dy 1.752	Cf
			Cu 1.278	Ag 1.445	Au 1.442		Tb 1.763	Bk
			Ni 1.246	Pd 1.376	Pt 1.388		Gd 1.787	Cm
			Co 1.253	Rh 1.345	Ir 1.357		Eu 1.995	Am
			Fe 1.241	Ru 1.325	Os 1.338		Sm	Pu 1.513
			Mn 1.366(1370°K)	Tc 1.352	Re 1.371		Pm ?	Np 1.31
			Cr 1.249	Mo 1.363	W 1.371	U 1.39	Nd 1.814	U 1.39
			V 1.311	Nb 1.429	Ta 1.43	Pa 1.606	Pr 1.820	Pa 1.606
			Ti 1.448	Zr 1.589	Hf 1.564	Th 1.798	Ce 1.825	Th 1.798
			Sc 1.606	Y 1.776	Rare earths	Ac 1.878	La 1.869	Ac 1.878
	Be 1.113	Mg 1.599	Ca 1.974	Sr 2.152	Ba 2.174	Ra ?		
H 0.37065	Li 1.519	Na 1.858	K 2.272	Rb 2.48	Cs 2.655	Fr ?		

Table 14.4 **Comparison of experimental internuclear distances with those obtained by adding covalent radii (in parentheses) from Table 14.3. The experimental distances tend to be shorter (up to 10%) than the bond sums, but usually less than 0.1 Å shorter. The very great shortenings, compared to additive values, for the bonds between elements widely separated in the periodic table (such as LiF, $MgCl_2$) are attributed to formation of ions (which we will discuss shortly). Only a few compounds thought to be highly ionic from other evidence are included in this table. For some carbon bonds see Table 14.2.**

Ag—SNC 2.43 (2.47)	H_2S—$AlBr_3$ 2.40 (2.46)	$AsBr_3$ 2.33 (2.39)	$AsCl_3$ 2.16 (2.24)	AsF_3 1.71 (1.96)	AsH_3 1.52 (1.55)	AsI_3 2.54 (2.58)
BBr_3 1.87 (1.94)	BCl_3 1.74 (1.79)	BF_3 1.29 (1.50)	BH_3 1.19 (1.10)	$BiCl_3$ 2.48 (2.54)	BrCl 2.14 (2.14)	BrF_3 1.81 (1.85)
BrH 1.41 (1.44)	CdI_2 2.58 (2.82)	ClF 1.63 (1.70)	Cl—CrO_2Cl 2.12 (2.24)	FH 0.917 (1.01)	$GeCl_4$ 2.08 (2.22)	Cl—GeH_3 2.15 (2.22)
GeH_4 1.53 (1.53)	$HgBr_2$ 2.41 (2.64)	$HgCl_2$ 2.29 (2.49)	HgH 1.74 (1.80)	HgI 2.59 (2.83)	ICl 2.32 (2.33)	IH 1.61 (1.63)
IrF_6 1.83 (2.06)	LiF 1.51 (2.23)	LiH 1.60 (1.82)	$MgCl_2$ 2.18 (2.59)	MnH 1.73 (1.67)	$(CH_3)_2N$—Cl 1.75 (1.72)	NH_3 1.01 (1.03)
NpF_6 1.98 (2.02)	OCl_2 1.70 (1.73)	OF_2 1.42 (1.45)	PCl_3 2.03 (2.09)	PF_3 1.54 (1.81)	PH_3 1.44 (1.40)	P_4Se_3 2.24 (2.26)
Br—SOBr 2.27 (2.17)	SCl_2 1.99 (2.02)	Cl—SSCl 2.07 (2.02)	SH_2 1.34 (1.33)	ClS—SCl 2.05 (2.06)	$SbBr_3$ 2.51 (2.59)	$SbCl_3$ 2.33 (2.44)
SbH_3 1.71 (1.75)	SeH_2 1.46 (1.46)	$SiBr_4$ 2.16 (2.32)	$SiCl_4$ 2.02 (2.17)	SiF_4 1.56 (1.88)	F—SiH_3 1.59 (1.88)	SiH_4 1.48 (1.48)
$SnBr_4$ 2.46 (2.54)	$SnCl_4$ 2.33 (2.40)	SnH_4 1.70 (1.71)	SnI_4 2.69 (2.74)	$TaCl_5$ 2.30 (2.42)	$TeBr_2$ 2.51 (2.57)	$TeCl_4$ 2.33 (2.43)
$TiBr_4$ 2.31 (2.59)	$TiCl_4$ 2.19 (2.44)	UF_6 1.99 (2.10)	VCl_4 2.03 (2.30)	WF_6 1.83 (2.08)	ZnH 1.59 (1.63)	$ZrCl_4$ 2.32 (2.58)

A clue to the assignment of ionic radii is shown in Table 14.5. Note that we would expect positive ions to be smaller than negative ions and to decrease in size (in any given family in the periodic table) as Z decreases. Now there is a set of compounds in which the I—I distance is 4.25 Å, as in LiI, and another set in which the Se—Se distance is 3.85 Å, as in MgSe. We interpret the constancy of the X—X distance in the compounds like LiI and like MgSe to indicate that the anions are in contact in these substances. Thus the effective radii of the anions should be half these internuclear distances. The positive ions fit in the holes between the negative

Table 14.5 **Internuclear distances in some crystals with sodium chloride structures.**

Distance	MX					
	LiI	NaI	KI	MgSe	CaSe	SrSe
M—X distance (Å)	3.02	3.23	3.53	2.72	2.96	3.11
X—X distance (Å)	4.25	4.57	5.00	3.85	4.19	4.41
Accepted X^{-n} radius	2.16			1.98		
Calculated M^{+n} radius	0.86	1.07	1.37	0.74	0.98	1.13
Accepted M^{+n} radius	0.61	0.96	1.33	0.65	0.99	1.13

Table 14.6 Observed and radius-sum (in parentheses) internuclear distances in some ionic crystals. Note the deviations from additivity above the solid lines, consistent with anion-anion contact.

	F^-	Cl^-	Br^-	I^-		$O^=$	$S^=$	$Se^=$	$Te^=$
	1.36	1.81	1.95	2.16		1.40	1.84	1.98	2.21
Li^+	2.01	2.57	2.75	3.02	Mg^{++}	2.10	2.54	2.72	
0.60	(1.96)	(2.41)	(2.55)	(2.76)	0.65	(2.05)	(2.49)	(2.63)	
Na^+	2.31	2.81	2.98	3.23	Ca^{++}	2.40	2.83	2.96	3.17
0.95	(2.31)	(2.76)	(2.90)	(3.11)	0.99	(2.39)	(2.83)	(2.97)	(3.20)
K^+	2.67	3.14	3.29	3.53	Sr^{++}	2.54	3.00	3.11	3.33
1.33	(2.69)	(3.14)	(3.28)	(3.49)	1.13	(2.53)	(2.97)	(3.11)	(3.34)
Rb^+	2.82	3.29	3.43	3.66	Ba^{++}	2.75	3.18	3.31	3.50
1.48	(2.84)	(3.29)	(3.43)	(3.64)	1.35	(2.75)	(3.19)	(3.33)	(3.56)
Cs^+	3.01	3.47	3.62	3.83					
1.69	(3.05)	(3.50)	(3.64)	(3.85)					

ions. Study of many ionic compounds leads to tables of ionic radii as given in Figure 4.9. The additivity of these numbers compared with observed internuclear distances in crystalline compounds with the sodium chloride structure is shown in Table 14.6.

VAN DER WAALS RADII

Nonbonding, or van der Waals, radii are also relatively constant, though subject to more variation than the bonding radii. These values are obtained by averaging the internuclear distance between atoms in adjacent molecules (for example, Cl to Cl where each Cl is in a different molecule) and dividing the average distance by two to get a radius. Table 14.7 lists some van der Waals radii. Note how similar they are to the anion radii of the same atoms in Table 14.6.

BOND ENTHALPIES

The most successful method for generalizing about bond enthalpies (often essentially identical with bond energies, as we will see later in Chapter 27), follows closely that just outlined for bond distances, but it is even more restrictive. Examination of the large number of data now available shows that the energy of the bond between any given pair of atoms is often remarkably constant, so long as the rest of the molecule is not greatly changed. But it does not appear possible (as it was with

Table 14.7 Some van der Waals radii.

Atom	H	F	Cl	Br	I	O	S	N	P	C	Si
Van der Waals radii (Å)	1.0	1.4	1.8	2.0	2.2	1.4	1.8	1.5	1.9	1.7	2.0

bond distances) to divide these relatively constant values into a bond energy characteristic of each "half-bond." Instead, it is necessary to tabulate energies as characteristic of the pair of atoms. Table 14.8 shows such a tabulation of average bond enthalpies.

Average bond enthalpies are "average" in two ways. They are the average of the values found in many compounds, and they are the average of the bond strengths in each of these compounds. Thus the table lists 110 kcal mole^{-1} as the average bond enthalpy for the O—H bond. This value not only represents an average value that can be used in water, alcohols, and other molecules containing the O—H group, but it also represents the average bond enthalpy in water. Thus the experimental value for dissociating the first O—H bond in water (to give H and OH) is 120 kcal mole^{-1}, but the energy to dissociate O—H (into H and O) is 102 kcal mole^{-1}. The total dissociation of water requires 222 kcal mole^{-1}, or an average of 111 kcal mole^{-1} for each bond.

Data for bond enthalpy calculations come from spectroscopy (measurement of the smallest amount of radiant energy which, upon absorption by a molecule, causes bond breaking), electron impact (measurement of the electron energy sufficient to allow a colliding electron to break a bond and form molecular fragments observable in a mass spectrometer), and heats (ΔH) of reaction (measurement of the total heat evolved in chemical reactions).

We may check the additivity of average bond enthalpies by calculating the enthalpy changes, ΔH, for a few reactions and comparing them with experimentally observed values, as in Table 14.9.

Experimentally measured bond energies vary from about 0.014 kcal mole^{-1} for He—He to 257 kcal mole^{-1} for carbon monoxide, CO (one of the

Table 14.8 Some average single bond enthalpies (kcal mole^{-1}) at 298°K (mostly those suggested by Pauling).

	Si	H	C	I	Br	Cl	N	O	F
F	129	135	105		61	61	65	44	38
O	88	110	84		57	49	53	33	
N		93	70			48	38		
Cl	86	103	79	50	52	58			
Br	69	87	66	43	46				
I	51	71	57	36					
C	69	99	83						
H	70	104							
Si	42								
Heats of atomization[a]	88.04	52.09	171.29 (graphite)	18.07	23.05	29.08	112.98	59.55	18.88

[a] The heats of atomization [mostly from NBS Technical Note 270-1 (1965)] represent the kcal mole^{-1} to create one mole of the gaseous atoms from the pure element at 298°K (from the gaseous diatomic molecule in all except silicon and graphite, where the solids are the comparison state). For most elements this heat of atomization equals half the average single-bond energy, as the table shows. For silicon the factor is 2, since silicon atoms are tetrahedrally bonded to four other atoms. The bonds in graphite, N_2, and O_2 are stronger than single bonds. Evidently graphite, N_2, and O_2 are not held together by single bonds as are the other substances. [See "Bond energies," Sidney W. Benson, *J. Chem. Ed.*, **42,** 502 (1965), for an excellent discussion.]

Table 14.9 **Comparison of experimental values of ΔH for some gas phase reactions at 298°K with those calculated from average bond enthalpies. The sum is obtained by summing the bond energies of the reactants, then subtracting the sum of the bond energies of the products. The uncertainty is about ± 10 kcal mole^{-1} or less than 1 kcal per bond change—a remarkable constancy.**

Reaction	ΔH_{sum}	ΔH_{exptl}	|Diff|
$2H_{2(g)} + O_{2(g)} = 2H_2O_{(g)}$	−114	−116	2
$4 \cdot 52 + 2 \cdot 59 - 4 \cdot 110 = 326 - 440 = -114$			
$5C_{(graphite)} + 6H_{2(g)} =$ 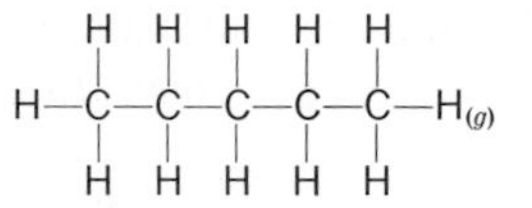	−29	−37	8
$(5 \cdot 171 + 12 \cdot 52) - (4 \cdot 80 + 12 \cdot 99) = 1479 - 1508 = -29$			
$N_{2(g)} + 3H_{2(g)} = 2NH_{3(g)}$	−20	−22	2
$2 \cdot 113 + 6 \cdot 52 - 6 \cdot 93 = 538 - 558 = -20$			
$N_{2(g)} + 2F_{2(g)} = N_2F_{4(g)}$	+4	−2	6
$(2 \cdot 113 + 4 \cdot 19) - (38 + 4 \cdot 65) = 302 - 298 = +4$			

strongest bonds known). Our bonding theory must account for this full range, for the relative constancies, and for the detailed variations in bond strengths. We shall use the symbol D for bond dissociation energies (enthalpies). Thus $D_{H\text{—}H} = 104.18$ kcal mole^{-1}, $D_{C\text{—}H} = 99$ kcal mole^{-1}, and so on.

Exercise 14.4

Calculate ΔH from average bond energies for the reaction $2CH_{4(g)} = C_2H_{6(g)} + H_{2(g)}$. *Answer:* Break two C—H bonds $= 2 \cdot 99$ kcal mole^{-1}; form C—C bond $= 83$ and H—H bond $= 104$ kcal mole^{-1}. $\Delta H = -83 - 104 + 2 \cdot 99 = +11$ kcal. Experimental (see Table 12.1) is $+14.9$. Discrepancy $= 4$ kcal.

BOND POLARITY

Experimental measurements show that molecules that are unsymmetrical in their atomic arrangement are also unsymmetrical in their distribution of electric charge. These unsymmetrical molecules exhibit dipole moments. The units in which dipole moments are measured and expressed are either electrostatic units · distance or Debye units, which differ from the first units by a factor of 10^{18}. Thus HCl has a dipole moment of $1.07 \cdot 10^{-18}$ esu · cm, or 1.07 Debye units. We shall discuss the experimental measurement of dipole moment in the next chapter.

There is only one internuclear distance in a diatomic molecule. Since the dipole moment is the product of an electric charge and a distance, we may calculate an effective electric charge separation in the molecule by assuming that the separated charges are centered at the internuclear distance. Since the electron charge is equal to $4.80 \cdot 10^{-10}$ esu, we obtain the effective charge, Q_{eff}, by dividing the observed dipole moment, expressed in Debye units, by $(4.80 \cdot d_{internuclear})$. This calculation has been carried out in Table 14.10 for some typical diatomic molecules.

In none of the cases in Table 14.10 (nor in any known case) is the resulting effective charge as large as the electron charge. The Q_{eff} does vary and, in general, is larger the farther the two elements are separated from one another in the periodic table. In other words, diatomic molecules made up of elements close to one another in the periodic table are not very unsymmetrical electrically, but the electrical asymmetry increases as the separation of the elements increases.

We already know that the ease of loss of electrons by a gaseous atom, as measured by its ionization energy, is a function of position in the periodic table. We might hazard a guess that the bond moments may have some relation to the ionization energies, since the bond moments also are related to the forces holding electrons to atoms.

Dipole moments are not, of course, limited to diatomic molecules. All molecules having an unsymmetrical atomic arrangement (lacking a center of symmetry) have dipole moments. But the interpretation of dipole moments in polyatomic molecules is less straightforward than in diatomic molecules, since many internuclear distances are involved.

However—as with bond distances and bond enthalpies, so here with bond polarities—it proves possible to assemble a set of bond moments that seem characteristic of individual bonds. These bond moments, usually expressed in Debye units, are rewardingly constant over a large range of compounds, but serious deviations from additivity do occur even in simple compounds, as seen in Table 14.11. If the bond distances remained constant and the bond angles were all tetrahedral, the dipole moments in each row of the table should remain almost constant. Actually the CX_2X_2 values should be 1.16 times as great as the $CXY_3 = CX_3Y$ values. That the values vary considerably indicates appreciable interaction between the various charge centers in a nonadditive fashion. The deviations for many molecules are much less than those shown, but it should be clear that caution must be exercised in adding bond polarities. Even if corrections are made for changing bond lengths and bond angles, it is still not possible to find a set of bond moments which will add to give all the experimental dipole moments in Table 14.11.

Table 14.12 shows data typical of benzene derivatives. Here there is a somewhat closer approximation to bond additivity. The benzene ring is a regular hexagon, each of whose corners holds a hydrogen atom for which another group can be substituted. The resulting shapes of the ortho, meta, and para isomers are shown in the table. Vector addition shows that the dipole moment of the meta disubstituted compound should be the same as that of the monosubstituted compound, that the dipole moment of the symmetrical para isomer should be zero, and that the ortho isomer should have a dipole moment 1.73 times as large as that of the monosubstituted compound. The calculated values for the meta and para values for dichlorobenzene agree well, but the calculated ortho value is 2.89; 2.51 is the experimental value.

When the two groups are different, vector addition (remembering the hexagonal shape of the benzene structure) should give the dipole moments of the disubstituted derivatives from those of the two monosubstituted ones. Test this additivity principle on the mixed chloronitro derivatives in the last line.

Again, as with bond angles, bond distances, bond frequencies, and bond enthalpies, we find that bond electrical polarities tend to be characteristic of the pair of atoms involved in the bond and to be only moderately changed by changes in the rest of the molecule.

Table 14.10 Gaseous molecules: μ = dipole moments (Debye units), d = internuclear distances (Å), Q_{eff} = effective charges (electron units). This table uses experimental values for the dipole moments and internuclear distances for some diatomic molecules to calculate the effective charge, Q_{eff}, in electron units centered on the nuclei separated by the observed internuclear distance. Notice that the gaseous alkali halide salts have effective charges close to 0.7 electron charges in all observed cases. The hydrogen and interhalogen compounds have Q_{eff} values varying from close to 0 to about 0.5 electron charges.

		H	K	Cs	F	Cl
F	μ	1.91	7.33	7.875		
	d	0.92	2.2	2.34		
	Q_{eff}	0.43	0.69	0.70		
Cl	μ	1.07	8.00	10.5	0.881	
	d	1.27	2.67	2.91	1.63	
	Q_{eff}	0.18	0.63	0.75	0.11	
Br	μ	0.788	9.22		1.29	0.57
	d	1.41	2.82		1.76	2.14
	Q_{eff}	0.12	0.6		0.15	0.06
I	μ	0.382	9.2	10.2		0.65
	d	1.61	3.05	3.31		2.32
	Q_{eff}	0.05	0.63	0.64		0.06

$$\mu = Q \cdot d = Q_{\mathrm{eff}} \cdot 4.80 \cdot 10^{-10} \cdot d, \text{ or } Q_{\mathrm{eff}} \text{ (electron charge units)} = \frac{\mu_{\mathrm{Debyes}}}{4.80 d_{\text{Å}}}$$

SOURCE: Mostly from A. L. McClellan, *Tables of Experimental Dipole Moments*, San Francisco, W. H. Freeman and Company (1963).

Table 14.11 Dipole moments of some gaseous molecules. C—H bond distances are given first, followed by C—halogen bond distance, except that, in the last group, C—F distance is given first, followed by C—Cl distance.

Note that, because of symmetry in a tetrahedral molecule, the sum of three equal vectors tetrahedral to one another equals a single vector of the same magnitude, directed at an angle of 180° from the fourth tetrahedral vector. Similarly, two equal tetrahedral vectors add to give a vector 1.16 times their magnitude, directed in the same plane as the two vectors and halfway between them. Thus CH_3X and CHX_3 should have identical dipole moments if bond polarities were strictly additive, and CH_2X_2 would have a moment 1.16 times greater. The CF_xCl_y series approximates this prediction best.

		CHX_3	CH_2X_2	CH_3X
F	μ (Debyes)	1.65	1.96	1.822
	bond distances (Å)	1.10, 1.33	1.09, 1.36	1.11, 1.39
	bond angles (degrees)	108.8 FCF	111.9 HCH, 108.3 FCF	110 HCH
Cl	μ (Debyes)	1.06	1.57	1.94
	bond distances (Å)	1.073, 1.77	1.07, 1.77	1.11, 1.78
	bond angles (degrees)	110.4 ClCCl	112 HCH, 112 ClCCl	110.5 HCH
Br	μ (Debyes)	—	1.43	1.79
	bond distances (Å)	1.07, 1.93	1.09, 1.91	1.11, 1.94
	bond angles (degrees)	110.8 BrCBr	109.5 HCH, 112 BrCBr	111.4 HCH

	$CFCl_3$	CF_2Cl_2	CF_3Cl
μ (Debyes)	0.45	0.55	0.39
bond distances (Å)	1.44, 1.76	1.35, 1.74	1.33, 1.75
bond angles (degrees)	113 ClCCl	109 FCF, 113 ClCCl	108.6 FCF

Table 14.12 **Dipole moments (in Debyes) of some derivatives of benzene measured in the gas phase. If bond moments were strictly additive, C_6H_5X and m-$C_6H_4X_2$ should have the same dipole moment, o-$C_6H_4X_2$ should be 1.73 times as great and p-$C_6H_4X_2$ should be zero. Furthermore p-C_6H_4XY should have a dipole moment equal to the difference between that in C_6H_5X and that in C_6H_5Y.**

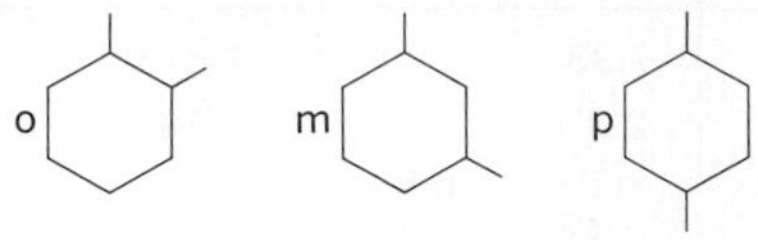

	o	m	p		
$C_6H_4Cl_2$	2.51	1.68	0.00	C_6H_5Cl	1.70
$C_6H_4F_2$	—	1.58	—	C_6H_5F	1.58
$C_6H_4(NO_2)_2$	—	—	—	$C_6H_5NO_2$	4.22
$C_6H_4ClNO_2$	4.63	3.72	2.81	—	—

Vector addition of bond dipoles in benzene derivatives

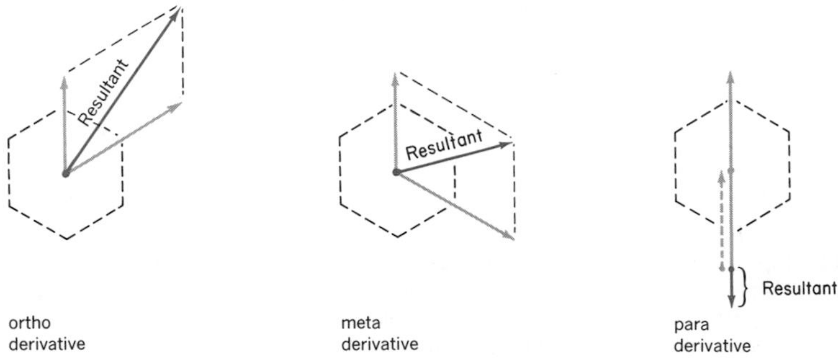

Exercise 14.5

Estimate the dipole moment of CsBr, p-C_6H_4FCl. *Answer:* CsBr, $\mu = 4.80 \cdot Q_{\text{eff}} \cdot d = 4.80 \cdot 0.70 \cdot 3.07 \cong 10.2$. p-$C_6H_4FCl = 1.70 - 1.58 = 0.12$.

RELATIVE ELECTRONEGATIVITY

In 1928 Pauling and Yost suggested that much of the data concerning bond enthalpies and bond polarities could be rationalized in terms of relative electronegativity, x. This concept has been empirically developed even further since then and provides a scale for correlating bond properties which is easy to remember.

Pauling and Yost noted that actual bonds in a binary gaseous molecule were almost always stronger than the average of the bonds in the parent elements. That is to say, the enthalpy of formation of the gaseous compound was usually negative; ΔH_{form} was negative (see Table 14.13). They also noted that the size of ΔH was a function of the separation of the elements in the periodic table. The size of ΔH also paralleled the dipole moment of the compound. Large dipole moments

Table 14.13 Comparison of bond energies (kcal mole^{-1}) in elements with those in some gaseous binary compounds. Note that bonds in compounds are stronger than the average of the bonds in the elements.

	H—H	F—F	Cl—Cl	Br—Br	I—I
Experimental bond enthalpy	104.18	38.76	58.16	46.10	36.14

	H—F	H—Cl	H—Br	H—I
Experimental bond enthalpy	134.3	103.3	87.6	71.4
$\frac{1}{2}(D_{\mathrm{H-H}} + D_{\mathrm{X-X}})$	71.5	81.2	75.2	70.2
$-\Delta H_{\mathrm{form}}$	64.8	22.1	12.4	1.2

	F—Cl	Br—Cl	I—Cl	I—Br
Experimental bond enthalpy	60.4	52.4	50.4	42.5
$\frac{1}{2}(D_{\mathrm{X-X}} + D_{\mathrm{Y-Y}})$	48.5	52.2	47.2	41.1
$-\Delta H_{\mathrm{form}}$	11.9	0.2	3.2	1.4

went with large negative values of enthalpy of formation of gaseous compounds.

A search was undertaken for some number which could be assigned to each element to measure its tendency to attract electrons. We have already seen that ionization energies are one such measure in gaseous atoms. Another is the electron affinity of the gaseous atoms—that is, the tendency of a neutral gaseous atom to acquire another electron and form a gaseous negative ion. The latest values calculated by Pauling for the relative electronegativity of an element are based on the following two equations:

$$D_{\mathrm{A-B}} = \tfrac{1}{2}[D_{\mathrm{A-A}} + D_{\mathrm{B-B}}] + 23(x_{\mathrm{A}} - x_{\mathrm{B}})^2 \qquad (14.1)$$

$$x_{\mathrm{A}} = \frac{(\text{ionization energy} - \text{electron affinity})_{\mathrm{A}}}{125} \qquad (14.2)$$

The numerical constants in Equations (14.1) and (14.2) are chosen to give a convenient numerical range to the values of the relative electronegativities, x, ranging from 0.7 for francium to the defined value of 4.0 for fluorine. The resulting values are given in Table 14.14 in the form of a periodic table and plotted in rough periodic table form in Figure 14.4. No claim can be made for a rigorous correlation of relative electronegativity with any single directly measurable property, but the values calculated from Equations (14.1) and (14.2) generally agree within ± 0.2 units in relative electronegativity and also correlate very well with other properties of the molecules such as dipole moments and chemical behavior. We shall find relative electronegativities useful in interpreting chemical properties.

Note that relative electronegativity usually increases from left to right in any row of the periodic table and from bottom to top in any column. This matches closely the trends in ionization energies, as would be expected. We would also expect that bonds would be more and more polar as the relative electronegativities of the two atoms involved differed more and more. This is found to be true. Bonds between elements with very different relative electronegativities are highly polar, or ionic. Those between elements differing only slightly in relative electronega-

Table 14.14 **The complete electronegativity scale. The values given refer to the common oxidation states of the elements. For some elements variation of the electronegativity with oxidation number is observed; for example, Fe^{II} 1.8, Fe^{III} 1.9; Cu^{I} 1.9, Cu^{II} 2.0; Sn^{II} 1.8, Sn^{IV} 1.9. [For other elements, see W. Gordy and W. J. O. Thomas, *J. Chem. Phys.*, 24, 439 (1956).]**

H = 2.1

Li	Be											B	C	N	O	F
1.0	1.5											2.0	2.5	3.0	3.5	4.0
Na	Mg											Al	Si	P	S	Cl
0.9	1.2											1.5	1.8	2.1	2.5	3.0
K	Ca	Sc	Ti	V	Cr	Mn	Fe	Co	Ni	Cu	Zn	Ga	Ge	As	Se	Br
0.8	1.0	1.3	1.5	1.6	1.6	1.5	1.8	1.8	1.8	1.9	1.6	1.6	1.8	1.0	2.4	2.8
Rb	Sr	Y	Zr	Nb	Mo	Tc	Ru	Rh	Pd	Ag	Cd	In	Sn	Sb	Te	I
0.8	1.0	1.2	1.4	1.6	1.8	1.9	2.2	2.2	2.2	1.9	1.7	1.7	1.8	1.9	2.1	2.5
Cs	Ba	La–Lu	Hf	Ta	W	Re	Os	Ir	Pt	Au	Hg	Tl	Pb	Bi	Po	At
0.7	0.9	1.1–1.2	1.3	1.5	1.7	1.9	2.2	2.2	2.2	2.4	1.9	1.8	1.8	1.9	2.0	2.2
Fr	Ra	Ac	Th	Pa	U	Np–No										
0.7	0.9	1.1	1.3	1.5	1.7	1.3										

SOURCE: Linus Pauling, *Nature of the Chemical Bond*, 3d ed., Cornell University Press, (1960).

tivity involve a more equal sharing of the electrons (covalency), and are sometimes almost nonpolar. Bond strengths, bond angles, bond lengths, and bond vibrational frequencies also are related to differences in relative electronegativities.

SUMMARY

We have now accumulated a great deal of experimental evidence concerning the forces acting between atoms in molecules. Much of this evidence is from spectroscopic and structural studies. It includes values for bond distances, bond angles, bond enthalpies, bond vibrational frequencies, bond polarities. Many of these data may be correlated in terms of radii and relative electronegativities for individual atoms. The properties of molecules are then predicted by adding the properties assigned the individual atoms. Better agreement is often obtained by assigning values of bond enthalpies, angles, frequencies, and polarities to bonds between pairs of atoms. These bond values may then be added to predict the properties of molecules.

None of these additive functions turns out to be as accurate as the available experimental data. It is clear that atoms are affected in various ways depending on the atoms to which they are bonded. The remarkable thing is that the additive functions give as good correlations as they do. After all, the internuclear distances in molecules are typically only about 10^{-8} cm and the forces acting are strong.

In the next chapter we shall see how well these additive functions and the properties of molecules can be interpreted in terms of atomic orbitals. Remember that atomic orbitals, as developed in Chapters 2, 3, and 4, are characteristic of isolated gaseous atoms. It will be interesting to see how these orbitals are affected by bringing two or more atoms close together, as happens when molecules form.

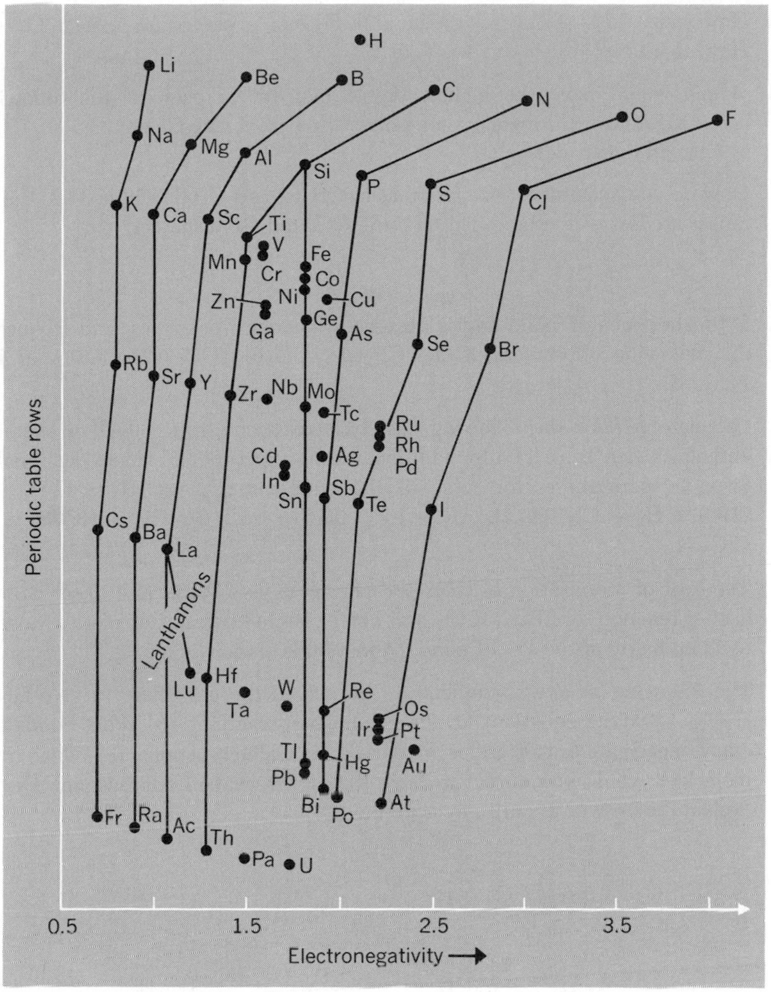

Figure 14.4 Electronegativity values of the elements. [Pauling, *Nature of the Chemical Bond*, 3d ed. © 1960 by Cornell University. Used by permission of Cornell University Press.]

The ambition of molecular biology is to interpret the essential properties of organisms in terms of molecular structures.
—*Jacques Monod,* Science, **154,** 475–482 (1966).

PROBLEMS

14.1. Suggest reasons for the general trend in bond length as Z increases (*a*) in the rows of the periodic table, (*b*) in the columns of the periodic table.

14.2. How many times stronger is the bond in O_2 than expected for a single O—O bond? How about N_2?

14.3. Which would have the highest dipole moment in each of the following sets: (*a*) *o*-C_6H_4FCl or the meta or para isomer; (*b*) CH_3F, CH_3Cl, or CH_3I; (*c*) CO_2, COS, or CS_2 (all linear molecules).

14.4. How do you account for the fact that in CH_3Cl and CH_3F (Table 14.2) the CH distances are less well established than the CCl and CF distances?

II

14.5. Estimate probable bond angles, distances, energies, polarities, and frequencies for the following substances: CD_4, CF_2Cl_2, CH_3Br, CF_4, $(H_2COH)_2$, $(CH_3)_2CO$, PCl_3, SF_6.

14.6. Calculate ΔH for the following gas-phase reactions from values of average bond enthalpies. See Table 14.4 for additional data. Experimental values (kcal mole^{-1}) are given in parentheses for some of the reactions: $H_2 + C_2H_4 = C_2H_6$ (-32.8), $2HCl = H_2 + Cl_2$ (44.2), $H_2 + F_2 = 2HF$ (-129.6), $Cl_2 + HCCH = HCl +$ ClCCH.

14.7. The heat of atomization of solid phosphorus to give $P_{(g)}$ is 75.18 kcal mole^{-1}. The heat of reaction for $2P_{(s)} + 3Cl_{2(g)} = 2PCl_{3(g)}$ is 144.0 kcal. Calculate a value for the bond enthalpy of the P—Cl bond. (About 30 kcal mole^{-1}.)

14.8. The following structural isomers are burned in the gas phase to give $CO_{2(g)}$ and $H_2O_{(g)}$. (*a*) Write equations for the combustion reactions. (*b*) What bonds and how many of each are broken and formed in the indicated reactions? (*c*) Which of the two molecules would you expect to have the higher heat of combustion? Discuss and explain the answer to part *c* in structural terms.

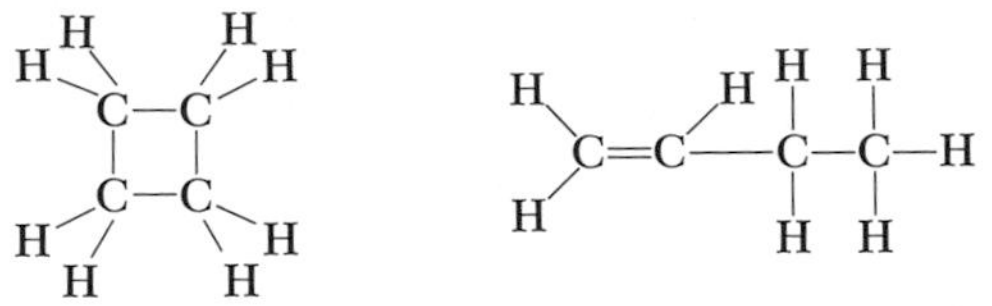

A B

14.9. Use the data in Tables 14.3 and 14.6 to calculate internuclear distances for all the molecules listed in Table 14.10. Compare with the experimental distances. Comment on the comparisons.

14.10. Plot relative electronegativity, *x*, versus first ionization energy (Table 3.1) for the first 20 elements in the periodic table. Any trends? Any remarkable exceptions? Discuss the case of hydrogen.

14.11. Calculate the heat of reaction (ΔH^0) for the formation of 1,3-butadiene ($H_2C{=}CH{-}CH{=}CH_2$) from carbon and hydrogen atoms in the gas phase:

$$4C_{(g)} + 6H_{(g)} = H_2C{=}CH{-}CH{=}CH_{2(g)}$$

Do this calculation in two ways, (*a*) by referring to the bond energy tables (about 970 kcal mole^{-1}) and (*b*) by using the heat of formation of 1,3-butadiene gas, which is $\Delta H_f^0 = +26.9$ kcal per mole (about 960 kcal mole^{-1}). Is the molecule observed to be more stable or less stable than bond energies would predict?

14.12. Arrange the numbers, I, II, III corresponding to the following three molecules in order of increasing dipole moment, highest moment last.

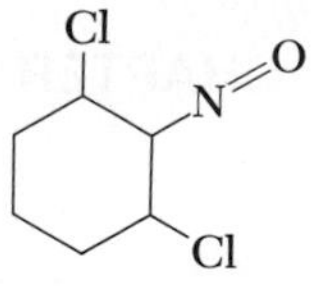

I

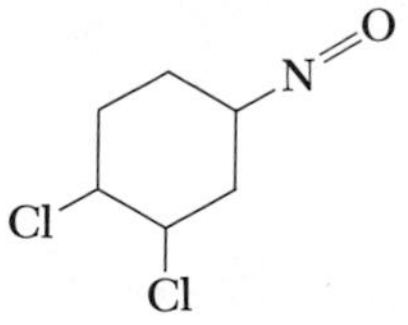

II

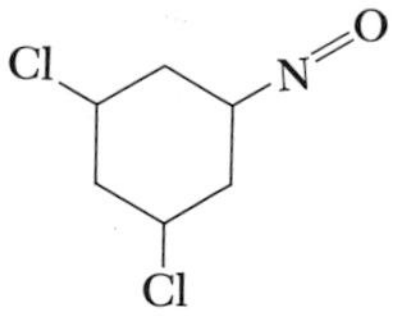

III

Both NO and Cl tend to attract electrons from the ring. NO is somewhat more effective at this; its "bond moment" is higher than that of Cl. Where would you place the molecule IV in this series?

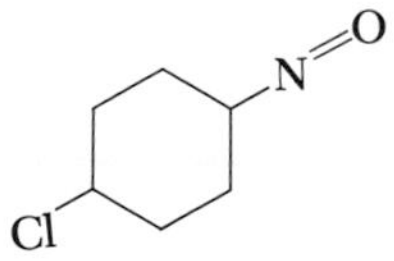

IV

See page 1091 for a list of references and readings in the recent chemical literature related to the material in this chapter.

CHAPTER **15**

Chemical Bonding in Terms of Atomic Orbitals

The general properties of chemical bonds may be interpreted in terms of the simultaneous interaction of one or more electrons with more than one nucleus.

We have seen in Chapter 14 that bond angles, bond frequencies, bond distances, bond enthalpies or energies, and bond polarities are, in many cases, rather characteristic of the atoms involved without regard to the rest of the molecule. We have already learned, in Chapters 2, 3, and 4, a great deal about atomic orbitals. Perhaps the properties of chemical bonds as well as the properties of isolated gaseous atoms may be interpreted in terms of atomic orbitals.

COMBINATIONS OF ATOMIC ORBITALS

One of the quantum mechanical treatments of bonding in terms of atomic orbitals is called the method of linear combination of atomic orbitals. In this treatment the bond between two atoms is described in terms of the interpenetration, or overlap, of two atomic orbitals—one from each of the atoms involved in the bond. Bonds formed by orbital overlap are called covalent bonds. We shall not go through the mathematical calculations, but we can achieve similar results with qualitative arguments.

Consider the situation as a hydrogen atom and a chlorine atom approach one another. We remember from Chapter 2 that a hydrogen atom consists of a nucleus plus one electron. The hydrogen electron, in its lowest energy level, is in a 1*s* orbital. This orbital is spherical in symmetry, with the nucleus at its center. Like all orbitals it can hold two electrons, though in the hydrogen atom it contains only one. The gaseous chlorine atoms consist of a nucleus surrounded by seventeen electrons. The orbital occupancy is $1s^2$; $2s^2$, $2p^6$; $3s^2$, $3p^5$. The spherical *s* orbitals are fully occupied (2 electrons per orbital), as are all but one of the perpendicular *p* orbitals. One of the perpendicular *p* orbitals (a $3p$ orbital) holds only one electron.

Could it be that, as the two atoms approach, the half-occupied *s* orbital of the hydrogen and the half-occupied *p* orbital of the chlorine can interpenetrate or overlap in such a way that a new orbital containing a pair of electrons forms? (See Figure 15.1.) This new orbital might be formed by a combination of the properties of the original *s* and *p* orbitals. The angle would have to be 180°, and the bond frequency, bond distance, bond energy, and bond polarity would be determined by the properties of the original *s* and *p* orbitals and by their interaction with the other orbitals and the two nuclei.

What might happen if hydrogen atoms approached sulfur atoms in a similar way? Each hydrogen has a single $1s$ electron in a spherical orbital. Each sulfur has an orbital population described as: $1s^2$; $2s^2$, $2p^6$; $3s^2$, $3p^4$. Two of the mutually perpendicular $3p$ orbitals are each half-occupied. If each of these perpendicular orbitals overlaps with a $1s$ orbital from a hydrogen atom, all the orbitals achieve their full occupancy of two electrons per orbital. We would expect the two resulting bonds in H_2S to be at right angles to one another, since the symmetry of *p* orbitals places *p* orbitals at right angles to one another (see Figure 4.3). The bond angle in H_2S is observed to be 93.3°, which is certainly close to the 90° predicted. Try drawing a figure like 15.1 to illustrate this prediction.

What can we predict about other bond properties, perhaps comparing hydrogen chloride to hydrogen sulfide? For example, isn't it reasonable to expect the HCl bond to be more polar than that in H_2S, since the chlorine nucleus is more highly charged than that of sulfur? Thus the electrons in the overlapping *s-p* orbital should be more strongly attracted toward the chlorine than toward the sulfur nucleus. The dipole moment of gaseous hydrogen sulfide is 0.92 Debye, whereas that of hydrogen chloride is 1.08. From the bond angle and respective bond dis-

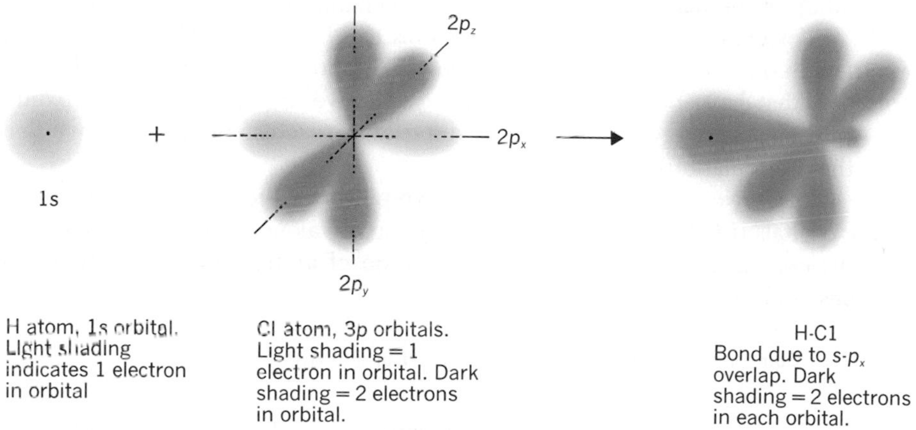
2p_z
2p_x
1s
2p_y
H atom, 1s orbital. Light shading indicates 1 electron in orbital
Cl atom, 3p orbitals. Light shading = 1 electron in orbital. Dark shading = 2 electrons in orbital.
H-C1 Bond due to s-p_x overlap. Dark shading = 2 electrons in each orbital.

Figure 15.1 A schematic interpretation of the reaction H + Cl = HCl in terms of a linear combination of atomic orbitals. The theory further suggests that the p_x orbital involved in overlap bonding does not remain a symmetrical dumbbell. It expands, or enlarges, on the hydrogen side and diminishes in volume on the opposite side of the chlorine, owing to the positive hydrogen nucleus.

tances—1.3455 Å in H_2S, 1.274$_5$ Å in HCl—we can calculate a bond moment in H_2S of 0.65 Debyes and an effective charge separation of 0.10 electron charges in H_2S as compared to an effective charge separation of 0.176 electron charges already calculated for HCl (Figure 14.1). The HCl bond is more polar, as predicted. Relative electronegativities predict the same result.

The HCl bond is also shorter than that in H_2S, as we might guess from the relative tendencies of the chlorine and sulfur nuclei to attract the hydrogen electron. This would lead us to believe that both the bond energy and the bond frequency would also be greater in HCl than in H_2S. The experimental values of bond energies are H—Cl = 103.2 kcal mole^{-1}, H—S = 81.1 kcal mole^{-1}. The experimental values of the bond frequencies are more difficult to compare; there are three vibrational frequencies in H_2S and only one in HCl. The HCl frequency is $8.65 \cdot 10^{13}$ cycles per second; the three hydrogen sulfide frequencies are 7.8, 3.5, and $7.8 \cdot 10^{13}$ cycles per second, with the $7.8 \cdot 10^{13}$ cycles per second being most comparable to the HCl frequency. The lower frequency in H_2S and the weaker bond there (compared to HCl) both reinforce our idea that bond properties can be predicted by linear combination of atomic orbitals.

The properties of phosphine, PH_3, might also be examined. We would again predict a bond angle of 90° (since the phosphorus will be using three of the perpendicular $3p$ orbitals in overlapping with three hydrogen atoms) and a bond polarity less than that in H_2S (since the nuclear charge of the phosphorus is less than that of sulfur), as well as a longer bond distance, lower bond strength, and lower bond vibration frequency. The experimental values for PH_3 are: bond angle = 93.5°, dipole moment = 0.55 Debye, bond distance = 1.4206 Å, bond energy = 76.4 kcal mole^{-1}, and comparable bond frequency = $7.0 \cdot 10^{13}$ cycles per second. All the predictions are borne out. Table 15.1 summarizes the above comparisons and trends. Differences in relative electronegativity are again consistent with the trends.

Study of many thousands of compounds would further indicate that many chemical bonds can be treated in terms of the combination of atomic orbitals. Application of the mathematics of quantum mechanics would further confirm this belief. Unfortunately, only a very few systems can be treated with mathematical exactness (molecular hydrogen, the species H_2^+, and methane are typical of the molecules that have been so treated) and qualitative arguments and approximations must almost always be introduced in order to reach solutions. Thus we shall leave these calculations until a later course.

Before we can use the full qualitative power of the linear combination of atomic orbitals (LCAO) or the simpler reasoning of valence bond (VB) theory, we must discuss three further factors: hybridization of atomic orbitals, nonbonding electrons, and multiple bonding.

Table 15.1 Comparison of the H—X bonds in HCl, H_2S, and H_3P.

Bond	Angle	Bond moment (Debye)	Distance	Enthalpy (kcal mole^{-1})	Frequency (sec^{-1})
H—Cl	—	1.07	1.274 Å	103.2	$8.65 \cdot 10^{13}$
H—SH	92.2°	0.65	1.328 Å	81.1	$7.8 \cdot 10^{13}$
H—PH_2	93.5°	0.35	1.437 Å	76.4	$7.0 \cdot 10^{13}$

HYBRIDIZATION OF ATOMIC ORBITALS

About two million compounds are known that contain carbon, contrasted to about a hundred thousand that contain no carbon. A very large fraction of these carbon compounds contain carbon atoms bonded to four other atoms, and the bond angles in these cases remain remarkably close to the tetrahedral angle of 109°28′, or 109.5° for short. How does the atomic orbital treatment handle the problem of the tetrahedral carbon atom?

Consider the simplest case—CH_4, methane. The ground energy level of a gaseous carbon atom is known to be $1s^2$; $2s^2$, $2p^2$, leaving one of the p orbitals unoccupied and two of them occupied by a single electron each. There is room in these orbitals, which are not fully occupied, for four more electrons. Thus the formula CH_4 is not surprising, since each of the four hydrogens can overlap one electron into the carbon orbitals. But what bond angles would we predict for the resulting CH_4 molecule?

Arguing as in the above, we can see that the three p orbitals, being directed at right angles to one another, should give three bonds, also at right angles to one another. What, then, happens to the fourth hydrogen? And what orbital does it use?

If the fourth hydrogen overlaps the carbon $2s$ orbital (which has spherical symmetry), this fourth hydrogen should be able to take any position around the carbon. Of course, three positions at right angles are preempted by the other three hydrogens, so we might expect the fourth hydrogen to wander around on the still vacant side of the carbon. It might even take up an equilibrium position equidistant from each of the other three hydrogens overlapping the carbon p orbitals. The molecule would then have the shape of a triangular pyramid. The three hydrogens overlapping the p orbitals would form bond angles at 90° to one another, forming an equilateral base to the pyramid. The fourth hydrogen, overlapping with the carbon s orbital, would occupy the apex of the pyramid and each side would be an isosceles triangle, as in Figure 15.2.

The experimentally observed shape of CH_4 is also shown in Figure 15.2. The four C—H bonds are identical in length, energy, frequency, polarity, and angular distribution. If they are formed by orbital overlap between the carbon and the hydrogens, each of the overlaps must be identical with the other three.

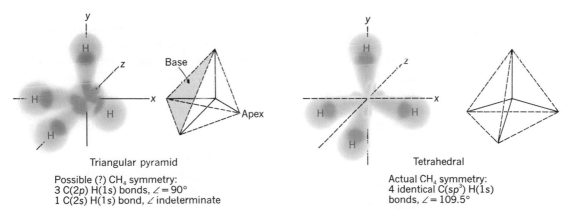

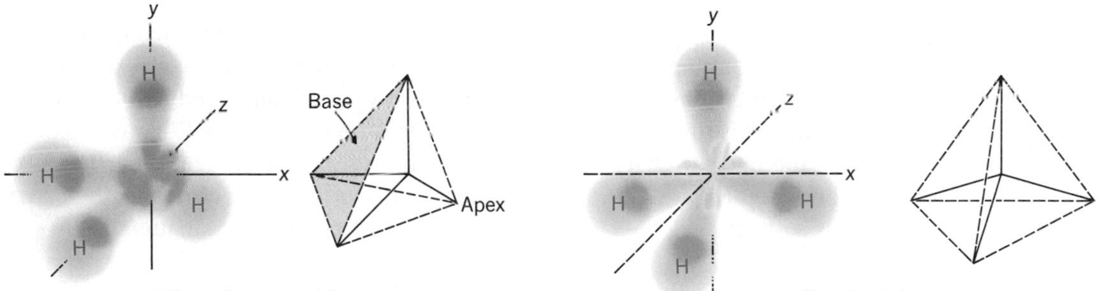

Triangular pyramid

Possible (?) CH_4 symmetry:
3 C(2p) H(1s) bonds, ∠ = 90°
1 C(2s) H(1s) bond, ∠ indeterminate

Tetrahedral

Actual CH_4 symmetry:
4 identical C(sp^3) H(1s) bonds, ∠ = 109.5°

Figure 15.2 Possible orbital occupancy in CH_4.

The problem of the tetrahedral carbon may be solved by the methods of quantum mechanics, but again the mathematics is unnecessary in order to comprehend the argument and the conclusions. The problem is to find the most stable set of orbitals for eight electrons (four from carbon and four from hydrogen) starting with the single 2*s* and the three 2*p* orbitals of the carbon. The experimental answer is a set of four identical bonds tetrahedrally distributed in space. The quantum mechanical answer is, of course, the same. This new set of four identical and tetrahedrally distributed orbitals is said to be a hybridized form of the original 2*s* and 2*p* orbitals—an sp^3 hybrid. This sp^3 hybridization is not found only around carbon. Identical hybridization accounts for the observed properties in most four-coordinated compounds of silicon, germanium, tin, lead, and many other substances.

The difference between the behavior of carbon and that of chlorine, sulfur, and phosphorus is that in HCl, H_2S, and PH_3, all the partly empty orbitals had the same angular symmetry—all were *p* orbitals. But the four bonds to carbon required a combination of the symmetries of the *p* and the *s* orbitals. The result is sp^3 tetrahedral hybridization. Some of the most common types of bonding combinations (including common hybridizations) and the resulting geometries are listed in Table 15.2.

Exercise 15.1

Suggest an atomic orbital set for bonding in each of the following: $HgCl_2$, BCl_3, PCl_4^+. *Answer:* $HgCl_2$ needs two Hg—Cl bonds. Hg has two 6*s* electrons and empty 6*p* orbitals; thus *sp* hybrid (linear). BCl_3 needs three orbitals, B has two 2*s* and one 2*p* electrons and empty 2*p* orbitals; thus sp^2 hybrid (trigonal plane). PCl_4^+ needs four orbitals, P^+ has two 3*s* and two 3*p* electrons and 2*p* orbitals to hold four more electrons; thus sp^3 hybrids (tetrahedral).

BONDING AND NONBONDING ELECTRONS

Examination of the known chemical compounds shows that, for almost all of them, the number of electrons per formula weight of compound is even. Apparently electrons tend to come in pairs in chemical compounds. This reminds us that atomic orbitals can hold no more than two electrons each and supports the interpretation of bond formation as the result of overlapping of atomic orbitals. When two orbitals overlap the resulting bonding orbital can hold no more than two electrons, thus acting in a fashion very similar to atomic orbitals that are not involved in bonding.

Some nonbonding orbitals are nonbonding because they are so strongly influenced by their "own" nucleus as to be relatively uninfluenced by other nuclei in the vicinity. It is for this reason that the 1*s* electron spectra, the *K* X-rays, depend mainly on the nuclear charge of the central nucleus, rather than on other nuclei in the vicinity (see Figure 5.1). The binding energy of these electrons to their own nucleus is so high that their energy level is almost completely unaffected by surrounding atoms.

A different behavior might be expected in electrons whose principal quantum number is the same as that of the bonding atomic orbitals. We can obtain interesting insights into this phenomenon by studying the halogen compounds listed in Table 13.4.

Table 15.2 Some atomic orbital combinations and molecular geometries. (Compare Table 14.1.)

Coordination number	Orbitals on central atom	Geometrical arrangement		Examples
2	*sp*	linear	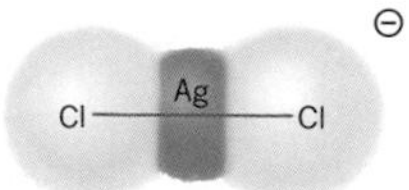	$CdBr_2$, $AgCl_2^-$
	p^2	bent	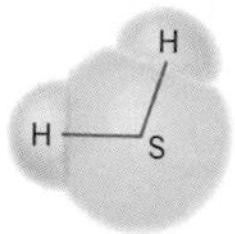	H_2S, $TeBr_2$
3	sp^2	trigonal plane	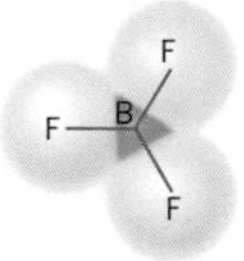	BF_3, GaI_3
	p^3	trigonal pyramid	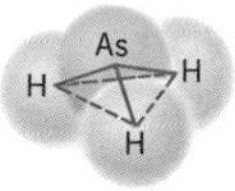	AsH_3, PCl_3
4	sp^3	tetrahedron	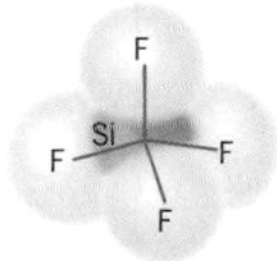	SiF_4, $TiCl_4$
	dsp^2	tetragonal plane	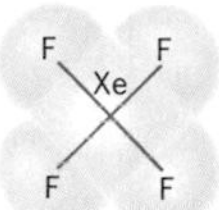	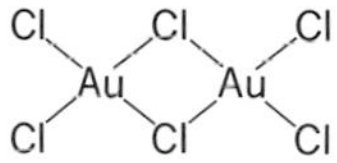
5	dsp^3	trigonal bipyramid	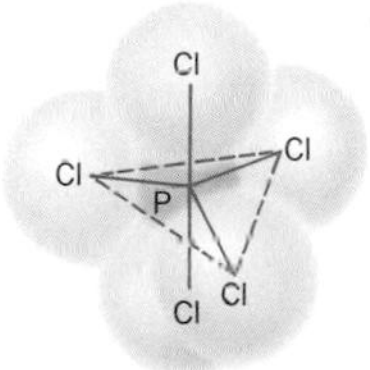	PCl_5, $NbBr_5$
6	d^2sp^3	octahedron	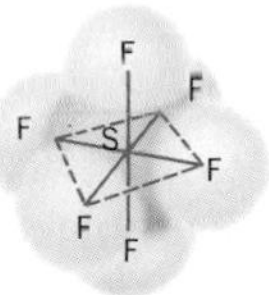	$CdCl_6^{-4}$, SF_6

The experimentally determined geometries of these compounds are shown in Figure 15.3. All these structures may be rationalized if we assume that each of the "peripheral" halogen atoms holds eight electrons in its sp^3 set of orbitals and overlaps one of its *p* orbitals with the "central" halogen atom. Each central halogen

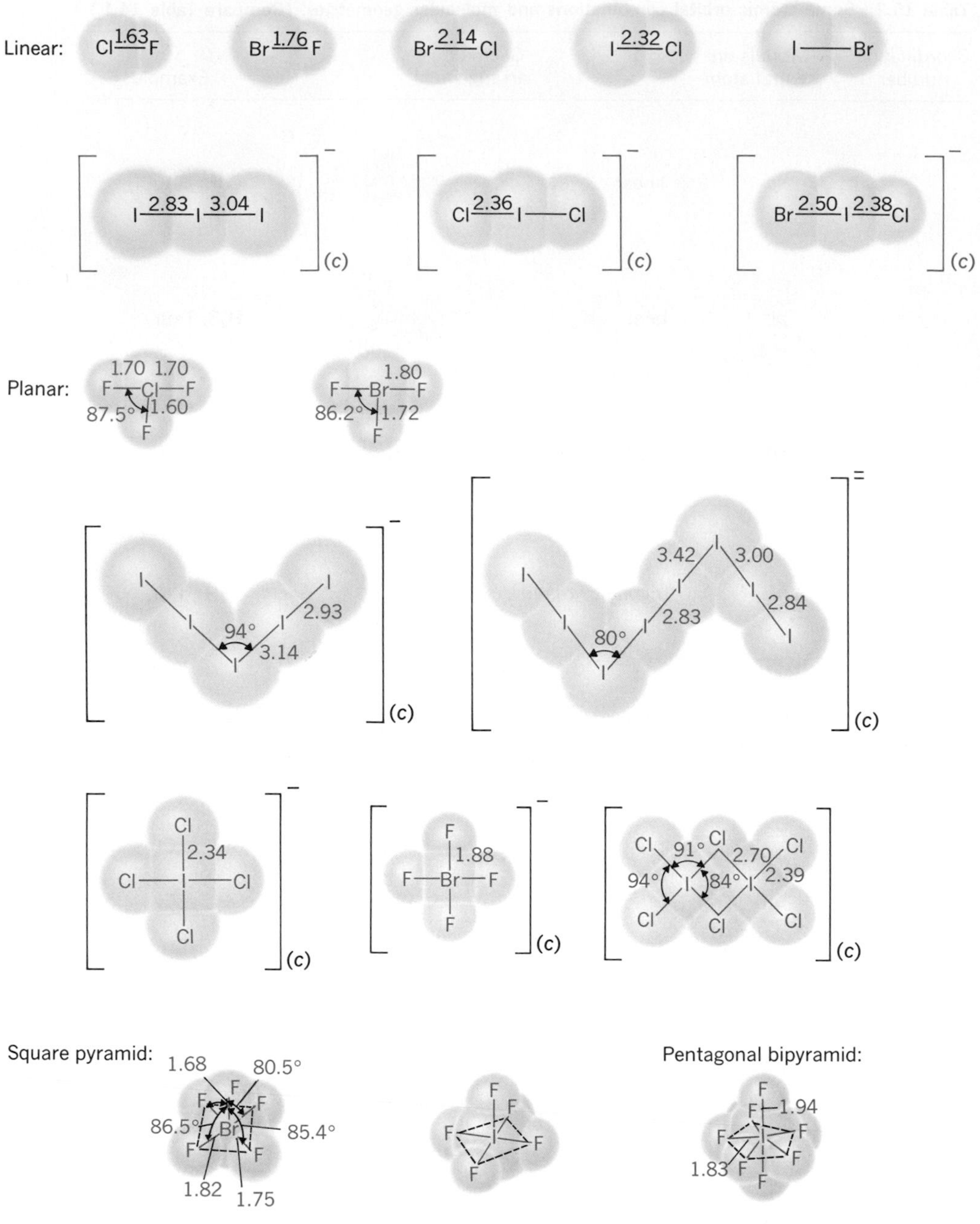

Figure 15.3 Geometries of the known halogen compounds. Determined in gas phase except as noted by subscript (c) for crystal (distances in Å, angles in degrees).

atom then is assumed to hold in its orbitals all the remaining valence electrons plus those in overlapping orbitals, symmetrically distributed if there is more than one "central" halogen atom. The interpretations of the diatomic molecules is straightforward, so we will turn to the polyatomic ones.

We show in Figure 15.4 an analysis of each of the halogen compounds in

Molecule	Total number of valence electrons (number around central atoms)	Probable electron distribution	Shape and hybridization about central atoms
ClF, BrF, BrCl, ICl, IBr, F_2, Cl_2, Br_2, I_2	14 (8)	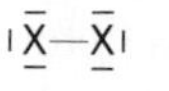	linear
$I_3^-{}_{(c)}$, $ICl_2^-{}_{(c)}$, $BrICl^-{}_{(c)}$	22 (10)	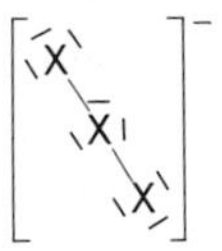	dsp^3, linear
ClF_3, BrF_3	28 (10)	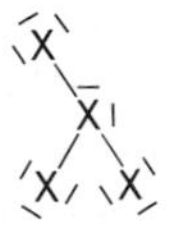	dsp^3, with only three of the bipyramidal orbitals bonding—two polar and one equatorial, giving a planar molecule.
$I_5^-{}_{(c)}$ (I_3^- + I_2)	36 (10,8)	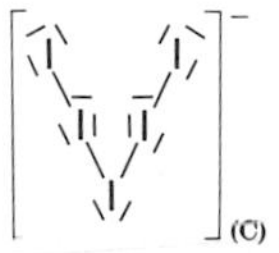	p^2, with only two orbitals bonding at central atom. dsp^3, with only two orbitals bonding at middle atom in each arm.
$I_8^={}_{(c)}$ ($2I_3^-$ + I_2)	58 (10,8)	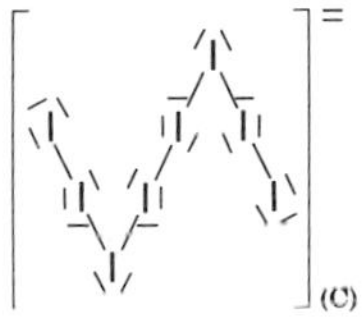	Similar to $I_5^-{}_{(c)}$
$ICl_4^-{}_{(c)}$, $BrF_4^-{}_{(c)}$	36 (12)	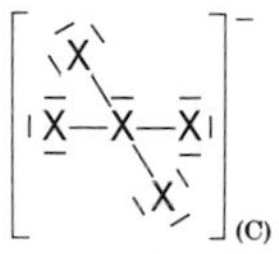	d^2sp^3, with only four of the octahedral orbitals bonding, giving a planar molecule.
I_2Cl_6	56 (12,8)	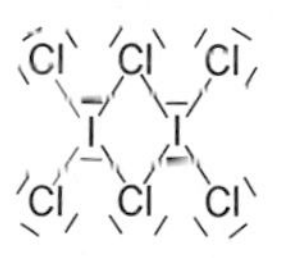	Like ICl_4^- with two chlorine p^2 bridging atoms, all planar.
BrF_5, IF_5	42 (12)	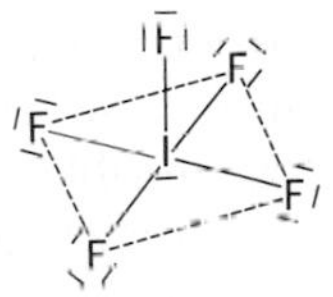	d^2sp^3 with only five bonding orbitals giving square pyramid.
IF_7	56 (14)	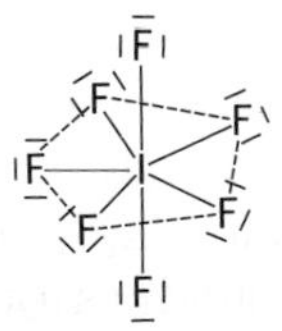	d^3sp^3 with all seven orbitals bonding giving a pentagonal bipyramid.

Figure 15.4 Nonbonding orbitals and molecular geometry.

terms of total number of valence electrons per molecule, assignment of valence electrons to the component atoms (8 for each peripheral atom), and assumed bonding orbitals or hybridization about each central atom. Combination of the bonding orbital assignments in Figure 15.4 with the corresponding geometries in Table 15.2 correctly predicts the experimental geometries of Figure 15.3, so long as one assumes that nonbonding valence electrons occupy directed orbitals and hence influence the geometry of the molecule.

The number of electrons for each molecule listed in Figure 15.4 is even. The number of valence electrons around any given atom is also even, and equal to eight or more. Both nonbonding and bonding electrons occupy valence orbitals, enter into hybridization, and affect the geometry of the molecule. Each set of overlapping orbitals is occupied by two electrons. The occupied orbitals are distributed quite symmetrically throughout the molecule. All these generalizations prove to be widely applicable to most of the chemical compounds we know today.

Exercise 15.2

Suggest a shape and atomic orbital structure for XeF_2 and $Ag(NH_3)_2^+$. *Answer:* XeF_2 has $8 + 2 \cdot 7 = 22$ valence electrons, and thus is like I_3^- (linear) with 3 nonbonding pairs on Xe to give sp^3d hybrid. $Ag(NH_3)_2^+$ needs two bonds using "basic electrons" from NH_3 in *sp* silver hybrid (linear).

ELECTRON CLOUDS— AN ALTERNATE POINT OF VIEW

Gillespie recently suggested that a simple alternative to the hybridization picture is available for interpreting molecular properties. Suppose we merely assume that in representing pairs of electrons in valence orbitals, both nonbonding and bonding pairs must be considered. The formulas are made more straightforward if E is used to represent a nonbonding pair. Thus ammonia equals NH_3E, water equals H_2OE_2, and so on.

If there are two filled sets of valence orbitals, the sets take up positions as far apart from one another as possible, and the resulting molecule will be linear. Three sets of valence electrons will lead to a trigonal plane distribution, four sets to tetrahedral bonding, five sets to a trigonal bipyramid, six sets to octahedral bonding. Each of these geometric figures is merely the result of the valence electron sets taking positions as far apart as possible. This generalization is certainly simple to apply and accurately describes a very large number of compounds, including most of the ones we have discussed. It is the easiest, most accurate model for beginning students to use.

Electron cloud repulsion comes up against two problems, however. One is the interpretation of the 90° bonds in the bent-linear halogen compounds (such as I_5^-) or in triatomic molecules (H_2S, PH_3, and others), and the other is the existence of square planar compounds (Au_2Cl_6, $AuBr_4^=$, $Ni(CN)_4^=$, and others). It is hard to see why the I_5^- or H_2S orbitals should assume right-angle configurations to one another, or why four pairs of valence electrons should take equilibrium positions at the corners of a square array. But these difficulties are rare.

Moreover, the idea of repulsions between sets of valence electrons is certainly valid, and it does allow us to remember quickly what the most likely configurations are. Furthermore, in most cases, one comes out with the same geometries as predicted by hybridization in Table 15.2, and counting sets of valence electrons is easy and fast, especially if we indicate an unshared pair by E in the chemical formula: $HgCl_2 = 2$, $BF_3 = 3$, $CF_4 = 4$, $PCl_5 = 5$, $SO_3 = 3$, $SO_2E = 3$, $NH_3E = 4$, $H_2OE_2 = 4$, $O_2OE = 3$. The bond angles are, rather closely ($\pm 5°$): 180° for 2, 120° for 3, 109.5° for 4, trigonal bipyramid for 5, and octahedral for 6 in all instances. Figure 15.5 shows Gillespie's predictions of molecular geometry. Note that atoms get as far apart as possible, leaving any "crowding" to the nonbonding electrons.

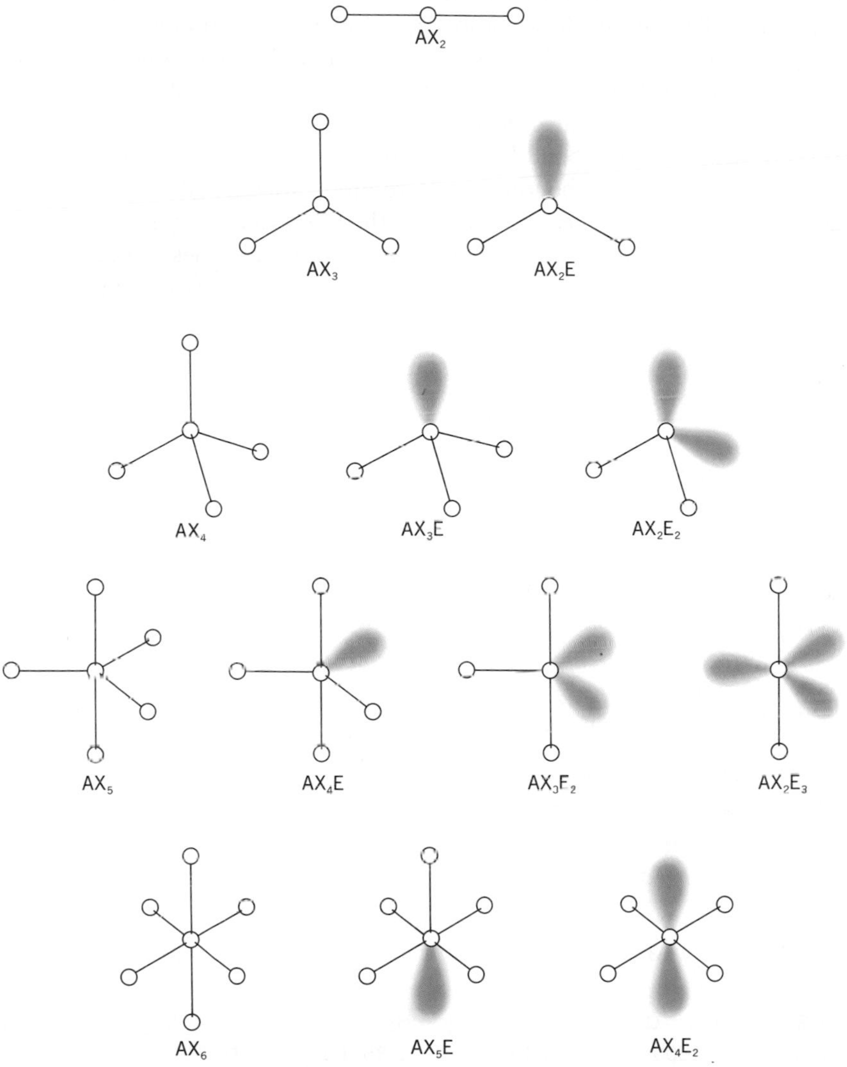

Figure 15.5 General shapes of some molecules, using the Gillespie principle. [R. J. Gillespie, *J. Chem. Ed.*, **40**, 295 (1963).]

Exercise 15.3

Suggest shapes for XeF_2, $Ag(NH_3)_2^+$, PtF_6, ICl_4^-. *Answer:* Using Gillespie's theory we get XeF_2E_3 (pentagonal pyramid with FXeF linear); $Ag(NH_3)_2^+$ (linear); PtF_6 (octahedral); $ICl_4^-E_2$ (octahedral with ICl_4 square coplanar).

MULTIPLE BONDING

We have so far neglected a rather large class of bonds which are short, strong, and have high stretching frequencies. These bonds most often involve carbon, oxygen, and/or nitrogen atoms. These strong bonds are typically found in compounds in which the coordination number around the carbon or nitrogen is less than four and that about oxygen is one rather than two. Table 15.3 lists some bond lengths for compounds illustrating these properties. Table 15.4 summarizes the lengths, strengths, and frequencies of common multiple bonds, together with the commonly assigned valence orbital population in terms of atomic orbitals.

As indicated in our past discussion, the bond energies and bond frequencies both increase as the bond length decreases. It appears that as more and more electrons are involved in bonding any two atoms together the nuclei move closer together, the bond becomes stronger, and the bond frequency rises.

We have confined our discussion of bond frequencies primarily to stretching modes. Multiple bonds have an interesting difference from single bonds with respect to torsion or twist about the bond axis.

Table 15.3 Experimental bond lengths of multiple bonds.

Ethylenic bonds (double bonds)

$H_2C{=}CH_2$	$F_2C{=}CF_2$	$Cl_2C{=}CCl_2$	$HBrC{=}CBr_2$	$HClC{=}CCl_2$
1.353	1.33	1.30	1.32	1.36
$HBrC{=}CBrH$	$HFC{=}CFH$	$H_2C{=}Cl_2$	$H_2C{=}CHBr$	
1.34	1.31	1.34	1.34	

Acetylenic bonds (triple bonds)

$HC{\equiv}CH$	$HC{\equiv}CCl$	$ClC{\equiv}CCl$	$BrC{\equiv}CCl$	$HC{\equiv}CBr$
1.201_0	1.211	1.195	1.20	1.20

Other multiple bonds

$H{-}C{\equiv}N$	$BrC{\equiv}N$	$ClC{\equiv}N$	$F_3CC{\equiv}N$			
1.156	1.158	1.163	1.15			
$HN{=}C{=}O$	$H{-}N{=}CS$	$N{=}CS$				
1.207 1.171	1.216	1.25				
$(NH_2)_2C{=}O$	$Cl_2C{=}O$	$Br_2C{=}O$	$F_2C{=}O$	$HFC{=}O$	$H_2C{=}O$	
1.24	1.166	1.13	1.17	1.192	1.21	
$H_3B{-}C{=}O$	$O{=}CS$	$O{=}C{=}O$	$Cl_3CHC{=}O$	$H_2C{=}C{=}O$	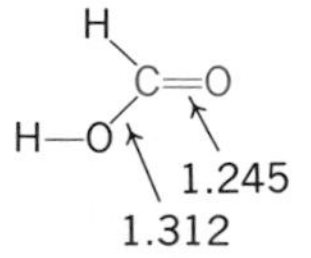	$H_3CON{=}O$
1.131	1.16	1.1600	1.15	1.35 1.17		1.22

Table 15.4 Typical properties of multiple bonds compared to single bonds.

	Average length (Å) ±0.04	Average energy ±5 (kcal $mole^{-1}$)	Average frequency ±1 (10^{13} cycles sec^{-1})	Orbitals involved in multiple bonds [(*sp*) indicates *sp* hybrid or σ bond]
C—C	1.54	83	2	—
C=C	1.33	146	5	(*sp*), *p*
C≡C	1.20	199	6	(*sp*), *p*, *p*
C—N	1.47	73	—	—
C=N	1.22	147	5	(*sp*), *p*
C≡N	1.16	213	6	(*sp*), *p*, *p*
C—O	1.40	85	3	(*sp*)
C=O	1.18	170	5	(*sp*), *p*
N—O	1.36	53	3	(*sp*)
N=O	1.12	145	4	(*sp*), *p*

The fact that, at room temperature, there is only one kind of ethane molecule, H_3CCH_3, and only one kind of the molecule, ClH_2CCH_2Cl, is taken as evidence that there is free rotation about the C—C sp^3 hybrid bond in these molecules—at least at room temperature. If the rotation were prevented, there might be several types of ethane. For example, if one looked along the C—C axis of the molecule, the hydrogens might be either staggered or lined up. Similarly, the two chlorines in ClH_2CCH_2Cl might be behind one another or opposite one another. These possibilities are illustrated in Figure 15.6. Moreover, all other evidence available also supports the idea that there is indeed essentially free rotation about the C—C bond at room temperature.

The situation in ClHC=CHCl is quite different. Two molecules are known with this formula. The two molecules are called *cis* (for adjacent) and *trans* (for across) dichloroethylene. The experimentally observed structures and some of their properties are listed in Table 15.5.

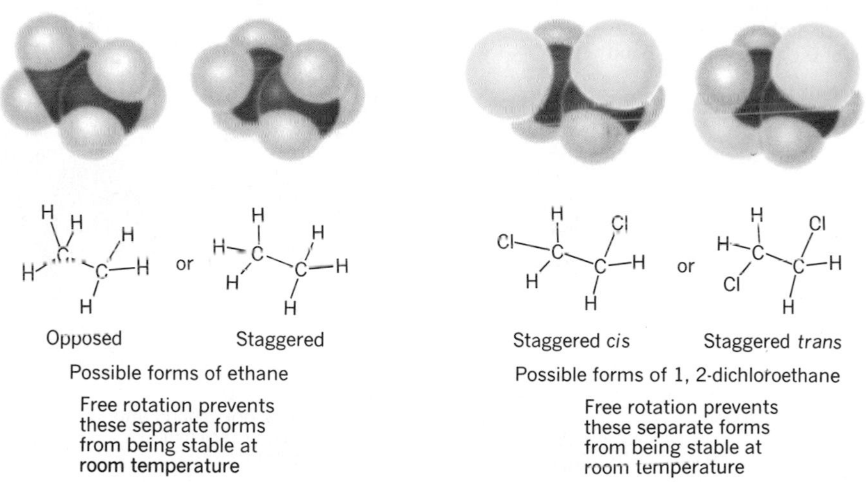

Figure 15.6 Free rotation.

Table 15.5 Comparison of *cis*- and *trans*-dichloroethylene.

Name	Structure (both planar)	B.P. (°K)	M.P. (°K)	Density at 298°K (g/ml)	Solubility in H_2O 293°K (g/100 g H_2O)
Cis-dichloroethylene	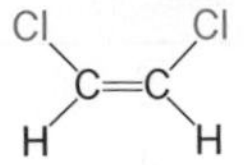	333.4	192.6	1.284	0.35
Trans-dichloroethylene	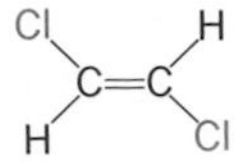	320.8	223.1	1.256	0.63

A very large number of pairs of molecules are known in which each member of the pair differs from the other only in rotation about the multiple bond. Yet the existence of the pair of molecules is proof that this rotation is not probable at room temperatures. At higher temperatures the rotation does become appreciable and the two molecules can convert into one another, giving further proof that rotation about the multiple bond is difficult at low temperatures.

The formation of multiple bonds from atomic orbitals can be pictured as in Figure 15.7. All the multiple bonds mentioned thus far have been between atoms of carbon, nitrogen, and/or oxygen, but other examples will be studied later. Multiple bonds are found when there are insufficient electrons and other atoms (the co-

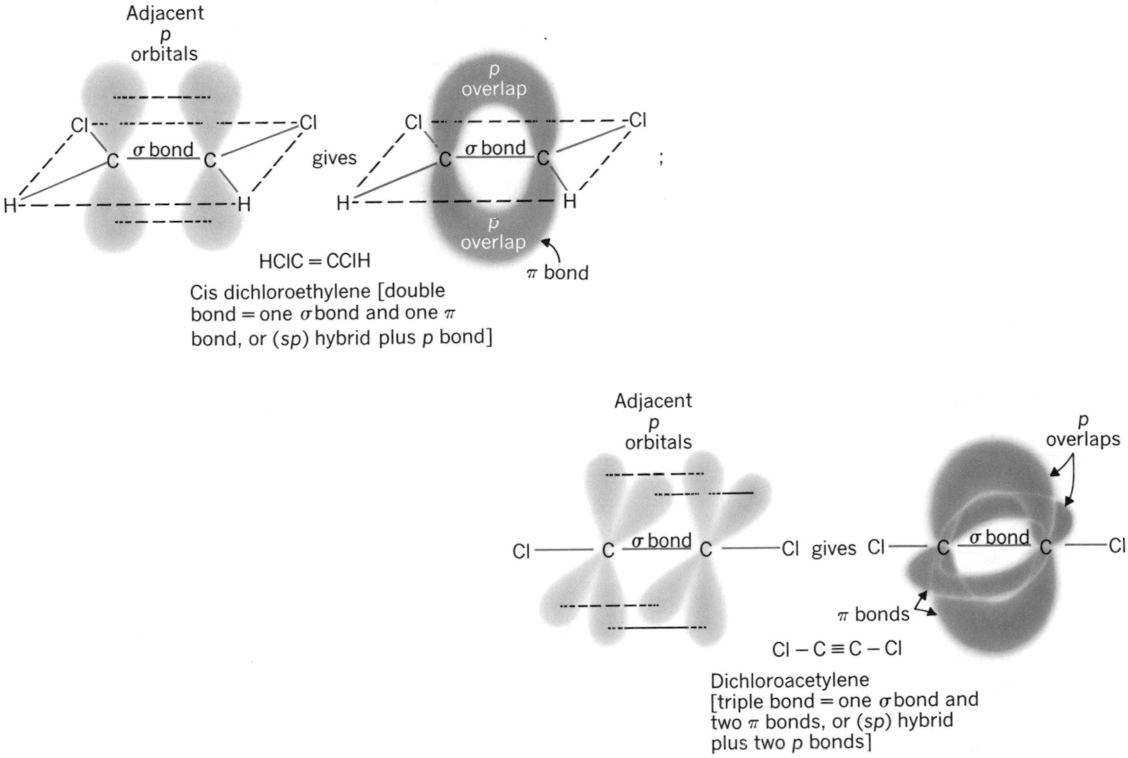

Figure 15.7 Multiple bonding due to *p* overlap.

ordination number, counting nonbonding pairs, is too low) to overlap each of the available valence orbitals of the central atom with a separate atom. Under these circumstances two or more orbitals are thought to overlap between the multiple-bonded atoms. In each case we assume that one pair of orbitals of the two atoms overlap "end-on" to form a bond directed along the internuclear axis. This bond is cylindrically symmetrical and is called a σ bond. Some of the p orbitals perpendicular to the σ bond (one or two per atom) then overlap the similarly perpendicular p orbitals of the other atoms in the molecule. It is the "sidewise" overlap of these perpendicularly directed p orbitals between the two atoms already overlapping their s or p or hybrid orbitals in a σ bond orbital that leads to a shortening and strengthening of the multiple bond. Since the p orbitals are strongly oriented in space, they can only overlap if the perpendicular p orbital on each atom is parallel to that on the other atom. This parallel condition cannot be maintained if there is free rotation about the bond, thus accounting for the lack of free rotation observed in the actual molecules. The overlap between these p orbitals perpendicular to the σ bond is called π bonding.

Note that the extension of the two overlapping p orbital sections (the π bond) above and below the plane in ethylene or dichloroethylene containing the σ bond and all the nuclei accounts for the fact that these molecules remain planar. That is, all six atoms are experimentally observed to lie in one plane which includes the σ bond. The observed bond angles of 120° are consistent with sp^2 hybrids as in Table 15.2. The double bond is then completed through out-of-plane overlap of the two remaining p orbitals, one from each of the carbon atoms. The 120° angles also follow from the Gillespie model: each carbon atom is surrounded by three sets of valence electrons: the two C—H or C—Cl σ sets and the C=C set of σ and π electrons.

Acetylene and its derivatives form a linear sp hybrid. The two carbons are joined to one another and to the two adjacent atoms by σ bonds. This leaves two half-filled p orbitals on each carbon atom. These p orbitals, which are perpendicular to the σ bonds, can then overlap between the two carbons. Since three orbitals are now overlapping between the two carbon atoms, the bond is shorter and stronger than that in ethylene and much shorter and stronger than that in ethane and other singly bonded carbon compounds. The linearity of acetylene derivatives follows from the sp hybridization consistent with Table 15.2, or from the two sets of valence electrons around each carbon according to Gillespie.

Exercise 15.4

Suggest a shape for $H_2C{=}C{=}CH_2$, allene. *Answer:* There will be three σ bonds around each of the outside C's, holding them to the two H's and the neighboring C. This leads to sp^2 hybridization around the end C's and sp hybridization around the central C. There now remain single p orbitals on the end C's and a pair of p orbitals on the central atom. The p orbitals on the central C are, of course, perpendicular to one another. This forces the p orbitals on the end C's also to be perpendicular to one another in order to overlap the central orbitals appropriately. This causes the two pairs of H's to be in mutually perpendicular planes. The molecule may be described as a linear arrangement of C's with the H's lying in mutually perpendicular planes which intersect in the line of C's.

Table 15.6 Comparison of observed and tabulated average values for bonds in gaseous $HONO_2$ and C_6H_6. Approximated values (~) are obtained by assuming that other bond energies in observed molecules have usual values. Note that the observed values of distance and enthalpy are always intermediate between the single and double bond values, and that the molecules are more stable than "expected" by 14 and 37 kcal mole^{-1}, respectively.

	HO^*NO_2	C_6H_6
Observed bond angles	137.8° 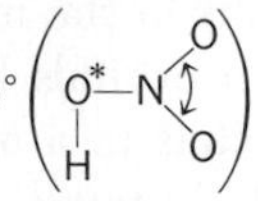	120°
Observed bond distances	1.20 (N—O) 1.44 (N—OH)	1.3973 (C—C)
Tabulated single bond distance	1.36 (N—O)	1.54 (C—C)
Tabulated double bond distance	1.12 (N=O)	1.33 (C=C)
Observed bond enthalpy	~106 (N to O)	~121 (C to C)
Tabulated single bond enthalpy	53 (N—O)	83 (C—C)
Tabulated double bond enthalpy	145 (N=O)	147 (C=C)
Average tabulated bond energy	99	115
Extra energy per bond	106 − 99 = 7	121 − 115 = 6
Total "resonance energy"	~14 (2 bonds)	37 (6 bonds)

RESONANCE

We have so far described molecules in terms of a linear combination of atomic orbitals. This resulted in electron distributions which involved two, or four, or six electrons holding any given pair of atoms together (single, double, or triple bonds respectively). But there is a group of molecules for which no single structure of this type is adequate. Consider nitric acid, HNO_3, and benzene, C_6H_6, as shown in Figure 15.8. For each of these molecules it is possible to write more than one linear combination of atomic orbitals which pairs up the available valence electrons in the available orbitals. Some experimental data for these molecules are given in Table 15.6 and compared to "average" values.

In $HONO_2$ and C_6H_6, as well as other molecules in which more than one

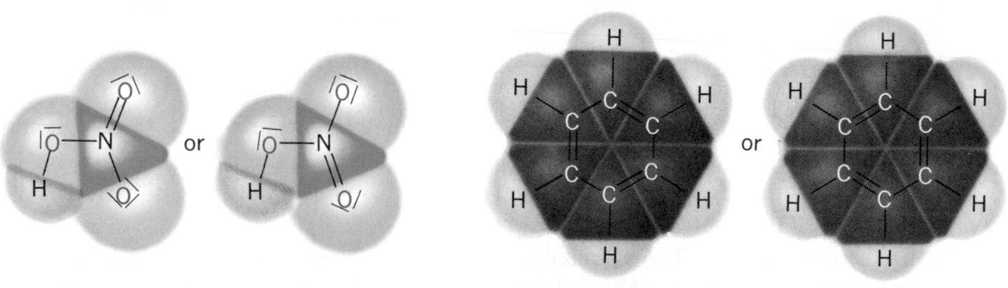

Figure 15.8 Both HNO_3 (number of valence electrons = 24) and C_6H_6 (number of valence electrons = 30) can be represented by two nonidentical LCAO electron structures. Because of the symmetry of the molecules, the two structures contain the same number of bonds but they are distributed differently. Each actual structure has been found experimentally to be intermediate between these two *resonance* structures, often called canonical forms.

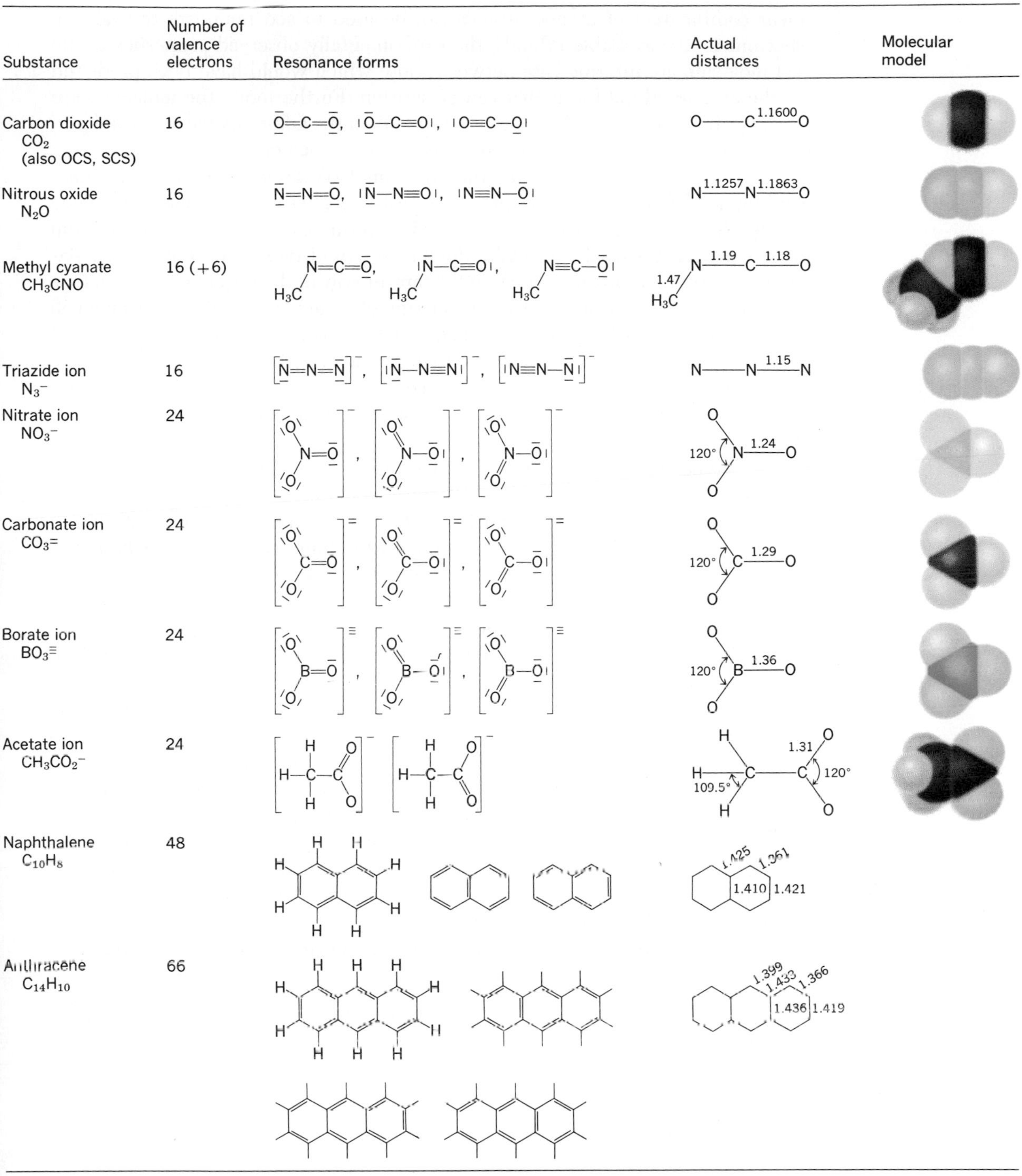
Substance
Number of valence electrons
Resonance forms
Actual distances
Molecular model
Carbon dioxide
CO2
(also OCS, SCS)
16
1.1600
Nitrous oxide
N2O
16
1.1257
1.1863
Methyl cyanate
CH3CNO
16 (+6)
1.19
1.18
1.47
Triazide ion
N3−
16
1.15
Nitrate ion
NO3−
24
1.24
120°
Carbonate ion
CO3=
24
1.29
120°
Borate ion
BO3≡
24
1.36
120°
Acetate ion
CH3CO2−
24
1.31
120°
109.5°
Naphthalene
C10H8
48
1.410
1.421
Anthracene
C14H10
66
1.436
1.419
1.366

Figure 15.9 Some resonant systems.

linear combination of atomic orbitals can be used to accommodate the valence electrons in the available orbitals, the experimentally observed properties of the real molecule are intermediate between those which would have been predicted for the atomic orbital forms that can be written. Furthermore, the molecules are more tightly bonded (and hence more stable) than the additivity values would predict. This "extra" stability is measured as the resonance energy.

Molecules whose actual structure cannot be described by a single linear combination of atomic orbitals are said to exist in a resonant ground state. They exhibit the phenomenon of resonance. (The term resonance is borrowed from physics, where it is used to describe the interaction of two systems of very similar energy; in such a resonant interaction the total energy of the system is lowered. One might argue that, in a similar way, the energy of an actual chemical molecule will be lower than that of any of the resonance forms made of linear combinations of atomic orbitals used to describe the actual ground state.)

Figure 15.9 shows some other common molecules for which resonant forms must be written in attempting to describe the actual molecules in terms of atomic orbitals.

Some remarkable observations can be made in Figure 15.9. One is that there are two sets of isoelectronic molecules, containing 16 and 24 valence electrons, respectively. Another is that the distances in naphthalene and anthracene parallel to a remarkable degree the fraction of the times each particular bond is a double bond in the resonance, or canonical, forms (see Figure 15.10).

Figure 15.11 is a plot of bond distance versus "bond order" for carbon-carbon bonds. Bond order is defined as the average bond multiplicity. If, as in benzene, a bond is single in half the resonance forms and double in the other half, the bond-order is $(1 + 2)/2 = \frac{3}{2}$. The bond order of the bridge bond in naphthalene (see Figure 15.9) is $(1 + 2 + 1)/3 = \frac{4}{3}$. The bond order of the shortest bond in naphthalene is $(1 + 2 + 2)/3 = \frac{5}{3}$, and so on. Curves like that in Figure 15.11 can be drawn for pairs of atoms other than two carbon atoms but the data for carbon are much more plentiful. We may summarize the data for carbon by saying that bond is roughly linear in bond order (±0.02 Å) from a bond order of 3 to about $\frac{4}{3}$. At lower bond orders the distance rises more rapidly to the single bond distance of 1.54 Å. Thus the introduction of a slight excess charge above that found for two electrons is much more effective at shortening and strengthening bonds than are further additional charge increases.

The fact that many resonant systems can be grouped into isoelectronic sets

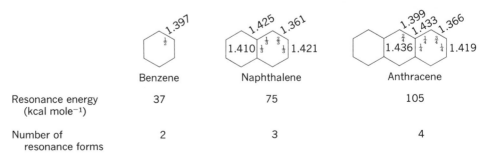

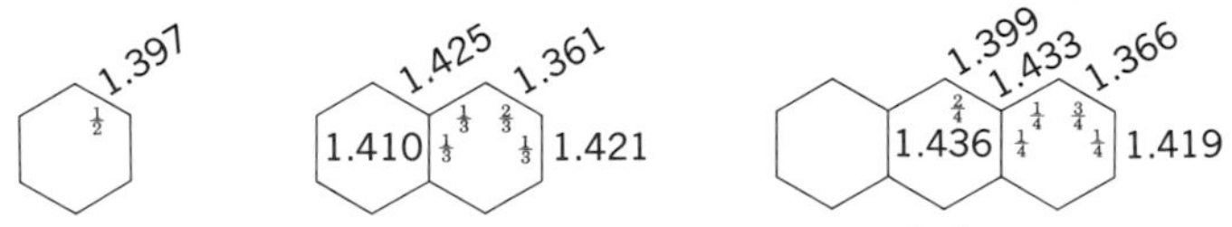

	Benzene	Naphthalene	Anthracene
Resonance energy (kcal mole^{-1})	37	75	105
Number of resonance forms	2	3	4

Figure 15.10 Correlation of bond distance (4 significant figures) with fraction of resonance forms in which a given bond is double ($\frac{1}{3}$, etc.), and of resonance energy (kcal mole^{-1}) with number of resonance forms.

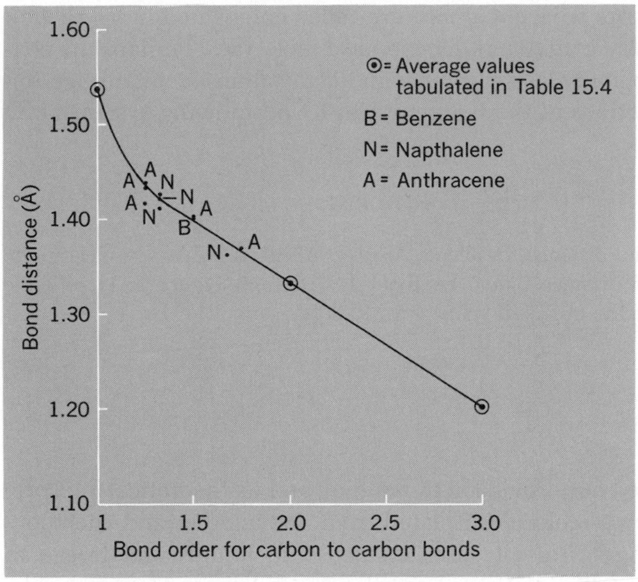

Figure 15.11 Bond order and bond distance.

provides an initial clue to describing electronic structures in molecules otherwise than in terms of atomic orbitals. So far we have used the approach known as the valence bond (VB) theory. It treats each bond as a simple overlap of atomic orbitals from the adjacent atom. Perhaps the orbitals can be viewed as spreading over the whole molecule rather than merely concentrating around a pair of atoms. We shall investigate this concept of molecular orbitals, MO, in Chapter 17.

Benzene, naphthalene, and anthracene, for example, can be represented in terms of atomic orbitals as in Figure 15.12. Such systems of multiple *p* overlap (*p*

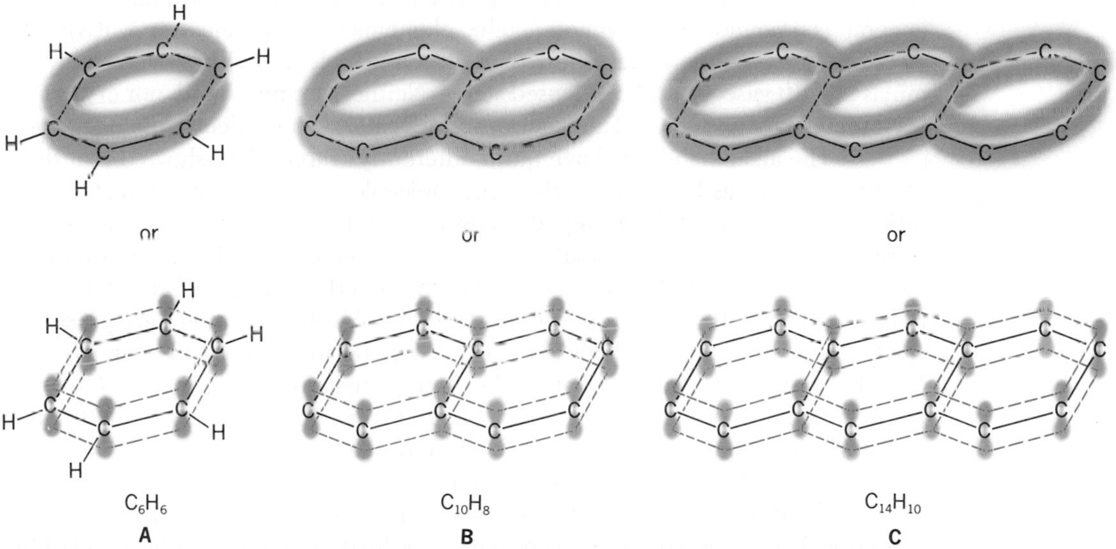

Figure 15.12 Continuous *p* orbital overlap or conjugation. (**A**) C_6H_6—each carbon has σ bonds to one hydrogen and two adjacent carbons plus π bonding all around the ring. (**B** and **C**) The situations in $C_{10}H_8$ and $C_{14}H_{10}$ are very similar to that in benzene except that the continuous π bonding extends throughout the ring system. The hydrogens are not shown.

overlap between four or more adjacent atoms) are called conjugated in VB theory. Conjugated systems are very common in biochemical molecules. Perhaps the continuous π orbitals extending over long distances and many atoms facilitate electron transfer and chemical reactions at the temperatures found in living systems. MO theory may be helpful here.

Exercise 15.5

Suggest a C—C bond distance for allene. *Answer:* Allene is $H_2C{=}C{=}CH_2$ so the carbon-carbon bond distance should be about 1.33 Å from Figure 15.11 or Table 15.4. Table 17.7 lists the observed value as 1.312 Å.

CONDENSED PHASES

We have, thus far, restricted our discussion of bonding and its theoretical interpretation to gaseous molecules—molecules isolated from one another and each containing relatively few atoms. But all gases condense to liquids and freeze to crystals. The liquid and crystalline state are less voluminous, less readily penetrable, and more resistant to flow than the corresponding gas. Each of these changes in properties indicates the formation of additional bonds. The new bonds must be between the molecules which existed in the gaseous state or between the atoms of the gas which have rearranged into new coordination patterns in the condensed states.

Detailed experiments on many crystals and liquids show that the same molecules are often present in the condensed phases as were present in the gas. The great majority of carbon compounds behave in this way. All the carbon-containing molecules discussed so far in this chapter have the same structure in gas, liquid, and crystalline state—for example, CH_4, C_6H_6, $C_{10}H_8$, C_2H_6, $(CH_2Cl)_2$, and others. In general, compounds between nonmetallic elements of similar electronegativity (an electronegativity difference of less than 1.5; see Table 14.14) have the same formulas in both gaseous and condensed states. Neither gas, nor liquid, nor crystal is a good electrical conductor. The electrons are localized in particular molecules.

The alkali halides behave quite differently. Table 14.10 showed that these compounds exist as highly polar diatomic molecules in the gaseous state. Condensation of the alkali halides to liquids gives mobile fluids of high electrical conductivity and the average coordination numbers increase to six to ten around each atom. The diatomic molecules, if they exist at all in the liquid, are rare and appear to have little effect on the properties of the liquid. Most of the atoms are present as singly charged ions. The alkali ions bear single positive electrical charges—Li^+, Na^+, K^+, Rb^+, Cs^+—and the halides bear single negative charges—F^-, Cl^-, Br^-, I^-. (Astatine and francium are radioactive and so rare we need not include them here.) All these ions are isoelectronic with noble gas atoms.

The crystalline alkaline halides have coordination numbers of six or eight. The coordination number six is the more common and is called the sodium chloride structure. The alkali halide structure with coordination number eight is called the cesium chloride structure. These two structures are shown in Figure 15.13 together with a list of the halides with each structure at normal laboratory conditions. Rais-

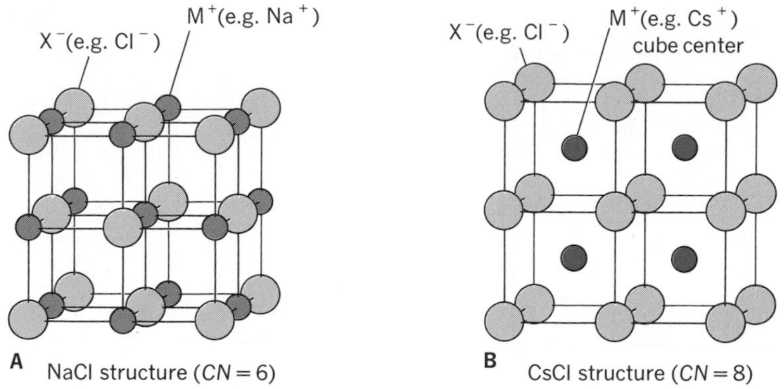

Figure 15.13 The NaCl ($CN = 6$) and CsCl ($CN = 8$) structures. All alkali halides have the NaCl structure at room temperature except CsCl, CsBr, and CsI. These three have the CsCl structure. An "expanded" form of each crystal structure is shown. In the actual crystals the ions are in contact.

ing or lowering the temperature or pressure may lead to modification of the crystal form to another structure. Thus RbCl, RbBr, and RbI all form cesium chloride structures above about 5000 kg cm^{-2} and CsCl has a sodium chloride structure above 460°C.

Many compounds containing both metallic and nonmetallic elements especially if the elements differ in electronegativity by more than 1.5 units (such as KCl, $CaBr_2$, ScF_3, Y_2O_3, LiH) form ionic liquids and crystals when their polar gaseous molecules condense. By ionic liquids and crystals we mean condensed phases in which individual electrons may be rather unambiguously assigned to individual charged molecules or atoms. Each electron spends most of its time localized on a particular ion. Electrical conductivity in the liquid is good because the ions are free to move past one another. But electrical conductivity in the crystal is low because the ions are restricted to well-defined sites in the crystal and the electrons are localized on individual ions. Since there are no charged particles which are free to move through the crystal, ionic crystals are poor conductors of electricity. We shall discuss ionic crystals in Chapter 16.

A considerable number of the metallic elements exist as neutral diatomic molecules in the gas phase (see Figure 5.10). The rest of the metallic elements are mainly monatomic and electrically neutral in the gas. Yet all metals condense to liquids and crystals, and form phases which are good conductors of electricity and have high coordination numbers, as shown in Figure 5.13. The electrical conductivity in liquid and crystalline metallic elements is almost entirely due to electron mobility, rather than ionic mobility. Apparently, condensed metals contain electrons which are not localized on a particular atom or small group of atoms. Some of the electrons in condensed metals are delocalized—they can move through the condensed phase even under small differences in electrical potential. We shall discuss metals in Chapters 16, 17, and 33.

There are a few molecules containing only nonmetallic elements which greatly change structure when they condense. Phosphorus pentachloride is an outstanding example. The gas contains PCl_5 molecules almost exclusively, as does the liquid. But the crystal contains only PCl_4^+ and PCl_6^- ions, in equal numbers of

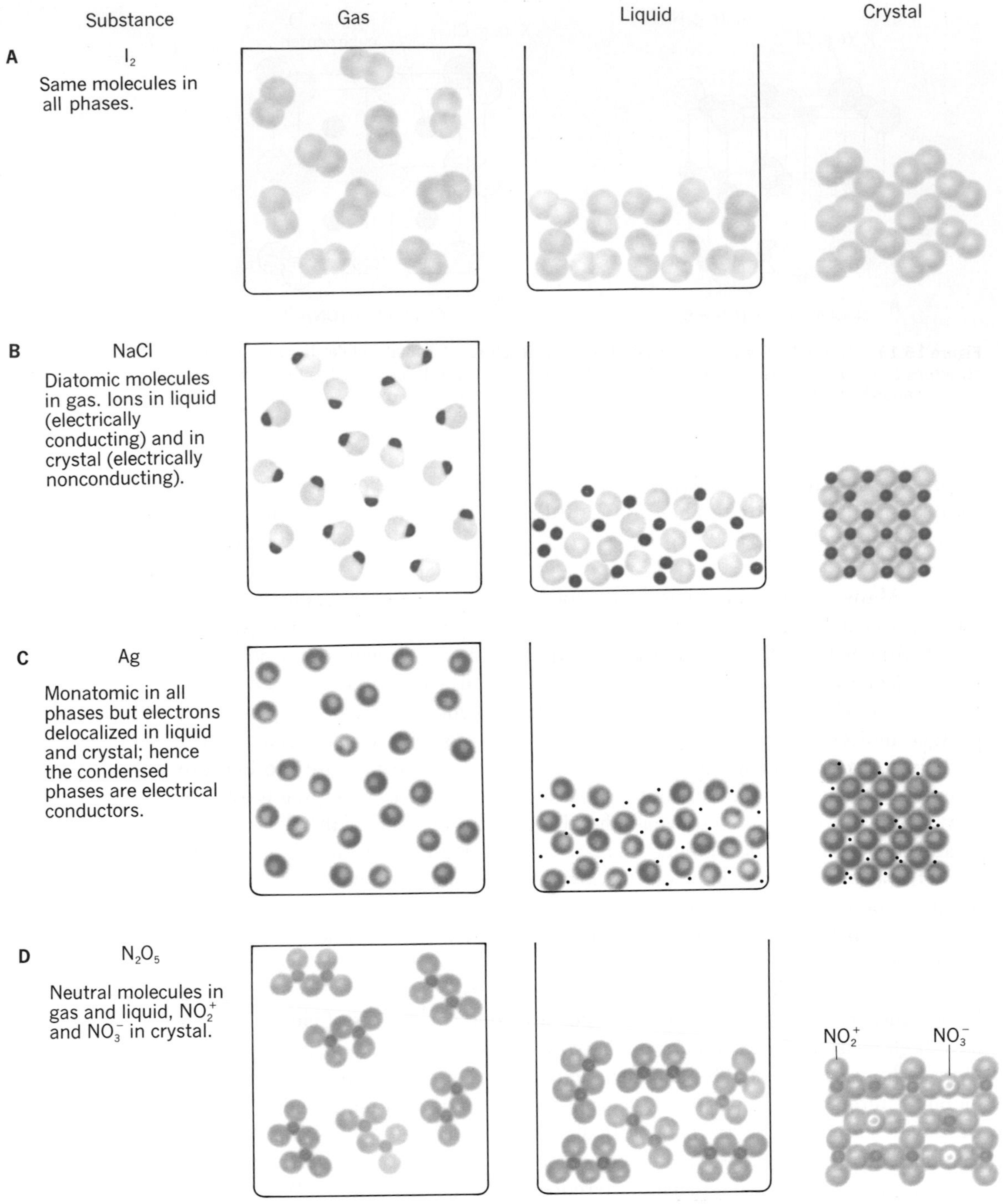
Substance
Gas
Liquid
Crystal
A
I2
Same molecules in all phases.
B
NaCl
Diatomic molecules in gas. Ions in liquid (electrically conducting) and in crystal (electrically nonconducting).
C
Ag
Monatomic in all phases but electrons delocalized in liquid and crystal; hence the condensed phases are electrical conductors.
D
N2O5
Neutral molecules in gas and liquid, NO2+ and NO3- in crystal.
NO2+
NO3-

Figure 15.14 Some variations in structure and properties from phase to phase.

course, consistent with the requirement of conservation of electrical charge. A similar example is nitrogen pentoxide, which consists of N_2O_5 molecules in gas and liquid, but of NO_2^+ and NO_3^- ions in the crystalline phase. A more complicated example is perchloric acid monohydrate. The gas contains $HClO_4$ and H_2O molecules, but the crystal contains only H_3O^+ and ClO_4^- ions. The liquid is a complicated system of these and other molecules. Figure 15.14 summarizes some of the above differences.

One lesson to draw from this section is the danger of generalizing on the behavior of a substance which has been studied in only one phase. It may have quite different structural properties in another phase. Another lesson is that the bonding entities and bonding types can vary from phase to phase. Let's look at some examples of the forces which act mainly in the condensed phases and hence may be causes of these differences.

Exercise 15.6

Crystal data on the monohydrate of nitric acid indicate that each nitrogen atom is surrounded by three identical oxygens. What conclusions does this lead to? *Answer:* If the three oxygens are identical, the entity should be NO_3^-, not $HNO_3(HONO_2)$. Thus the proton is probably associated with a water molecule as H_3O^+.

VAN DER WAALS AND REPULSIVE FORCES

We pointed out in Table 6.1 that no gases behave ideally. This was interpreted in terms of repulsive and attractive forces acting between the molecules. These forces are formalized in the

VAN DER WAALS EQUATION: $RT = (\overline{V} - b)\left(P + \frac{a}{\overline{V}^2}\right)$

Here b represents the effect of the repulsive forces and a is a measure of the attractive forces. We also demonstrated that at large to moderate values of $\overline{V}$ the attractive forces had the larger effect, but at small values of $\overline{V}$ the repulsive forces were predominant.

We also identified repulsive forces in our discussions of the interactions of electrons and nuclei. Close approach of two electrons or of two nuclei leads to strong repulsions. Such close approaches become more common if the molar volume, $\overline{V}$, becomes small. Thus the repulsive forces found in gases at small molar volumes and the repulsive forces which prevent liquids and solids from condensing to an infinitely small volume can be attributed to the repulsions of electrons for one another and of nuclei for one another. The repulsive energy, U_{rep}, is often represented as inversely proportional to some high power, usually 9–12, of the internuclear distance, d. Thus

$$U_{\text{rep}} = \frac{B}{d^n} \qquad (15.1)$$

where $n = 9$ to 12.

The van der Waals attractions can also be rationalized in terms of our model for the nuclear atom. Regardless of which model we select for discussion—the probability atom of quantum mechanics or the pulsing atom of wave mechanics or any other dynamic model—the electric charge density is not constant in any given volume of space around the nucleus. Thus there will be instantaneous fluctuations in the charge density in any given direction from the nucleus. These fluctuations in effective charge will tend to induce opposite fluctuations in nearby spots in other atoms. An electrically positive fluctuation in one atom will tend to produce an electrically negative fluctuation in the neighboring volume of any nearby atom. A net attractive force will result. The attractive forces due to these statistical fluctuations in the electric charge density will be present between every pair of atoms. If the two atoms are nonpolar and have all their low-lying orbitals already filled, like the noble gas atoms, these forces are the only ones that can lead to interatomic attraction.

These forces were treated systematically by F. London in 1930 and are called London, or dispersion, forces. The magnitude of the interaction energy is proportional to the inverse sixth power of internuclear distance, d. It is also related to the ease with which the electron field about the atom can be distorted. The ease of distortion is measured as the polarizability of the atom, α; α may be defined in terms of the induced dipole moment, μ_{ind}, which may be caused in the atom by an electric field, $\mathcal{E}$:

$$\text{polarizability} = \alpha = \frac{\mu_{\text{ind}}}{\mathcal{E}} \tag{15.2}$$

α has the dimensions of volume, and is usually expressed as Å^3.

Then the London energy,

$$U_{\text{London}} = \frac{-ch\nu\alpha^2}{d^6} \tag{15.3}$$

The value of $ch\nu$ varies from substance to substance but approximates $2.6 \cdot 10^3$ kcal mole^{-1} for many molecules: ν is the frequency of electron field oscillation, h is Planck's constant, and c is a numerical factor depending on the nature of the interacting molecules.

London forces exist between any pair of atoms or molecules. In the noble gases they are the only forces. They must generally be weak, as evidenced by the low melting and boiling points of the noble gases (see Table 11.2). Few other substances have such low melting and boiling points, so most substances must have other and more powerful forces acting between their atoms and molecules. London forces are, however, related to total molecular area and can result in melting and boiling points well above room temperature. The paraffin of candle wax is a good example, as is the polyethylene used in flexible bottles.

Polar molecules contain a permanent net asymmetry in their distribution of electric charge; they have dipole moments. The dipole moment in each molecule can induce a dipole in its neighbors (just as London forces are due to induced charge asymmetries), but permanent dipoles can also interact directly by "lining up." Figure 15.15 illustrates the source and magnitude of London forces, induced dipole forces, and dipole-dipole interactions.

All these interactions, lumped together as van der Waals interactions, exist in gases. The relative contributions and the values of α differ from gas to gas, hence the value of a in the van der Waals equation also differs from gas to gas. Clearly these interactions will be much larger in condensed phases than in gases of large molar volume.

Table 15.7 shows the relative contributions of dipole-dipole, dipole–induced-dipole, and London forces to the interactions in some common substances that exist as the same kind of molecules in all phases. The London interactions are

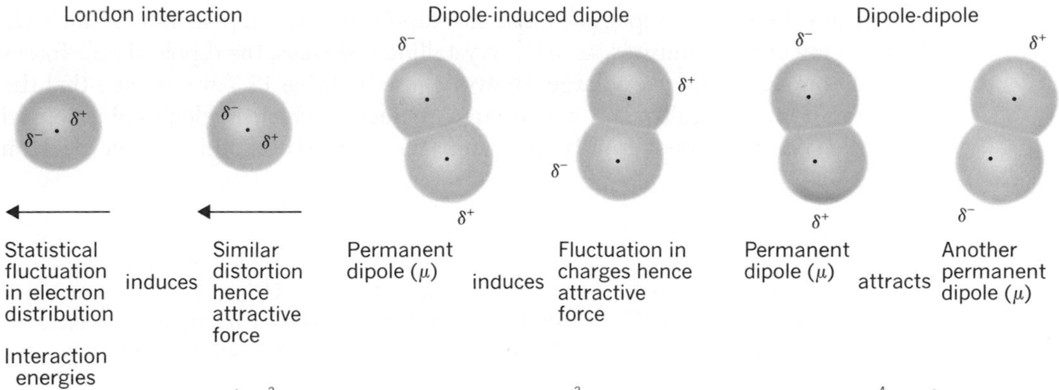

$$U_{\text{London}} = -\frac{ch\nu\alpha^2}{d^6} \qquad U_{\text{ind}} = -\frac{e\alpha\mu^2}{d^6} \qquad U_{D\text{-}D} = -f\,\frac{\mu^4}{d^6}\,\frac{1}{kT}$$

Figure 15.15 Types of attractive interactions between electrically neutral molecules (van der Waals forces) and their mathematical description. Note that $U_{D\text{-}D}$ is affected by temperature, since rising T increases the molecular gyrations and thus minimizes the possibility of alignment. The other two effects are insensitive to T (except as it may effect d). Numerical factors c, e, and f are dependent on the nature of the interacting molecules: commonly $c = \frac{1}{2}$, $e = 2$, and $f = \frac{2}{3}$.

Table 15.7 Intermolecular-attraction terms for some pairs of simple molecules at a constant distance of 5 Å. The first five substances listed are nonpolar but have increasing polarizability. Their properties listed in the last four columns generally increase in the same sequence. The other substances are listed in order of increasing dipole moment. Their values of ΔH, a, and $T_{\text{b.p.}}$ usually also increase in order of U_{tot}. Note, however, that U_{tot} values for NH_3 and H_2O are anomalous (due to low polarizability). This indicates that some additional bonding is probably present in these substances. We shall identify these bonds as hydrogen bonds. They are directional and not included in the Mie equation (15.8), which assumes essentially random orientations for the molecules.

Molecule	Dipole moment (Debye)	Polarizability (Å^3)	Interaction energy (kcal mole^{-1}) at $d = 5$Å and $T = 298$°K				ΔH_{vap} (kcal/mole)	a van der Waals $\frac{l^2 \cdot \text{atm}}{\text{mole}^2}$	$T_{\text{b.p.}}$ (°K)
			$U_{\text{D-D}}$	U_{ind}	U_{London}	U_{tot}			
Nonpolar									
He	0	0.2	0	0	0.0007	0.0007	0.022	.0341	4.2
Ar	0	1.6	0	0	0.042	0.042	1.59	1.34	87.2
N_2	0	1.8	0	0	0.064	0.064	1.34	1.39	77.0
Xe	0	4.0	0	0	0.26	0.26	3.11	4.19	165.0
CCl_4	0	10.5	0	0	1.8	1.8	7.14	20.39	350.9
Dipolar									
CO	0.12	2.0	$3 \cdot 10^{-6}$	$5.3 \cdot 10^{-5}$	0.07	0.07	1.44	1.49	81.0
HI	0.38	5.4	0.0003	0.0014	0.50	0.50	4.34	6.23	237.7
HBr	0.78	3.6	0.0056	0.0040	0.22	0.23	4.21	4.45	206.1
HCl	1.03	2.6	0.017	0.0052	0.11	0.13	3.86	3.67	189.4
NH_3	1.5	2.2	0.075	0.0091	0.08	0.17	5.58	4.17	239.8
H_2O	1.84	1.5	0.171	0.0094	0.037	0.22	9.42	5.46	373.1

almost always the principal ones and the dipole–induced-dipole interactions are least. At lower temperatures, as in the crystalline materials, the dipole-dipole forces can, of course, become very large. In every case in Table 15.7 we assume that the electrons remain localized in a particular molecule which is electrically neutral over-all. The attractions result from asymmetries in the distribution of the electron cloud.

Exercise 15.7

Calculate the percent contribution of U_{D-D}, U_{ind}, and U_{London} to U_{tot} for each substance in Table 15.7. *Answer:* London forces are 100% for nonpolar molecules, and from about 25 to 99% in all cases. U_{D-D} is next most important—up to 80%, with large dipoles like H_2O. U_{ind} is never more than 2 or 3%.

Exercise 15.8

Note in Table 15.7 that polarizability seems to decrease as dipole moment increases. Rationalize this fact. *Answer:* Highly polar molecules contain atoms of large electronegativity which attract electrons strongly. Thus, it is not surprising that the polarizability, which measures the ease of deformation of the molecular electric field, is low.

MEASUREMENT OF DIPOLE MOMENTS OF PURE SUBSTANCES

Dipole moments are very helpful in understanding molecular structure, chemical bonds, and chemical reactivities. Their measurement is straightforward, but not precise, so various tabulations give various values.

Most measurements involve placing a sample in a parallel plate condenser. If its capacitance (that is, the stored charge per unit of applied potential) is C_0 in a vacuum, placing a nonconducting substance between the plates will give a capacitance, $C = \epsilon C_0$, where ϵ is the dielectric constant of the substance and is always greater than 1. Measurements are usually made with alternating current to minimize electrode effects. We interpret the increased ability of the condenser to store charge as due to charge alignment in the substance. This may be caused by two general effects: (1) orientation of polar molecules between the charged plates, called orientation polarizability, P_o, and (2) distortion of the normally nonpolar electric fields of the molecules by the applied field, called distortion (or induced) polarizability, P_d.

The total molar polarizability $P_M = P_d + P_o$. O. F. Mossotti in 1850 showed that

$$P_M = \frac{\epsilon - 1}{\epsilon + 2}\frac{M}{\rho} \tag{15.4}$$

where M/ρ is the molar volume and ϵ is the dielectric constant.

Debye later calculated $P_o = (\frac{4}{3})\pi N_0(\mu^2/3kT)$, where μ is the permanent dipole moment of the molecule. The exact calculation of P_d is difficult but the assumptions normally used in calculations on condensed liquid phases of nonpolar molecules, either pure or containing a dilute solution of polar molecules, give

$$P_d = \frac{4\pi N_0}{3}\alpha$$

where α is the molecular polarizability in cm^3: α turns out to be somewhat less than the molecular volume (see Table 15.7).

Thus we get

$$\frac{\epsilon - 1}{\epsilon + 2}\frac{M}{\rho} = P_M = \frac{4\pi N_0}{3}\left(\alpha + \frac{\mu^2}{3kT}\right) = a + \frac{b}{T} \tag{15.5}$$

The decrease of P_M with rising T should not surprise you. After all, the increase in T increases the thermal motion of all the molecules and reduces the ability of the molecules to line-up in the applied field.

For pure substances, a plot of $[(\epsilon - 1)/(\epsilon + 2)](M/\rho)$ versus $1/T$ gives a straight line for which both α and μ can be calculated (from intercept and slope, respectively).

INDEX OF REFRACTION

Maxwell's theory of light led to the conclusion that at high frequencies $\epsilon = n^2$, where n is the refractive index of the substance. Substitution in Equation (15.4) gives, at high frequencies,

$$P_M = \frac{n^2 - 1}{n^2 + 2}\frac{M}{\rho} \tag{15.6}$$

Elementary consideration of the nature of light shows that this P_M can be due only to interactions between molecular electrons and the rapidly oscillating electromagnetic field of the visible light, frequency about 10^{15} sec^{-1} (see Figure 9.2). Permanent dipoles of rotation frequencies about 10^{10} sec^{-1} cannot follow this rapid pulsation nor can nuclear framework vibrations (of frequency about 10^{12} sec^{-1}). Thus the equation $\epsilon = n^2$ may be interpreted in terms of the refractive index representing the relative velocity, c, of light in a vacuum and, c_s, in the substance, $n = c/c_s$. The slowing down of light in the substance is due to the interaction between its oscillating electromagnetic field and the bound electrons in the molecule. The less tightly bound they are, the higher the interaction, leading to larger values of n and of ϵ.

This means that the total polarizability at any frequency can be considered as made up of three terms, $P_M = P_e + P_a + P_o$, where P_e is polarizability due to induced distortion of the electron cloud, P_a represents induced distortion due to deformation of the nuclear framework, and P_o is polarizability due to alignment of polar molecules by the applied field. In many cases P_a is less than 10% of $P_e = P_c + P_a$, so $P_d = P_e = [(n^2 - 1)/(n^2 + 2)](M/\rho)$, readily calculable from index of refraction measurements and density data.

MEASUREMENTS OF DIPOLE MOMENTS IN SOLUTION

Solutions of polar molecules in nonpolar solvents often show effects due to interactions between the dipoles. These effects diminish as the solution is diluted and the dipoles are separated. Thus it is customary to study ϵ as a function of concentration at constant T. Instead of M/ρ (used for pure substances), we use $\overline{V}$ to get

$$\frac{\epsilon - 1}{\epsilon + 2}\overline{V} = P_M - X_1(P_e + P_a)_{\text{solvent}} + X_2(P_e + P_a + P_o)_{\text{solute}}$$

P_a for each is assumed to be negligible. P_e is calculated from index of refraction measurements and $(P_o)_{\text{solute}}$ calculated as a function of $\overline{V}$. Plotting $(P_o)_{\text{solute}}$ versus $1/\overline{V}$ allows extrapolation to infinite dilution where interactions between the dipoles is zero. The value of $(P_o)_{\text{solute}}$ at infinite dilution is then used for the calculation of μ for the unhindered molecules from the Debye equation.

POTENTIAL ENERGY CURVES FOR ELECTRICALLY NEUTRAL MOLECULES

The three equations of Figure 15.15 show that the attractive energies for electrically neutral molecules are all inversely proportional to the sixth power of the internuclear distance. Equation (15.1) showed that the repulsive energies may be represented by an inverse higher power of the internuclear distance. Let us assume

Table 15.8 **Intermolecular energy constants of the Mie equation $U_{tot} = Bd^{-12}—Ad^{-6}$, and the calculated values of equilibrium intermolecular distance and "bond" strength. Compare Table 15.7.**

Gas	$B \cdot 10^{105}$ (erg cm^{12})	$A \cdot 10^{60}$ (erg cm^6)	Minimum in U vs d curve [d (Å)]	D (kcal $mole^{-1}$)
He	0.3605	1.17	2.917	0.0137
Ne	3.545	8.32	3.049	0.0700
Ar	162	103.4	3.819	0.237
H_2	6.49	10.5	3.276	0.0609
N_2	370	140	4.174	0.191
CH_4	620	226	4.20	0.296
CF_4	9788	908	5.28	0.304

this repulsive exponent is 12, which is found to be appropriate in many instances. The total potential energy of interaction may then be expressed as

$$U_{tot} = -\left[\frac{ch\nu\alpha^2}{d^6} + \frac{e\alpha\mu^2}{d^6} + \frac{f\mu^4}{d^6kT}\right] + \frac{B}{d^{12}} \tag{15.7}$$

At any constant T this reduces to an equation of the form suggested by Mie,*

$$U_{tot} = -Ad^{-6} + Bd^{-12} \tag{15.8}$$

The value of A can be calculated from Equation (15.7) or both A and B can be calculated empirically from accurate equations of state. Some tabulated values for nonpolar molecules are given in Table 15.8.

Figure 15.16 shows the total interaction energy, U_{tot}, as a function of d for several nonpolar molecules. Figure 15.17 shows the attractive and repulsive terms plotted separately as well as the U_{tot} obtained by adding the two effects for He and Ar.

All molecules for which data are available have potential energy relationships similar to those of Figures 15.16 and 15.17. The interaction energy for small molecules is essentially zero at distances greater than 10 Å, there is a minimum in the potential energy curve at about 3 to 6 Å, and the potential energy rises rapidly at small distances. This may be translated to mean that there is great resistance to squeezing molecules very closely together, that there is almost no interaction between molecules at large distances, and that there is an intermediate equilibrium distance at which the repulsive and attractive forces just balance to produce a minimum potential energy—that is, an intermolecular bond. The distance corresponding to the potential energy minimum corresponds to the distance at which the bond strength is greatest. This distance will approximate the internuclear distance from one molecule to the next in the crystal and liquid phases.

Exercise 15.9

Calculate the value of d for which $U = 0$ during a Ne–Ne collision. *Answer:* $U = 3.545 \cdot 10^{-105} d^{-12} - 8.32 \cdot 10^{-60} d^{-6} = 0$. If d is in Å, $3.545 \cdot 10^{-105} \cdot d^{-12} \cdot 10^{96} = 8.32 \cdot 10^{-60} \cdot d^{-6} \cdot 10^{48}$, $d^6 = 3.545 \cdot 10^{-9}/8.32 \cdot 10^{-12} = 4.26 \cdot 10^2$, $d =$

* *Ann. Physik*, **11**, 657 (1903).

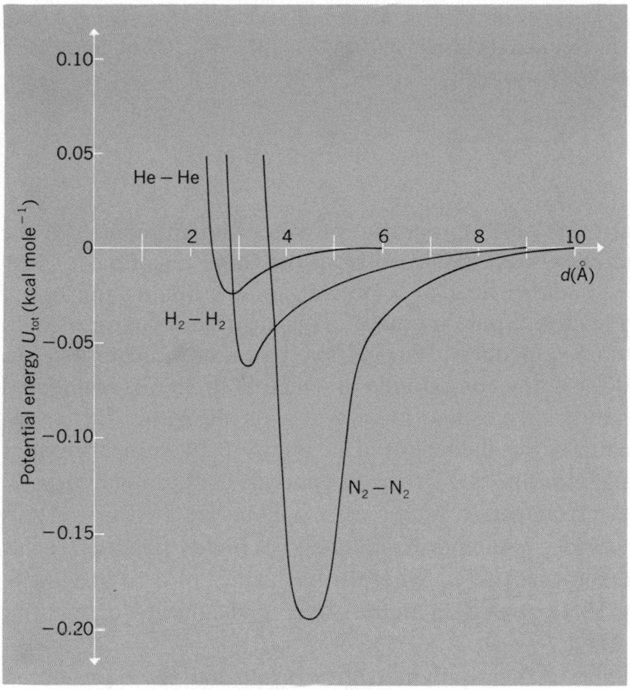

Figure 15.16 Mutual potential energy of pairs of molecules calculated from Equation (15.8).

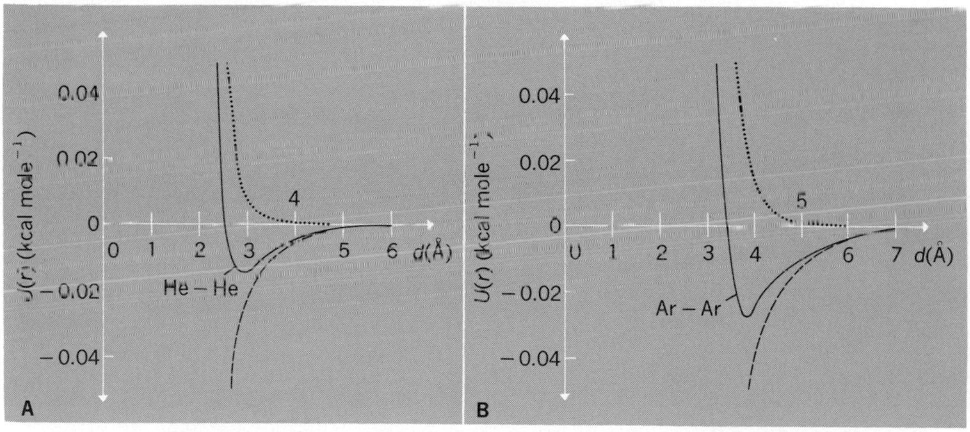

Figure 15.17 Potential energy for interaction of (**A**) two helium atoms and (**B**) two argon atoms. ···· = repulsive energy, ---- = attractive energy, —— = net energy as a function of d. Note different coordinate scales.

2.74 Å. Note that U_{min} occurs at 3.049 Å according to Table 15.8. Thus, during collisions, neon atoms interpenetrate by about 0.4 Å or a little over 10% of their radius if they had zero kinetic energy initially.

HYDROGEN BONDING

We noted in Table 15.7 that some of the properties of water and ammonia did not parallel the total interaction energy as calculated from the three equations of Figure 15.15. These properties, such as heat of vaporization and boiling point, did roughly parallel the change in the dipole moment. This suggests that there is an additional force which is more dependent on polarity than any indicated so far. Similar anomalies are found for many compounds in which hydrogen is connected to a highly electronegative atom, such as fluorine, oxygen, or nitrogen.

Remember, for example, the data plotted in Figure 6.14, indicating that acetic acid dimerizes in the gaseous phase. Other compounds containing hydrogen connected to the highly electronegative atoms also polymerize in the gaseous phase. Gaseous hydrogen fluoride, monomer formula HF, is highly polymerized as a gas. Molecules of general formula $(HF)_n$, where n has values of 2 to at least 6, have been identified. Figure 15.18 gives data on the effect of H-bonding on melting points, boiling points, and ΔH_{vap}.

Studies of the structure of these polymers give results like those presented in Figure 15.19. Similar structural arrangements are found in many condensed phases. In every case the hydrogen is on or close to the internuclear axis between two atoms of high electronegativity (usually F, O, or N).

Hydrogen bonds are very common and have an important structural function in many molecules of biological importance, especially proteins and carbohy-

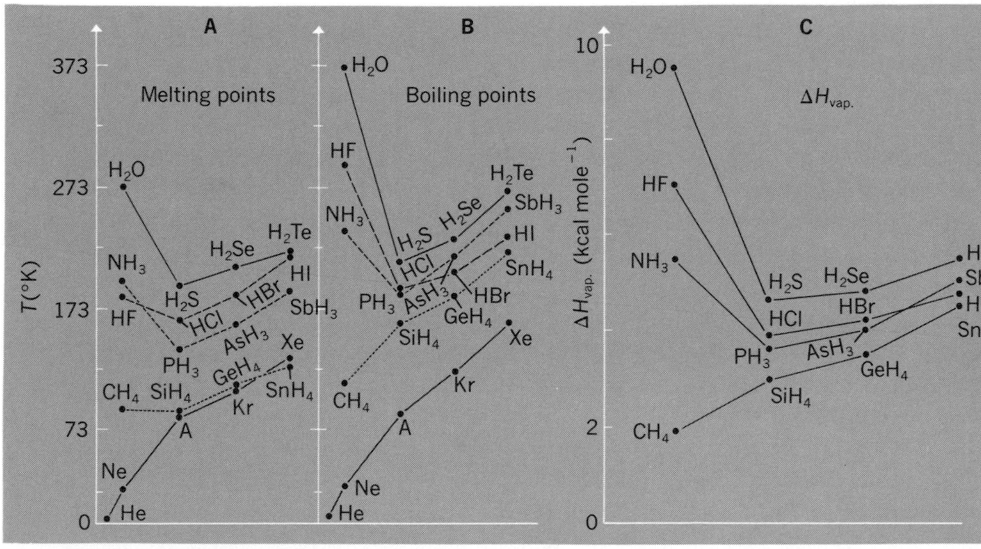

Figure 15.18 Effect of H-bonding on (**A**) some melting points, (**B**) some boiling points, and (**C**) ΔH_{vap}. Compare the noble gases and the hydrogen compounds of the carbon family with the hydrogen compounds of the nitrogen, oxygen, and halogen families. Which substance exhibits the biggest effects due to H-bonding?

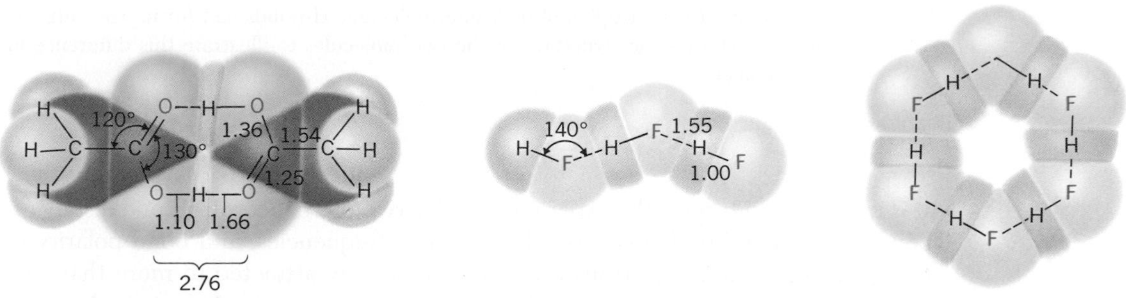

Figure 15.19 Structures of some hydrogen-bonded gaseous polymers. Note that the X—H--X bond is linear and X is always an atom of high relative electronegativity.

drates. The bond strength of hydrogen bonds varies from about 1 to 10 kcal mole^{-1}. You will remember from Chapter 6 that $E_{\text{trans}} = \frac{3}{2}RT$. Thus the average translational kinetic energy at human body temperature, 37°C = 310°K, is about 1 kcal mole^{-1}. Thus many hydrogen bonds are strong enough to withstand the continuous buffeting of the surrounding molecules and yet will break and reform if their energy is changed slightly. The constant breaking and reforming of hydrogen bonds is a major part of metabolic and other physiological processes. Were the bonds any weaker, living systems would either have to operate at a lower temperature or disintegrate. Were the bonds much stronger, the rate of change would be so slow as to immobilize the living system. It is interesting to note that only hydrogen bonds, of all the interactions we know, have both the requisite strength and the strongly directional character required to hold highly organized molecular structures together while still allowing them to change rapidly from one structure to another at normal body temperatures.

The theoretical interpretation of hydrogen bonding is straightforward. Any highly electronegative atom strongly attracts electrons from neighboring atoms. Hydrogen can hold only two electrons in its bonding orbital. If these are strongly attracted in one direction—for example, toward an oxygen atom with which the hydrogen is bonded (engaged in σ bonding)—the other side of the hydrogen is made highly positive, especially along the extension of the internuclear axis. After all, there are no other electrons in lower energy orbitals to shield the nucleus. When hydrogen is connected to a highly electronegative atom, the bond dipole is high and is enhanced along the extension of the internuclear axis by the relative exposure of the hydrogen nucleus. When another highly electronegative atom approaches along this extension of the internuclear axis, strong attractive forces occur. These forces weaken if the hydrogen moves away from the axis joining the nuclei of the two neighboring electronegative atoms, since the hydrogen nucleus becomes better and better shielded as this deviation increases.

Exercise 15.10

The boiling point of $p\text{C}_6\text{H}_4(\text{NO}_2)\text{OH}$ is much higher than that of $o\text{C}_6\text{H}_4(\text{NO}_2)\text{OH}$. Suggest an interpretation. *Answer:* Both substances tend to form hydrogen bonds between the hydroxyl hydrogen and the nitro oxygens. In *o*-nitrophenol, intramolecular H-bonds can form, so the resulting molecules are easy to separate and the boiling point is low. In *p*-nitrophenol only intermolecular H-bonds can form, lowering the volatility. Draw scale structures of the two molecules to illustrate this difference in their geometry.

SUMMARY

It is possible to interpret the experimental observations concerning bond distances, bond angles, bond enthalpies, bond vibrational frequencies, and bond polarity in terms of one or more electrons being simultaneously attracted to more than one nucleus and occupying atomic orbitals which are interpenetrating or overlapping. Strong bonds occur when there is considerable overlap either in terms of the number of orbitals overlapping (multiple bonds) or of the extent of overlap between a given pair of orbitals. Strong bonds are short bonds and have high vibrational frequencies. High bond polarities indicate that the electrons are attracted unsymmetrically by the two nuclei. In polar bonds the electrons are, on the average, closer to one nucleus than to the other. This normally represents a strengthening of the bond compared to nonpolar bonding, and leads to a shorter bond.

A large number of molecules and condensed phases may be given electron structures for their valence electrons by assigning the available valence electrons to the available atomic orbitals, using a combination of the same orbitals that are known to be present in the gaseous atom. In many cases atomic orbitals of different energy form bonding orbitals that all have the same energy. This is called VB hybridization. In other cases the orbital assignment seems to be unambiguous; in still others, several possible assignments, or resonant forms, are found. Such resonance is present in molecules that are experimentally more stable than the simple linear combination of atomic orbitals would indicate.

We know from past experience with gaseous atoms that energy levels split when the field strength in the vicinity increases. It should not be surprising if the energies of the orbitals found in isolated gaseous atoms are influenced when atoms come near one another, as in forming a chemical bond. Such splitting might be small if the bond interaction was not great, but could be quite large if strong interaction occurred. It is then that we use terms such as hybridization and resonance to describe systems that are considerably more stable than a simple combination of valence bonds would indicate. It is here that one would expect to find molecular orbitals most useful, orbitals which are characteristic of the atomic and electronic conformation in the molecule rather than in the isolated gaseous atoms.

If the simultaneous interaction of one or more electrons with more than one nucleus results in the localization of electrons more or less between a given pair of atoms, we say a covalent bond has formed. If the interaction is between neutral molecules each containing localized electrons, we say London forces, induced dipole forces, and/or dipole-dipole interactions are present. These forces are often generalized as van der Waals forces. Especially strong intermolecular forces occur when highly electronegative atoms covalently bonded to hydrogen are present. The hydrogen can form a strong bridge—a hydrogen bond—when it is on the line of centers between two atoms of high electronegativity.

Atomic orbital theory is surprisingly adequate to describe interatomic interactions so long as the electrons are localized. As the interatomic forces increase (giving larger field strengths) appreciable energy shifts occur in the orbitals. Hybridization and resonance are attempts to fit these shifts into atomic orbital theory.

Now the smallest particles of matter may cohere by the strongest Attractions, and compose bigger Particles of weaker Virtue; and many of these may cohere and compose bigger Particles whose Virtue is still weaker, and so on for divers Successions, until the Progression end in the biggest Particles on which the Operations in Chemistry, and the Colours of natural Bodies depend, and which by cohereing compose Bodies of a sensible Magnitude.
There are therefore Agents in Nature able to make the Particles of Bodies stick together by very strong Attractions. And it is the Business of experimental Philosophy to find them out.—Isaac Newton, Opticks (1704).

PROBLEMS

15.1. Why is the 18-electron molecule F_2 more reactive than the 18-electron molecule Ar?

15.2. XeF_4 is a rather stable compound. What are some possible ways of explaining the bonding in this molecule? Why do you think such compounds are absent for He and Ne?

15.3. How would you describe the bonding in a vinyl alcohol molecule ($CH_2{=}CHOH$) in terms of hybridized orbitals? What shape is the molecule?

15.4. Would you expect the bond energy of the P—Cl bonds to be greater in PCl_3 or in PCl_5?

15.5. Which of the following molecules (ions) are linear? (*a*) CO_2, (*b*) ClO_2, (*c*) $Ag(Cl)_2^-$, (*d*) H_2O_2, (*e*) NCF.

15.6. Which of the following are planar? (*a*) BF_3, (*b*) PH_3, (*c*) $Ni(CN)_4^=$, (*d*) P_4, (*e*) $CO_3^=$, (*f*) SO_3, (*g*) $SO_3^=$.

II

15.7. Represent the reaction between hydrogen and oxygen atoms to give water in a figure similar to Figure 15.1.

15.8. From the single bond energies Si—F, 135; Si—O, 112; H—F, 135; and H—O, 119 kcal, estimate ΔH for the reaction ($\Delta H \cong -30$ kcal per mole SiF_4)

$$SiO_2\,(s) + 4HF\,(g) \longrightarrow SiF_4\,(g) + 2H_2O\,(g)$$

15.9. In the vapor phase, $AlCl_3$ exists to the extent of about 0.027%, and the remainder of the material is primarily a dimer, Al_2Cl_6. Explain the existence of this dimer in the language of atomic orbitals (VB). At the same T, the mixture AlI_3 and Al_2I_6 contains the monomer to the extent of about 24%. Explain why the iodide dimer is less stable than the chloride dimer.

15.10. The heat of combustion of liquid cyclopentane is 734.0 kcal mole^{-1}, giving gaseous H_2O and CO_2 as products. Assuming the heat of vaporization of cyclopentane (C_5H_{10}) is 6.8 kcal/mole, estimate the strain energy of cyclopentane (about 10 kcal mole^{-1}). Write equations to justify your work showing ΔH for each step.

15.11. Predict the geometrical shape and as many of the following as possible for the listed gaseous molecules: bond lengths, dipole moments, bond polarities, bonding orbitals (including hybridization and resonance structures).

BCl_3, CO, $TeCl_4$, H_2CCCl_2, ONO^-, SO_2, $C_{14}H_{10}$ 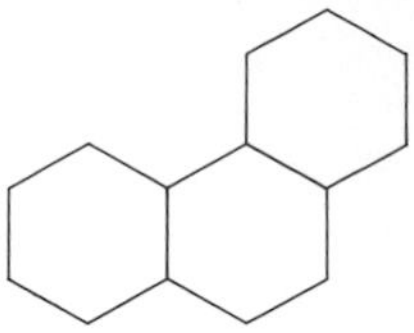

15.12. The free radical NH_2 has been studied spectroscopically with the following results. In the ground state the molecule is bent with a bond angle of 130°20′. In the first excited electronic state the molecule is linear. A simple valence bond argument can explain the geometry of the molecule in terms of orbitals of the central atom that are used for bond formation. Assuming that the excitation changes an electron from an $n = 2$ to an $n = 3$ state, and keeping the lowest bonding orbital of nitrogen ($2s$) fully occupied, assign the seven valence electrons to atomic orbitals (hybrid if necessary) of the nitrogen atom in a way that accounts for the observed geometry.

15.13. One theoretical description of the water molecule is based upon the use of the p orbitals of the oxygen atom to form the bonds with the hydrogen atoms. The increase of the bond angle from the theoretical value associated with two p orbitals of 90° to the observed value of 105° may be interpreted in terms of coulombic repulsion between the two hydrogen atoms due to partial ionic character of the oxygen to hydrogen bonds. One interpretation of the vibration spectrum of gaseous water is based upon an approximation in which the only forces considered are those between the atomic centers: $O—H_1$, $O—H_2$, and $H_1—H_2$. Analysis of the spectral data in terms of this simple model gives a force constant for the $H_1—H_2$ interaction of $1.85 \cdot 10^5$ dynes cm^{-1}. It is assumed that Hooke's law applies to the $H_1—H_2$ interaction, with the zero point of the force system corresponding to a bond angle of 90°, and that the OH bond distances remain constant at 0.960 Å.

(*a*) What must be the partial ionic charge (in esu) on each hydrogen atom in order for the coulombic repulsion between them to give an equilibrium bond angle equal to the observed value of 105°? (About 0.1 e^-.)

(*b*) Calculate the dipole moment of this theoretical model of the water molecule resulting from the charge separation calculated in (*a*), and compare it with the experimental value. Comment on the validity of the model. (About 1 Debye.)

15.14. The spectroscopic heat of dissociation of O_2 has been determined as 119.1 kcal ($O_2 \longrightarrow 2O$, $\Delta H = 119.1$ kcal). ($H_2 \longrightarrow 2H$, $\Delta H = 104.2$ kcal.) From these data and the standard enthalpy of formation of water, −57.8 kcal, find the bond energy of the H—OH bond in water (about 120 kcal mole^{-1}). Compare this value with the spectroscopic dissociation energy of the OH molecule, 102 kcal. Can you suggest any explanation for the difference?

15.15. The tripositive auric ion is known to form a complex with bromide ion which has the formula $AuBr_4^-$. Write the ground state electronic configuration for Au and for Au^{+3}. The bonds of the complex ion may be either weak "ionic" bonds or strong covalent bonds. In either case, the bromine ions are regarded as providing four pairs of electrons which must occupy orbitals of the gold ion. What orbitals are available and what is the predicted configuration of the ion (*a*) if it is assumed that weak bonds are formed and that the ground state of the ion is unchanged by the formation of the complex, and (*b*) if it is assumed that the four *lowest* energy orbitals are used in bond formation? What experiment, if any, could you suggest that would distinguish between the two possibilities.

See page 1091 for a list of references and readings in the recent chemical literature related to the material in this chapter.

CHAPTER 16

Ionic Substances and Metals

The close agreement between crystal energies calculated from the Madelung formula and from the Born-Haber cycles gives us confidence that we understand ionic bonding reasonably well.

Most of the substances treated in Chapter 15 may be viewed in terms of electrically neutral molecules with bonding electrons filling all low-lying orbitals and localized between pairs of atoms differing only slightly in relative electronegativity. The neutral molecules are held together by van der Waals forces. When the relative electronegativity difference between the constituent atoms is large, the resulting compounds contain ions and the principal force between the ions is coulombic. These substances are called ionic. The electrons are highly localized and seldom move from one ion to another.

At the opposite extreme—that of electron delocalization—are the metals. Metals result when atoms with many empty orbitals and small differences in electronegativity intermingle. The resulting systems often have many highly delocalized electrons.

IONS

High electrical conductivity in liquid compounds indicates the presence of charged molecules, or ions. Electrons in almost all liquid compounds are localized on individual molecules and translate through the liquid only as the whole molecule moves. Free electrons are found commonly only in liquid and crystalline metals. Ions are found in compounds containing elements of considerable difference in relative electronegativity; a difference greater than about 2 will give highly ionic compounds.

Ions may be monatomic in the liquid state, as are the positive ions of most of the metals in groups IA, IIA, and IIIA of the periodic table, and the simple halide ions of group VIIA. Monatomic oxide, $O^{=}$, and sulfide ions, $S^{=}$, may exist in some high temperature melts. But most ions exist as polyatomic ions. The ones most often met in beginning chemistry courses are nitrate ion, NO_3^-, carbonate ion, $CO_3^{=}$, perchlorate ion, ClO_4^-, sulfate ion, $SO_4^{=}$, chromate ion, $CrO_4^{=}$, hydroxide ion, OH^-, phosphate ion, $PO_4^{\equiv}$, and ammonium ion, NH_4^+. Hydrogen ion is also common and we have already discussed its probable state, at least in aqueous solutions, in Chapter 12. In other liquids, just as in aqueous solutions, simple hydrogen ions, H^+, do not exist at any appreciable concentration.

The above ions also make up most of the ionic crystals we shall deal with. You should memorize the names and formulas of these ions if you do not already know them. The periodic table can be most helpful here.

Ions differ in symmetry. Monatomic ions have spherical symmetry under most circumstances, but nitrates and carbonates are planar triangles, XY_3^{-n}; sulfate, chromate, phosphate, perchlorate, and ammonium ions are tetrahedral, $XY_4^{\pm n}$. Hydroxide ions are, of course, linear. The shape of the ions will influence the shape of the electric field around the ion and the magnitude of the interactions with other molecules will vary with direction. We shall deal here only with spherically symmetrical ions. From the arguments developed you will be able to extend the reasoning to ions of lower symmetry, at least qualitatively. Ionic symmetry can almost always be predicted from Gillespie's theory.

INTERIONIC FORCES

The electrical interactions between two spherical ions will follow Coulomb's law

$$U_{\text{ionic}} = -\frac{Q_1Q_2}{d}e^2 \tag{16.1}$$

where U is the potential energy, each Q refers to the number of electron charges on the respective ions, d is the internuclear distance, and e is the charge on an electron. Coulomb's law states that each ion will repel other ions of similar charge and attract those of opposite electrical charge. Both in gases, liquids, and crystals, ions of one charge tend to be coordinated to, or surrounded by, ions of opposite charge. Experimental evidence indicates that the repulsive forces between ions of opposite charge follow approximately the same relationship as that for neutral molecules:

$$U_{\text{rep}} = \frac{B}{d^n}$$

where n varies from about 9 to 12, with 12 common for monatomic ions. Thus the interaction between two ions of opposite charge is given by

$$U_{\text{to}} = \frac{B}{d^{12}} - \frac{Q_1Q_2}{d}e^2 \tag{16.2}$$

Comparison of Equation (16.2) with Equation (15.8) shows that appreciable interionic energies (proportional to d^{-1}) extend to greater distances than do those between electrically neutral molecules (energies proportional to d^{-6}). Interionic energies are relatively long-range interactions. (All our formulations so far have been in terms of potential energy. The force acting at any distance, d, is the rate of change of the potential energy at distance d: $F = dU/dd$.) Equation (16.2) describes quite accurately the bonding in such diatomic gases as NaCl, KBr, and CaO.

Figure 16.1 shows the potential energy of gaseous NaCl calculated from Equation (16.2), assuming completely ionic bonding. A potential energy curve is also shown based on calculations assuming *sp* orbital overlap between the sodium and chlorine to form Na—Cl, in which electrons are shared by orbitals on both atoms. The separated gaseous ions, Na^+ and Cl^-, are defined as having zero potential energy. Experimental evidence shows that the separated gaseous atoms, Na and Cl, are 31 kcal $mole^{-1}$ lower in energy than the ions (as shown in Figure 16.3). Thus, as the diagram shows, sodium chloride gas dissociates into neutral atoms, but the experimental molecular properties of gaseous diatomic NaCl agree with those calculated for a pair of adjacent ions, Na^+Cl^-, rather than a pair of atoms sharing an *sp* common orbital. At short distances the ions are the more stable pair. At long distances the neutral atoms are more stable.

Equation (16.2) fails to describe the behavior of ionic liquids and crystals. This failure is due to the long-range nature of interionic forces. In dilute diatomic gases one needs to consider only the interactions between pairs of atoms in a molecule, since other molecules are so far away. In liquids and crystals there are many other atoms within the 10 to 20 Å distance in which interionic forces are appreciable and many interionic interactions must be considered. These interactions will depend on the arrangement of the ions around one another. Not enough is known about ionic liquids to solve the problem mathematically. A great deal, however, is known about the arrangements of ions in crystals. Remember, for example, Figure 15.13, which shows the arrangements of the ions in the sodium chloride structures.

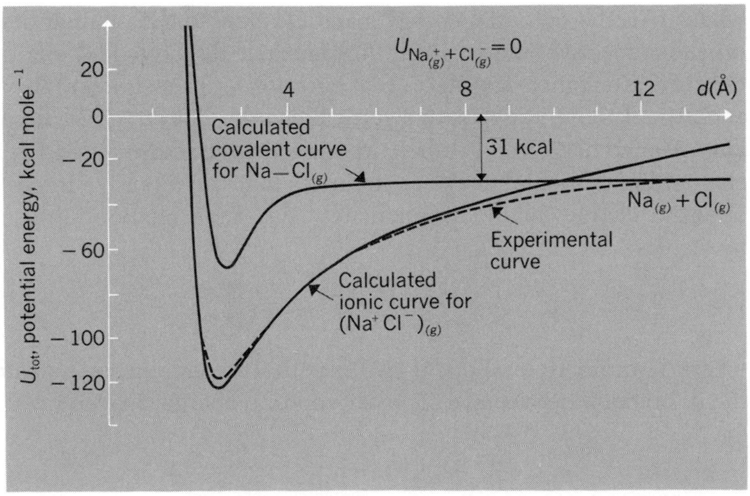

Figure 16.1 Potential energy for gaseous forms of NaCl as a function of internuclear distance. The calculated ionic curve is from Equation (16.2). Note that $NaCl_{(g)}$ dissociates into neutral atoms.

Exercise 16.1

What species will be most abundant in gaseous potassium chloride? *Answer:* Assume that relations are similar to those in NaCl. At low T, $KCl_{(g)}$ molecules will be most common, held together largely as ion pairs. At higher T, dissociation into $K_{(g)}$ and $Cl_{(g)}$ will occur, not into the ions. Thus, for example, gaseous KCl should be a poor electrical conductor at all T's.

MADELUNG CONSTANTS

In crystals it is possible to sum over the interionic coulombic attractions and repulsions. For cubic crystals—that is, crystals which can be considered to be composed of a large number of cubes of identical atomic composition and symmetry—the resulting formula is quite simple, and is called the

MADELUNG EQUATION:

$$\overline{U}_{\text{tot}} = \frac{N_0 M Q_1 Q_2 e^2}{d}\left(1 - \frac{1}{n}\right) \tag{16.3}$$

$\overline{U}_{\text{tot}}$ is the energy required to dissociate one mole of the crystal into gaseous ions, N_0 is Avogadro's number, Q_1, Q_2, and e have the same meaning as in Equation (16.1), n is the repulsive exponent (9 to 12), and d is the shortest distance between unlike nuclei in the crystal. M is a constant, originally calculated for many crystal types by Madelung* which depends only on the experimentally determined arrangement of ions in the crystal. Table 16.1 tabulates values of M for some common cubic structures.

Calculations based on Equation (16.3), using Madelung constants, experimental values of d, and values of n calculated from precise equations of state, agree well with values of crystal dissociation energies calculated in other ways. Our calculations for the diatomic gaseous molecules also afford good checks. This gives us confidence that the nature of bonding between ions is reasonably well understood. Only coulombic forces and the usual repulsive energies need be considered. There is little contribution from orbital overlap.

We should note, however, that all the ions we have discussed are composed of atoms which have achieved fully occupied orbitals. Some of the polyatomic ions are further stabilized by resonance. When we study crystals or liquids that might contain ions all of whose orbitals are not filled, we can expect to find bonding that arises from this fact. Thus ferric chloride, $FeCl_3$, and compounds of many other elements from the middle of the periodic table (where atoms with partly filled d orbitals are common) cannot be described in terms of ionic bonding involving only coulombic forces.

THE BORN-HABER CYCLE

Considerable insight into chemical reactions and into the forces acting in crystals can be obtained through breaking an over-all reaction down into separate steps, for each of which the energy is known. According to the first law of thermody-

---

* *Physikaliscle Zeitschrift,* 19, 524 (1918).

Table 16.1 Madelung constants for some common cubic crystals.

Crystal type	Madelung constant (M)	Crystal structure
NaCl (rock salt)	1.747558	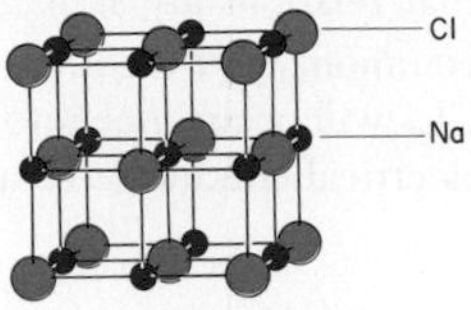
CsCl (cesium chloride)	1.762670	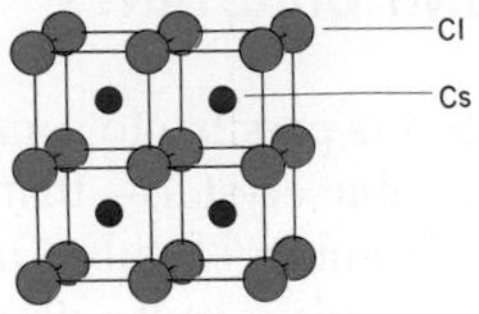
ZnS (sphalerite)	6.5221	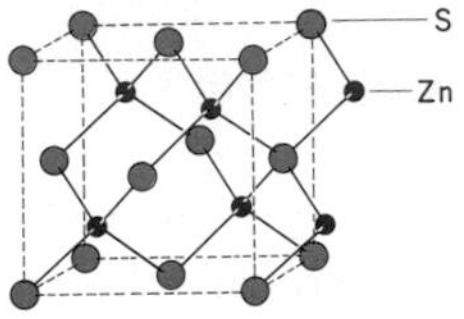
CaF_2 (fluorite)	5.03878	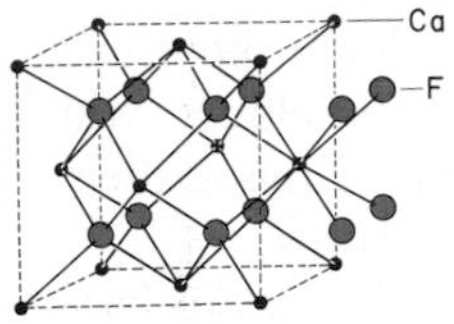
Cu_2O (cuprite)	4.3224	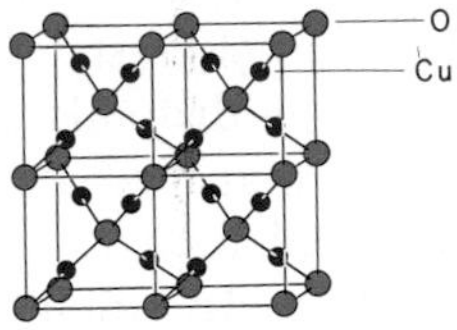

namics the energy change of a system is independent of the mechanism of the change. Thus the sum of the energies of a set of individual reactions will be the same as the energy of the over-all reaction accomplished through the individual steps.

Consider the reaction of an alkali metal, $M_{(c)}$, with a gaseous halogen, $X_{2(g)}$. The net reaction can be written

$$M_{(c)} + \tfrac{1}{2}X_{2(g)} = MX_{(c)}, \qquad \Delta H = \Delta H_{\text{formation }MX(c)} = \Delta H_f \tag{16.4}$$

Figure 16.2 shows ΔH_f for all the alkali halides. There is always a monotonic change in ΔH when the halide coupled with any given alkali is varied. But the changes are neither monotonic nor in the same direction when the halogen is kept constant and the alkali is varied. No single variable seems capable of accounting for the experimental trends in ΔH_f. The experimental evidence is overwhelming, however, that all these crystals are highly ionic. Let us apply the ionic bonding theory we have been discussing in an attempt to interpret these trends.

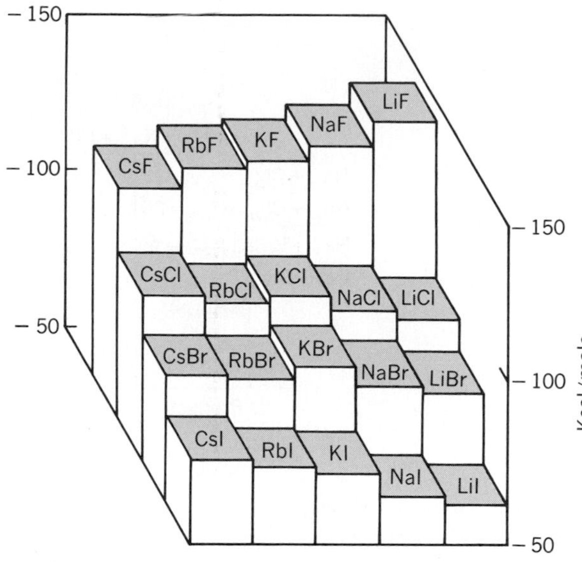

Figure 16.2 Standard enthalpies of formation for the alkali metal halides at 25°C and 1 atm. [Strong and Stratton, *Chemical Energy*, Reinhold, 1965.]

The net reaction in (16.4) is also the sum of the following possible steps.

	Reactions	*Process and energy*
1.	$M_{(c)} + \frac{1}{2}X_{2(g)} = M_{(c)} + X_{(g)}$	Dissociation of $X_{2(g)} = \frac{1}{2}D$
2.	$M_{(c)} + X_{(g)} = M_{(g)} + X_{(g)}$	Sublimation of $M_{(c)} = \Delta H_{subl}$
3.	$M_{(g)} + X_{(g)} = M^+_{(g)} + e^- + X_{(g)}$	Ionization of $M_{(g)} =$ I.E.
4.	$M^+_{(g)} + e^- + X_{(g)} = M^+_{(g)} + X^-_{(g)}$	Electron acquisition, by $X_{(g)} =$ E.A.
5.	$M^+_{(g)} + X^-_{(g)} = MX_{(c)}$	Condensation of gaseous ions to crystal $= -U_{tot}$
6.	Net: $M_{(c)} + \frac{1}{2}X_2 = MX_{(c)}$	Net $= \Delta H_f$

The Born-Haber equation, based on the first law of thermodynamics, is

$$U_{tot} = -\Delta H_f + \tfrac{1}{2}D + \Delta H_{subl} + \text{I.E.} + \text{E.A.} \qquad (16.5)$$

with appropriate concern for the sign of each energy term. Reactions 1, 2, and 3 are all endothermic. Reactions 4, 5, and 6 are all exothermic. Furthermore, the energy of reaction 6 is the sum of the energies of reactions 1, 2, 3, 4, and 5. We can represent these energy relationships as in Figure 16.3.

Figure 16.4 is a similar Born-Haber diagram for $CaO_{(c)}$. Note that there is a different scale, that U_{tot} is much larger than for $NaCl_{(c)}$, and that $O^- + e^- = O^=$ is strongly endothermic. Oxygen does not "want to gain two electrons to form $O^=$." Since CaO and NaCl have the same Madelung constants, Equation (16.3) predicts a ratio of U_{tot} of $2^2 \cdot d_{NaCl}/d_{CaO} = 4 \cdot 2.70/2.40 = 4.50$. The experimental ratio is $851/185 = 4.59$, a difference of only 2 percent.

Table 16.2 contains the energy terms for the Born-Haber cycles for some of the alkali halides. It also contains the crystal energies, U_{tot}, calculated from Equation (16.3). The close agreement, in spite of the complete independence of the two methods of calculation, gives us further confidence that we understand ionic bonding reasonably well.

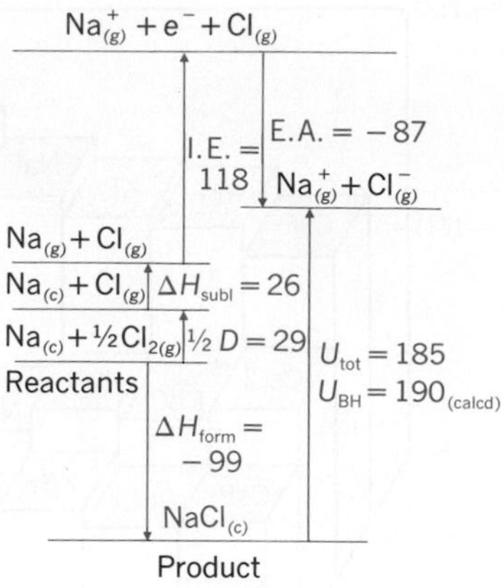

Figure 16.3 Born-Haber diagram for $Na_{(c)} + \frac{1}{2}Cl_{2(g)} = NaCl_{(c)}$. All energies given in kcal mole^{-1}. Note that the difference in ionic interaction, U_{tot}, between gas and crystal is the largest energy term.

Exercise 16.2

Comment on the phrase "sodium atoms want to lose electrons." *Answer:* The ionization energy of $Na_{(g)}$ is 118 kcal mole^{-1}, higher than the dissociation energy of most chemical bonds. Sodium clearly does *not* want to lose electrons. In general, the stability of ionic substances is due to the large coulombic forces that exist at small distances. Hence U_{tot} and the E.A. of the nonmetals are the principal sources of energy encouraging the formation of ionic substances.

COORDINATION NUMBERS IN IONIC COMPOUNDS

If monatomic ions interact primarily through a simple coulomb-type force, and if they are spherically symmetrical—both of which assumptions are consistent with the above treatment of ionic bonding—one might expect that the coordina-

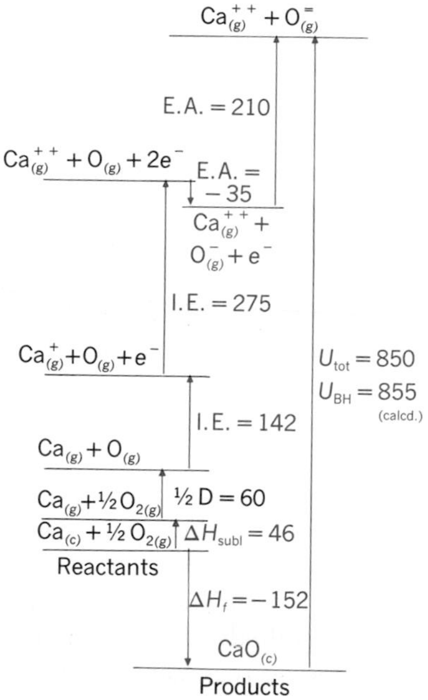

Figure 16.4 Born-Haber cycle for $Ca_{(c)} + \frac{1}{2}O_{2(g)} = CaO_{(c)}$. All energies in kcal mole^{-1}. Note that the acquisition of the second electron by oxygen ($O^- + e^- = O^=$) is a strongly endothermic process.

Table 16.2 The Born-Haber cycle. (Energy terms in kcal mole^{-1}.) Note the excellent agreement between the two values for all the alkali halides and the disparity for the silver halides, indicating, in the silver compounds, a fair amount of covalent bonding.

Crystal	$-\Delta H_f$	$\frac{1}{2}D$	ΔH_{subl}	I.E.	E.A.	U_{BH}	U_{calc}[a]	U_{London}	U_{tot}	Diff. $U_{calc} - U_{BH}$
LiF	146	18	37	124	−81	244	239	3	242	−2
LiCl	98	29	37	124	−87	201	192	7	199	−2
LiBr	87	23	37	124	−83	188	182	7	189	1
LiI	67	18	37	124	−71	175	170	6	176	1
KF	136	18	21	99	−81	192	189	3	192	0
KCl	104	29	21	99	−87	166	163	4	167	1
KBr	101	23	21	99	−83	161	157	4	161	0
KI	84	18	21	99	−71	151	148	4	152	1
CsF	128	18	19	90	−81	174	172	4	176	2
CsCl	102	29	19	90	−87	153	148	5	153	0
CsBr	99	23	19	90	−83	148	142	7	149	1
CsI	84	18	19	90	−71	140	135	7	142	2
AgF	55	18	61	174	−81	227	197	22	219	−8
AgCl	38	29	61	174	−87	215	175	28	203	−12
AgBr	38	23	61	174	−83	213	170	26	196	−17
AgI	28	18	61	174	−71	210	160	30	190	−20

[a] Calculated from Equation (16.3).

tion numbers observed in ionic crystals would be predictable from simple geometric considerations. In any ionic crystal each ion should be surrounded by ions of opposite electrical charge packed together as closely as possible. "As closely as possible" would be interpreted as ions of opposite charge being in contact, but ions of like charge out of contact. See Tables 14.5 and 14.6 and the accompanying discussion.

Positive ions result when atoms lose electrons. Thus positive ions are smaller than their parent atom. Negative ions, on the other hand, are larger than their parent atom, since each atom gains one or more electrons in forming negative ions. Thus, negative ions are generally larger than positive ions. It is, therefore, negative ions that are most likely to be in contact (since they occupy most of the volume of the crystal) and it is their packing we might consider first. The positive ions, being smaller, may be able to fit into the holes between the spherical negative ions.

The size of the hole left between tangent spheres depends on the number of spheres surrounding the hole and on the diameter of the spheres. However, the radius of the hole relative to the radius of the surrounding spheres is independent of the size of the spheres. Large tangential spheres give large holes, while smaller tangential spheres of the same packing give correspondingly smaller holes, as indicated in Figure 16.5.

The radius ratio of the hole to the surrounding spheres is related to the number of surrounding spheres and their type of packing, as shown in Table 16.3.

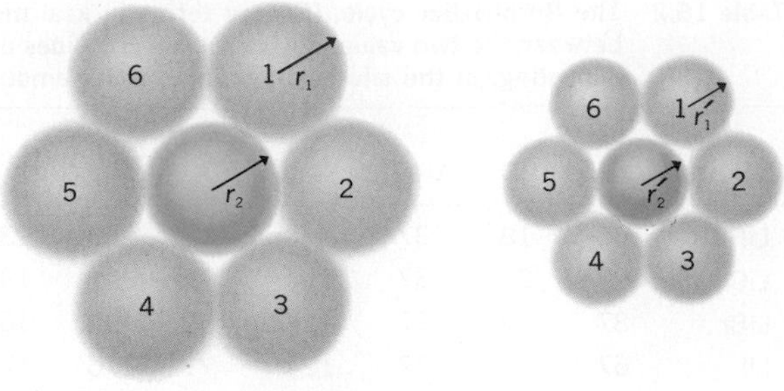

Figure 16.5 Six spheres of radius r_1 packed in a plane always leave a hole just large enough for a sphere of the same radius, $r_2 = r_1$. The radius ratio, $r_2/r_1 = 1$, for this packing.

If negative ions pack according to any of the structures outlined for the larger spheres in Table 16.3, we would predict that the smaller positive ions would have to give radius ratios slightly larger than those listed in Table 16.3 if the negative ions are to be kept out of contact. Tables 16.4 and 16.5, based on the radii of Figure 4.9, show some results for a few known structures. The correlation of observed radius ratios with the predictions is gratifying, and again confirms our confidence in present ideas concerning ionic bonding. Ionic bonds are primarily coulombic between electrically charged molecules, with little intermolecular overlapping of orbitals. Ionic bonds are nondirectional, the structure of the crystal being primarily determined by the radius ratio. In the case of polyatomic ions the symmetry of the ion will help determine the crystal structure.

FLOW IN IONIC CRYSTALS

Ionic crystals subjected to stress usually fracture. These fractures normally occur along planes parallel to the planes of ions and are attributed to the ionic repulsions that occur in the crystals if the ionic planes slip so that positive ions approach positive ions and negatives approach negatives. It is also possible, however, for ionic crystals to flow without fracture, as shown in Figure 16.6. Examination of Table

Table 16.3 Some common geometries.

Geometry of packing	trigonal plane	tetrahedral	octahedral	simple cubic	closest packed
Structure[a]	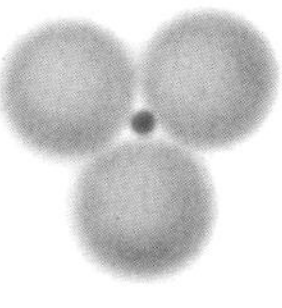	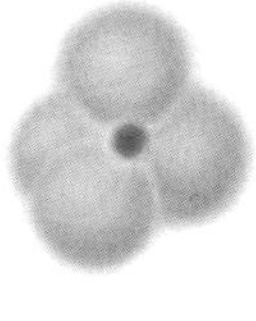	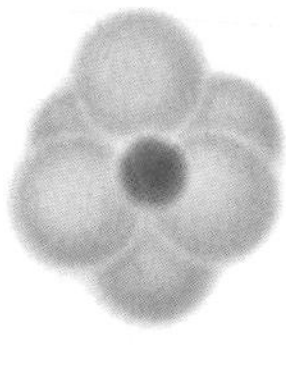	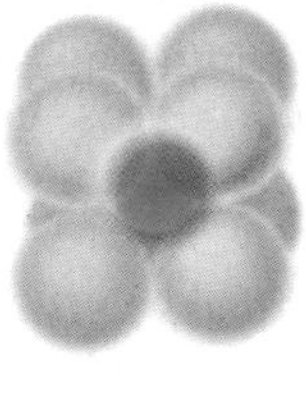	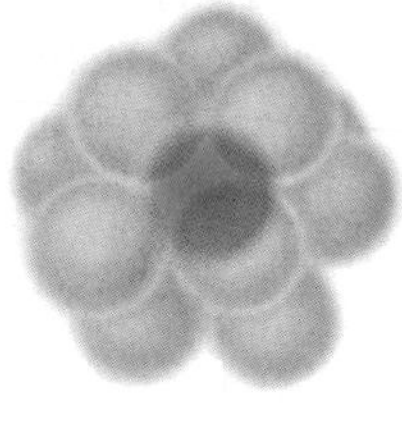
Coordination number	3	4	6	8	12
Radius ratio (hole/sphere)	0.155	0.225	0.414	0.732	1.000

[a] Note that the size of the hole increases as the coordination number around it increases.

Table 16.4 **Correlation of radius ratio with crystal structures. (See Figure 15.13 for NaCl, CsCl, and CaF_2 structures. The CaF_2 structure is like the CsCl structure but with half the cube centers empty of Ca^{++} ions.) Note that NaCl and CsCl structures are for one-to-one compounds, while rutile and fluorite are for two-to-one compounds. Note the small number of compounds which have radius ratios appreciably under the theoretical minimum in any class, or (except for the one-to-one NaCl type compounds) over the minimum for a class of higher *CN*. Most monatomic ionic crystals are halides or oxides, with a few sulfides.**

Crystal type	*CN* (negative around positive ions)	*CN* (positive around negative ions)	Predicted minimum radius ratio (r+/r−)	Substances and radius ratios				
Tetrahedral	4	2	0.225	GeO_2 0.38	SiO_2 0.29	BeF_2 0.23		
Sodium chloride	6	6	0.414	LiF 0.44	NaF 0.70	KF 0.97	RbF 1.09	CsF 1.24
				LiCl 0.33	NaCl 0.53	KCl 0.74	RbCl 0.82	CaO 0.71
				LiBr 0.31	NaBr 0.49	KBr 0.68	RbBr 0.76	SrS 0.61
				LiI 0.28	NaI 0.44	KI 0.62	RbI 0.68	BaO 0.96
Rutile (TiO_2)	6	3	0.414	MnO_2 0.40	SnO_2 0.51			
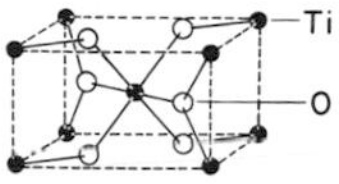				VO_2 0.43	MnF_2 0.51			
				MgF_2 0.47	ZnF_2 0.54			
				TiO_2 0.49	PbO_2 0.60			
Cesium chloride	8	8	0.732	CsCl 0.93				
				CsBr 0.87				
				CsI 0.78				
Fluorite (CaF_2)	8	4	0.732	ZrO_2 0.57	CaF_2 0.73	BaF_2 0.99		
				$SrCl_2$ 0.63	$BaCl_2$ 0.75			
				CuF_2 0.71	SrF_2 0.76			
				CdF_2 0.71	HgF_2 0.81			
				CeO_2 0.72	LaOF 0.83			

Table 16.5 **Coordination number (*CN*) of oxide ions around some cations as a function of the radius ratio. (Based on radius of $O^{=}$ ion = 1.40 Å.)**

Cation	(*r* Å)	Radius ratio	Theoretical *CN*	Observed *CN*
B^{+++}	(0.20)	0.14	3 or 4	3, 4
Be^{++}	(0.31)	0.22	4	4
Al^{+++}	(0.50)	0.36	4 or 6	4, 5, 6
Ti^{++++}	(0.68)	0.49	6	6
Zr^{++++}	(0.80)	0.57	6 or 8	6, 8
Na^{+}	(0.95)	0.68	6 or 8	6, 7, 8, 9, 10, 12
K^{+}	(1.33)	0.95	8 or 12	6, 8
Cs^{+}	(1.69)	1.2	12	12

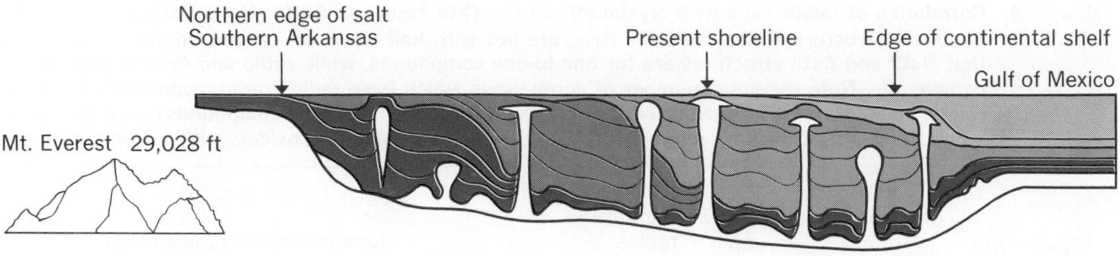

Figure 16.6 Flow in an ionic solid as indicated in the underground salt domes of the southern United States. Note height compared to Mt. Everest.

16.1 will show that there are ionic planes composed of only one kind of ion and that these planes are between other planes composed only of ions of the opposite charge. Stress applied slowly parallel to these planes leads to smooth flow without fracture.

BONDING IN METALS

We recognize metals by such bulk properties as luster, ductility, and electrical and thermal conductivity. Detailed structural studies show that most crystalline and liquid metals exhibit high coordination numbers (8 or greater), as shown in Figure 5.13. (A tentative model was presented in Figure 15.14.) Detailed studies also show that the unique properties we call metallic are directly related to the presence of delocalized electrons in condensed phases, either liquid or crystal. The electrons do not appear to remain attached to any atom or small group of atoms but rather to wander with little hindrance throughout the condensed phase.

Application of a small external electric field causes the delocalized electrons to have a net translational vector parallel to the field. Electrical conductivity occurs. Because the delocalized electrons are effective transmitters of kinetic energy, the metals are good thermal conductors, and because the delocalized electrons interact strongly with incident light, reflecting most of it, the metals are lustrous. The delocalized electrons are associated with relatively nondirectional bonding, and the atoms can thus flow rather readily from one equilibrium position to another, resulting in ductility. The variations in these properties from one metal to another correlate rather well with the degree of delocalization of the electrons.

Consider, for example, the alkali metals—Li, Na, K, Rb, and Cs. Each alkali metal can form diatomic molecules in the gaseous state, presumably by sharing *s* electrons to form a sigma bond by *s*—*s* overlap. But the crystal of each of these metals shows a coordination number of 8. They all crystallize in a body-centered cubic structure—like the cesium chloride structure of Figure 15.13 except that all the atoms are alike. The ductility is high, as are the electrical and thermal conductivities, the luster, and the chemical reactivity (in both the large amount of energy evolved and the high rate of reaction). The electrons in the condensed phases give every evidence of being highly delocalized.

There is also considerable evidence that there is only one delocalized electron available per atom in the crystal of each metal, and the condensed phase has many of the properties to be expected of a system of singly charged positive ions surrounded by a numerically equal sea of electrons. For example, the boiling points, melting points, and hardness of the alkali metals decrease in a regular fashion as one moves down the family from lithium to cesium. This would fit with the idea that the size of the positive ion is strongly determinative of the forces holding the condensed phase together. The small lithium ions would attract the surrounding electrons more strongly than would the large sodium ions, and so on down the family as the ionic size continues to increase. This leaves us with the interesting problem of how a single atom coordinates to eight others when there is only one available bonding electron per atom, and also raises the question why the coordination number is eight rather than some other number. For example, we might expect a coordination number of twelve, as is found in most of the metals. After all, this is the maximum number of spheres that will pack tangentially around a given identical sphere if no directional forces are involved.

The simplest model of bonding in metals available to us at this stage is the overlap of atomic orbitals that do not contain enough electrons to fill all the orbitals. The electrons would, then, move from orbital to orbital in a statistical fashion such that the average bond strength to each of the surrounding atoms was the same. We might remember that the alkali metals have a set of closely spaced s and p orbitals, so sp^3 hybridization might occur. The sp^3 hybrid orbitals would point toward four of the surrounding eight atoms, and the "tails" of the sp^3 hybrids would point toward the other four of the coordinated atoms. Thus a periodic simple inversion of the sp^3 hybrid pattern might account for the bonding to eight coordinated atoms arranged at the corners of a surrounding cube. The exchange of electrons from one atom to another would account for the delocalization, at least qualitatively. The coordination number of 8, rather than 12, would be justified by arguing that a total of eight bonds (involving sp^3 hybrids having an average of only one electron per atom) would be stronger than a total of twelve bonds required by close packing (but still having only one electron available per atom and hence somewhat weaker). This argument, which is not too tortured, would then account for the more common coordination number of 12 when the number of valence electrons increased, as in the alkaline earth family—Be, Mg, Ca, Sr, Ba, Ra. Of course, the vanadium and chromium families and iron (see Figure 5.13), with their $CN = 8$, cause problems.

Such a model, which explains bonding in metals in terms of overlap of atomic orbitals populated by delocalized electrons, is simple and accounts qualitatively for many experimental observations. But there are a great many experimental properties that the model does not handle, and there are other models that are more successful than the valence-bond model. We shall explore some of these later after accumulating more experimental information and a firmer base for different theoretical approaches. One of the fundamental problems is that LCAO-VB is not highly successful in systems having delocalized electrons. We ran into a similar problem in hybridization and in resonance systems, where additional ad hoc assumptions had to be added to atomic orbital theory to fit the experimental facts. Perhaps it would pay to look at the problem of bonding in condensed phases, or even in large molecules, from another point of view. One such view is that of molecular orbitals, which we shall discuss in the next chapter.

SUMMARY

Ionic bonds can be interpreted in terms of Coulomb's law, which describes the forces between electrically charged particles (here charged atoms and molecules that retain their own localized electrons). Metallic bonds are characteristic of phases in which there are many delocalized electrons—electrons which can move throughout the phase with relative freedom.

The monuments of wit survive the monuments of power.
—*Francis Bacon,* Essex's Device (1595).

PROBLEMS

16.1. Use a Born-Haber cycle approach to estimate ΔH_f for NaF. ΔH_{subl} for Na is 26 kcal mole^{-1}. The experimental value of ΔH_f is -136 ncal mole^{-1}. Use the experimental value of U_{BH} to calculate a value of n, the repulsive exponent, for the crystal. ($n \cong 7$.)

16.2. Gaseous NaF and Ne_2 are isoelectronic. Account for the fact that one is stable at room temperature and the other not.

16.3. What is the probable state, shape, and valence electron distribution in each of the following at room temperature: H_2Se, SiC, CaC_2, XeF_6, $Fe(CO)_5$, FrF, InAs, $Hg_2{}^{++}{}_{(aq)}$, $NO_2{}^-{}_{(aq)}$, SO_2, SO_3, N_2O, NO_2, Cl_2O, ClO_2.

16.4. Will the elements of atomic number 12 and 17 form a compound? Will it be ionic or covalent? Show how a possible formula may be deduced from the electron structures. If any oxidation-reduction is involved, point it out.

16.5. Elements A, B, C have atomic numbers of 4, 9, and 18 and weights of 9, 19, and 40, respectively. (*a*) Indicate as much as possible about the structure of the atoms. (*b*) Classify the elements as nonmetals or metals. (*c*) Give the formulas of any substances they may form among themselves and tell whether these molecules are ionic, polar, or nonpolar.

16.6. (*a*) Make a comparison between a solid metallic oxide such as CaO and a solid nonmetallic oxide such as H_2O (ice) as to melting point, hardness, and density. (*b*) Show how one may interpret these differences in properties with the aid of rough structural diagrams (plus a little discussion).

II

16.7. Which of the following substances would be largely covalent and which largely ionic in the crystalline state? Give formulas of the species you would expect to find in the crystal; for example, $NaNO_{3(c)}$ would contain Na^+ and covalent $NO_3{}^-$ ions. XeF_4, F_2O, SrF_2, YCl_3, $SiBr_4$, PBr_3, BaO, $(CH_3)_2SO_4$, Li_2SO_4, $C_2H_5ONO_2$, $NaONO_2$, $NOCl_2$.

16.8. PCl_5 occurs in the gas and liquid as PCl_5 molecules, in the crystal as PCl_4^+ and PCl_6^-. Why is the ionic crystal more stable energetically than the PCl_5 crystal?

16.9. Which would have the higher vapor pressure at 500°C, NaCl or CaO? Which has the higher melting point, RbBr or BaS? SrO or SrS?

16.10. Are the bonds in the gaseous diatomic molecule RbF (rubidium fluoride) best described as ionic, or covalent? Would the products of thermal dissociation be Rb and F, or Rb^+ and F^-?

16.11. CaF_2 is a crystalline macromolecule that involves the packing of Ca^{++} and F^- ions. The fluoride ions have four neighboring Ca^{++} ions in a tetrahedral arrangement. How many F^- ions must be around each of the calcium ions to account for the observed stoichiometry?

III

16.12. Estimate the internuclear distance in NaCl *(c)* whose density is 2.16 g ml^{-1}. Compare the accepted value.

16.13. Estimate from Coulomb's law the bond energy in $NaCl_{(g)}$ (about 120 kcal mole^{-1}). Estimate the heat of vaporization of $NaCl_{(s)} \longrightarrow NaCl_{(g)}$ (about 70 kcal mole^{-1}). Compare ΔH_{vap} to U_{BH} for NaCl. Use these data to comment on the composition of gaseous NaCl as a function of *T*.

16.14. Use Coulomb's law to calculate *D* for $CaO_{(g)}$. ($D \cong 700$ kcal mole^{-1}.) The *IR* spectrum of the gas indicates $d = 1.822$ Å. Now calculate ΔH for the process $CaO_{(c)} = CaO_{(g)}$. ($\Delta H_{vap} \cong 130$ kcal.) Compare to the same value for NaCl (Problem 16.13). Compare U_{tot} for CaO and NaCl. Comment on these two comparisons.

16.15. Rationalize the melting points *(a)* and boiling points *(b)* of the alkali halides in terms of the forces acting.

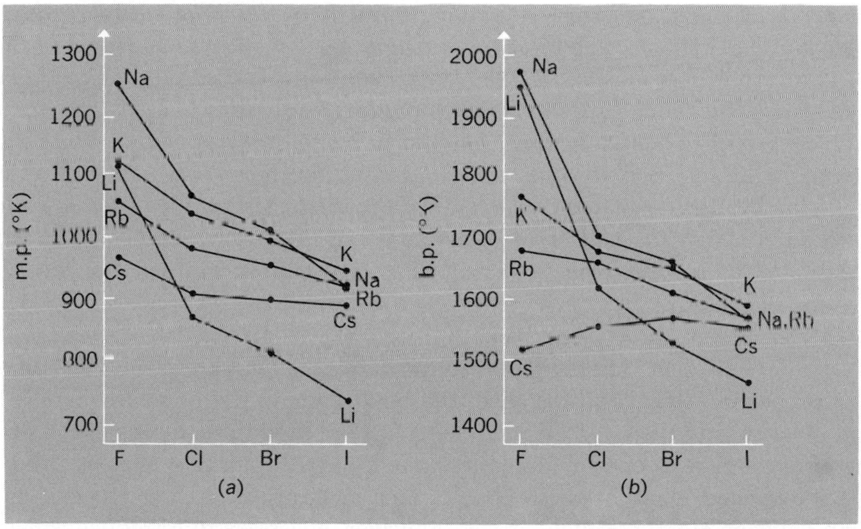

See page 1092 for a list of references and readings in the recent chemical literature related to the material in this chapter.

CHAPTER **17**

Chemical Bonding—Delocalized Electrons

When two or more theories can be applied to the description of a given phenomenon, the simpler one is usually tried first, even though the user knows there is another more exact theory available.

With due acknowledgment to G. B. Shaw for the inspiration, it might be said that theories of chemical bonding—neglecting not a few which are entirely valueless—fall into one of two categories: those which are too good to be true and those which are too true to be good. "True" in this context is intended to mean "having physical validity" and "good" to mean "providing useful results, especially quantitative ones, with a relatively small amount of computational effort." The proper, rigorous wave equation for any molecular situation represents a theory of that situation which is too true to be good. Most theories which are too good to be true are those in which the real problem per se is not treated, but rather an artificial analogue to the real problem, contrived so as to make the mathematics tractable, is set up and solved.—F. ALBERT COTTON (1964)

We have seen that the forces acting between atoms are related to—among other properties—the bond distance, the bond energy, the bond frequency, the bond polarity, and the bond angles. We have attributed these forces to the simultaneous attraction of one or more electrons by more than one nucleus. And we have interpreted many of these observations in terms of the overlap and interaction between atomic orbitals. It was, however, necessary to introduce concepts like hybridization, resonance, and delocalization of electrons in order to allow the concept of atomic orbitals to become broad enough to account for the experimental observations.

In this chapter we shall investigate some other methods of describing chemical bonding. These methods will utilize the ideas of atomic orbitals, but will consider more explicitly the effect on the electronic energy levels when atoms pack closely together.

MOLECULAR IONIZATION ENERGIES

Great insight into atomic orbitals came from studying the ionization energies of atoms (see Chapter 3). Ionization energies of molecules can also be studied, as can the effect which ionization has on bond energies, distances, and frequencies. Unfortunately there are few data on the ionization energies of gaseous molecules. The first ionization energy of some molecules has been measured but for only a very few has the second ionization energy been measured, and no measurements appear to have been made on the higher ionization energies. Thus we are limited to comparing bond properties of the un-ionized molecules with those of the corresponding singly ionized molecule.

Before we look at the data available, let us consider the general problem, and especially the relationship between the ionization energies of atoms and of diatomic molecules. Consider the following series of steps, all referring to gaseous species.

	$AB = AB^+ + e^-$	ionization of molecule	I.E.(AB)
	$AB^+ = A + B^+$	bond breaking in molecular ion	$D(AB^+)$
	$B^+ + e^- = B$	electron capture by atomic ion	$-$I.E.(B)
Sum:	$AB = A + B$	bond breaking in molecule	D(AB)

Thus

$$D(AB) = D(AB^+) + \text{I.E.}(AB) - \text{I.E.}(B)$$

or

$$D(AB) - D(AB^+) = \text{I.E.}(AB) - \text{I.E.}(B) \tag{17.1}$$

This relationship is summarized in Figure 17.1. Remember that all species are gaseous. Note too that this assumes that AB^+ decomposes into A and B^+ (not A^+ and B). Only experiment can show which way a heteronuclear molecule actually does decompose most readily. If A and B are identical (homonuclear molecules), no ambiguity arises.

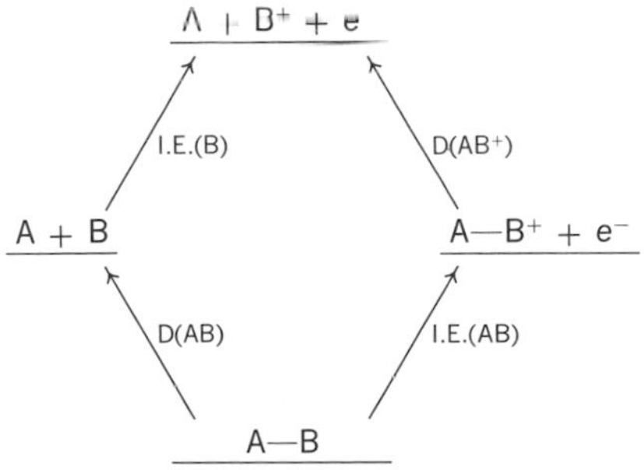

Figure 17.1 Relationship between ionization energy of a diatomic molecule and the bond strengths in the neutral and ionized molecule. We assume that all species are in their ground states.

Equation (17.1) states that, if the ionization energy of the diatomic molecule exceeds the ionization energy of the atom (remember this refers to the atom which actually becomes the positive ion when the molecular ion dissociates), then the bond in the neutral diatomic molecule is stronger than the bond in the molecular ion. If the ionization energy of the diatomic neutral molecule is smaller than that of the neutral atom, then the bond in the neutral molecule must be weaker than that in the molecular ion. Molecules in which this occurs contain antibonding electrons—that is, electrons which diminish the bond strength of the molecule. Table 17.1 gives some experimental data.

The compounds in Table 17.1 may be separated into three groups: (1) those whose A—B bond strength weakens considerably upon ionization (H_2, N_2, CO), (2) those whose bond strength increases appreciably upon ionization (He_2, O_2, F_2, Cl_2, Br_2, I_2, NO), and (3) those whose bond strength is little changed by ionization (HC, HO, HCl, HBr, HI). We could list OH as doubtful as to category, but have placed it with the other bonds to H.

We would expect that bond strengthening would be accompanied by bond shortening. This happens in the four molecules in Table 17.1 for which data are available (He_2, O_2, Cl_2, and NO). Similar shortening will almost certainly be found in halogen ions such as F_2^+ (compared to F_2). In all the other molecules the bond is longer in the ion, except for CO, in which a shortening from 1.128 to 1.115 has been observed. This shortening of 0.013 Å is considerably less than that observed when the bond strength increases.

Apparently the molecules in group I lose bonding electrons when ionized, those in group II lose antibonding electrons, and those in group III lose electrons that have little effect on the bonding—essentially nonbonding electrons. We shall treat these experimental observations as operational definitions of these three types of electrons.

Table 17.1 Bond and ionization energies (kcal mole^{-1}) in diatomic molecules.

	AB	*D(AB)*	I.E. (*B*)	I.E. (*AB*)	$D(AB^+)$ [to give $A + B^+$]	$D(AB) - D(AB^+)$	d_{AB} (Å)	d_{AB^+} (Å)
I	H_2	104	314	< 356	62	42	0.741	< 1.06
	N_2	226	335	< 360	200	26	1.098	≅ 1.117
	CO	257	260	< 323	194	63	1.128	≅ 1.115
II	He_2	0.01	567	> 517	50	−50	2.92	> 1.08
	O_2	119	314	> 279	168	−49	1.207	> 1.123
	F_2	38	402	> 380(?)	>60	>−22	1.418	
	Cl_2	58	300	> 265	93	−35	1.988	> 1.891
	Br_2	46	275	> 245	74	−32	2.284	
	I_2	36	243	> 214	65	−29	2.667	
	NO	151	314	> 214	251	100	1.150	> 1.062
III	HC	81	260	≅ 256	85	−4		
	HO	102	314	≅ 298(?)	118(?)	−16	0.971	
	HCl	103	300	≅ 294	109	−6	1.274	< 1.315
	HBr	88	275	≅ 269	94	−6	1.408	< 1.448
	HI	71	243	≅ 240	74	−3	1.609	

It is interesting to recall valence bond theory here. It could have accounted for the bonding and nonbonding electrons, but it made no provision for antibonding electrons.

SEPARATED AND UNITED ATOMS

Consider for a moment a process that might occur were two separate atoms brought closer and closer together. At very large distances the atoms would be essentially independent of one another. The atomic orbitals in each atom would depend only on its own nuclear charge and its own electron content. As the atoms approached, their electric fields would begin to interact. The atomic orbitals would be split and their energies would shift. If the atoms were brought still closer together, the splitting would increase. Finally, were the atoms to unite, the two separate nuclei would become one nucleus and the electrons would be found in a set of orbitals characteristic of the new nucleus and its surrounding electrons.

There seems to be no reason for the occurrence of any discontinuities in this fusion process of two separated atoms. It then follows that the atomic orbitals of the separated atoms must undergo a continuous transformation into the atomic orbitals of the united atom. Our problem is to trace this continuous process for each orbital.

The fusion process would probably be simplest if the two separated atoms were homonuclear. In such a case the electric field would retain cylindrical symmetry at all times and each set of atomic orbitals would be perturbed in an identical fashion at any given distance.

Fusion of two heteronuclear atoms would lead to fields which were circularly symmetrical about the bond axis, but the two nuclei would generate different fields at either end of the bond. This lowers the symmetry compared to the homonuclear case, and, of course, complicates the mathematical treatment.

The orbitals that exist in the stages intermediate between the two separated atoms and the final state of the united atom are called molecular orbitals. Their properties will depend on the fields of both nuclei—not that of just one nucleus as atomic orbitals do.

HOMONUCLEAR MOLECULAR ORBITALS

Application of quantum mechanics and symmetry theory has led, in the hands of Robert Mulliken and others, to a theoretical treatment of the fusion process. The theoretical results are usually summarized in a correlation diagram. A schematic correlation diagram for the homonuclear case is given in Figure 17.2 for the molecular orbital, MO, theory.

Note that all the curved lines traversing the diagram are continuous and have no maxima or minima. The molecular orbitals lying on the downward sloping (right to left) lines are more stable than the atomic orbitals from which they come—they are bonding molecular orbitals. The molecular orbitals lying on the upward sloping (right to left) lines are less stable than the atomic orbitals from which they come—they are antibonding molecular orbitals identified by stars (*). Molecular

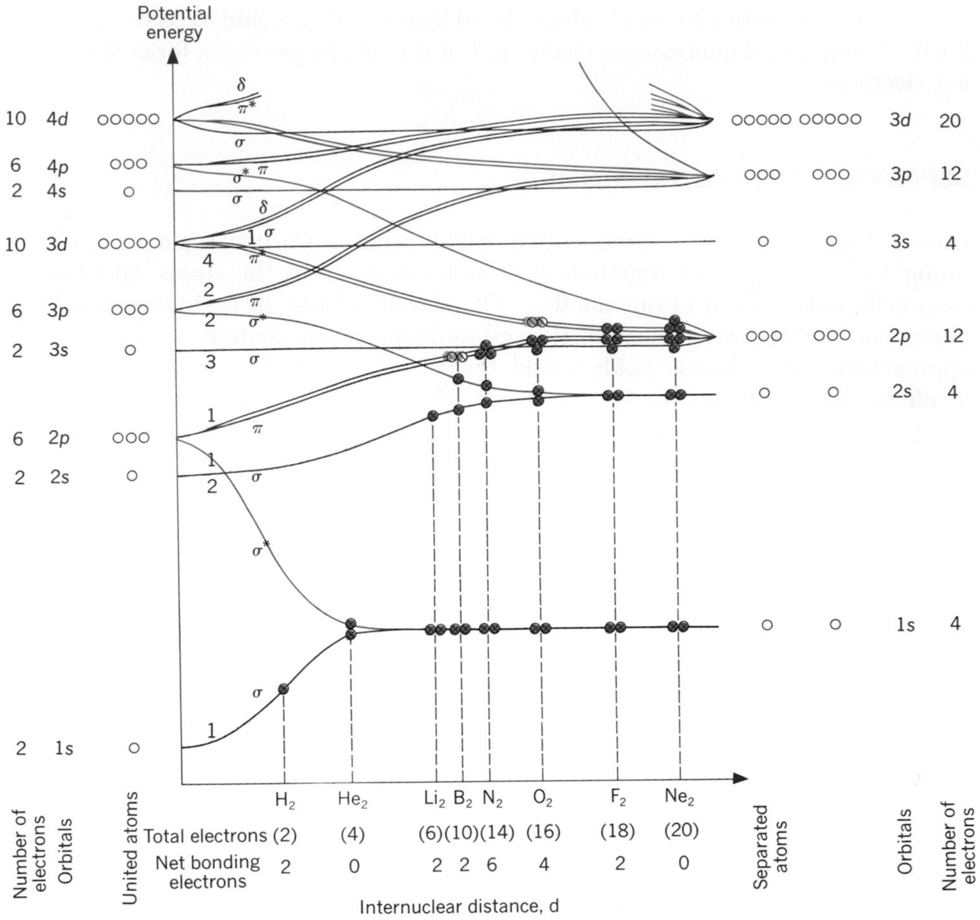

Figure 17.2 Homonuclear correlation diagram. Schematic representation of variation of molecular orbital energy with internuclear distance for homonuclear (A_2) diatomic molecules. The variation with nuclear charge is not shown. The molecular orbital electron structures for some homonuclear diatomic molecules are indicated. Molecular orbitals are indicated as σ, π, and δ, containing 2, 4, and 4 electrons per set, respectively, and differing in symmetry. The asterisks indicate antibonding orbitals. Note that the d scale is far from linear, being increasingly compressed as one moves from left to right.

orbitals are nonbonding when they lie on a line of no slope. Each molecular orbital can hold zero, one, or two electrons.

Here are some of the generalizations that may be made about Figure 17.2.

1. Every set of orbitals in the separated atoms splits into an equal number of bonding and antibonding orbitals.
2. The s orbitals in the united atom come by way of a bonding molecular orbital from a single orbital in the separated atoms.
3. The p orbitals in the combined atom come by way of an antibonding σ orbital and a bonding pair of π orbitals from two separate sets of orbitals in the separated atoms.
4. The d orbitals in the united atom come from three separate sets of orbitals in the separated atoms by way of three separate molecular orbitals. One

of these is almost nonbonding, another is strongly antibonding, and the third is strongly bonding.

5. The σ molecular orbitals occur singly and can hold, of course, up to two electrons each. The π orbitals come in sets of two, thus holding a total of four electrons. The δ orbitals come in sets of two and can also hold a total of four electrons per set. (We shall not discuss δ orbitals further.)
6. Low-lying orbitals, such as 1*s*, do not split as readily as higher orbitals. They deviate from simple atomic orbitals only at small internuclear distances.
7. There is considerable crossing of molecular orbitals at intermediate distances, but not much at distances corresponding to very small or very large internuclear separations.

Observations 6 and 7 are quite comparable to similar observations already made in Chapter 3 about atomic orbitals.

Figure 17.2 also shows the molecular orbital electron structure for several diatomic molecules. A circle with crossed strokes indicates a full molecular orbital. A circle with one slant stroke, like that for O_2, indicates a half-filled molecular orbital.

The correlation diagram in Figure 17.2 accounts for all the experimental observations on homonuclear molecules summarized in Table 17.1. He_2 is an unstable molecule (bond energy of 0.01 kcal mole^{-1}), since it has an equal number of bonding and antibonding electrons. All the other homonuclear molecules (H_2, N_2, O_2, F_2, Cl_2, Br_2, I_2) are stable, since they have more electrons in bonding molecular orbitals than in nonbonding molecular orbitals. Thus, each of these represents a system of lower total energy than the corresponding separated atoms. The decreasing bond energy upon ionization of H_2 and N_2 is consistent with Figure 17.2, which indicates that their highest energy electrons are bonding electrons. The increasing bond energy upon ionization of He_2, O_2, F_2, and the rest of the halogens is consistent with the indication in Figure 17.2 that all of these have their highest energy electrons in antibonding orbitals (assuming the other halogens have an orbital pattern similar to that of fluorine). We can also predict that Ne_2^+ should be more stable than Ne_2, as shown in the diagram.

A particularly interesting feature of the correlation diagram is brought out if we examine the predicted electron structure of O_2. The two highest energy electrons are indicated as being in a π^* (read "pi star") set of orbitals. The π^* orbitals can hold four electrons, two in each of the orbitals. But O_2 has only two electrons in this set of orbitals. If molecular energy levels behave as do atomic orbitals, each of the two π^* orbitals should hold only one electron; furthermore, these two electrons should be unpaired. Experimental work shows that molecular oxygen does indeed contain two unpaired electrons per molecule in the ground electronic state. This correlation is one of the greatest triumphs of the molecular orbital theory, since simple valence bond theory predicts an incorrect structure in this case. $\langle O{=}O \rangle$, with all electrons paired, rather than a structure in which there are unpaired electrons, as found experimentally.

The structure of molecular oxygen is sometimes represented as in the central section of Figure 17.3. The synthesis of these molecular orbitals from the separated atomic orbitals is also indicated (compare with Figure 17.2).

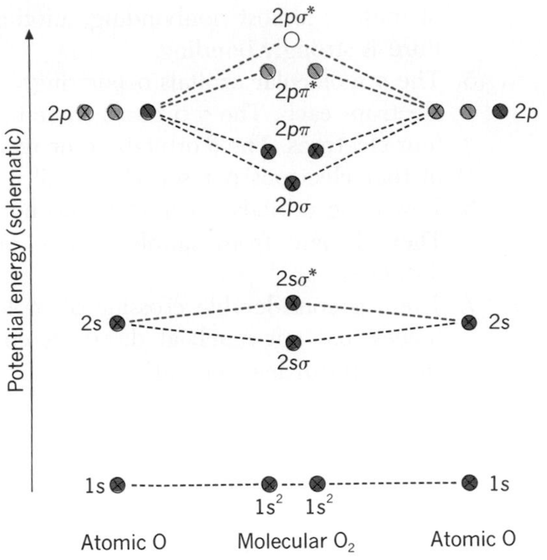

Figure 17.3 Molecular orbital electron structure of oxygen, O_2, and its relation to the atomic orbitals in monatomic oxygen, O. Note that there is a net of four bonding electrons in O_2 and that the two most energetic antibonding electrons are unpaired. Note also the system by which molecular orbitals are identified. Consider the uppermost one shown: the source atomic orbital (2*p*); the symmetry of the molecular orbital (σ); whether the molecular orbital is bonding or antibonding (*). Total symbol, $2p\sigma^*$. Finally, note that the 1s electrons remain in essentially atomic orbitals even in molecular O_2.

The ions O_2^- and $O_2^=$ are also known, and their properties have been measured in crystalline compounds such as KO_2 and Na_2O_2. The internuclear distances are 1.28 and 1.49 Å, respectively. Presumably the additional electrons (compared to O_2, $d = 1.208$ Å) are entering the $2p\pi^*$ orbitals, are acting as antibonding electrons, and lead to the continuous lengthening of the bond.

Figure 17.4 shows some electron density maps for molecular orbitals similar to those of Figures 4.1 to 4.5 for atomic orbitals. Note the strong overlap found in bonding orbitals, and the repulsions (indicated by contour crowding) in antibonding orbitals.

Exercise 17.1

Which would have the longer bond: N_2 or N_2^+, F_2 or F_2^+? *Answer:* According to Figure 17.2, N_2 loses a bonding electron in forming N_2^+; its bond should lengthen. F_2 loses an antibonding electron in forming F_2^+; its bond should shorten (see Table 17.1).

HETERONUCLEAR MOLECULAR ORBITALS

The calculation of the molecular orbitals for heteronuclear bonding is considerably more difficult than for homonuclear bonding, since electric field asymmetry along the bond axis must be considered. Figure 17.5 is a schematic representation of a heteronuclear correlation diagram. The atomic orbitals of similar quantum number in the separated atoms are no longer at the same energy, and the transitions to the atomic orbitals of the united atom follow paths different from those found with homonuclear molecules. These paths are actually a function of the nuclear charges of the two atoms but the diagram in Figure 17.5 is satisfactory for many of the bonds between elements of nuclear charge 5 to 10.

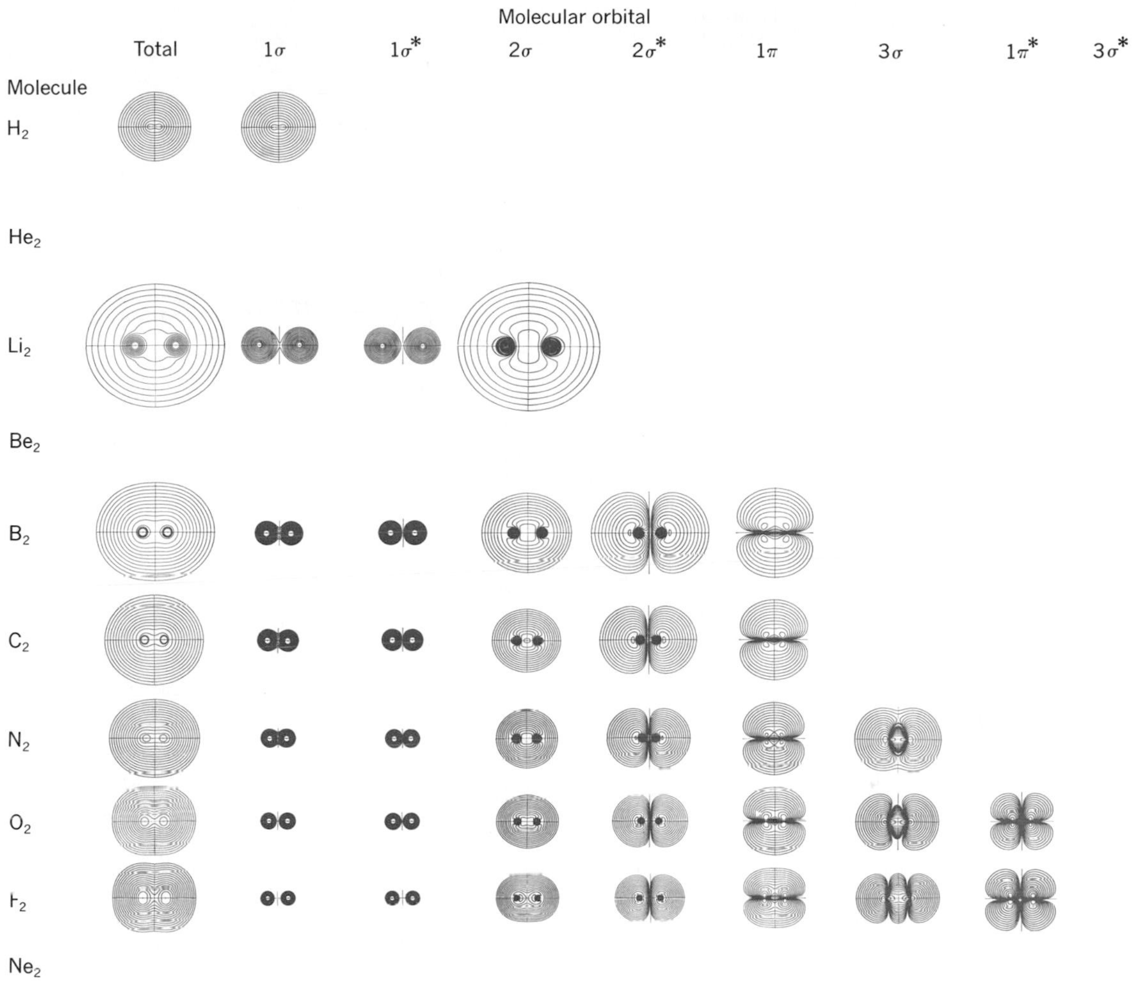

Figure 17.4 The shell model of molecules. This chart consists of contour diagrams of the electron densities characteristic of the shell model of the molecules H_2, Li_2, B_2, C_2, N_2, O_2, and F_2. Both the total molecular density and the constituent shell densities are displayed at the experimental internuclear distance of each molecule. (He_2, Be_2, and Ne_2, which are members of this homonuclear series, are not bound in their ground state and are not displayed.) [A. C. Wahl, *Science*, **151**, 961 (1966). Copyright 1966 by the American Association for the Advancement of Science.]

Molecular orbital assignments are shown for CO and NO. CO has a net sum of six bonding electrons, accounting for its very strong bond, short internuclear distance, and high bond frequency.

Molecular NO has an odd number of electrons per molecule, 11. Thus, at least one of these must be unpaired. The molecular orbital diagram indicates that only one should be unpaired. This is found to be consistent with the experimental data. NO has a net sum of five bonding electrons, accounting for the fact that its bond is weaker, longer, and of lower vibrational frequency than that in CO. The fact that the highest energy electron is an antibonding electron also accounts for the increase in bond strength upon ionization of NO. The bond in NO^+ (250 kcal

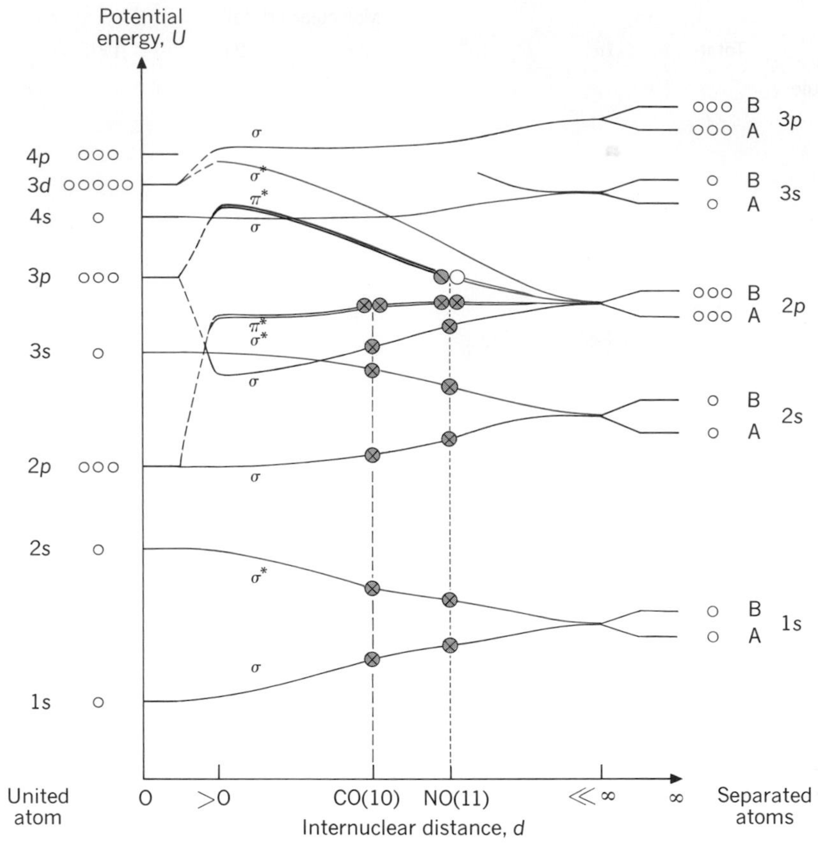

Figure 17.5 Heteronuclear correlation diagram. Schematic representation of variation of molecular orbital energy with internuclear distance for heteronuclear (AB) diatomic molecules. The variation with nuclear charge is not shown. The molecular orbital electron structures for CO and NO are indicated, as well as their total number of electrons (14 and 15).

mole^{-1}) is isoelectronic with that in CO (257 kcal mole^{-1}), accounting for the very similar bond properties found experimentally in these two molecules. Note that N_2 is also isoelectronic with CO and NO^+ (except that N_2 is homonuclear), and that the bonding properties in N_2 are remarkably similar to those in CO and NO^+. The molecules will, of course, differ chemically because of their differing polarity and the difference in the atomic orbitals of the separated atoms. Table 17.2 compares some properties of these isoelectronic substances.

Table 17.2 Comparison of some properties of several isoelectronic molecules. Note the great similarities of the properties; their differences are consistent with differences in nuclear charges and polarity of the bond.

	D (kcal mole^{-1})	d (Å)	ν (10^{13} sec^{-1})	μ (Debyes)	α (Å^3)	$T_{\text{b.p.}}$ (°K)	a $\left(\frac{l^2 \text{ atm}}{\text{mole}^2}\right)$	Solubility in H_2O, 0°C (cm^3/l)
N_2	226	1.098	7.00	0	1.79	77.3	1.39	23.3
CO	257	1.128	6.50	0.13	1.99	82.0	1.49	35
NO^+	251	1.062	—	—	—	—	—	

Figure 17.5 accounts very satisfactorily for the changes in properties in the sequence CN^+, CN, CN^- with bond distances of 1.1727, 1.1718, and 1.15, respectively (the first two measured in the gas phase, the last one in crystalline LiCN and the gaseous halogen cyanides, XCN). Note that CN is also isoelectronic with N_2 and the other molecules in Table 17.2.

π ORBITAL OVERLAP

Since 1950 chemists have synthesized a rapidly increasing number of compounds in which π bonds in a stable molecule form further bonds to other atoms or molecules. Two outstanding examples are the π-bonded complexes made from benzene and its derivatives or related compounds, and those made from cyclopentadiene, C_5H_6, when it is converted into the cyclopentadienyl ion, $C_5H_5^-$. Figure 17.6 illustrates some of these structures, and the molecular orbital picture of benzene and the cyclopentadienyl ion.

The silver perchlorate-benzene addition compound and ferrocene can be interpreted by theorizing that electrons in π orbitals are not very tightly held to their "own" molecule. After all, the electrons are in orbitals that extend considerably above and below the plane of atoms formed by the benzene and cyclopentadienyl rings. These loosely held electrons can interact strongly with the positive silver ion or doubly positive iron ion, leading to bond formation.

The trinitrobenzene-anthracene addition compound can be interpreted in very similar terms if we remember that oxygen is a much more electronegative element than nitrogen, carbon, or hydrogen. Thus, the NO_2 groups will tend to drain electrons out of the π system of their benzene ring, leaving it relatively electron-deficient. This electron-deficient set of π orbitals can then interact with the full π orbitals of the anthracene to give net attraction or bonding.

The π orbital overlap between molecules can thus account for the occurrence of all these interactions. Most of the other known π compounds, like those illustrated in Figure 17.6, are made up of alternating π systems: one system tends to donate electrons to the intermolecular bond, the other tends to accept electrons from the π donor. The alternating structure of these compounds suggests their common name—sandwich compounds.

Some other compounds very similar to ferrocene are $(C_5H_5)_2M$ (where M can be Ni, Co, Cr, V, Ru), C_5H_5NiNO (where the cyclopentadienyl ion is on one side of the nickel atom and the NO group occupies the opposite side), and C_5H_5Tl (the compound with Tl^+ ion).

The details of the bonding in sandwich compounds is not yet known. It is rather well established that the two rings in ferrocene are rotating freely around the axis through the iron and perpendicular to the rings, at least at room temperature. Thus π overlap does not necessarily lead to strongly directional bonding. This might be expected from the circular symmetry of the π orbitals involved in the bonding and from the highly delocalized electrons in the π bonds.

It is possible that π overlap is an important source of bonding in some biological systems—remember our discussion of hydrogen bonding. The bond strengths (1–10 kcal $mole^{-1}$) are about right but the bonds are generally not as highly directional as hydrogen bonds and do not normally lead to such highly

Name	Formula	Suggested orbital structure	Shorthand structure
Benzene	C_6H_6	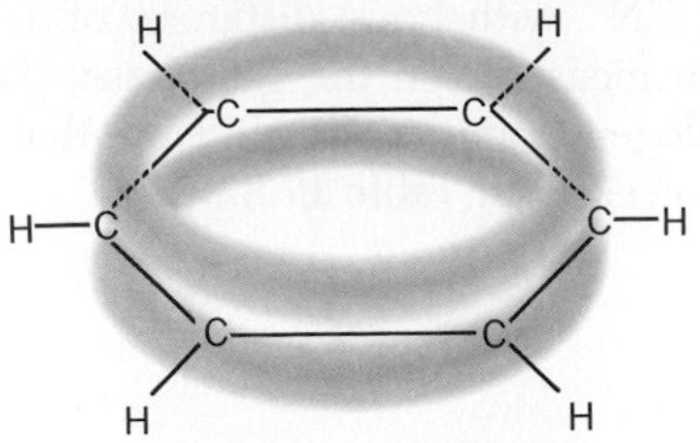	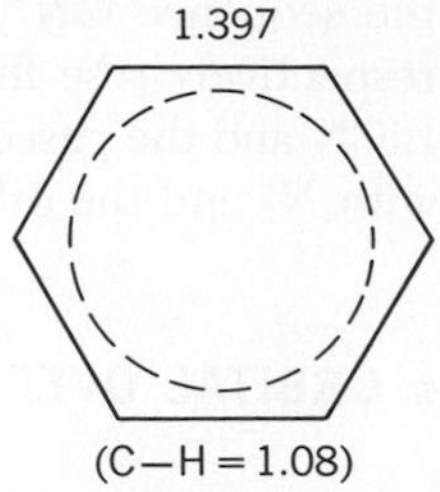
Cyclopentadienyl ion	$C_5H_5^-$	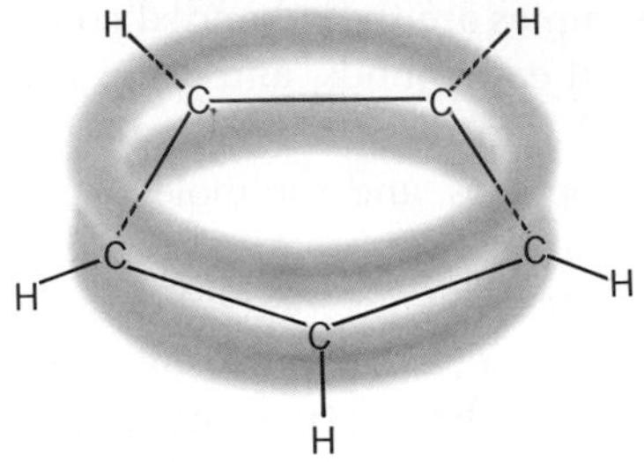	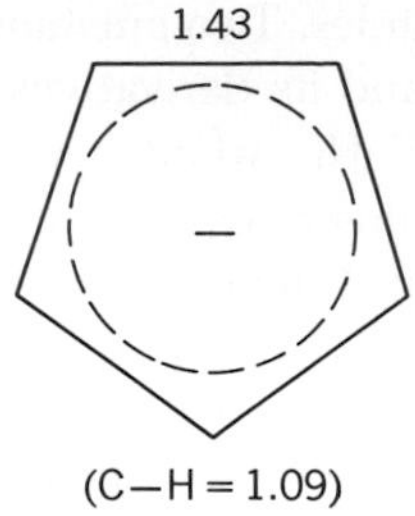
Silver perchlorate—benzene 1-1 addition compound	$AgClO_4 \cdot C_6H_{6(c)}$	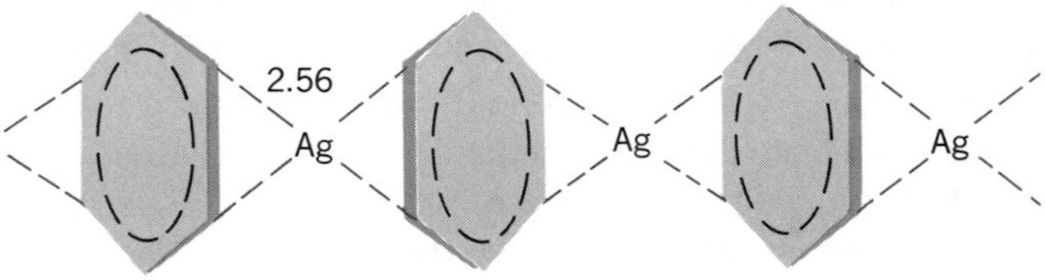	
Ferrocene	$Fe(C_5H_5)_2$	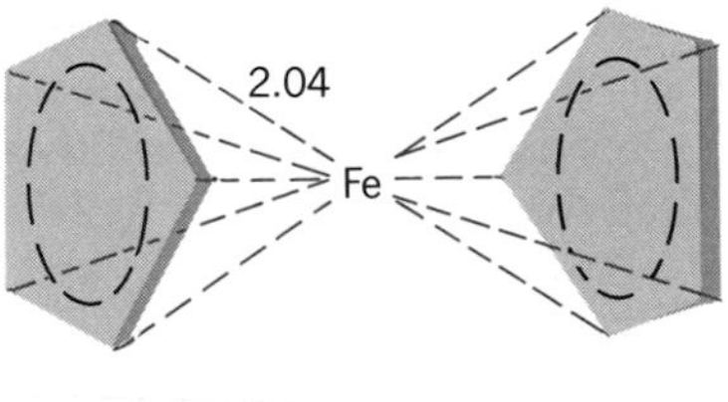	
Trinitrobenzene—anthracene addition compound	$C_6H_3(NO_2)_3 \cdot C_{14}H_{10}$	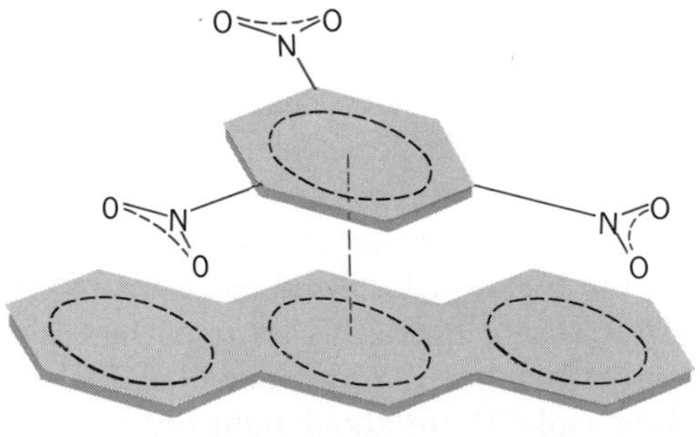	

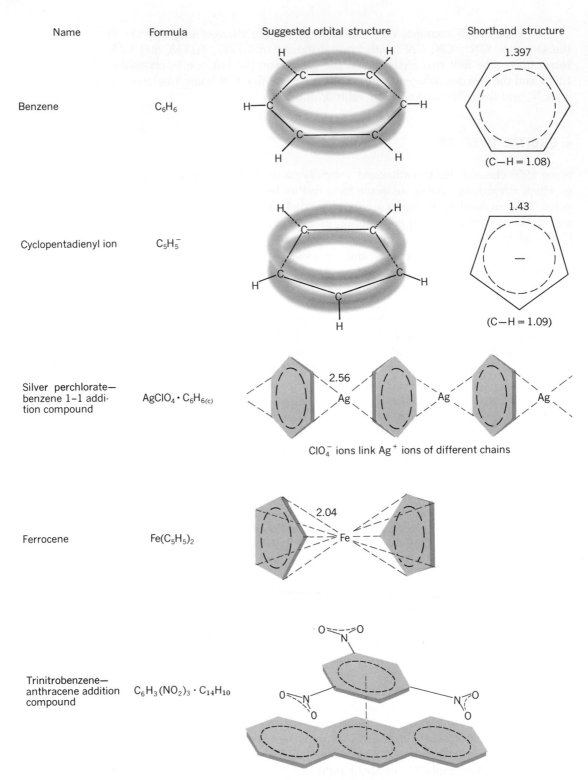

Figure 17.6 Some compounds having π overlap bonding.

organized structures as those found with hydrogen-bonded molecules (see Figure 15.18). A π overlap could, however, be useful in transferring electrons from one system to another, whereas hydrogen bonding is not highly effective in electron transfer.

MOLECULAR ORBITALS IN GRAPHITE

The two common forms of carbon—diamond and graphite—differ greatly in crystal structure and in properties. Diamond forms one of the hardest crystals known. Each atom is tetrahedrally coordinated to its four nearest neighbors. We interpret this as the result of the formation of four identical σ molecular orbitals (hybridization) from the $2s$ and three $2p$ atomic orbitals of each carbon atom. These molecular orbitals are strongly directed in space toward the corners of a tetrahedron; the orbitals contain only bonding electrons, and the bonds are short. Hence the bonds are strong and the crystal is hard—that is, hard to deform. When the crystal is struck a sharp blow, the energy is absorbed by the breaking of bonds and the crystal cleaves or shatters. If the blow is carefully directed along the crystal planes, one can obtain two fragments from the cleavage process. If the blow is not in line with the crystal planes, the energy will dissipate along several sets of planes and shattering will occur.

Graphite is much softer, indicating the presence of some weak bonds. The energy of a blow may be absorbed by deformation of the crystal along the glide planes (the planes of atoms between which the interatomic forces are relatively weak). The energy is then dissipated over many atoms as thermal energy rather than by breaking a few strong bonds, as in diamond. But graphite has a high melting point, indicating that it also contains strong bonds. Indeed, careful experimentation shows that some of the bonds in graphite are even stronger than the strongest bonds in diamond. The strong graphite bonds are concentrated into two-dimensional planar structures. Atoms in any given plane are very tightly bonded together, but the forces between the planes are much weaker. Figure 17.7 illustrates possible structures for a plane of atoms in crystalline graphite and for interplanar attractions.

The strong bonds within the layers can be attributed to σ bonds and π bonds in the molecular orbitals formed from the $2s$ and three $2p$ orbitals of each carbon atom. These bonds should be almost as strong as those in benzene (where the average carbon to carbon bond strength is known to be about 121 kcal mole^{-1}; see Table 15.6). The bond strength of the planar bonds in graphite is found to be about 114 kcal mole^{-1}. That in diamond is about 83 kcal mole^{-1}. We see that graphite can be treated approximately as an infinite-planar molecule, with bonding comparable to that in benzene.

The bonds between the atomic layers in graphite can be attributed to π orbital overlap very similar to that found in the sandwich compounds. These bonds will be relatively nondirected, so that graphite will flow under stress as the π orbitals slide over one another.

(We should probably point out here that the use of graphite as a lubricant relies on the existence of very strong bonds within each atomic layer to form a tough film for separating moving parts. However, lubricating graphite owes its

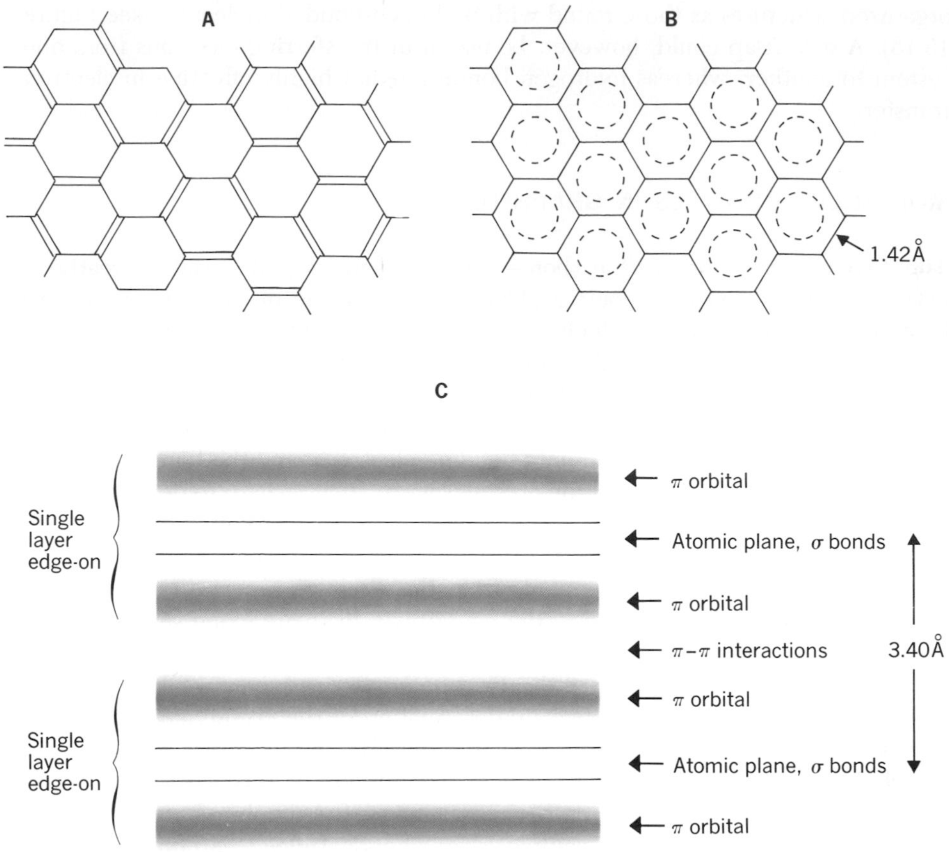

Figure 17.7 Possible representations of the graphite orbital structure. (**A**) Valence bond resonating systems—every bond averages $\frac{2}{3}$ single bond, $\frac{1}{3}$ double bond character. (**B**) Molecular orbitals— three σ orbitals at 120° angles about each carbon atom plus continuous π orbitals above and below plane of atoms. (**C**) Crystal layers edge-on, showing possible π orbital interactions between atomic layers.

easy sliding to the existence of additional molecules—from air or from the suspending fluid—which are adsorbed on the π orbitals of the graphite planes and which allow the graphite crystallites to slide past one another even more readily than do the pure graphite layers. Pure graphite is not nearly as good a lubricant, for example, in a vacuum, after these additional molecules are removed.)

The electrical properties of graphite are also consistent with this model. Graphite is a good conductor of electricity (and of heat) parallel to the atomic planes, but is a poor conductor normal to the planes. Thus it is a good conductor in two dimensions but poor in the third. This fits the idea that π electrons are delocalized. In graphite the delocalization is great, extending throughout each plane. Thus the electrons can move quite freely in the planes to conduct electricity and heat. Conduction perpendicular to the atomic planes requires the transfer of electrons or energy from one set of π orbitals into another set. The experimental observations on conductivity and molecular orbital theory agree that this transfer is not accomplished easily.

BONDING IN METALS

Metals are characterized by high electrical conductivity and other properties that indicate that they have highly delocalized electrons. Monatomic gaseous atoms of metals are characterized by sets of atomic orbitals that are far from being filled with electrons. Furthermore, the ionization energies of these gaseous atoms are low, indicating that the nuclei of the atoms that form metals do not hold their "own" electrons very tightly compared to the atoms of the nonmetals. Figure 17.8 suggests schematically how the atomic orbitals merge into the bonding molecular orbitals found in condensed metallic phases. Remember, from MO theory, that every pair of atomic orbital splits (one from each atom) into a bonding and an antibonding orbital as the nuclei approach. With high CN, as in metals, the splitting is considerable and the bonding orbitals are at much lower energies and have broader allowed energies than the original atomic orbitals.

We have already noted that some metals form molecules even in the gaseous state (see Figure 5.10). All of the metals condense at room temperature to give conducting phases with highly delocalized electrons. The low ionization energies plus the delocalized molecular orbitals (or crystal orbitals, since they extend throughout the crystal) combine to give the electrical and thermal as well as many of the other properties of metallic crystals.

Great progress has been made recently in developing theories of the metallic state though the mathematical treatment for delocalized electrons in small molecules is not complete. It is possible to describe the situation in extended arrays such as crystals, partly because of the much higher long-range symmetry in a crystal. Nor is it necessary to consider boundary conditions and edge effects to as great an extent as in the smaller aggregates.

Figure 17.9 presents a theoretical picture of the potential energy surface for electrons in crystalline aluminum. The projection is along one of the atomic

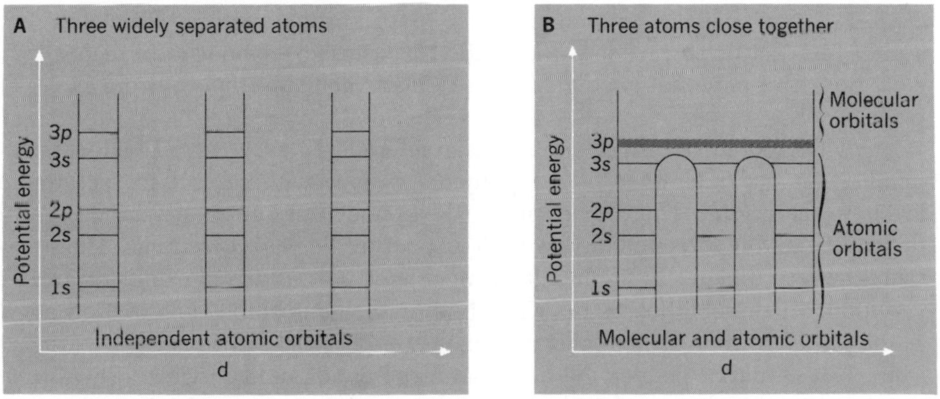

Figure 17.8 Schematic transition from independent atomic orbitals to a mixture of atomic and molecular orbitals for a metal such as aluminum ($1s^2$; $2s^2$, $2p^6$; $3s^2$, $3p^1$). The 1s, 2s, and 2*p* orbitals are relatively unaffected as atoms approach one another. The 3*s* bonding orbitals are somewhat lowered in energy, since these electrons now "feel" the presence of more than one nucleus. The 3*p* bonding orbitals are not only lowered, but are considerably broadened, or split. Thus the atomic 3*p* orbitals become delocalized and are influenced by the crystal geometry as much as by their "own" nucleus. They merge into crystal, or molecular, orbitals. The more atoms that condense together, the greater the effect.

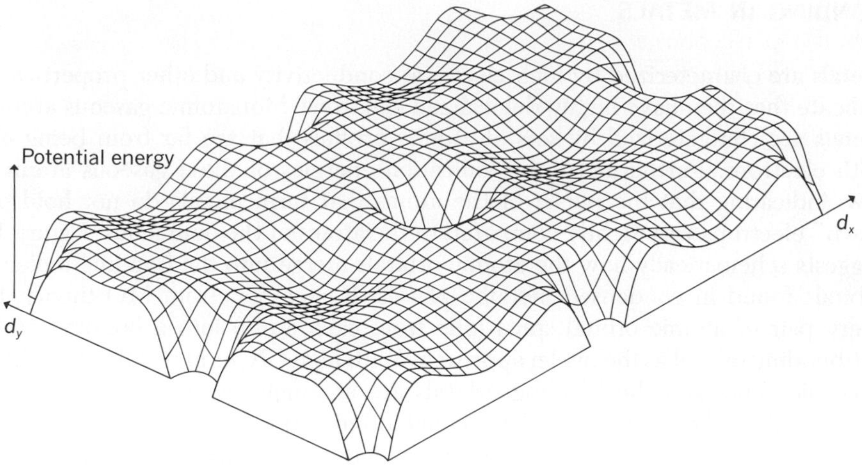

Figure 17.9 Potential energy, *U*, of electrons in one atomic plane of crystalline aluminum. Note the small variation of *U* with position except near the nuclei, whose positions correspond to the deep potential wells. [From W. A. Harrison, *Pseudo Potentials in the Theory of Metals*, Benjamin, 1966.]

planes. The holes correspond to the position of the atomic nuclei and the hollows to the places in which conductivity electrons are most likely to be found. Note, however, that many of the hollows are very shallow, so that the electrons can move under a very small potential gradient in almost any direction in this plane. The nuclear potential wells destroy the smooth surface of the plane, but most of these potential wells will be filled with electrons in the atomic orbitals of the aluminum atoms. Thus the presence of the wells does not grossly interfere with the movements of the delocalized electrons. The delocalized electrons can not fall into the already full wells.

The simplest interpretation of the crystal orbital picture of metals views a metal as a set of positive ions surrounded by a rather mobile sea of delocalized electrons. The potential energy in the sea may vary only slightly from place to place.

The potential energy surfaces characteristic of each crystal will vary depending on the orientation of the potential surface with respect to the atomic layers in the crystal. Thus, for example, the conductivity in the crystal may vary depending on the direction of flow with respect to the planes of atoms. The situation is comparable to that in graphite, though most metals do not exhibit as great a variation with orientation as does graphite, and some exhibit no variation at all as the direction through the crystal is changed.

It should be pointed out here that representations like Figure 17.9 assume that one has a single crystal with no bounding surfaces or imperfections. Any real sample of metal will have boundaries, and most samples will consist of a large number of tiny crystals and some impurities. These crystals will meet at their respective boundaries, and their potential energy surfaces will show marked changes across these boundaries. The presence of impurities and imperfections in a crystal will cause similar distortions in the potential energy surfaces. Thus, in many cases, the properties of a real crystal are more strongly influenced by crystal boundaries, crystal imperfections, and impurities than by the potential energy surfaces characteristic of a pure single crystal. But all these effects may be understood as distortions in the potential energy surfaces, and suitable allowances can be made. For example, almost any impurity lowers the electrical conductivity of a pure metal: the resistivity of copper to electric current flow is increased 200% by contamination with 2 mole % of nickel.

Thermal agitation also distorts the potential energy surfaces. The electrical conductivity of almost all metals decreases with rising temperature because of such distortion. Conversely, at very low temperatures, the surfaces may become almost flat.

In some metals—and most semiconductors and poor conductors—the electrical conductivity increases with rise in temperature. Our theory quickly interprets these experimental observations. The increased distortion of the potential surfaces tends to decrease the conductivity in these crystals, as outlined above, but there are very few electrons available at low temperatures to conduct; hence the low conductivity. Raising the temperature increases the likelihood that additional electrons will escape from the potential wells about the nuclei. Depending on the energy required to get the electrons out of the potential wells, the effect of rising temperature may be either to increase or to decrease the observed conductivity. Remember the Boltzmann factor and the role of entropy and energy in determining any change which occurs.

Thus the conductivity of semiconductors often is given by the equation

$$\text{conductivity} = Ae^{-\epsilon/kT}$$

where A is a constant, characteristic of the material, ϵ is the activation energy required to get an electron from its potential well into the conduction orbital, k is Boltzmann's constant, and $T =$ °K. Figure 17.10 shows the effect in several materials. Note that ϵ (proportional to the slope) actually decreases slowly as T increases.

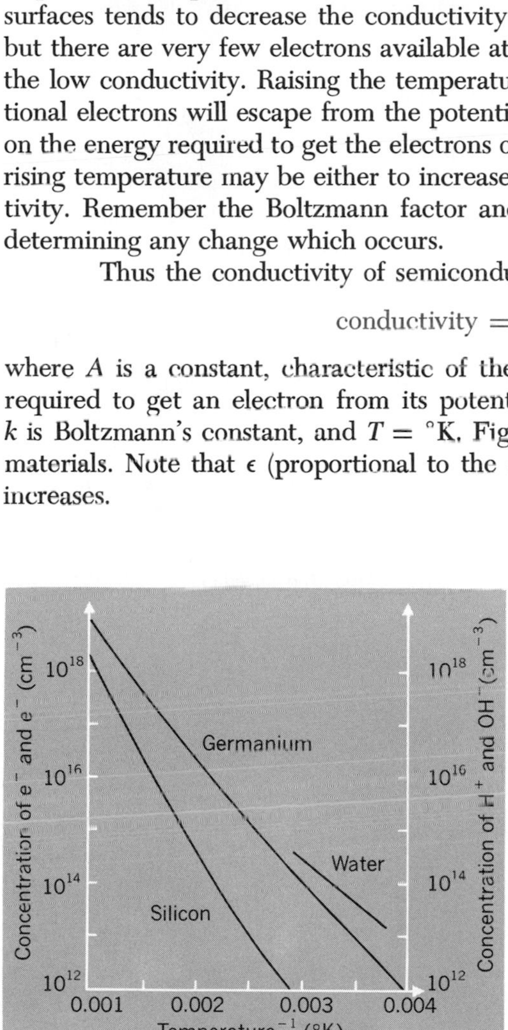

Figure 17.10 Temperature-dependence of the self-dissociation of water and intrinsic conductivity of silicon and germanium. The concentration of ions and charge carriers is about the same order of magnitude and varies exponentially with the temperature. [A. Rabenau, *Endeavour,* **25,** 160 (1966).]

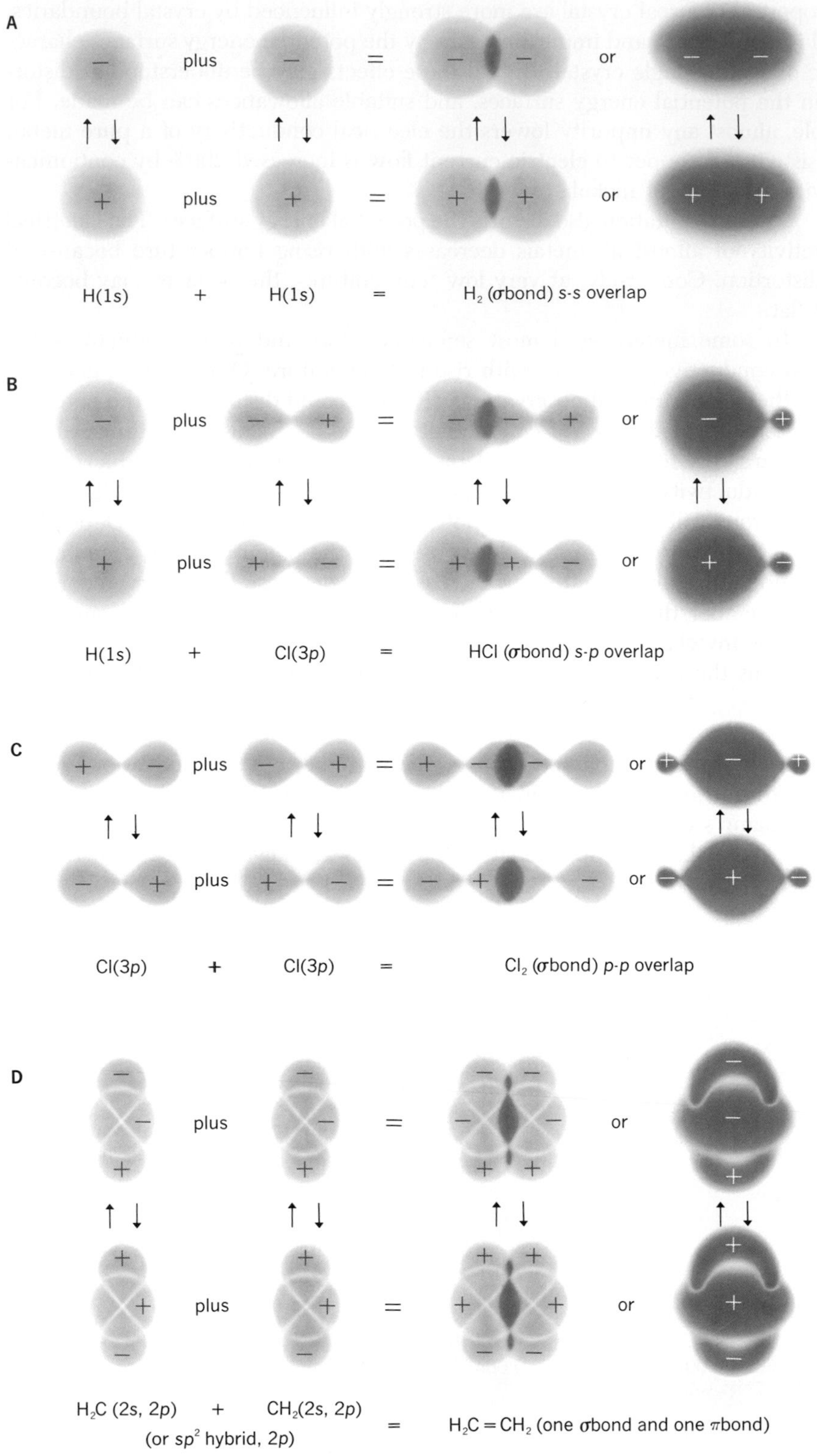

A
plus
=
or
plus
=
or
H(1s) + H(1s) = H_2 (σbond) s-s overlap
B
plus
=
or
plus
=
or
H(1s) + Cl(3p) = HCl (σbond) s-p overlap
C
plus
=
or
plus
=
or
Cl(3p) + Cl(3p) = Cl_2 (σbond) p-p overlap
D
plus
=
or
plus
=
or
H_2C (2s, 2p) + CH_2(2s, 2p)
(or sp^2 hybrid, 2p)
= $H_2C=CH_2$ (one σbond and one πbond)

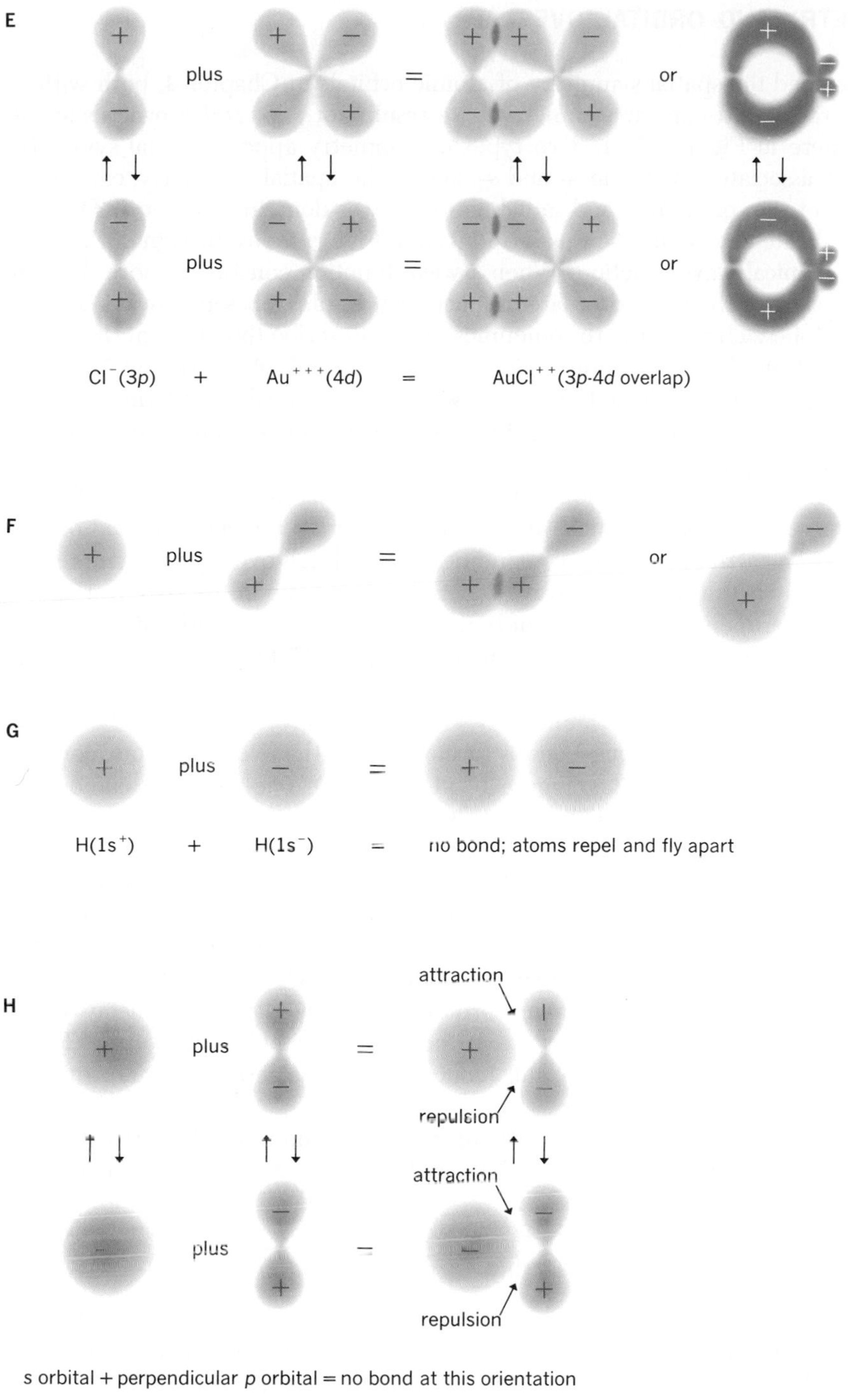

Figure 17.11 Bond strength and orbital overlap. Strong orbital bonding occurs when the overlapping orbitals have the same sign and the overlap gives a symmetrical pattern. (**A–E**) Strong overlap, symmetrical in space and in sign of wave function, gives strong bonding. (**F–H**) Examples of poor overlap and weak bonding due to poor symmetry or opposed signs of the wave functions.

SYMMETRY AND ORBITAL OVERLAP

We discussed the spatial symmetry of atomic orbitals in Chapter 4, both with regard to radial and angular symmetry. The results for *s*, *p*, and *d* orbitals are repeated here in Figure 17.11. Two types of symmetry appear: spatial symmetry, and that associated with the + and − signs. The spatial symmetry can be described in terms of angular and radial nodes, as was done in Chapter 4. The symmetry indicated by + and − was introduced in Figure 4.5 as the sign of the quantum mechanical wave function. When a wave function consists of more than one lobe, the signs of the lobes alternate in space: that is, plus lobes are always adjacent to minus lobes. These signs are sometimes said to describe the phase of the motion of the electron cloud. As a crude picture, we may think of the sign as indicating whether the cloud is pulsing toward or away from its nodal boundaries. The lobe which is positive one instant is negative the next, the changes in sign for a given orbital occurring at the same instant.

Theoretical examination of the orbital patterns (which are, after all, theoretical rather than experimental) indicates that overlap between unfilled orbitals leads to strong attractive forces, or bonding, if the orbitals overlap in a symmetrical way and only if the sign of the wave function is the same in the two overlapping orbitals. Experimental observation of bonding is in agreement with this theoretical prediction. These conditions are outlined in Figure 17.11. We see that unfilled *s* orbitals can overlap in any direction with *s* orbitals of the same sign to form a strong bond (Figure 17-11, A). Similarly, *s* orbitals can overlap with *p* or *d* orbitals of the same sign, but a strong bond is formed only if the overlap occurs along the long axis of the *p* or *d* orbital (Figure 17.11, B and F). The *p* orbitals can overlap *p* orbitals either along their long axes (Figure 17.11, C), to give σ bonds, or with their axes perpendicular to the internuclear axis (Figure 17.11, D), to give π bonds, so long as the signs of the wave functions are appropriately paired. The *d* orbitals can have end-on overlap with *s*, *p*, or *d* orbitals, or can overlap two of their four lobes simultaneously either with another *d* orbital or with a *p* orbital (Figure 17.11, E) so long as the signs of the wave function pair. Orbitals of opposite sign do not overlap (Figure 17.11, G). An *s* orbital cannot overlap simultaneously with both the lobes of a *p* orbital because of the lack of suitable sign pairing (Figure 17.11, H). Two orbitals already full (containing two electrons) cannot overlap; they can only repel one another.

Thus, for bonding to occur there must be (1) no more than two electrons per orbital, (2) favorable symmetry, (3) matching signs of the wave functions.

ELECTRON SPIN AND *d* ORBITAL SPLITTING

We know from our discussion in Chapter 3 that electrons tend to spread out as much as possible among the available orbitals. This reduces electron-electron repulsion and produces unpaired electrons with net resultant spin. (A pair of electrons in a single orbital give spin cancellation and no resultant spin.) Thus a pair of electrons in a single orbital have a higher potential energy than the same two electrons in separate orbitals. The difference in these two terms we shall call pair-repulsion energy, *P*. Thus, *d* electrons tend to spread out among the available orbitals in as uniform a fashion as possible when the orbitals all have the same energy. But consider what happens as orbital splitting occurs. In octahedral complexes the five *d* orbitals split into a low energy group of three and a high energy group of two orbitals differing

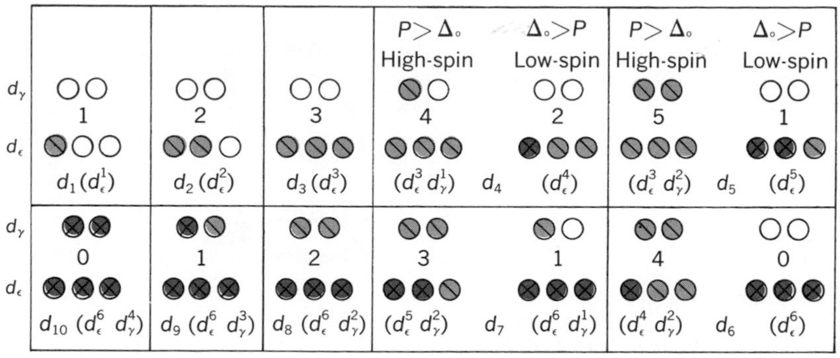

Figure 17.12 Possible electron distributions among the d orbitals of an octahedrally coordinated ion. The ions are identified as d_1, d_2, d_3, etc., in terms of the number of d electrons in the orbitals, and (in parentheses) the d_ϵ and d_γ population. Only one possible spin state exists for the d_1, d_2, d_3, d_8, d_9, and d_{10} ions, but two possible spin states exist for the d_4, d_5, d_6, and d_7 ions. These two states (high-spin when $P > \Delta$, low-spin when $\Delta > P$) are differentiated in terms of the relative populations of the d_ϵ and d_γ sets of orbitals, as indicated in the figure. The resulting number of unpaired electrons in the ion is listed in the middle of each orbital representation.

in energy by an amount Δ. If Δ exceeds P, the electrons will be found in the lower set of three orbitals (called d_ϵ; the other two being called d_γ), even though they must pair up to give that configuration. Figure 17.12 illustrates the expected different electron spin configurations for octahedral coordination, depending on whether $P > \Delta_0$ (high-spin configuration) or $\Delta_0 > P$ (low-spin configuration).

Unpaired electrons in a substance may be detected and counted by suspending a sample containing a known number of molecules of the substance from an analytical balance and weighing the sample twice—when it is outside a magnetic field and when it is partly inside the magnetic field. The sample appears to lose weight slightly in the magnetic field if all the electrons are paired: such substances are said to be diamagnetic. Samples containing unpaired electrons appear to gain markedly in weight when placed partly in the field: such substances are said to be paramagnetic. From the known properties of the field, the concentration of the unknown, and the measured gain in weight it is possible to calculate the number of unpaired electrons per molecule of sample. The apparatus used for these measurements is known as a Gouy balance (see Figure 17.13).

The relative effects of P and Δ may be considered in terms of some experimental data on octahedral complexes of Co^{+++} and Fe^{++}. Each of these contains 24 electrons and is a d_6 ion. Studies on the spectra of the ions in the gas phase indicate that P for Co^{+++} is about 50 kcal mole^{-1}, and for Fe^{++} is about 40 kcal mole^{-1}. Studies on the spectra of aqueous solutions of $CoF_6^{\equiv}$, $Co(NH_3)_6^{+++}$, and $Fe(NH_3)_6^{++}$ give the values of Δ_0 summarized in Table 17.3. The predicted values for the number of unpaired electrons per ion are also compared with the experimental values in Table 17.3. Similar agreement is found in other cases.

Table 17.3 Correlation of P, Δ_0, and net electron spin.

Solution	$P_{Co^{+++}}$	$P_{Fe^{++}}$	Δ_0	Net electron spin: Values predicted from Figure 17.12		Net electron spin: Experimental values
$CoF_6^{\equiv}$	50		37	$P > \Delta_0$	4	4
$Co(NH_3)_6^{+++}$	50		66	$\Delta_0 > P$	0	0
$Fe(NH_3)_6^{++}$		40	35	$P > \Delta_0$	4	4

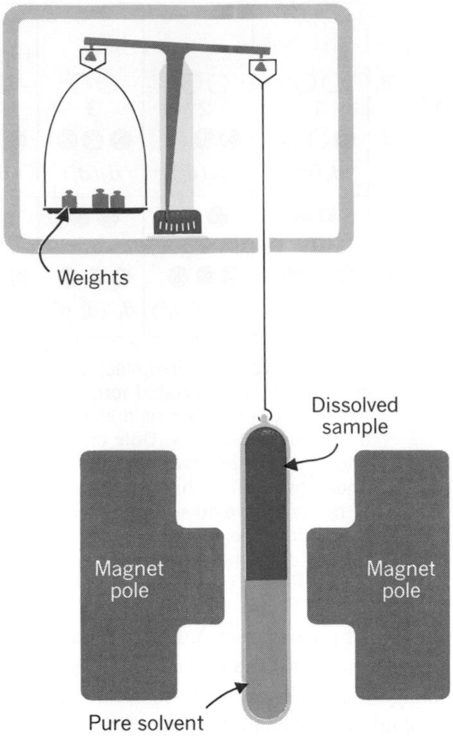

Figure 17.13 Schematic Gouy balance. The sample, usually dissolved in a solvent, is hung from one arm of an analytical balance and weighed in the absence of the magnetic field. It is then weighed again in the presence of the magnetic field. The sample tube is centered in the magnetic field, the bottom half being full of pure solvent, the top half full of solution. A larger weight in the second weighing indicates unpaired electrons in the sample.

Many of the bonding properties of the elements in the main groups of the periodic table (the two groups at the left and the six groups at the right in the most common form of the table) may be explained in terms of *s* and *p* orbitals alone, especially for the elements in the first two rows of the periodic table. However, *d* orbitals appear to become more commonly involved in the bonding interactions for groups near the center of the periodic table, and for elements in the lower rows. Compare our discussion of the interhalogen compounds in Figure 15.4. The elements in the central portion of the periodic table appear to involve their *d* orbitals in many of their atomic interactions both in compounds, as discussed above, and as the pure elements, especially in the metallic state, where high coordination and highly delocalized electrons are common.

ISOELECTRONIC SPECIES

We have mentioned on numerous occasions the occurrence of molecules of similar properties, which also contained the same number of valence electrons. The isoelectronic atoms and ions of Table 11.1 are a good example, as are the isoelectronic species in Figures 11.3 and 15.9. Let us explore this idea a little further.

We have accumulated considerable evidence that in many molecules electrons are not localized between two individual atoms. Molecular orbital theory also suggests that electrons wander throughout molecules, restricted primarily by considerations of symmetry and energy. If this is true, molecules of similar symmetry and the same number of electrons might well have similar molecular orbital populations and similar chemistry (see Table 17.2). The effect of varying symmetry when the molecules are isoelectronic has been briefly shown in Table 15.5.

Table 17.4 lists groups of energetically stable isoelectronic substances and categorizes them with respect to existence at room temperature or at high temperature in the gaseous state. Note that the only numbers of electrons which give isoelectronic species at room temperature are 2, 10, 14, 16, 18, and 22, but that other numbers of electrons give gaseous species that are stable at higher temperatures. (Stable means that the species will not decompose exothermically.) The

Table 17.4 Some isoelectronic species with less than 23 electrons. Ground state configurations are shown.

Total number of electrons	Room-temperature species (gaseous unless ions)	High-temperature gaseous species
0		H^+
1		H, $H\overset{1.06}{—}H^+$
2	He, $H\overset{0.741}{—}H$, H^-, Li^+, Be^{++}	$He—H^+$, $H—H—H^+$
3		Li, $Li—H^+$, $He\overset{1.08}{—}He^+$
4		Be, $Be\overset{1.312}{—}H^+$
5		B, $Be\overset{1.343}{—}H$, $B\overset{1.215}{—}H^+$
6		C, Li—Li, $B\overset{1.233}{—}H$, $C\overset{1.131}{—}H^+$
7		N, $C\overset{1.120}{—}H$, $\dot{B}H_2$ (H—B—H, bent), $N\overset{1.084}{—}H^+$
8		O, $N\overset{1.038}{—}H$, $O\overset{1.029}{—}H^+$ $H\overset{1.03}{—}\ddot{C}—H$
9		F, NH_2 (N—H 1.024, 103°), $O\overset{0.971}{—}H$, CH_3 (appears to be almost planar)
10	Ne, $F\overset{0.917}{—}H$, H_2O (O—H 0.957, 105°), NH_3 (N—H 1.014, 107°) CH_4 (C—H 1.093, 109°), $O\overset{0.984}{—}H^-$, $H_3O^{\oplus}$ (O—H ~0.99) $NH_2^{\ominus}$ (N—H 1.03, 104°), $NH_4^{\oplus}$ (N—H 1.032, 109°), $BH_4^{\ominus}$ (109°) $N^{\equiv}$, $O^{=}$, F^-, Na^+, Mg^{++}, Al^{+++}	$B\overset{1.589}{—}B$
11		Na
12		Mg, $C\overset{1.312}{—}C$, $B\overset{1.281}{—}N$, $C\overset{1.173}{—}N^+$
13		Al, $Be\overset{1.361}{—}F$, $B\overset{1.205}{—}O$, $C\overset{1.172}{—}N$, $N\overset{1.116}{—}N^+$, $C\overset{1.115}{—}O^+$, $Al\overset{1.646}{—}H^+$
14	$N\overset{1.098}{—}N$, $C\overset{1.128}{—}O$, $H\overset{1.066}{—}C\overset{1.156}{—}N$ $H\overset{1.058}{—}C\overset{1.205}{—}C—H$, $C\overset{1.07}{—}N^-$, $C\overset{1.28}{—}C^{=}$	Si, $B\overset{1.265}{—}F$, $N\overset{1.062}{—}O^+$, $Al\overset{1.648}{—}H$
15	$N\overset{1.150}{—}O$	P, $Si\overset{1.521}{—}H$, $P\overset{1.425}{—}H^+$, $C\overset{1.271}{—}F$, HCO (H—C 1.08, C—O 1.198, 120°), $O\overset{1.123}{—}O^+$

(continued)

Table 17.4 contd.

Total number of electrons	Room-temperature species (gaseous unless ions)	High-temperature gaseous species
16	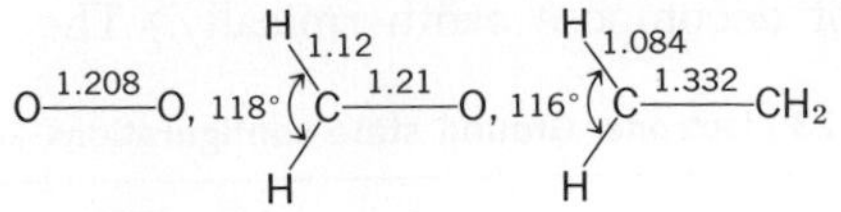 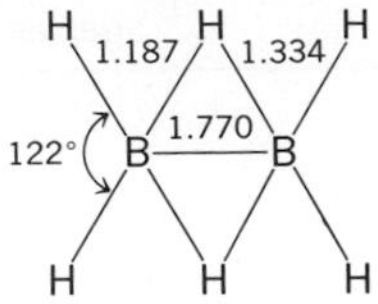 (2 perpendicular planes see Fig. 17.7)	S, $P\overset{1.433}{\text{—}}H$, 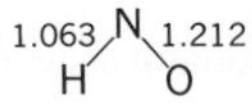
17	$O\overset{1.28}{\text{—}}O^-$	Cl, $S\overset{1.350}{\text{—}}H$, 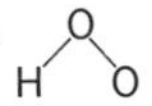
18	Ar, $Cl\overset{1.274}{\text{—}}H$, 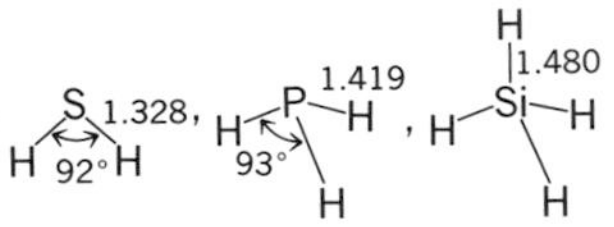 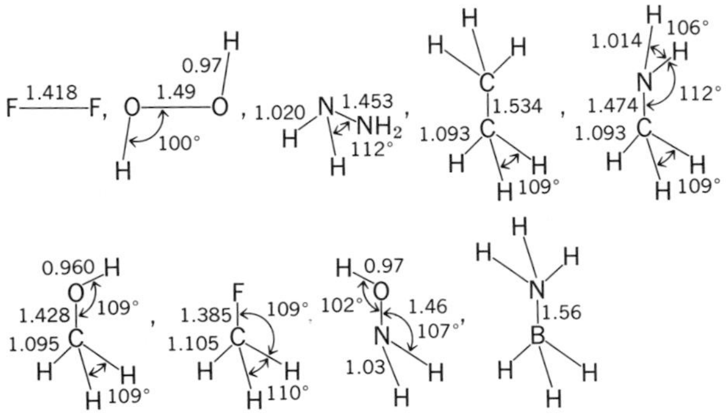 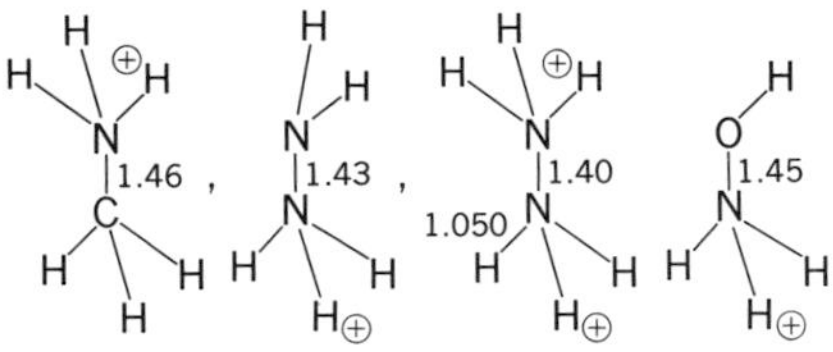 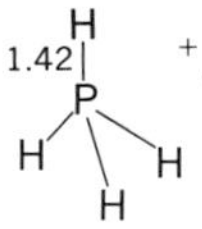 $^+$, $O\overset{1.49}{\text{—}}O^=$, $P^\equiv$, $S^=$, Cl^-, K^+, Ca^{++}, Sc^{+++}, Ti^{+4}, V^{+5}, Cr^{+6}, Mn^{+7}	$C\overset{1.277}{\text{—}}C\text{—}C$
19		K
20		Ca, N—C—N
21		Sc, $Al\overset{1.618}{\text{—}}O$, $Si\overset{1.572}{\text{—}}N$, $Si\overset{1.504}{\text{—}}O^+$ $C\overset{1.562}{\text{—}}P$, $O\overset{1.265}{\text{—}}B\text{—}O$, $O\text{—}C\text{—}O^+$, N—C—O, N—N—O, N—N—N, C—N—O

(continued)

Table 17.4 contd.

Total number of electrons	Room-temperature species (gaseous unless ions)	High-temperature gaseous species
22	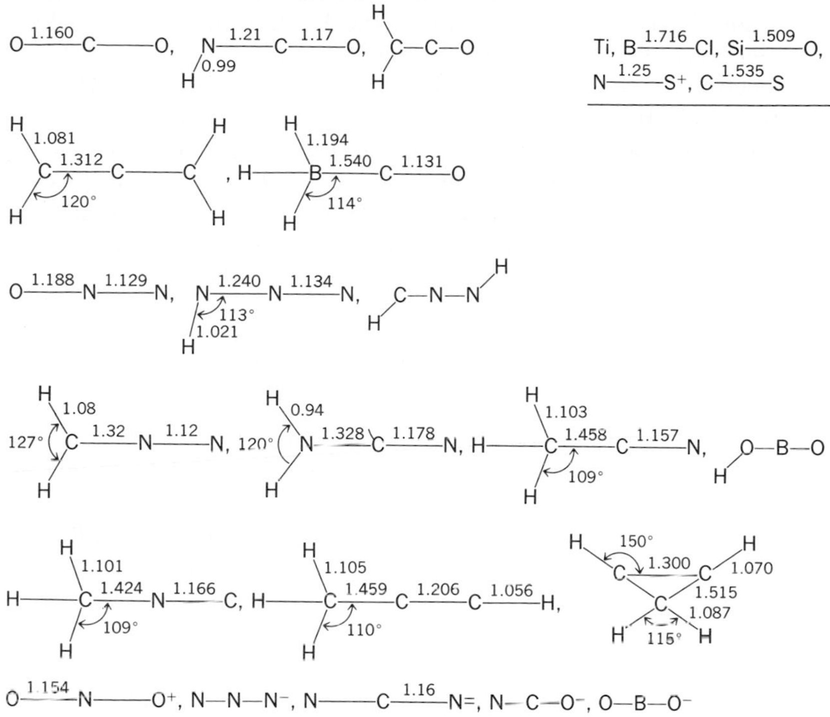	Ti, $B\overset{1.716}{—}Cl$, $Si\overset{1.509}{—}O$, $N\overset{1.491}{—}P$ $N\overset{1.25}{—}S^{+}$, $C\overset{1.535}{—}S$

neutral, room-temperature species can all exist as gases; the ionic species exist in crystals with appropriate ions of opposite charge. Note that a good many of the room-temperature species can be created by allowing the high-temperature species to combine with one another. For example, the high-temperature species with 8 and 9 electrons combine to give a good many of the room-temperature species with 16 and 18 electrons, respectively, and all the 22 electron species are combinations of 8 and 14 electron species. Many of the elements are of course highly polymerized at room temperature—for example, Li, Be, B, C, and all the elements in the third row of the periodic table ($Z = 11$ to 18) except argon. Only two common stable compounds—BN and SiC—having less than 23 electrons per formula weight are not listed in the table. Both BN and SiC are polymeric substances isoelectronic with diamond, and they have the same crystal structure as diamond. Most other substances with less than 23 electrons per formula weight are either listed or are thought to be made of some of the listed units. For example, BeH_2 contains Be^{++} and H^- ions, MgH_2 contains Mg^{++} and H^- ions, LiF contains Li^+ and F^-, and so on.

A short inspection of Table 17.4 immediately indicates that only certain numbers of electrons—2, 10, 14, 16, 18, and 22—commonly give stable species at room temperature. All of these numbers are even. Only O_2^- and NO are "odd molecules" stable at room temperature.

Furthermore, were we to count only valence electrons (for example, eliminate 1*s* electrons from the count, except for H and He), a further simplification would occur. All the 10-electron species would prove to have 8 valence electrons, the 14-electron species would have 10 valence electrons, the 16-electron species would have 12 valence electrons, the 18-electron species would have 8 valence electrons (if they contained a single "central" nucleus, as in H_2S) or 14 valence electrons (if they contained two "central" nuclei, as in H—O—O—H). Similarly, the 22-electron species, all of which contain three first-row nuclei, would contain 16 valence electrons. We thus see that the numbers of valence electrons commonly found at room temperature are 2, 8, 10, 12, 14, and 16: all the even numbers beyond (and including) 8 are found, but odd numbers are rare. At high temperatures, however, many of the species have odd numbers of electrons.

This apparent predilection for even numbers of bonding electrons is found in the great majority of chemical compounds. One concomitant fact is that practically all of the compounds of the main group elements have an even number of electrons per formula weight. Compounds of the transition elements may have an uneven number of electrons per formula weight, but even here the number of electrons involved in bonding, especially covalent bonding, tends to be even. This result is rather remarkable when one remembers the large values of P, the pairing repulsion, found in atoms—of the order of 40 kcal $mole^{-1}$.

In the strictest sense, the isoelectronic principle is limited to molecules which have both the same number of electrons and the same number of heavy nuclei (not counting H). Thus H_2O and NH_3 are isoelectronic (10 electrons and 1 heavy nucleus each), but B_2 cannot be compared to them (10 electrons but 2 heavy nuclei).

The principle is often extended, however, to groups of atoms that may differ in total number of electrons so long as they have the same number of valence electrons and the same number of heavy nuclei (not counting hydrogen). Thus the following groups can be interchanged in many substances and are often called isoelectronic. The properties of the resulting molecules are often readily correlated: $—CH_3$, $—NH_2$, —OH, —F, $—SiH_3$, $—PH_2$, —SH, —Cl, —Br, —I.

A closer examination of Table 17.4 produces more insights into chemical bonding. (1) In a series of isoelectronic species in which the total charge on the species remains constant, but in which one nuclear charge increases as another decreases, the bond length is shortest for the species in which the nuclei are most nearly the same charge: N—N 1.098, C—O 1.128, B—F 1.265; C—N 1.172, B—O 1.205, Be—F 1.361. (2) Increasing one nuclear charge while the nuclear charge at the other end of the bond remains constant normally shortens the bonds: BeH 1.343, BH^+ 1.215; $H_3C—CH_3$ 1.534, $H_3C—NH_2$ 1.474, $H_3C—OH$ 1.428, $H_3C—F$ 1.385. (Can you think of a way to rationalize trends 1 and 2, both of which involve changing nuclear charges at the ends of a bond?) (3) Adding protons while keeping the nuclear charges unchanged normally decreases the bond lengths: $H_2N—NH_2$ 1.453, $(H_2N—NH_3)^+$ 1.43, $(H_3N—NH_3)^+$ 1.40. These three generalizations seem to account for most of the effects observed in the data of Table 17.4.

Table 17.4 includes, of course, only species that have a total of 22 electrons or less. Similar families and generalizations apply to species having more electrons. The concept of isoelectronic species is very useful in studying the relationships between chemical species and in predicting the properties—including the stability—of previously unknown species.

Exercise 17.2

Compare the relative likelihood of existence of the molecules H_3BCH_3, H_3BNH_3, and H_3BOH_2. *Answer:* H_3BCH_3 has $6 \cdot 1 + 3 + 4 = 13$ valence electrons, an unlikely number because it is odd. H_3BNH_3 has $6 \cdot 1 + 3 + 5 = 14$ valence electrons, a likely number. H_3BNH_3 should have a structure like C_2H_6, with which it would be isoelectronic. H_3BOH_2 also has 14 valence electrons. It has, apparently, not been synthesized yet but should be stable. Note that $H_3BCH_3^-$ would also be isoelectronic with C_2H_6 and should be stable. It does not appear to have been synthesized either. The reason for this lack of synthesis is, almost certainly, that these substances are stable to simple dissociation, for example, into H_3B and H_2O, but are unstable with respect to other products, such as H_2 and $B(OH)_3$.

VALENCE BOND VERSUS MOLECULAR ORBITAL DESCRIPTIONS OF MOLECULES

The valence bond structural representations were invented to describe the compounds that have been known for the longest time. Thus valence bond structures are quite adequate, especially when extended by the concepts of hybridization and resonance, to describe the general electron distribution in the great majority of chemical compounds. Many of the compounds discovered since World War II do not lend themselves to a valence bond description—for example, the electron-deficient compounds, the compounds involving "π orbital overlap," metals, and intermetallic compounds (which we hae not even discussed as yet).

Molecular orbital (MO) theory is much newer than valence bond (VB) theory. MO theory has scored some great successes (the oxygen molecule, *d* orbital splitting) and is continually adding to the list. Unfortunately the calculations and the ideas behind MO theory are more complicated than those for the VB approach.

For this reason, most chemists—strongly influenced by their own educational background, which generally emphasized VB theory—try to describe chemical species in terms of valence bond structures. When this fails, even after invoking hybridization and resonance, MO methods are used. We shall follow this practice in discussing the chemical systems we study from now on. You will find similar multiple approaches used in almost every branch of science. When two or more theories can be applied to the description of a given phenomenon, the simpler one is usually tried first, even though the user knows that there is a more exact theory available. Remember, for example, the common use of Newton's laws of motion, even though they are only a special case of the more general (and more complicated) theories of Einstein.

SUMMARY

We are rapidly accumulating a great deal of quite accurate information about internuclear distances, bond strengths, bond frequencies, bond dipole moments, and the variation in these quantities with temperature and the nature of the surrounding fields. We are increasingly able to predict what will happen to all of these properties as molecules approach one another and the intensity of the interactions varies.

What we do not know in detail is the role of the electrons and their distribution within the molecules. Present theories are aptly described by the quotation that opens this chapter. Bonding theory is one of the great unsolved mysteries of chemistry, and its solution is receiving central emphasis in contemporary chemistry. Presumably a good theory describing the interactions between electrons and nuclei would not only correlate most chemical information but would allow chemists to design new compounds that would have properties desired by the experimenter and would provide valuable guidance in the synthesis of the compounds. The remarkable thing is that chemists continue to synthesize several hundreds of thousands of new substances each year and, in many cases, can be quite sure of the properties of these substances even before they are made. Thus, although the theoretical picture is far from completed, even in its present state it gives powerful insights into the nature of chemical bonds.

More and more it appears that chemical bonds can be treated as the resultant of attractive and repulsive electrical forces that occur when one or more electrons are simultaneously attracted to more than one nucleus. The electrons repel one another, as do the nuclei, but the nuclei and electrons attract one another. Actual molecular and crystal structures are the result of minimizing the free energies of these attractions and repulsions over the whole structure. The potential energy tends to minimize ($\Delta H = -$), but the entropy remains positive at all T's above 0°K: $G = H - TS$ minimizes.

Valence bond theory adheres as closely as possible to atomic orbitals in interpreting chemical bonds. In many cases the bonds have the same symmetry as the atomic orbitals. In some cases (hybrid bonds and resonance systems) the bonding symmetry is a combination of the atomic orbital symmetries. In general, each valence orbital of the atom contributes to a single orbital in the molecule, and this orbital may be bonding or nonbonding. VB theory is relatively simple to apply.

Molecular orbital theory requires each pair of atomic orbitals to split into a bonding and an antibonding orbital as two atoms interact. The stability and other properties of the resulting molecule depend on the ratio of the number of bonding electrons to the number of antibonding electrons. There may also be nonbonding electrons that have little effect on the bond properties. MO theory can interpret many properties that are inscrutable from the standpoint of simple VB theory, but MO theory is usually more difficult to apply.

No present theory accounts quantitatively for the properties of all known substances, but most of the properties of more than 95% of known substances can be adequately described by VB and/or MO theory. Plenty of work remains for the theorist, spurred on by the recent discoveries of stable gaseous molecules such as CH_5^+ (Munsen and Field), H_5^+ (1962), O_{12}^+ (1965), $C_2H_7^+$ (1965), $H_3O^+ \cdot (1\text{–}8)H_2O$ (1965), $NH_4^+ \cdot (1\text{–}20)NH_3$ (1965), and others. Nor are these compounds held by weak bonds; for the reaction $CH_4\,(g) + H^+\,(g) = CH_5^+\,(g)$, $\Delta H = -118 \pm 5$ kcal.

The scientist must develop enormous tolerance in seeking for ideas which may please nature, and enormous patience, self-restraint, and humility when his ideas over and over again are rejected by nature before he arrives at one to please her. When the scientist does finally find such an idea, there is something very intimate in his feeling of communion with nature.
—*Robert S. Mulliken,* Science, **154,** 746 (1966).

PROBLEMS

17.1. Which of each of the following pairs would absorb the lower frequency IR radiation? (*a*) N_2, CO; (*b*) HC, HO; (*c*) NO, HBr. Consider both vibration and rotation.

17.2. The compound N≡C—C≡C—C≡N, dicyanoacetylene, burns in O_2 to give the hottest flame known. Can you suggest why this flame is much hotter than other flames?

17.3. Aluminum wires for electrical conductors are sometimes made hollow and filled with metallic sodium. Why? Are there any problems in using such wires?

17.4. High-speed motor valves are sometimes made hollow and partly filled with sodium. Why sodium? Why only partly filled? Any problems in using such valves?

17.5. Gaseous HeH is energetically stable with respect to decomposition into He and H, but not with respect to decomposition into He and $\frac{1}{2}H_2$. Rationalize these two experimental observations.

17.6. Copper crystals of exceptionally high purity (less than 0.1 ppm impurity) have been grown by A. F. Clark et al. [*J. Appl. Phys.*, **36,** 3358 (1965)]. These have electrical resistances only one-tenth those of previously prepared copper crystals. Suggest a mechanism by which lowering impurity levels from 1 ppm to 0.1 ppm can have such a remarkable effect on electrical resistance.

II

17.7. The compound

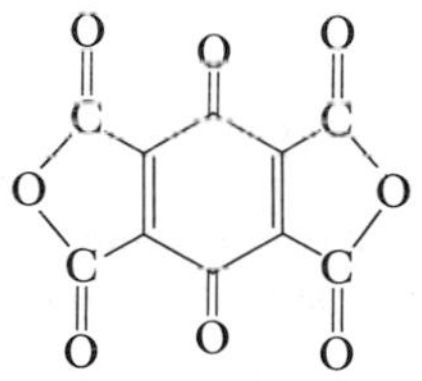

, formula $C_{10}O_8$, appears to be stable in benzene solution and as a one-to-one addition compound with benzene, but is not stable when pure. Can you interpret this? Into what might the pure material decompose?

17.8. Predict relative ionization energies, bond strengths, and bond lengths for O_2^{++} and O_2^{+++}, and defend your predictions. (O_2^{++}, I.E. $\cong$ 500 kcal, D $\cong$ 170 kcal, $d \cong 1.1$ Å.)

17.9. Sketch a figure like Figure 17.8 for the condensation of gaseous sodium to crystalline sodium. How do you account for the fact that sodium is a better conductor of electricity and heat than is aluminum?

17.10. $FeCl_3$ dimerizes to Fe_2Cl_6 with tetrahedral coordination of Cl about Fe, whereas $Fe(CN)_3$ polymerizes in crystals to give octahedral coordination of *CN* about each iron. Can you rationalize these two observations?

17.11. Discuss the changes that would occur during the conversion of Ne into the eight isoelectronic molecules listed in Table 17.4. Use the idea of the fused to separated atom. Which of the other isoelectronic species would you expect to be most similar to NH_2^- in chemistry?

17.12. Below is a table of properties of the crystalline elements in the second row of the periodic table. (*BCC* = body-centered cubic; *HCP* = hexagonal closest-packed; *CCP* = cubic closest-packed; and *DIAM* = diamond structure, a variant of cubic.)

Property	Li	Be	B	C	N	O	F	Ne
Melting point, °C	108	1277	2030	3770	−210	−219	−220	−249
Molar density, moles/cm³	0.076	0.205	0.216	0.292	0.058	0.071	0.058	0.059
Electrical conductivity, mho	0.117	0.25	10^{-12}	$<10^{-10}$	All very small: $<10^{-20}$			
Structure	*BCC*	*HCP*	Fig. 25.17	*DIAM*	*HCP*	*HCP*	—	*CCP*
Classification								

(*a*) Fill in the blanks above which are labeled "classification," using Mo for molecular crystal, *C* for covalent macromolecular, *M* for metallic, and *I* for ionic.

(*b*) Explain why N, O, F, and Ne exhibit low melting points and low molar densities but Li, Be, B, and C exhibit relatively high melting points and high molar densities. Do not merely restate your answers to part *a* above; discuss the forces that hold these crystals together.

17.13. Which in each of the following pairs will have the stronger bond? (*a*) CN, CN^+; (*b*) CN^-, CN; (*c*) NF^-, NF; (*d*) CF, CF^+.

17.14. Which in each pair of the following gaseous reactions is energetically more likely?
(*a*) $CH_3F \longrightarrow CH_3 + F$ or $CH_3F \longrightarrow CH_3^+ + F^-$, $I.E._{CH_3} = 228$ kcal mole^{-1}.
(*b*) $N_2 \longrightarrow 2N$, or $N_2 \longrightarrow N_2^+ + e^-$.
(*c*) $Na + Cl_2 \longrightarrow NaCl + Cl$, or $Na + Cl_2 \longrightarrow Na^+ + Cl^- + Cl$.
Comment on the relative likelihood of gaseous reactions producing ions or producing neutral species.

III

17.15. Can you see any reasons for questioning the value of $I.E._{F_2}$? Estimate a "more reasonable" value and justify your estimate as thoroughly as possible?

17.16. Would you expect the $C_{2(g)}$ molecule to be stable with respect to $2C_{(g)}$ (*a*) from VB theory, (*b*) from MO theory? What is the most common species in gaseous carbon near the boiling point?

17.17. Comment on the relative stabilities with respect to their atoms of He_2, Li_2, Be_2, B_2. The observed bond strengths are 0.01, 25.8, 16(?), and 66 kcal mole^{-1}, respectively. Does the 16(?) indicate doubtfully high or doubtfully low in your opinion? Would the ions He_2^+, Li_2^+, Be_2^+, B_2^+ have a stronger or weaker bond than the corresponding neutral molecules?

17.18. HCN and HCCH are isoelectronic with the molecules in Table 17.2. Estimate some of their molecular properties and then check your predictions against the literature values. Account for any surprises.

17.19. Two thermistors have resistance-temperature relationships as follows.
A. 0.0°C, 4598 ohms; 20.0°C, 2182 ohms; 98.7°C, 229 ohms.
B. 0.0°C, 10802 ohms; 21.8°C, 4614 ohms; 97.1°C, 410 ohms.
Which thermistor has the larger activation energy to produce conductivity electrons? How about 0.0°C, 89.5; 17.5°C, 60.7; 97.9°C, 17.3 ohms?

17.20. Draw orbital overlap representations for the following gaseous molecules and predict their bond angles, bond lengths, and polarity:
$HgCl_2$, Hg_2Cl_2, Fe_2Cl_6, SCl_2, S_2Cl_2, H_2O_2, H_2O, C_3O_2, F_2O.

17.21. The energies of the following reactions have been determined experimentally:

$Cl_2 \longrightarrow Cl_2^+ + e^-$ 11.64 ±0.5 ev[1]

$Cl_2 \longrightarrow Cl_2^{++} + 2e^-$ 32.6 ev[1]

$Cl_2 \longrightarrow 2Cl$ 2.47 ev[2]

$Cl \longrightarrow Cl^+ + e^-$ 13.00 ev[3]

$Cl^+ \longrightarrow Cl^{++} + e^-$ 23.80 ev[3]

[1] J. T. Herron and V. H. Dibeler, *J. Chem. Phys.*, **22**, 1884 (1960).
[2] W. H. Evans, T. R. Munson, and D. D. Wagman, *J. Res. National Bureau of Standards*, **55**, 1947 (1955).
[3] G. Herzberg, *Atomic Spectra and Atomic Structure*, Dover, 1944.

(*a*) Calculate the dissociation energy of Cl_2^+. [About 4 ev]
(*b*) Determine the products of dissociation of the stable species Cl_2^{++} and determine the dissociation energy.
(*c*) Compare the dissociation energies of Cl_2, Cl_2^+, and Cl_2^{++}, and discuss the results in terms of MO theory.

17.22. The ionization energy (of electrons by photons—photo electrons) versus intensity of ionization for isoelectronic Ar and HCl is illustrated. Rationalize the following features of the curves: (*a*) the close doublet in Ar, (*b*) the two broad regions of ionization in HCl, (*c*) the "fine structure" in each region for HCl. [Price, *Endeavour*, **25**, 78 (1966).]

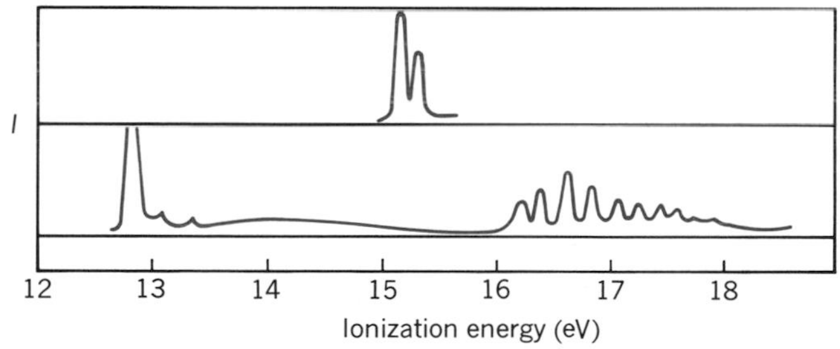

17.23. The ionization energy (of electrons by photons—photo electrons) versus intensity of ionization for isoelectronic N_2 and CO is shown. Rationalize the following features of the curves: (*a*) the three broad regions of ionization, (*b*) the "fine structure", (*c*) the different values of I.E. in the two curves for the three broad regions. [Price, *Endeavour,* **25,** 78 (1966).]

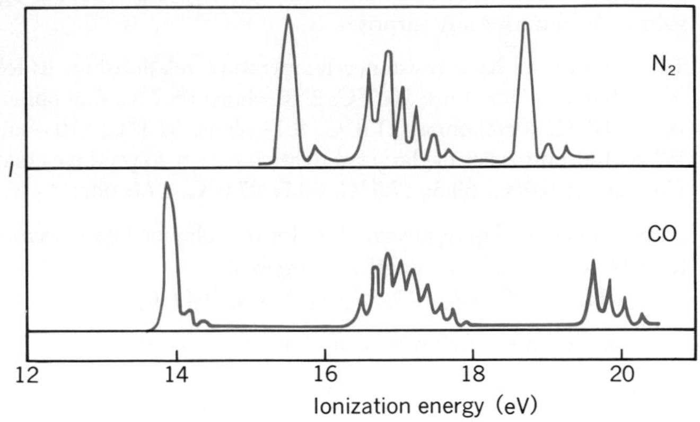

See page 1092 for a list of references and readings in the recent chemical literature related to the material in this chapter.

PART 3

Dynamic Equilibria

TO WHAT EXTENT DO REACTIONS OCCUR?

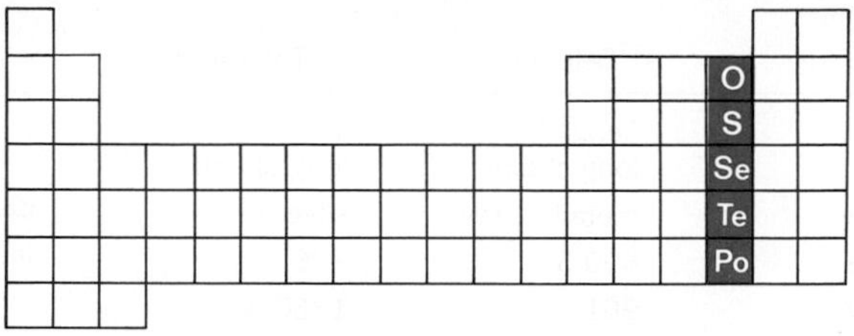

CHAPTER 18

The Chalcogens—Group VIA

Oxygen atoms account for 90% of the volume of the earth's crust.

The elements of the fluorine, chlorine, bromine, iodine group are called halogens, as we saw in Chapter 13, from the Greek stems *hals*, salt from the sea, and *genes*, to be born—that is, elements that come from sea salt. Similarly, the elements of the oxygen, sulfur, selenium, tellurium group are called chalcogens, from the Greek stem *chalkos*, referring to copper—that is, elements that come from some of the ores of copper. (The pronunciation is kăl′-kō-jens.)

Polonium, in this second group, is radioactive (like astatine, in the halogens), and we will therefore not include it in our treatment of the group. Unlike astatine, polonium was first found in naturally occurring radioactive ores as an intermediate in the conversion of radium into lead; astatine was first synthesized in the laboratory by bombarding bismuth with alpha particles in a cyclotron.

SOME FAMILY RELATIONSHIPS

Table 18.1 compares some properties of the chalcogens as a function of increasing atomic number.

There should be few obvious surprises in the tabulated data. The trend in each row of data is monotonic (except for S^0) and in a direction consistent with those in the other rows. The big jumps are between oxygen and sulfur, reminiscent of the halogen family (see Table 13.1). The transition from nonmetallic character to metallic character goes further and faster than with the halogens. (However, we should recall the metallic luster of iodine.) None of the chalcogens is a good electrical or thermal conductor, and the conductivity in selenium and tellurium

Table 18.1 Some properties of the chalcogens.

Property	Oxygen	Sulfur	Selenium	Tellurium	Trend (⟶)
Formula (room *T*)	$O_{2(g)}$	$S_{8(c)}$	$Se_{n(c)}$ long chains	$Te_{n(c)}$ long chains	
Color (room *T*)	—	yellow	metallic grey	silvery	deepens
Melting point (°K)	54.3	392.3	490.5	726	increase
Boiling point (°K)	90	717.7	961	1360.3	increase
Ionization energy (kcal mole^{-1})	314	239	225	208	decrease
X—X bond energy (kcal mole^{-1})	117	101	65	52	decrease
S°_{298} (eu)	48.996 (O_2)	60.80 (rhombic S_8)	10.144 (Se)	11.88 (Te)	varies
Electron structure (gaseous atom)	2, 6	2, 8, 6	2, 8, 18, 6	2, 8, 18, 18, 6	

crystals varies markedly with orientation of the crystal, just as one would expect in a crystal made up of long chains of atoms. (Remember graphite.)

All of these elements exist in a variety of molecular modifications. We have discussed some of these for oxygen and sulfur and have shown part of the phase diagram for pure sulfur (Figure 5.14). The electron structure of molecular oxygen was discussed in Chapter 17 in terms of molecular orbital theory, which accounts in a most satisfying way for the experimental observation that molecular oxygen has two unpaired electrons per molecule.

Unlike oxygen, however, sulfur, selenium, and tellurium have structures that may be interpreted satisfactorily in terms of atomic orbitals, possibly as a result of the additional shielding for the valence electrons around these nuclei. The splitting of the atomic energy levels by the closely bonded oxygen nuclei proceeds to such an extent that molecular orbital theory must be invoked. This splitting appears to be much less for the other members of the group.

Sulfur normally occurs as eight-membered rings at room temperature. The most stable states for selenium and tellurium are long chains. The bond distances are 2.05, 2.32, and 2.86 Å respectively and the bond angles are 105°, 104°, and 104°. The chain formation itself, whether closed into a ring or extended, is consistent with the existence of six valence electrons in a closely spaced *s*-*p* set of orbitals. There are two vacancies in the *p* set, allowing covalent overlap with two other atoms to give chains of atoms in which the coordination number is, of course, two. The difference in stability of the ring and chain forms in sulfur is not great, as is shown by the formation of chains when the sulfur is heated slightly above its melting point.

Exercise 18.1

Account for the trend in color in the chalcogens. *Answer:* As Z increases, the energy levels get closer together (Figure 4.6), especially in the condensed phase (Figure 17.8) of high *CN*. Thus the absorption bands (*a*) move from the *UV* into the visible and (*b*) broaden as crystal orbitals get more important.

Table 18.2 The most common elements (nuclei) in various fractions of the earth. Note that several elements vital to ocean life are present in truly minute concentrations—for example, N ($2 \cdot 10^{-5}$%), P (10^{-6}%), Fe (10^{-7}%).

Ocean		Solid crust		Total earth	
Element	Atomic percent	Element	Atomic percent	Element	Atomic percent
H	66.	O	62.	O	49.3
O	33.	Si	21.	Fe	16.5
Cl	0.32	Al	6.3	Si	14.5
Na	0.28	Na	2.5	Mg	14.2
Mg	0.035	Ca	1.9	S	1.6
S	0.014	Fe	1.9	Al	1.1
Ca	0.0061	Mg	1.6	Ni	1.1
K	0.0061	K	1.4	Ca	0.7
C	0.0014	Cl	0.5	others	1.
Br	0.00050	H	0.3		
B	0.00026	Ti	0.3		
Si	0.00007	C	0.1		
Sr	0.00005	P	0.05		

OXYGEN

Examination of the earth's outer surface shows that the most common element (that is, most common nucleus) is oxygen. The figures given in Table 18.2 are, of course, estimates; they will vary with the authority quoted, but the general order, and the fact that oxygen nuclei are most common, is widely agreed upon. A more detailed analysis is presented in Figure 18.1. The compositions of representative samples of the known universe again indicate that oxygen is a common element, as shown in Table 18.3.

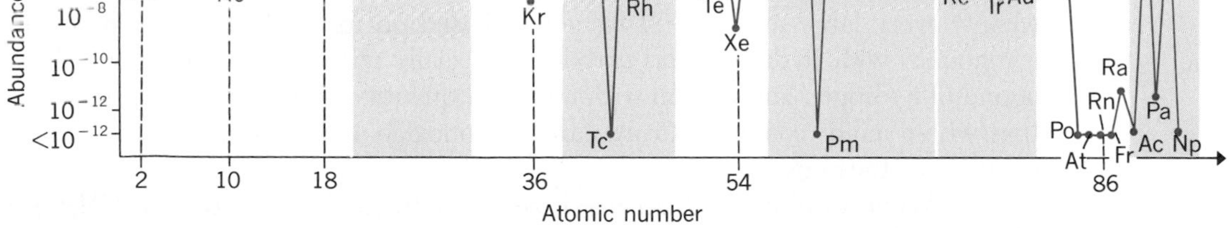

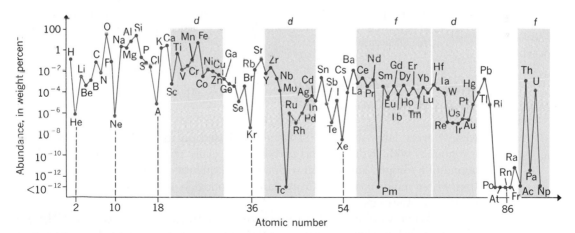

Figure 18.1 Crustal abundance of elements of atomic numbers 1–93. Note the logarithmic abundance coordinate. [M. Fleischer and R. L. Parker, U.S. Geol. Surv. Prof. Paper 440-D (1967).]

Table 18.3 Common elements in some natural systems.

Earth's surface	Meteorites	Solar atmosphere	Star τ Scorpii	Nebula NGC 7027
O	O	H	H	H
Si	Si	He	He	He
Al	Fe	O	Ne	C
Na	Al	Si	C	N
Fe	Mg	N	O	O
Ca	S	C	N	Si

The two most readily available forms of oxygen today are the gaseous molecule, O_2, and water, H_2O. But the most abundant forms containing oxygen are the silicate rocks immediately beneath us. Table 18.2 and Figure 14.4 show that oxygen is the only one of the common elements that has a high electronegativity and thus tends to form negative ions. Because these negative ions are usually larger than positive ions, oxygen atoms account for more than 90% of the volume of the earth's crust. The smaller positive ions fit into the interstices and consequently increase the total volume only a little. Obtaining pure oxygen from these crystalline oxides is a highly endothermic process. Even the decomposition of water into the elements is highly endothermic—68 kcal mole^{-1} of water decomposed. Therefore almost all of the pure oxygen made commercially is produced by the distillation of liquid air. In 1968 the daily rate of production was about 100,000 tons of oxygen of better than 95% purity, at a cost of about $10 per ton. (Twenty years earlier the cost was $1 per pound.) About half of this is used in steelmaking, slightly less in the production of other chemicals, about 5 percent in missile propulsion, and a few percent in medicine and in welding.

Exercise 18.2

Why are negative ions generally larger than positive ions? *Answer:* Loss of electrons (forming positive ions) tends to decrease atomic size, partly by depopulating outer energy levels, partly by drawing all electrons closer to the nucleus; the reverse is true for negative ions.

CHEMICAL USES OF OXYGEN ON A COMMERCIAL SCALE

Almost every large-scale use of oxygen is based on its tendency to form stable compounds with hydrogen and carbon—especially with carbon. Heating a compound of hydrogen and carbon with a limited quantity of oxygen produces a mixture whose major constituents are carbon monoxide and hydrogen. This mixture is called synthesis gas.

When synthesis gas is passed over certain catalysts, methanol (CH_3OH) is formed. When synthesis gas is passed over other catalysts in the presence of additional oxygen, the carbon monoxide is almost quantitatively converted to carbon dioxide, leaving the hydrogen unreacted. It is in this way that a gaseous solution suitable for the Haber process (see Chapter 12) may be made. About half of the purified oxygen used commercially goes into the making of ammonia by the Haber process.

The use of purified oxygen in industry is still in its infancy. Almost none was used twenty years ago. Very large savings have already been achieved over past industrial processes, and the oxygen tonnage used approximately doubles every six years.

Exercise 18.3

Write the net equation for synthesis gas production.

Answer: $C_nH_m + \frac{n}{2}O_2 = nCO + \frac{m}{2}H_2$

OXIDATION NUMBERS

We all know that many metals lose their luster and corrode when exposed to the atmosphere. Iron turns black when heated in air but rusts to a red-brown substance when exposed to moist air at room temperature. These two changes can be represented by equations:

$$3Fe_{(c)} + 2O_{2(g)} \xrightarrow{\text{hot}} \underset{\text{black iron oxide}}{Fe_3O_{4(c)}}$$

$$2Fe_{(c)} + \tfrac{3}{2}O_{2(g)} + nH_2O_{(l)} \xrightarrow[\text{T}]{\text{room}} \underset{\text{red iron rust}}{Fe_2O_3 \cdot nH_2O}$$

Similarly, all the other elements, except the noble gases, react with oxygen to form oxides. This process of combination with oxygen has for many years been called oxidation. Modern structural studies show, however, that many other changes produce quite similar results. For example, metallic sodium can combine with either oxygen or chlorine. In both cases sodium ions are produced, surrounded by oxide ions in one case and by chloride ions in the other:

$$2Na_{(c)} + \tfrac{1}{2}O_{2(g)} = (Na^+)_2O^{=}{}_{(c)} \equiv Na_2O_{(c)}$$
$$Na_{(c)} + \tfrac{1}{2}Cl_{2(g)} = Na^+Cl^-{}_{(c)} \equiv NaCl_{(c)}$$

As far as the sodium is involved the two changes are very similar. When this was first discovered, the term oxidation was extended to cover all such cases and oxidation was defined as the loss of electrons by a substance, in this case by the sodium. Thus the reaction of hydrogen with oxygen and the reaction of hydrogen with bromine were both called oxidations, since polarity studies indicated that the hydrogen was the more positive constituent in both the resulting molecules:

$$H_{2(g)} + \tfrac{1}{2}O_{2(g)} = (H^{\delta+})_2O^{2\delta-}{}_{(g)} \equiv H_2O_{(g)}$$
$$\tfrac{1}{2}H_{2(g)} + \tfrac{1}{2}Br_{2(g)} = H^{\delta+}Br^{\delta-}{}_{(g)} \equiv HBr_{(g)}$$

The more these reactions were studied, however, the less certain it seemed that the substance oxidized always lost electrons. Suppose a gaseous sulfur atom reacts with gaseous oxygen to produce gaseous sulfur dioxide. There is universal agreement that the sulfur has been oxidized, but each atom of sulfur seems actually to have gained electrons rather than lost any:

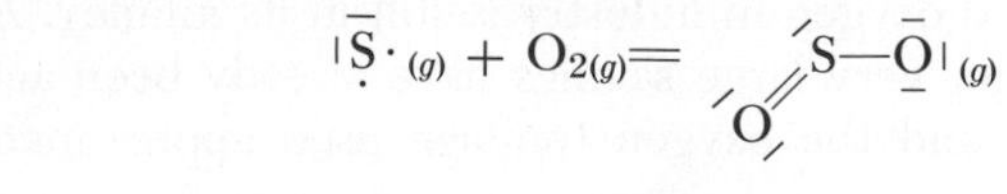

Since similar anomalies arise in hundreds of other instances oxidation is now defined as an increase in the positive oxidation number of an element. Changes in oxidation states are identified by applying some simple rules.

1. The sum of the oxidation numbers of the atoms in any species equals the electrical charge on the species. *Corollary:* Any element in the pure elementary state has an oxidation state of zero. This is true because all pure elements are electrically neutral.
2. The elements of main groups IA, IIA, and IIIA (except boron) in the periodic table always have positive oxidation states of +1, +2, and +3, respectively.
3. Hydrogen has an oxidation state of +1 in all of its compounds except those with the elements of groups IA, IIA, and IIIA.
4. Fluorine always has an oxidation state of −1 in compounds.
5. Oxygen usually has an oxidation state of −2 in compounds, except for some compounds to which rules 2, 3, and/or 4 apply.
6. The maximum positive oxidation state of an element equals its group number in the periodic table. The most negative oxidation state is this maximum positive number minus eight.
7. The oxidation states of other elements are determined by applying the above rules, as appropriate, in the order given. In case of doubt the more electronegative element is given its most negative oxidation number; thus Cl = −1, and I = +1, in ICl.

Table 18.4 shows some application of the rules. Note that rules 1 and 7 are most commonly used. Thus it is rules 2, 3, 4, and 6 which must be especially remembered as to content and sequence of application.

Table 18.4 Examples of calculating oxidation numbers. Note that rules 1 and 7 are most commonly used. Thus it is rules 2, 3, 4, 5, and 6 which must be especially remembered as to content and sequence of application.

Substance	S_8	H_2S	LiH	RbO_2	$CaSO_4$	$BrCl_4^-$
Oxidation states	0	+1, −2	+1, −1	+1, $-\frac{1}{2}$	2+, ?, 2−	Cl, −1
Rules	1	1, 3	1, 2	1, 2	by 1, 2, 5, and 7 S = +6	by 1, 6, 7 Br = +3
Substance	HF	SF_6	CH_3CHO	$KMnO_4$	$Na_2S_2O_3$	Mn_3O_4
Oxidation states	+1, −1	+6, −1	H = +1, O = −2	+1, +7, −2	+1, +2, −2	O = −2
Rules	1, 3, or 4	1, 4	C = −1 from 1, 3, 5, 7	1, 2, 5, 7	1, 2, 5, 7	Mn = $+\frac{8}{3}$ from 1, 5

Many complicated compounds are composed of simpler species. For example, NH_3, CO, CN^-, NO, and similar groups can enter into complexes such as $Cu(NH_3)_4^{++}$, $Ni(CO)_4$, $Ag(CN)_2^-$, $FeNO^+$. In such compounds the complexing species are assumed not to have changed oxidation number. Thus NH_3 is always 0, as are CO and NO, and CN^- is always -1. This gives the metals the following oxidation states in the complexes listed: Cu = +2, Ni = 0, Ag = +1, Fe = +2. Note that it is possible to have an element of zero oxidation state in a compound, such as $Ni(CO)_4$, CH_2O, SiH_2Cl_2.

Though oxidation and reduction are now defined in terms of changes in oxidation numbers (obtained by applying the rules above), it is often possible to detect real gains and losses of electrons by individual atoms. In many redox reactions (see next paragraph) atoms exchange electrons, and the changes in oxidation numbers indicate the numbers of electrons exchanged.

Just as oxidation is defined as gain, or increase in positive oxidation number, so the opposite process of reduction is defined as loss, or decrease in positive oxidation number. Every increase in the oxidation number of one atom must be exactly offset by a compensating decrease in the positive oxidation number of another atom. Oxidation and reduction are inextricably linked—one always accompanies the other. Reactions that are described in terms of reduction and oxidation are commonly called redox reactions. Any reaction in which the oxidation numbers change is a redox reaction.

One of the uses of oxidation numbers is to predict and correlate the changes that occur in redox reactions. Thus a change involving an increase in positive oxidation number requires an oxidizing agent to accomplish it. Another use is to predict and correlate the properties of different chemical species. Thus all species containing oxygen in the -1 oxidation state will have some similar properties, all species containing sulfur in oxidation state +6 will have some similar properties, and so on. A third use is to name substances. Thus $FeCl_2$ is called iron (II) chloride, Hg_2Cl_2 is called dimercury (I) dichloride, and so forth. But oxidation numbers themselves, though useful, are determined by arbitrary rules and do not necessarily indicate the presence of electric charge differences of the same magnitude.

Exercise 18.1

Assign oxidation numbers to each atom in the following: C_3O_2; $Fe(CO)_5$; Sb_2S_4; K_2MnO_4; $C_{12}H_{22}O_{11}$; $K_2Cr_3O_{10}$; Al_2Cl_6; $Na_2S_2O_3$. *Answer:* $+\frac{4}{3}$, -2; 0, +2, -2; +4, -2; +1, +6, -2; 0, +1, -2; +1, +6, -2; +3, -1; +1, +2, -2. Assign H, Na, K = +1 first; then O = -2; Cl = -1. Get other by difference.

OXIDATION STATES OF THE CHALCOGENS

The most common oxidation states of the chalcogens are listed in Table 18.5. The -2, +6, and +4 states are most commonly found. Typically the -2 state involves gaining two electrons in the vacant p orbitals (either to form an X^{2-} ion or a covalent molecule), the -1 state involves a sharing of electrons between two chalcogen

Table 18.5 Some common oxidation states of the chalcogens. Values of $\Delta G^0_{\mathrm{form}}$ are given in parentheses to indicate the degree of stability of these compounds with respect to the elements. Note the absence of double bonds in selenium and tellurium compounds compared to oxygen and sulfur, and the frequency of sp^3 hybrids. (ΔG^0 in kcal $mole^{-1}$.)

Element	−2	−1	0	+2	+4	+6
Oxygen (sp^3)	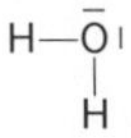 (−56.688) $Ca^{++}(\lvert O\rvert)^{=}$ (−144.4)	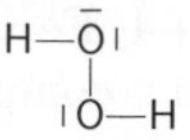 (−28.78) $(Na^+)_2(\lvert O—O\rvert)^{=}$ (−102.8)	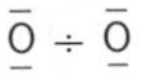 (0) 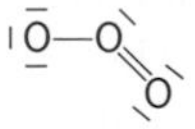 (39.0)			
Sulfur (sp^3, sp^3d^2)	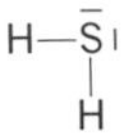 (−8.02) $Fe^{++}(\lvert S\rvert)^{=}$ (−23.32)	$\lvert S—S\rvert^{=}$ (19.0)	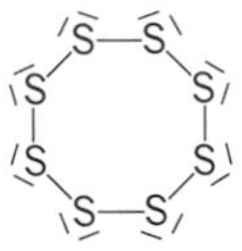 (0)	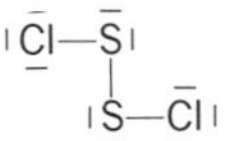 (−7.6$_{(g)}$)	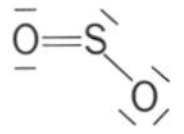 (−71.749)	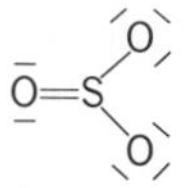 (−88.69) 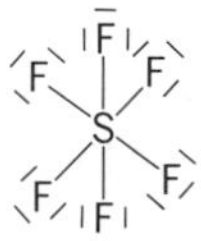 (−264.1)
Selenium (sp^3, sp^3d^2)	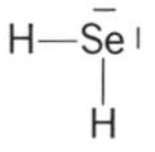 (3.8) NH_4^+ $(H—Se\rvert)^-$ (−5.6)		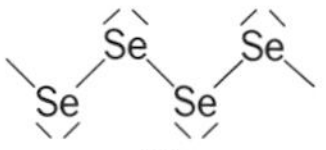 (0)		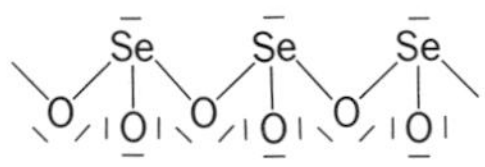 (−41.5)	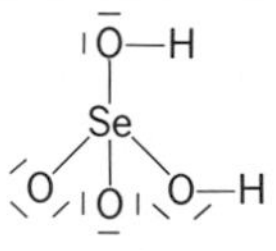 (∼−100) 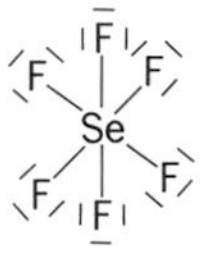 (−243)
Tellurium (sp^3, sp^3d, sp^3d^2)	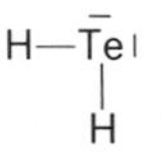 (33.1) $Cu^{++}(\lvert Te\rvert)^{=}$ (∼−6)		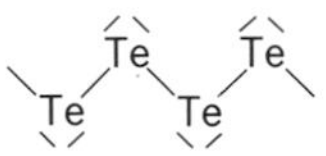 (0)		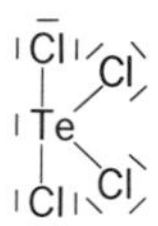 (−56.7)	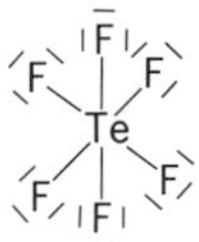 (−292)

atoms ($O_2^=$), and the +6 state involves sharing at least eight (sp^3) and maybe more (sp^3d^2) electrons with electronegative atoms—usually oxygen or fluorine.

Exercise 18.5

What kind of reactant (oxidizing, reducing, or other) is needed for each of the following changes? $O_2 \longrightarrow O_3$; $H_2O_2 \longrightarrow O_2$; $H_2O_2 \longrightarrow H_2O$; $H_2O_2 \longrightarrow H_2$. *Answer:* $0 \longrightarrow 0$, other; $-1 \longrightarrow 0$, oxidizing; $-1 \longrightarrow -2$, reducing; $+1 \longrightarrow 0$, reducing.

REACTIONS BETWEEN THE ELEMENTS AND OXYGEN

Elementary oxygen reacts with most of the other elements to form binary compounds called oxides, in which the oxidation state of the oxygen is -2. Some of the alkali metals and alkaline earth metals react to give other compounds, as shown in Table 18.6. The stability of the peroxides (containing $O_2^=$ ions) and superoxides (containing O_2^- ions) may result from the large sizes of the corresponding cations, which will give stable crystals with large anions; smaller cations could not keep the large peroxide or superoxide anions apart. Thus lithium peroxide is prepared only with great difficulty, and the peroxide of beryllium does not appear to be known.

Each of the elements except the noble gases appears to have at least one oxygen compound, which is energetically stable at room temperatures, but many elements do not react appreciably with oxygen at room temperature—probably because a protective oxide coating immediately forms on the surface of the element.

The oxides of the metallic elements are generally ionic, especially when the metallic element is in its lower oxidation states and when the electronegativity of the metal differs greatly from that of oxygen. As the oxidation state of the metallic element increases, the oxides become more and more covalent, as the nucleus of the metallic element becomes more and more exposed and increasingly attracts the oxygen electrons. Consider, for example, the relative forces acting in MnO_4^- ions ($+7$ manganese) and MnO ($+2$ manganese). Or consider the likelihood of covalent bond formation with the *s* and *p* orbitals of the alkali metal ions, compared to the likelihood of covalent bonding with the *s*, *p*, and *d* orbitals found in the transition metal ions.

The rate of reaction of oxygen in forming oxides is lower than might be expected, compared to the rates of chlorine, fluorine, and bromine. This may well be due to the higher bond strength in molecular oxygen (see Table 14.8), which is only partly offset by the tendency of molecules with unpaired electrons to react rapidly (molecular oxygen has two unpaired electrons). This rationalization of the low rate of reaction of oxygen in forming oxides is borne out by examining the rates of reaction at which peroxides and superoxides form. In these reactions, the oxygen-to-oxygen bond is not broken and the reactions are faster than those leading to oxide formation. Further evidence is given by the rapid rate of reaction between hemoglobin and oxygen. Here the entire oxygen molecule attaches to the hemoglobin molecule, apparently through the interaction between the unpaired electrons and a ferric ion bound to the hemoglobin, and without bond breaking in the O_2 molecule.

The world would be a very different place if molecular oxygen were a rapid oxidizing agent. For example, few if any of the living systems we know would exist, since most living materials (proteins, carbohydrates, fats) are oxidizable by molecular oxygen at room temperature.

Thus oxygen is a powerful oxidizing agent with most of the elements and many of their compounds, but its rate of reaction is relatively low at room temperature.

Exercise 18.6

Interpret the fact that powdered aluminum reacts very slowly with atmospheric oxygen, but can detonate when mixed with liquid oxygen. *Answer:* Liquid O_2 contains no other materials which would absorb heat to slow the exothermic Al—O_2 reaction; liquid O_2 is more concentrated than air by a factor of about 100; the difference in energy required to raise liquid O_2 to the explosion temperature compared to gaseous O_2 is not appreciable compared to ΔH.

OXIDES OF METALS

The properties of many of the oxides of the metals may be interpreted in terms of ionic bonding. The crystal structures are generally consistent with the idea that the large negative oxide ions pack together closely with the smaller cations in the interstices (see Tables 16.4 and 16.5). Table 18.7 lists some of the more common oxides in terms of their crystal structures to indicate further the wide-ranging effect of ionic forces in crystalline oxides.

The available evidence—the effect of radius ratio, the anion-anion internuclear distances, physical properties, and chemical properties—indicates that the substances listed in Table 18.7 are highly ionic in the crystal state. The properties of the oxides in Table 18.8, on the other hand, indicate a high degree of covalent character. For example, the latter table contains many compounds with large oxygen-oxygen distances, a high degree of electron conductivity, and low correlation of structure with radius ratio—all of which indicate directional bonding, often involving delocalized electrons, and thus strongly suggesting covalent bonding consistent with the relatively small differences from oxygen in electronegativity and/or the high oxidation states.

We would, therefore, expect molten oxides of most metals to be good conductors of electricity, even though the solids would be expected to be insulators. Ions should be present in both the phases, but they would be immobilized by the crystal structure and free to move in the liquid. Many of the oxides have such

Table 18.6 Crystalline products of direct reaction of some metals with excess oxygen at room temperature. ΔG^0_{298} values (in parentheses) indicate stability with respect to the elements. (ΔG^0 in kcal mole^{-1}.)

Oxidation state of oxygen	Oxygen species	Metals								Type of product
		Li	Na	K	Rb	Cs	Be, Mg, Ca	Sr	Ba	
-2	$O^=$	Li_2O (-133.9)	Na_2O (-90.0)				MO	SrO (-133.8)		oxides
-1	$O_2^=$		Na_2O_2 (-102.8)	K_2O_2 (-100.1)				SrO_2 (-139)	BaO_2 (-135.8)	peroxides
$-\frac{1}{2}$	O_2^-			KO_2 (-49.8)	RbO_2 (-47.3)	CsO_2 (-46.3)				superoxides

Table 18.7 **Some metal oxide structures with a high degree of ionic bonding. Note that six crystal types (NaCl, CaF_2, TiO_2, Cr_2O_3, Tl_2O_3, and La_2O_3) account for the great majority of metallic oxide structures. Note also that ionic character decreases from left to right in the periodic table and also decreases with increasing oxidation number of the cation.**

Oxidation state of cation	Cation-anion ratio	Substances	Crystal type (and Table, if any)	*CN* of oxygen atoms about cations
+1	2–1	(*a*) K_2O, Li_2O, Na_2O, Rb_2O	Anti-CaF_2 (16.4) (cations and anions reversed compared to CaF_2)	4
		(*b*) Cs_2O	$CdCl_2$	6
+2	1–1	(*a*) BeO, ZnO		4
		(*b*) AmO, BaO, CaO, CdO, CoO, FeO, MgO, MnO, NbO, NiO, PaO, PuO, SmO, SrO, TaO, TiO, UO, VO	NaCl (15.8)	6
+3	2–3	(*a*) Al_2O_3, Cr_2O_3, Fe_2O_3, Ga_2O_3 Rh_2O_3, Ti_2O_3, V_2O_3	Cr_2O_3	6
		(*b*) Dy_2O_3, Er_2O_3, Eu_2O_3, Gd_2O_3, Ho_2O_3, In_2O_3, Lu_2O_3, Mn_2O_3, Sc_2O_3, Sm_2O_3, Tb_2O_3, Tl_2O_3, Tm_2O_3, Y_2O_3, Yb_2O_3	Tl_2O_3	6
		(*c*) Ac_2O_3, Ce_2O_3, La_2O_3, Nd_2O_3, Pr_2O_3	La_2O_3	7
+4	1–2	(*a*) CrO_2, GeO_2, IrO_2, MnO_2, MoO_2, NbO_2, OsO_2, PbO_2, RuO_2, SnO_2, TaO_2, TeO_2, TiO_2, VO_2, WO_2	TiO_2 (16.4)	6
		(*b*) AmO_2, CeO_2, HfO_2, NpO_2, PaO_2, PoO_2, PrO_2, PuO_2, ThO_2, UO_2, ZrO_2	CaF_2 (16.4)	8
+5	2–5	V_2O_5		5 (or 4)
+6	1–3	ReO_3, WO_3, MoO_3, UO_3	Three different structures	6
+8	1–4	OsO_4	Like CH_4 (Fig. 15.2)	4
$+\frac{8}{3}$	3–4	Fe_3O_4, Mn_3O_4, Co_3O_4	Some cations in tetrahedral holes, some in octahedral holes	4 and 6

a high melting point that their electrical conductivity in the liquid state has not been studied, but those of low melting point, such as the molten alkali metal oxides, are good conductors of electricity by ionic transport. Consistent with our prediction, most of the crystalline oxides listed by crystal class in Table 18.7 are poor conductors of electricity.

Table 18.8 **Some metal oxide structures with a high degree of covalent bonding. All oxides of nonmetals are highly covalent.**

2–1	Cu_2O, Ag_2O, Pb_2O (see Table 16.9)
1–1	PbO, SnO, PtO, PdO, CuO, HgO
2–3	Bi_2O_3, Ag_2O_3, B_2O_3, Pb_2O_3
1–2	SeO_2, SiO_2, PtO_2
2–5	Nb_2O_5, Ta_2O_5, U_2O_5
1–3	CrO_3
2–7	Mn_2O_7
3–4	Pt_3O_4, Pb_3O_4
others	U_3O_8, Mo_4O_{11}, V_6O_{13}, Mo_8O_{23}, Mo_9O_{26}, $W_{18}O_{49}$

Exercise 18.7

Rationalize the fact that highly positive oxidation states are less apt to be ionic than are the less positive states of the same element. *Answer:* I.E. rises rapidly with each electron removed (Figure 3.3), much more rapidly than coulombic interaction of the resulting positive ions. Thus, highly positive states are energetically difficult to attain and stabilize compared to the lower states. Assignment of oxidation numbers is done by rule ($O = -2$); thus a high atomic ratio of oxide ions, for example, automatically gives a high positive oxidation number even though the bonds are covalent.

OXIDE COATINGS ON METALS

We have already stated that all metals react directly with oxygen to form oxides. All of these reactions can occur at room temperatures. Yet many metals remain bright, shiny, and uncorroded even when exposed to the atmosphere for years. The jewelry metals are outstanding examples, but even highly reactive aluminum can be cited, as shown by the bright aluminum pots and pans in many kitchens.

A clue to this behavior can be reached by studying the corrosion of iron. Rusting occurs in moist air and continues until the sample is completely converted to the flaky, hydrous ferric oxide we call rust. Its formula is indefinite under most conditions but can be written $Fe_2O_3 \cdot nH_2O$, in which the value of n depends on the conditions of formation and can vary greatly in a single sample of rust from one spot to another. Hence, for example, the varied colors of most rusty objects. Hot iron, on the other hand, turns black quickly in air but then becomes quite inert to further reaction. This black coating is highly resistant to rusting. Analysis of the black material shows it to be Fe_3O_4, black iron oxide. The black oxide, unlike rust, adheres tightly to the iron surface. It is this adherence (plus the general inertness of the oxide itself) that inhibits further corrosion.

Similar oxide coats form on all metals. Some are transparently thin, adherent, and insoluble in water so that the metal appears to be inert toward atmospheric oxidation, as with the jewelry metals and aluminum. Chromium-plated objects are also protected by a similar coat as, indeed, are all metals which remain shiny when exposed to the atmosphere. The alkali and most of the alkaline earth metals form water-soluble, flaky oxides aand thus corrode rapidly in air.

One may well ask why some oxides adhere and others flake off. A little

Table 18.9 Properties of some metals and their common oxides.

Atomic number Z	Metal	Oxide	Densities (g cm^{-3}) ρ metal	ρ oxide (ρ metal in oxide)	Solubility of oxide in water	Coating
13	Al	Al_2O_3	2.70	3.97 (2.10)	insoluble	protective
12	Mg	MgO	1.74	3.58 (2.15)	slightly soluble	moderately protective
11	Na	Na_2O	0.97	2.27 (1.69)	soluble	nonprotective
26	Fe	$Fe_2O_3 \cdot nH_2O$	7.86	~3 (~2)	insoluble	nonprotective
		Fe_3O_4	7.86	4.18 (3.03)	insoluble	protective

thought will indicate that it must have to do with how close a match exists between the crystal structure of the metal and that of the oxide. If the structures match, there may be very little change in effective volume of the surface layer with respect to the metal. In such a case cracks will not form, the oxide can adhere, and further reaction is inhibited (if the oxide is insoluble), since the atmosphere can no longer come in contact with the reactive metal surface. Formation of surface coatings having quite different volumes and/or structures than the metals from which they come will lead to shrinkage or expansion of the surface layer as it forms. This will cause cracking of each new layer and will continue to expose fresh metal surfaces to continuing reaction. Table 18.9 gives some data to evaluate these arguments.

OXIDES OF THE NONMETALLIC ELEMENTS

Most of the oxides of the nonmetals can be prepared in forms which are relatively volatile. Many of them also polymerize into larger molecules. But in every case the bonding is primarily covalent, as indicated by low coordination numbers, the volatility itself, and the lack of electrical conduction in any phase. Some of the more common oxides are listed in Table 18.10, with the most common one listed at the top of each set. Most of these molecular oxides have structures predictable from valence bond theory. For example, C_3O_2 is O=C=C=C=O, a linear molecule.

Exercise 18.8

Draw a possible VB structure for Cl_2O and for ClO_2. *Answer:* Cl has 7 valence electrons, O has 6. Cl_2O has 20 valence electrons, possibly as

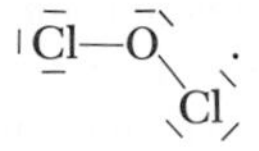

. ClO_2 has

Table 18.10 Some oxides of nonmetals arranged according to the periodic table. All have essentially covalent bonds. $\Delta G^0_{\text{form } 298}$ values (in parentheses) indicate relative stability of the more common species with respect to the elements; note many are unstable in the standard state (have ΔG^0_f values, which are positive). Note that $(\ )_n$ indicates a polymeric, or macromolecular, solid. The other substances are molecular. (ΔG^0 in kcal $mole^{-1}$.)

			H_2O
CO_2 (−94.258) CO (−32.781) C_3O_2	N_2O_5, $(NO_2^+, NO_3^-)_{(c)}$ (27.5) (27.2) N_2O_4, NO_2 (23.38) (12.26) N_2O_3, NO, N_2O (33.32) (20.69) (24.90)	O_2 O_3 (39.0)	F_2O (−1.1) F_2O_2
$(SiO_2)_n$ (−204.75)	$P_4O_{10(c)}$ (−644.8) $P_4O_{6(c)}$	SO_2 (71.749) SO_3 and $(\ )_n$ (88.69) S_2O, S_2O_3, S_2O_7	Cl_2O (23.4) ClO_2 (28.8) ClO_3 Cl_2O_7
	$As_4O_{6(c)}$ (−275.46) $(As_2O_5)_n$ (−187.0)	$(SeO_2)_{n(c)}$ SeO_3 and $(\ )_n$	Br_2O $(BrO_2)_n$ Br_3O_5
	$Sb_4O_{6(c)}$ (−303.1) $(Sb_2O_5)_n$ (−198.2)	$(TeO_2)_n$ $(TeO_3)_n$	I_2O_5 I_4O_9 $(IO_2)_n$
	$(Bi_2O_3)_n$ (−118.0) $(Bi_2O_5)_n$		

19 valence electrons and is an odd molecule, possibly as 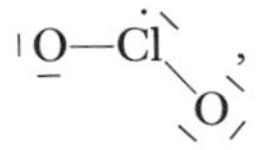, but MO theory would probably be better to use. Both molecules are probably bent with rather long and weak bonds.

SPECIES PRESENT IN PURE WATER

Water is the most common relatively pure chemical in nature and the laboratory. It is also the most common constituent of reacting chemical systems. If we are to understand these systems, it helps to have some understanding of the properties and behavior of water. We have already discussed some of its general properties resulting from the electron structure, bent shape, moderately large difference in relative electronegativity of H and O, and the resulting strong ($\sim$3 kcal mole^{-1}) intermolecular hydrogen bonds. But it is worth noting that water is also a complicated equilibrium system.

Consider the species present. Although it is true that covalent molecules composed of two atoms of hydrogen and one of oxygen are by far the most common, you should note that there are present two stable isotopes of hydrogen (H^1, 98.985%; $H^2 \equiv D$, 0.0149%) and three of oxygen (O^{16}, 99.759%; O^{17}, 0.037%; O^{18}, 0.204%). Tritium, hydrogen of mass three ($H^3 \equiv T$), is also present from cosmic ray reactions. It is radioactive but has a steady-state abundance which is measurable. All radioactive isotopes of oxygen are too short-lived (a 2 minute half-life or less) to be present in detectable amounts. Thus there are many types of water molecules: H_2O^{16}, DHO^{17}, T_2O^{18}, and others. The total possible, counting all six isotopes, is eighteen different isotopic combinations. The relative likelihood of any one kind is, of course, the product of the percent isotopic abundances of the atoms in it, assuming that all bonds are equally strong regardless of isotopic mass. Thus the relative amounts of H_2O^{16} and D_2O^{18} will be

$$(0.98985^2 \cdot 0.99759/0.000149^2 \cdot 0.204) = 2.16 \cdot 10^8$$

In addition, of course, these species can all ionize, as in

$$H_2O_{(l)} \rightleftarrows H^+{}_{(aq)} + OH^-{}_{(aq)}$$

or

$$OH^-{}_{(aq)} \rightleftarrows O^={}_{(aq)} + H^+{}_{(aq)}$$

These equilibria add fifteen more species (neglecting variations in hydration).

Thus there are at least thirty-three species in water, all engaged in dynamic equilibria. Fortunately for the person interested in the reactions and properties of water, the differences in isotopic composition cause only small variations in properties. Also, the $O^=_{(aq)}$ are so very rare (considerably less than one $O^=_{(aq)}$ per liter on average) that they can be neglected. For most purposes the properties of water may be correlated in terms of only H_2O, $H^+{}_{(aq)}$, and $OH^-{}_{(aq)}$ species.

REACTIONS OF OXIDES AND WATER

If an oxide is added to water, interaction with the water will occur. Many oxides are rather insoluble in water and others may dissolve only slowly, but some interaction occurs. One effect of the interactions is to change the concentration of hydrogen ions. Any change in the hydrogen ion concentration will be reflected in an opposite change in the hydroxide ion concentration, since

$$K_{eq} = [H^+][OH^-] = 10^{-14}$$

Addition of some oxides to water causes an increase in the hydrogen ion concentration, and the solution becomes more acidic. These are called acidic oxides. Other oxides reduce the hydrogen ion concentration, and the solution becomes more basic. These are called basic oxides. Still others have no appreciable effect on the acidity of the water. This third class includes the highly insoluble oxides, as well as those whose acid strength is essentially the same as water and those whose rate of reaction with water is very small. However, most of the soluble oxides give large enough changes in the acidity to be known as acidic or basic oxides. CO, NO, and NNO are the only common soluble oxides which undergo no appreciable reaction with water at room temperature. The other oxides of the nonmetals generally dissolve and give an acid solution. The halogen oxides may also undergo oxidation-reduction reactions, such as

$$4I_4O_{9(c)} + 6H_2O_{(l)} = 2I_{2(aq)} + 12HIO_{3(aq)} + 3O_{2(g)}$$

Some typical reactions are the following:

Alkali metal oxides—all are very soluble:

$$M_2O_{(c)} + H_2O_{(l)} = 2M^+{}_{(aq)} + 2OH^-{}_{(aq)}$$

$$Na_2O_{(c)} + H_2O_{(l)} = 2NaOH_{(c)} = 2Na^+{}_{(aq)} + 2OH^-{}_{(aq)}$$

[since all these hydroxides are soluble]

Alkaline earth metal oxides—solubility is low with BeO, increases toward BaO:

$$MO_{(c)} + H_2O_{(l)} = M^{++}{}_{(aq)} + 2OH^-{}_{(aq)}$$

$$BeO_{(c)} + H_2O_{(l)} = Be(OH)_{2(c)}$$

Group three oxides—Y^{+++}, Sc^{+++}, La^{+++}—dissolve appreciably, with solubility increasing in the order given:

$$M_2O_{3(c)} + 3H_2O_{(l)} = 2M^{+++}{}_{(aq)} + 6OH^-{}_{(aq)}$$

$$Al_2O_{3(c)} + 3H_2O_{(l)} = 2Al(OH)_{3(c)} \quad \text{[slow reaction, } Al(OH)_3 \text{ very insoluble]}$$

$$B_2O_{3(c)} + 3H_2O_{(l)} = 2B(OH)_{3(aq)}, \quad B(OH)_{3(aq)} + H_2O \overset{\text{slightly}}{=} B(OH)_4{}^-{}_{(aq)} + H^+{}_{(aq)}$$

The trends in these reactions indicate that increasing the positive oxidation state of the metal, or decreasing the radius of the positive cation, decreases the solubility of the oxide as well as that of the hydroxide. And even when these oxides give soluble products, as does B_2O_3, the small, highly charged central atom has little tendency to break its bond with the surrounding oxygens. Rather, in such a reaction, a proton is freed from the periphery of the $B(OH)_3$ molecule to give an acid solution.

Some typical reactions between the oxides of the nonmetals and water are

$$CO_{2(aq)} + H_2O_{(l)} = CO(OH)_{2(aq)} = CO_2OH^-{}_{(aq)} + H^+{}_{(aq)}$$
$$\text{[or } H_2CO_{3(aq)}\text{][or } HCO_3{}^-{}_{(aq)}\text{]}$$

$$SO_{2(g)} + H_2O_{(l)} = SO(OH)_{2(aq)} = SO_2OH^-{}_{(aq)} + H^+{}_{(aq)}$$
$$\text{[or } H_2SO_{3(aq)}\text{][or } HSO_3{}^-{}_{(aq)}\text{]}$$

$$P_4O_{10(c)} + H_2O_{(l)} = 4PO(OH)_{3(aq)} = 4PO_2(OH)_2{}^-{}_{(aq)} + 4H^+{}_{(aq)}$$
$$\text{[or } H_3PO_{4(aq)}\text{][or } H_2PO_4{}^-{}_{(aq)}\text{]}$$

$$BiO_{3(c)} + H_2O_{(l)} = Bi(OH)_{3(c)} \quad \text{[} Bi(OH)_3 \text{ is very insoluble]}$$

All of these reactions, both those of the metallic and those of the nonmetallic oxides, can be generalized in the following way. Assume that the initial step is the conversion of an oxide ion into two hydroxide groups by reaction with water:

$$MO + H_2O = M(OH)_2$$

This gives a substance in which hydroxide groups are surrounding a central atom that has a positive oxidation number. One of three possible events may now occur. The newly formed OH group can dissociate to form an $OH^-_{(aq)}$ ion and a hydrated positive ion, as do the soluble metallic oxides:

$$\tfrac{1}{2}M_2O_{(c)} + \tfrac{1}{2}H_2O_{(l)} = MOH_{(c)}, \qquad MOH_{(c)} = M^+_{(aq)} + OH^-_{(aq)}$$

Or the newly formed OH group can dissociate a proton to give a $H^+_{(aq)}$ ion and a hydrated negative ion, as do the soluble nonmetallic oxides:

$$YO_{2(g)} + H_2O_{(l)} = H_2YO_{3(aq)}, \qquad H_2YO_{3(aq)} = H^+_{(aq)} + HYO_3{}^-_{(aq)}$$

Or the newly formed OH group can remain without further change, forming no soluble ions at all. The resulting species may dissolve as a neutral molecule, $B(OH)_3$ or H_2CO_3, or may remain almost completely insoluble, as do $Al(OH)_3$ or $Bi(OH)_3$:

$$\tfrac{1}{2}Z_2O_{3(c)} + \tfrac{3}{2}H_2O_{(l)} = Z(OH)_{3(c)} \overset{\text{or maybe}}{=} Z(OH)_{3(aq)}$$

The entropy principle states that each of these processes will occur to some extent. (Remember that all possible things will happen.) But which of these possibilities occurs to the greatest extent depends on the relative bond strengths in the X—O—X entity. If the X—O bond is stronger, H^+ will ionize. If the O—H bond is stronger, OH^- will ionize. If the bonds are both strong, there will be no appreciable ionization.

Exercise 18.9

Which of the following are most apt to be acidic and which basic oxides? CO_2, Cl_2O_7, BaO, La_2O_3, Cs_2O. *Answer:* Metallic oxides are usually basic—Cs_2O, BaO, La_2O_3. Oxides of nonmetals are usually acidic—Cl_2O_7, CO_2. Correlate this difference with relative electronegativities.

EFFECTIVE CHARGE DENSITY

One of the factors that affect the relative strengths of H—O—X bonds is the positive charge density of X. A low positive charge density (especially if accompanied by outer *sp* orbitals which are full) should give a highly ionic bond between X and OH and strengthen the covalent O—H bond. A highly positive charge density on X should increase the tendency of the proton to ionize and, at the same time, concentrate electrons in the X—O bond and strengthen that bond, as in Figure 18.2.

It is not possible to calculate exact charge densities for atoms in molecules, but we can define charge density as net charge divided by the volume through which the charge spreads. For an isolated gaseous atom,

$$\text{charge density} = \frac{\text{net electronic charge}}{\tfrac{4}{3}\pi r^3} \tag{18.1}$$

where r is the effective ionic radius. We may obtain rough approximations to charge densities in condensed phases by using Equation (18.1), and the results will be quite useful for highly ionic species. In covalent species it is customary to

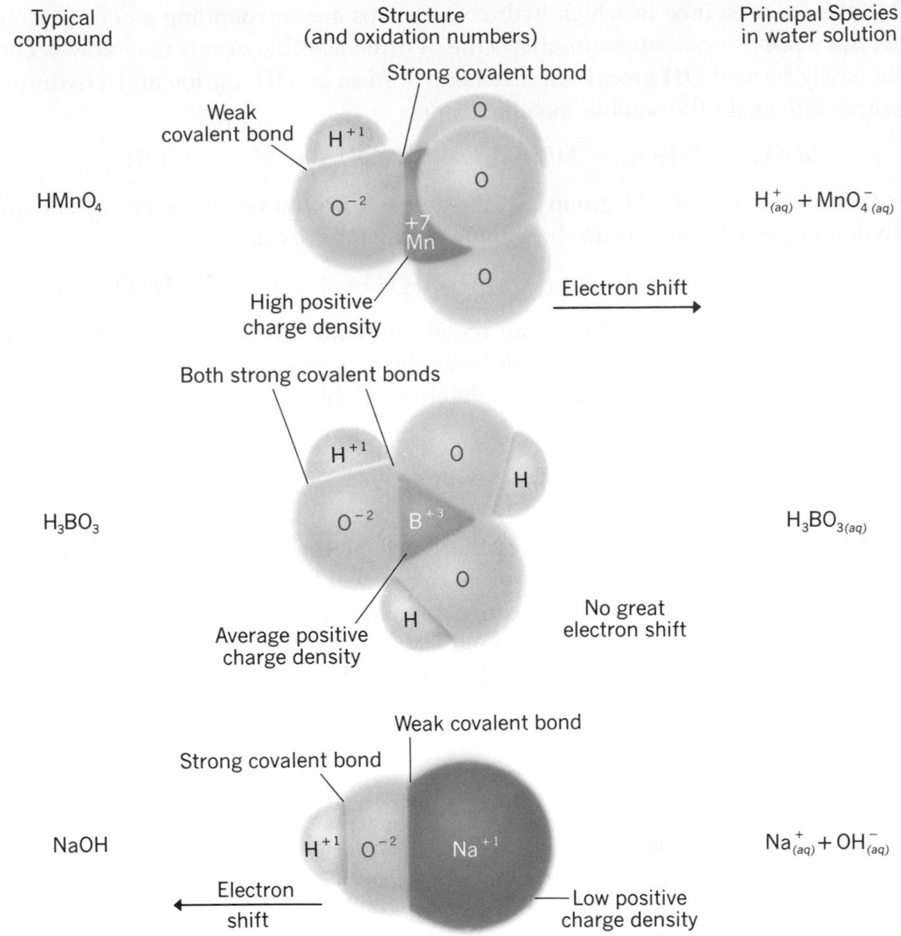

Figure 18.2 Effect of oxidation state and size (charge density) of neighboring atom on the strength of the covalent bond with oxygen, and the degree of ionization in aqueous solutions.

use the oxidation number as an effective charge, and to calculate an effective ionic radius as though the atom were an ion bearing a charge equal to the oxidation number. Tables of such ionic radii are available; see Figure 4.9. For our purposes qualitative arguments will prove sufficient. We shall use oxidation numbers and trends in atomic size (as discussed in Chapters 14 through 17) to evaluate the effects of charge density.

On this basis we would expect the effective positive charge density on the Br in $HBrO_3$ to be less than that on the Cl of $HClO_3$. Both have the same oxidation number, $+5$, but bromine atoms are larger than chlorine atoms. The effective negative charge density on the oxygen in water should be greater than that on the S of H_2S. Again, both have the same oxidation state, but oxygen atoms are smaller than sulfur atoms. The effective positive charge density on the As of H_3AsO_4 should be less than that on the Se of H_2SeO_4, since the sizes are not very different (with As slightly larger), whereas the oxidation state of the arsenic is $+5$ and that of the selenium is $+6$. In each of these cases we find experimentally that more H^+ is released to solution by the molecules having the more positive charge density on the "central" atom.

Exercise 18.10

Select the substance in each following pair which will more readily release OH^- into aqueous solution: NaOH, CsOH; $Ba(OH)_2$, RbOH; $CO(OH)_2$, $SiO(OH)_2$; ClO_3OH, $SO_2(OH)_2$. *Answer:* Low positive charge densities on the atom holding the OH tend to lead to easy release of OH^-. Thus CsOH > NaOH (Cs^+ larger than Na^+); RbOH > $Ba(OH)_2$ (Rb +1, Ba +2); $SiO(OH)_2$ > $CO(OH)_2$ (C +4, Si +4 but larger atom); $SO_2(OH)_2$ > ClO_3OH (S +6 compared to Cl +7). The Si, C, S, and Cl "hydroxides" listed actually act principally as acids in aqueous solutions.

ARRHENIUS ACID-BASE THEORY

The very earliest use of the terms acid and base was in connection with oxides. Metallic oxides were said to be basic oxides and nonmetallic oxides to be acidic oxides. It was thought, in fact, that all acids had to contain oxygen. Bases were known to give slippery aqueous solutions and to have an astringent taste. Acids were sour (the name comes from Latin *acidus,* sour), and attacked metals like zinc and iron but not copper or the coinage metals. Acids and bases reacted with one another to produce salts, which also had a rather characteristic taste.

The earliest theory of acid-base action that we still use to any great extent was suggested by Arrhenius toward the end of the nineteenth century. Arrhenius did a great deal of experimentation on the electrical properties of solutions and became convinced that these solutions contained charged particles, which he called ions. His work, like that of many young innovators, was widely scorned at first, but it still serves as the basis for our present ideas about acids, bases, and ions.

Lavoisier had originally suggested that all acids contain oxygen; most of the early acids were actually oxides. As the study of aqueous solution chemistry developed, it became apparent that a more likely common constituent, at least in the presence of water, was hydrogen. At the very end of the eighteenth century Berthollet showed, for example, that muriatic acid contained no oxygen, but was indeed HCl, now called hydrochloric acid. One hundred years later Arrhenius tied these ideas together in terms of the existence of hydrogen ions in acidic aqueous solutions and hydroxide ions in basic aqueous solutions. However, the notion of chemical equilibrium was just beginning to be understood, and almost nothing was known of the interaction of ions with the surrounding solvent or with one another. Modern applications of Arrhenius' theory are quite different than those he originally suggested. Applying these modifications, we will restate the Arrhenius theory.

An acid is a substance which releases hydrogen ions when placed in a solvent such as water. Strong acids have large equilibrium constants. Weak acids have small equilibrium constants. Many common acids are weak acids.

A base is a substance which releases hydroxide ions when placed in a solvent such as water. Strong bases have large equilibrium constants. Weak bases have small equilibrium constants. Most common bases are strong bases.

Additions of an acid solution to a basic solution result in the formation of water ($H^+ + OH^- = H_2O$) and the formation of a solution of a salt. The salt will precipitate if its solubility is exceeded:

$$H^+{}_{(aq)} + Cl^-{}_{(aq)} + Na^+{}_{(aq)} + OH^-{}_{(aq)} = H_2O + Na^+{}_{(aq)} + Cl^-{}_{(aq)}$$

[$NaCl_{(c)}$ is obtained by evaporating the water]

$$H^+{}_{(aq)} + SO_4{}^{=}{}_{(aq)} + Ba^{++}{}_{(aq)} + OH^-{}_{(aq)} = H_2O + BaSO_{4(c)}$$

The acidity or basicity of the solution may be tested by adding colored substances which are themselves acids and bases and which change color as they gain and lose hydrogen ions or hydroxide ions. Litmus is the best known, but there are many other acid-base indicators that are more useful. Some frequently used indicators are methyl orange, methyl red, bromthymol blue, and phenolphthalein. All of these are complicated molecules with an extended carbon skeleton, as indicated in Table 18.11. We shall represent their respective acid forms as HMO, HMR, HBTB, and HPP. The color changes involve the ionization of a proton (as indicated in Figure 21.26) and may be represented by the following equations. All acid-base indicators are weak acids, as shown in Table 18.11. Table 18.12 gives the color changes of a commonly used set of acid-base indicators. Note that pH is the negative logarithm of the hydrogen ion concentration.

Acidity is also associated with acid attack on metals. The reactions of protons with metals usually involve simple oxidation-reduction:

$$Zn_{(c)} + 2H^+{}_{(aq)} = H_{2(g)} + Zn^{++}{}_{(aq)}$$

$$Al_{(c)} + 3H^+{}_{(aq)} = \tfrac{3}{2}H_{2(g)} + Al^{+++}{}_{(aq)}$$

$$Cu_{(c)} + H^+ = \text{negligible reaction}$$

Hydrogen ions will be reduced by metals when either (or both) of the following energy conditions is satisfied: (1) the metal holds onto electrons much less tightly than does hydrogen, making the transfer of electrons from metal to hydrogen energetically favorable, or (2) the hydration energy of the metal ion (compared to its interaction energy in the elementary state) is large relative to that of the hydrogen ion, making it energetically favorable for the hydrated metallic ion to exist instead of the hydrated hydrogen ion. The entropy change will normally favor the reaction giving hydrogen, since hydrogen gas has a higher entropy than the crystalline metal and this effect usually more than offsets the loss in entropy of

Table 18.11 **Formulas of some acid-base indicators. The ionizable hydrogen for the usual indicator range is colored.**

Indicator		K_{eq}
Methyl orange	$HMO = H^+{}_{(aq)} + MO^-$ (HMO red, MO^- orange)	$\dfrac{[H^+][MO^-]}{[HMO]} = 5.6 \cdot 10^{-4}$
Methyl red	$HMR = H^+{}_{(aq)} + MR^-$ (HMR red, MR^- yellow)	$\dfrac{[H^+][MR^-]}{[HMR]} = 5 \cdot 10^{-6}$
Bromthymol blue	$HBTB = H^+{}_{(aq)} + BTB^-$ (HBTB yellow, BTB^- blue)	$\dfrac{[H^+][BTB^-]}{[HBTB]} = 1.0 \cdot 10^{-7}$
Phenolphthalein	$HPP = H^+{}_{(aq)} + PP^-$ (HPP colorless, PP^- red)	$\dfrac{[H^+][PP^-]}{[HPP]} = 1.0 \cdot 10^{-9}$

Table 18.12 Approximate indicator colors. (Abbreviations: b = blue, c = colorless, g = green, o = orange, r = red, y = yellow, v = violet, t = transition.)

Concentration of H^+	Concentration of OH^-	*p*H	Methyl violet	Methyl orange	Bromphenol blue	Bromcresol green	Litmus	Bromthymol blue	Cresol red	Phenolphthalein	Alizarin yellow *R*	Indigo carmine	Solutions of certain common substances giving the corresponding *p*H
1	10^{-14}	0	y	r	y	y	r	y	y	c	y	b	1 *M* HCl
10^{-1}	10^{-13}	1	g	r	y	y	r	y	y	c	y	b	0.1 *M* HCl
10^{-2}	10^{-12}	2	b	r	y	y	r	y	y	c	y	b	0.01 *M* HCl
10^{-3}	10^{-11}	3	v	r	y	y	r	y	y	c	y	b	0.05 *M* $HC_2H_3O_2$
10^{-4}	10^{-10}	4	v	o	g	y	r	y	y	c	y	b	H_2CO_3 (CO_2 at 1 atm)
10^{-5}	10^{-9}	5	v	y	b	g	r	y	y	c	y	b	0.2 *M* NH_4Cl
10^{-6}	10^{-8}	6	v	y	b	b	r	y	y	c	y	b	
10^{-7}	10^{-7}	7	v	y	b	b	t	g	y	c	y	b	"neutral point," 1 *M* NH_4OAc
10^{-8}	10^{-6}	8	v	y	b	b	b	b	t	c	y	b	1 *M* $NaHCO_3$
10^{-9}	10^{-5}	9	v	y	b	b	b	b	r	t	y	b	0.2 *M* $NaC_2H_3O_2$
10^{-10}	10^{-4}	10	v	y	b	b	b	b	r	r	y	b	
10^{-11}	10^{-3}	11	v	y	b	b	b	b	r	r	o	b	0.05 *M* NH_4OH; or 0.4 *M* Na_2CO_3
10^{-12}	10^{-2}	12	v	y	b	b	b	b	r	r	r	b	0.01 *M* NaOH
10^{-13}	10^{-1}	13	v	y	b	b	b	b	r	r	r	g	0.1 *M* NaOH
10^{-14}	1	14	v	y	b	b	b	b	r	r	r	y	1 *M* NaOH

hydration when moving from hydrated hydrogen ions (which create a good deal of order in the water around them) to hydrated larger cations (which have less ordering effect on the water; see p. 31).

Exercise 18.11

Rationalize the fact that Cu does not dissolve in acid but Zn does. *Answer:* The second I.E. of Cu is much higher than that for Zn and the hydration energies of both Zn^+ and Cu^+ are too low to give these ions. Thus Zn^+, Cu^+, and Cu^{++} do not form in reaction with hydrogen ion, but Zn^{++} (low I.E. compared to hydration energy) does.

BRÖNSTED ACID-BASE THEORY

It soon became apparent that there were many ways to adjust the hydrogen ion concentration in a solution other than by adding an acid or adding a substance that contained potential hydroxide ions. Not only would sodium hydroxide react with, or neutralize, hydrochloric acid, but so would cyanide, thiosulfate, or acetate ions, and a host of other substances. It was possible to account for these observations by using Arrhenius theory, but a more direct approach was suggested by Brönsted. He defined a base as a substance that could accept a proton from an acid. The reactions just mentioned would then be described by the following equations:

Base	*Equation*	K_{eq}
Hydroxide ion	$OH^- + HCl = H_2O + Cl^-$	large
Cyanide ion	$CN^- + HCl = HCN + Cl^-$	large
Thiosulfate ion	$S_2O_3^= + HCl = HS_2O_3^- + Cl^-$	large
Ammonia	$NH_3 + HOAc = NH_4^+ + OAc^-$	$1.0 = \frac{[NH_4^+][OAc^-]}{[NH_3][HOAc]}$
Acetate ion ($CH_3CO_2^- = OAc^-$)	$OAc^- + HCN = HOAc + CN^-$	$2.6 \cdot 10^{-5} = \frac{[HOAc][CN^-]}{[OAc^-][HCN]}$

Indicator reactions could be written as

$$OH^- + HMO = H_2O + MO^- \qquad 4 \cdot 10^{10} = \frac{[MO^-]}{[OH^-][HMO]}$$

$$CN^- + HMR = HCN + MR^- \qquad 1 \cdot 10^4 = \frac{[HCN][MR^-]}{[CN^-][HMR]}$$

$$NH_3 + HBTB = NH_4^+ + BTB^- \qquad 1.8 \cdot 10^2 = \frac{[NH_4^+][BTB^-]}{[NH_3][HBTB]}$$

$$OAc^- + HPP = HOAc + PP^- \qquad 6 \cdot 10^{-5} = \frac{[HOAc][PP^-]}{[OAc^-][HPP]}$$

Examination of all these equations shows that each has a proton transferring from one substance to another. The reverse reaction would have the proton transferring back. The equilibrium constants show that most of these reactions do not go nearly to completion; thus there is appreciable reverse reaction in most cases. Careful experimental work shows that all of the reactions can proceed in either direction. Brönsted's suggestions may be summarized: (1) acid-base reactions involve the competition between two different bases for protons, (2) when an acid (proton donor) reacts with a base (proton acceptor), the acid forms its conjugate base, the base forms its conjugate acid, (3) acid-base reactions are readily reversible. A few equations should clarify these ideas.

	Acid	*Base*		*Conjugate base*	*Conjugate acid*	K_{eq}
General equation	HA	$+ B^-$	$\rightleftarrows$	A^-	$+ HB$	$\frac{[A^-][HB]}{[HA][B^-]}$
Examples	HOAc	$+ OH^-$	$\rightleftarrows$	OAc^-	$+ H_2O$	$1.8 \cdot 10^9$
	H_2S	$+ CN^-$	$\rightleftarrows$	HS^-	$+ HCN$	$2.0 \cdot 10^2$
	$H_2PO_4^-$	$+ OCl^-$	$\rightleftarrows$	$HPO_4^=$	$+ HOCl$	0.93
	HCO_3^-	$+ NH_3$	$\rightleftarrows$	$CO_3^=$	$+ NH_4^+$	$8.4 \cdot 10^{-2}$

Thus every Brönsted reaction can be considered as the sum of two competing Arrhenius reactions. In general,

Arrhenius equations
$$\begin{cases} HA = \cancel{H^+} + A^- \\ \cancel{H^+} + B^- = HB \end{cases}$$

Brönsted equation
$$HA + B^- = A^- + HB$$

Note also that the equilibrium constant for a Brönsted equation can be directly obtained from the equilibrium constants of two Arrhenius equations:

Arrhenius equations
$$\begin{cases} HA = H^+ + A^-, \; K_1 = \dfrac{[H^+][A^-]}{[HA]} \\ HB = H^+ + B^-, \; K_2 = \dfrac{[H^+][B^-]}{[HB]} \end{cases}$$

Brönsted equation
$$HA + B^- = A^- + HB, \; K_3 = \frac{[A^-][HB]}{[HA][B^-]} = \frac{[\cancel{H^+}][A^-][HB]}{[HA][\cancel{H^+}][B^-]}$$

In other words, we have

$$K_3 = K_1 \cdot \frac{1}{K_2} = \frac{K_1}{K_2} \tag{18.2}$$

Tabulations of Arrhenius equilibrium constants exist for a very large number of reactions. We list constants for some common acids in Table 18.13. Note that the strong acids are at the top of the left column of the "reactants" and the strong bases are at the bottom of the right column of "products."

It is interesting that the Arrhenius constants themselves can be thought of as special Brönsted constants in which water is the base, and $[H^+]$ is defined to equal $[H_3O^+]$:

$$HA_{(aq)} + H_2O = H_3O^+{}_{(aq)} + A^-{}_{(aq)}, \qquad K = \frac{[H_3O^+][A^-]}{[HA]} = \frac{[H^+][A^-]}{[HA]}$$

Table 18.13 Ionization constants for some common acids (all species in aqueous solutions). HCl, HBr, HI, HNO_3, H_2SO_4, and $HClO_4$ are the common very strong acids, $K > 1$.

Type equation: $HA_{(aq)} = H^+{}_{(aq)} + A^-{}_{(aq)}$, $K = \frac{[H^+][A^-]}{[HA]}$, $pK = \log(1/K) = -\log K$

Name	Formula	Equilibrium	K_{eq} (25°K)	pK[a]
Sulfurous	H_2SO_3	$SO(OH)_2 \rightleftarrows H^+ + SO_2OH^-$	$1.7 \cdot 10^{-2}$	1.76
Monohydrogen sulfate	HSO_4^-	$SO_3OH^- \rightleftarrows H^+ + SO_4^=$	$1.6 \cdot 10^{-2}$	1.80
Phosphoric	H_3PO_4	$PO(OH)_3 \rightleftarrows H^+ + PO_2(OH)_2^-$	$7.11 \cdot 10^{-3}$	2.148
Hydrofluoric	HF	$HF \rightleftarrows H^+ + F^-$	$6.8 \cdot 10^{-4}$	3.17
Methyl orange	HMO	$HMO \rightleftarrows H^+ + MO^-$	$4 \cdot 10^{-4}$	3.4
Acetic	$CH_3COOH(HOAc)$	$HOAc \rightleftarrows H^+ + OAc^-$	$1.8 \cdot 10^{-5}$	4.75
Aluminum ion	$Al(H_2O)_6^{+++}$	$Al(H_2O)_6^{+++} \rightleftarrows H^+ + Al(H_2O)_5OH^{++}$	$7.9 \cdot 10^{-6}$	5.10
Methyl red	HMR	$HMR \rightleftarrows H^+ + MR^-$	$8 \cdot 10^{-6}$	5.1
Carbonic	H_2CO_3	$CO(OH)_2 \rightleftarrows H^+ + CO_2OH^-$	$4.34 \cdot 10^{-7}$	6.352
Bromthymol blue	HBTB	$HBTB \rightleftarrows H^+ + BTB^-$	$1 \cdot 10^{-7}$	7.0
Hydrogen sulfide	H_2S	$H_2S \rightleftarrows H^+ + HS^-$	$1.0 \cdot 10^{-7}$	7.00
Hypochlorous	HOCl	$HOCl \rightleftarrows H^+ + OCl^-$	$6.8 \cdot 10^{-8}$	7.17
Dihydrogen phosphate	$H_2PO_4^-$	$PO_2(OH)_2^- \rightleftarrows H^+ + PO_3OH^=$	$6.34 \cdot 10^{-8}$	7.198
Monohydrogen sulfite	HSO_3^-	$SO_2OH^- \rightleftarrows H^+ + SO_3^=$	$6.3 \cdot 10^{-8}$	7.20
Phenolphthalein	HPP	$HPP \rightleftarrows H^+ + PP^-$	$1 \cdot 10^{-9}$	9.0
Ammonium ion	NH_4^+	$NH_4^+ \rightleftarrows H^+ + NH_3$	$5.69 \cdot 10^{-10}$	9.245
Hydrocyanic	HCN	$HCN \rightleftarrows H^+ + CN^-$	$4.9 \cdot 10^{-10}$	9.31
Monohydrogen carbonate (bicarbonate)	HCO_3^-	$CO_2OH^- \rightleftarrows H^+ + CO_3^=$	$4.79 \cdot 10^{-11}$	10.320
Hydrogen peroxide	H_2O_2	$H_2O_2 \rightleftarrows H^+ + OOH^-$	$2.4 \cdot 10^{-12}$	11.62
Monohydrogen phosphate	$HPO_4^=$	$PO_3OH^= \rightleftarrows H^+ + PO_4^{\equiv}$	$4.4 \cdot 10^{-13}$	12.360
Monohydrogen sulfide	HS^-	$HS^- \rightleftarrows H^+ + S^=$	$1.3 \cdot 10^{-13}$	12.90
Water	H_2O	$H_2O \rightleftarrows H^+ + OH^-$	$1.82 \cdot 10^{-16}$[b]	15.740
Hydroxide ion	OH^-	$OH^- \rightleftarrows H^+ + O^=$	$<10^{-36}$	>36

[a] *pK* is the negative logarithm of the equilibrium constant. Using *pK* values simplifies the arithmetic of equilibrium calculations, since one algebraically adds values of *pK* instead of multiplying values of *K* to get constants for composite equilibria, as in Equation (18.2). All concentrations are to be expressed as moles/liter and all the *K*'s above have the units of (moles l^{-1}).

[b] Note that this K_{eq} value for water explicitly uses the concentration of H_2O, 55.51 *F*. The more commonly used $K_w = 1.00 \cdot 10^{-14}$ ($pK = 14.00$) does not.

Exercise 18.12

Rationalize the fact that most acids in aqueous solutions are weak acids. *Answer:* Brönsted acids typically form a negative ion when they lose H^+ to a competing water molecule. Normally the negative ion is a more effective competitor for the proton than is a neutral water molecule; thus acids are weak in water unless their negative ion charge density is small, as in Cl^-, NO_3^-, HSO_4^-, ClO_4^-.

LEWIS ACID-BASE THEORY

The Brönsted theory successfully generalized the idea of a base but kept the proton as necessary to explain acid behavior. Experimentation in nonaqueous solvents and even many reactions in aqueous systems indicated that it might be desirable to generalize the concept even further. One such generalization is that of Lewis. He noted that ammonia, NH_3, not only combined with protons, but also combined with Ag^+, Cu^{++}, Ni^{++}, BF_3 and many other substances and that there were many other similar reactions. Lewis, therefore, defined an acid as a substance that could accept a pair of electrons to form a covalent bond. He defined a base as a substance with a pair of electrons that could be donated to an acid to form a covalent bond. The reactions listed above would be written as follows.

Equation	K_{eq}
$H^+_{(aq)} + :NH_{3(aq)} = H—NH_3{}^+_{(aq)}$	$1.8 \cdot 10^9$
$Ag^+_{(aq)} + :NH_{3(aq)} = (Ag—NH_3)^+_{(aq)}$	$1.6 \cdot 10^3$
$Cu^{++}_{(aq)} + :NH_{3(aq)} = (Cu—NH_3)^+_{(aq)}$	$2 \cdot 10^4$
$Co^{+++}_{(aq)} + :NH_{3(aq)} = (Co—NH_3)^{+++}_{(aq)}$	$2 \cdot 10^7$

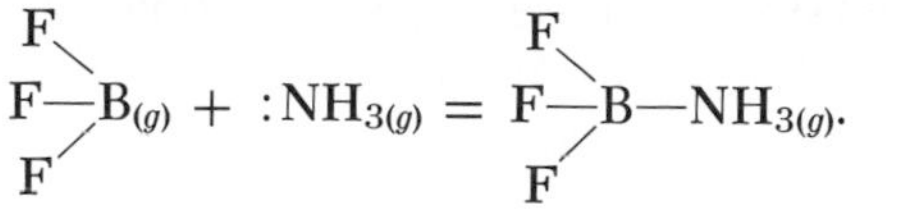

The Ag, Cu, Co ions with ammonia are called complex ions. Lewis theory accounts very simply for their formation in terms of unshared pairs on the $:NH_3$ and empty orbitals on the Ag^+, Cu^{++}, and Co^{+++} ions. We have shown the one-to-one complexes, where the changing *K*'s clearly indicate increasing acidity of the cations as the positive charge increases. This increased acidity with higher charge density on the positive acidic ion also shows up in an ability to coordinate larger numbers of NH_3's. Thus the usual maximum *CN*'s are, respectively, $Ag(NH_3)_2{}^+$, $Cu(NH_3)_4{}^{++}$, $Co(NH_3)_6{}^{+++}$.

The Brönsted reactions of the preceding section can also be written as Lewis reactions, all in aqueous systems.

Equation	K_{eq}
$H—OAc + :OH^- = :OAc^- + H—OH$	$1.8 \cdot 10^9$
$H—SH + :CN^- = :SH^- + H—CN$	$2.0 \cdot 10^2$
$H—OPO_3H^- + :OCl^- = :OPO_3H^= + H—OCl$	0.93
$H—OCO_2{}^- + :NH_3 = :O—CO_2{}^= + H—NH_3{}^+$	$8.4 \cdot 10^{-2}$

But neither Brönsted nor Arrhenius theory will account for the reaction between BF_3 and NH_3.

The Lewis theory is the most general of the three we have discussed, since it allows for many acids and many bases. Application of Lewis theory requires a knowledge of the structure of the substance and of its electron orbital population. The other two theories require only a knowledge of the chemical formula. Which theory is most directly applicable to a particular problem depends on the problem. All three theories emphasize the competitive nature of acid-base reactions: the Arrhenius theory in terms of hydroxide ions trying to capture hydrogen ions; the Brönsted theory in terms of various bases competing with one another for protons; the Lewis theory in terms of various acids competing for the unshared electrons of various bases and vice versa. The equilibrium state in each case can be described in terms of an equilibrium constant involving the concentrations of the substances that are competing in the equilibrium state. Since this equilibrium constant is an experimentally measurable number, we can determine it once and then use it to calculate expected performance in related systems. We hope to find good agreement between the calculations and the observed experimental observations, and this expectation is normally met very satisfactorily.

The Brönsted and Lewis theories account for the experimental observation that some acids and bases are stronger than others; some are better competitors for the protons or electron pairs. In general, as we would expect, those acids with large positive charge densities on their central atoms are the strongest (see Table 16.13). In Brönsted terms they donate protons most strongly. In Lewis terms they are most able to accept electron pairs to form covalent bonds. Similarly, those bases which have the highest negative charge density are the strongest: they are most "willing" to accept positive protons (Brönsted) or to donate unshared pairs of electrons to form a covalent bond (Lewis). We shall find the correlation of relative charge density and acid strength a useful generalization. Charge density is, of course, related to ΔH and bond strengths. We must also remember to consider entropy effects in correlating acid-base behavior.

Exercise 18.13

Arrange the following in probable order of acid strength as Lewis acids for OH^- base: H^+, Na^+, Fe^{+++}, Zn^{++}, Ba^{++}. *Answer:* High positive charge density and readily available (low lying) orbitals give strong Lewis acids. Aqueous H^+ has both and is one of the strongest acids known. The other ions are larger and more comparable in size (about 1 Å radius) but vary in charge and orbitals. Probable sequence (strongest acid first) is Fe^{+++}, Zn^{++}, Ba^{++}, Na^+.

HYDROLYSIS REACTIONS

Reactions with water are called hydrolysis. From our discussion of acids and bases so far we would expect several possible reactions: (1) the water could donate a pair of its unshared electrons and act as a base, or (2) it could donate a proton to an unshared pair of electrons and act as an acid. As a redox reactant (3) water could donate electrons to an oxidizing agent and form hydrogen peroxide, or oxygen plus hydrogen ions, or (4) the water could accept electrons and form hydrogen gas and hydroxide ions. These four possibilities may be represented by equations.

Water as a base

$$\begin{array}{l} H-\ddot{O}: \\ \quad\;\, | \\ \quad\;\, H \end{array} + Cu^{++} = [H-\underset{\cdot\cdot}{\ddot{O}}-Cu]^+ + H^+$$

Thus, positive ions tend to hydrolyze to yield an acidic solution; positive ions are usually Lewis acids

Water as an acid

$$\begin{array}{l} H-\ddot{O}: \\ \quad\;\, | \\ \quad\;\, H \end{array} + :CN^- = H-\underset{\cdot\cdot}{\ddot{O}}:^- + H-CN$$

Thus negative ions tend to hydrolyze to give a basic solution; negative ions are usually Lewis bases

Water as a reducing agent	$2H_2O = H_2O_2 + 2H^+ + 2e^-$ or $H_2O = \frac{1}{2}O_2 + 2H^+ + 2e^-$	Water may be oxidized to peroxide or oxygen by good oxidizing agents
Water as an oxidizing agent	$H_2O + e^- = \frac{1}{2}H_2 + OH^-$	Water may be reduced to hydrogen by good reducing agents

Hydrolysis, as a term, is usually reserved for the acid-base reactions in which the oxidation state of neither the hydrogen nor the oxygen change.

Consider the following experiment. Addition of aluminum chloride to water leads to a vigorous exothermic reaction, which results in an acidic solution. Analysis of the solution shows the presence of negative chloride ions and positive ions containing aluminum. Addition of sodium hydroxide lowers the acidity of the solution but also leads to the formation of a gelatinous white precipitate which dissolves in excess hydroxide solution. If this basic solution is neutralized with some strong acid (HCl or HNO_3), the gelatinous white precipitate reforms, but dissolves as excess acid is added. The following equations describe the best interpretation currently available for these observations.

Solution in water:

$$AlCl_{3(c)} + 6H_2O = Al(H_2O)_6{}^{+++}{}_{(aq)} + 3Cl^-{}_{(aq)} + \text{energy}$$

[Hydration energy of Al^{+++} is great.]

$$Al(H_2O)_6{}^{+++}{}_{(aq)} = Al(H_2O)_5OH^{++}{}_{(aq)} + H^+{}_{(aq)}$$

[High positive charge of Al^{+++} repels H^+, so little energy is required for H^+ to ionize into aqueous solution. Entropy increases.]

Precipitation upon addition of base:

$$Al(H_2O)_6{}^{+++}{}_{(aq)} + OH^-{}_{(aq)} = Al(H_2O)_5OH^{++}{}_{(aq)} + H_2O$$

$$Al(H_2O)_5OH^{++}{}_{(aq)} + OH^-{}_{(aq)} = Al(H_2O)_4(OH)_2{}^+{}_{(aq)} + H_2O$$

$$Al(H_2O)_4(OH)_2{}^+{}_{(aq)} + OH^-{}_{(aq)} = Al(H_2O)_3(OH)_3(OH)_{3(s)}$$

[$Al(H_2O)_3(OH)_3$, being electrically neutral, aggregates and precipitates. The solid contains a great deal of additional water and is held together by hydrogen bonds; hence it is gelatinous rather than crystalline. The aquation also minimizes the entropy decrease.]

Precipitate dissolves upon addition of excess strong base:

$$Al(H_2O)_3(OH)_{3(s)} + OH^-{}_{(aq)} = Al(H_2O)_2(OH)_4{}^-{}_{(aq)} + H_2O$$

$$Al(H_2O)_2(OH)_4{}^-{}_{(aq)} + OH^-{}_{(aq)} = Al(H_2O)(OH)_5{}^={}_{(aq)} + H_2O$$

$$Al(H_2O)(OH)_5{}^={}_{(aq)} + OH^-{}_{(aq)} = Al(OH)_6{}^{\equiv}{}_{(aq)} + H_2O$$

Addition of strong acid reforms the gelatinous precipitate:

$$Al(OH)_6{}^{\equiv}{}_{(aq)} + 3H^+{}_{(aq)} = Al(H_2O)_3(OH)_{3(s)}$$

[Three steps summed in one equation.]

Further addition of strong acid dissolves the precipitate:

$$Al(H_2O)_3(OH)_{3(s)} + 3H^+{}_{(aq)} = Al(H_2O)_6{}^{+++}{}_{(aq)}$$

[Three steps summed in one equation.]

The high positive charge density of Al^{+++} attracts and holds the surrounding six oxygens very tightly. It is primarily the changes in the peripheral hydrogens which account for the observed changes in the system as base and acid are added.

There are many compounds which, like $Al(H_2O)_3(OH)_3$, can (1) in the Arrhenius sense react with either hydrogen ions or hydroxide ions, or (2) in the Brönsted sense donate or accept protons, or (3) in the Lewis sense donate or accept a pair of unshared electrons. These substances can act either as acids or bases. They are said to be amphoteric. HSO_4^-, HCO_3^-, $H_2PO_4^-$, $HPO_4^=$, $CuOH^+$, $Sn(H_2O)_2(OH)_4$, $Cr(H_2O)_3(OH)_3$ and many, many other substances are amphoteric. With strong acids they react as bases, with strong bases they react as acids. Normally, however, the term amphoteric is reserved for water-insoluble, hydroxide-containing species such as $Al(H_2O)_3(OH)_3$, which can dissolve in either acidic or basic solutions. These are the amphoteric hydroxides. They are hydroxides of the elements which lie, for the most part, near a diagonal line running from Al to Bi in the periodic table, but the hydroxides of Zn^{++} and Cr^{+++} must be included as outstanding examples of this class of hydroxides. These elements, you should not be surprised to note, are situated in the periodic table between the highly metallic elements (which form basic oxides and hydroxides) and the nonmetallic elements (which form acidic oxides and hydroxides).

Exercise 18.14

Write a net equation for $Zn(OH)_2$ acting (*a*) as a base, (*b*) as an acid. *Answer:* (*a*) $Zn(OH)_{2(c)} + H_3O^+_{(aq)} = ZnOH^+_{(aq)} + 2H_2O$, or $Zn(H_2O)_2(OH)_{2(c)} + H_3O^+_{(aq)} = Zn(H_2O)_3OH^+_{(aq)} + H_2O$. (*b*) $Zn(OH)_{2(c)} + OH^-_{(aq)} = Zn(OH)_3{}^-_{(aq)}$, or $Zn(H_2O)_2(OH)_{2(c)} + OH^- = Zn(H_2O)(OH)_3{}^-_{(aq)} + H_2O$.

PEROXIDES

Many of the peroxides of the metals may be made by heating the metal in excess oxygen, as already mentioned (see Table 18.6). Hydrogen peroxide may then be formed by carefully acidifying an aqueous solution of the peroxide. Sodium peroxide, for example, might be used:

$$Na_2O_{2(c)} = 2Na^+_{(aq)} + O_2{}^=_{(aq)};\ O_2{}^=_{(aq)} + 2H^+_{(aq)} = H_2O_{2(aq)}$$

Treatment of BaO_2 with cold dilute acid is used commercially to give H_2O_2, but the principal reaction when water is added to alkali metal peroxides at room temperature is the generation of oxygen gas. In fact, this is a convenient way to generate small quantities of oxygen. The reaction is exothermic, accompanied by a large increase in entropy and must be done with care:

	ΔH^0	ΔS^0	ΔG^0
$Na_2O_{2(c)} + H_2O = 2Na^+_{(aq)} + 2OH^-_{(aq)} + \frac{1}{2}O_{2(g)}$,	-35.6	15.6	-40.9

The most common synthesis of hydrogen peroxide is achieved electrochemically. Two electrodes are introduced into an aqueous solution containing HSO_4^- (from H_2SO_4 or NH_4HSO_4), and direct current is passed through the cell. The anode reaction is

$$2HSO_4^-{}_{(aq)} = S_2O_8^={}_{(aq)} + 2H^+{}_{(aq)} + 2e^-, \qquad \mathcal{E}^\circ = 2.11 \text{ volts}$$

peroxydisulfate

followed by

$$S_2O_8^={}_{(aq)} + 2H_2O = 2HSO_4^-{}_{(aq)} + H_2O_{2(aq)}$$

At the cathode hydrogen is generated:

$$2e^- + 2H^+{}_{(aq)} = H_{2(g)}, \qquad \mathcal{E}^0 = 0.00$$

The solution is stirred so that the acidity does not change, since hydrogen is produced at the anode and consumed at the cathode.

		ΔH^0	ΔS^0	ΔG^0
Net reaction:	$2H_2O_{(l)} = H_2O_{2(aq)} + H_{2(g)}$,	90.9	32.2	81.3

A 30% aqueous solution of H_2O_2 results, from which pure H_2O_2 can be distilled under low pressure. The boiling point of H_2O_2 is 152°C, at which temperature it can explode, but it can be distilled safely at 80°C, at which temperature its vapor pressure is about 60 mm of mercury. Its melting point is −1.7°C. Thus H_2O_2 has physical properties similar to water, as we would expect from the tendency of each substance to form hydrogen bonds in quite similar manners.

As you may have gathered from the above, H_2O_2 is an exothermic compound with respect to decomposition into oxygen and water: $H_2O_{2(l)} = H_2O_{(g)} + \frac{1}{2}O_{2(g)} + 12.9$ kcal. This reaction is autocatalytic in the sense that the intermediate molecules produced in the reaction (probably OH radicals) catalyze the decomposition and increase the rate of decomposition. Commercial hydrogen peroxide contains inhibitors which react rapidly with these autocatalysts and thus lower the rate of decomposition. These inhibitors are sometimes called negative catalysts, a misleading term. Actually the inhibitors themselves do not slow down the rate of reaction. Rather they react very rapidly with the free radical intermediate (probably OH) necessary to the decomposition reaction, and thus lessen the chance that further reaction can occur.

The exothermic nature of the reaction, the ease with which it can be catalyzed and controlled, and the low molecular weights of the products are the bases for the use of hydrogen peroxide jets in space "walks" and other navigational tasks which must be carefully controlled in space technology.

SULFUR CHEMISTRY

Much of the chemistry of sulfur is similar to that of oxygen, especially the chemistry of sulfur in the −2 and −1 oxidation states. Sulfides, like oxides, are usually insoluble in water, form crystals whose structures are strongly influenced by ionic forces (radius ratio, crystal field), and give acid-base and redox reactions analogous to those of oxygen. The differences are normally in the direction to be expected, resulting from the increased size and lower negative charge density of the sulfur ions.

Sulfur is, however, much more apt to form long chains than is oxygen. Ozone, O_3 is the longest known oxygen chain, but sulfur chains can be very long indeed, as in liquid sulfur just above its melting point (Figure 5.14). Elementary sulfur is, for example, quite soluble in an aqueous solution containing sulfide ions, since polysulfide ions can form. These ions are disintegrated by the addition of hydrogen ions, since hydrogen ion is a stronger acid than sulfur:

Lewis base   Lewis acid

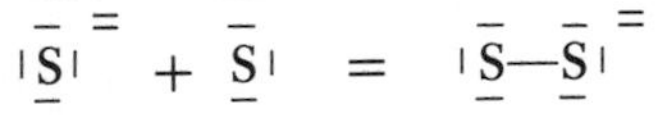

Sulfide ion   Sulfur atom   Polysulfide ion

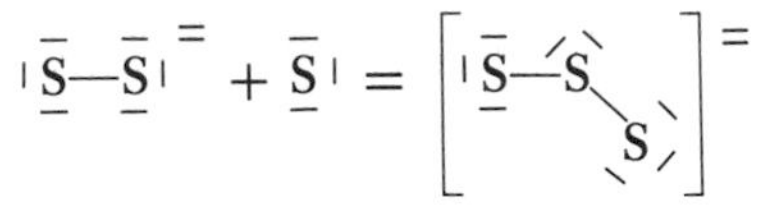

and so on, to give $S_n^{=}$, where n can be 6 or larger. But $S_n^{=} + H^+ = HS^- + S_{n-1(c)}$, since S_{n-1} is a weaker Lewis acid than is $H^+_{(aq)}$.

Oxygen has no positive oxidation states (except in its fluorine compounds), so the behavior of sulfur in these positive oxidation states cannot be learned by studying oxygen. The two common states are +4 (as in SO_2 and the sulfites, containing $SO_3^{=}$ and +6 (as in SO_3 and the sulfates, containing $SO_4^{=}$). Sulfur dioxide, SO_2, is the principal product obtained from burning sulfur in air or oxygen. But SO_3 is energetically more stable and is kept from forming only by a slow rate of reaction between SO_2 and O_2. This reaction can be catalyzed and is carried out on a very large scale commercially; sulfuric acid (obtained by indirectly dissolving SO_3 in water) is one of the chemicals produced in the largest tonnage. The oxidation can be catalyzed by NO_2 at about room temperature. However, since the rate of reaction is small at this temperature, this gas phase reaction requires very voluminous reaction chambers (sometimes 50 feet or more on a side). The only satisfactory lining for these chambers is metallic lead, so the resultant product is contaminated with lead and is limited in concentration range, because high concentrations of acid would rapidly dissolve the lead. Lead chamber acid is typically used in industrial applications that require neither high purity nor concentrated acid.

Sulfur dioxide will also react with oxygen, over platinum or vanadium oxide catalysts, to give sulfur trioxide. The highly exothermic reaction maintains the solid catalyst at red heat (about 1000°C). The rate of reaction is so rapid at this temperature that less than one square foot of cross section contains the catalyst over which the gases flow rapidly. The product is dissolved in sulfuric acid to give a very high concentration of sulfur trioxide, which can then be diluted with water to give acid of the desired concentration. The entire process may be formulated as follows:

	$\Delta H°$	$\Delta S°$	$\Delta G°$
$S_{(c)} + O_{2(g)} = SO_{2(g)}$	−70.9	2.7	−71.7
$SO_{2(g)} + \frac{1}{2}O_{2(g)} = SO_{3(g)}$	−23.7	−22.5	−17.0
$SO_{3(g)} + H_2SO_{4(l)} = H_2SO_4 \cdot SO_{3(l)}$			
$H_2SO_4 \cdot SO_{3(l)} + H_2O_{(l)} \longrightarrow H_2SO_{4(aq)}$			
or			
$SO_{3(g)} + H_2O_{(l)} = H_2SO_{4(aq)}$	−55.4	−73.2	−32.5

The $H_2SO_4 \cdot SO_{3(l)}$, or fuming sulfuric acid, goes by the commercial name of "oleum."

Water cannot be used to dissolve the SO_3 directly, since the SO_3 would react with the gaseous water above the liquid to produce a fog of liquid droplets. Each droplet would immediately adsorb air molecules on its surface and become impervious to coalescence with other droplets or to dissolving in bulk liquid water. Thus the sulfuric fog would go right past the liquid water and escape from the plant.

Sulfur, like oxygen, forms strong bonds to many positive ions, often even stronger (more covalent) than the oxygen bonds. For example, a sulfide is usually more insoluble in water than is the corresponding oxide. Similarly, sulfur compounds often act as bases, forming covalent bonds to positive metal ions. The photographic industry utilizes this phenomenon to render developed photographic film insensitive to further exposure to light. The initial latent image on the film is formed where light hits granules of silver bromide suspended in a gelatin emulsion. (The presence of $S^=$ impurities in the granules apparently catalyzes the absorption of light by creating strains in the crystals.) These light-struck granules are then reduced chemically to silver by a developing agent (a chemical reducing agent that reduces only the light-struck granules). The unaffected silver bromide is then dissolved (or fixed) in hypo (aqueous sodium thiosulfate containing $S_2O_3^=$ ions). The $S_2O_3^=$ ions dissolve only the undeveloped silver bromide. The dissolved materials are carefully washed out of the emulsion, which is then dried. This sequence is summarized in the following equations and in Figure 18.3.

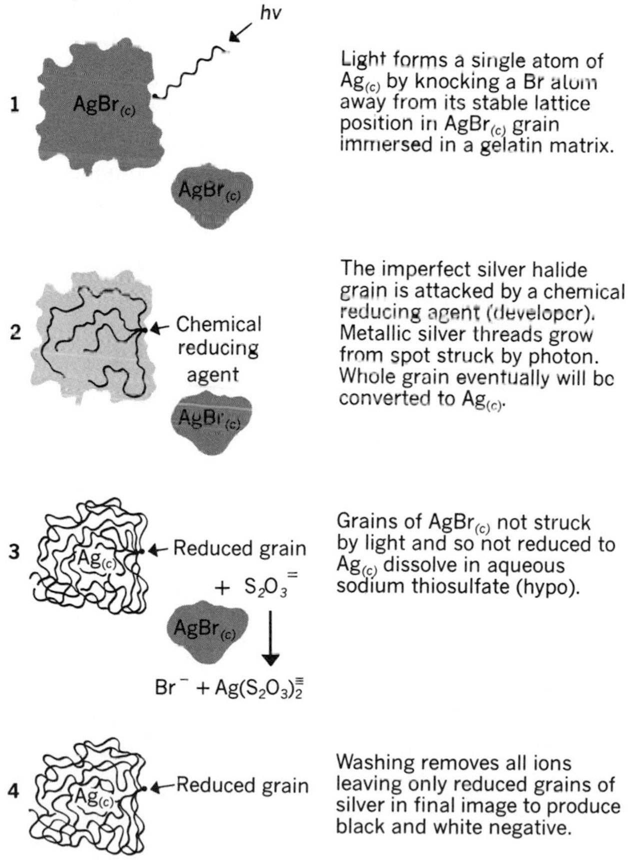
hv
1
AgBr(c)
Light forms a single atom of Ag(c) by knocking a Br atom away from its stable lattice position in AgBr(c) grain immersed in a gelatin matrix.
AgBr(c)
2
Chemical reducing agent
The imperfect silver halide grain is attacked by a chemical reducing agent (developer). Metallic silver threads grow from spot struck by photon. Whole grain eventually will be converted to Ag(c).
AgBr(c)
3
Ag(c)
Reduced grain
+ S2O3=
Grains of AgBr(c) not struck by light and so not reduced to Ag(c) dissolve in aqueous sodium thiosulfate (hypo).
AgBr(c)
Br⁻ + Ag(S2O3)2≡
4
Ag(c)
Reduced grain
Washing removes all ions leaving only reduced grains of silver in final image to produce black and white negative.

Figure 18.3 Schematic representation of the photographic process.

Exposure	$AgBr_{(c)} + h\nu = AgBr^*_{(c)}$
Development	$AgBr^*_{(c)}$ + reducing agent $(e^-) = Ag_{(c)} + Br^-_{(aq)}$
Fixing	$AgBr_{(c)} + 2S_2O_3{}^{=}{}_{(aq)} = Ag(S_2O_3)_2{}^{-3}{}_{(aq)} + Br^-_{(aq)}$
Washing	All ions are removed by carefully washing the emulsion
Net Result	Grains of $Ag_{(c)}$ wherever light struck the film initially

The $Ag(S_2O_3)_2{}^{\equiv}$ has the structure $[O_3S—S—Ag—S—SO_3]^{\equiv}$, indicating that silver forms tighter bonds to sulfur than to oxygen. Similarly, $Ag_2S_{(c)}$ ($\Delta G^0_{\text{form}} = -9.62$ kcal mole^{-1}) is much more stable with respect to decomposition into the elements and to solubility than is $Ag_2O_{(c)}$ ($\Delta G^0_{\text{form}} = -2.68$ kcal mole^{-1}).

Exercise 18.15

Acidification of aqueous hypo gives a sulfur precipitate. Account for this. *Answer:* $S_2O_3{}^{=}{}_{(aq)} + 2H^+_{(aq)} = S_{(c)} + H_2SO_{3(aq)}$. This may be thought of as an acid-base reaction in which $:\ddot{S}$ is competing with H^+ for the base, $SO_3{}^{=}$. H^+ is the stronger acid, helped by the fact that S can form chains acting amphoterically toward itself.

SULFUR-SULFUR BONDS

We have seen that oxygen-to-oxygen bonds exist in peroxides and superoxides. Sulfur also bonds to itself (remember the thiosulfate ion, $S_2O_3{}^{=}$ and the eight-membered rings in the element). In general, sulfur-to-sulfur bonds ($\sim$ 63 kcal mole^{-1}) are more stable with respect to decomposition than are oxygen-to-oxygen ($\sim$ 33 kcal mole^{-1}) bonds. For example, sulfur-to-sulfur bonds are of importance in holding the amino acids of enzymes in their proper orientation, as will be shown in Chapter 40. When these intermolecular sulfur bonds are broken, the enzymes lose their specific configuration and, usually, the power to catalyze biochemical reactions. Of the twenty essential amino acids listed in Table 40.1, only two, cysteine and methionine, contain sulfur atoms, and only the cysteine can easily use its sulfur in forming the disulfide bridges mentioned above. Thus one of the essential functions of cysteine in living systems must be the formation of such bridges.

THE OXIDES OF SULFUR IN WATER SOLUTION

Both sulfur dioxide and sulfur trioxide are soluble in water; the sulfur trioxide is very soluble indeed, although, as mentioned above, there are problems with the mechanism of the solution process. Some properties of the substances and their aqueous solutions are listed in Table 18.14.

The high aqueous solubility and high acid strength of sulfur trioxide and sulfuric acid (compared to sulfur dioxide and sulfurous acid) are consistent with the higher positive charge density in the +6 compounds. This higher positive charge density will hold coordinated water more tightly, increasing the interaction with water (and hence the solubility) and increasing the ionization of the peripheral hydrogens. The lower acid strengths of the monohydrogen sulfate and monohydrogen sulfite ions (compared to the neutral acids) are consistent with the

Table 18.14 Some properties of sulfur dioxide and sulfur trioxide. Note that the entropy effect ($T\ \Delta S$) is larger than the enthalpy effect in several of the aqueous equilibria, primarily because of the high degree of hydration of H_{aq}^{+}. (ΔH^0 and ΔG^0 in kcal mole^{-1}; S^0 in cal mole^{-1} °K^{-1}.)

	Oxidation state of sulfur	Melting point (°K)	Boiling point (°K)	Solubility in H_2O at 25°C (M at 1 atm (pressure)	Principal aqueous equilibria	K_{eq}	ΔH^0 (kcal mole^{-1})	ΔS^0_{298} (eu)
SO_2	+4	200.5	263	1.5	$SO_{2(g)} + H_2O_{(l)} = H_2SO_{3(aq)}$ sulfurous acid	$9.01 \cdot 10^{-5}$	−6.250	−20.6
$SO_{2(g)}$ formation	ΔH^0 −70.944	S^0 59.30	ΔG^0 −71.749		$H_2SO_{3(aq)} = H^+_{(aq)} + HSO_3{}^-_{(aq)}$ monohydrogen sulfite	$1.7 \cdot 10^{-2}$	−4.16	−22.1
					$HSO_3{}^-_{(aq)} = H^+_{(aq)} + SO_3{}^{=}_{(aq)}$ sulfite	$6.3 \cdot 10^{-8}$	−2.7	−40
SO_3	+6	290	318	Infinite (any amount of SO_3 can be dissolved in any quantity of water at 25°C)	$SO_{3(g)} + H_2O_{(l)} = H_2SO_{4(aq)}$	$8 \cdot 10^{23}$	−54.42	−73.3
$SO_{3(g)}$ formation	ΔH^0 −94.58	S^0 61.34	ΔG^0 −88.69		$H_2SO_{4(aq)} = H^+_{(aq)} + HSO_4{}^-_{(aq)}$ monohydrogen sulfate	10^2	5.24	26.7
					$HSO_4{}^-_{(aq)} = H^+_{(aq)} + SO_4{}^{=}_{(aq)}$ sulfate	$1.6 \cdot 10^{-2}$	−5.24	−21.9

negative charges of the ions, which make it more difficult for the protons to ionize, but again the +6 compound is the stronger acid.

Note that the nomenclature here follows the same rules as in the halogen compounds. The acid of higher positive oxidation state has a name ending in -ic, and its ion ends in -ate. The acid of lower positive oxidation state ends in -ous, and its ion in -ite. Thus, sulfuric acid and sulfates have a +6 oxidation state, and sulfurous acid and sulfites have a +4 oxidation state for the sulfur. Compare the discussion of nomenclature in Table 13.5.

SULFIDES

As indicated in Chapter 5, sulfides are the most common ore for many of the elements, and sulfur metallurgy is thus of great interest commercially. Sulfide chemistry is coincident with one of the fields that give chemistry its reputation of being such a "stinky" subject—qualitative chemical analysis.

As with the oxides, so with the sulfides—most cations form substances insoluble in aqueous solutions. Since hydrogen sulfide, like the oxide, is a weak acid, the solubilities of these sulfides vary markedly as the acidity of the solution changes:

$$H_2S_{(aq)} = H^+{}_{(aq)} + HS^-{}_{(aq)}, \qquad K_1 = \frac{[H^+][HS^-]}{[H_2S]} = 1.0 \cdot 10^{-7} \quad (18.3)$$

$$HS^-{}_{(aq)} = H^+{}_{(aq)} + S^={}_{(aq)}, \qquad K_2 = \frac{[H^+][S^=]}{[HS^-]} = 1.3 \cdot 10^{-13} \quad (18.4)$$

(Note that H_2S, though a weak acid, is a stronger acid than water, as would be expected from the smaller negative charge density on the sulfur. Note also that the difference factor between K_1 and K_2 is the same that was found in sulfurous acid, 10^6. (This factor is between 10^4 and 10^6 for many acids: see Table 18.13.) One atmosphere pressure of H_2S gives 0.01 *F* aqueous H_2S as a saturated solution.

Data for the solubility equilibria for several sulfides are given in Table 18.15. Two equilibrium constants are given, the solubility product constant, K_{sp},

$$MS_{(c)} = M^{++}{}_{(aq)} + S^={}_{(aq)}, \qquad K_{sp} = [M^{++}][S^=]$$

and the equilibrium constant for dissolving in acid to form $H_2S_{(aq)}$, K_{eq},

$$MS_{(c)} + 2H^+{}_{(aq)} = M^{++}{}_{(aq)} + H_2S_{(aq)}, \qquad K_{eq} = \frac{[M^{++}][H_2S]}{[H^+]^2}$$

Note that the values for [MS] are included in *K* in both cases, since the concentration of a solid is itself a constant.

Exercise 18.16

How likely is it that HgS will exist in well-defined equilibrium with saturated H_2S in 1 *M* acid? *Answer:* The $[Hg^{++}]$ calculated is $2.3 \cdot 10^{-23}$ or about one ion per liter of solution. In the usual one ml sample there should be less than one ion. This is, of course, possible on the average, but one would expect considerable statistical fluctuation from the equilibrium state.

Table 18.15 Data on some sulfide equilibria in aqueous solutions.

Equilibrium	Cations						
	Hg^{++}	Cu^{++}	Cd^{++}	Co^{++}	Ni^{++}	Zn^{++}	Mn^{++}
$MS_{(c)} = M^{++}{}_{(aq)} + S^{=}{}_{(aq)}$ $K_{sp} = (M^{++})(S^{=})$	$3 \cdot 10^{-54}$	$3.5 \cdot 10^{-42}$	$7.1 \cdot 10^{-28}$	$1.9 \cdot 10^{-27}$	$1.1 \cdot 10^{-27}$	$6.9 \cdot 10^{-26}$	$6.2 \cdot 10^{-22}$
$MS_{(c)} + 2H^{+}{}_{(aq)} = M^{++}{}_{(aq)} + H_2S_{(aq)}$ $K_{eq} = \frac{(M^{++})(H_2S)}{(H^{+})^2} = \frac{K_{sp}}{K_1K_2}$	$2.3 \cdot 10^{-34}$	$2.7 \cdot 10^{-22}$	$5.5 \cdot 10^{-8}$	$1.5 \cdot 10^{-7}$	$8.5 \cdot 10^{-6}$	$5.3 \cdot 10^{-6}$	$4.8 \cdot 10^{-2}$

SELENIUM AND TELLURIUM

Many of the properties of selenium and tellurium can be deduced by extrapolation from the properties of sulfur, making allowances for the increased atomic size, the narrower separation in energy between the *s*, *p*, and *d* orbitals, and the increased nuclear charge. The elements usually occur in compounds mixed in with comparable sulfur ores. They are prepared as by-products of the refining of the sulfur ores. Their compounds have formulas and properties analogous to those of the sulfur compounds. Both hydrogen selenide and hydrogen telluride have strong odors and are very toxic. Traces of the elements, when ingested, have the unfortunate property of appearing in the breath as malodorous compounds. The elements and their compounds have electrical properties that lend them to applications as semiconductors and solid-state electrical components, as might be guessed from the increasingly metallic nature (lower ionization energies) as the atomic number increases in these families to the right of the periodic table.

There is much more to know than any of us are ever going to catch up with; and this is not just the trivial fact that we don't work hard enough; it is not the trivial fact that things are difficult to learn. It is that any form of knowledge really precludes other forms; that any serious study of one thing cuts out some other part of your life.
—*J. Robert Oppenheimer* (1955).

PROBLEMS

18.1. How do you account for the fact that SO_2 reacts rapidly with $H_2O_{(l)}$ but slowly with $O_{2(g)}$ at the same temperature, yet both reactions have large negative values of ΔG?

18.2. Which is a more rapid oxidizing agent, H_2O_2 or O_2? Both have large ΔG's with similar reducing agents.

18.3. H_2O_2 is both an oxidizing and a reducing agent. Show this by (*a*) half-reactions, (*b*) valence bond structures, (*c*) oxidation states.

18.4. $PbSO_4$ is much more insoluble in aqueous systems than is $Pb(HSO_4)_2$. Can you rationalize this fact? How does this solubility difference affect the operation of a lead chamber plant making H_2SO_4?

18.5. What physical properties would you predict for liquid selenium?

18.6. How do you account for the trend in I.E. in the chalcogens? the trend in bond energy? the trend in boiling point? the trend in color?

18.7. Would the change listed require an oxidizing agent, a reducing agent, or some other type of reagent? (*a*) H_2O to H_2O_2; (*b*) H_2SO_4 to H_2SO_3; (*c*) H_3PO_4 to P_4O_{10}; (*d*) P_4 to P_4S_3; (*e*) MnO_2 to $KMnO_4$; (*f*) $KClO_3$ to $KClO_4$; (*g*) HCl to YCl_3; (*h*) $Th_3(PO_4)_4$ to Th; (*i*) U_3O_8 to UF_6; (*j*) $AgNO_3$ to $Ag(CN)_2^-$; (*k*) $S_4O_6^=$ to $S_2O_3^=$; (*l*) Fe^{++} to Fe^{+++}; (*m*) Cr_2O_3 to $Cr_2O_7^=$; (*n*) CH_4 to CH_3OH; (*o*) Fe to $Fe(CO)_5$.

18.8. Elementary sulfur is quite soluble in liquid carbon disulfide, CS_2, but not very soluble in benzene, C_6H_6, and almost insoluble in water. Can you account for these differences?

18.9. Why does H_2O_2 have a higher boiling point than water but a similar melting point?

18.10. How would the amount of H_2S which would dissolve in 100 ml of water be affected by each of the following separate changes? Interpret each answer in terms of the kinetic theory and the equilibria involved. Write equations for any reactions.
(*a*) Hotter water is used.
(*b*) The pressure of H_2S above the water is increased.
(*c*) Sodium hydroxide is added to the water.
(*d*) Copper nitrate is added to the water.

18.11. Partly filled bottles of aqueous H_2S solution soon begin to show the presence of free elementary sulfur. Write the equation for the reaction producing the sulfur. How is this consistent with the relative positions of sulfur and oxygen in the periodic table and with the relative sizes of their atoms?

18.12. What proof can you cite that the oxygen molecule is diatomic?

18.13. Apply a Born-Haber cycle (being as quantitative as possible) and rationalize the tendency of SF_6, rather than SF_4, to form when the elements are mixed. (Difference in $\Delta H_{\text{form}} \cong 100$ kcal mole^{-1}.)

18.14. Which of the following can act as Lewis acids? (*a*) Al^{+++}, (*b*) BCl_3, (*c*) BrF_3, (*d*) Fe^{++}, (*e*) SiF_4.

18.15. Which of the following can act as Lewis bases? (*a*) $S^=$, (*b*) H_2O, (*c*) Br^-, (*d*) CO, (*e*) CN^-.

II

18.16. Careful soldering to give good electrical connections uses rosin, principally abietic acid, as a flux. The structure is probably $C_{15}H_{19}(CH_3)_4COOH$.

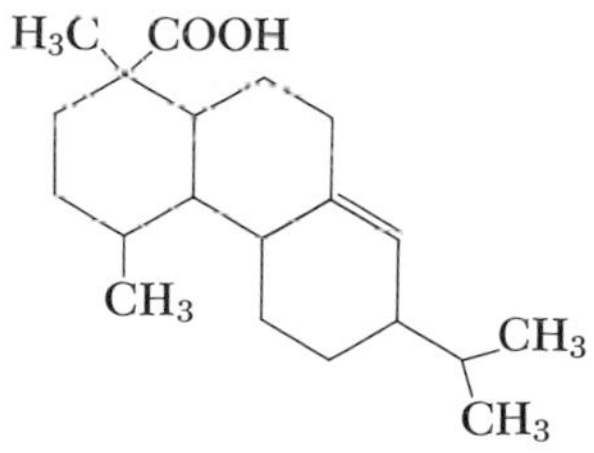

What properties make rosin superior to $ZnCl_2$ as a flux for electrical connections? Why is $ZnCl_2$ better for large mechanical joints?

18.17. CO_2 reacts more slowly with water than does SO_2, although ΔG for both processes is similar. Write down correct orbital and structural formulas and interpret the difference in rate.

18.18. P_4O_{10} forms many different complex acids as it hydrolyzes toward H_3PO_4, the most stable form in dilute solution. Two of the well-known intermediates are $H_4P_2O_7$ and

$(HPO_3)_n$. Use structural formulas to decide which forms first. Suggest a step-by-step mechanism, using structural formulas for the conversion of P_4O_{10} to H_3PO_4 by hydrolysis.

18.19. Write equations showing each of the following acting as an acid or base (as the case may be) toward water. Draw valence electron structures for each substance. Calculate as many K values as possible, using data in this chapter. HBr, KOH, HOBr, $Te(OH)_6$, Na_2SiO_3, PH_3, CH_3NH_2, KH_2PO_4, $RbHSO_3$, $NaHCO_3$, Na_2O_2.

18.20. 0.1 F solutions of each of the following in water give the colors indicated when a few drops of methyl red, phenolphthalein, methyl orange, or bromthymol blue are added. Estimate values of K for the principal equilibrium in each system, using only these data. Arrange the species in order of decreasing acid strength from the data in this problem alone. Compare your K values with Table 18.13 when possible.

	MR	PP	MO	BTB
HF	r	c	r	y
H_2O_2	y	c	o	y
$NaHSO_3$	r	c	o	y
KCN	y	r	o	b
HCN	y	c	o	y

18.21. Calculate the $[H^+]$ and $[OH^-]$ in each of the following solutions. (*a*) 1 F HI, (*b*) 0.1 F HOAc ($[H^+] \cong 10^{-3}\ M$), (*c*) 0.01 F HCN, (*d*) 0.1 F H_2S, (*e*) 0.01 F H_2CO_3, (*f*) 0.1 F $AlCl_3$ ($[H^+] \cong 10^{-3}\ M$), (*g*) 1 F KCN, (*h*) 1 F $NaHSO_3$ ($[H^+] \cong 10^{-4}\ M$), (*i*) 0.1 F KHO_2, (*j*) 10^{-3} F HF ($[H^+] \cong 10^{-3}\ M$).

18.22. Write net equations for the reactions between the listed aqueous solutions and write valence electron structural formulas for each species. Which reactions can be interpreted in terms of Brönsted theory, in terms of Lewis theory, in terms of neither of these theories? Add H^+, OH^-, H_2O as necessary to get an equation; in other words, assume aqueous solution throughout. (*a*) HCl + NaOH, (*b*) $Cr(NO_3)_3$ and KOH (remember to write formulas for the principal species actually present in these solutions; for example, Cr^{+++} is very similar in its chemistry to Al^{+++}), (*c*) $Na_2O_{2(c)}$ and H_2O, (*d*) $Zn(H_2O)_4^{++}$ and NH_3 to give $Zn(NH_3)_4^{++}$, (*e*) $Fe(H_2O)_6^{+++}$ and I_2 to give $Fe(H_2O)_6^{++}$ and I^-, (*f*) $Fe(H_2O)_6^{+++}$ and HCl to give $FeCl_6^{\equiv}$, (*g*) $AgCl_{(c)}$ and KCN to give $Ag(CN)_2^-$.

18.23. About twenty million tons of sulfuric acid, more tons than of any other pure chemical, are produced annually in the United States. How much sulfur is required? (About 10^7 tons.) This is about $\frac{3}{4}$ of all the sulfur mined annually in this country.

18.24. Aqueous photographic fixing solutions are made by adding about 240 g of $Na_2S_2O_3 \cdot 5H_2O$ per liter. Assume that when 90% of this hypo is complexed the bath must be renewed. What is the value of the silver in a 5-gallon tank of used hypo? (About \$40.) The price of silver is about \$1.35 per ounce. How would you reclaim the silver cheaply?

18.25. Lead sulfide, formula PbS, heated in air forms gaseous sulfur dioxide, formula SO_2, and an oxide of lead. 0.797 g of the sulfide form 0.744 g of the pure oxide. What is the formula of the oxide? Write an equation for the reaction.

18.26. Four identical bottles in the storeroom of a laboratory have lost their labels. The liquids are known to be 9 M ammonia, 9 M hydrochloric acid, phosgene dissolved in CCl_4 (very poisonous if inhaled), and 36 N sulfuric acid. Describe in detail a method of deciding without question which bottle is which, without leaving the vicinity of the shelf on which the bottles are stored.

18.27. A sample of SCl_2 weighing 15.5 grams contains (*a*) ______ moles of SCl_2, (*b*) ______ gram-atoms of chlorine, and (*c*) ______ atoms of sulfur. The oxidation number of sulfur in this compound is (*d*) ______. The density of SCl_2 vapor at 300°K and 0.10 atmosphere would be (*e*) ______ g/liter. If 0.10 mole of SCl_2 is prepared by burning sulfur in chlorine, (*f*) ______ liters of chlorine (Cl_2), at STP, would be required. If the chlorine is prepared by the following reaction

$$4HCl + MnO_{2(s)} = MnCl_2 + Cl_{2(g)} + 2H_2O$$

(g) ______ grams of MnO_2 would be required. Adding SCl_2 to water produces a disproportionation reaction in which part of the sulfur is (*h*) ______ to $S_{8(s)}$ and part is (*i*) ______ to sulfurous acid (H_2SO_3). Write a balanced equation for this hydrolysis reaction. ($SCl_2 + H_2O =$ (*j*) ______.) (*k*) ______ ml of 0.20 *F* NaOH would be required to neutralize the acid produced by the hydrolysis of 0.0010 moles of SCl_2.

III

18.28. The solubility of $PbCl_2$ in water at 25°C is 0.039 *F*; $K_{sp} = 1.7 \cdot 10^{-5}$. Assume all the apparent discrepancy is due to hydrolysis of Pb^{++} to $PbOH^+$ and calculate *K* for the reaction $Pb^{++}{}_{(aq)} + H_2O = PbOH^+{}_{(aq)} + H^+{}_{(aq)}$. ($K \cong 0.5$)

18.29. A solution which is 0.1 *F* in Ag^+, 0.1 *F* in Hg^{++}, 0.1 *F* in Cu^{++}, and 0.1 *F* in Cd^{++} is treated with potassium cyanide, such that the cupric ions are reduced and the final equilibrium cyanide concentration is 0.1 *F*. If this solution is to be saturated with hydrogen sulfide, show by suitable calculations (*a*) that cuprous sulfide will not precipitate, (*b*) that cadmium sulfide will precipitate, and (*c*) whether the sulfides of silver and mercury will precipitate.

Solubility products		*Dissociation constants*	
Cu_2S	$2.0 \cdot 10^{-47}$	$Cu(CN)_3^{=}$	$5 \cdot 10^{-28}$
CdS	$7.1 \cdot 10^{-28}$	$Cd(CN)_4^{=}$	$1.4 \cdot 10^{-17}$
Ag_2S	$4.0 \cdot 10^{-52}$	$Ag(CN)_2^-$	$8 \cdot 10^{-23}$
HgS	$3.0 \cdot 10^{-54}$	$Hg(CN)_4^{=}$	$4 \cdot 10^{-42}$

For saturated aqueous hydrogen sulfide solutions: $[S^{=}] = 1.3 \cdot 10^{-21} \cdot [H^+]^{-2}$.

See page 1092 for a list of references and readings in the recent chemical literature related to the material in this chapter.

CHAPTER **19**

Molecular Motions and Dynamic Equilibria

Chemical reactions occur when substances interact to give new substances; these interactions usually involve molecular collisions lasting about 10^{-11} sec at room temperature.

The world, as we generally observe it, is a rather stable place in a physical sense. True, people move from spot to spot, cars move somewhat more rapidly, and planes and rockets move still more rapidly. But most of the objects we see are relatively stationary and their motions are rather slow, even gentle. It is hard to maintain a constant awareness of the fact that the atoms and molecules in all these apparently quiescent objects are themselves engaged in very rapid random motion, with velocities of about 500 to 1000 miles per hour. We shall review some of the evidence for this molecular motion, and then see how it applies to equilibrium systems.

MOLECULAR MOTIONS AT ROOM TEMPERATURE

Figure 14.2 shows that most bonds will be in their ground vibrational state at room temperatures, and all but the most unusual molecules will also be in their ground electronic state at this temperature. Thus chemistry and chemical reactions at room temperatures will involve molecules that are translating vigorously, rotating vigorously, but vibrating in their ground vibrational and electronic states. Many molecular collisions will occur because of the rapid translational motions, since molecular velocities are in the range of 4000 to 40,000 cm sec^{-1}, as shown on page 223. Collision rates, Z, in gases at atmospheric pressure and 25°C are about 10^{10} collisions per molecule per second.

Table 19.1 Some average rates of molecular motion in gases at 1 atm at 25°C.

Translational velocities	10^4 cm sec^{-1}
Collision frequencies	10^{10} sec^{-1}
Rotation frequencies	10^{11} sec^{-1}
Vibration frequencies	10^{13} sec^{-1}

For many molecules the frequency of rotation is about 10^{11} sec^{-1}. Since the collision rate is about 10^{10} sec^{-1}, a molecule completes about 10 rotations between collisions in a gas at 25°C and 1 atm pressure.

Molecular vibrations have a frequency of about 10^{13} sec^{-1}, varying with the reduced mass and the force constant of the bond,

$$\nu = \frac{1}{2\pi}\sqrt{\frac{k}{\mu}}$$

Thus bonds vibrate about a hundred times during each molecular rotation and about a thousand times between collisions in gases at room temperature and pressure. These results are summarized in Table 19.1.

Motions in condensed phases are more difficult to treat exactly. Translation from place to place is difficult, since the molecules are tightly packed. Even rotations may be rare unless the molecules are almost spherical, or nearly cylindrical about one axis. The rotations tend to be transformed into oscillations or twisting motions, and the translations tend to be transformed into rapid back-and-forth motions as the molecule bangs into its neighbors and bounces. There are, of course, a great many collisions per second (about 10^{12} in many instances) because the molecules are so close to one another. Even in condensed phases, however, the bond vibration frequencies tend to be higher than the oscillations and reboundings by a factor of almost ten.

Exercise 19.1

Which decreases fastest with increase in mass—translational velocity or rotational or vibrational frequency? *Answer:* Translational velocity and vibrational frequency are inversely proportional to a function of mass to the $\frac{1}{2}$ power, but rotational frequency is more sensitive to change in mass due to its inverse first-power relationship.

INTERMOLECULAR ENERGY TRANSFER

At room temperature, molecules usually exchange only rotational and translational energies. They seldom acquire enough energy in a collision to move out of the ground vibrational level, unless they undergo reaction. The energy of reaction may then be sufficient to excite vibrations in the products. After such excitation, or after a high-temperature collision that excites higher vibrational states, the molecules will probably vibrate several times before undergoing another collision. During these vibrations the added vibrational energy may distribute itself among other bonds if the molecule is polyatomic. This redistribution cannot, of course, occur in a diatomic molecule. The redistribution in a polyatomic molecule may stabilize the molecule with respect to decomposition by averaging the energy over several bonds, or it may make the molecule dissociate if the energy concentrates in a relatively weak bond. Thus the molecule may pick up energy at one point, but undergo reaction at another point because of the redistribution of the energy (see Figure 19.1).

As the temperature increases, the average translational energy also increases and there is a greater likelihood of large energy transfers. Bond-breaking reactions become more and more common as it becomes more and more likely that higher vibrational states will be excited. Bond breaking may indeed be viewed as a vibration of infinite amplitude. At still higher temperatures electronic excitation can occur, including ionization of the molecules. At extremely high temperatures, nuclear reactions become possible. Much of the present search for a feasible nuclear fusion reaction for large-scale power generation is in the direction of creating and maintaining very high temperatures (10^7°K or higher) in a relatively concentrated gas. Figure 19.2 indicates some of the kinds of equilibrium states that exist at various temperatures. Figure 19.3 gives actual equilibrium concentrations in gaseous oxygen over a portion of the temperature range.

Exercise 19.2

Comment on the statement found in many discussions of radioactivity—"the rate of radioactive change is independent of the temperature." *Answer:* Since most nuclear changes involve energies of the order of 10^6 kcal mole^{-1} or more, the statement is valid unless $\frac{3}{2}RT$ (usually called RT) is this large, that is, unless T approximates 10^9°K.

THE NATURE OF CHEMICAL REACTIONS

Net chemical reactions occur when substances interact to give new substances; these interactions usually involve molecular collisions lasting about 10^{-11} sec at room temperature. The substances must get close enough together to influence one another, and this is what we mean by a collision. We have already discussed briefly the nature of these collisions and the effects of temperature, pressure, and concentration on the likelihood that they will lead to reaction. Among others, see the discussions on the blast furnace, on sulfur chemistry, and on hydrogenation and the Haber process.

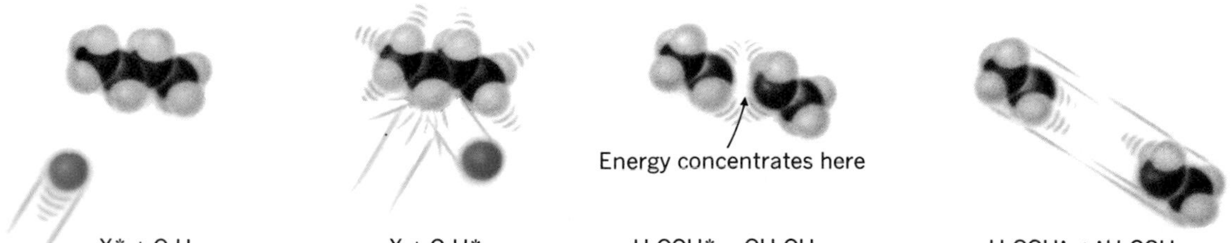

$X^* + C_4H_{10} \rightarrow X + C_4H_{10}^* \rightarrow H_3CCH_2^* - CH_2CH_3 \rightarrow H_3CCH_2^{\cdot} + {}^{\cdot}H_2CCH_3$

which later collide with other molecules and react

Figure 19.1 A schematic mechanism of energy transfer. X* represents a high-energy molecule.

$(\bar{E}_{trans})_{ave}$ (kcal mole^{-1})	°K	
$3 \cdot 10^{10}$	10^{13}	Meson generation occurs
	10^{12}	
$3 \cdot 10^{8}$	10^{11}	Nuclear reactions are common
	10^{10}	Most atoms are completely ionized
$3 \cdot 10^{6}$	10^{9}	Some nuclear reactions occur X-rays become common
	10^{8}	
$3 \cdot 10^{4}$	10^{7}	Soft X-rays are generated
	10^{6}	Multiple ionization becomes common in gases Only monatomic gases exist
300	10^{5}	Only monatomic and diatomic gases exist at any but the highest pressures Thermal ionization becomes common in gases
	10^{4}	Electronic states excited in many gases Most materials are gaseous Most molecules begin to disintegrate into atoms or diatomic molecules
3	10^{3}	Vibrations above the ground state begin to be important Electronic states can be excited in condensed phases—"red hot"
	273.16	Triple point of water defining the temperature scale
	100	Many substances melt and boil as translation and rotation occur Appreciable rotation begins in gaseous hydrogen Hydrogen melts and boils
$3 \cdot 10^{-2}$	10	
		Translation well established in gases
	1	Superconductivity and superfluidity are observed Most substances are crystalline; only helium exists as liquid
		(Note break in scale)
0	0	No changes are possible, only zero point vibration

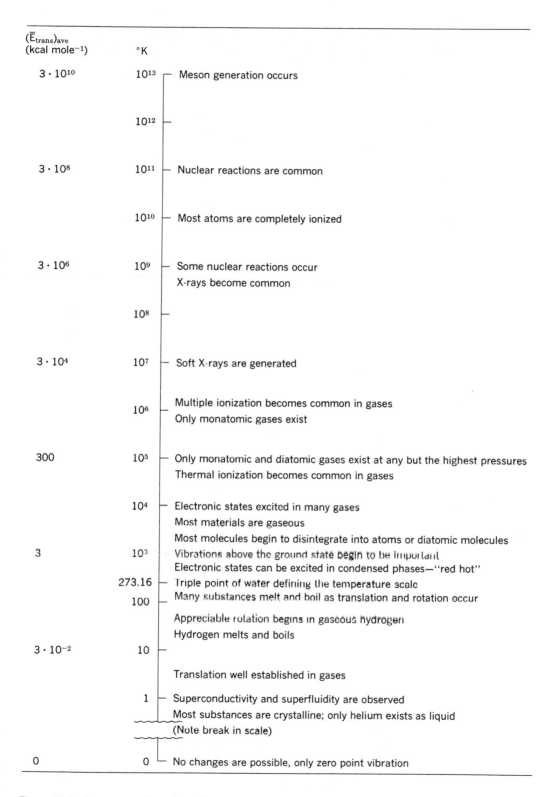

Figure 19.2 Some properties of equilibrium states as a function of temperature.

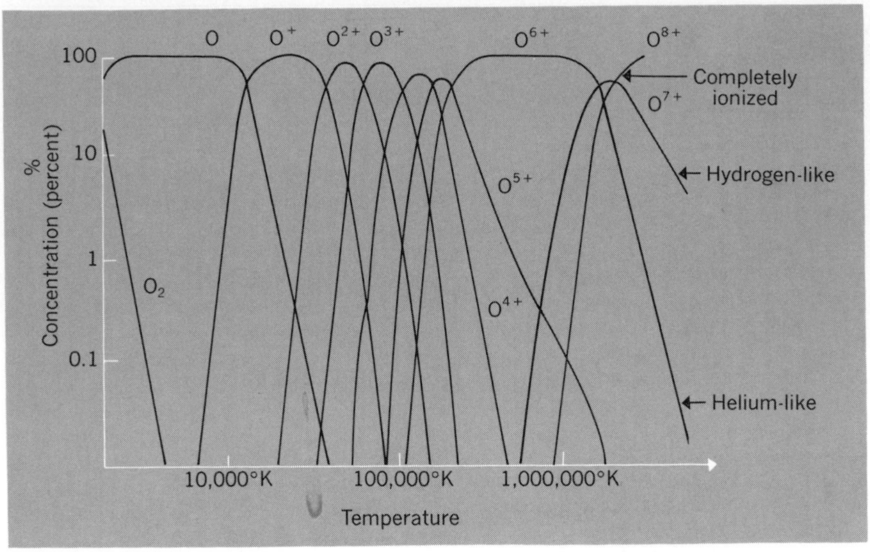

Figure 19.3 Concentration versus temperature in pure oxygen.

We shall continue these discussions in considerable detail in the chapters on the kinetics and mechanisms of reactions. It should be clear even now, however, that molecules engaged in random translational motions, with energies distributed according to Boltzmann statistics, will collide frequently and in random ways. Furthermore, the molecules stay together during a collision for a length of time comparable to that of a bond vibration. Some of these collisions will lead to exchanges of energy and some will lead to bond breaking and bond forming. Since the processes are random, they can be described in statistical terms. For example, the likelihood of reaction will depend on the likelihood of collision (and thus on the concentrations of the molecules), and also on the available energy (and thus on the temperatures of the system). There may be other variables as well, as we shall see in Chapters 22 and 23. We shall, in this chapter, explore the nature of chemical equilibria and equilibrium states, and their relationships to molecular motion.

DISCOVERY OF THE EQUILIBRIUM CONSTANT EXPRESSION

In preceding chapters we have used equilibrium constants in a purely empirical fashion. We shall now look into their history and detailed interpretation.

From the earliest days of chemistry it has been apparent that some reactions went "to completion" and others did not. A particularly simple example is the solubility of a crystal in a liquid. At any temperature below the melting point of the solid, the system always reaches a condition in which the liquid solution is saturated with crystal. Addition of more crystals has no effect on the concentration of the dissolved material. Similar effects have been noted in other reactions occurring in a single phase.

It was Guldberg and Waage who first stated clearly, in a series of papers published from 1863 to 1867, that the extent of reaction (at least in some systems) could be described by what we now call an equilibrium constant—that is, a ratio of concentration terms, each raised to an appropriate exponent. Their evidence was experimental. Their conclusion was empirical, but it was consistent with arguments based on rates of reaction.

In the 1870's their conclusion was generalized, by the application of exact thermodynamic arguments to assert that there exists for any reaction a concentration ratio that at constant temperature is independent of concentration changes. This ratio is obtained by multiplying together the concentrations of the species on the right side of the chemical equation, to obtain the numerator, and multiplying the concentrations of the species on the left side, to obtain the denominator. Each concentration is raised to a power (exponent) equal to the coefficient of that species in the net chemical equation. Thus, for the general equation

$$aA + bB + cC = dD + eE$$

we get the

EQUILIBRIUM CONSTANT EXPRESSION: $$K_{\text{eq}} = \frac{[D]^d[E]^e}{[A]^a[B]^b[C]^c}$$

or, in general,

$$K_{\text{eq}} = \frac{\prod_P [P]^p}{\prod_R [R]^r} \tag{19.1}$$

where $[P]$ reads "concentration of product P" and p is its coefficient in the chemical equation; similarly for R. K is a numerical constant independent of concentration, but K does depend on temperature. Note that K is a dimensional number; thus the numerical value of K will differ depending on the units used to express concentrations. Since Equation (19.1) is a general one, we conclude that a reaction which goes "to completion" merely has a very large value of K; the equilibrium concentration of reactants is very small. A reaction which "does not occur" merely has a very small value of K; the equilibrium concentration of products is very small. Thus, strictly speaking, all reactions occur and none goes to completion. Every isolated chemical system will eventually come to equilibrium. An important question is: Does reaction cease in a system at chemical equilibrium or is a dynamic state of equal rates of counterbalancing reaction achieved?

MICROSCOPIC REVERSIBILITY

Suppose we consider a reaction mechanism that is known in some detail. The hydrolysis of an ester, for example, actually proceeds through the following steps in basic solutions.

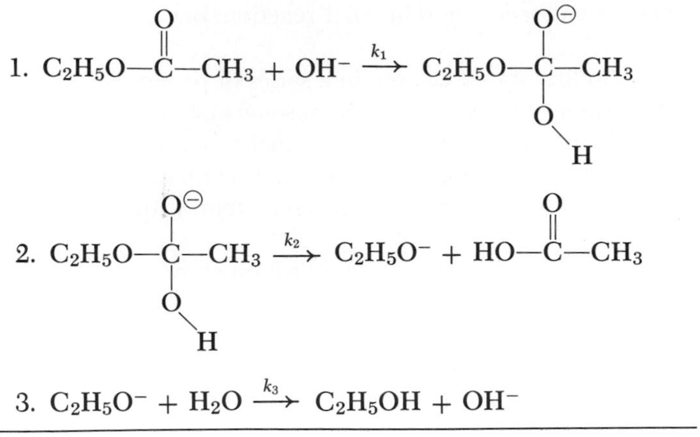

Net: 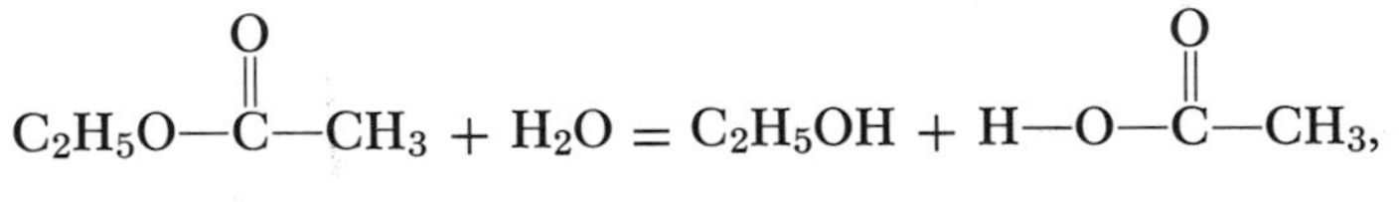 $K_{eq} = \dfrac{[\text{ROH}][\text{HOAc}]}{[\text{ROAc}][\text{H}_2\text{O}]}$ (19.2)

Initially only the reactions listed occur, since only $C_2H_5OOCH_3$, OH^-, and H_2O are present to react. But at equilibrium each of these forward reactions becomes exactly balanced by a reverse reaction, and the rate of each forward reaction exactly equals the rate of its reverse reaction.

Reaction	*Rate*	
1. 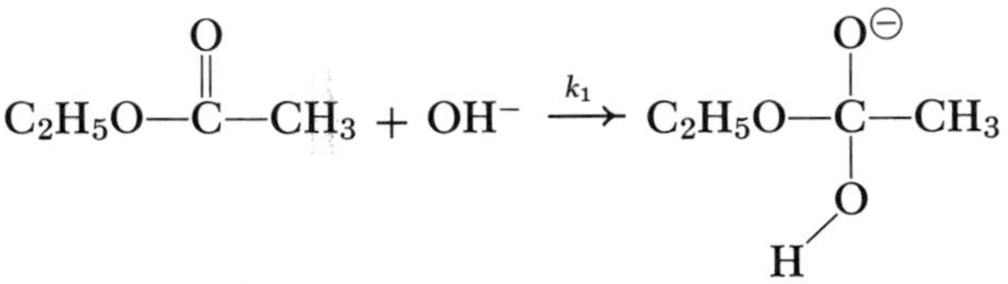	$rate_1 = k_1[\text{ROAc}][\text{OH}^-]$	(19.3)
2. 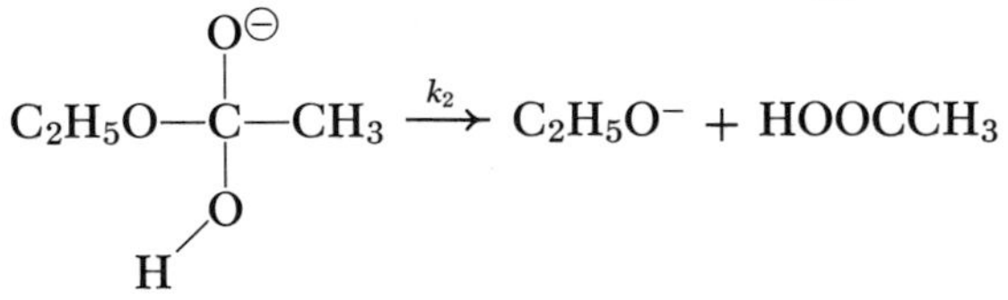	$rate_2 = k_2[\text{ROOHAc}^-]$	(19.4)
3. $C_2H_5O^- + H_2O \xrightarrow{k_3} C_2H_5OH + OH^-$	$rate_3 = k_3[\text{RO}^-][\text{H}_2\text{O}]$	(19.5)
−3. $C_2H_5OH + OH^- \xrightarrow{k_{-3}} C_2H_5O^- + H_2O$	$rate_{-3} = k_{-3}[\text{ROH}][\text{OH}^-]$	(19.6)
−2. 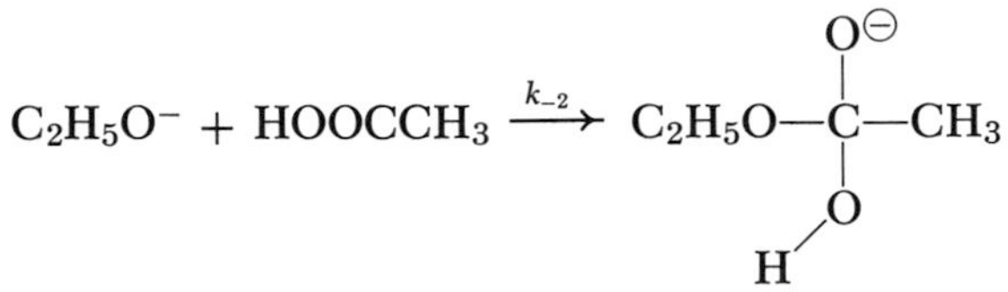	$rate_{-2} = k_{-2}[\text{RO}^-][\text{HOAc}]$	(19.7)
−1. 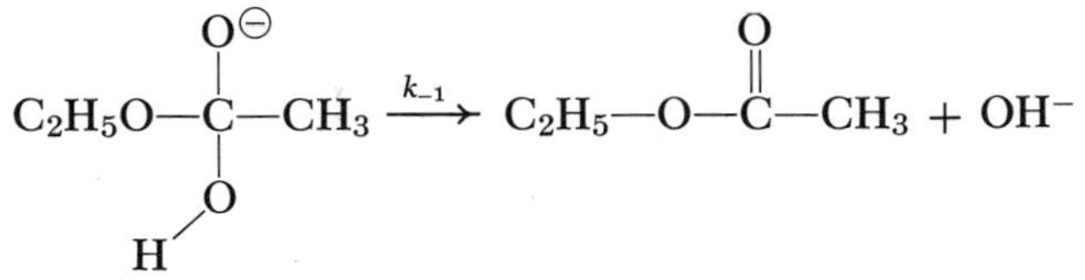	$rate_{-1} = k_{-1}[\text{ROOHAc}^-]$	(19.8)

But $\text{rate}_3 = \text{rate}_{-3}$ at equilibrium. Thus

$$k_3[\text{RO}^-][\text{H}_2\text{O}] = k_{-3}[\text{ROH}][\text{OH}^-] \qquad \text{or} \qquad \frac{k_3}{k_{-3}} = \frac{[\text{ROH}][\text{OH}^-]}{[\text{RO}^-][\text{H}_2\text{O}]}$$

Similarly, since $\text{rate}_2 = \text{rate}_{-2}$ and $\text{rate}_1 = \text{rate}_{-1}$ at equilibrium,

$$k_2[\text{ROOHAc}^-] = k_{-2}[\text{RO}^-][\text{HOAc}], \qquad \frac{k_2}{k_{-2}} = \frac{[\text{RO}^-][\text{HOAc}]}{[\text{ROOHAc}^-]}$$

$$k_1[\text{ROAc}][\text{OH}^-] = k_{-1}[\text{ROOHAc}^-], \qquad \frac{k_1}{k_{-1}} = \frac{[\text{ROOHAc}^-]}{[\text{ROAc}][\text{OH}^-]}$$

Note what happens, however, if we multiply these three rate quotients together:

$$\left[\frac{k_1}{k_{-1}}\right]\left[\frac{k_2}{k_{-2}}\right]\left[\frac{k_3}{k_{-3}}\right] = \left[\frac{[\text{ROOHAc}^-]}{[\text{ROAc}][\text{OH}^-]}\right]\left[\frac{[\text{RO}^-][\text{HOAc}]}{[\text{ROOHAc}^-]}\right]\left[\frac{[\text{ROH}][\text{OH}^-]}{[\text{RO}^-][\text{H}_2\text{O}]}\right]$$

$$= \frac{[\text{HOAc}][\text{ROH}]}{[\text{ROAc}][\text{H}_2\text{O}]} = K_{\text{eq}} \tag{19.9}$$

which is the same as the experimental equilibrium constant of Equation (19.2). This derivation is completely consistent with the experimental observations on the reaction mechanism and assumes only that, at equilibrium, each step in the mechanism becomes equal in rate to its reverse. In other words, the proof assumes that each apparently static equilibrium state is made up of *dynamic* microscopic states in which molecules are continually moving, colliding, and reacting in a random way such that the likelihood of their reacting is related to their concentrations. All available evidence is consistent with this principle of microscopic reversibility in chemical systems. Chemical equilibria are dynamic states.

Exercise 19.3

Comment on the statement, "The principle of microscopic reversibility assumes that the rates of all reactions are identical at equilibrium." *Answer:* Not valid; the assumption is that the rate of each "forward" reaction becomes identical to the rate of its own "reverse" reaction.

DYNAMIC CHEMICAL EQUILIBRIUM

The principle of chemical microscopic reversibility gives an equilibrium constant expression consistent with the experimental observations in all cases for which the mechanism is known. It also gives a proper equilibrium constant expression if one merely guesses a mechanism (correct or incorrect) and carries out the equating of the supposed rate constants step by step. The principle of microscopic reversibility, in fact, is a perfectly general method of getting K. Since it is so general, we need never bother to go through it; we can simply write down the equilibrium constant expression from an examination of the equation for the net reaction. But the principle of microscopic reversibility does assume that reversibility occurs and that chemical equilibria are dynamic. What experimental evidence do we have for this?

Table 19.2 **Hydrogen, iodine, and hydrogen iodide equilibrium at 698.6°K. The first five lines give data on equilibrium systems obtained by heating hydrogen and iodine together. The last three lines give data on equilibrium systems obtained by heating pure hydrogen iodide. Note that the same constant is obtained by each method.**

$[H_2]$ (moles/liter)	$[I_2]$ (moles/liter)	$[HI]$ (moles/liter)	$K = \frac{[H_2][I_2]}{[HI]^2}$
$1.8313 \cdot 10^{-3}$	$3.1292 \cdot 10^{-3}$	$17.671 \cdot 10^{-3}$	$1.835 \cdot 10^{-2}$
$2.2523 \cdot 10^{-3}$	$2.3360 \cdot 10^{-3}$	$16.850 \cdot 10^{-3}$	$1.853 \cdot 10^{-2}$
$2.9070 \cdot 10^{-3}$	$1.7069 \cdot 10^{-3}$	$16.482 \cdot 10^{-3}$	$1.827 \cdot 10^{-2}$
$3.5600 \cdot 10^{-3}$	$1.2500 \cdot 10^{-3}$	$15.588 \cdot 10^{-3}$	$1.831 \cdot 10^{-2}$
$4.5647 \cdot 10^{-3}$	$0.7378 \cdot 10^{-3}$	$13.544 \cdot 10^{-3}$	$1.835 \cdot 10^{-2}$
$0.4789 \cdot 10^{-3}$	$0.4789 \cdot 10^{-3}$	$3.531 \cdot 10^{-3}$	$1.840 \cdot 10^{-2}$
$0.4953 \cdot 10^{-3}$	$0.4953 \cdot 10^{-3}$	$3.655 \cdot 10^{-3}$	$1.832 \cdot 10^{-2}$
$1.1409 \cdot 10^{-3}$	$1.1409 \cdot 10^{-3}$	$8.410 \cdot 10^{-3}$	$1.840 \cdot 10^{-2}$
		Average	$1.837 \cdot 10^{-2}$ or 0.01837

SOURCE: A. H. Taylor and R. H. Crist, *J. Am. Chem. Soc.*, **63,** 1377 (1941).

Often cited is evidence like that carefully obtained by Taylor and Crist on the hydrogen-iodine reaction:

$$2HI_{(g)} = H_{2(g)} + I_{2(g)}, \qquad K_{eq} = \frac{[H_2][I_2]}{[HI]^2}$$

Some of their data are given in Table 19.2. A remarkably constant "constant" is obtained, the experimental uncertainty being about ±1%.

One method of checking on the possible dynamism of the equilibrium state is to allow a system to come to equilibrium and to remain in that condition long enough to ensure that equilibrium has really been attained. Samples can be removed from time to time and analyzed to determine if all concentrations remain constant. Or spectroscopic methods can be used on the otherwise undisturbed equilibrium system to determine the concentrations of all the species present. A small amount of one of the ingredients containing some radioactive atoms can then be introduced—for example, radioactive iodine could be introduced into the hydrogen-iodine equilibrium system. (The system will shift slightly because of the addition of the radioactive iodine, but this shift can be kept so small as to be immeasurable.) If we now periodically remove samples of the equilibrium mix and analyze for radioactivity in the hydrogen iodide, we find that the amount of radioactive iodine in the HI increases rapidly at first but then reaches a constant value exactly matching that predicted on the assumption that the radioactive iodine has become randomly distributed between the iodine and the HI. This is possible only if molecules react at equilibrium and if the equilibrium state is dynamic.

All the available experimental evidence, as well as all current chemical theories, supports the idea that chemical equilibria are dynamic: (1) all possible reactions are occurring, (2) each reaction is exactly counterbalanced at equilibrium by an opposite, but otherwise identical, reaction proceeding at the same rate, (3) no net change occurs in any concentration at equilibrium.

EQUILIBRIUM CONSTANTS AND FREE ENERGIES OF REACTION

We earlier developed the idea that probable reactions in closed systems at constant T and P were associated with negative values of ΔG^0, and improbable reactions with positive values of ΔG^0. We now see that the equilibrium constant, K, is also related to reaction probability. Large values of K (> 1) represent probable reactions; small values (< 1) improbable reactions. We gave the relationship between ΔG^0 and K in Chapter 1. We shall derive this relationship in Chapter 29; it is merely stated again here:

$$\Delta G^0 = -RT \ln K_{eq}$$

Note that this is consistent with past discussions. If $K > 1$, $\Delta G^0 = -$; if $K < 1$, $\Delta G^0 = +$.

CALCULATION OF THE EQUILIBRIUM CONSTANT

The equilibrium constant expression for any reaction may be immediately written from an examination of the chemical equation. Thus the initial step in approaching any equilibrium problem is to write the chemical equation. A few examples are given in Table 19.3.

We give an additional useful generalization: concentrations that are constant in an equilibrium state are included in the equilibrium constant. There is so much water present in these dilute solutions that the small changes in volume in the liquid phase do not appreciably change its concentration. If this concentration is constant, it may be included in the value of K_{eq} and so simplify the algebraic calculations. This is universally done in chemistry. Tabulated values for equilibrium constants in aqueous solutions always include in the K_{eq} the concentration of water, 55.51 M, if needed, according to the chemical reaction.

Now consider the problem of pure condensed phases. In many reactions a pure condensed phase may form, especially through the precipitation of a crystalline phase from solution. The concentration of the crystalline phase is constant, so long as the crystals are pure. Thus twice as many crystals contain twice as many

Table 19.3 Examples of equilibrium constant expressions.

Equation	Equilibrium constant expression	Comment
$HgCl_{2(aq)} = Hg^{++}{}_{(aq)} + 2Cl^{-}{}_{(aq)}$	$K_{eq} = \dfrac{[Hg^{++}][Cl^-]^2}{[HgCl_2]}$	concentration of H_2O is assumed constant
$PbCl_{2(c)} = Pb^{++}{}_{(aq)} + 2Cl^{-}{}_{(aq)}$	$K_{eq} = [Pb^{++}][Cl^-]^2$	$[PbCl_{2(c)}]$ is a constant and is included in K_{eq}
$CN^{-}{}_{(aq)} + H_2O = HCN_{(aq)} + OH^{-}{}_{(aq)}$	$K_{eq} = \dfrac{[HCN][OH^-]}{[CN^-]}$	concentration of H_2O is a constant included in K_{eq}
$Na_{(c)} + H_2O_{(l)} = Na^{+}{}_{(aq)} + OH^{-}{}_{(aq)} + \frac{1}{2}H_{2(g)}$	$K_{eq} = [Na^+][OH^-][H_2]^{1/2}$	$[Na_{(c)}]$ and $[H_2O]$ are constants included in K_{eq}

moles, but these moles occupy twice the volume, so that the concentration (the number of moles per liter of the crystalline phase) remains constant regardless of the number of moles present. Concentrations of pure condensed phases (most commonly solid phases) are included in the values tabulated for K_{eq}. This is not done for pure gaseous phases, since the concentration there is dependent on the pressure; the concentrations in condensed phases are only slightly affected by changes in pressure, since condensed phases are normally rather incompressible.

The calculation of the value of the equilibrium constant at any temperature involves, then, the determination of the concentration at equilibrium of each species involved in the dynamic equilibrium, except for any solvent and any pure condensed phases. Concentrations of dissolved species are expressed as formality, F (molarity, M); concentrations of gases are expressed as partial pressure in atmospheres. Let us examine a few experimental systems.

Exercise 19.4

Calculate a numerical value for the equilibrium constant for the aqueous reaction $Cl_2 + 2Br^- = 2Cl^- + Br_2$. The equilibrium concentration of Br^- is found to be $5 \cdot 10^{-4}\ M$ when the two reactant concentrations are initially 0.1 M. *Answer:* From the stoichiometry, the other equilibrium concentrations must be $[Cl_2] = 0.05\ M$, $[Br_2] = 0.05\ M$, $[Cl^-] = 0.1\ M$. Then $K = \{[Cl^-]^2[Br_2]/[Cl_2][Br^-]^2\}_{eq} = 4 \cdot 10^4$.

IONIZATION OF WATER

We have already pointed out that pure water contains many species but that most of its properties may be accounted for in terms of the ions resulting from the collision-induced self-ionization, written

$$H_2O_{(l)} = H^+{}_{(aq)} + OH^-{}_{(aq)}, \qquad K_w = [H^+][OH^-]$$

$$OH^-{}_{(aq)} = H^+{}_{(aq)} + O^={}_{(aq)}$$

We can neglect the second ionization to a very good approximation. Any ions present in pure water should, then, be due to the first reaction, the one which produces equal concentrations of H^+ and OH^-.

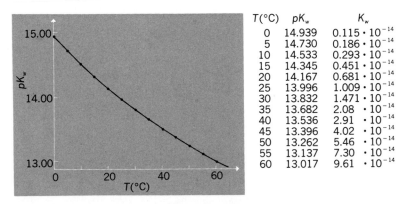

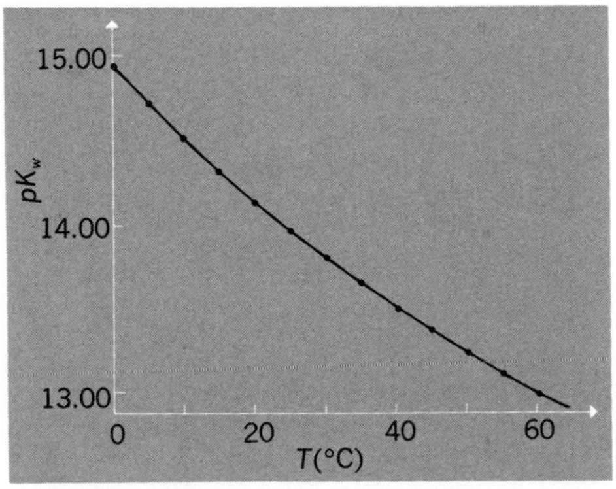

T(°C)	pK_w	K_w
0	14.939	$0.115 \cdot 10^{-14}$
5	14.730	$0.186 \cdot 10^{-14}$
10	14.533	$0.293 \cdot 10^{-14}$
15	14.345	$0.451 \cdot 10^{-14}$
20	14.167	$0.681 \cdot 10^{-14}$
25	13.996	$1.009 \cdot 10^{-14}$
30	13.832	$1.471 \cdot 10^{-14}$
35	13.682	$2.08 \cdot 10^{-14}$
40	13.536	$2.91 \cdot 10^{-14}$
45	13.396	$4.02 \cdot 10^{-14}$
50	13.262	$5.46 \cdot 10^{-14}$
55	13.137	$7.30 \cdot 10^{-14}$
60	13.017	$9.61 \cdot 10^{-14}$

Figure 19.4 *pK* as a function of *T*. [H. S. Harned and W. J. Hamer, *J. Am. Chem. Soc.*, **55**, 2194, 4496 (1933). Copyright 1933 by the American Chemical Society.]

Measuring the electrical conductivity of pure water and comparing it to the conductivity of solutions containing known quantities of hydrogen ions and hydroxide ions allows the estimation of these concentrations. This experiment has been done very carefully at least three times. The values of K_w at 298°K were found to be $1.10 \cdot 10^{-14}$ (1893), $0.81 \cdot 10^{-14}$ (1907), and $1.05 \cdot 10^{-14}$ (1907). The concentration can also be studied by their catalytic effect on the rates of various reactions and by their effect on the voltage of an electric cell in which $H^+_{(aq)}$ or $OH^-_{(aq)}$ are reactants. From all these and other methods we get values of K_w as in Figure 19.4. In addition to values of K_w itself, the figure gives pK_w, the negative logarithm of K_w, and shows pK_w plotted versus T, where $pK = -\log_{10}K$. We shall find pK values most useful.

We shall use the value

$$K_w = 1.00 \cdot 10^{-14} = [H^+][OH^-] \qquad \text{at } 298°\text{K}$$

It is easy to remember, easy to use, and within 1% of the best value. This means that in pure water at 25°C

$$[H^+] = [OH^-] = (1.00 \cdot 10^{-14})^{1/2} = 1.00 \cdot 10^{-7}\, M$$

The units of K_w are (moles/liter)^2.

We can also calculate the free energy of ionization of water:

$$\Delta G^0 = -RT \ln K_w = -\frac{1.987 \cdot 298.2 \cdot 2.303}{1000} \log 10^{-14.00} = 19.11 \text{ kcal mole}^{-1}$$

The positive value is consistent with the small, but appreciable, ionization of the water.

Exercise 19.5

Rationalize the increase in K_w with increasing T. *Answer:* The net reaction may be written $H_2O + H_2O = H_3O^+_{(aq)} + OH^-_{(aq)}$. Electrostatic theory and the experimental value of K_w suggest that the ground energy state strongly favors the neutral molecules. At higher T the excited state (ions) becomes more likely as the available KE ($\frac{3}{2}RT$) rises and molecular collisions become more and more vigorous.

Exercise 19.6

Calculate $[OH^-]$ in an aqueous solution at 25°C, when $[H^+] = 1.0 \cdot 10^{-6}\, M$. *Answer:* $K_{25°C} = [OH^-][H^+] = 1.0 \cdot 10^{-14}$; $[OH^-] = 1.0 \cdot 10^{-14}/1.0 \cdot 10^{-6} = 1.0 \cdot 10^{-8}\, M$.

IONIZATION OF A WEAK ACID

Now consider the process of ionization of another solute in water. We could, for example, use any of the weak acids listed in Table 18.13. Let us select HOCl and calculate the concentration of hydrogen ions obtained if we dissolve x moles of pure HOCl in 1 liter of pure water. Since HOCl is an acid we expect the solution to be acidic. Thus $[H^+]$ should be greater than $10^{-7}\, M$.

We may then write

Principal equilibrium: $HOCl_{(aq)} = H^+_{(aq)} + OCl^-_{(aq)}$

Equilibrium constant expression: $$K = \frac{[H^+][OCl^-]}{[HOCl]} = 6.8 \cdot 10^{-8}$$

Both HOCl and H_2O can yield hydrogen ions upon ionization, but HOCl, with $K_{eq} = 6.8 \cdot 10^{-8}$, is far stronger as an acid than H_2O, with $K_w = 1.0 \cdot 10^{-14}$. The H—OCl bond is weaker than the H—OH bond and breaks more often as molecules collide and $[H^+]$ should therefore be considerably greater than 10^{-7} *M*. Thus, as a first approximation, let us assume that all of the hydrogen ions come from the HOCl. We see from the stoichiometric equation that hydrogen ions and hypochlorite ions are produced simultaneously and in equal concentration. We also see that one hypochlorous acid molecule is used up each time a hydrogen-ion–hypochlorite-ion pair are produced. We may express these facts algebraically in the following equations representing the equilibrium state:

Principal equilibrium: $HOCl_{(aq)} = H^+{}_{(aq)} + OCl^-{}_{(aq)}$

Charge balance: $[H^+] = [OCl^-]$

Mass balance: $[HOCl] = x - [H^+]$

since x moles/l of HOCl were dissolved. Thus

Equilibrium constant expression: $$K_{eq} = \frac{[H^+][OCl^-]}{[HOCl]} = \frac{[H^+][H^+]}{x - [H^+]}$$

$$\frac{[H^+]^2}{x - [H^+]} = 6.8 \cdot 10^{-8} \qquad (19.10)$$

Clearly, knowledge of x allows calculation of the equilibrium concentration of hydrogen ions, $[H^+]$. Equation (19.10) may be solved exactly for $[H^+]$, assuming x is known, by the binomial theorem. But is that the easiest way? Note that HOCl is a weak acid (K is small). Thus little of it will be ionized. It is likely that $x \gg [H^+]$. This assumption greatly simplifies Equation (19.10), to give

$$\frac{[H^+]^2}{x} = 6.8 \cdot 10^{-8}$$

$$[H^+] = \sqrt{6.8 \cdot 10^{-8}\, x} = 2.6 \cdot 10^{-4}\, x^{1/2}$$

Table 19.4 tabulates some solutions of this equation, giving $[H^+]$ as a function of x.

Table 19.4 shows that our two assumptions are justified over a wide range of concentrations. K_{eq} is known to about 1 percent. Within this degree of accuracy the hydrogen ion concentration, $[H^+]$, is negligible compared to x, down to values of x of about $1.00 \cdot 10^{-4}$, and is only just appreciable at this value. Furthermore, not until the value of x drops to about $1.00 \cdot 10^{-5}$ is the $[H^+]$ from the ionization of HOCl low enough that it begins to compare with the 10^{-7} *M* hydrogen ion found in pure water. Thus, only with values of x below 10^{-4} need we employ the binomial solution of Equation (19.10) or need we worry about the ions coming from the ionization of water.

In this instance, as in practically all instances, you can most quickly solve equilibrium constant expressions if you assume that the ionization of water contributes negligibly to the total ion concentration $[K_{eq} \gg K_w]$ and that the amount of ionization of the weak acid is negligible compared to the amount of acid present ($x \gg [H^+]$). But it is *always* wise, having solved a problem using these two assumptions, to look at the answers and see if the assumptions were justified. If not, more exact methods are used in repeating the solution.

Table 19.4 Equilibrium concentrations (moles/liter) when x moles of HOCl are dissolved to give 1.00 liter of aqueous solution, assuming that $x \gg [H^+]$ and that ionization of water is negligible compared to HOCl.

	$x(F)$									
	1.00	0.500	0.100	0.0500	0.0100	$1.00 \cdot 10^{-3}$	$1.00 \cdot 10^{-4}$	$1.00 \cdot 10^{-5}$	$1.00 \cdot 10^{-6}$	$1.00 \cdot 10^{-7}$
$[H^+]_{eq}$	$2.6 \cdot 10^{-4}$	$1.8 \cdot 10^{-4}$	$8.2 \cdot 10^{-5}$	$5.8 \cdot 10^{-5}$	$2.6 \cdot 10^{-5}$	$8.2 \cdot 10^{-6}$	$2.6 \cdot 10^{-6}$	$7.9 \cdot 10^{-7}$	$2.5 \cdot 10^{-7}$	
$[OCl^-]_{eq}$	$2.6 \cdot 10^{-4}$	$1.8 \cdot 10^{-4}$	$8.2 \cdot 10^{-5}$	$5.8 \cdot 10^{-5}$	$2.6 \cdot 10^{-5}$	$8.2 \cdot 10^{-6}$	$2.6 \cdot 10^{-6}$	$7.8 \cdot 10^{-7}$	$2.1 \cdot 10^{-7}$	
$[HOCl]_{eq}$	1.00	0.500	0.100	0.0500	0.0100	$0.99 \cdot 10^{-3}$	$0.97 \cdot 10^{-4}$	$0.92 \cdot 10^{-5}$	$7.8 \cdot 10^{-7}$	
							x no longer $\gg [H^+]$	$[H^+]$ from water is appreciable		

Now suppose that instead of adding pure HOCl to pure water we add both HOCl and NaOCl to pure water. NaOCl, sodium hypochlorite, like all sodium salts, consists of elements with greatly differing relative electronegativities. That is, sodium is far less electronegative than are oxygen and chlorine, though the latter two are quite similar in relative electronegativity (see Figure 14.4). Thus NaOCl will be almost completely ionized in water into Na^+ and OCl^- ions. The sodium ions are isoelectronic with Ne atoms, as shown in Table 19.4, and are normally quite inert toward other chemical species. Such chemically inert ions are often called "spectator ions." They must be present in order to balance the electrical charges in the system, but they exert little effect on the changes that are occurring and undergo few changes themselves. You should assume, unless there is evidence to the contrary, that all compounds containing both metallic, M, and nonmetallic, X, elements ionize completely into M^{+m} and X^{-n} ions in aqueous solution.

Exercise 19.7

Calculate $[H^+]$ in a 1 M aqueous solution of HCN. *Answer:* From Table 18.13, $K = 4.9 \cdot 10^{-10} = [H^+][CN^-]/[HCN] = [H^+]^2/{\sim}1$, since $HCN = H^+ + CN^-$, so that $[H^+] = [CN^-]$. Thus $[H^+] = \sqrt{4.9 \cdot 10^{-10}} = 2.2 \cdot 10^{-5}\ M$. This value is negligible compared to 1 M, and is an acceptable answer.

IONIZATION OF A WEAK ACID IN THE PRESENCE OF A "COMMON ION"

Consider the equilibrium state that will result if we dissolve x moles of HOCl and w moles of NaOCl (w moles Na^+ and w moles OCl^-) in 1 liter of pure water. These two substances both release OCl^- in an aqueous solution and are said to have a "common ion." The equilibria are

Principal equilibria:

$$HOCl_{(aq)} = H^+{}_{(aq)} + OCl^-{}_{(aq)}, \qquad K = 6.8 \cdot 10^{-8} \qquad (19.11)$$

$$NaOCl_{(aq)} = Na^+{}_{(aq)} + OCl^-{}_{(aq)}, \qquad K = \text{very large} \qquad (19.12)$$

Because the presence of the additional OCl^-—the common ion—from NaOCl will lower the acidity, we expect this solution to be less acid than that considered in the preceding section. Thus $[H^+]$ will be less than $10^{-4}\ M$ and may even be less than $10^{-7}\ M$ if enough of the OCl^- ions (Lewis base) are present.

The reaction in Equation (19.11) will produce y moles of H^+ and y moles of OCl^-, and reaction (19.12) will produce w moles of OCl^-. Remember that compounds containing both metallic and nonmetallic elements are assumed to be completely ionized (at least in solutions which are 1 M or less in the compound). Thus, at equilibrium,

Mass and charge balance:

$$[HOCl] = x - y, \qquad [H^+] = y, \qquad [OCl^-] = w + y$$

Equilibrium constant expression:

$$K = 6.8 \cdot 10^{-8} = \frac{[H^+][OCl^-]}{[HOCl]} = \frac{y \cdot (w + y)}{x - y} \qquad (19.13)$$

where x and w are known, since they represent the numbers of moles of HOCl and NaOCl added per liter of solution.

Again we have a relatively complex equation, but again it can normally be greatly simplified. Let us apply Le Châtelier's principle, or the principle of microscopic reversibility, to the net reactions in Equations (19.11) and (19.12). The complete ionization of the NaOCl (remember salts ionize) will give free OCl^- ions. The presence of these ions will tend to diminish the extent of ionization of the HOCl by favoring the reverse reaction. Thus, even more than in pure HOCl, $x \gg y$. This decrease in y also tends to make $w \gg y$. Assuming that both $x \gg y$ and $w \gg y$, we obtain

$$K = 6.8 \cdot 10^{-8} = \frac{y \cdot w}{x} = \frac{[H^+]w}{x}$$

or

$$[H^+] = \frac{x}{w} \cdot 6.8 \cdot 10^{-8}$$

Note that if the ratio x/w equals one or less, the two assumptions seem apt to be fulfilled. Again a quick calculation gives values that can be checked against the assumptions. The "common ion" effect, as predicted, has lowered the $[H^+]$ below what the acid gives when present alone. In fact the solution may have become slightly basic.

If we have a solution made by adding $1.0 \cdot 10^{-2}$ moles of HOCl and $1.0 \cdot 10^{-3}$ moles of NaOCl to give 100 ml of solution in water, what are the equilibrium concentrations? Since 100 ml is one-tenth of a liter, the additions were at the rate of $10 \cdot 1.0 \cdot 10^{-2} = 1.0 \cdot 10^{-1}$ moles of HOCl and $10 \cdot 1.0 \cdot 10^{-3} = 1.0 \cdot 10^{-2}$ moles of NaOCl per liter of solution. The NaOCl will, of course, be essentially completely ionized at this concentration. Thus OCl^- (from NaOCl) is $1.0 \cdot 10^{-2}$ M. The net equation for the principal reaction at equilibrium is

Principal equilibrium: $HOCl_{(aq)} = H^+{}_{(aq)} + OCl^-{}_{(aq)}$

Equilibrium constant expression: $K = \frac{[H^+][OCl^-]}{[HOCl]} = 6.8 \cdot 10^{-8}$

Mass balance: $[OCl^-]_{eq} = 1.0 \cdot 10^{-2} + [H^+]_{eq}$

$[HOCl]_{eq} = 1.0 \cdot 10^{-1} - [H^+]_{eq}$

and

$$K = 6.8 \cdot 10^{-8} = \frac{[H^+]\{1.0 \cdot 10^{-2} + [H^+]\}}{\{1.0 \cdot 10^{-1} - [H^+]\}} \tag{19.14}$$

Equation (19.14) can, of course, be solved exactly, but it is far quicker to assume (since K is small) that $[H^+] \ll 1.0 \cdot 10^{-2}$ and, therefore, that $[H^+] \ll 1.0 \cdot 10^{-1}$. This gives

$$K = 6.8 \cdot 10^{-8} = \frac{[H^+]1.0 \cdot 10^{-2}}{1.0 \cdot 10^{-1}}$$

$$[H^+] = \frac{6.8 \cdot 10^{-8} \cdot 1.0 \cdot 10^{-1}}{1.0 \cdot 10^{-2}} = 6.8 \cdot 10^{-7}\ M$$

Note that the assumptions are justified. But what about the contribution made by the ionization of water?

Table 19.5 **Equilibrium concentrations when $1.0 \cdot 10^{-3}$ moles of NaOCl and $1.0 \cdot 10^{-2}$ moles of HOCl are dissolved to give 100 ml of aqueous solution.**

$[OCl^-]$	$[HOCl]$	$[H^+]$	$[OH^-]$	$[Na^+]$
$1.0 \cdot 10^{-2}$ *M*	$1.0 \cdot 10^{-1}$ *M*	$6.8 \cdot 10^{-7}$ *M*	$1.5 \cdot 10^{-8}$ *M*	$1.0 \cdot 10^{-2}$ *M*

Pure water has $[H^+] = [OH^-] = 1.0 \cdot 10^{-7}$ *M*. This value of $1.0 \cdot 10^{-7}$ *M* is not negligible compared to the $6.8 \cdot 10^{-7}$ *M* of the last equation. But remember—all constants for all equilibria occurring must be satisfied at equilibrium in any system. Thus, it must also be true that

$$K_w = 1.00 \cdot 10^{-14} = [H^+][OH^-]$$

where $[H^+]$ = sum of all hydrogen ion concentrations (from HOCl and from H_2O). If there were no HOCl present, $[H^+]$ would be $1.00 \cdot 10^{-7}$ *M* from the water (assuming 25°C). The presence of HOCl adds to the total $[H^+]$, thus decreasing the amount of ionization by the water compared to that of pure water. (Le Châtelier's principle and the principle of microscopic reversibility again hold.) Therefore

$$K_w = 1.00 \cdot 10^{-14} = [H^+][OH^-] = \{[H^+]_{H_2O} + [H^+]_{HOCl}\}\{[H^+]_{H_2O}\}$$

Since $[H^+]_{HOCl} > [H^+]_{H_2O}$, as shown above, let us assume that $[H^+]_{H_2O}$ is negligible compared to $[H^+]_{HOCl}$. Then

$$1.00 \cdot 10^{-14} = [H^+]_{HOCl}[H^+]_{H_2O} \cong 6.8 \cdot 10^{-7}[H^+]_{H_2O}$$

$$[H^+]_{H_2O} \cong \frac{10^{-14}}{6.8 \cdot 10^{-7}} = 0.15 \cdot 10^{-7}\ M$$

This value of $0.15 \cdot 10^{-7}$ *M* hydrogen ion might be just barely appreciable compared to $6.8 \cdot 10^{-7}$ *M*. However, equilibrium constants are seldom known to better than ±5%, so we would normally state that the ionization of water in this solution is negligible compared to the ionization of HOCl.

Thus we have found the final equilibrium concentrations (see Table 19.5) for a solution made by mixing $1.0 \cdot 10^{-2}$ moles of HOCl and $1.0 \cdot 10^{-3}$ moles of NaOCl in 100 ml of H_2O.

Exercise 19.8

Which is a more acid aqueous solution—1 *M* HCN or 1 *M* HCN in the presence of 1 *M* KCN? *Answer:* The net reaction for the ionization of HCN is $HCN_{(aq)} = H^+_{(aq)} + CN^-_{(aq)}$. The presence of additional CN^- ions from added KCN (which is completely ionized, as are all potassium salts) makes the reverse reaction to the net reaction more probable and decreases the $[H^+]$. The argument can be justified (*a*) in terms of rates of reaction and microscopic reversibility, (*b*) in terms of Le Châtelier's principle, (*c*) in terms of the equilibrium constant expression, (*d*) quantitatively by carrying out the equilibrium calculations to get $[H^+] = 2.2 \cdot 10^{-5}$ *M* in 1 *M* HCN, and $[H^+] = 4.9 \cdot 10^{-10}$ *M* in 1 *M* HCN which is also 1 *M* in KCN. Note: $K = 4.9 \cdot 10^{-10}$ in Table 18.13.

HYDROLYSIS OF A SALT OF A WEAK ACID

What happens if we add only NaOCl to water? What equilibrium concentrations are then reached? The NaOCl will ionize to give Na^+ and OCl^- ions, and the Na^+, as usual, will merely be a spectator to the equilibrium. Can the OCl^- react? The only other species present in large concentration is H_2O. (This situation should remind us of our discussion of acid-base reactions in Chapter 18.) The OCl^- ions are certainly basic. They can compete for hydrogen ions as required by Brönsted theory, and they have unshared pairs of electrons as required by Lewis theory. The OCl^- ions should compete with hydroxide ions for the protons in water and come to dynamic equilibrium as in the net equation

Principal equilibrium: $OCl^-_{(aq)} + HOH_{(l)} = HOCl_{(aq)} + OH^-_{(aq)}$

Equilibrium constant expression:
$$K = \frac{[HOCl][OH^-]}{[OCl^-]} \qquad (19.15)$$

(Remember that [HOH] is included in K.) As you should have surmised, the hydrolysis of the negative OCl^- (Lewis base) should make the solution basic.

We see from the net equation that, at equilibrium, $[HOCl] = [OH^-]$, but we do not know the value of K. However, note that it includes the terms $[HOCl]/[OCl^-]$, which should remind you of the K in Equation (19.14), $K = 6.8 \cdot 10^{-8} = [H^+][OCl^-]/[HOCl]$. Let us alter Equation (19.15) slightly to give

$$K = \frac{[HOCl][H^+][OH^-]}{[H^+][OCl^-]} = \frac{K_W}{K_{HOCl}} = \frac{1.00 \cdot 10^{-14}}{6.8 \cdot 10^{-8}} = 1.47 \cdot 10^{-7} \qquad (19.16)$$

Thus

$$K = 1.47 \cdot 10^{-7} = \frac{[HOCl][OH^-]}{[OCl^-]}$$

Since the solution was made by dissolving y moles of NaOCl to give one liter of aqueous solution, we obtain

Principal equilibrium: $OCl^-_{(aq)} + H_2O_{(l)} = HOCl_{(aq)} + OH^-_{(aq)}$

Mass balance:
$$[HOCl] = [OH^-]$$
$$[OCl^-] = y - [OH^-]$$

Equilibrium constant expression:
$$K = \frac{[OH^-][OH^-]}{\{y - [OH^-]\}} = 1.47 \cdot 10^{-7}$$

Again we will make our two simplifying assumptions—that $y \gg [OH^-]$ and that $[OH^-]$ from the direct ionization of water is negligible. Then

$$K = \frac{[OH^-]^2}{y} = 1.47 \cdot 10^{-7}$$

$$[OH^-] = \sqrt{1.47 \cdot 10^{-7} y} = 3.8 \cdot 10^{-4} y^{1/2}$$

Values of $[OH^-]$ are tabulated in Table 19.6 as a function of y. Again our assumptions are justified (within the usual ±5%) over a wide range of concentrations. Very dilute solutions give appreciable deviations, however, as would be expected. All the solutions are basic, as predicted.

Now note that we could have solved our problem concerning the simultaneous addition of HOCl and NaOCl with Equations (19.15) and (19.16). To repeat: at equilibrium,

Table 19.6 **Equilibrium concentrations (moles/liter) when *y* moles of NaOCl are dissolved to give 1.0 liter of aqueous solution, assuming $[OH^-] \ll y$ and negligible direct ionization of H_2O.**

	$y = [Na^+]$							
	1.00	0.50	0.100	0.050	$1.00 \cdot 10^{-2}$	$1.00 \cdot 10^{-3}$	$1.00 \cdot 10^{-4}$	$1.00 \cdot 10^{-5}$
$[OH^-]$	$3.8 \cdot 10^{-4}$	$2.7 \cdot 10^{-4}$	$1.2 \cdot 10^{-4}$	$8.5 \cdot 10^{-5}$	$3.8 \cdot 10^{-5}$	$1.2 \cdot 10^{-5}$	$3.8 \cdot 10^{-6}$	$1.2 \cdot 10^{-6}$
$[HOCl]$	$3.8 \cdot 10^{-4}$	$2.7 \cdot 10^{-4}$	$1.2 \cdot 10^{-4}$	$8.5 \cdot 10^{-5}$	$3.8 \cdot 10^{-5}$	$1.2 \cdot 10^{-5}$	$3.8 \cdot 10^{-6}$	$1.2 \cdot 10^{-6}$
$[OCl^-]$	1.00	0.500	0.100	0.0500	$1.00 \cdot 10^{-2}$	$0.99 \cdot 10^{-3}$	$0.96 \cdot 10^{-4}$	$0.88 \cdot 10^{-5}$ $[OH^-]$ appreciable compared to $[OCl^-]$

Principal equilibrium: $OCl^-_{(aq)} + HOH_{(l)} = HOCl_{(aq)} + OH^-_{(aq)}$

Equilibrium constant expression: $$K = \frac{[HOCl][OH^-]}{[OCl^-]} = 1.47 \cdot 10^{-7}$$

If we add NaOCl at the rate of $1.0 \cdot 10^{-2}$ moles per liter and HOCl at the rate of $1.0 \cdot 10^{-1}$ moles per liter, from the net reaction we get (at equilibrium)

Mass balance: $$[OCl^-] = 1.0 \cdot 10^{-2} - [OH^-]$$
$$[HOCl] = 1.0 \cdot 10^{-1} + [OH^-]$$
$$K = 1.47 \cdot 10^{-7} = \frac{[HOCl][OH^-]}{[OCl^-]} = \frac{\{1.0 \cdot 10^{-1} + [OH^-]\}[OH^-]}{\{1.0 \cdot 10^{-2} - [OH^-]\}}$$

Again we make our two assumptions—that $[OH^-] \ll 1.0 \cdot 10^{-2}$ and that direct ionization of water is negligible.

$$K = 1.47 \cdot 10^{-7} = \frac{1.0 \cdot 10^{-1}[OH^-]}{1.0 \cdot 10^{-2}}$$
$$[OH^-] = 1.5 \cdot 10^{-8}\ M$$

This is, of course, the same value we obtained in the previous section (for the same problem using the same assumptions). You may wish to amuse yourself by showing that the answers must be the same. Since the answers are consistent with the assumptions, the answers are also acceptable ones.

Most negative ions hydrolyze in water to produce solutions in which $[OH^-] > [H^+]$. Similarly most positive ions hydrolyze to give solutions in which $[H^+] > [OH^-]$. Since every solution containing ions must contain both positive and negative ions, the final concentration of H^+ and OH^- will be determined by the relative hydrolyses of the positive and negative ions—that is, by the relative strengths of the various acids and bases present. The extent of hydrolysis may be calculated if the appropriate K's (as in Table 18.13) are known. Equilibrium concentrations may usually be calculated by (*a*) determining the formulas of the principal species actually present (salts are written as their separated ions; weak electrolytes as molecules), (*b*) writing the net equation for the principal equilibrium and the corresponding equilibrium constant expression, (*c*) applying mass and/or charge balance, (*d*) assuming that the ions contributed by water are negligible, (*e*) checking for other possible simplifying assumptions and making them, (*f*) calculating tentative equilibrium concentrations, and (*g*) checking the assumptions until acceptable results are obtained.

Exercise 19.9

Which is more basic—1 *M* KCN or 1 *M* KOCl? *Answer:* Note that both will be basic, $[OH^-] > 10^{-7}\ M$, since both are potassium salts of weak acids. The acid ion hydrolyzes ($X^- + H_2O = HX + OH^-$) but the K^+ does not. $K_{HOCl} = 6.8 \cdot 10^{-8}$, $K_{HCN} = 4.9 \cdot 10^{-10}$. Thus HCN is the weaker acid, will have the greater tendency to form, and its 1 *M* potassium salt will have the more basic solution. Calculation gives $[OH^-] = 3.8 \cdot 10^{-4}\ M$ in 1 *M* KOCl, and $[OH^-] = 4.5 \cdot 10^{-2}\ M$ in 1 *M* KCN in agreement with prediction.

BUFFERS

Living systems rely on many acid-base reactions in their metabolism, and many of these reactions are critically affected by changes in pH. For example, most enzymes will operate efficiently only over a narrow range of pH. Deviations from this range seriously inhibit the metabolic reactions. Human blood is maintained at about $p\text{H} = 7.4$, the stomach at about $p\text{H} = 2$. Thus, it is important for a living organism not only to regulate its pH, but to maintain different pH's in various parts of its metabolic system. This is accomplished by buffer solutions. Buffer solutions are also much used in chemical experimentation to maintain constant pH in a system under study. ($p\text{H} = -\log[\text{H}^+]$, analogous to $pK = -\log K$.)

A buffered system is one which changes very little in pH upon addition of either an acid or a base. Clearly the buffer must contain an acid to react with added bases and a base to react with added acids. Examination of a generalized acid-base equilibrium equation shows this is readily possible.

$$\underset{\text{acid}}{\text{HX}} = \text{H}^+ + \underset{\text{base}}{\text{X}^-}, \qquad K = \frac{[\text{H}^+][\text{X}^-]}{[\text{HX}]}$$

HX will act as an acid toward added base and X^- will act as a base toward added acid.

For maximum efficiency in handling large additions of either acid or base the concentrations of HX and X^- should be large and should be equal: $[\text{HX}] = [\text{X}^-]$ in the buffer. At these conditions of maximum effectiveness of the buffer,

$$K = \frac{[\text{H}^+][\text{X}^-]}{[\text{HX}]} = [\text{H}^+]$$

Thus any acid-base conjugate pair exhibits its greatest buffering ability at $p\text{H} = pK$.

Consider a buffer based on the equilibrium

$$\text{HOAc}_{(aq)} = \text{H}^+{}_{(aq)} + \text{OAc}^-{}_{(aq)}, \qquad K = \frac{[\text{H}^+][\text{OAc}^-]}{[\text{HOAc}]} = 1.8 \cdot 10^{-5}$$

in a solution which is 1 F in HOAc and 1 F in OAc^- (added in the form of sodium acetate).

$$K = \frac{[\text{H}^+][\text{OAc}^-]}{[\text{HOAc}]} = \frac{[\text{H}^+]1}{1} = [\text{H}^+] = 1.8 \cdot 10^{-5}\ F;\ p\text{H} = 4.75$$

Addition of 0.1 mole of HCl, a strong acid, per liter of solution would cause the net reaction

$$\text{H}^+{}_{(aq)} + \text{OAc}^-{}_{(aq)} = \text{HOAc}_{(aq)}$$

and reduce the $[\text{OAc}^-]$ from 1 M to 0.9 M, and increase [HOAc] from 1 M to 1.1 M. Let us calculate the new pH.

$$K = \frac{[\text{H}^+][\text{OAc}^-]}{[\text{HOAc}]} = \frac{[\text{H}^+] \cdot 0.9}{1.1} = 0.8[\text{H}^+] = 1.8 \cdot 10^{-5}\ F$$

$$[\text{H}^+] = 2.3 \cdot 10^{-5},\ p\text{H} = 4.65$$

The pH has decreased by 0.10 unit. Similarly, addition of 0.1 mole of NaOH per liter of the original buffer would only increase the pH by 0.10 unit.

If 0.1 mole of HCl were added to 1 liter of pure water, the pH would change from $p\text{H} = 7.0$ in pure water to $p\text{H} = 1.0$ after the HCl was added, a factor of 10^6 in $[H^+]$ and of 6 in pH. Acetate buffer is clearly effective at minimizing pH changes.

The bicarbonate and phosphate buffers found most commonly in living systems are equally effective and help account for the wide tolerance in diet exhibited by many living systems.

Exercise 19.10

How would you prepare a buffer solution of pH 9.2? *Answer:* A buffer has maximum effectiveness for an equilibrium such as $HX = H^+ + X^-$, when $[HX] = [X^-]$. This equivalence corresponds to $pH = pK$. From Table 18.14, $pK = 9.245$ for the equilibrium, $NH_4^+ = H^+ + NH_3$. Thus, a 1 M solution of NH_3, which is also 1 M in NH_4Cl (or any other salt of NH_4^+ with an anion of a strong acid) would be satisfactory. Then adjust the pH to as close to 9.2 as desired by adding a small amount of strong acid, such as HCl or HNO_3.

SUMMARY

The random translational motions and the quantized rotational, vibrational, and electronic states of molecules assure that molecular collisions will occur and that energy can be transferred at all conditions except 0°K. Not only can energy be transferred, but so also can atoms, electrons, and even relatively large molecular fragments. In other words, molecules can undergo reaction upon collision. The likelihood of reaction will depend on collision frequency, available energy, and collisional orientation. Net reactions will occur in any system until equilibrium is established. At equilibrium, reactions still continue, but for each reaction there is a reverse reaction proceeding at exactly the same rate but in the opposite direction. The dynamic state of the system ensures that it will not depart appreciably from the equilibrium state as long as there are no outside influences. Thus, in effect, an equilibrium system is always an isolated system; there are no net flows in or out of it.

We may think of any chemical system as one in which molecules are competing with one another to form the strongest set of bonds possible. But the random nature of the collisions and the transfers of energy ensure that all bonds will break sometime and, thus, that atoms will be moving from one molecule to another more or less often.

The concentrations in the dynamic equilibrium state may be correlated in terms of equilibrium constants—one constant, K, for each equilibrium. Values of many equilibrium constants have been determined and tabulated, so that it is now possible to do a very large number of calculations concerning equilibrium conditions without further experimentation. Equilibrium calculations typically involve writing the equation for the principal equilibrium, calculating mass and charge balance, and applying the equilibrium constant expression with suitable simplifying assumptions.

When we view the reaction mixture as a macroscopic system the molecular turmoil is invisible, and what we see instead is a seemingly purposeful drive to equilibrium, rapid at first, then slower, until finally equilibrium is achieved and the chemical reaction is at an end. At the molecular level, however, the reaction is not at an end, the interactions, the transitions from state to state, and the violent disruptions being just as frequent and as confused as ever.
—*B. Wisdom*, Science, **148**; 1555 (1965).

PROBLEMS

19.1. A detailed study of activation energies shows that the apparent activation energy for a given gas-phase reaction may depend on the nature of other nonreacting gaseous molecules present. The more atoms the nonreactive molecules contain, the lower is the apparent activation energy. Can you interpret this effect?

19.2. Benzoic acid, C_6H_5COOH, has an equilibrium constant of $6.46 \cdot 10^{-5}$. Sodium benzoate, C_6H_5COONa, is used as a food preservative (in catsup, for example). The human stomach fluid is about 0.1 F H^+. Calculate the ratio of the concentrations of benzoate ion and benzoic acid in your stomach after eating a hamburger with catsup on it. (Ratio $\cong 10^{-3}$.)

19.3. Why does an upset stomach give you a sour taste in your mouth? Why does drinking a solution of baking soda alleviate the symptom? Baking soda is $NaHCO_3$.

19.4. The pH of the blood is about 7.4. Calculate the ratio of $[HCO_3^-]$ to $[CO_3^=]$ in the blood. (Ratio $\cong 10^3$.) Would vigorous exercise increase or decrease this ratio?

19.5. Use Table 18.2 to discuss the relative likelihood that forms of life on land might have more serious phosphorus deficiencies than forms in the sea.

19.6. Why is it necessary to consider the relative stabilities of reagents and products in discussing chemical reactions and not just the stabilities of the reagents alone?

19.7. Spilled NaOH has caused a yellow spot on your blue coat. What treatment do you recommend?

19.8. Discuss the effect on the concentration of hydroxide ion in an ammonia solution when the listed changes are made. The equilibrium is $NH_3 + H_2O = NH_4^+ + OH^-$.
(*a*) Addition of a solution of hydrochloric acid.
(*b*) Addition of solid NH_4Cl.
(*c*) Addition of solid AgCl.
(*d*) Addition of solid NaCl.
(*e*) Boiling the solution.
(*f*) Addition of water.

19.9. When sodium hydroxide is added to a bottle of vinegar the typical odor of vinegar disappears. How do you account for this?

II

19.10. Determine the concentration of $[H^+]$ and $[CN^-]$ in a 0.001 molar aqueous solution of potassium cyanide at 25°C. K_a for HCN is $4.9 \cdot 10^{-10}$. ($[H^+] \cong 10^{-10}$ *M*.)

19.11. Which of the following indicators would you use for the titration of 0.1 *F* boric acid with sodium hydroxide? Indicate clearly why you would use the indicator.

Indicator	*Indicator ionization constant*
Methyl orange	10^{-4}
Methyl red	10^{-5}
Litmus	10^{-7}
Phenolphthalein	10^{-9}

19.12. In how many ways (merely describe them and the effect which is to be observed) could you determine experimentally whether thiocyanic acid were a strong or weak electrolyte in aqueous solution?

19.13. Classify the following solutions as acidic, basic, or neutral: (*a*) 55.5 *M* H_2O, (*b*) 18 *M* H_2SO_4, (*c*) 2.67 *M* NaCl, (*d*) 0.15 *M* NaOAc, (*e*) 0.05 *M* Cl_2.

19.14. (*a*) $Al(NO_3)_3$ solution is more acid than $Y(NO_3)_3$ of the same concentration. Which is the stronger base, $Al(OH)_3$ or $Y(OH)_3$? (*b*) Write the equation for the hydrolysis of $CO_3^=$; of NH_4^+.

19.15. (*a*) Calculate the equilibrium concentrations of H_2, I_2, and HI obtained when 0.0800 g of HI are introduced into a 5.00-liter flask at 698.6°K. (*b*) Calculate the new equilibrium concentrations if 0.0200 g of iodine are added to the flask. (*c*) Interpret these shifts in terms of (*i*) Le Châtelier's principle, (*ii*) the principle of microscopic reversibility and rates, (*iii*) the equilibrium constant. ($[H_2] \cong 10^{-5}$ *M*.)

19.16. Calculate K_w at 27°C. What are $[H^+]$ and $[OH^-]$ at this temperature? The temperature of the human body is about 37°C. Calculate K_w at this temperature. The *p*H of blood is about 7.4; what is the $[OH^-]$ in blood? (*p*OH $\cong$ 6.5.)

19.17. A *p*H meter is a device by which the *p*H of a solution may be read on a dial when the electrodes of the machine are dipped in the solution. If we are titrating 150 ml of 0.15 *F* HCNO with 0.45 *F* NaOH, what should the machine read at the equivalence point? ($K_{a(HCNO)} = 2.10^{-4}$.) [*p*H $\cong$ 9.]

19.18. K_1 and K_2 for *o*-phthalic acid 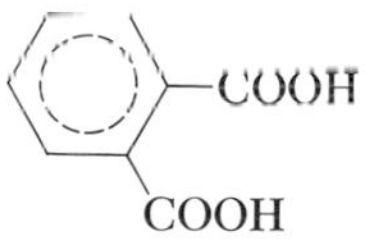

are respectively $1.3 \cdot 10^{-3}$ and $3.9 \cdot 10^{-6}$.

Calculate the hydrogen ion concentration of a buffer solution which is 0.100 *F* in phthalic acid and 0.200 *F* in potassium hydrogen phthalate. ($[H^+] \cong 10^{-3}$ *M*.)

19.19. A buffer solution is prepared by dissolving 0.4 moles of acetic acid (ionization constant $1.8 \cdot 10^{-5}$) and 0.20 moles of sodium acetate in 2.00 liters of water. What is the *p*H of the solution? [*p*H $\cong$ 4.]

19.20. Which one of the four forms of aqueous phosphate (H_3PO_4, $H_2PO_4^-$, HPO_4^{2-}, or PO_4^{3-}) will be present in highest concentration if one-tenth of 1 mole of phosphoric acid is dissolved in 1 liter of water and the *p*H is adjusted to 10.0. Give a thorough explanation of your reasoning, including computations where necessary. ($HPO_4^=$.)

III

19.21. Some thermodynamic quantities related to ionization (i) [$acid_{(aq)} \longrightarrow H^+_{(aq)} + RCO_2^-{}_{(aq)}$] and neutralization ($n$) [$acid_{(aq)} + OH^-{}_{(aq)} = H_2O + RCOO^-{}_{(aq)}$] for certain RCOOH acids have been determined calorimetrically at 298°K by L. Avedikian [*Bull. Soc. Chim. France,* **1**, 254 (1967)].

R—	pK	ΔG_i^0 (kcal mole^{-1})	ΔH_i^0 (kcal mole^{-1})	ΔS_i^0 (eu)	ΔH_n^0 (± 0.05) (kcal mole^{-1})
CH_3—	4.756	6.49	−0.09	−22.1	−13.61
NH_2CH_2—	9.780	13.29	10.64	−8.90	−2.88
$NH_2(CH_2)_2$—	10.235	13.90	11.27	−8.82	−2.25
$NH_2(CH_2)_3$—	10.556	14.35	11.95	−8.05	−1.57

Suggest a structural interpretation for the very similar values for all the amino acids as contrasted with the different values for acetic acid (and other similar acids). Discuss all five terms given above. From the above data, calculate ΔH for the reaction $H^+_{(aq)} + OH^-{}_{(aq)} = H_2O$.

See page 1092 for a list of references and readings in the recent chemical literature related to the material in this chapter.

CHAPTER **20**

Solubility and Redox Equilibria

The tendency of any reaction to occur depends on the concentrations of the reactants.

In this chapter we shall further explore the interpretation of equilibria in terms of dynamic molecular systems.

SOLUBILITY EQUILIBRIA

All solids when shaken with a liquid eventually come to equilibrium with a saturated solution of the solid in the liquid. This statement may be generalized: any dissimilar phases (solid-liquid, gas-liquid, gas-solid) in intimate contact for a sufficient period of time will come to mutual equilibrium if neither phase is completely used up—but only if there is a change in phase during the solution process. At equilibrium the molecules move between the two phases at equal rates and no net change occurs. Mixing two gases, or two liquids, or two solids often gives single-phase systems that do not form saturated solutions—each component can dissolve any amount of the other; they form an infinite series of solutions.

A particularly simple two-phase system to study is $AgCl_{(c)} - H_2O_{(l)}$. Shaking excess AgCl with water gives a saturated liquid solution of AgCl in water (and a solid solution of water in AgCl). The solubility of water in crystalline AgCl is very low indeed, but that of AgCl in water is readily measurable. For example, one can evaporate a known amount of the saturated liquid solution and measure the residual, nonvolatile AgCl. Evaporation of 1 liter of solution saturated at 25°C leaves about $1.7 \cdot 10^{-2}$ g of AgCl (formula weight 143 g mole^{-1}):

$$\frac{1.7 \cdot 10^{-2}\text{ g}}{143\text{ g mole}^{-1}} = 1.2 \cdot 10^{-5}\text{ moles AgCl per liter of saturated solution}$$

Conductivity measurements confirm this value and indicate that the AgCl is almost completely ionized into Ag^+ and Cl^- in the saturated solution (as you should have assumed). From the net equation for the solution process we get

Principal equilibrium: $AgCl_{(c)} = Ag^+_{(aq)} + Cl^-_{(aq)}$

Equilibrium constant expression: $K_{sp} = [Ag^+][Cl^-] = [Ag^+]^2 = (1.2 \cdot 10^{-5})^2 = 1.4 \cdot 10^{-10}$

(Current best value $= 1.8 \cdot 10^{-10}$.)

Notice that we assumed, consistent with charge and atomic balance, that the concentrations of silver ions and of chloride ions were equal at equilibrium and that each was equal to the molarity of the saturated solution. There is good supporting evidence for these assumptions, and the equilibrium constant for the solubility of silver chloride in water is one of the best established K's.

Values for some other K's (normally called K_{sp}'s), pK_{sp}'s, the corresponding net equation, and the equilibrium constant expression are given in Table 20.1 (see also Table 18.16). Remember that pK is the negative $\log_{10}$ of K. To use the values of K in Table 20.1, all concentrations must be expressed as moles/liter of solution. Since all the K's are less than 1, we expect all the values of ΔG^0 to be positive, consistent with the limited extent to which the solubility reactions occur.

Exercise 20.1

Calculate the solubility of AgI in 0.1 M NaI. *Answer:* The net reaction is $AgI_{(c)} = Ag^+ + I^-$, $K_{sp} = [Ag^+][I^-] = 4.5 \cdot 10^{-17}$. But $[I^-]$ initially equals 0.1 (NaI is completely ionized), so only a tiny amount of AgI will dissolve, adding infinitesimally to the iodide concentration but giving some silver ion concentration, $[Ag^+]$. Thus $[Ag^+][I^-] = [Ag^+]\ 0.1 = 4.5 \cdot 10^{-17}$. $[Ag^+] = 4.5 \cdot 10^{-16}$ M at equilibrium. F wt.

Table 20.1 Values of some K_{sp}'s at 25°C.

Net reaction	K_{sp}	pK_{sp}
$AgCl_{(c)} = Ag^+_{(aq)} + Cl^-_{(aq)}$	$[Ag^+][Cl^-] = 1.8 \cdot 10^{-10}$	9.75
$AgBr_{(c)} = Ag^+_{(aq)} + Br^-_{(aq)}$	$[Ag^+][Br^-] = 5.2 \cdot 10^{-13}$	12.28
$AgI_{(c)} = Ag^+_{(aq)} + I^-_{(aq)}$	$[Ag^+][I^-] = 4.5 \cdot 10^{-17}$	16.35
$CaCO_{3(c)} = Ca^{++}_{(aq)} + CO_3{}^{=}_{(aq)}$	$[Ca^{++}][CO_3{}^{=}] = 7.2 \cdot 10^{-9}$	8.14
$BaCO_{3(c)} = Ba^{++}_{(aq)} + CO_3{}^{=}_{(aq)}$	$[Ba^{++}][CO_3{}^{=}] = 5.5 \cdot 10^{-9}$	9.26
$SrSO_{4(c)} = Sr^{++}_{(aq)} + SO_4{}^{=}_{(aq)}$	$[Sr^{++}][SO_4{}^{=}] = 2.9 \cdot 10^{-7}$	6.53
$BaSO_{4(c)} = Ba^{++}_{(aq)} + SO_4{}^{=}_{(aq)}$	$[Ba^{++}][SO_4{}^{=}] = 8.7 \cdot 10^{-11}$	10.06
$BaCrO_{4(c)} = Ba^{++}_{(aq)} + CrO_4{}^{=}_{(aq)}$	$[Ba^{++}][CrO_4{}^{=}] = 1.2 \cdot 10^{-10}$	9.93
$AgCN_{(c)} = Ag^+_{(aq)} + CN^-_{(aq)}$	$[Ag^+][CN^-] = 1.2 \cdot 10^{-16}$	15.92
$CuCl_{(c)} = Cu^+_{(aq)} + Cl^-_{(aq)}$	$[Cu^+][Cl^-] = 1.9 \cdot 10^{-7}$	6.73
$CaF_{2(c)} = Ca^{++}_{(aq)} + 2F^-_{(aq)}$	$[Ca^{++}][F^-]^2 = 4.0 \cdot 10^{-11}$	10.40
$Hg_2Cl_{2(c)} = Hg_2{}^{++}_{(aq)} + 2Cl^-_{(aq)}$	$[Hg_2{}^{++}][Cl^-]^2 = 1.3 \cdot 10^{-18}$	17.88
$Cr(H_2O)_3(OH)_{3(c)} + 3H_2O = Cr(H_2O)_6{}^{+++}_{(aq)} + 3OH^-_{(aq)}$	$[Cr(H_2O)_6{}^{+++}][OH^-]^3 = 10^{-30}$	30
$Al(H_2O)_3(OH)_{3(c)} + 3H_2O = Al(H_2O)_6{}^{+++}_{(aq)} + 3OH^-_{(aq)}$	$[Al(H_2O)_6{}^{+++}][OH^-]^2 = 10^{-32}$	32

AgI = 245. Thus, solubility of AgI $= 4.5 \cdot 10^{-16} \cdot 245 = 1.1 \cdot 10^{-13}$ g AgI liter^{-1}, assuming that the only appreciable reaction is the net reaction given.

Exercise 20.2

$K_{sp} = 2.1 \cdot 10^{-22}$ for $Gd(OH)_{3(c)}$. Estimate its solubility in water. *Answer:* Assuming the only appreciable equilibrium is $Gd(OH)_{3(c)} = Gd^{+++}{}_{(aq)} + 3\ OH^{-}{}_{(aq)}$ (that is, no hydrolysis of Gd^{+++}), $[Gd^{+++}]_{eq} = m$, $[OH^{-}]_{eq} = 3m$. $K_{sp} = m \cdot (3m)^3 = 27m^4 = 2.1 \cdot 10^{-22}$, and $m = 1.7 \cdot 10^{-6}\ M\ Gd^{+++}$, which is the same as the molar solubility of $Gd(OH)_3$. Of course, $[OH^{-}]_{eq} = 3m = 5.1 \cdot 10^{-6}\ M$.

REDOX EQUILIBRIA

Since you now have a general method of writing an equilibrium constant expression for any net reaction, little is to be gained by cataloging further reactions by type. It is, however, worth pointing out that equilibrium constants are also associated with redox equations and that data from electric cells in which redox reactions are occurring provide one of our most accurate sources of experimental data for the determination of equilibrium constants.

The reactions we have discussed so far in this chapter involve competition for some common atom (as in the Brönsted acid-base treatment), competition between solution and crystal for ions (as in the solubility equilibria of Table 20.1), or, in general, random wandering of atoms from one set of partners to another without change in oxidation state.

Some molecular collisions actually lead to exchange of electrons between the colliding atoms. We then say that redox has occurred. Such reactions can often be carried out in electric cells, and the tendency of the reaction to occur can be measured in terms of the voltage, or potential, generated by the cell. Thus the voltage of an electric cell depends on the factors we have already discussed as affecting equilibria—concentration of reactants and temperature. Many systems give electric cells that are highly reproducible in voltage if they are operated at a reproducible temperature and set of concentrations. Furthermore, voltage can be measured accurately and quickly with a voltmeter, thus simplifying the experimental determination of the tendency of the reaction to occur.

All redox reactions can be written as the sum of two half-reactions: one in which electrons are gained and another in which electrons are lost. Thus all redox reactions can be viewed as a competition for electrons. Equilibrium will be reached when concentrations are such that reverse reactions are equally probable. We may reduce all redox reactions to the following types of equations:

$$\begin{array}{ll} \text{Oxidation:} & M = M^{+} + e^{-} \\ \text{Reduction:} & e^{-} + Y = Y^{-} \\ \hline \text{Net:} & M + Y = M^{+} + Y^{-} \end{array} \qquad (20.1)$$

or, conversely,

$$\begin{array}{ll} \text{Reduction:} & e^{-} + M^{+} = M \\ \text{Oxidation:} & Y^{-} = Y + e^{-} \\ \hline \text{Net:} & M^{+} + Y^{-} = M + Y \end{array} \qquad (20.2)$$

Note that Equations (20.1) and (20.2) are merely the reverse of one another. Which way the reaction *will go* depends upon the nature of M and of Y and upon the conditions at the time of reaction. For example, changing the temperature, or the pressure, or the concentrations of the reactants would tend to favor one of the directions more than it would the other. Thus, increasing, then decreasing, any one of these variables would drive the reaction first one way and then the other.

STANDARD REDOX POTENTIALS—$\mathcal{E}^0$

If we keep conditions of temperature, pressure, and concentration constant at some standard values, we can measure the relative tendencies of various species to gain and lose electrons and tabulate the results. The most common standard conditions are 25°C (298°K), 1 atm pressure, with all species in their pure state or else in solution in some solvent (usually water) at a concentration of 1 mole per liter of solution ($1\ F = 1\ M$). The standard state for gases is a partial pressure of one atmosphere. The voltages measured under these conditions are called standard potentials, or standard electromotive forces (EMF), and are given the symbol $\mathcal{E}^0$.*

These standard potentials, measuring the relative ability of various species to compete for electrons in liquid systems, may be obtained by building electric cells. The cell is constructed so that each of the two half-reactions of interest can occur independently in one of the halves of the cell. An external electrical conductor allows electrons to flow from one side of the cell to the other through a meter which measures the direction of flow and the tendency of flow to occur. An internal conducting solution allows ions to move internally from each side of the cell to the other to complete the electrical circuit. Figure 20.1 represents a diagram of such an experimental arrangement.

We shall, for the moment, stick to aqueous solutions and shall use the hydrogen electrode (made by bubbling gaseous hydrogen over a rough platinum surface) as a standard comparison electrode. The net reaction at the hydrogen electrode may be written

$$H^+{}_{(aq)} + e^- = \tfrac{1}{2}H_{2(g)}$$

The meter on the cell will measure the *difference* between the tendency of the hydrogen side of the cell to gain or lose electrons and the tendency of the other side of the cell to gain or lose electrons. If electrons flow from the hydrogen side to the cadmium side, hydrogen clearly has the greater tendency to lose electrons. If electrons flow toward the hydrogen side, the relative tendencies are reversed. The meter, if it is a voltmeter, will not only measure direction but also difference in electric potential. This difference in electric potential between the two sides is a measure of the difference in tendency to lose electrons on the two sides of the cell. The usual unit applied to electrical measurements of potential is the volt, and $\mathcal{E}^0$ values are usually given in volts. Volts may be readily converted into kcal per

* An accurate statement would be that $\mathcal{E}^\circ$ is the cell voltage at 298°K when every reactant is at unit activity. For most practical work, unit activity is assumed to be found in a 1 M solution or in a pure substance at 1 atm pressure. In data tables considerable confusion exists as to $\mathcal{E}^\circ$ values because of the unwarranted use of this assumption. For this course the errors involved in using the assumption are not important, but in work with real systems a close check should be made on all $\mathcal{E}$ values taken from the literature. See Chapter 29 for an extended discussion of activity.

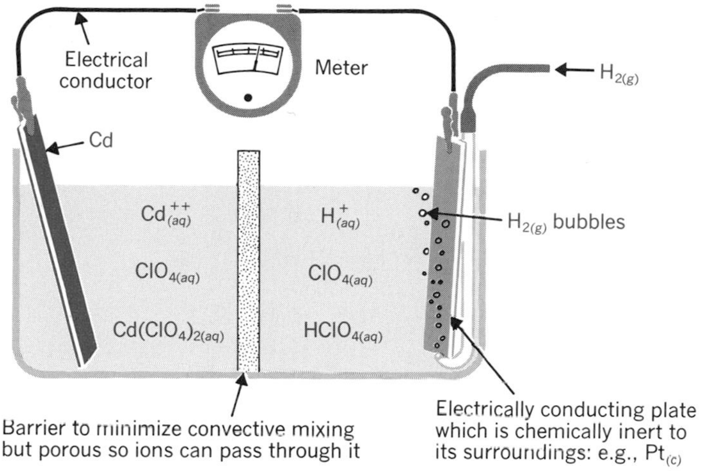

Figure 20.1 An electric cell for the experimental determination of relative tendencies of H_2-H^+ and Cd-Cd^{++} to gain and lose electrons. Perchlorate solutions are used because of the lack of reactivity of ClO_4 under these conditions.

mole of electrons transferred (abbreviated kcal equivalent^{-1}, or kcal equiv^{-1}) by multiplying the voltage figure by 23.053 kcal equiv^{-1} per volt.

The values of $\mathcal{E}^0$ obtained from potential measurements at standard conditions have another valuable attribute. They are directly related to the equilibrium constant, K, and to ΔG^0 for the reaction. The equations(derived later in Chapter 29) are

$$-\Delta G^0/(23{,}053n) = \mathcal{E}^0 = (RT/n\mathcal{F}) \ln K = (2.303 \cdot 1.987 \cdot T)/(n \cdot 23{,}053) \log K$$

At 25°C these become,

$$\mathcal{E}^0 = -\frac{0.0592}{n} pK = \frac{0.0592}{n} \log K = \frac{-\Delta G^0}{(n \cdot 23{,}053)} \qquad (20.3)$$

These are most commonly written

$$\Delta G^0 = -n\mathcal{F}\mathcal{E}^0 = -RT \ln K$$

where ΔG^0 is in cal mole^{-1}; $\mathcal{F} = 23{,}053$ (the Faraday conversion factor from volt equivalents to cal mole^{-1}); 2.303 converts ln K to log K; n is the number of electron equivalents exchanged in the net reaction written; $\mathcal{E}^0$ is the standard cell potential; $R = 1.9872$ cal mole^{-1} °K^{-1}; and K is the equilibrium constant for the net reaction written. Note that positive voltages, indicating probable reactions, are associated with negative values of ΔG^0 and values of $K > 1$, as would be expected.

Not all voltages can be measured directly against a hydrogen electrode in aqueous solution. But such voltages can often be measured in other ways. We shall discuss some of these experimental problems later and merely list here the results of many independent measurements. Thus Table 20.2 contains a list of half-reactions arranged in order of increasing tendency to gain electrons. We can only measure *differences* in this tendency, and so we arbitrarily define the tendency

Table 20.2 Standard reduction potentials, $\mathcal{E}^0$, for some half-reactions in aqueous solution at 25°C. (All unsubscripted species have 1 *M* solutions as their standard states.)

Number	Half-reaction	$\mathcal{E}_{1/2}^0$	$pK_{1/2}$[a]	$K_{1/2}$[a]
1	$Na^+ + e^- = Na_{(c)}$	−2.174	45.8	$1.6 \cdot 10^{-46}$
2	$\frac{1}{2}Mg^{++} + e^- = \frac{1}{2}Mg_{(c)}$	−2.375	40.10	$7.9 \cdot 10^{-41}$
3	$\frac{1}{3}AlF_6^{-3} + e^- = \frac{1}{3}Al_{(c)} + 2F^-$	−2.07	35.0	$1.0 \cdot 10^{-35}$
4	$\frac{1}{3}Al(H_2O)_6^{+3} + e^- = \frac{1}{3}Al_{(c)} + 2H_2O$	−1.66	28.1	$8 \cdot 10^{-29}$
5	$H_2O + e^- = \frac{1}{2}H_{2(g)} + OH^-$	−0.8277	13.99	$9.5 \cdot 10^{-15}$
6	$\frac{1}{2}Zn^{++} + e^- = \frac{1}{2}Zn_{(c)}$	−0.7628	12.89	$1.29 \cdot 10^{-13}$
7	$\frac{1}{2}Fe^{++} + e^- = \frac{1}{2}Fe_{(c)}$	−0.440	7.43	$3.7 \cdot 10^{-8}$
8	$Cr^{+3} + e^- = Cr^{++}$	−0.41	6.9	$1.3 \cdot 10^{-7}$
9	$\frac{1}{2}Cd^{++} + e^- = \frac{1}{2}Cd_{(c)}$	−0.403	6.81	$1.5 \cdot 10^{-7}$
10	$CuI + e^- = Cu_{(c)} + I^-$	−0.185	3.12	$7.6 \cdot 10^{-4}$
11	$\frac{1}{2}Sn^{++} + e^- = \frac{1}{2}Sn_{(c)}$	−0.136	2.30	$5.0 \cdot 10^{-3}$
12	$D^+ + e^- = \frac{1}{2}D_{2(g)}$	−0.044	0.74	0.18
13	$\frac{1}{3}Fe^{+++} + e^- = \frac{1}{3}Fe_{(c)}$	−0.024	0.41	0.39
14	$H^+ + e^- = \frac{1}{2}H_{2(g)}$	zero	zero	1.00
15	$CuBr_{(c)} + e^- = Cu_{(c)} + Br^-$	0.033	−0.56	3.6
16	$\frac{1}{2}Sn^{+4} + e^- = \frac{1}{2}Sn^{++}$ (in 1 *M* HCl)	0.139	−2.35	$2.2 \cdot 10^{2}$
17	$Cu^{++} + e^- = Cu^+$	0.158	−2.67	$4.7 \cdot 10^{2}$
18	$\frac{1}{2}S_4O_6^{=} + e^- = S_2O_3^{=}$	0.17	−2.9	$8 \cdot 10^{2}$
19	$AgCl_{(c)} + e^- = Ag_{(c)} + Cl^-$	0.2223	−3.75	$5.6 \cdot 10^{3}$
20	$\frac{1}{2}Cu^{++} + e^- = \frac{1}{2}Cu_{(c)}$	0.3402	−5.75	$5.6 \cdot 10^{5}$
21	$H_2O + OCl^- + e^- = \frac{1}{2}Cl_{2(g)} + 2OH^-$	0.52	−8.80	$6 \cdot 10^{8}$
22	$Cu^+ + e^- = Cu_{(c)}$	0.522	−8.82	$6.6 \cdot 10^{8}$
23	$\frac{1}{2}I_{2(c)} + e^- = I^-$	0.5355	−9.05	$1.1 \cdot 10^{9}$
24	$\frac{1}{2}H_3AsO_4 + H^+ + e^- = \frac{1}{2}H_3AsO_3 + \frac{1}{2}H_2O$	0.559	−9.40	$4.0 \cdot 10^{10}$
25	$Fe(CN)_6^{-3} + e^- = Fe(CN)_6^{-4}$ (in 1 *M* H_2SO_4)	0.69	−12.0	$1 \cdot 10^{12}$
26	$Fe^{+++} + e^- = Fe^{++}$ (in 1 *M* $HClO_4$)	0.747	−12.61	$4.1 \cdot 10^{12}$
27	$\frac{1}{2}Hg_2^{++} + e^- = Hg_{(l)}$	0.7986	−13.49	$3.1 \cdot 10^{13}$
28	$Ag^+ + e^- = Ag_{(c)}$	0.7996	−13.50	$3.2 \cdot 10^{13}$
29	$Hg^{++} + e^- = \frac{1}{2}Hg_2^{++}$	0.920	−15.5	$3 \cdot 10^{15}$
30	$\frac{1}{2}Br_{2(l)} + e^- = Br^-$	1.087	−18.35	$2.2 \cdot 10^{18}$
31	$\frac{1}{6}Cr_2O_7^{-2} + \frac{7}{3}H^+ + e^- = \frac{1}{3}Cr^{+++} + \frac{7}{6}H_2O$ (in 2 *M* H_2SO_4)	1.10	−18.6	$4 \cdot 10^{18}$
32	$\frac{1}{2}MnO_{2(c)} + 2H^+ + e^- = \frac{1}{2}Mn^{++} + H_2O$	1.208	−20.40	$2.5 \cdot 10^{20}$
33	$\frac{1}{4}O_{2(g)} + H^+ + e^- = \frac{1}{2}H_2O$	1.229	−20.78	$6.0 \cdot 10^{20}$
34	$\frac{1}{2}Cl_{2(g)} + e^- = Cl^-$	1.3583	−22.95	$8.9 \cdot 10^{22}$
35	$Ce^{+4} + e^- = Ce^{+3}$ (in 0.5 *M* H_2SO_4)	1.4589	−24.62	$4.2 \cdot 10^{24}$
36	$\frac{1}{5}MnO_4^- + \frac{8}{5}H^+ + e^- = \frac{1}{5}Mn^{++} + \frac{4}{5}H_2O$	1.491	−25.2	$1.6 \cdot 10^{25}$
37	$\frac{1}{2}F_{2(g)} + e^- = F^-$	2.87	−48.5	$3 \cdot 10^{48}$

[a] The values of $K_{1/2}$ and $pK_{1/2}$ do not have the usual physical significance attached to equilibrium constants for net reactions, since they would include a term for electron concentration which is not experimentally observable. However, the values of $K_{1/2}$ and $pK_{1/2}$ are very useful in calculating values of *K* and *pK* for net reactions obtained by combining two half-reactions. The values of *K* and *pK* so obtained have the same significance as *K*'s determined in other ways. All aqueous concentrations must be expressed as moles/liter of solution. In the case of gases, partial pressures in atmospheres must be used in equilibrium constant expressions.

In a few cases involving ions with large charges (and hence high charge densities), measurements are quoted for solutions of specified acidity. Such ions tend to hydrolyze extensively; thus their potential varies markedly with the acidity of the solution.

of hydrogen to lose electrons as zero. This means we assign $\mathcal{E}^0 = 0$ as the potential of the standard hydrogen electrode. The numbers tabulated are, then, the cell voltages that would be observed if we could measure each of the listed half-reactions against a hydrogen electrode, all conditions being standard. Negative values mean that the half-reaction listed has less tendency than that of hydrogen ion to gain electrons. Positive values mean that the half-reaction has a greater tendency than the $H^+_{(aq)} + e^- = \frac{1}{2}H_{2(g)}$ half-reaction to gain electrons. The pK and K values are calculated from Equation (20.3). Note that $n = 1$ for all reactions in Table 20.2.

Exercise 20.3

The $\mathcal{E}^0$ value for the net reaction $\frac{1}{2}H_{2(g)} + \frac{1}{2}I_{2(c)} = H^+_{(aq)} + I^-_{(aq)}$ is found to be 0.5355. Calculate K for this reaction in water solution. *Answer:* $\mathcal{E}^0 = 0.0592/n \log K$, $n = 1$. Thus $\mathcal{E}^0 = 0.0592 \log K = 0.5355$; $K = 1.1 \cdot 10^9$. This large value indicates a likely reaction, since $K = [H^+][I^-]/p_{H_2}{}^{1/2}[I_2]^{1/2}$.

ADDITION OF HALF-REACTIONS AND OF $\mathcal{E}^0$ VALUES

Reversing any half-reaction leads to the reversal of the sign of its voltage. Half-reactions may be added as in Table 20.3, so that their electron changes cancel and yield net reactions. The voltages of two half-reactions add to give the voltage of the net reaction. The pK values also add to give new pK's. Values of K multiply to give new K's. Table 20.3 has some examples. The electron change, n, always equals the net change in oxidation state in each half-reaction.

Note in Table 20.3 that, when half-reactions are added to give a net reaction, one of the half-reactions must always be written in the reverse direction to that found in Table 20.2, or the electrons will not drop out upon addition of the half-reactions. Whenever a half-reaction is reversed, its value of $\mathcal{E}^0$ changes sign, its value of pK changes sign, and its value of K becomes the reciprocal of the value in Table 20.2. It is left to you to prove that this last statement must be true.

We thus see that any two half-reactions in Table 20.2 can be combined to give a net reaction. This is done by reversing one of the two half-reactions, adding it to the other half-reaction to give the net equation, and manipulating the $\mathcal{E}^0$, pK, and K values as described. If the resulting $\mathcal{E}^0$ is positive, ΔG^0 will be negative, and the net reaction will proceed as written if all the species are mixed in their standard states, as represented in the equation for the net reaction. Under these conditions the value of pK for the net reaction will be negative, and the value of K will be greater than 1. Net reaction in V Table 20.3 proceeds as written when the species are all mixed in their standard states.

If the value of $\mathcal{E}^0$ for a net reaction is negative, ΔG^0 will be positive, the value of pK will be positive, and the value of K less than 1. The ingredients will then react, if mixed in their standard states, in a direction opposite to that for which the net reaction is written. In other words, reaction will occur among the substances on the right side of the equation to give net formation of those written on the left. Net reactions II and III (Table 20.3) both go "backward" if the species are mixed in their standard states.

Table 20.3 Addition of half-reactions, $\mathcal{E}^0$, *pK*, and multiplication of *K*'s. (Ref. = number of reaction in Table 20.2.)

	Ref.	Reaction	$\mathcal{E}^0$ (volts)	*pK*		*K*
I. Reduction	(16)	$\frac{1}{2}Sn^{+4} + e^- = \frac{1}{2}Sn^{++}$	0.139	−2.35	$2.2 \cdot 10^2$	
Oxidation	−(11)	$\frac{1}{2}Sn = \frac{1}{2}Sn^{++} + e^-$	0.136	−2.30	$(5.0 \cdot 10^{-3})^{-1}$	
Net:		$\frac{1}{2}Sn_{(c)} + \frac{1}{2}Sn^{+4}{}_{(aq)} = Sn^{++}{}_{(aq)}$	0.275	−4.65	$4.4 \cdot 10^4 =$	$\dfrac{[Sn^{++}]}{[Sn^{+4}]^{1/2}}$
$\mathcal{E}^0 > 0, K > 1$; ∴ net reaction goes to the right at standard conditions						
II. Reduction	(17)	$Cu^{++} + e^- = Cu^+$	+0.158	−2.67	$4.7 \cdot 10^2$	
Oxidation	−(22)	$Cu = Cu^+ + e^-$	−0.522	8.82	$(6.6 \cdot 10^8)^{-1}$	
Net:		$Cu_{(c)} + Cu^{++}{}_{(aq)} = 2Cu^+{}_{(aq)}$	−0.364	6.15	$7.1 \cdot 10^{-7} =$	$\dfrac{[Cu^+]^2}{[Cu^{++}]}$
$\mathcal{E}^0 < 0, K < 1$; ∴ net reaction goes to left (backward) at standard conditions						
III. Reduction	(18)	$\frac{1}{2}S_4O_6{}^{=} + e^- = S_2O_3{}^{=}$	+0.17	−2.9	$8 \cdot 10^2$	
Oxidation	−(24)	$Fe(CN)_6{}^{-4} = Fe(CN)_6{}^{\equiv} + e^-$	−0.69	+12	10^{-12}	
Net:		$Fe(CN)_6{}^{-4}{}_{(aq)} + \frac{1}{2}S_4O_6{}^{=}{}_{(aq)} = Fe(CN)_6{}^{\equiv}{}_{(aq)} + S_2O_3{}^{=}{}_{(aq)}$	−0.52	+9	$8 \cdot 10^{-10} =$	$\dfrac{[Fe(CN)_6{}^{\equiv}][S_2O_3{}^{=}]}{[Fe(CN)_6{}^{-4}][S_4O_6{}^{=}]^{1/2}}$
$\mathcal{E}^0 < 0, K < 1$; ∴ net reaction goes to left (backward) at standard conditions						
IV. Reduction	(31)	$\frac{1}{2}MnO_2 + 2H^+ + e^- = \frac{1}{2}Mn^{++} + H_2O$	+1.208	−20.40	$2.5 \cdot 10^{20}$	
Oxidation	−(30)	$\frac{1}{3}Cr^{+++} + \frac{7}{6}H_2O = \frac{1}{6}Cr_2O_7{}^{=} + \frac{7}{3}H^+ + e^-$	−1.10	+18.6	$(4 \cdot 10^{18})^{-1}$	
Net:		$\frac{1}{3}Cr^{+++}{}_{(aq)} + \frac{1}{2}MnO_{2(c)} + \frac{1}{6}H_2O = \frac{1}{6}Cr_2O_7{}^{=}{}_{(aq)} + \frac{1}{2}Mn^{++}{}_{(aq)} + \frac{1}{3}H^+{}_{(aq)}$	0.11	−1.8	$6 \cdot 10^2 =$	$\dfrac{[Mn^{++}]^{1/2}[Cr_2O_7{}^{=}]^{1/6}[H^+]^{1/3}}{[Cr^{+++}]^{1/3}}$
$\mathcal{E}^0 > 0, K > 1$; ∴ net reaction goes to right at standard conditions						
V. Reduction	(22)	$Cu^+ + e^- = Cu$	+0.522	−8.82	$6.6 \cdot 10^8$	
Oxidation	−(15)	$Cu + Br^- = CuBr + e^-$	−0.033	+0.56	$(3.6)^{-1}$	
Net:		$Cu^+{}_{(aq)} + Br^-{}_{(aq)} = CuBr_{(c)}$	+0.489	−8.26	$1.8 \cdot 10^9 =$	$\dfrac{1}{[Cu^+][Br^-]} = \dfrac{1}{K_{sp}}$
$\mathcal{E}^0 > 0, K > 1$; ∴ net reaction proceeds as written (to right) at standard conditions						

Very extensive tables of half-reactions and their values of $\mathcal{E}^0$ are available in the chemical literature, containing as many as several hundred half-reactions. Note the large amount of information in such a table. If it contains 200 half-reactions, it can predict the direction of all the reactions among any combination of these half-reactions. New half-reactions can also be obtained by adding half-reactions (see p. 758 and following). Thus, considerable information concerning well over 20,000 reactions is compressed into a table of 200 half-reactions.

Exercise 20.4

Which of the following net reactions occur as written in the aqueous standard state? (*a*) $Cd^{++} + Fe = Fe^{++} + Cd$, (*b*) $D^+ + \frac{1}{2}H_2 = H^+ + \frac{1}{2}D_2$, (*c*) $\frac{1}{2}Br_2 + \frac{1}{2}H_2O = Br^- + \frac{1}{4}O_2 + H^+$, (*d*) $I^- + CuBr = CuI + Br^-$. *Answer:* (*a*) 9 − 7, $\mathcal{E}^0 = 0.037$; positive, so reaction occurs as written (initial numbers refer to half-reactions in Table 20.2). (*b*) 12 − 14, $\mathcal{E}^0 = -0.044$; negative, so reaction is unlikely, and reverse reaction is more likely. (*c*) 29 − 32, $\mathcal{E}^0 = -0.142$; negative, so reaction is unlikely, and reverse reaction is more likely. (*d*) 15 − 10, $\mathcal{E}^0 = 0.218$; positive, so reaction occurs as written. Remember, these predictions are only for the net reaction that will occur if all species are initially present in their standard states. Note that some of these net voltages are small. This indicates that tendencies to react are not great and that appreciable amounts of all species will be present at equilibrium.

Exercise 20.5

What net reaction will occur if the system $\frac{1}{2}I_{2(c)} + CuI_{(c)} = Cu^{++}{}_{(aq)} + 2I^-{}_{(aq)}$ is constructed with the ions present at 0.1 *M*? *Answer:* From Table 20.2 we combine 10, 22, 17, and 23 to give

	$pK_{1/2}$	
$CuI_{(c)} + e^- = Cu_{(c)} + I^-$	3.12	
$Cu_{(c)} = Cu^+ + e^-$	8.82	
$Cu^+ = Cu^{++} + e^-$	2.67	
$\frac{1}{2}I_2 + e^- = I^-$	−9.05	
Net: $\frac{1}{2}I_{2(c)} + CuI_{(c)} = Cu^{++} + 2I^-$	5.56,	$K = 2.8 \cdot 10^{-6}$

Thus $K = 2.8 \cdot 10^{-6}$, but initially $[Cu^{++}][I^-]^2 = 10^{-3}$, so net reaction must occur to lower $[Cu^{++}]$ and $[I^-]$. Thus $CuI_{(c)}$ and $I_{2(c)}$ will form until $[Cu^{++}][I^-]^2 = 2.8 \cdot 10^{-6}$.

SOLUBILITY PRODUCTS AND DISSOCIATION CONSTANTS FROM $\mathcal{E}^0$ VALUES

It is interesting, and probably surprising to you, that the net reaction in example V of Table 20.3 does not involve oxidation-reduction:

$$Cu^+{}_{(aq)} + Br^-{}_{(aq)} = CuBr_{(c)}, \qquad K = 1.8 \cdot 10^9 = \frac{1}{K_{sp}}$$

You may correctly interpret this as revealing the arbitrary nature of our definition of redox, as pointed out in Chapter 18. Practically, however, it means that many solubility product constants can be determined from electric cell measurements.

The electric cell measurements are often much simpler to accomplish than direct chemical analysis of the composition of equilibrium systems, and electrical measurements thus provide a valuable tool for studying many equilibria that would otherwise be quite intractable. It is only necessary that the experimenter be clever enough to design an electric cell whose half-reactions give a net reaction related to his desired equilibrium constant.

Consider the following combinations of half-reactions from Table 20.2 as further examples of the use of EMF data. Cells I, II, and IV are diagrammed in Figure 20.2.

	Number[a]	Half-reaction	$\mathcal{E}^0$	$pK_{1/2}$	$K_{1/2}$
I	(4)	$\frac{1}{3}Al(H_2O)_6^{+++} + e^- = \frac{1}{3}Al + 2H_2O$	−1.66	28.1	$8 \cdot 10^{-29}$
	−(3)	$2F^- + \frac{1}{3}Al = \frac{1}{3}AlF_6^{\equiv} + e^-$	2.07	−35.0	$1/(1.0 \cdot 10^{-35})$
	Net:	$\frac{1}{3}Al(H_2O)_6^{+++}{}_{(aq)} + 2F^-{}_{(aq)} = \frac{1}{3}AlF_6^{\equiv}{}_{(aq)} + 2H_2O_{(l)}$	0.41	−6.9	$8 \cdot 10^6 =$ $[AlF_6^{\equiv}]^{1/3}/\{[Al(H_2O)_6^{+++}]^{1/3}[F^-]^2\}$
$\mathcal{E}^0 > 0$, $K > 1$; ∴ F^- complexes Al^{+++} more tightly than does H_2O, or F^- is a stronger base than is H_2O with the acid Al^{+++}					
II	(10)	$CuI + e^- = Cu + I^-$	−0.185	3.12	$7.6 \cdot 10^{-4}$
	−(15)	$Cu + Br^- = CuBr + e^-$	−0.033	0.56	1/3.6
	Net:	$CuI_{(c)} + Br^-{}_{(aq)} = CuBr_{(c)} + I^-{}_{(aq)}$	−0.218	3.68	$2.1 \cdot 10^{-4} =$ $[I^-]/[Br^-]$
$\mathcal{E}^0 < 0$, $K < 1$; ∴ $CuI_{(c)}$ is more insoluble than $CuBr_{(c)}$ in H_2O, or I^- is a stronger base than is Br^- with the acid Cu^+					
III	(10)	$CuI + e^- = Cu + I^-$	−0.185	3.12	$7.6 \cdot 10^{-4}$
	−(22)	$Cu = Cu^+ + e^-$	−0.52	8.8	$1/(6 \cdot 10^8)$
	Net:	$CuI_{(c)} = Cu^+{}_{(aq)} + I^-{}_{(aq)}$	−0.71	11.9	$1.3 \cdot 10^{-12} =$ $K_{sp} = [Cu^+][I^-]$
$\mathcal{E}^0 < 0$, $K < 1$; ∴ $CuI_{(c)}$ is not very soluble in H_2O					
IV	−(7)	$\frac{1}{2}Fe = \frac{1}{2}Fe^{++} + e^-$	0.409	−6.91	$1/(1.23 \cdot 10^{-7})$
	(26)	$Fe^{+++} + e^- = Fe^{++}$	0.747	−12.61	$4.1 \cdot 10^{12}$
	Net:	$\frac{1}{2}Fe_{(c)} + Fe^{+++}{}_{(aq)} = \frac{3}{2}Fe^{++}{}_{(aq)}$	1.156	−19.52	$3.3 \cdot 10^{19} =$ $[Fe^{++}]^{3/2}/[Fe^{+++}]$
$\mathcal{E}^0 > 0$, $K > 1$; ∴ metallic iron will reduce Fe^{+++} to Fe^{++}					

[a] From Table 20.2.

In cases I, II, and III we have used EMF data from electric cells to calculate an equilibrium constant for net reactions not involving redox. We may interpret this possibility in a straightforward manner.

The tendency of any reaction to occur depends on the concentrations of the reactants. Thus the tendency of any electric cell to produce an EMF (as measured by the magnitude of the EMF) depends on the concentrations of the reactants in the cell. But the concentrations of these reactants may be varied, not only by adding various amounts of the reactants but also by adding other substances which can react with them. Adding bromide ions to a solution of Ag^+ ions around a silver electrode will precipitate some of the silver ions and change the potential gener-

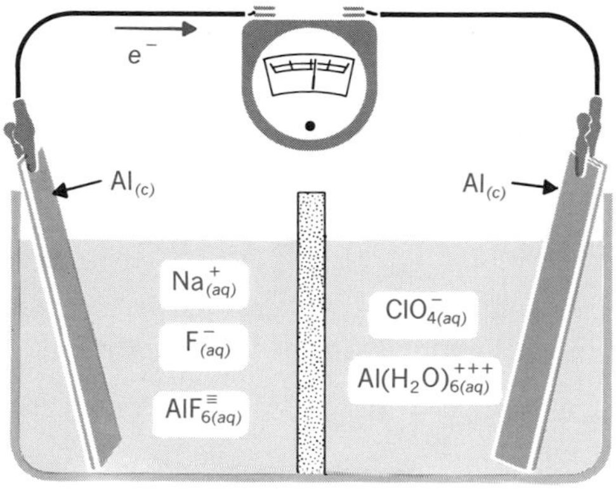

A. Cell I

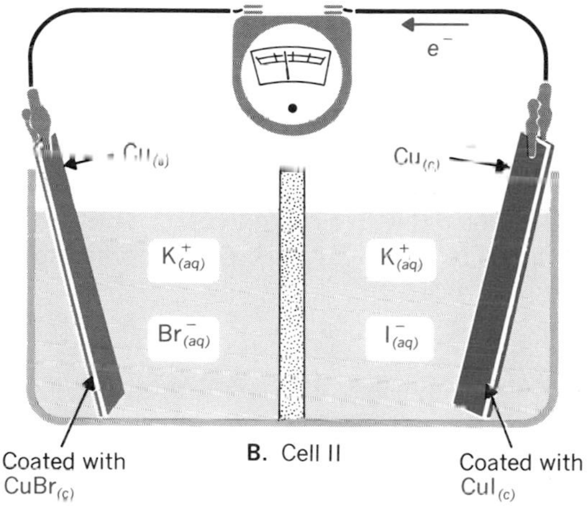

B. Cell II

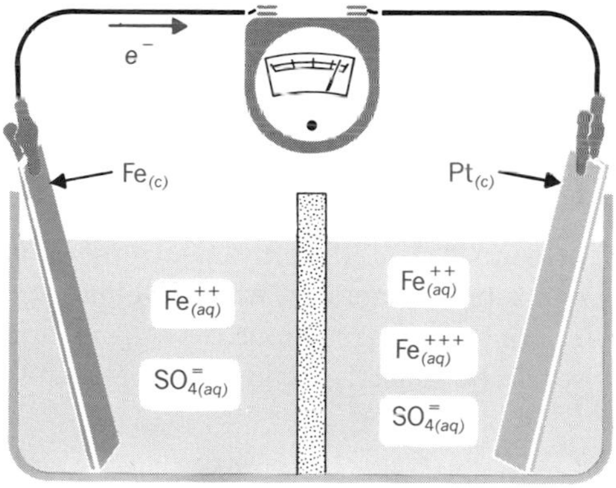

C. Cell IV

Figure 20.2 Schematic diagrams of cells I, II, and IV. Cell III cannot be constructed, since $Cu^{+}_{(aq)}$ is not stable with respect to disproportionation at 1 *M* concentration.

ated at the electrode. Addition of bromide ions to such a solution will decrease the tendency of silver ions to form silver atoms, since bromide ions reduce the concentration of silver ions. Or we may restate the result: addition of bromide ions will remove silver ions and so decrease the tendency of silver ions to gain electrons at the electrode and become silver atoms. Thus, the $\mathcal{E}$ value for the half-reaction

$$Ag^{+}_{(aq)} + e^{-} = Ag_{(c)}, \qquad K_{1/2} = 3.2 \cdot 10^{13}, \qquad \mathcal{E}^{0} = 0.7996$$

is dependent on the concentration of Ag^+, which is, in turn, dependent on the concentration of Br^- in the solution through the equilibrium

$$AgBr_{(c)} = Ag^{+}_{(aq)} + Br^{-}_{(aq)}, \qquad K_{sp} = 5.2 \cdot 10^{-13}$$

Therefore the effect of precipitating agents on a cell potential can always be interpreted in terms of the effect of the precipitating agent on the concentration of one or more of the reacting species. Similarly, the concentration of reacting species may be changed by formation of complex molecules, as in $Ag^+ + 2NH_3 = Ag(NH_3)_2{}^+$ and other similar acid-base reactions. This extends the advantages of electric cell potential measurements to most acid-base equilibrium constants for reactions occurring in liquid phases. Gas phase reactions are less amenable to measurement by means of electric cells, since gas phases do not usually conduct electricity. Even in these cases, however, the gas phase equilibria can sometimes be studied. For example, the pressure of a gas helps determine its solubility in a liquid, which may be correlated with a cell potential. Thus one may even be able to use electric cell potentials to study gas phase equilibria in special cases.

Exercise 20.6

Calculate K for the net reaction $AlF_6{}^{-3} + 6H_2O = Al(H_2O)_6{}^{+++} + 6F^-$.

Answer:

$$(3) \qquad \tfrac{1}{3}AlF_6{}^{-3} + e^- = \tfrac{1}{3}Al + 2F^-, \qquad K_{1/2} = 1.0 \cdot 10^{-35}$$

$$(-4) \qquad \tfrac{1}{3}Al + 2H_2O = \tfrac{1}{3}Al(H_2O)_6{}^{+++} + e^-, \qquad K_{1/2} = 1/(8 \cdot 10^{-29})$$

$$\text{Net: } \tfrac{1}{3}AlF_6{}^{-3} + 2H_2O = \tfrac{1}{3}Al(H_2O)_6{}^{+++} + 2F^-, \qquad K = 1.3 \cdot 10^{-7}$$

$K^3 = 2.2 \cdot 10^{-21}$, the desired K. Thus $AlF_6{}^{-3}$ is not greatly hydrolyzed by H_2O. If $[AlF_6{}^{-3}] = 1\ M$, then $[Al(H_2O)_6{}^{+++}] = \tfrac{1}{6}[F^-] = 2.2 \cdot 10^{-4}\ M$.

REDOX AND BORN-HABER CYCLES

Variations in $\mathcal{E}^0$ are, of course, related both to entropy and enthalpy effects. At room temperature, as with most reactions, entropy effects may be the smaller of the two, at least in comparing similar reactions. You should anticipate, for example, that entropy changes would be small in the first two of the following reactions, but not in the third.

	ΔS^0 (eu)	ΔH^0 (kcal mole^{-1})	ΔG^0 (kcal mole^{-1})
$Zn_{(c)} + Cu^{++}_{(aq)} = Zn^{++}_{(aq)} + Cu_{(c)}$	−3.7	−51.8	−50.7
$Fe_{(c)} + Cu^{++}_{(aq)} = Fe^{++}_{(aq)} + Cu_{(c)}$	−2.0	−36.4	−35.8
$Zn_{(c)} + 2Ag^{+}_{(aq)} = Zn^{++}_{(aq)} + 2Ag_{(c)}$	−50.3	−87.1	−72.0

Figure 20.3 uses a Born-Haber cycle to investigate the differences in ΔH^0. Note that it is the differences in heats of vaporization of the metals which account for most of the over-all effect.

Exercise 20.7

Predict ΔS^0, ΔH^0, and ΔG^0 for the reaction $Cu_{(c)} + 2Ag^+{}_{(aq)} = Cu^{++}{}_{(aq)} + 2Ag_{(c)}$. *Answer:* ΔS^0 should be similar to that for $Zn_{(c)} + 2Ag^+{}_{(aq)}$. ΔH^0 should be negative, since ΔH_{vap} for 2 moles of silver is greater than for 1 mole of copper, but less negative than ΔH^0 for $Zn_{(c)} + 2Ag^+{}_{(aq)}$, since ΔH_{vap} of Zn is small compared to that of Cu. Thus ΔG^0 should be less negative for the Cu than for the Zn reaction with Ag—largely because of variations in ΔH_{vap} of Zn and Cu. The observed values are $\Delta S^0 = -46.5$ eu, $\Delta H^0 = -35.2$ kcal mole^{-1}, $\Delta G^0 = -21.3$ kcal mole^{-1}, in good agreement with predictions.

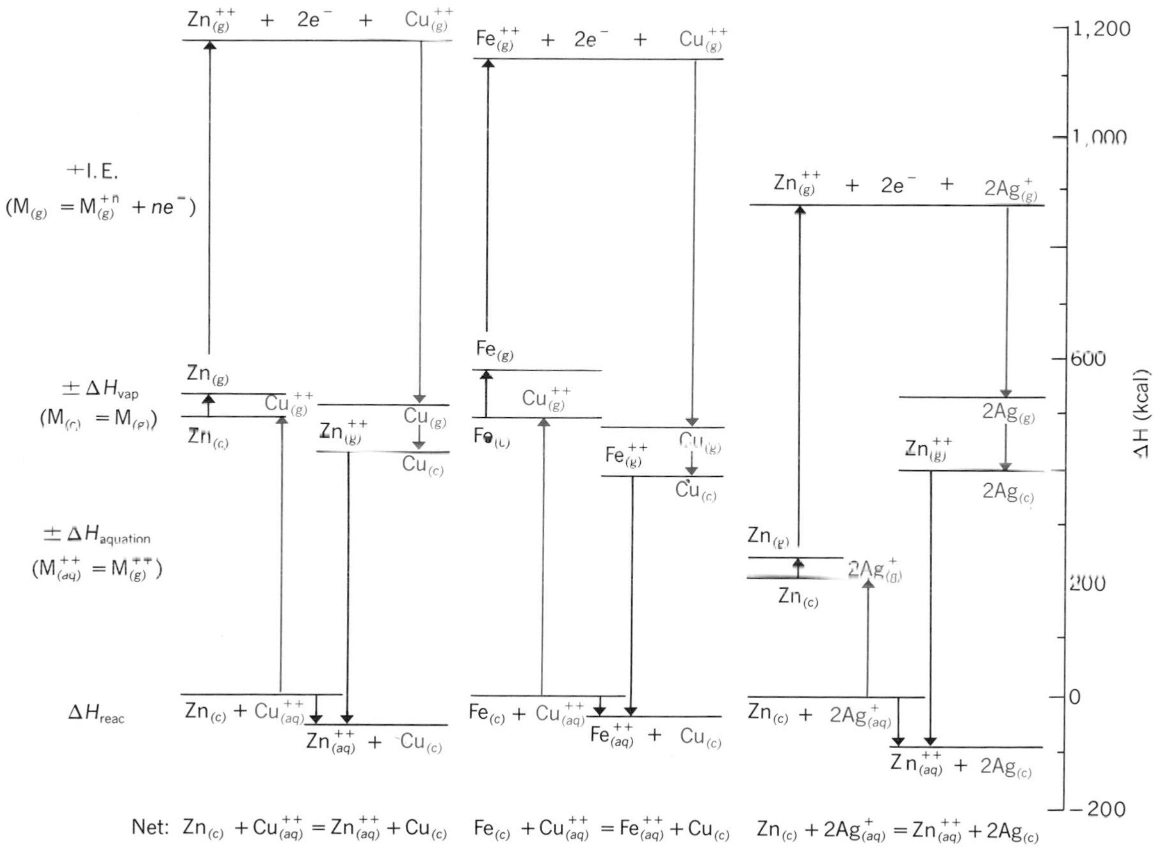

Figure 20.3 Born-Haber cycles and some redox reactions. The large terms are the I. E. and the aquation heats. However, with ions of similar size and charge, these tend to offset one another; that is, ΔH_{aq} + I. E. $\cong$ constant, as with Cu, Zn, and Ag. (Ions which hold water tightly may also hold electrons tightly.) Thus, the ΔH_{reac} may approximate the difference in the two heats of vaporization. It is probably the *d* orbitals in iron that put it out of line with the other three.

GAS PHASE EQUILIBRIA

The ideas presented above, mainly in connection with ionic equilibria in water, are also applicable to other equilibrium systems including gas phase reactions. For a system such as

$$C_2H_{6(g)} = C_2H_{4(g)} + H_{2(g)}, \qquad K_c = \frac{[C_2H_4][H_2]}{[C_2H_6]}$$

where the concentrations are expressed as moles per liter (M), we have $K = M_{C_2H_4}M_{H_2}/M_{C_2H_6}$.

It is often more convenient, however, to measure gaseous pressures, rather than molarities. Gas pressures in a mixture sum to give the total pressure according to

DALTON'S LAW:

$$p_A + p_B + p_C = P_{tot} = \sum_i p_i$$

From the ideal gas law

$$p = RT(n/V) = RT\,M$$

Thus, partial pressure, p_i, is directly proportional to M, so, for the above system,

$$K_c = \frac{M_{C_2H_4}M_{H_2}}{M_{C_2H_6}} = \frac{(p/RT)_{C_2H_4}(p/RT)_{H_2}}{(p/RT)_{C_2H_6}} = \frac{p_{C_2H_4}p_{H_2}}{p_{C_2H_6}} \cdot (RT)^{-1}$$

Since K_c and RT are constants, the pressure terms must also give a constant:

$$\frac{p_{C_2H_4}p_{H_2}}{p_{C_2H_6}} = K_p = K_c(RT)$$

In the general case of gas reactions, where Δn is the change in number of moles as the reaction proceeds from left to right, we get

$$K_p = K_c(RT)^{\Delta n} \tag{20.4}$$

It is much more common to use K_p than K_c for gas phase reactions, but note the potential ambiguity here. Always be careful to see which type of K is being discussed. Only if $\Delta n = 0$ does $K_p = K_c$. Since the standard state for gases is 1 atm, it is pressures and K_p that are almost always used. Thus $\Delta G^0 = -RT \ln K_p$.

SIMULTANEOUS EQUILIBRIA

Most of the systems we have discussed so far in this chapter involve competition among only a few species for a single common species—say protons, or electrons, or some single ion. There is a single, principal equilibrium. It is, of course, quite possible to find systems in which many interacting competitions are occurring: redox, acid-base, and precipitation reactions may all be competing at once for several species. The final equilibrium state will find all these equilibria in a dynamic state such that the equilibrium concentration of each species will simultaneously satisfy all the equilibrium constants of every reaction in which it can participate. A living system is a fine example of extremely complex, simultaneous equilibria. One of the difficulties of studying living systems arises from the interdependent nature of the numerous equilibria.

Consider, for example, the problem facing the physiology of a mollusc in maintaining his shell. The shell itself is a complicated chemical mixture but we, unlike the mollusc, can assume that the shell is pure calcium carbonate, $CaCO_3$. The shell, if it is to be stable, must be essentially in equilibrium with the surrounding sea, as in the equation

$$CaCO_{3(c)} = Ca^{++}{}_{(aq)} + CO_3{}^{=}{}_{(aq)}, \qquad K = [Ca^{++}][CO_3{}^{=}] \cong 10^{-8} \tag{20.5}$$

The evidence is strong that Ca^{++} is quite unreactive with seawater. Ca^{++} is not appreciably hydrolyzed, but $CO_3{}^{=}$ hydrolyzes extensively, as in the reactions

$$CO_3{}^{=}{}_{(aq)} + H_2O_{(l)} = HCO_3{}^{-}{}_{(aq)} + OH^{-}{}_{(aq)}, \qquad K = \frac{[HCO_3{}^{-}][OH^{-}]}{[CO_3{}^{=}]} = 2 \cdot 10^{-4} \tag{20.6}$$

$$HCO_3{}^{-}{}_{(aq)} + H_2O_{(l)} = H_2CO_{3(aq)} + OH^{-}{}_{(aq)}, \qquad K = \frac{[H_2CO_3][OH^{-}]}{[HCO_3{}^{-}]} = 2 \cdot 10^{-10} \tag{20.7}$$

Furthermore, the final hydrolysis product, H_2CO_3, can engage in further equilibria:

$$H_2CO_{3(aq)} = H_2O_{(l)} + CO_{2(aq)}, \qquad K = \frac{[CO_2]}{[H_2CO_3]} = 10^2 \tag{20.8}$$

$$CO_{2(aq)} = CO_{2(g)}, \qquad K = \frac{p_{CO_2}}{[CO_2]} = 30. \tag{20.9}$$

Most molluscs must be able to change their shells, which requires two abilities. The molluscs must be able to grow a new shell as a covering, and they must be able to dissolve the old shell as it gets in the way of their continued growth. How do they do this? (And without being able to carry out equilibrium calculations, either!)

$CaCO_3$ will precipitate whenever the concentrations of Ca^{++} and $CO_3{}^{=}$ are such that their product exceeds the solubility product, K_{sp}. The concentration of Ca^{++} is relatively unaffected by other equilibria, but the $CO_3{}^{=}$ concentration depends on the total available carbon in the water, on the concentration of OH^-, and on the partial pressure of gaseous carbon dioxide (since the carbon can be present in any of several forms: $CO_3{}^{=}$, $HCO_3{}^{-}$, H_2CO_3, $CO_{2(aq)}$, and $CO_{2(g)}$. Thus the mollusc can control the precipitation of $CaCO_3$ by controlling the acidity of the solution, the partial pressure of CO_2, and/or the total available carbon.

The mollusc is of course metabolizing and producing CO_2, and he is surrounded by and continually ingesting ocean water containing Ca^{++} and all the other species involved in these equilibria. None of these total concentrations is subject to much variation. But the concentration of acid helps determine all the individual concentrations except that of Ca^{++}, and living systems (including molluscs) can often regulate acidity quite well. Let us see what the mollusc might do.

The concentration of Ca^{++} in the ocean is about $1.0 \cdot 10^{-2}\,M$. Since $[Ca^{++}][CO_3{}^{-}] \cong 10^{-8}$ at equilibrium, the $[CO_3{}^{=}]$ must be about $10^{-6}\,M$ if the $CaCO_3$ is to be in equilibrium with the ocean water. The total concentration of "inorganic" C (in one or another of the species in equilibrium here) is $2.3 \cdot 10^{-3}\,M$ in ocean water. Shell precipitation and solution will, therefore, be in equilibrium if the ratio $CO_3{}^{=}$/total "inorganic" carbon in the water $= 10^{-6}/2.3 \cdot 10^{-3} \cong 5 \cdot 10^{-4}$. Thus

$$\frac{[CO_3{}^{=}]}{[CO_3{}^{=}] + [HCO_3{}^{-}] + [H_2CO_3] + [CO_2]} \cong 5 \cdot 10^{-4} \tag{20.10}$$

Equations (20.5), (20.6), (20.7), (20.8), and (20.10) contain a total of six variables: the concentrations of Ca^{++}, $CO_3{}^{=}$, $HCO_3{}^{-}$, H_2CO_3, $CO_{2(aq)}$, and OH^-. [We can eliminate Equation (20.9) from consideration, since this is merely one more equation in one more unknown and contributes nothing to the solution of the problem.] Five independent equations involving six unknowns means that determination of any one unknown determines all of them, but just as importantly it means that the system does have the possibility of change. The mollusc can change the $CO_3^=$ by adjusting the concentration of OH^-. The sixth restriction is that the $[Ca^{++}]$ be 10^{-2} *M*. The five equations plus this single fixed concentration means that there is a unique solution to the problem. Molluscs, presumably, found this solution by trial and error over geologic time. Perhaps we can find it somewhat more rapidly:

$$[Ca^{++}] = 10^{-2},\ [Ca^{++}][CO_3^=] = 10^{-8} = [10^{-2}][CO_3^=];\ \therefore\ [CO_3^=] = 10^{-6}$$

$$2 \cdot 10^{-4} = \frac{[HCO_3^-][OH^-]}{[CO_3^=]} = \frac{[HCO_3^-][OH^-]}{10^{-6}}, \qquad [OH^-] = \frac{2 \cdot 10^{-10}}{[HCO_3^-]}$$

$$2 \cdot 10^{-10} = \frac{[H_2CO_3][OH^-]}{[HCO_3^-]} = \frac{[H_2CO_3] \cdot 2 \cdot 10^{-10}}{[HCO_3^-]^2}, \qquad [H_2CO_3] = [HCO_3^-]^2$$

$$10^2 = \frac{[CO_2]}{[H_2CO_3]} = \frac{[CO_2]}{[HCO_3^-]^2}, \qquad [CO_2] = 10^2[HCO_3^-]^2$$

$$5 \cdot 10^{-4} = \frac{[CO_3^=]}{[CO_3^=] + [HCO_3^-] + [H_2CO_3] + [CO_2]}$$

$$= \frac{10^{-6}}{10^{-6} + [HCO_3^-] + [HCO_3^-]^2 + 10^2[HCO_3^-]^2}$$

The value of $[HCO_3^-]$ may be calculated exactly or approximated. It must be less than $2 \cdot 10^{-3}$ *M*, since this value represents the total "inorganic" carbon. Thus higher-power terms should quickly become negligible in the sum; we shall assume this. Then we obtain

$$5 \cdot 10^{-4} = \frac{10^{-6}}{10^{-6} + [HCO_3^-]}$$

$$[HCO_3^-]_{eq} = 2 \cdot 10^{-3}\ M$$

This figure indicates that essentially all the inorganic carbon is in the form of HCO_3^- ions. Now we can calculate all the other equilibrium concentrations:

$$[OH^-]_{eq} = \frac{2 \cdot 10^{-10}}{[HCO_3^-]} = \frac{2 \cdot 10^{-10}}{2 \cdot 10^{-3}} = 10^{-7}\ M$$

$$[H_2CO_3]_{eq} = [HCO_3^-]^2 = (2 \cdot 10^{-3})^2 = 4 \cdot 10^{-6}\ M$$

$$[CO_2]_{eq} = 10^2[HCO_3^-]^2 = 10^2 \cdot 4 \cdot 10^{-6} = 4 \cdot 10^{-4}\ M$$

Remember that $[CO_3^=]_{eq} = 10^{-6}$ *M*.

All of these values are consistent with our assumptions. The mollusc should maintain the $[OH^-] \cong 10^{-7}$ *M* or greater to form $CaCO_{3(c)}$, and should lower the $[OH^-]$ to less than 10^{-7} *M* to dissolve $CaCO_{3(c)}$. Since the concentration of hydroxide ion in the ocean is about 10^{-6} *M*, we see that $CaCO_3$ would normally precipitate (accounting for limestone strata beneath ancient oceans). Thus the established shell is stable to solution in ocean water, but can be dissolved by a small increase in the acidity, which the mollusc apparently controls very well. Birds control the same equilibria in forming eggshell, also of $CaCO_3$. Vertebrates also control the same equilibria, as well as similar equilibria yielding calcium phosphates such as $Ca_3(PO_4)_2$, in controlling skeletal growth.

For an example of simultaneous gaseous equilibria involving CH_4 and H_2O (in equilibrium with H_2, CO, C, C_2H_6, and CO_2) see E. E. Stone, *J. Chem. Ed., 43,* 241 (1966). This is the synthesis gas equilibrium system and is of great industrial importance. Figure 20.4 gives the results of computer calculations on a set of equilibria that includes eight species.

Exercise 20.8

Would $Al(H_2O)_3(OH)_3$ dissolve appreciably in 1 *M* NaF? *Answer:* The following equilibria must be considered.

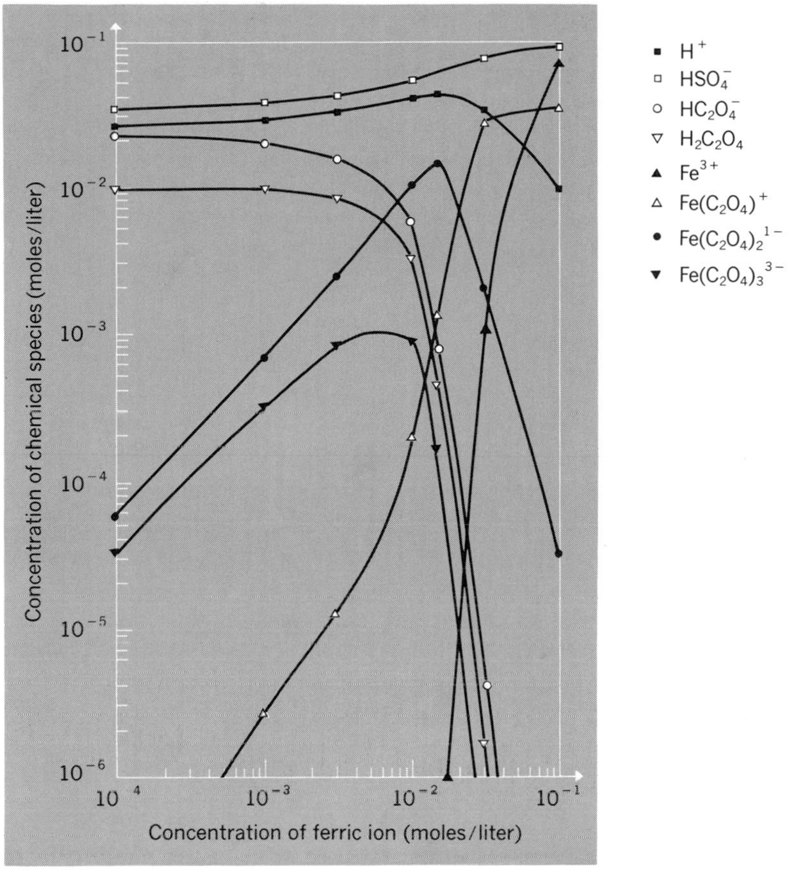

Figure 20.4 Concentration of the various species in 0.03 *M* potassium oxalate, 0.1 *N* sulfuric acid on addition of ferric ammonium sulfate. [From J. W. Swinnerton and W. W. Miller, *J. Chem. Ed.*, **36,** 488 (1959).]

From Table 20.1:	$Al(H_2O)_3(OH)_{3(c)} + 3H_2O = Al(H_2O)_6^{+++} + 3OH^-,$	$K = 10^{-32}$
From Exer. 20.6:	$Al(H_2O)_6^{+++} + 6F^- = AlF_6^{\equiv} + 6H_2O,$	$K = 4.5 \cdot 10^{20}$
From Table 18.13:	$HF = F^- + H^+,$	$K = 6.8 \cdot 10^{-4}$
K_w:	$H^+ + OH^- = H_2O,$	$1/K_w = 10^{14}$

Thus we have five unknown concentrations: $Al(H_2O)_6^{+++}$, OH^-, F^-, $AlF_6^{\equiv}$, HF, H^+, if we assume we need not consider any other possible complexes of Al^{+++}. We have four values of K. The fifth restriction can be the mass balance: $[F^-] + 6[AlF_6^{\equiv}] + [HF] = 1\ M$. Can you guess the result by examining the values of K? Can you carry out the solution? It is that the $Al(H_2O)_3(OH)_3$ is slightly soluble, which gives $[AlF_6^{\equiv}]_{eq} \cong 10^{-3}\ M$, $[F^-]_{eq} = 1\ M$, $[OH^-] \cong 2 \cdot 10^{-3}\ M$ as the appreciable concentrations.

EQUILIBRIA IN NONAQUEOUS CONDENSED SYSTEMS

It is true that our discussion of equilibria has been almost completely limited to aqueous solution and gaseous systems. However, the idea of dynamic equilibria involving solubility, dissociation, redox, acid-base, and so on, is equally applicable to nonaqueous systems. Values of equilibrium constants are known for many such systems. In fact nonaqueous condensed systems often approximate ideality more closely than aqueous solutions, and thus the constants hold over a wider concentration range. Semiconductors containing a doping element are one type of interesting, almost ideal, nonaqueous system. For a system such as Sb in crystalline Ge we get $Sb = Sb^+ + e^-$, $K = [Sb^+][e^-]/Sb$. The electrical conductivity is directly proportional to $[e^-]$. Experiments on the variation of conductivity with [Sb] and with temperature show that K is remarkably constant at constant temperature as Sb varies, and that the variation of K with temperature is like that of other equilibrium constants.

SUMMARY

Typical equilibria are (*a*) those involving acid-base systems in which competition may be said to be for hydrogen ions (Brönsted theory) or for pairing free electron pairs with empty orbitals (Lewis theory), (*b*) those involving redox in which the competition may be said to be for electrons, and (*c*) those involving phase equilibria in which the competition may often be viewed in terms of Lewis acid-base theory, with the solvent and the crystal state competing for the molecules.

In every closed system at constant temperature and pressure we may view the competitions in terms of the tendency for energy and matter to spread out as much as possible (drive to increase the entropy of the system) and the tendency of strong bonds to form (drive to decrease the enthalpy of the system). The net effect, which also includes the effect of temperature, is given by the equation

$$\Delta G = \Delta H - T\,\Delta S$$

We have already shown in Chapter 9 that this is identical to saying that all processes tend to increase the entropy of the universe.

Since ΔG^0, K, and $\mathcal{E}^0$ are all related to the likelihood of a reaction occurring, we are not surprised to find that there are simple relationships between ΔG^0 and K and $\mathcal{E}^0$:

$$\Delta G^0 = -RT \ln K = -n\mathcal{F}\mathcal{E}^0 \qquad (20.11)$$

where ΔG^0 and $\mathcal{E}^0$ refer, respectively, to the change in free energy and to the cell voltage of a reaction which starts with all reactants and products initially mixed in their standard conditions—as pure materials or, if in solution, as 1 *F* or, if gases, at 1 atm partial pressure—and proceeds at constant T and P.

Atoms move in the void and catching each other up jostle together, and some recoil in any direction that may chance, and others become entangled with one another in various degrees according to the symmetry of their shapes and sizes and positions and order, and they remain together and thus the coming into being of composite things is affected.
—*Simplicius,* De caelo, (~400 B.C.)

PROBLEMS

20.1. Calculate $\mathcal{E}^0$, K, and pK for the following reactions. (a. $pK \cong -6$.)

	(a)	(b)	(c)	(d)	(e)
oxidizing half-reaction	Cd^{++}—Cd	Cu^{++}—Cu	$S_2O_3^{=}$—$S_4O_6^{=}$	MnO_4^{-}—Mn^{++}	Ce^{+4}—Ce^{+++}
reducing half-reaction	Zn—Zn^{++}	Fe—Fe^{++}	Fe^{++}—Fe^{+++}	Hg_2^{++}—Hg^{++}	I^-—I_2

20.2. Calculate the solubility product for $AgCl_{(c)}$ from Table 20.2. Compare with the value in Table 20.1.

20.3. One liter of water will just dissolve 6.24 g of Ag_2SO_4. Calculate K_{sp} for silver sulfate. ($K_{sp} \cong 10^{-5}$.)

20.4. Some solid silver oxalate, $Ag_2C_2O_4$, is shaken with 0.05 F sodium oxalate until equilibrium is attained. The silver ion concentration is found to be $1.4 \cdot 10^{-5}$ F. Calculate the solubility product of silver oxalate. ($K_{sp} \cong 10^{-11}$.)

20.5. At a certain temperature, T, the equilibrium between NO, O_2, and NO_2 gases in a flask can be described by the equation

$$2NO_{(g)} + O_{2(g)} = 2NO_{2(g)} + 27 \text{ kcal}$$

In what way will the number of moles of NO_2 in the flask at equilibrium be altered by (a) increasing the temperature, (b) removing NO from the flask, (c) adding a catalyst, (d) adding O_2 to the flask, (e) compressing the flask to a smaller volume?

20.6. Ordinarily the lungs inhale air with about 20% oxygen and 80% nitrogen, and exhale air with about 19% oxygen, 80% nitrogen, and 1% carbon dioxide. Why is it fatal to breathe air containing 20% oxygen, 70% nitrogen, and 10% carbon dioxide?

20.7. The hexahydrate of ferric chloride, when heated until no further change occurs, leaves a red-brown residue insoluble in water. At the same time a gas is given off which turns blue litmus red. Write an equation for the net reaction and explain why the reaction proceeds in the above manner rather than in the reverse direction.

20.8. The following oxidation-reduction reactions take place as written:

$$Fe^{+++} + Ag + Cl^- = Fe^{++} + AgCl$$
$$Fe + 2H^+ = Fe^{++} + H_2$$
$$2AgCl + H_2 = 2Ag + 2H^+ + 2Cl^-$$

Give by formula the reduced and oxidized form of the four oxidizing and reducing couples involved in these reactions, followed by the corresponding half-reaction. Making use of the above data only, arrange the half-reactions in order of increasing $\mathcal{E}^0$ as reaction potentials and determine the direction in which the reactions below would take place:

$$Fe + 2AgCl = Fe^{++} + 2Ag + 2Cl^-$$
$$3Fe^{++} = 2Fe^{+++} + Fe$$

20.9. Calculate the pH at which $Al(H_2O)_3(OH)_3$ should just begin to precipitate from a 0.1 F solution of aluminum nitrate. ($pH \cong 4.$)

II

20.10. Calculate the solubility of $AgCN_{(c)}$ in water assuming (*a*) no hydrolysis of either ion, (*b*) hydrolysis of the CN^- only. (*a*. $s \cong 10^{-8}\ M$.)

20.11. Calculate the equilibrium concentrations in a system made by mixing the following species so that each was in its standard state before reaction: Ag^+, Hg_2^{++} plus $Ag_{(c)}$ and $Hg_{(l)}$. ($[Ag^+] \cong 1M$.)

20.12. A solution of 0.1 F $AgNO_3$ is slowly added with stirring to a solution 0.1 F in Cl^- and 0.1 F in Br^-. Will $AgCl_{(c)}$ precipitate first? At what concentration of Ag^+ will the second precipitate begin to form? What percentage of the first anion to precipitate will still be in solution when the second anion just begins to precipitate? ($[Ag^+] \cong 10^{-9}M$.)

20.13. Gaseous NO_2 was introduced into a hot, isothermal, constant-volume system. Its initial pressure was 263 mm. The equilibrium pressure in the system was 312 mm. Assume that the only appreciable equilibrium is $NO_{2(g)} = NO_{(g)} + \frac{1}{2}O_{2(g)}$ and calculate K_P for the system. ($K_P \cong 4\ mm^{1/2}$.)

20.14. Write equilibrium constant expressions for K_P for each of the following gaseous systems in terms of total pressure, P_t, and x, the fraction of the first reactant on the left which has reacted at equilibrium starting with equimolar reactants only. (*a*) $H_2 = 2H$, (*b*) $H_2 + \frac{1}{2}O_2 = H_2O$, (*c*) $C_2H_2 + 2H_2 = C_2H_6$. The answer to *b* is

$$K_P = \frac{x\left(2 - \frac{x}{2}\right)^{1/2}}{\left(1 - x\right)\left(1 - \frac{x}{2}\right)^{1/2}} P_t$$

20.15. An excess of metallic copper was brought into equilibrium with a solution which was originally 0.5 M cupric sulfate ($CuSO_4$). (*a*) Calculate the equilibrium concentrations of all species present, assuming that sulfate does not enter into the reaction in any way. (*b*) Explain the fact that this reaction proceeds almost to completion when a high concentration of chloride ion is present. ($[Cu^+]_{eq} \cong 10^{-3}M$.)

20.16. What is the pH of a solution made up from 0.1 mole of NaOH and 0.1 mole of $CaCl_2$ added to one liter of water? The solubility equilibrium constant for $Ca(OH)_2$ is $8 \cdot 10^{-6}$. ($pH \cong 10.$)

20.17. Given the following standard oxidation potentials, calculate the dissociation constant for the tetrammine copper(II) ion. ($K_d \cong 10^{-14}$.)

$$Cu_{(c)} = Cu^{++} + 2e^-, \qquad \mathcal{E}^0 = -0.345\ v$$

$$Cu_{(c)} + 4NH_3 = Cu(NH_3)_4^{++} + 2e^-, \qquad \mathcal{E}^0 = +0.053\ v$$

20.18. At some temperature, T, the equilibrium constant, K, for the reaction

$$H_{2(g)} + CO_{2(g)} = H_2O_{(g)} + CO_{(g)}$$

is $\frac{7}{3}$. Calculate the molar concentration of each component in the final equilibrium system obtained by adding 1.00 mole of H_2, 2.00 moles of CO_2, 3.00 moles of H_2O, and 4.00 moles of CO to a 5.00-liter vessel at temperature T. ($p_{H_2} \cong 0.4$ atm.)

20.19. At 900°C the partial pressure of CO_2 in equilibrium with $CaCO_{3(c)}$ and $CaO_{(c)}$ is 800 mm. If 1.530 g of calcium carbonate is placed in a cooled, evacuated 1-liter flask, and the flask is sealed and heated to 900°C, what will be the phases present in the flask? In what amount will each phase be present? (About 10^{-2} moles CaO.)

20.20. The equilibrium constant for the reaction $PbCl_{2(s)} = Pb^{++}{}_{(aq)} + 2Cl^{-}{}_{(aq)}$ is $1.7 \cdot 10^{-5}$; however, the solubility in water at the same temperature (25°C) is 0.039 *M*. Assume that the entire discrepancy can be attributed to the reaction $Pb^{2+}{}_{(aq)} + H_2O = PbOH^{+}{}_{(aq)} + H^{+}{}_{(aq)}$ which would tend to increase the solubility of the $PbCl_2$; then, calculate the equilibrium constant for this reaction. ($K_{\text{hyd}} \cong 0.5$.)

III

20.21. Calculate the equilibrium concentration of CH_4 from the gas phase reaction $CH_3CHO_{(g)} = CH_{4(g)} + CO_{(g)}$ when the initial concentration of pure CH_3CHO is 0.24 *M* and the equilibrium constant, K_c, is $9.5 \cdot 10^{-5}$. Calculate all the final concentrations if the initial mixture had been as above but also contained 0.16 *M* CH_4. ($[CH_4] \cong 10^{-3} M$.)

20.22. The thermodynamic values at 298°K for the reaction of a mole of some metals with aqueous hydrogen ion to produce hydrogen gas and aqueous metal ions are given below. Rationalize the differences in ΔS^0 and in ΔH^0 in terms of atomic properties. You need not look up data.

	ΔS^0	ΔH^0	ΔG^0
Mg	−4.76	−110.41	−108.99
Pb	20.81	0.39	−5.81
Na	17.8	−57.28	−62.59
Al	−34.99	−125.4	−115.0

20.23. Dipositive tin, Sn^{++}, forms the complex ion, $SnCl_4^{=}$; dipositive iron, Fe^{++}, does not form a chloro complex. When a solution of Sn^{++}, Fe^{++}, and Cl^- is equilibrated with excess metallic iron and tin, the resulting equilibrium concentrations are $[SnCl_4^{-}] = 0.040\ M$, $[Fe^{++}] = 0.60\ M$, and $[Cl^-] = 0.90\ M$. Calculate the dissociation constant of the $SnCl_4^{=}$. ($K \cong 10^{-10}$.)

See page 1092 for a list of references and readings in the recent chemical literature related to the material in this chapter.

PART 4

Rates and Mechanisms

HOW DO REACTIONS OCCUR?

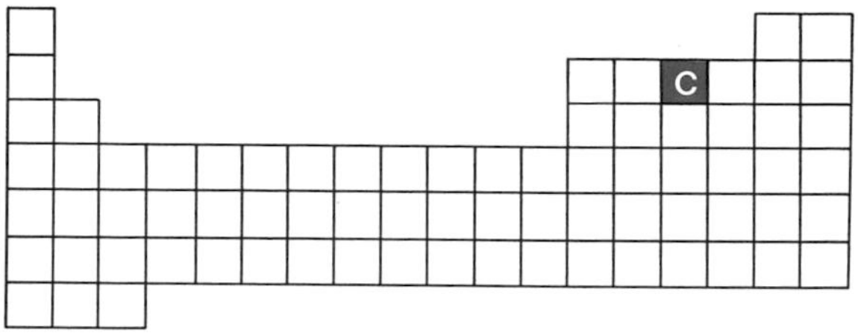

CHAPTER 21

Carbon Compounds

KENNETH M. HARMON

Catenation, isomerization, and the incorporation of one or many other elements leads to an infinite array of carbon-containing substances; one of our greatest problems is to classify them in a usable way.

Professors, research chemists, textbooks, or journals that deal with the study of chemical syntheses and reactions are usually identified as dealing either with organic or inorganic chemistry. The organic label is reserved for the study of the compounds of carbon; the study of all the other elements is lumped together under the label "inorganic chemistry." Why was the chemistry of carbon singled out in this way? There are both historical and practical answers to this question.

ORGANIC CHEMISTRY

The first complex carbon compounds isolated by early chemists—ethyl alcohol, acetic acid, cane sugar, and uric acid—were derived from living organisms, and so were termed organic substances. It was believed at first that there was a fundamental difference between materials derived from living and nonliving sources; the former were held to have a *vital force* which was not present in substances of mineral origin. But in 1828 the German chemist Woehler synthesized urea from ammonium cyanate, a compound of inorganic origin:

$$\underset{\text{ammonium cyanate}}{NH_4CNO} \overset{\text{heat}}{=} \underset{\text{urea}}{H_2N{-}\overset{\overset{\displaystyle O}{\|}}{C}{-}NH_2}$$

This synthesis began the downfall of the vitalistic theory, but the classification of the study of carbon compounds as the distinct field of organic chemistry was retained, and has persisted to this day.

It is true that most of the carbon-containing materials that we use come to us by way of living organisms. The carbon dioxide of the atmosphere is incorporated into the growth of plants, which are in turn eaten by animals. This continuous photosynthetic route provides a considerable supply of carbon compounds including the foods we eat, wood, fibers, medicines, leather, our own bodies, and many more. A much larger source of carbon compounds is the earth's reserve of petroleum, natural gas, and oil shale. These too appear to result from the incorporation of atmospheric carbon dioxide into living organisms in ages past. Although mined from the earth like minerals, these substances are truly organic in origin.

It has not been entirely because of their derivation from living organisms, however, that carbon compounds have been grouped into a separate class for study. There have been two good practical reasons for it: the nature of carbon compounds has called for specialized approaches and techniques, and the number of carbon compounds is so great that the chemistry of this one element is equal in scope and diversity to that of all the others combined.

In the early days of chemistry the study of most elements involved primarily the study of salts, acids, bases, and aqueous solutions, but the known carbon compounds were almost all covalent molecular species. Scientists working with organic molecules were faced, from the start, with special problems in purification, identification, and synthesis. In particular, since they were dealing with complex molecules instead of salts, they were forced to consider the problems of chemical structure, of the shape of molecules, and of the order of connection of the constituent atoms.

NUMBER OF CARBON COMPOUNDS

By isolation from natural sources and by laboratory syntheses, the number of known carbon compounds has increased rapidly, until today more than $3 \cdot 10^6$ such compounds have been identified, and new ones are continually being synthesized and/or isolated at a rate of more than a thousand per day. This makes known carbon compounds almost ten times as numerous as the known compounds of all the other elements, a ratio that will probably be maintained indefinitely.

Elemental carbon is found in nature as diamond (see p. 385) and graphite (see p. 386). Two oxides of carbon occur commonly (carbon monoxide, CO, and carbon dioxide, CO_2) and several others are known through laboratory synthesis (for example, carbon suboxide, C_3O_2, and mellitic anhydride, $C_{12}O_9$; see Figure 21.1). Carbon combines with halogens to form tetrahalides (CX_4, where X = F, Cl, Br, or I), and several ions containing carbon and nitrogen are frequently encountered (such as cyanide, CN^-, and cyanate, NCO^-). Solution of carbon dioxide in water gives carbonic acid, H_2CO_3, which, along with bicarbonate ion, HCO_3^-, plays an important role in biological processes (see p. 485), and which provides the source of carbonate ion in rocks and minerals.

We are making a slow start in enumerating some $3 \cdot 10^6$ carbon compounds, but this problem is quickly overcome when we consider the compounds

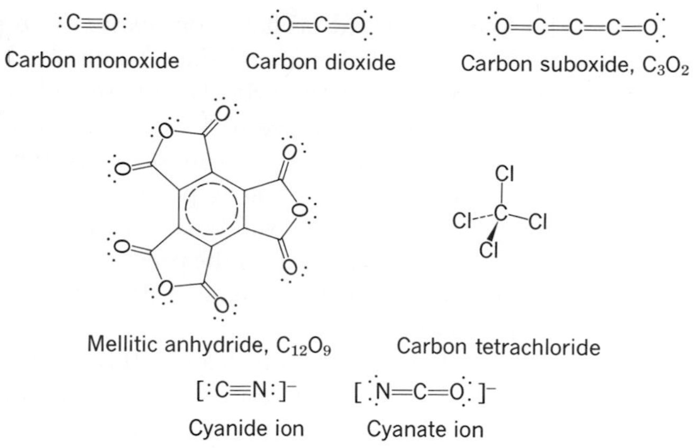

Figure 21.1 Bonding and structure of some "inorganic" compounds of carbon.

containing only carbon and hydrogen, called hydrocarbons (Figure 21.2). Hydrocarbons are rendered unique by the fact that carbon-hydrogen bonds react very, very slowly with atmospheric moisture and oxygen at room temperature, and the strength of a bond from one carbon to another is not weakened markedly by the presence of other carbon-carbon bonds attached to either atom. If we consider the first-row hydrides (see Chapter 12), we find that lithium, beryllium, and boron hydrides react violently with the atmosphere, and the hydrogen-fluorine bond in HF is ionized by contact with moisture. Water and ammonia, the hydrides of oxygen and nitrogen, are stable substances, but slightly more complicated hydrides of these elements (hydrogen peroxide, HO—OH, and hydrazine, $H_2N—NH_2$) have very reactive oxygen-oxygen or nitrogen-nitrogen bonds; higher hydrides are even less stable.

In methane, CH_4, the simplest hydrocarbon, the bonds are said to form

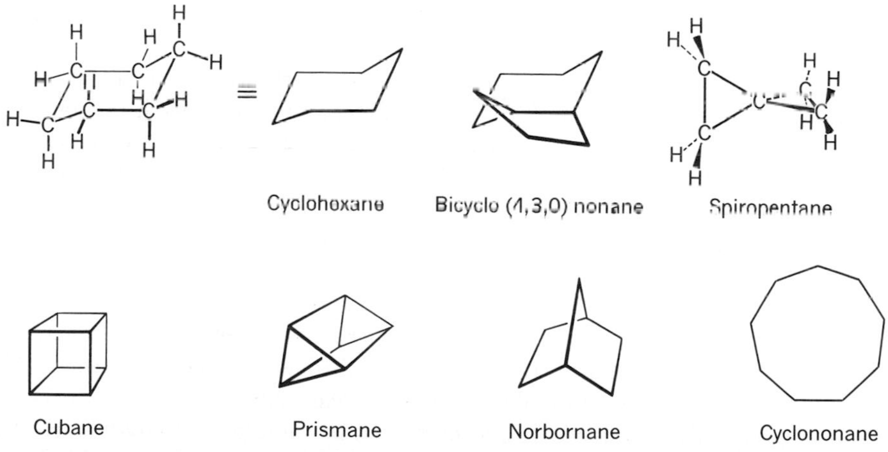

Figure 21.2 Structures of some hydrocarbons, and some representations. In spiropentane plain lines indicate bonds in the plane of the paper; wedges, bonds above the paper; dotted lines, bonds below the paper. Perspective and labelling are also used to indicate lack of planarity. In each of the six figures without chemical atomic symbols there is a carbon at each corner or vertex, lines are carbon-carbon bonds, and hydrogens are understood to bring the number of bonds at each carbon to four.

by four sp^3 hybrid orbitals from carbon (see p. 329), each overlapping with a 1*s* orbital of a hydrogen atom. Each bonding orbital has two electrons; there are no empty or partly empty orbitals and no nonbonding pairs of electrons. In addition, the electronegativity (see p. 320) of carbon is very close to that of hydrogen, and the bonds in methane are almost completely nonpolar. These conditions give a low melting point and boiling point and render the molecule slow to react at room temperature; methane will burn if ignited by a flame or spark in air or will react with molecular halogens in the presence of sunlight, but under ordinary conditions it is practically inert to chemical attack because of the slow rates of reaction (high activation energy).

If we were to break a C—H bond in a methane molecule so that one electron went with each portion formed, we would form a hydrogen atom and a methyl radical. (The name methyl is applied to the group CH_3— and is derived from methane by removing the "-ane" and adding "-yl.") In our hypothetical bond-breaking process we would have exerted an amount of energy equivalent to 104 kcal per mole of bonds broken. If we now allow two methyl radicals to combine, so that the two sp^3 orbitals (each with one electron) overlap to form a bond, we would find that 88 kcal of energy would be liberated for each mole of bonds formed. Thus the carbon-carbon bond is almost as strong as the carbon-hydrogen bond. The new molecule formed is called ethane, H_3C—CH_3; like methane, it has no empty orbitals or unshared electrons, its bonds are nonpolar, and it is chemically quite inert, again primarily due to high activation energies. If we removed a hydrogen atom from ethane (98 kcal $mole^{-1}$ required) to form an ethyl radical, CH_3—CH_2—, and joined it to a methyl radical (85 kcal $mole^{-1}$ released), we would have a new compound called propane, CH_3—CH_2—CH_3. We could repeat the process to form butane, CH_3—CH_2—CH_2—CH_3, or we could form butane by combination of two ethyl radicals (about 83 kcal $mole^{-1}$ released). This process can be continued indefinitely on paper and—what is more important—the predicted substances have been isolated in the laboratory; in the first approximation there is no loss of stability as the size of the molecule increases. There is little change in the bond energies.

The reason for the great number of hydrocarbons lies in this ability of carbon to form stable chains, a process called catenation. Since each carbon atom can be bonded to one, two, three, or four other carbons, the chains may be branched and rebranched, joined in rings, and closed in polyhedra. Without introducing any other structural factor than simple covalent carbon-carbon and carbon-hydrogen bonds, the number of molecular types we can postulate is limitless.

Another feature adding to the complexity of the situation is the ability of carbon to form strong covalent bonds to elements other than hydrogen (see Table 14.8). This is particularly true for oxygen, nitrogen, halogen, and sulfur, but there are compounds known involving bonds of reasonable strength from carbon to almost every other element. If one hydrogen in each possible hydrocarbon is replaced by a chlorine atom, the number of possible compounds is doubled and, since the hydrogens are often not equivalent and the number and nature of substituent groups can be varied extensively, the total number of possible compounds becomes even larger. The number $3 \cdot 10^6$ is very small compared to the number of compounds of carbon possible. There is still some work left for the synthetic chemist.

Organic chemistry thus owes its existence as a separate branch of chemistry to the particular origins, properties, and diversity of the compounds of carbon. It is reasonable to ask if this arbitrary decision makes sense today. Many so-called organic chemists today spend their time studying physical properties, spectroscopic measurements, and thermodynamic values of compounds, in investigating the kinetics and mechanisms of reactions, or in observing the properties of carbon-containing salts, acids, and bases in aqueous or polar solutions. At the same time a vast array of recently synthesized inorganic compounds are molecular species and call for understanding of the preparation and purification techniques and the constant attention to form and structure that has characterized organic chemistry in the past. It would seem more reasonable in the future to classify chemists by the type of work they do—physical measurements, reaction kinetics, analysis, or synthesis—rather than by the chemical elements involved in the compounds they happen to work with.

Exercise 21.1

Rationalize the fact that carbon undergoes catenation whereas nitrogen and oxygen do not. *Answer:* Actually both N and O do catenate (for example, $H_2N—NH_2$, $HO—OH$) but only to a very limited extent and then only in compounds which decompose at room conditions ($H_2O_2 = H_2O + \frac{1}{2}O_2$). Entropy, of course, always opposes catenation. When, as in N_2 and O_2, multiple bonds of great strength can form, the catenated compounds become unstable with respect to the elements and smaller molecules; that is, $\Delta H = -$ for the decomposition of the catenated compounds and $\Delta G = -$. Carbon, as an element, cannot form multiple bonds of order 3 (as does N_2) nor even of order 2 (as does O_2). Thus catenated carbon is more stable than nitrogen or oxygen with respect to the free element, both because of relative bond strengths and because carbon forms a solid with a resulting lower value for its entropy.

ISOMERISM

It is well to consider the subject of isomerism before attempting to classify organic compounds. Two molecules are said to be isomeric if they contain the same atoms in the same numbers (that is, have the same formula) but differ in the arrangement of the atoms. Since the physical properties of a molecule are direct reflections of its structure, two isomeric molecules will differ, if only slightly, in physical properties. Quite clearly the number of possible arrangements of atoms in a molecule increases as the number of atoms increases; among the complex molecules of carbon compounds the question of isomer formation is of paramount importance (see pp. 274, 318, 337).

SKELETON ISOMERS

The principal types of isomerization of importance to the organic chemist can be observed in relatively simple hydrocarbons or their derivatives. Carbon has four orbitals that may be involved in bonding and hydrogen has only one; thus in methane the four hydrogens must be linked to the central carbon and not to each

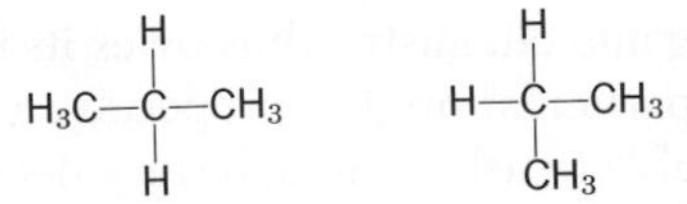

Two possible isomeric forms of a flat plane structure.

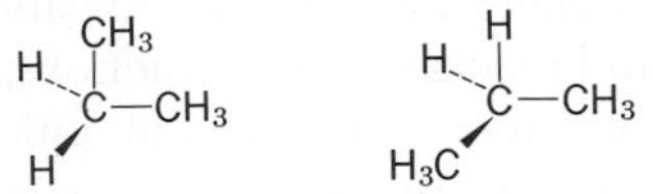

Two possible isomeric forms of a distorted pyramid structure.

Figure 21.3 Some possible structures of propane. Actually only one isomer is known so the above structures are incorrect.

other. In fact each hydrogen is at a vertex of a regular tetrahedron about the carbon atom; this arrangement places the hydrogens as far from each other in space as possible, and minimizes repulsions between the bonding electrons. No other arrangement of atoms in a CH_4 molecule has been detected. In ethane each carbon atom is again surrounded by a tetrahedron of other atoms, three hydrogens and a carbon in each case. If we retain the normal bonding numbers of the atoms, there is only one way to connect the atoms in ethane, and there is also only one way to connect the atoms in propane, C_3H_8. The fact that disubstituted methanes such as propane (which can be thought of as a methane molecule in which two hydrogens have had methyl groups substituted for them) exist in only a single form first suggested the tetrahedral arrangement of bonding about the carbon atom. If the bonds were directed toward the corners of a square, there should be two propanes: the methyls could be on adjacent corners or they could be on opposite corners. Similarly, an unsymmetrical trigonal pyramid could have two forms: one with two methyls on the base and one with a methyl in the base and another at the apex (see Figures 21.3 and 21.4).

The molecule butane, C_4H_{10}, does exist in two forms, however: four carbons could be linked in a chain or three could be linked in a chain with one attached to the middle atom of the chain. In either arrangement it takes just ten hydrogens to fill out the remaining tetrahedral bonds of the carbons that are not involved in carbon-carbon bonds. Both of these molecular species are familiar

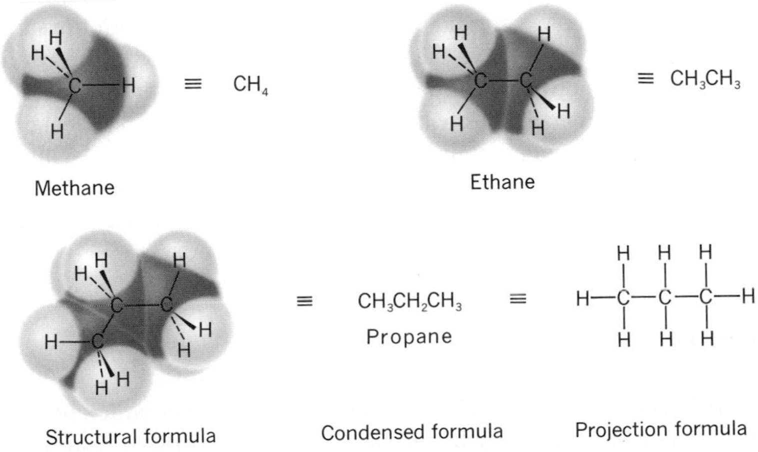

Figure 21.4 Structures and representations of some simple hydrocarbons.

$CH_3—CH_2—CH_2—CH_3$		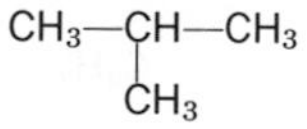
n-Butane m.p. −138.3°C b.p. −0.5°C n_D = 1.3543^{-13} ρ = 0.6012$^{20}_{4}$	C_4H_{10}	*i*-Butane m.p. −145°C b.p. 10.2°C n_D —— ρ 0.557$^{20}_{4}$
$CH_3CH_2CH_2CH_2CH_3$		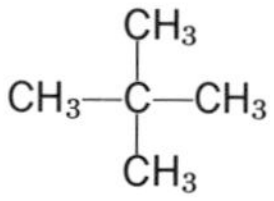
n-Pentane m.p. −130°C b.p. 36°C n_D 1.3579^{20} ρ 0.6262$^{20}_{4}$	C_5H_{12}	*neo*-Pentane m.p. −20°C b.p. 9.5°C n_D 1.3476^{6} ρ 0.6135$^{20}_{4}$
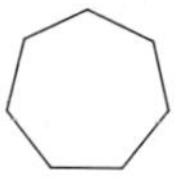		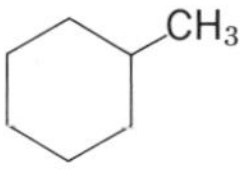
Cycloheptane m.p. −12°C b.p. 118°C n_D 1.4449^{20} ρ 0.8109$^{20}_{4}$	C_7H_{14}	Methylcyclohexane m.p. −126°C b.p. 100°C n_D 1.4253^{15} ρ 0.7695$^{20}_{4}$

Figure 21.5 Some pairs of skeleton isomers and their melting and boiling points, refractive indices (n_D), and densities (ρ).

substances to the chemist; the straight chain compound is commonly called *normal* butane (*n*-butane) and the branched compound *iso*butane (*i*-butane). Isomers that differ only in the arrangement of the carbon skeleton are called "skeleton isomers" (see Figure 21.5).

Exercise 21.2

Write skeletal formulas (showing only the carbons) for the isomers of C_6H_{14}. *Answer:*

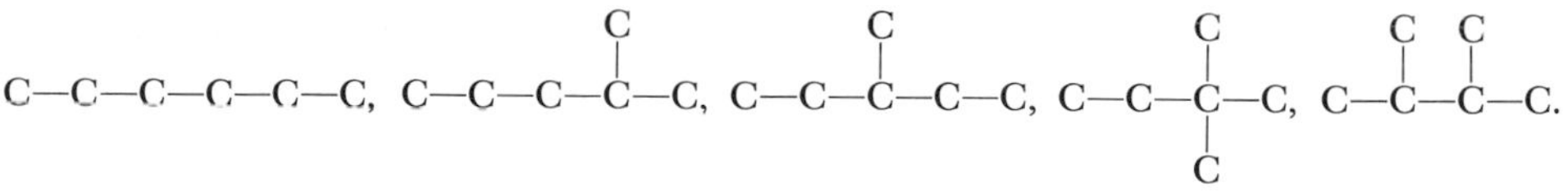

GEOMETRIC ISOMERS

At first glance it might seem that there are a number of possible arrangements of *n*-butane, depending on how the chain is bent. Similarly, rotation of one methyl group in ethane about the axis of the carbon-carbon bond would give two forms: one in which the hydrogens all line up (eclipsed position) and one in which each

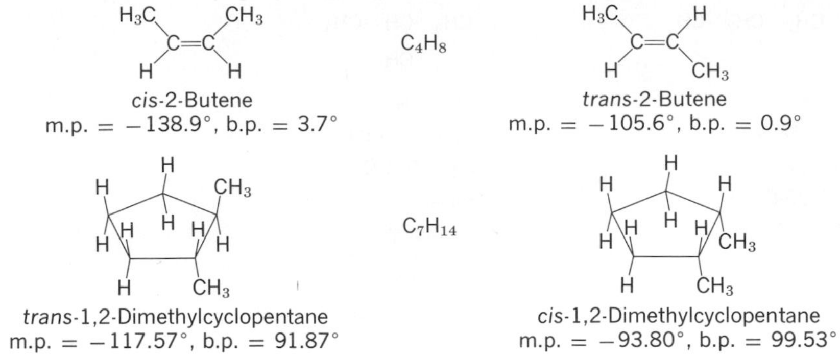

Figure 21.6 Some geometric isomers.

hydrogen on one carbon lies opposite the bisector of the angle between two hydrogens on the other carbon (staggered position; see Figure 15.6). Molecular arrangements that differ only by rotation about a carbon-carbon single bond are a special form of isomers called "conformers." The study of conformers is often of importance in complex molecules, but in simple species the thermal motions of the molecules at room temperature usually cause the molecules to move rapidly from one form to another and so average out any differences in "conformation," or spacial arrangement about a single bond.

In many hydrocarbons a portion of the molecule is not free to rotate even well above room temperature. This is observed, for example, in compounds with carbon-carbon double bonds (Table 15.5) or in compounds that contain small rings of atoms. The molecule 2-butene, C_4H_8, contains a four-carbon chain with a carbon-carbon double bond between the two central carbons. Each of these carbons is attached to a methyl group and a hydrogen by sp^2 hybrid bonds; the four carbons and the two hydrogens attached to the central carbons lie in a plane. Thus two isomers are possible: one in which the two methyls lie on the same side of the double bond (*cis*-2-butene) and one in which the methyls are on opposite sides of the double bond (*trans*-2-butene) (see Figure 21.6).

In cyclopentane, C_5H_{10}, the five carbons are bonded in a ring to form a pentagon. Each carbon has two sp^3 bonds directed toward two other carbons; these bonds are slightly distorted from the normal tetrahedral angle, and as a result the ring is very slightly more reactive (weaker bonds) than pentane itself. The remaining two bonds are directed at nearly the normal tetrahedral angle above and below the ring and a bit out from it. Since in a small ring the carbon cannot rotate —rotation would bring the two groups attached to it into the center of the ring, where there is simply no room—it follows that a bond above the ring stays above, and one below stays below. Thus in 1,2-dimethylcyclopentane, in which the methyls are attached to adjacent carbons, there can be one isomer where both methyls are on the same side of the ring (*cis* form) and one in which the methyls are on opposite sides of the ring (*trans* form). Isomers which result from the placement of groups around a site of restricted rotation in a molecule are called "geometric isomers."

Exercise 21.3

Use LCAO theory to rationalize the lack of rotation about a C=C double bond.

Answer: C=C can also be written as 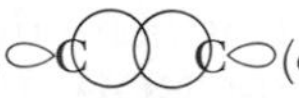 (σ bond) plus  (π bond).

There can be free rotation about the σ bond, which is cylindrically symmetrical along the bond axis. The π bond does not have cylindrical symmetry along the bond axis, and hence has a barrier to rotation accounting for the hindered rotation in a double bond, C=C.

POSITION ISOMERS

If one of the hydrogen atoms in a hydrocarbon molecule is replaced by another kind of atom or group of atoms, the addendum is termed a "functional group." A common functional group is the hydroxyl group —OH; hydrocarbons in which a hydrogen atom is replaced by a hydroxyl group are called alcohols. Examination of the structures of methane and ethane, with NMR for instance will show that all the hydrogens are equivalent in each of these molecules. If we replace one of the hydrogens in a methane molecule with an —OH group to form methyl alcohol, H_3C—OH, the same species will result, no matter which hydrogen is replaced. Similarly, replacement of any one of the hydrogens of an ethane molecule with —OH gives identical molecules of ethyl alcohol, H_3CCH_2—OH, since there is free rotation about the single C—C bond at room temperature, conformers of this compound are not normally observed (see Figure 21.7). In propane, however,

CH_3CH_2OH Ethyl alcohol (beverages, medicine)	CH_3OCH_3 Dimethyl ether (refrigerant)	
$CH_3CH_2CH_2OH$ *n*-Propyl alcohol (solvent and intermediate for chemical synthesis)	CH_3CHCH_3 with OH on the central C *i*-Propyl alcohol (rubbing alcohol)	$CH_3OCH_2CH_3$ Methyl ethyl ether (fumigant)
$CH_3CH_2CH_2CH_2OH$ *n*-Butyl alcohol	CH_3CHCH_2OH with CH_3 on the second C *i*-Butyl alcohol	$CH_3CH_2CHCH_3$ with OH on the third C *s*-Butyl alcohol
CH_3C—OH with two CH_3 on the C *t*-Butyl alcohol	$CH_3CH_2OCH_2CH_3$ Diethyl ether (anesthetic)	

Figure 21.7 Condensed formulas of some isomeric alcohols and ethers, and some uses.

there are two dissimilar types of hydrogen atoms: those attached to a terminal methyl group and those on the central —CH_2—, or methylene, group. If a hydroxyl group is substituted for a methyl hydrogen in a propane molecule, the species that results, $H_3CCH_2CH_2$—OH, is quite different from that formed by replacing a methylene hydrogen, $(H_3C)_2CHOH$; the first compound is often called *normal* propyl alcohol and the second *iso*propyl alcohol. Isomers that differ in the position of a functional group on a hydrocarbon skeleton are called "position isomers."

FUNCTIONAL ISOMERS

There is still another way to link together the atoms that form ethyl or propyl alcohols. Since oxygen forms two strong covalent bonds to either carbon or hydrogen, a molecule can be prepared with the oxygen bound to two carbons, with all of the hydrogens also being bound to carbon. Such a rearrangement with the ingredients of ethyl alcohol, C_2H_6O, would give the molecule H_3C—O—CH_3, and a shuffle of the atoms of propyl alcohol, C_3H_8O, would yield H_3CCH_2—O—CH_3. Compounds of this type are known as ethers; the first is dimethyl ether and the second is methyl ethyl ether. The ether linkage C—O—C constitutes a different functional group than the hydroxyl group, —OH; two molecules that contain the same numbers and kinds of atoms so arranged as to have different functional groups are called "functional isomers." (See Figure 12.9 for another set of examples and their NMR spectra.)

ISOMERIZATION EFFECTS ON MOLECULAR PROPERTIES

Two molecular species that are skeleton, geometric, position, or functional isomers of each other, or which differ by a combination of these isomerization types, will have different physical properties—such as boiling point, melting point, dipole moment, dielectric constant, index of refraction, electromagnetic spectrum, and so on. Conformers that can not readily interconvert by rotation about single bonds will also show such differences. These differences between isomers may be minute or gross depending on the species involved, but they always exist. Small or large (but always finite) differences in chemical reactivity exist between members of such isomeric pairs. There is one more type of isomerization, however, in which the difference between members of a pair of isomers is reflected in a single physical property and very limited differences in chemical reactivity. This type of isomerization is called "optical isomerization," and the physical property involved is the interactions of molecules with plane-polarized light.

Exercise 21.4

Use simple van der Waals theory to rationalize the difference in boiling point of cycloheptane and methylcyclohexane in Figure 21.5. *Answer:* In this, and most other examples, the more symmetrical isomer has the higher melting and higher boiling points. We may assume that this is because the more symmetrical molecules can on the average pack more closely together, thus reducing the average intermolecular distance, increasing the intermolecular forces, increasing ΔH of phase changes, and

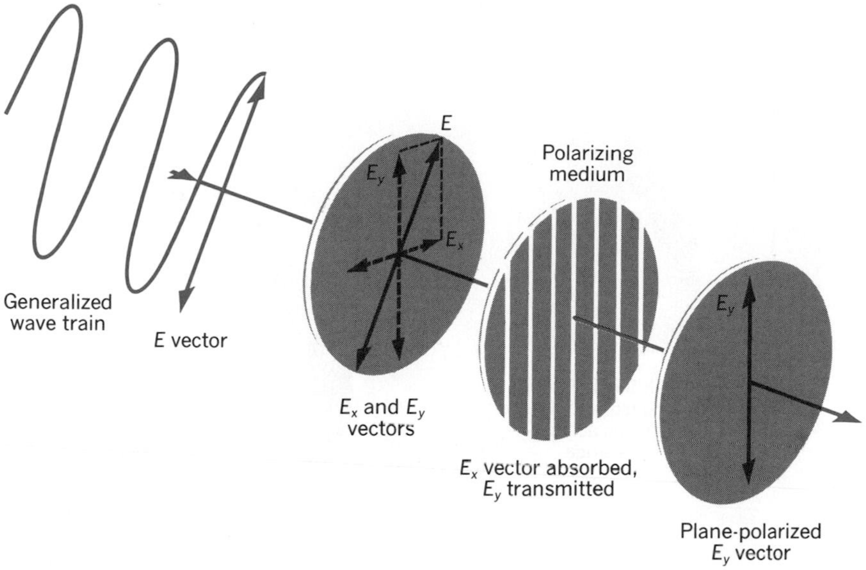

Figure 21.8 Plane-polarized light production. A generalized wave train of electromagnetic radiation (light) of electric vector E may be treated as composed of two vectors, E_x and E_y. Certain prisms (Nicol, made of $CaCO_3$) and crystals (Polaroid, a quinine salt) can absorb one of the vectors transmitting the other as plane-polarized light.

raising the m.p. and b.p. The effect on m.p. is often greater than on b.p., since high order is a crystalline property, not a liquid one. The ΔS of melting and boiling also tend to favor lower m.p.'s and b.p.'s for unsymmetrical molecules. Do you see why? Remember, $T_{pc} = \Delta H_{pc}/\Delta S_{pc}$, since $\Delta S = q_{rev}/T$.

OPTICAL ISOMERS

Electromagnetic radiation (light) can be thought of as photons whose planes of vibration are randomly oriented. Their electric vectors, as indicated in Figure 21.8, can be treated as composed of two mutually perpendicular vectors, E_x and E_y. Various optical instruments will absorb all of one of the vectors, transmitting only photons which have electric vectors in the same plane; such light is called plane-polarized light. The orientation of the plane of polarization, and any rotations of the plane, may be measured very accurately ($\pm 0.001°$) in an instrument called a polarimeter.

When a beam of plane-polarized light is passed through many solid, liquid, or gaseous chemical compounds or through solutions of such compounds, it emerges unchanged from the other side. There are other substances, however, that affect a beam of plane-polarized light passing through them; the light emerges with the plane of vibration rotated from the incident plane. Such substances are called "optically active," and for each such substance an isomeric substance can be found that has identical physical properties with the exception of its interaction with plane-polarized light. Identical amounts of such optical isomers rotate the plane of a beam of plane-polarized light to the same extent, but in opposite directions

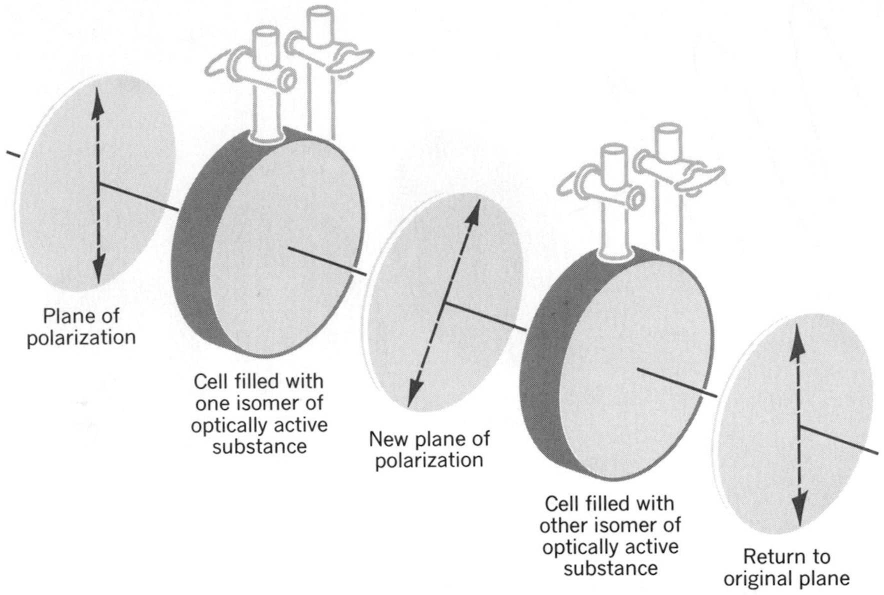

Figure 21.9 Rotation of plane-polarized light equally, but in opposite directions, by solution of *d* and *l* isomers of a single substance at the same concentration.

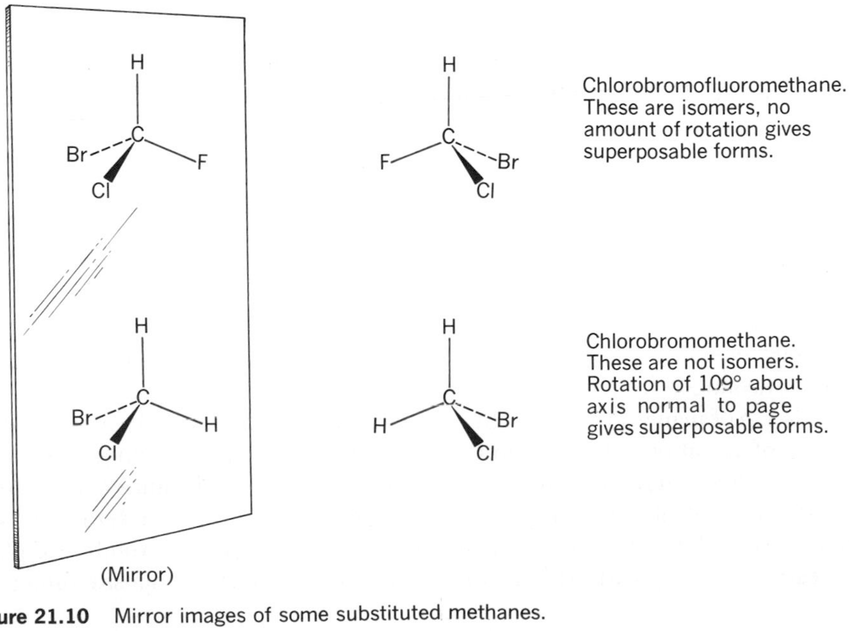

Figure 21.10 Mirror images of some substituted methanes.

(see Figure 21.9). The rotation is usually measured as the specific rotation, $[\alpha]$, where $[\alpha] = \theta V/ml$ = degrees · cm^3/g · cm; m/V = g of isomer per liter of solution, and l = optical length through the solution.

Optical isomers differ only in the arrangement of their atoms in space, one isomer being the mirror image of the other. The most common type of optical isomerization is shown by molecules in which a tetrahedrally bonded carbon atom is attached to four different groups. In chlorobromofluoromethane, CHFClBr, there are two ways (mirror images) in which the four groups can be attached to the central carbon, and no amount of rotating one form of this molecule about in space will cause the groups to line up as in the other molecule. We may also draw a mirror image of chlorobromomethane, CH_2ClBr, but examination of the molecule will show that a simple rotation of one image proves it to be identical to the other (see Figure 21.10).

Imagine a molecule of chlorobromomethane fixed in space, all by itself. This molecule represents an asymmetric cluster of electric and magnetic fields associated with the differing electron clouds of the several types of atoms and the several types of chemical bonds. A ray of plane-polarized light approaching this molecule will interact with this asymmetric field and be rotated out of its plane of vibration as it passes by the molecule; a single isolated molecule will be optically active. However, in any observable sample of a substance there are always a very large number of molecules—a microgram of chlorobromomethane contains about $6 \cdot 10^{15}$ molecules—and in liquids, gases, or solutions these molecules are randomly distributed by thermal motions. For any conceivable orientation of a chlorobromomethane molecule in such a sample there will be, somewhere else in the sample, another molecule so oriented as to be its exact mirror image. The electrical fields of the first will twist a beam of plane-polarized light one way, but the fields of the mirror image will twist it equally the other way, and it will emerge unchanged.

In a sample of chlorobromofluoromethane in which all of the molecules have an identical spatial arrangement around the central carbon, a different situation exists. Each possible orientation of the molecule will have a different effect on a beam of plane-polarized light, but there are no orientations possible that are mirror images of any other orientations. Thus the plane of the light will be changed by an amount that is the sum of the effects of all possible orientations. In a sample of chlorobromofluoromethane composed entirely of molecules whose spatial arrangement was the mirror image of that of the molecules in the first sample and containing the same number of molecules, all these manifold effects would be of the same magnitude but of opposite direction. Thus the plane of the light would be changed by an amount equal to that shown by the first sample, but in the opposite direction.

There are a number of other structural arrangements having low symmetry that can result in optical activity due to low symmetry; a carbon atom with four differing groups is simply the most common one encountered. In every case there will be a pair of optical isomers that are mirror images of each other. Such molecules are said to be members of an "enantiomorphic" pair, or to be "enantiomorphs" of each other. A mixture of equal amounts of each member of an enantiomorphic pair is called a "racemic" mixture; racemic mixtures do not show any optical activity, since the effects of each molecular type are canceled by those of the other.

Table 21.1 summarizes the kinds of isomerization we have discussed.

Table 21.1 Types of isomerization shown by carbon compounds.

Isomer type	Molecules differ by:
Skeleton	Arrangement of carbons in skeleton of molecule
Conformers	Degree of rotation about a single bond
Geometric (*cis, trans*)	Position of substituent groups in space about a point of restricted rotation in molecule
Position	Position of functional groups on carbon skeleton
Functional	Arrangement of atoms into functional groups
Optical (enantiomers)	Atomic arrangements giving nonsuperposable mirror images

Exercise 21.5

Simple hexose sugars can be written:

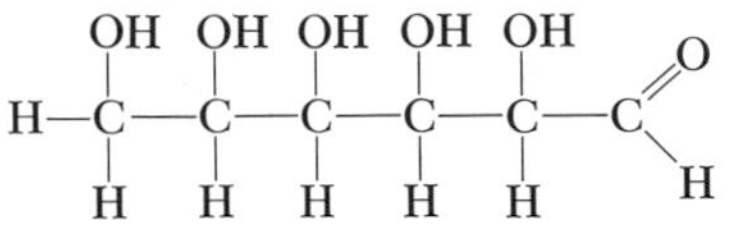

as in glucose, mannose, and others. How many asymmetric carbon atoms are there per molecule? How many optical isomers of formula $C_6H_{12}O_6$? *Answer:* There are four carbons (all but the two terminal ones) which are connected to four different groups. Thus there are four asymmetric carbons. There are two possible arrangements of the groups around each of the four carbons. Thus there are $2^4 = 16$ optical isomers of this type of hexose. All of these 16 isomers have been isolated. (Hexoses actually have a ring structure but still contain 4 asymmetric carbon atoms.)

CLASSIFICATION BY FUNCTIONAL GROUPS

Catenation, isomerization, and the incorporation of one or many other elements leads to an infinite array of carbon-containing substances; one of our greatest problems is to classify them in a usable way. We have already noted that carbon-hydrogen and carbon-carbon single bonds are rather unreactive; in general, the properties of a complex organic molecule are determined more by the functional groups present than by the hydrocarbon portion of the molecule. Thus it is convenient to classify organic molecules by functional group.

There are many known functional groups, and they can appear in many combinations. The examples that follow represent only a few common types that are often met in the laboratory or in everyday life.

HYDROCARBONS

The simplest organic molecules, in terms of structural features, are those that contain only carbon-carbon and carbon-hydrogen single (σ) bonds. These compounds are called paraffin hydrocarbons or "alkanes" (see Figure 21.11). Strictly speaking, the name alkane refers to straight or branched open-chain compounds; when the

Alkane	Common name	IUC name
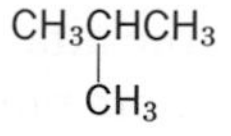 CH$_3$CHCH$_3$ 　　| 　　CH$_3$	isobutane (converted to gasoline)	2-methylpropane
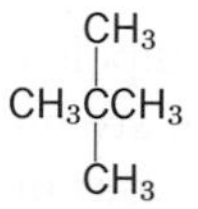 　　CH$_3$ 　　| CH$_3$CCH$_3$ 　　| 　　CH$_3$	neopentane	2,2-dimethylpropane
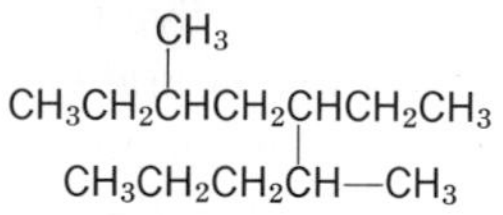 　　　　CH$_3$ 　　　　| CH$_3$CH$_2$CHCH$_2$CHCH$_2$CH$_3$ 　CH$_3$CH$_2$CH$_2$CH—CH$_3$	none	3,6-dimethyl-5-ethylnonane
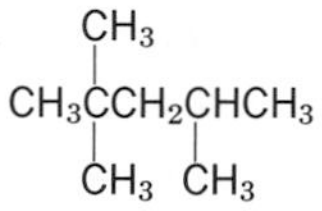 　　CH$_3$ 　　| CH$_3$CCH$_2$CHCH$_3$ 　　|　　| 　　CH$_3$　CH$_3$	isooctane (high octane fuel)	2,2,4-trimethylpentane
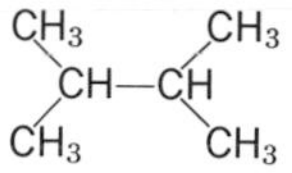 CH$_3$　　　CH$_3$ 　\\　　　/ 　CH—CH 　/　　　\\ CH$_3$　　　CH$_3$	diisopropyl (solvent)	2,3-dimethylbutane

Figure 21.11　Common and *IUC* names of some alkanes, and some uses.

carbons are joined in a single ring, several rings, or closed in polyhedra, the compounds are referred to as cyclic, polycyclic, or birdcage hydrocarbons respectively, but as long as such species have only single bonds and no other functional groups they tend to resemble the alkanes quite closely.

We have already noted several (Figures 21.4 and 21.5) simple alkanes (methane, ethane, propane, and butane) which are straight chain compounds containing from one to four carbon atoms. These compounds are named for the alcohols with the same number of carbon atoms, which were known to chemists before the respective hydrocarbons had been identified. The straight chain alkanes containing from five to ten carbons are called, in order, pentane, hexane, heptane, octane, nonane, and decane. The *ane* ending is common to all alkanes; the prefixes of the compounds of higher molecular weight stem from the Greek (except for the Latin *non-*) and indicate the number of carbons in the compound. Similarly, names are derived for compounds with more carbon atoms; these are less commonly met with, and memorization of them can be delayed until a course in "organic" chemistry.

As soon as we consider branched chain alkanes we run into a problem that appears again and again throughout organic chemistry. Early chemists assigned an individual name to each compound, since they had only a relatively few known substances to deal with, and even today a chemist preparing a new type of compound often gives it a convenient individual name. However, as more and more compounds are identified and prepared, it quickly becomes impossible to keep track of their names. In a series of meetings, beginning in 1930, the International Union of Chemistry (IUC) developed a standard system of nomenclature for alkanes and their derivatives. In this system a branched alkane is considered to be a derivative of the longest unbranched alkane skeleton that can be found within the structure. This chain is numbered in such a way that the sum of the numbers of the carbons bearing substituents will be as low as possible. The name of the branched hydrocarbon is then composed by naming and numbering the attached "alkyl groups" (see below), after a pattern that can be deduced much more rapidly by perusal of Figure 21.11 than it can be explained in words.

The bonds in simple alkanes have almost no ionic nature or dipole character, and the forces that hold the molecules together in a bulk sample are mainly of the van der Waals type (see Figure 15.15). Thus alkanes containing four or less carbons are gases at room temperature, and those containing from five to about twenty carbons are usually liquids. The chief source of alkanes is natural gas and petroleum. Natural petroleum is distilled to give fractions containing numerous compounds; these include gasolines (b.p. 50–200°C), kerosenes (b.p. 175–275°C), fuel oils (b.p. 250–400°C), and lubricating oils (which must be distilled under reduced pressure). After the removal of the liquid components the residues yield paraffin, multitudinous organic chemicals (so-called "coal tar chemicals"), and finally, asphalt. Natural gas consists mainly of methane and ethane, but contains propanes and butanes also. Commercial "LP" is mainly butanes.

Exercise 21.6

The heats of combustion of the gaseous normal (straight chain) hydrocarbons are given by the formula $\Delta H_{C_2H_{2n+2}} = (157.2n + 59.3)$ kcal mole^{-1}, where $n > 3$. Rationalize this formula. *Answer:* Each hydrocarbon differs from that of $n - 1$ by a CH_2 group. Thus, the term 157.2 kcal mole^{-1} in the equation represents the heat of combustion of one CH_2 group to CO_2 and H_2O. The 59.3 kcal mole^{-1} term represents the additional heat of combustion of the terminal CH_3 groups and other "end effects," which become constant above $n = 3$.

SUBSTITUTED HYDROCARBONS

When one of the hydrogens of an alkane has been replaced by a substituent we can adopt either of two points of view (not unlike those of the two sets of in-laws at a wedding). We can consider that the alkane has had some new substituent attached to it or, on the other hand, we can consider that most of the alkane has been attached to the substituent. Many of the problems of alkane nomenclature can be dealt with at once if we digress a moment to consider the attachment of some simple alkanes and a bromine atom (to use an arbitrary example) from our two viewpoints.

There is only one compound with the formula H_3CBr, formed by substituting a bromine atom for one hydrogen in methane. From the first point of view the material is a substituted methane; it would be called bromomethane, and this is the IUC name of this compound. From the second point of view it is a bromine with most of an alkane attached; it would be called methyl bromide, and this is the common name of the compound. A meth*yl* group is an alk*yl* group; the name is formed by dropping the *-ane* from the corresponding alk*ane* and adding *-yl*. Similarly, H_3CCH_2Br would be bromoethane or ethyl bromide. With a three-carbon chain the bromine atom could be (*a*) on an end carbon or (*b*) on the center carbon to give two position isomers; the IUC names are (*a*) 1-bromopropane and (*b*) 2-bromopropane, but the common names are (*a*) *n*-propyl bromide (the *n*- standing for *normal*, indicating attachment to the end carbon of a straight chain) and (*b*) *i*-propyl bromide (the *i*- standing for *iso-*, indicating that there is a $(CH_3)_2CH$— grouping on the end of the molecule opposite the functional group).

With four carbons the situation becomes complicated further by the introduction of skeleton isomers (see Figure 21.12). A straight four-carbon chain with a bromine on the end is called 1-bromobutane or *n*-butyl bromide; however, a straight four-carbon chain with a bromine on one of the two center carbons, although clearly—we may hope it is clear by this time—called 2-bromobutane by the IUC system, demands a new common name. It is called *s*-butyl bromide, in which the *s*- stands for *secondary*. A carbon having no more than one carbon-carbon bond attached to it is called a *primary carbon*, one which has two carbon-carbon bonds attached to it is called a *secondary carbon*, and one with three carbon-carbon bonds attached to it is called a *tertiary carbon*. The name *s*-butyl bromide indicates that the bromine is attached to a secondary carbon. If the four-carbon chain is branched, in such a way that three carbons are attached to a central carbon, then the bromine could be either on one of the three equivalent primary carbons or on the central tertiary carbon. The first compound is called 1-bromo-2-methylpropane by the IUC system, and bears the common name of *i*-butyl bromide (note that it contains a $(CH_3)_2CH$— grouping). The second compound is 2-bromo-2-methylpropane (by the IUC system) and has the common name of *t*-butyl bromide, in which the *t*- stands for *tertiary*. A carbon surrounded by four others is *neo*.

Figure 21.12 shows the alkyl groups derived from compounds having from

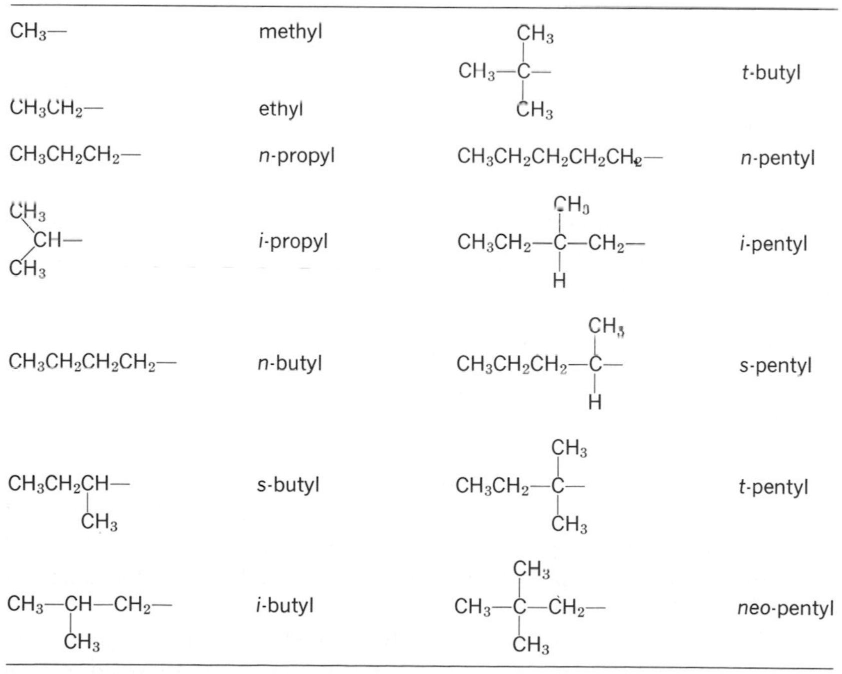

Figure 21.12 Common alkyl groups—CH_3, C_2H_5, C_3H_7, C_4H_9, C_5H_{11}.

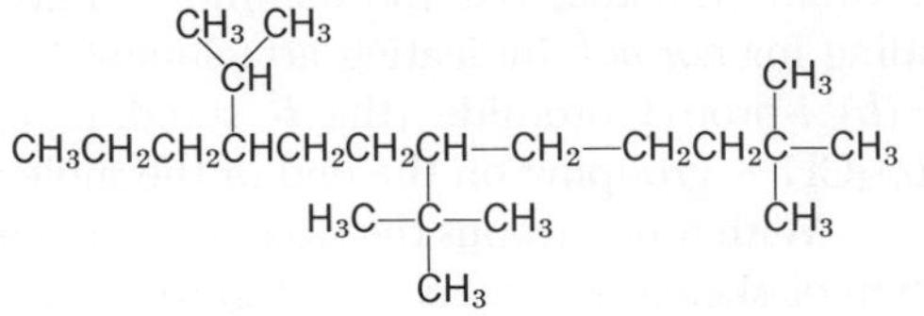

Figure 21.13 A complex hydrocarbon.

2,2-dimethyl-6-*t*-butyl-9-*i*-propyldodecane
or
2,2-dimethyl-6-(1,1-dimethylethyl)-9-(1-methylethyl)dodecane

one to five carbons. The common names through butyl have been accepted by the IUC and may be used in naming more complicated organic compounds. Groups with more than four carbons are named as derivatives of the corresponding alkane with the longest chain of carbons, with the group names enclosed in parentheses. An example of such a name is shown in Figure 21.13.

Exercise 21.7

Write structural formulas for: (*a*) 2-fluoro-3-methyl butane, (*b*) *i*-butyl alcohol, (*c*) 2-butanol, (*d*) neopentyl bromide. *Answer:* (most H's not shown)

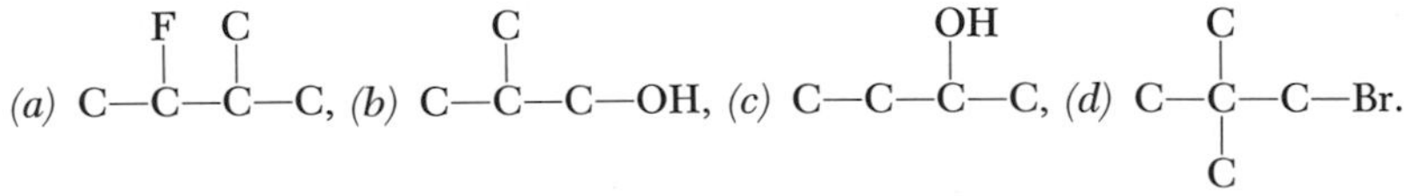

HYDROCARBONS CONTAINING MULTIPLE BONDS

The alkanes, as we have noted before, are quite unreactive chemically. There are other hydrocarbons, however, which are much more reactive. These contain carbon-carbon multiple bonds (π bonds) and include the "alkenes" or "olefins," and the "alkynes" or "acetylenes."

The multiple bonding in these compounds has been discussed in Chapter 15. In the alkenes two carbons are joined by a double bond composed of a σ bond formed by overlap of an sp^2 orbital from each carbon and a π bond formed by overlap of a p_z orbital from each carbon. The remaining four bonds of this two-carbon unit lie in a plane, at angles of about 120° from the line connecting the two double-bonded carbons. Rotation about the double bond is difficult, and as we have seen, gives rise to geometric isomers.

Simple alkenes are named much as are the alkanes, with the ending *-ene* substituted for the *-ane* in the alkane name. The carbon chain is so numbered as to give the lowest number possible to the carbon bearing the double bond. To indicate the arrangement of the groups in space about the double bond, the prefixes *cis-* (same side) and *trans-* (opposite) are used. Figure 21.14 lists some alkenes with examples of how they are named.

Like the alkanes, alkenes are mainly derived from natural gas and petroleum; however, there are many ways in which they can be synthesized from other types of organic molecules. The carbon-carbon double bond is much more reactive

Alkene	Common name	IUC name
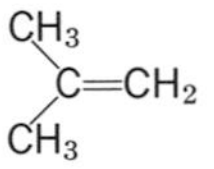	isobutylene (synthetic butyl) rubber)	2-methylpropene
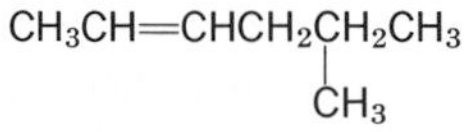	none	5-methyl-2-hexene
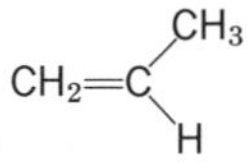	allene, or propylene (plastic lab ware, Nalgene)	propene
$H_2C{=}CH_2$	ethylene (polymers)	ethene
	cyclohexene (organic syntheses)	cyclohexene
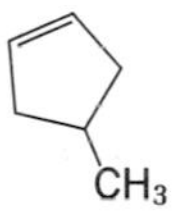	none	4-methylcyclopentene
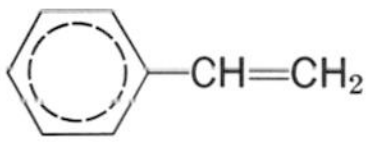	styrene (polystyrene)	phenylethene

Figure 21.14 Some common alkenes, and some uses.

than a carbon-carbon single bond, and alkenes react readily with halogens, peroxides, acids, and oxidizing agents. Alkenes play a very important role in industrial organic chemistry, as they can be converted into a wide variety of useful products.

In the alkynes, the carbon-carbon triple bond is formed by overlap of an *sp* orbital from each carbon to form a σ bond, and overlap of two perpendicular sets of *p* orbitals to form two π bonds. The remaining *sp* bond on either carbon is directed away from the triple bond and lies in the same line as the σ bond of the triple bond; thus four atoms of an alkyne always lie in a straight line. Some alkynes are found in nature, but most of them are synthesized in the laboratory—often from alkenes. The triple bond of the alkynes usually reacts more rapidly and with more negative ΔG^0 than the double bond of the alkenes. A special feature of alkynes is that a hydrogen attached to one of the carbons involved in the triple bond is quite acidic (relative to other hydrocarbons), and metal salts of acetylenic anions can be prepared.

Acetylene itself, $HC{\equiv}CH$, can be readily converted into ethene, ethyl alcohol, acetic acid, benzene, or a host of other compounds. During the latter days of World War II the German nation, cut off from substantial petroleum reserves, produced many needed organic chemicals through the intermediate of acetylene. Coke, from coal, was heated with calcium oxide, from limestone, to give calcium

Figure 21.15 Some alkynes and derivatives.

H—C≡C—H
Acetylene
or ethyne
(high energy fuel)

$CH_3C{\equiv}CCH_3$
Dimethylacetylene
or 2-butyne

$:C{\equiv}C:^{-2}$
Carbide or
acetylide ion
(fuel for acetylene
lamps)

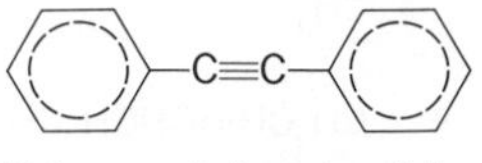

Tolan or diphenylacetylene
or diphenylethyne

carbide (Figure 21.15), and the calcium carbide then reacted with water to yield acetylene and calcium hydroxide. From the acetylene the Germans prepared fuels, oils, drugs, plastics, and many other substances needed in both the war effort and in daily life.

Another important group of hydrocarbons is the "aromatic" or "arene" hydrocarbons. In the structure of benzene (see Figure 15.12) the electrons in the π system are delocalized over the whole molecule and thus cannot be thought of as forming a functional group in the same way that the π bonds in an alkene or alkyne do; nonetheless, it is these delocalized electrons that lead to both the remarkable stabilities and the specific chemical reactivities of aromatic hydrocarbons (see Figure 21.16).

Many substituted derivatives of benzene are known. A number of substituted benzenes have been given a specific name of their own; several of the more

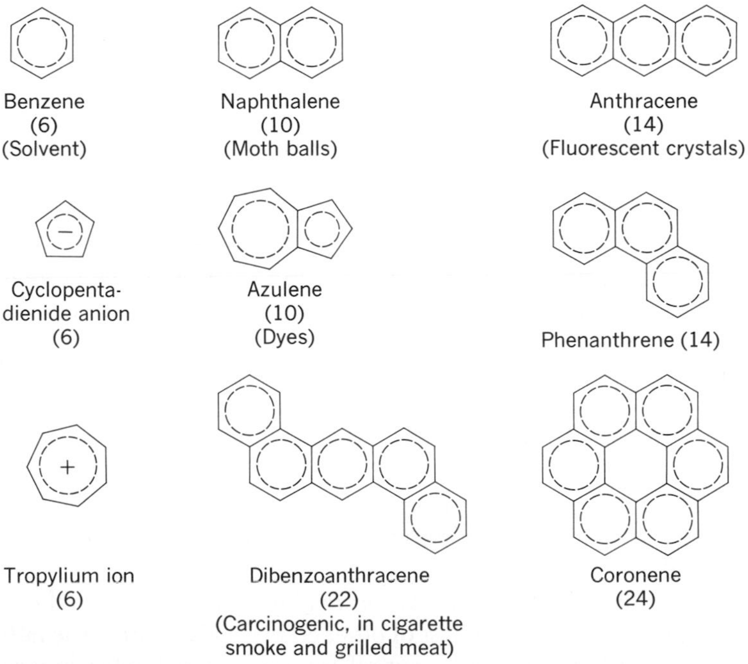

Figure 21.16 Some representative arenes. The number of delocalized electrons (in parentheses) equals $4n + 2$ (where n gives the number of rings of carbon atoms) except for coronene.

Preferred name listed first

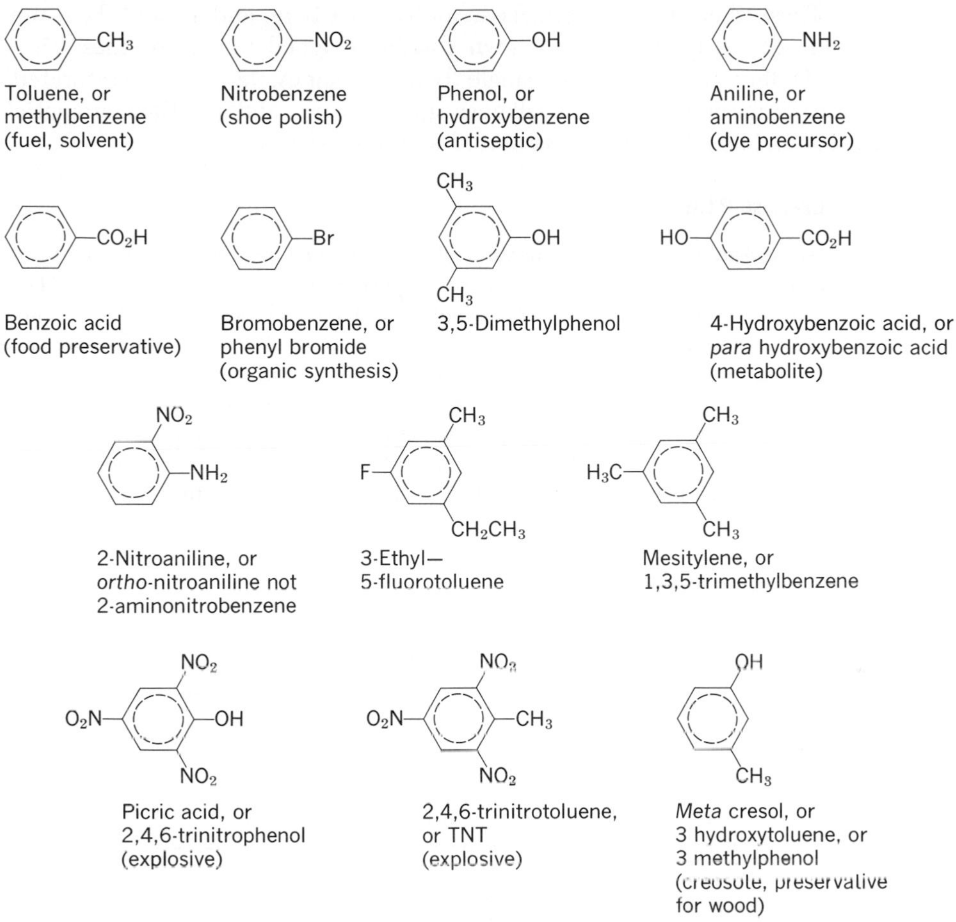

Figure 21.17 Structures and alternative names of benzene derivatives, and some uses.

familiar are shown in Figure 21.17. When more than one substituent is on the ring the compound may be named as a derivative of benzene; however, if one of the substituents (if present by itself) would give a specific name to the molecule, then the polysubstituted molecule will be named as a derivative of that specific name. Examination of Figure 21.17 should clarify this issue a bit, and indicate the type of numbering systems used.

Another type of benzene nomenclature is often met with—and often used incorrectly. When there are two substituents on a benzene ring there are three possible position isomers, depending on whether the groups are adjacent (*ortho*-isomer), separated by one carbon (*meta*-isomer), or by two carbons (*para*-isomer). Several examples of the use of these prefixes are included in Figure 21.17. Two things about this method of nomenclature should be stressed: (1) the system should be used when there are two, and only two, substituents on the ring, and (2) the ortho-meta-para system must not be mixed with systems in which numbers are used.

These, then, are the main classes of hydrocarbons, and most of the countless multitude of hydrocarbons known can be assigned to one of these three classes: (1) the "saturated" (all single bonds) alkanes, (2) the "unsaturated" (carbon-carbon multiple bonds) alkenes and alkynes, and (3) the "aromatic" (resonance-stabilized, cyclic, unsaturated systems) arenes.

Exercise 21.8

Rationalize the fact that alkenes and alkynes are much more reactive (both rate and equilibrium) than aromatics. *Answer:* Consider hydrogenation: $C_nH_m + H_2 = C_nH_{m+2}$. Molecular entropy changes are unfavorable both as to rate and equilibrium, but for most alkenes and alkynes the hydrogenation is of low activation energy and exothermic, and so equilibrium and rate are both favorable. Aromatics, because of electron delocalization (resonance), are highly symmetric in electric field. Thus rates are low, since there are no polar points of attack and the equilibrium is less favorable because the delocalized electrons are more stable (higher electron entropy) than the resulting "localized" molecules which would be formed by their hydrogenation.

OXYGEN COMPOUNDS

Among organic compounds that contain elements other than carbon and hydrogen, oxygen-containing compounds are the most familiar. We have already met two of the simplest types of oxygenated organic compounds, the alcohols, R—OH, and the ethers, R—O—R. (We introduce, somewhat abruptly, a new symbol, R—. This simply means an "alkyl" group; it could be methyl, ethyl, butyl, or any other group derived by removing a single hydrogen from an alkane.) An ether can be thought of as a derivative of water in which both hydrogens are replaced by alkyl groups. Like water, an ether molecule is not linear and possesses a dipole moment; thus ethers are good polar solvents. Unlike water, however, the ether molecule has no hydrogens attached to oxygen, and thus has no intermolecular hydrogen bonding (see p. 354); as a result, ethers have low viscosities and much lower boiling points than water. Ethers are inert toward many other substances though highly reactive with oxygen. They find their greatest use as solvents. Ethyl ether is used for anesthesia in surgery.

Alcohols may also be considered as derivatives of water in which one hydrogen is replaced by a hydrocarbon group. Alcohols are excellent polar solvents, and have much higher boiling points and greater viscosities than ethers since hydrogen bonding is still possible. *n*-Butyl alcohol, $CH_3CH_2CH_2CH_2OH$, is isomeric with ethyl ether (b.p. 37°C), but boils at 117°C.

The common names of the alcohols are formed by using the alkyl group which would be left if the —OH were removed, and then adding the word alcohol, as in *n*-butyl alcohol above. Obviously this system breaks down as the groups become complicated. In the IUC system the name of an alcohol is derived from that of the parent hydrocarbon by changing the *-ane* in the name of the alk*ane* to *-ol*, and indicating the position of the hydroxy group with a number. A moment's doodling will convince the student that *n*-butyl alcohol is 1-butanol, *s*-butyl alcohol

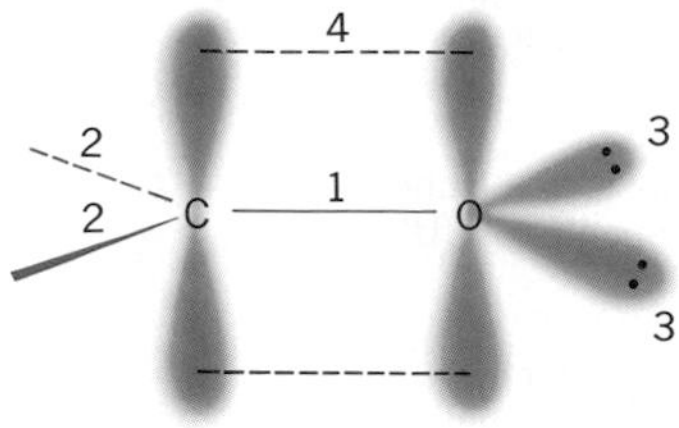

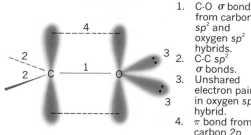

1. C-O σ bond from carbon sp^2 and oxygen sp^2 hybrids.
2. C-C sp^2 σ bonds.
3. Unshared electron pairs in oxygen sp^2 hybrid.
4. π bond from carbon $2p$ and oxygen $2p$.

Figure 21.18 Orbitals in the carbonyl group, each holding two electrons.

is 2-butanol, *i*-butyl alcohol is 2-methyl-1-propanol, and *t*-butyl alcohol is 2-methyl-2-propanol; and so it goes.

Unlike ethers, alcohols are quite reactive in a number of chemical processes; they are, for example, susceptible to chemical oxidation. Oxidation and reduction in organic systems are often not easily identified as such, but a general rule that is applicable in a wide variety of situations is that *oxidation* is accompanied by a gain in oxygen and/or a loss of hydrogen from a molecule, and *reduction* is accompanied by a loss of oxygen and/or a gain of hydrogen within a molecule. Prove to yourself that this is consistent with the oxidation number and half-reaction concepts of oxidation and reduction.

Certain chemical oxidants—such as (1) oxygen in the presence of hot copper or (2) a carefully measured equivalent amount of chromium trioxide, CrO_3 —will remove a molecule of hydrogen from an alcohol; one hydrogen is lost from the oxygen and one from the carbon to which the oxygen is attached. The oxygen and the carbon are now joined by a double bond (composed of a σ and a π bond) that is quite similar to a carbon-carbon double bond in its orbital makeup (Figure 21.18). This double-bonded oxygen functional group is known as a "carbonyl" group; if a primary alcohol (—OH on a primary carbon) is oxidized, the resulting carbonyl compound is known as an aldehyde, and if a secondary alcohol (—OH on a secondary carbon) is oxidized, the resulting carbonyl compound is known as a ketone. Examples of aldehydes and ketones are shown in Figure 21.19. The carbonyl group has a considerable dipole moment, with the negative end on the oxygen. This polar character makes carbonyl compounds liquids with relatively high boiling points (compared with hydrocarbons with the same molecular area). Ketones are good solvents, but aldehydes are too reactive to be useful in this way. The chemistry of aldehydes and ketones is too extensive and varied to be treated in this short survey, but it forms a significant portion of any course in organic chemistry.

Aldehydes are very sensitive to further oxidation, which is why the amount of oxidizing agent must be carefully controlled in the oxidation of a primary alcohol. When an aldehyde is treated with a mild oxidizing agent—or a primary alcohol is treated with an excess of strong oxidizing agent—a second atom of oxygen is introduced to form a new functional group, the "carboxyl" group (see Figure 21.20), in which both a carbonyl and a hydroxyl group are attached to the same carbon:

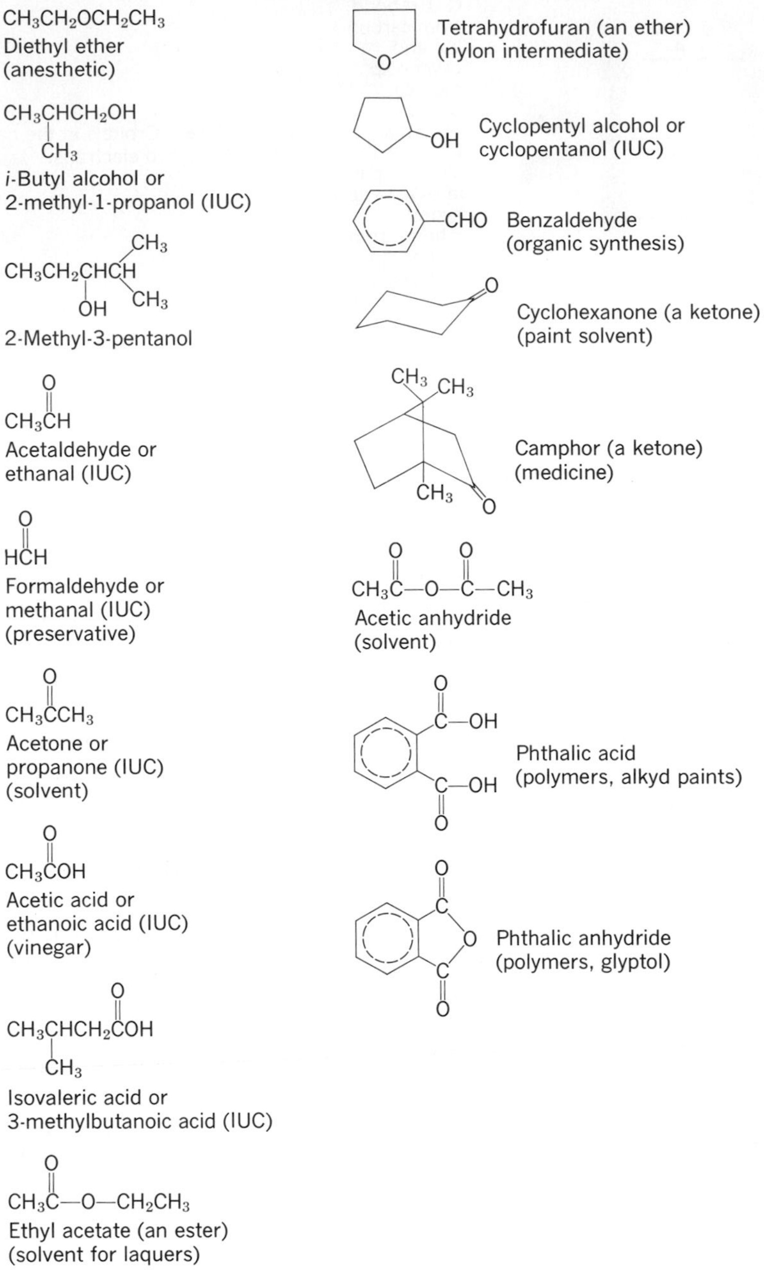

Figure 21.19 Some oxygen-containing organic compounds.

$$R\text{—}CH_2OH + \tfrac{1}{2}O_2 = RCHO + H_2O \qquad \text{(alcohol to aldehyde)}$$
$$RCHO + \tfrac{1}{2}O_2 = RCO_2H \qquad \text{(aldehyde to acid)}$$

Ketones cannot oxidize to carboxyl groups without rupturing a carbon-carbon bond, and are thus quite insensitive to oxidation. It is not necessary to control the amount of oxidizing agent carefully in preparing a ketone from a secondary alcohol.

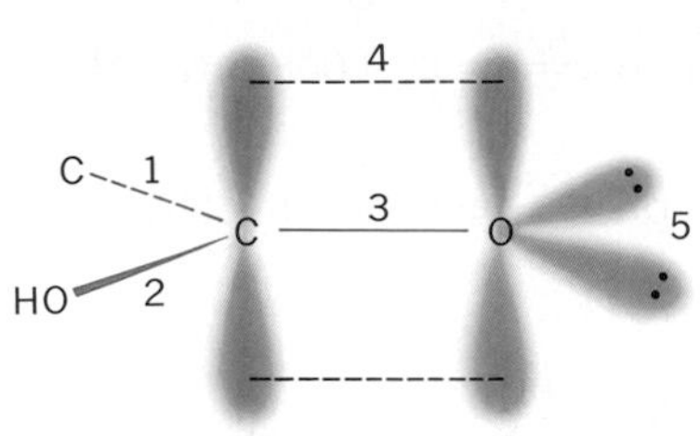

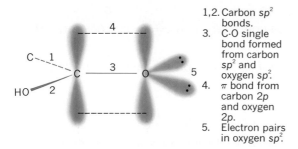

1,2. Carbon sp^2 bonds.
3. C-O single bond formed from carbon sp^2 and oxygen sp^2.
4. π bond from carbon $2p$ and oxygen $2p$.
5. Electron pairs in oxygen sp^2.

Figure 21.20 The carboxyl group orbitals, each holding two electrons.

The hydroxyl hydrogen of a carboxyl group is quite acidic (K_a about $1 \cdot 10^{-5}$), much more so than the hydroxyl hydrogen of an alcohol. When a base (B^-) removes a proton from an alcohol, —OH, group there is a positive enthalpy term from the

$$ROH + B^- = RO^- + HB$$

breaking of the O—H bond and a negative enthalpy term from the forming of the H—B bond. If the hydroxyl hydrogen is removed from a carboxyl group by the *same* base, as in

$$RCO_2H + B^- = \left(R{-}C\begin{smallmatrix}O\\ \\O\end{smallmatrix}\right)^- + HB$$

the above two enthalpy terms will be about the same, but in addition there will be another negative enthalpy term equal to the resonance energy of the carboxylate anion (see Figure 15.9); thus the neutralization process will have a more negative heat of reaction for the carboxyl compound. If experimental conditions are designed to keep the entropy change in the two reactions about the same (same solvent, same general size and shape of molecules, same concentrations) we see that the change in free energy is proportional to the change in enthalpy, and, since the ionization of the carboxyl group will result in the more negative change in free energy, the carboxyl group is the stronger acid.

Compounds containing carboxyl groups are called "carboxylic acids." The IUC name of a carboxylic acid is formed by dropping the *-e* from the name of the parent alkane and adding *-oic acid.* Thus a one-carbon acid is methanoic acid, a two-carbon acid ethanoic acid, and so on. Many acids are known by their common names, which have been in use for a very long time, and which usually reflect the natural source of the acid. Thus methanoic acid is formic acid (L. *formica,* ant), ethanoic acid is acetic acid (L. *acetum,* vinegar), propanoic acid is propionic acid (Gr. *proto,* first; *pion,* fat), butanoic acid is butyric acid (L. *butyrum,* butter), pentanoic acid is valeric acid (from its occurrence in the root of the valerian plant), and hexanoic acid is caproic acid (L. *caper,* goat).

Carboxylic acids form many important derivatives; among these are the "esters," formed by removal of the elements of water from a molecule of carboxylic acid and a molecule of alcohol (see Figure 21.21), and the "anhydrides," formed by removal of the elements of water from two molecules of carboxylic acid. Both find wide use as solvents and reaction intermediates.

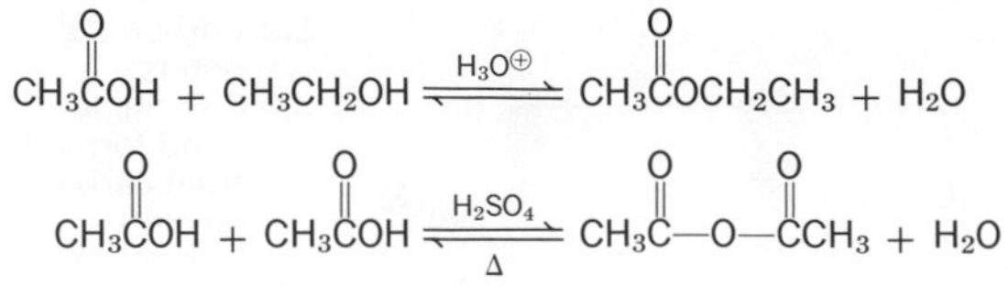

$$CH_3\overset{\overset{O}{\|}}{C}OH + CH_3CH_2OH \underset{}{\overset{H_3O^{\oplus}}{\rightleftharpoons}} CH_3\overset{\overset{O}{\|}}{C}OCH_2CH_3 + H_2O$$

Figure 21.21 Formation of an ester and an anhydride.

$$CH_3\overset{\overset{O}{\|}}{C}OH + CH_3\overset{\overset{O}{\|}}{C}OH \underset{\Delta}{\overset{H_2SO_4}{\rightleftharpoons}} CH_3\overset{\overset{O}{\|}}{C}-O-\overset{\overset{O}{\|}}{C}CH_3 + H_2O$$

Exercise 21.9

Balance equations for the oxidation of ethane to acetaldehyde by (*a*) inspection, (*b*) oxidation number change, (*c*) half-reactions. Which method is probably most used? *Answer:* Try each. Organic chemists usually balance by inspection. Do you see why?

HALOGEN COMPOUNDS

Halogen atoms can be made to replace one, many, or all of the hydrogens in an alkane, alkene, or arene by choosing the proper path for the synthesis among the many paths developed by organic chemists. The number of such compounds is so great that only a few generalizations can be made here.

Compounds containing "fluorine atoms" are often not stable unless all the hydrogens in the molecule have been replaced by halogens, but perfluorinated substances are highly resistant to chemical attack. "Teflon," a polymer which is particularly resistant, is formed of long carbon chains which are completely fluorinated. The "freons," gases of low boiling point used in refrigeration equipment, are fully halogenated methanes in which one or several of the halogens are fluorines.

Many compounds containing chlorine are familiar substances. Chloromethane, H_3CCl, is a gas; however, dichloromethane (methylene chloride), H_2CCl_2, trichloromethane (chloroform), $HCCl_3$, and tetrachloromethane (carbon tetrachloride), CCl_4, are liquids at room temperature and are common solvents. Millions of pounds per year of trichloroethylene (see Figure 21.22) are used in coin-operated and other dry cleaning shops. Many other chlorocarbons are used as solvents and synthetic intermediates.

Chlorocarbons are generally toxic, and the toxicity generally increases as the number of chlorines per molecule goes up. The two chemicals responsible for the most poisonings among chemists and workers in the chemical industry are benzene and carbon tetrachloride. Neither has particularly dramatic immediate effects—and so are often treated with contempt—but these and similar compounds accumulate in the body and even low and intermittent exposure can cause serious poisoning after a few years. These substances should always be handled in a fume hood if possible. Many chlorinated hydrocarbons are particularly toxic to insects, and insecticides such as DDT, dieldren, aldren, and hexachlor are of this type (see Figure 21.22). Such compounds often do not break down under the action of the atmosphere and thus may accumulate in the soil, in water, and in animal organisms. There is considerable concern with the problem of widespread dissemination of insecticides throughout our environment and their effects on other forms of life, including humans.

The reactivities of alkyl halides are a good example of the "effect of structure on reactivity." Thus 1-chlorobutane is much less reactive than the isomeric 2-chloro-2-methylpropane, which reacts with acids, bases, metal ions, and even water. The nature of such structural effects will be discussed in Chapter 24.

Alkyl bromides are much like alkyl chlorides. They are generally more reactive (weaker C—X bond) and so are used more widely in the laboratory than the alkyl chlorides; however, the bromine-containing compounds are more expensive, and chlorine-containing substances find a wider use in industrial chemistry. Alkyl iodides are sensitive to light and oxygen; they are useful chemicals in the synthesis of organic compounds, but need to be handled with special techniques to prevent decomposition.

Exercise 21.10

Some chlorinated insecticides are almost identical with naturally occurring molecules except that OH is replaced with Cl. Can you suggest why these might be toxic? *Answer:* Cl and OH have about the same size and charge density, but differ greatly in reactivity. Thus the chlorinated molecule might "fit" geometrically on an enzyme and block its action on the normal hydroxyl compounds.

CH_3Cl
Methyl chloride, or chloromethane (IUC) (refrigerant)

CH_2Cl_2
Methylene chloride, or dichloromethane (IUC) (solvent, local anesthetic by cooling)

$HCCl_3$
Chloroform or trichloromethane (IUC) (anesthetic)

CCl_4
Carbon tetrachloride, or tetrachloromethane (IUC) (solvent, cleaning fluid)

$BrCH_2CH_2CH_2Br$
1,3-Dibromopropane (IUC) (vermicide)

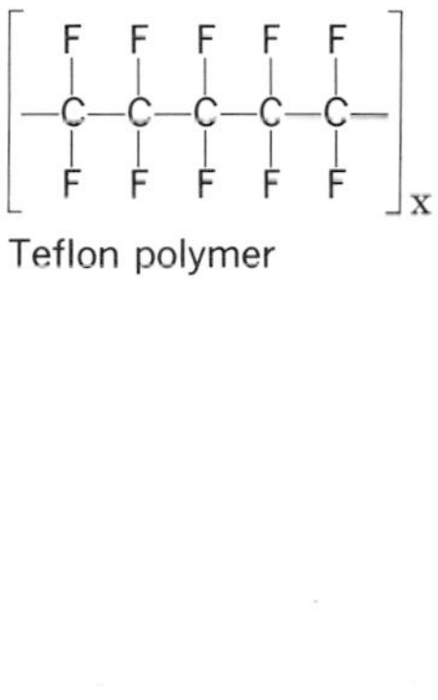

Teflon polymer

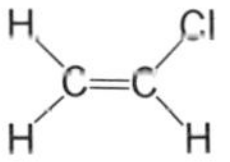

Vinyl chloride, or chloroethane (IUC) (polymers)

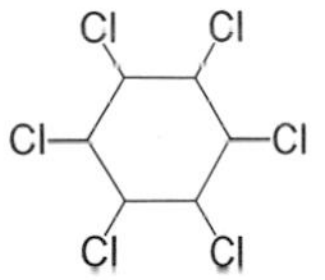

Hexachlor, $C_6H_6Cl_6$ (insecticide)

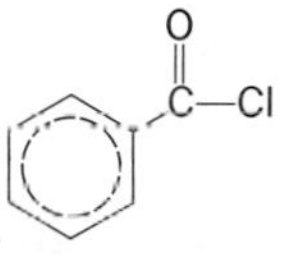

Benzoyl chloride (tear gas)

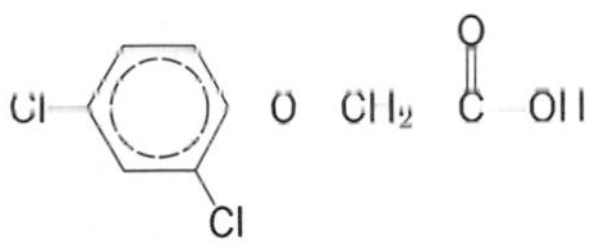

2,4-Dichlorophenoxyacetic acid, or (2,4-D) (weed killer)

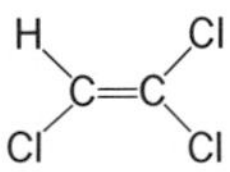

Trichloroethylene (dry cleaning solvent)

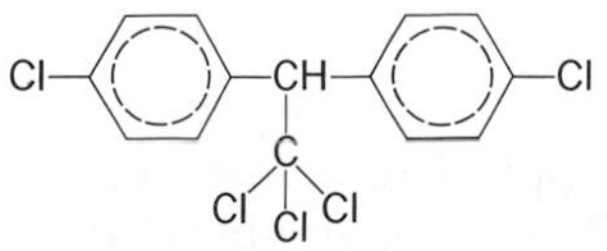

2,2-*Bis*-4-chlorophenyl-1,1,1-trichloroethane (DDT) (insecticide)

Figure 21.22 Some common halocarbons.

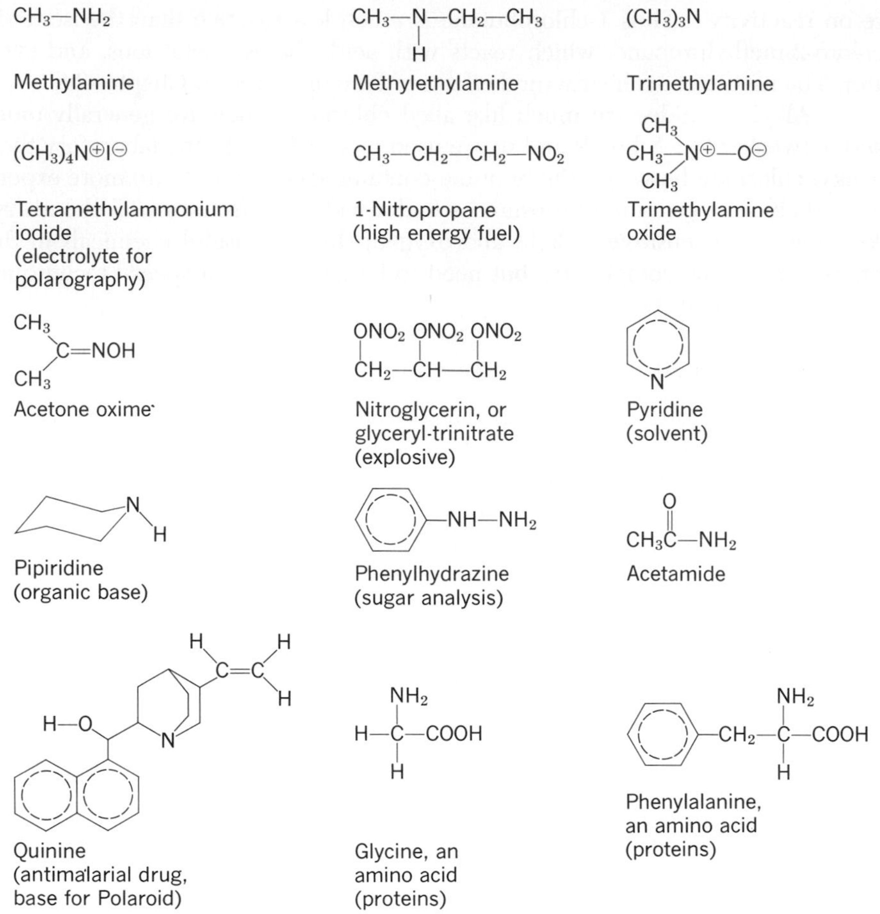

Figure 21.23 Some organic nitrogen compounds.

NITROGEN COMPOUNDS

There are a multitude of organic compounds containing nitrogen (a few are given in Figure 21.23) of which we will discuss only two classes—the amines and the amides.

The "amines" are alkyl or aryl derivatives of ammonia. (An "aryl" group, symbolized Ar— is a group derived from an arene by removal of one hydrogen.) If one hydrogen of ammonia is replaced by a hydrocarbon group, the compound is called a "primary amine," $R{-}\ddot{N}H_2$; if two hydrogens are replaced, the compound is called a "secondary amine," $R_2\ddot{N}H$; and if three hydrogens are replaced, the compound is called a "tertiary amine," $R_3\ddot{N}$. The terms primary, secondary, and tertiary when applied to amines have different meanings than when applied to alkyl groups. Thus *secondary*-butyl alcohol is a secondary alcohol, but *secondary*-butylamine is a primary amine. Draw their structures to clarify this point.

The amines have a fair dipole moment, some hydrogen bonding, and, with

$$CH_3\overset{O}{\overset{\|}{C}}—OH + NH_3 \underset{\Delta}{\rightleftharpoons} CH_3\overset{O}{\overset{\|}{C}}—NH_2 + H_2O$$

Figure 21.24 Amide formation.

the exception of a few very simple ones, comparatively high boiling points. They have foul, fishy odors (which is reasonable, since they account for the odor of fish) and are often discolored by oxidation products. The amines, like ammonia, are bases; the lone pair of electrons on the nitrogen atom will react with Brönsted or Lewis acids to form salts or complexes. Tertiary amines can react with alkyl halides to yield cations in which four alkyl groups are attached to the nitrogen; these ions are known as "quaternary ammonium ions." Salts of these ions are completely ionized, and a quaternary ammonium hydroxide is as strong a base as sodium hydroxide.

If the elements of water are removed from a molecule of ammonia and a carboxylic acid, the resultant compound is known as an amide (Figure 21.24). If an amine is used instead of ammonia, the product will be an alkyl-substituted amide. The amide linkage is of great importance in both industrial and biological chemistry; as we will see in a later chapter on macromolecules, both synthetic polymers (such as nylon) and natural polymers (such as the proteins) are held together with amide linkages.

Exercise 21.11

There are about 20 amino acids which make up all known proteins by amide linkages. How many possible tripeptides (molecules made up of three amino acid molecules) are there? Comment on the implications concerning the synthesis of proteins that may contain 1000 amide linkages. *Answer:* 20^3. Each additional linkage increases by 20 the possible polypeptides. 1000 linkages mean 20^{1000} possible proteins. But only certain proteins are useful to living organisms. Some highly reliable system must exist for assuring that the linkages form in exactly the "right" order.

OTHER COMPOUNDS

There are many more functional groups containing oxygen, halogens, or nitrogen, or combinations of them, and in addition there are functional groups based on sulfur, phosphorus, boron, and, indeed, almost every other element. The few listed above are only those most commonly met; however, some consideration of the way in which these compounds are arranged and named will indicate the approach that is used to bring order out of the chaotic number of organic compounds.

BONDING IN CARBON COMPOUNDS

Although a few exceptions are known, such as $[Al(CH_3)_3]_2$, almost all carbon atoms found in nature are characterized by atoms made up of a nucleus of charge +6, a pair of nonbonding 1*s* electrons, and a set of eight valence electrons with principal quantum number 2. When the CN about the carbon atom is four, these eight valence electrons are arranged in four pairs as four single (σ) bonds. These single

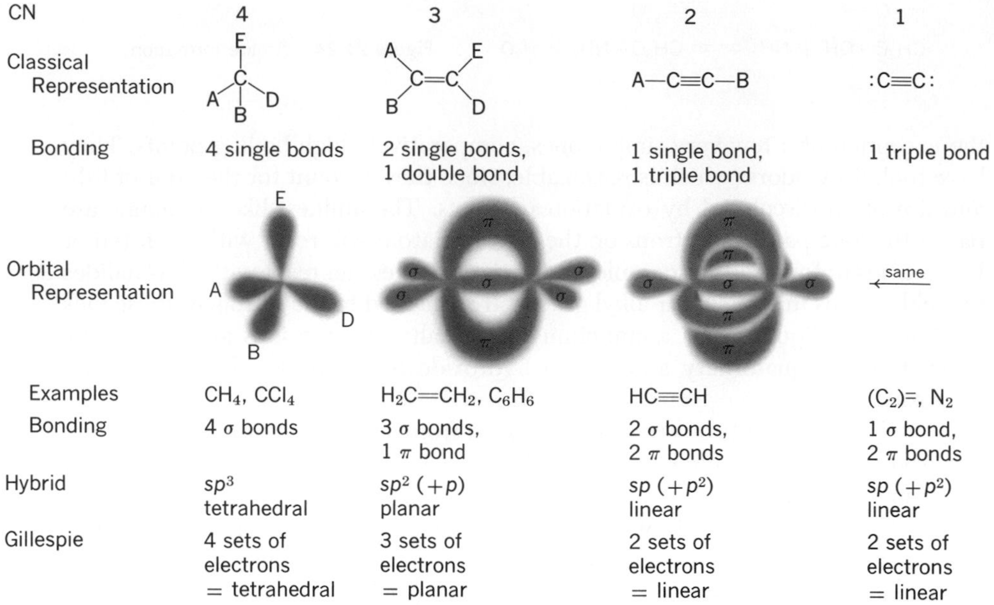
CN | 4 | 3 | 2 | 1
Classical Representation
A—C≡C—B
:C≡C:
Bonding | 4 single bonds | 2 single bonds, 1 double bond | 1 single bond, 1 triple bond | 1 triple bond
Orbital Representation
same
Examples | CH4, CCl4 | H2C=CH2, C6H6 | HC≡CH | (C2)=, N2
Bonding | 4 σ bonds | 3 σ bonds, 1 π bond | 2 σ bonds, 2 π bonds | 1 σ bond, 2 π bonds
Hybrid | sp3 tetrahedral | sp2 (+p) planar | sp (+p2) linear | sp (+p2) linear
Gillespie | 4 sets of electrons = tetrahedral | 3 sets of electrons = planar | 2 sets of electrons = linear | 2 sets of electrons = linear

Figure 21.25 Four possible descriptions of bonding configurations as a function of coordination number.

bonds are very close to tetrahedral in orientation as predicted either by Gillespie theory, or by sp^3 hybridization, including σ-π bond theory.

When the coordination number about the carbon is 3, the bond angles are all close to 120°, which is consistent both with Gillespie and sp^2 $(+p)$ hybridization. When the coordination number is 2, the bond angles are 180°, again consistent with both Gillespie and sp $(+p^2)$ hybridization. With $CN = 1$, we find sp $(+p^2)$ hybridization involving a nonbonding pair and a bonding pair in the sp hybrid plus 4 electrons in two π bonds (as in $C_2^=$).

The proposed distributions of electrons and orbitals for these *CN*'s are shown in Figure 21.25. The fact that these various types of bonds are formed both between carbon atoms and with many other atoms helps account for the enormous number of carbon compounds.

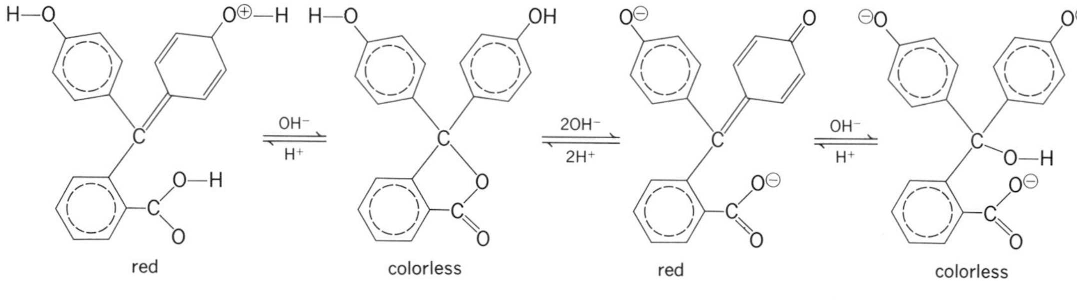

pk = 8.3

Figure 21.26 Color and structure in phenolphthalein. Note that many resonance structures must be used to describe the two red forms. This multiplicity is common in colored substances.

COLOR AND ELECTRONIC FORMS

Many compounds containing carbon are colored. Dyes are notable examples, as are the well-known acid-base indicators. Consider phenolphthalein. It is commonly known to be colorless in acid and pink in basic solutions. Actually the situation is much more complicated, as Figure 21.26 shows. There are four possible species, depending on the acidity of the solution—two are pink and two are colorless, giving three color-change ranges for the indicator. Note the similarity of the electron structures of the two colorless forms and, of the two colored forms. Color is, in general, an indication of a molecule's electronic energy levels, separated by about 50 kcal (see Figure 8.2). Such separations are common in π electron systems like phenolphthalein; hence many dyes contain linked benzene rings, or long carbon chains with alternating double bonds.

INTERRELATION OF ORGANIC COMPOUNDS

One thing that we should stress before moving too far from this classification of organic compounds is that the various classes, called by separate names, containing different functional groups, and possessing remarkably diverse physical and chemical properties, are not really separate entities. They are all related, and are, in a sense, different states of the same things. Thus ethane, ethene, and ethyne are different oxidation states of the same species just as truly as ferric iron, ferrous iron, and iron metal are. The same could be said of ethanol, acetaldehyde, and acetic acid; they exhibit oxidation states just as do hypochlorous, chlorous, chloric, and perchloric acid.

Synthetic organic chemistry can be divided into two main areas: (1) the synthesis of carbon skeletons, and (2) the interconversion of functional groups. The first area lies outside the scope of this introductory survey (unfortunately, since some of the most challenging and exciting problems of organic chemistry arise in this area), and we will be able to only take a brief glance at the second. Figure 21.27 is an outline of chemical methods of converting any of the functional groups that we have considered into any of the others. The reagents needed are listed over the arrows; naturally the mere naming of a reagent does not convey enough information to allow one to run a reaction. Detailed information on temperature, rate and order of addition, concentrations, molar ratios, solvents, and methods of separation are needed, and many, many alternate routes exist. However, this outline may help to point out that the various classes of organic compounds are not isolated entities. The raw materials of organic chemistry are few, and the end products are many; it is the task of the organic chemist to find the ever-branching paths that lead between them.

Exercise 21.12

Suggest two methods of converting *n*-propanol into propene. Write net equations for each step. *Answer:* See Figure 21.27. Four possible paths are shown, assuming that *n*-propanol behaves like C_2H_5OH.

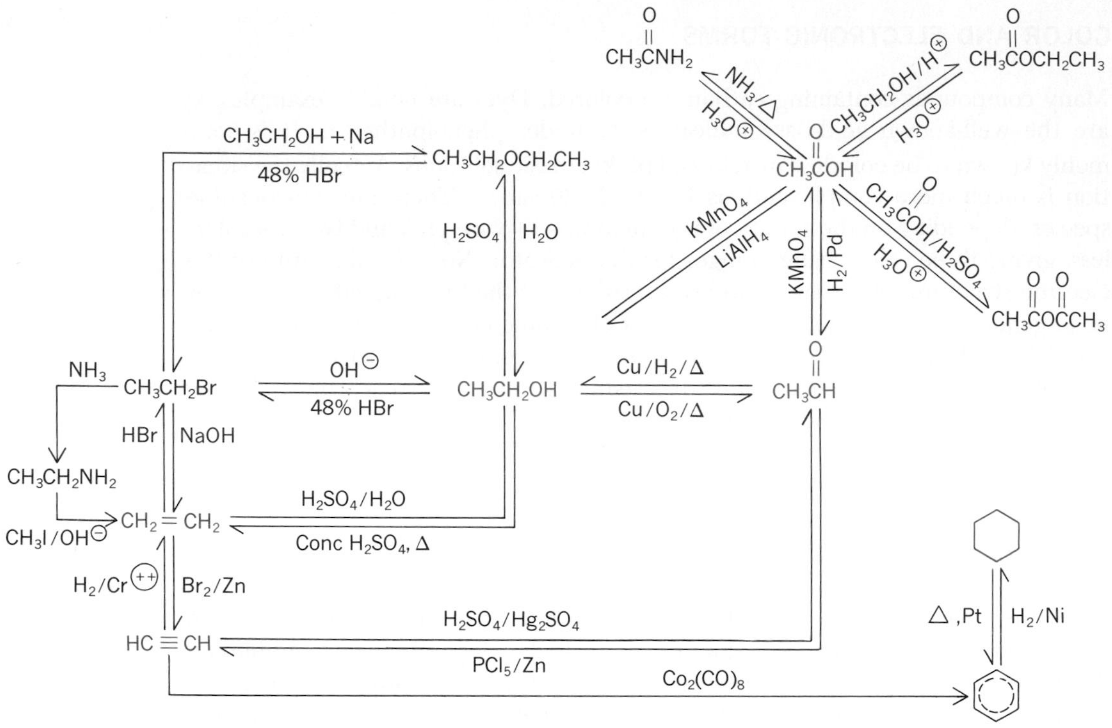

Figure 21.27 Interrelations of simple organic compounds (Δ = heat). Color is used to indicate some commonly available starting materials.

THE TASKS OF ORGANIC CHEMISTRY

Early in this chapter we pointed out that the classical division of the profession of chemistry into organic, inorganic, physical, and analytical is becoming less and less valid; scientists who call themselves organic chemists can be found working in each of these four areas as they were once defined. It will be some time, however, until textbooks, university curricula, and industrial tables of organization cease to be arranged in accord with this pattern, and until that time we will still find a large group of people who call themselves organic chemists, doing a wide variety of things.

What are the things that organic chemists do? Succinctly put, organic chemists isolate, synthesize, identify, and study systems containing carbon compounds.

ISOLATION

There are two great natural reservoirs of organic chemicals, the mineral substances coal and petroleum and the living substances plants and animals. The nature of coal and petroleum, although complex and varied, is fairly well understood, and most chemists who are interested in the study of substances found in nature are working with materials derived from plants and animals; such chemists are called "natural-product chemists."

The first chore of the natural-product chemist is to isolate a pure substance from the complex mixture that one nearly always obtains from a living source. The task of isolation can range from the trivial to the fantastic; the heartwood of some cedar trees contains pure crystals of an eleven-carbon carboxylic acid, while certain animal glands may contain less than a part per million of a medicinally important hormone, mixed not only with blood, tissue, cell fluids, and proteins, but with a dozen or a score of other hormones of almost identical chemical structure and physical properties. The chemist must bring an arsenal of separation techniques to bear on such problems, including distillation, crystallization, electrophoresis, chromatography, and many more, and he must develop methods to monitor the substance that he is after, so that he can tell when a fraction has been enriched in it.

SYNTHESIS

Perhaps more organic chemists are involved in synthesis than any other single task. There are a variety of reasons why a chemist sets out to make a substance: to confirm the identity of a natural product by preparing it from known starting materials, to prepare a new substance believed to be of industrial use or medical importance, or to create compounds which are of theoretical interest. In any case, the chemist must consider his goal in light of the available chemicals with which he can begin, survey the existing literature for routes to close the gap between source and product, and, if no reasonable routes exist, to create new methods of synthesis by drawing on his knowledge of chemical structures and reactions.

IDENTIFICATION

When a new compound has been obtained (whether by isolation from a natural source or by synthesis in the laboratory), two questions must be answered about it: (1) is it pure, and (2) what is it? All the hue and cry, all the sweat and glamor of organic chemistry are condensed—when the chips are down—into a handful of numbers, a melting point or boiling point, an index of refraction, some elemental percentages, some wavelengths of light absorbed. It is these that separate the "haves" from the "have nots."

The decision whether a substance is pure is usually based on analysis (see below) or on physical constants. If a compound has been previously prepared and analyzed by other workers, then a chemist will usually judge his sample pure if its physical constants (melting point, boiling point, index of refraction, spectra, and others) match those reported in the literature. For a new substance the decision may be more difficult, but usually a compound is judged pure if—in addition to possessing the proper analysis—it has a very narrow boiling or melting range, and is not separable into components by chromatographic techniques.

The analysis of the compound is the most important single criterion for purity and identification. Organic compounds are ordinarily analyzed for carbon and hydrogen by combustion techniques. A small, carefully weighed sample of the compound is heated in a stream of pure oxygen in an electrically heated furnace, and the exit gases are passed through preweighed tubes containing specific absorbents for carbon dioxide and water. From the weight of carbon dioxide and water produced, the percent of carbon and hydrogen in the molecule can be calculated. Other elements are determined by standard microquantitative techniques. An organic compound is judged acceptably pure—or its composition is judged acceptably close to the presumed composition—if all of the elemental percentages are found to be within 0.3% of the calculated value. When the compound is found to be pure and the elemental composition is known from analysis, the molecular weight should be determined by such methods as gas density measurements (Chapter 6) or colligative properties (Chapter 34). When this has been done, the formula of the molecule will have been determined.

Further identification of the molecule to determine the exact molecular structure can be carried out through the use of specific tests for the various functional groups and by a detailed examination of the electromagnetic spectrum (Figure 8.2). Of particular interest to the organic chemist are the ultraviolet-visible spectrum (which gives information on π and nonbonding electrons in organic molecules), the infrared spectrum (which gives information on the types of chemical bonds in a molecule—see Table 14.2), and the nuclear magnetic spectrum (which identifies the types and numbers of hydrogens in a molecule—see Figure 12.8).

Exercise 21.13

You have a compound of formula unknown to you, but known to have been studied before. What measurements would you make to identify the substance? *Answer:* (1) Try to ash it by heating on a steel plate. If there is no ash, it is likely to be a carbon compound. Assume this is so. (2) Determine its refractive index—very easy and accurate, with tabulated values widely available. (3) Determine m.p. and/or b.p., as in step 2. (4) Take IR spectrum, as in 2. These should be sufficient. They are also sufficient for noncarbon compounds, but measurements are more difficult and tables are less readily available. Elementary analysis or X-ray spectroscopy is usually used for inorganic compounds. (A professional chemist in a well-equipped laboratory would probably use NMR, infrared, and mass spectroscopy.)

STUDY

Much of the work of organic chemists is focused on detailed physical studies of molecules and the way in which they interact. Such studies can be divided into three general types, which are closely connected. The first is the study of the "structure" of molecules: their shape and size, bond angles and bond strain, electronic effects, spectral effects, and the presence or absence of resonance and the amount of stability arising therefrom. The second is the study of "kinetic" effects: the rates at which molecules react and the structural and environmental factors that affect these rates. The third, which draws heavily on both the first two, is the study of "reaction mechanisms." In all of the complex transformations that we have described in this chapter—the oxidations of alcohols, the formations of

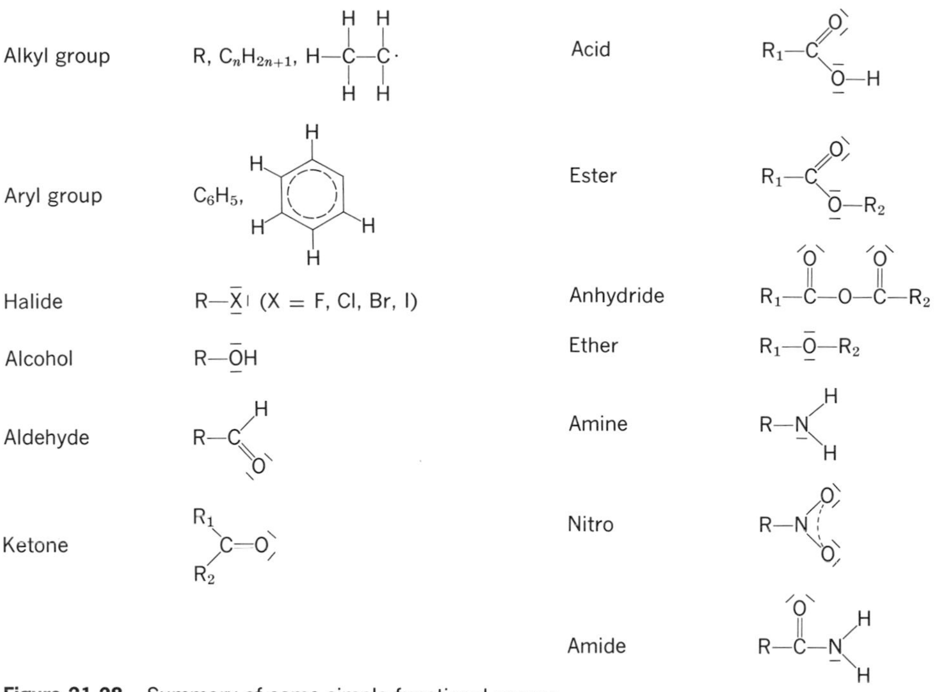

Figure 21.28 Summary of some simple functional groups.

amides, anhydrides, and esters, and all the useful conversions of Figure 21.27—a number of complicated atomic rearrangements must take place as one set of substances is transformed to another. A great task of organic chemistry has been to develop an understanding of the detailed, step-by-step processes by which molecules come together and interact to form new substances. We discuss some of these in Chapters 22 and 23.

SYNTHESIS OF CARBON COMPOUNDS IN NATURE

The evidence is overwhelming that most carbon compounds found in nature are of biogenic origin. Thus the recent discovery of meteorites containing carbonaceous material excited great interest in the possibility of extraterrestrial life. Simple laboratory experiments have shown, however, that the same range of compounds (and in the same ratio) found in the meteorites may be formed by heating CO and CH_4 to 900°C in one end of a glass tube at 1 atm pressure, while keeping the other end cool. Typical products are hydrogen, benzene, toluene, naphthalene, anthracene, plus more complicated compounds.

Similarly, amino acids can be synthesized by passing an electric arc through a mixture of NH_3, CH_4, and CO. Thus there is at present no distinction between compounds of biogenic origin and those which can be synthesized by nonliving systems in nature. The discovery of 22 different amino acids in fossilized organisms in a pre-Cambrian sedimentary rock at least 3.1 billion years old (J. W. Schopf, 1967) indicates that early living systems were based on the same amino acids as current ones.

SUMMARY

The study of carbon compounds is often classified as a field of chemistry known as organic chemistry. This special emphasis has been placed on carbon compounds because of the unusual number of compounds of this element (results of catenation and isomerization), and the generally covalent or molecular nature of the compounds of carbon. Detailed systems of classification have been developed to separate isomeric compounds and to arrange species by functional groups (Figure 21.28), and standard systems of nomenclature have been adopted.

Drugs affect different people in different ways and at different times for reasons that can seldom be explained until many thousands of patients have taken them. For example, a few persons out of every 100,000, owing to a peculiar genetic defect in their biochemistry, become violently ill if given sulfa drugs, but only if they eat cheese or other foods containing certain proteins.
Quinine, for example, would probably never reach the market if it were discovered today. Repeated doses cause blindness in dogs, though not in human beings. Aspirin, too, would be quickly eliminated because it harms rat embryos. Besides, it is only mildly effective in its original role as a pain-killer, yet most specialists now agree that it is the best weapon available against rheumatoid arthritis.
—George A. W. Boehm,
The New York Times Magazine (May 15, 1966).

PROBLEMS

21.1. Write full structural, projection, and condensed formulas for both dimethyl cyclobutanes shown in Figure 21.6.

21.2. Write equations for the reactions of acetylene to form ethane, ethyl alcohol, acetic acid, and benzene.

21.3. Suggest a reason why coronene in Figure 21.16 might be an exception to the $4n + 2$ rule which is followed by the other molecules.

21.4. Suggest a reason why some of the substances in Figure 21.14 are used to form commercial polymers, while those in Figure 21.11 are not.

21.5. Extend the argument on p. 519 to account for the fact that CF_3COOH (K = very large) is a stronger acid than CH_3COOH ($K = 1.8 \cdot 10^{-5}$).

21.6. Assign oxidation states to each atom in the following series: ethane, ethene, ethyne; ethanol, acetaldehyde, acetic acid; CH_3NH_2, CH_3NHOH, CH_3NO, CH_3NO_2. (CH_3NH_2; -2, $+1$, -3, $+1$.)

21.7. Analysis of a compound known to contain only C, H, and Cl shows that 0.116 g of compound gives 0.270 g of CO_2 and 0.047 g of H_2O when it is burned in O_2. Calculate several likely formulas. How would you proceed to distinguish between them? ($[C_6H_5Cl]_n$.)

21.8. Write out structural formulas for some possible molecules not discussed in this book and name the substances, using a standard system such as IUC.

21.9. Two organic compounds have the same molecular formula C_2H_6O. Compound A boils at 79°C, while compound B boils at -24°C. Suggest structural formulas for compounds A and B. Account clearly for the difference in boiling points.

21.10. Describe the rotations necessary to superpose the two forms of CH_2BrCl shown in Figure 21.10.

21.11. An organic compound has a molecular weight of 46 and contains 52.1% C, 13.1% H, balance oxygen. Its NMR spectrum is shown. Write its structural formula.

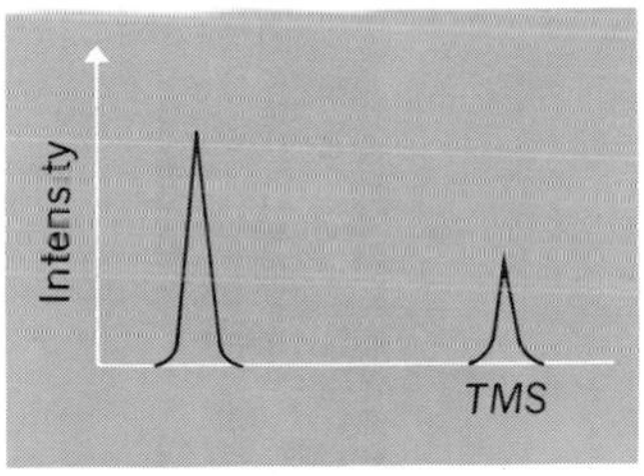

21.12. Rationalize the melting point differences in the pairs of isomers in Figure 21.5. Why do the melting points generally differ more than the boiling points in each pair? Suggest a method for separating the isomers from a 50-50 liquid solution.

21.13. Calcium carbide, CaC_2, is ionic calcium acetylide. Write an electron structure for CaC_2. Outline a possible crystal structure and estimate the C—C and Ca—C internuclear distances. CaC_2 reacts vigorously with water to give acetylene. Write an equation.

21.14. Which of the compounds in Figure 21.27 seem most available as starting points for industrial syntheses? List a source, or method of preparation, for each compound you select.

21.15. Write structural formulas for all the isomers of empirical formula: C_3H_6, C_3H_6O, $C_3H_4Cl_2$, C_3H_4ClF.

21.16. (*a*) Propionic acid (b.p. 141°C, solub in H_2O ∞), methylacetate (b.p. 57°C, solub in H_2O 33%) and ethyl formate (b.p. 54°C, solub in H_2O 11%) are isomeric. Draw their structural formulas and interpret the variations in b.p. and in solubility in H_2O. (*b*) Repeat for the following set: *n*-butyric acid (168°C, ∞), *n*-propyl formate (81°C, 2.2%), ethyl acetate (77°C, 9%), and methyl propionate (80°C, 0.5%).

See page 1092 for a list of references and readings in the recent chemical literature related to the material in this chapter.

CHAPTER 22

The Experimental Basis of Chemical Kinetics

STEPHEN V. FILSETH

A reliable set of kinetic data serves mainly to permit us to discard various otherwise seemingly plausible mechanistic steps whose predictions are at variance with our observations. Even if we can conjure up a mechanism that agrees in detail with our kinetic data, we have not proved the mechanism, nor can we ever prove it. This is typical of human ideas, but even negative information provides enormous insight into natural systems.

Chemical kinetics is not so much a separate area of study in chemistry as it is an emphasis of interest. The techniques, concepts, and utility of kinetics transcend the artificial boundaries of organic, inorganic, analytical, and physical chemistry. We minimize the emphasis on why a chemical reaction occurs, and, accepting the fact that chemical reactions do occur, interest ourselves now in the speed with which they take place. An understanding of this information enables us to reach certain conclusions regarding the more fundamental question of how chemical reactions take place.

The rate of a chemical reaction, which may also be called its velocity, is not an unambiguous quantity easily derived from experiment. Great care must be taken in the design and interpretation of the experiment if meaningful results are to be obtained. We will describe some of the experimental techniques that have been employed successfully by kineticists to measure the rates of chemical reactions. The real gauge of success of a kinetics experiment is seldom available to the kineticist himself, for it lies basically in the test of time. Although theory and interpretation may evolve and modify the conclusions reached on the basis of experiment, the experiment can be considered successful if the data remain unimpeachable.

The techniques chosen for the study of the rate of a chemical reaction are in large part determined by the time scale of the reaction. It is possible to characterize chemical reactions in terms of the length of time required for the reaction to proceed to the point of half-completion. We will consider the slower reactions first, since they present a more straightforward experimental problem.

THE RELATIONSHIPS BETWEEN TEMPERATURE AND RATE

Almost everyone realizes that rates of reaction are affected by a change in temperature. We cook food by heating it to make it more palatable and digestible. We ignite fuels to get them to burn at an appreciable rate. We refrigerate food to keep it from spoiling. And in a chemistry lab we watch reaction temperatures very carefully lest they rise and lead to violently rapid reactions.

Not all rates of reaction behave identically with temperature change. Most net rates increase, but some decrease. Furthermore, the change in rate is different for different reactions for the same temperature change; and in many cases the effect is not monotonic. Figure 22.1 illustrates some possible relationships between rate and temperature when all other variables, especially initial concentrations, are constant.

The falloff in enzyme reaction rates at high temperature (Figure 22.1, C) is easiest to interpret: the enzyme decomposes above the temperature corresponding to the maximum in the curve, and reactions involving it must have lower apparent rates. A falloff in rate as in Figure 22.1, B, occurs because of a "back reaction" whose rate increases faster than the rate of the "forward reaction" as the temperature rises. Thus the apparent decreases in rate with rising temperature in Figure 22.1, B and C are both due to the presence of competing reactions. This is apparently always true. All single-step reactions, or mechanistic steps, increase in rate as the temperature increases.

The usual case of an exponential increase in rate with rising temperature, as in Figure 22.1, A, is found empirically to fit the equation (if all concentrations are unity):

$$\text{rate} = Ae^{-\Delta E_{\text{act}}/RT} \qquad \text{or} \qquad \ln(\text{rate}/A) = -\Delta E_{\text{act}}/RT \tag{22.1}$$

where ΔE_{act} is called the activation energy, R is the gas constant, T is the Kelvin temperature, and A is the Arrhenius pre-exponential factor. This empirical dis-

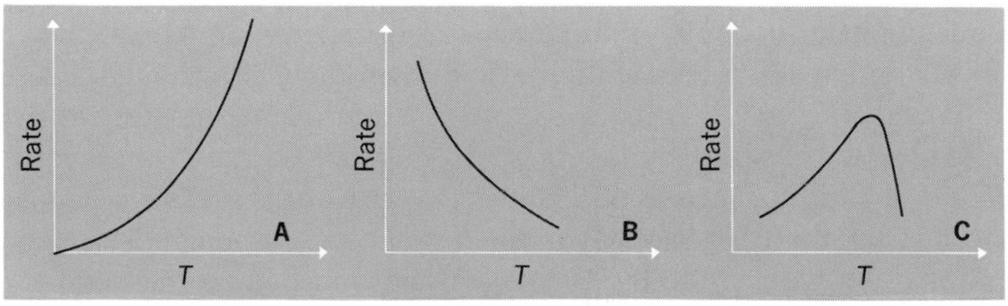

Figure 22.1 Possible dependence of rate on temperature: **(A)** typical single-step reaction, **(B)** bimolecular net reaction to give a single molecule; **(C)** enzyme-catalyzed net reaction.

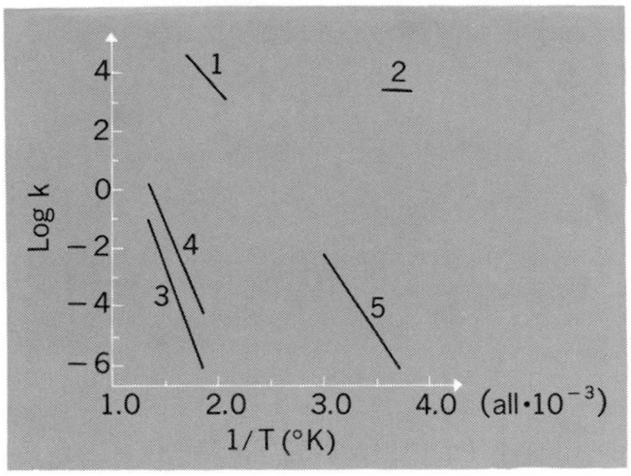

Figure 22.2 Arrhenius plots—logarithm of the rate versus reciprocal °K (all concentrations being at unit activity) for a few simple gas-phase reactions, and the calculation of ΔE_{act}.

covery came from noting that ln (rate) plotted versus $1/T$ gave a straight line (of slope $-\Delta E_{act}/R$) as shown in Figure 22.2.

Since rate is an exponential function of ΔE_{act}, it is mandatory that temperature be closely controlled if other factors affecting rates are to be studied. Note also that large values of ΔE_{act} cause a more rapid change of rate with temperature than do small values of ΔE_{act}. If $\Delta E_{act} = 0$, there is very little effect on the rate if T varies within a small range.

Exercise 22.1

It is commonly said that "reactions double in rate for a 10° rise in temperature." Calculate and comment on the intimations of this statement. *Answer:* (*a*) The statement should be applied only to single-step processes; others may decrease in net rate. (*b*) The temperature scale is not stated, but we'll assume it is centigrade. (*c*) If rate follows Arrhenius form,

$$\text{rate} = Ae^{-\Delta E_{act}/RT}, \qquad \text{rate}_1/\text{rate}_2 = e^{-(\Delta E/R)[(1/T_1)-(1/T_2)]} = \tfrac{1}{2}$$

There are still two variables, ΔE and T. Assuming $T_1 = 298°K$ and $T_2 = 308°K$, we get $\Delta E_{act} = 13$ kcal. The quoted statement thus contains implicit assumptions about the system, about T, and about ΔE_{act} which may or may not be valid.

THERMAL REACTIONS

Measurements upon systems having half-lives of more than one minute, whether in a gas phase or a condensed phase, may be made in a relatively leisurely fashion. The most common approach is to enclose the reaction mixture in a glass or metal container held in a thermostat and to make measurements of the compositions of the mixture at suitable intervals of time. This technique is commonly referred to as the static method.

Thermostats may range in complexity from simple, mechanically stirred liquid baths (typical for kinetic studies in condensed phases) to circulating air ovens (common in gas kinetic experiments). Since reaction rates depend exponentially on the temperature of the reaction mixture (which determines the availability of the activation energy), great care must be taken to assure both temporal and dimensional uniformity of temperature. If this cannot be done, the measured rate may be some relatively meaningless average value.

Thermostating is difficult because most reactions have an appreciable ΔE or ΔH. Thus, in recombination reactions of monatomic species,

$$\mathrm{I} + \mathrm{I} + \mathrm{M} \longrightarrow \mathrm{I}_2 + \mathrm{M}$$

(where M is any molecule capable of removing the vibrational energy generated on combination), intense local temperature gradients are established by the release of bond energy.

Exercise 22.2

A thermostat has an experimental uncertainty of $\pm 1^\circ$K at 500°K. What is the experimental uncertainty in the rate if $\Delta E_{\text{act}} = 40$ kcal? *Answer:* Assuming the Arrhenius law holds,

$$\text{rate}_1/\text{rate}_2 = \exp\{-(\Delta E_{\text{act}}/R)[(1/T_1) - (1/T_2)]\} \cong \exp\{(\Delta E_{\text{act}}/R)(T_2 - T_1)T^{-2}\}$$

assuming $T \gg \Delta T$. If $T = 500^\circ$K, $\Delta T = 2^\circ$K, $\Delta E_{\text{act}} = 40$ kcal, we get $\text{rate}_1/\text{rate}_2 =$ 0.85 as the factor of uncertainty in the rate. Thus there is about $\pm 8\%$ uncertainty in the rate for $\pm 1^\circ$K uncertainty in T. Note the large effect.

DETERMINATION OF CONCENTRATION

Almost all properties of chemical materials have been employed in the analysis of the composition of the reaction mixture as a function of time. The following discussion is representative but by no means exhaustive.

Perhaps the simplest technique is illustrated by the manometric study of the thermal decomposition of gaseous cyclopentene. At pressures of the order of 50 to 200 torr and temperatures near 500°C, over 95% of the reaction can be described by the stoichiometry

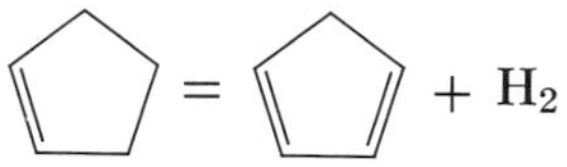

$$C_5H_8 = C_5H_6 + H_2$$

Since all species present are gaseous under the conditions of the experiment, the progress of the reaction may be followed quite simply by manometric means. The rate expression could be any of the following:

$$-\frac{d[C_5H_8]}{dt} = +\frac{d[C_5H_6]}{dt} = +\frac{d[H_2]}{dt}$$

We can write these differential* relations by knowing only the stoichiometric equation. The relationship of rate to pressure cannot be written until the experimental data on rate are available. Such experiments on this system give

*The differential operator, d, is used by chemists to indicate a vanishingly small change. Thus dx means an infinitesimal change in x. The delta operator, Δ, is used to indicate a finite change: $\Delta x = x_2 - x_1$. Thus limit $(\Delta t \rightarrow 0)\ \Delta x/\Delta t = dx/dt$.

$$-\frac{d[C_5H_8]}{dt} = kp_{C_5H_8}$$

where $p_{C_5H_8}$ = pressure of C_5H_8 at time t.

Kineticists are not usually presented with such simple systems, however. More common are reactions that may proceed along a variety of different paths, yielding many reaction products. An extreme example is the decomposition of butene-1 in the presence of photoexcited (that is, excited by photons) gaseous mercury atoms. This reaction results in the formation of some forty distinct, stable chemical species. In a situation like this, there are many ways to define the rate of the reaction, and a thorough treatment of the problem calls for a quantitative separation and analysis of all of the products. For this the technique of vapor-phase chromatography (see Chapter 36) has proved invaluable in recent years.

When measurement of composition may be made without disturbing the system, as with the cyclopentene above, a great simplification is achieved. The principal method employed in these techniques is the absorption or dispersion of electromagnetic radiation, ranging from the radio frequency region to the far ultraviolet. For example, the bromination of benzene may be conveniently followed by spectrophotometric (visible, UV, or infrared) observation of the disappearance of the bromine and/or benzene. The stoichiometry is

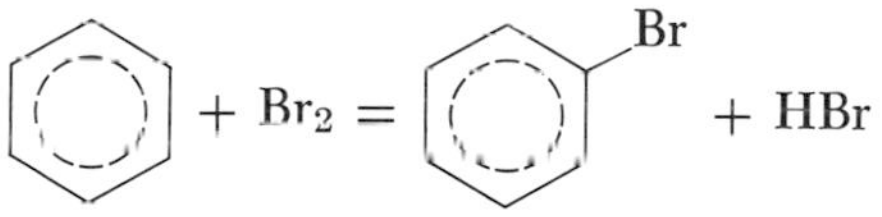

The rate could be represented by any of the following:

$$-\frac{d[C_6H_6]}{dt} = -\frac{d[Br_2]}{dt} = \frac{d[C_6H_5Br]}{dt} = \frac{d[HBr]}{dt}$$

The experimental data then provide the relationship of these time derivatives to the concentrations of the reactants.

In addition to the physical methods that can be employed to follow the course of a reaction, a variety of chemical techniques are available, which usually involve either stopping the reaction suddenly or removing small aliquots for analysis. An illustration of this approach is the study of the velocity of the reaction between silver ions and formate ions in aqueous solution:

$$2Ag^+{}_{(aq)} + HCOO^-{}_{(aq)} \longrightarrow 2Ag_{(c)} + CO_{2(g)} + H^+{}_{(aq)}$$

The rate could be expressed variously as

$$-\frac{d[Ag^+]}{dt} = -2\frac{d[HCOO^-]}{dt} = 2\frac{d[CO_2]}{dt} = 2\frac{d[H^+]}{dt}$$

The concentrations as a function of time are followed by periodically removing aliquots of the reaction mixture, quenching (stopping) the reaction by precipitating (hence removing) the silver ion with a known amount of excess chloride ion, and finally titrating the residual chloride to determine the silver ion concentration at the time of quenching. As in equilibrium constant calculations, concentrations of species in condensed phases are here usually represented in units of formality ($F = M$); gases in units of atmospheres partial pressure.

In many gas kinetic studies, analytical problems are compounded by the minuscule quantities of material involved. To minimize the participation of competing side reactions, the reaction may be allowed to proceed to only a few tenths percent conversion; product yields in the nanomole (10^{-9} mole $= 6 \cdot 10^{14}$ molecules) region are not uncommon. In such studies chemical analysis is inconvenient, and sensitive physical techniques such as vapor-phase chromatography, mass spectrometry, and radioisotopic labeling are employed.

Exercise 22.3

Suggest means of determining the concentration of some species versus time for each of these slow gaseous net reactions: (*a*) $H_2 + I_2 = 2HI$, (*b*) $C_2H_4 + H_2 = C_2H_6$, (*c*) $N_2 + O_2 = 2NO$, (*d*) $I_2 + Br_2 = 2IBr$. *Answer:* Absorption spectra would work for all in the infrared range (HI, C_2H_4, C_2H_6, NO, IBr only), and for *a* and *d* in the visible range (I_2, Br_2, IBr). Pressure would work for *b* only. Thermal conductivity would work well for *b*, as would heat capacity. Mass spectrometry would work in all.

PHOTOCHEMICAL REACTIONS

An important area of gas kinetics employs photons as the energizing agent rather than molecular collisions (heat). A singular advantage of this technique is the well-defined energy of monochromatic light compared to the continuous distribution of energies produced in thermal activation (molecular collisions); see Figure 8.12. A typical photochemical experiment might utilize the equipment shown in Figure 22.3.

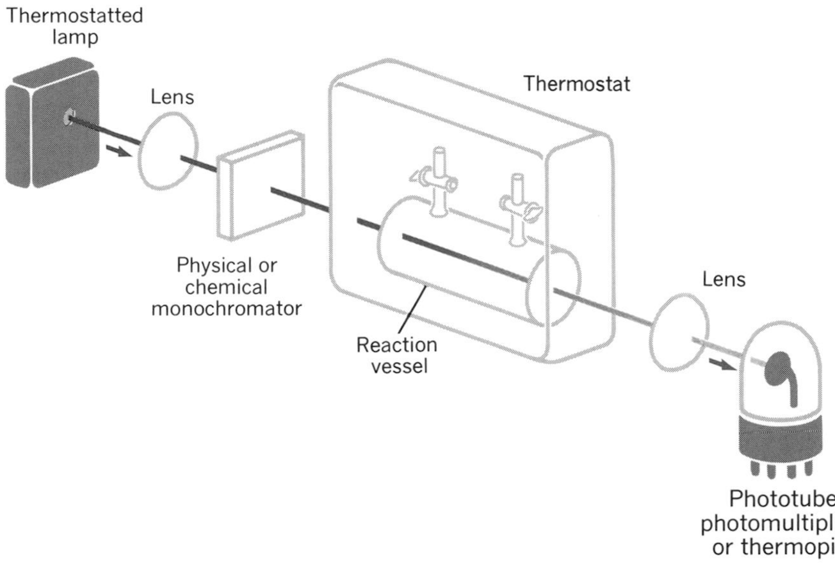

Figure 22.3 Schematic photochemical apparatus for gas kinetic study.

Since lamp intensity is frequently a strong function of lamp envelope temperature, a thermostated enclosure is necessary. The light from the lamp is collimated to illuminate the reaction vessel uniformly and is then passed through a chemical or physical monochromator to select the desired wavelength of radiation. After passing through a thermostated reaction vessel, the light may be collected by a photosensitive device that monitors the transmitted intensity. The extent of reaction may be measured by absorption measurements at right angles to the exciting beam, by removing samples from time to time, by pressure measurements, and so on.

The rates of photochemical reactions depend upon the intensity of radiation employed, and an integral feature of the photochemical experiment is the measurement of the intensity of this radiation. [The usual unit of photochemical intensity is the einstein (energy of one mole of photons = $Nh\nu$) per second.] Most commonly employed is a chemical actinometer—a chemical system with a quantitatively known behavior. Acetone is a commonly used system. The photochemistry of acetone has been well studied, and it is known that at temperatures above 130°C and for the commonly used wavelengths of 2537 and 3130 Å (see Appendix III to convert to frequencies), the decomposition is described by the following mechanism:

$$\begin{aligned} CH_3COCH_3 + h\nu &\longrightarrow CH_3\cdot + CH_3CO\cdot \\ CH_3CO\cdot &\longrightarrow CH_3\cdot + CO \\ CH_3\cdot + CH_3COCH_3 &\longrightarrow CH_4 + CH_3COCH_2\cdot \\ CH_3\cdot + CH_3COCH_2\cdot &\longrightarrow CH_3COC_2H_5 \\ 2CH_3\cdot &\longrightarrow C_2H_6 \end{aligned}$$

Since one molecule of CO is produced by each absorbed photon (the quantum yield is one), a simple measurement of the amount of CO produced in a certain time interval can be readily translated into a lamp intensity, I_0, if the fraction of the incident light absorbed, P, is known:

$$\frac{d[CO]}{dt} = kI_0P = k'I_{abs}$$

Homogeneous media containing a single absorbing species of molar concentration, c, are found to absorb acording to the relationship

$$-dI/I = \epsilon' c\, dl = 2.303\, \epsilon c\, dl \qquad (22.2)$$

where I is the intensity of the light which has passed a distance l into the medium, and ϵ is the molar absorptivity. When the value of ϵ is independent of c, the system is said to follow the Beer-Lambert law, often given by integrating Equation (22.2) between the limits $I = I_0$ at $l = 0$ and I, l to obtain

BEER'S LAW: $$I = I_0 e^{-\epsilon' cl}$$

$$I_{abs} = I_0 - I = I_0(1 - e^{-\epsilon' cl})$$

The molar absorptivity, ϵ, is normally a function of the frequency of the light, so it must be evaluated separately for each frequency and each species in the light path:

$$\ln (I_0/I) = \epsilon' cl$$
$$\log (I_0/I) = \epsilon cl = A, \text{ the absorbance}$$

Another reliable technique for light intensity measurements at 2537 Å is the methyl iodide-radioiodine system. A mixture of methyl iodide and molecular iodine is irradiated for a fixed period of time. If the molecular iodine contains a small percentage of iodine-131 (a radioactive isotope of iodine), some of this isotope will be found in the methyl iodide when the irradiation has been completed. This can be accounted for on the basis of the mechanism

$$CH_3I + h\nu \longrightarrow CH_3\cdot + I\cdot$$
$$CH_3\cdot + II^{131} \longrightarrow CH_3I^{131} + I\cdot$$
$$I\cdot + I\cdot \longrightarrow I_2$$

A simple measurement of the ratio of iodine-131 found in the methyl iodide to that found in molecular iodine permits the rate of the reaction to be followed. In a system such as this, the final products differ only slightly from the original reactants, and only isotopic techniques allow one to follow the course of the reaction.

Exercise 22.4

Irradiation of propionaldehyde at 200 mm pressure with 3020 Å light at 30°C gives a quantum yield for CO of 0.54. Calculate the light absorption in moles of photons per second and kcal sec^{-1} if the rate of CO formation is 0.001 mole hr^{-1}.

Answer: n = moles photons/sec

$$= 0.001 \frac{\text{moles CO}}{\text{hr}} \cdot \frac{1}{3600} \frac{\text{hr}}{\text{sec}} \cdot \frac{1}{0.54} \frac{\text{moles photons}}{\text{moles CO}}$$

$$= 5.3 \cdot 10^{-7} \text{ moles photons sec}^{-1}$$

$$\frac{\text{no. of kcal}}{\text{sec}} = nN_0 h\nu = \frac{nN_0hc}{\lambda} = \frac{5.3 \cdot 10^{-7} \cdot 6.02 \cdot 10^{23} \cdot 6.63 \cdot 10^{-27} \cdot 3.00 \cdot 10^{10}}{3.02 \cdot 10^{3} \cdot 10^{-8} \cdot 4.18 \cdot 10^{7} \cdot 10^{3}}$$

$$= 5.0 \cdot 10^{-5} \text{ kcal sec}^{-1}$$

REACTIONS WITH HALF-TIMES BETWEEN 10^{-3} AND 10^{2} SECONDS

Reactions having half-times shorter than a minute lead to new complications. In the first place, it is frequently difficult to define clearly the starting time of a reaction, and hence impossible to learn the exact extent of reaction in a measured interval. In thermal reactions it is frequently not possible to bring a reaction mixture up to the desired temperature of reaction in a period of time which is much shorter than the reaction time. It may thus be impossible to define the conditions of the reaction. In addition, for those reactions in which the rate is followed continuously, it may be difficult to make a measurement in a period of time which is short compared to the reaction time.

The principal approach to these problems has been to utilize flow techniques, in which the reaction mixture spends only a short time within a reaction zone before it is swept out to an analysis zone. The time limit on this technique is of

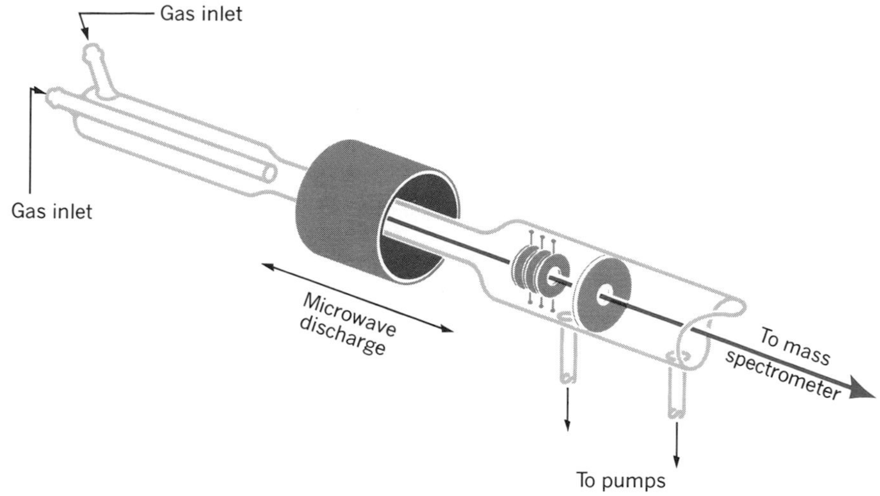

Figure 22.4 Apparatus for studying reactivity of transient species

the order of milliseconds (10^{-3} seconds) and is determined by the efficiency of mixing of the components of the reaction mixture.

In a typical flow experiment, the composition of the reaction mixture is measured either continuously or at intervals, both before and after the mixture has entered the reaction zone. From a knowledge of the dimensions of the reaction chamber and the flow rate of the mixture, the residence time in the reaction zone, and thence the rate of reaction, can be computed. A common problem is uncertainty about residence time, arising from nonuniform flow or difficulty in defining the reaction zone.

A similar technique has been employed to study the lifetimes and rates of disappearance of transient species formed in a microwave discharge. A typical apparatus is shown in Figure 22.4. From the known flow rates and the known distance between the discharge and the inlet of the mass spectrometer, it is possible to establish a time scale that permits the lifetimes of transient species to be determined.

A variation of the flow technique, which combines some of the best features of the flow and static methods, is the stopped-flow technique. Reactants are forced into a mixing chamber, where thorough mixing may occur in a few milliseconds, and then into a reaction vessel, whereupon flow is stopped. Measurements (usually spectroscopic) are then carried out upon the reacting mixture. The particular advantage of this technique is that the rate is no longer dependent upon somewhat variable flow rates and flow behavior.

REACTIONS WITH HALF-TIMES LESS THAN 10^{-3} SECONDS

Because reactions that are complete in microseconds (10^{-6} seconds) or less cannot be studied in static systems or in flow systems, a variety of specialized techniques have been developed.

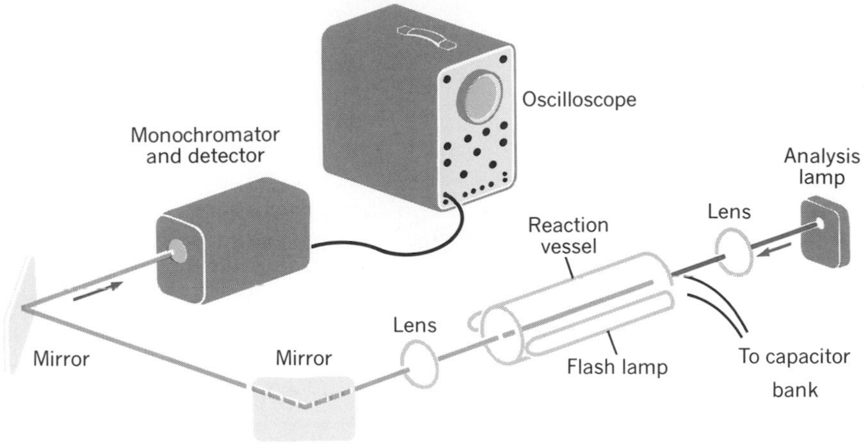

Figure 22.5 The basic components of a flash photolysis experiment.

One of the most successful of these is the flash photolysis method, also sometimes called the kinetic spectroscopy method. Discovery and use of this technique brought the Nobel Prize in Chemistry to Porter and Norrish in 1967. The essential components of a flash photolysis experiment are shown in Figure 22.5. A bank of capacitors is discharged in periods of time of the order of one microsecond through a lamp, which releases a burst of light quanta that may be of sufficient intensity to dissociate every molecule in the reaction vessel. Absorption spectroscopy is then used as the analytical technique to measure concentrations in the reaction vessel as a function of time. In a typical experiment involving the recombination of iodine atoms, the following reactions would take place:

$$\text{Primary process:} \qquad I_2 + h\nu \longrightarrow 2I$$
$$\text{Secondary reaction:} \qquad I + I + M \longrightarrow I_2 + M$$

The course of the reaction is typically followed by connecting the detector of the monochromator to a triggered oscilloscope and observing the increase in concentration of molecular iodine through its absorption band in the visible portion of the spectrum: analysis of a representative oscilloscope display is shown in Figure 22.6. Or the spectrum of the contents of the reaction vessel may be recorded photographically as a function of time as in Figure 22.7.

Figure 22.6 Oscilloscope display from a flash photolytic experiment in atom recombination.

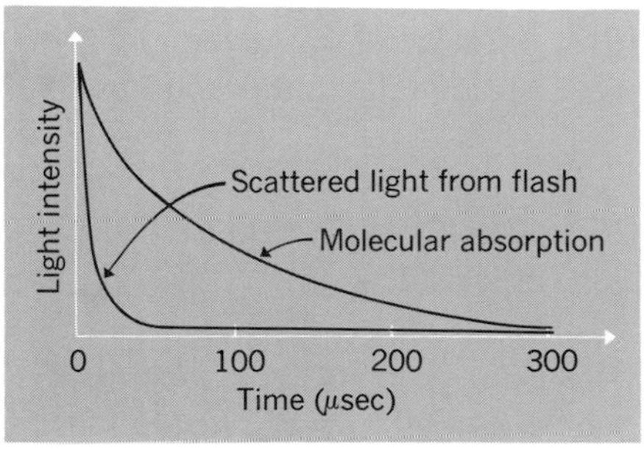

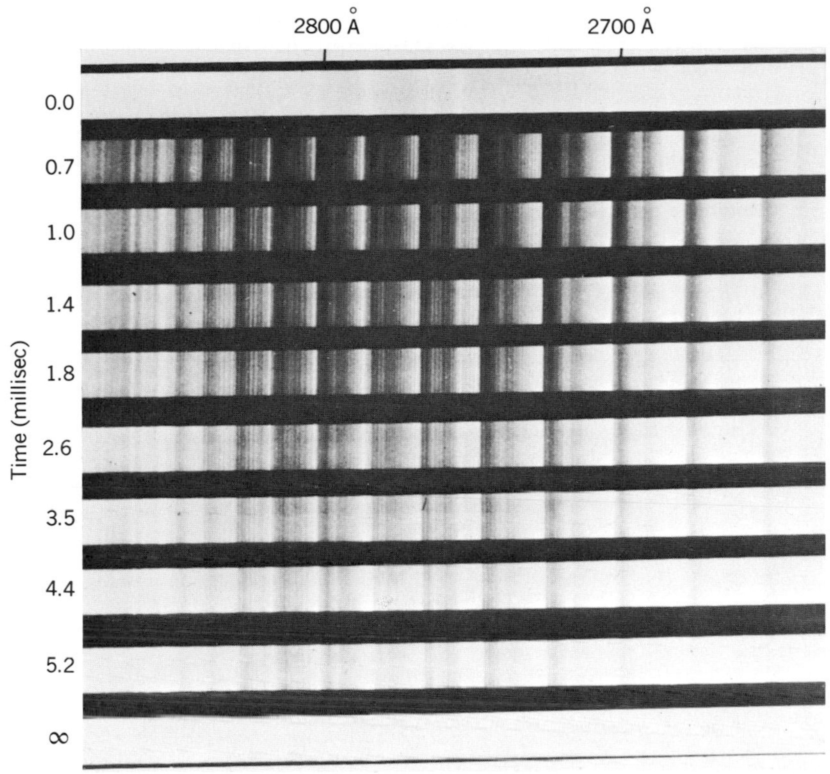

Figure 22.7 Photographic record of the disappearance of ClO produced by the flash photolysis of a mixture of Cl_2 and O_2. The rate of disappearance is proportional to $[ClO]^2$. [R. G. W. Norrish, *Science*, **149**, 1470 (1965). Copyright 1965 by the American Association for the Advancement of Science.]

An analogous technique is available for the study of thermal reactions. In shock-tube experiments, a glass or steel tube, perhaps 15 feet long and half a foot in diameter, is separated into two sections by a thin plastic or metal foil membrane. One side contains an inert "driver" gas at a pressure of the order of 10 atm and the other side contains a mixture of inert gas and reactant at a lower pressure (perhaps a few mm). When the membrane is punctured, a shock wave passes down the tube at velocities of the order of Mach 3 to 8, instantaneously (less than 10^{-10} sec) raising the temperature of the reaction mixture to temperature of from 5000°to 10,000°C. The resulting chemical changes can be conveniently measured by spectroscopic or mass spectrometric techniques as a function of the elapsed time following the passage of the shock. See Table 22.1 for some rate constants, k, and ΔE_{act} values determined in this way.

Nuclear magnetic resonance provides evidence on rates whose half-lives are in the range 10^{-1} to 10^{-7} sec, especially rates involving hydrogen atoms. If hydrogen atoms remain in a given environment for more than about 10^{-1} sec, they produce sharp, individual NMR absorption peaks. But if the hydrogen atoms are exchanging between two positions, the peaks corresponding to the two positions tend to merge into another single peak, whose width is related to the rate of exchange. Both the degree of merging and the peak width are related to the exchange

Table 22.1 **Rate data from shock tube experiments. Arrhenius pre-exponential factors, *A*, and activation energies, ΔE , for gas-phase dissociation steps in tertiary butyl hydrocarbons and in tertiary butyl halides obtained from shock tube experiments using standard known reactions (1 and 5) for comparison. Note that the *A* values are essentially constant in each group but that ΔE_{act} decreases either as more and more methyl groups surround the carbon-carbon bond that breaks, or as the polarizability of the attached halogen increases. This may mean that activation energies for the decompositions of these hydrocarbons decrease as the electron cloud in the vicinity is more and more diffuse.**

	Mechanistic step	$k = Ae^{-\Delta E_{act}/RT}$ sec^{-1}	
		A	ΔE_{act} (kcal mole)
	Tertiary butyl hydrocarbons		
1.	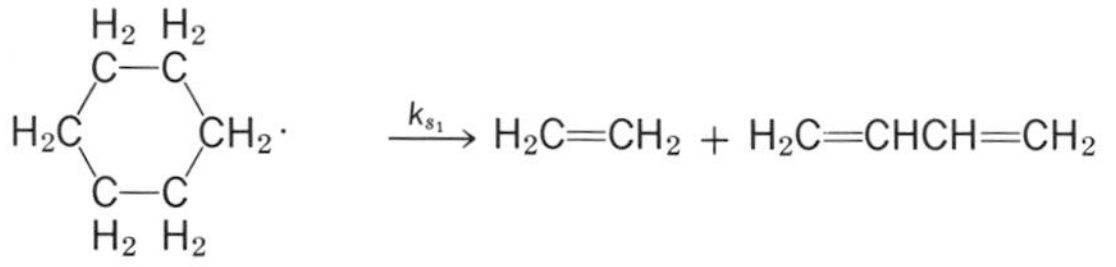	$10^{15.02}$ (primary standard)	66.7
2.	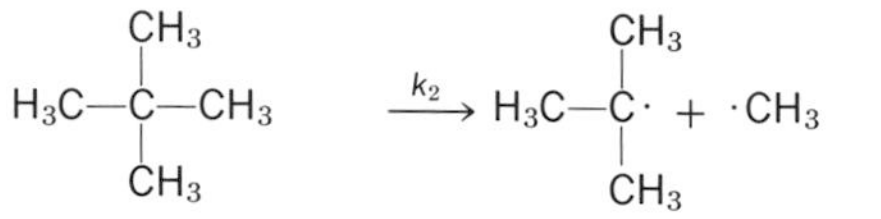	$10^{16.1}$	78.2
3.	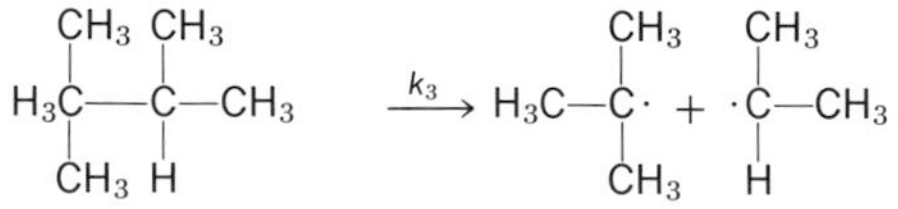	$10^{16.2}$	73.0
4.	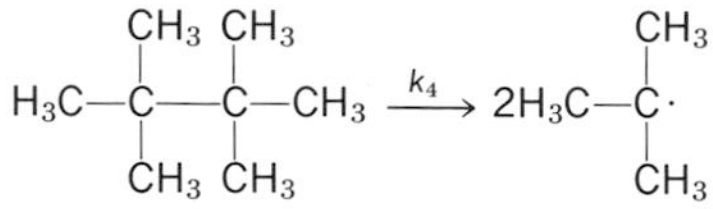	$10^{16.3}$	68.5
	Tertiary butyl halides		
5.	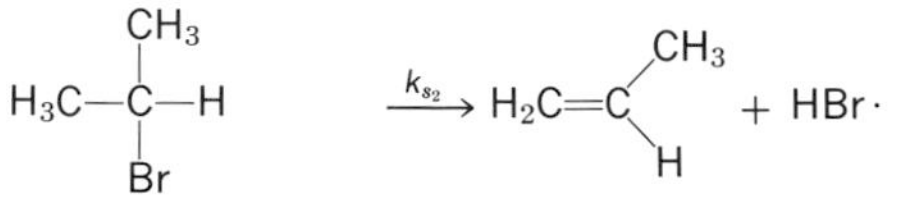	$10^{13.62}$ (primary standard)	47.8
6.	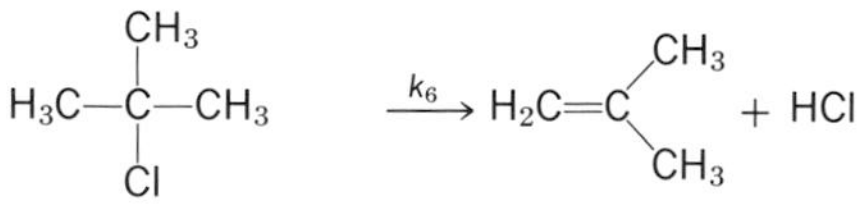	$10^{13.7}$	44.7
7.	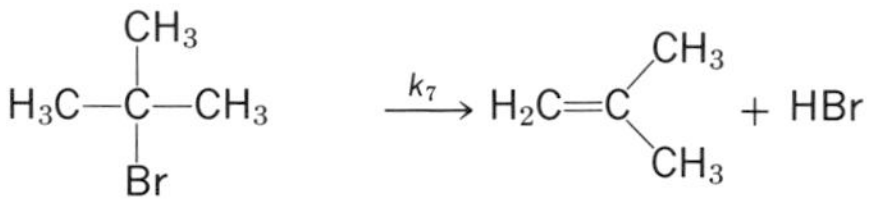	$10^{13.9}$	41.49
8.	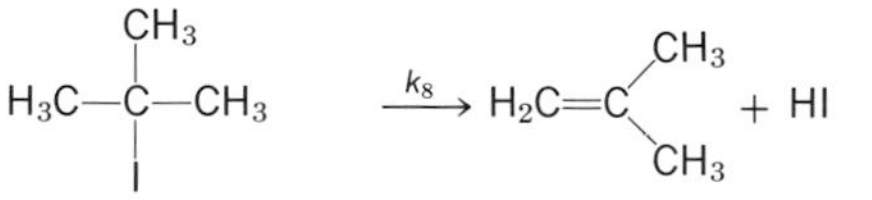	$10^{13.7}$	38.08

SOURCE: Results of Wing Tsang, *J. Chem. Phys.*, **44**, 4283 (1966).

Table 22.2 **Rate constants of some reactions involving aqueous ions. All reactions in water around room temperature 20°C ±10. *EDTA*$^{4-}$ = ethylene diamine tetra-acetate ion = $(^-OOCCH_2)_2NCH_2CH_2N(CH_2COO^-)_2$. *PAS*$^-$ = *p*-amino salicylate ion = $H_2NC_6H_3$-$(OH)CO_2^-$.**

Reaction	$k_f\,(M^{-1}\,sec^{-1})$[a]	$k_r\,(sec^{-1})$[b]	$K_{eq} = k_r/k_f$
$H^+ + OH^- \rightleftarrows H_2O$	$1.4 \cdot 10^{11}$	$2.6 \cdot 10^{-5}$	$1.9 \cdot 10^{-16}$
$CH_3COO^- + H^+ \rightleftarrows CH_3COOH$	$4.5 \cdot 10^{10}$	$8 \cdot 10^{5}$	$1.8 \cdot 10^{-5}$
$NH_3 + H^+ \rightleftarrows NH_4^+$	$4.3 \cdot 10^{10}$	24	$5.6 \cdot 10^{-10}$
$NH_4^+ + OH^- \rightleftarrows NH_3 + H_2O$	$3.4 \cdot 10^{10}$	$5 \cdot 10^{5}$	$1.5 \cdot 10^{-5}$
$C_3N_2H_5^+ + OH^- \rightleftarrows C_3N_2H_4 + H_2O$	$2.3 \cdot 10^{10}$	$2.5 \cdot 10^{3}$	$1.1 \cdot 10^{-7}$
$C_3N_2H_4 + H^+ \rightleftarrows C_3N_2H_5^+$	$1.5 \cdot 10^{10}$	$1.7 \cdot 10^{3}$	$1.1 \cdot 10^{-7}$
$OH^- + HEDTA^{3-} \rightleftarrows EDTA^{4-} + H_2O$	$3.8 \cdot 10^{7}$	$6.9 \cdot 10^{3}$	$1.8 \cdot 10^{-4}$
$OH^- + PAS^- \rightleftarrows PAS^{2-} + H_2O$	$3 \cdot 10^{7}$	$3 \cdot 10^{4}$	$1 \cdot 10^{-3}$

SOURCE: Adapted from G. G. Hammes, *Science*, **151**, 1509 (1966).
[a] Rate constant for the reaction in the forward direction.
[b] Rate constant for the reaction in the reverse direction.

rates. Table 22.2 shows some typical results for some simple, single-step reactions whose mechanism agrees with the net equation shown. Note that the forward reactions are all much faster than the reverse ones, consistent with the idea that oppositely charged ions will unite more rapidly than they will separate. In the first six cases in Table 22.2, the molecules, often positive and negative ions, react on every collision, accounting for the very similar values of k_f. In the last two cases, the rate of the forward reaction is about 1000 times slower, partly because both reactants have the same charge. Note also that $K_{eq} = k_r/k_f$, as required by the principle of microscopic reversibility (see p. 451).

Exercise 22.5

Estimate the collision rate in molecules sec^{-1} for $H^+ + CH_3COO^-$ in 1 *M* CH_3COOH. *Answer:* Assume that reaction occurs with each collision. Then collision rate $= d[H^+]/dt = k[H^+][CH_3CO_2^-]$ moles sec^{-1} $liter^{-1}$ $= k[H^+]^2 \cdot 6.02 \cdot 10^{23}$ molecules sec^{-1} $liter^{-1}$. In 1 *M* HOAc, $[H^+] = 4 \cdot 10^{-3}$, since $K = 1.8 \cdot 10^{-5}$. So the collision rate $= 4.5 \cdot 10^{10} \cdot (4 \cdot 10^{-3})^2 \cdot 6.02 \cdot 10^{23} \cong 1 \cdot 10^{29}$ molecules $liter^{-1}$ sec^{-1}. Since there are, on average, about $4 \cdot 10^{-3} \cdot 6 \cdot 10^{23} = 2 \cdot 10^{21}$ hydrogen ions per liter, each ion makes about 10^8 collisions per second. This frequency is not likely. The mechanism probably involves collisions of H_2O and OAc in which a proton is transferred. This mechanism gives a more reasonable collision frequency.

INFERENCE OF MECHANISM FROM KINETIC MEASUREMENTS

From a mechanistic point of view, rate data are principally negative information. A reliable set of kinetic data serves mainly to permit us to discard various otherwise seemingly plausible mechanistic steps whose predictions are at variance with our observations. Even if we can conjure up a mechanism that agrees in detail with our kinetic data, we have not proved that the mechanism is correct, nor can we ever prove it. We have only provided some supporting evidence in favor of it. There may be other mechanisms we are unfamiliar with which would agree with the data just as well. This is typical of human ideas, but even negative information provides enormous insights into natural systems.

A second point of considerable importance concerns the correspondence between the over-all stoichiometry of a chemical reaction and its mechanism. There is, in general, none.

Let us consider a simple example. In the photochemical decomposition of gaseous hydrogen bromide, the over-all stoichiometry is

$$2HBr \longrightarrow H_2 + Br_2$$

However, as far as we know there is no detectable step in the mechanism of this reaction that involves a collisional reaction of two molecules of hydrogen bromide. Instead, we have good reason to believe that the reaction actually occurs according to the following mechanism:

$$HBr + h\nu \longrightarrow H + Br$$
$$H + HBr \longrightarrow H_2 + Br$$
$$2Br \longrightarrow Br_2$$

It is only by coincidence that we will find any correspondence between the stoichiometry and the mechanism of a chemical reaction. Stoichiometry alone cannot reveal mechanisms.

Exercise 22.6

What can you deduce about the kinetics of the net reaction $C_3H_8 \longrightarrow CH_4 + C_2H_4$? *Answer:* Only that the sum of the mechanistic steps must add to give this net reaction; nothing else.

With these admonitions in mind, we can proceed to the definition of two quantities we shall need for a discussion of reaction mechanisms: reaction order and reaction molecularity.

REACTION ORDER

In general, the rate of a reaction is a function of concentrations of some of the species taking part in the reaction. The nature of the dependence is commonly described by giving the differential rate equation of the reaction. Thus, in the formation of hydrogen chloride from iodine chloride and iodine, the reaction is seen to proceed according to the stoichiometry

Net equation: $$2ICl + H_2 \longrightarrow 2HCl + I_2$$

The rate of this reaction is observed to depend on the concentrations of reactants:

Differential rate equation:

$$\text{rate} = \text{const}\,[ICl][H_2] = -\frac{d[ICl]}{dt} = -2\frac{d[H_2]}{dt} = \frac{d[HCl]}{dt} = 2\frac{d[I_2]}{dt}$$

This situation is described by saying that the reaction is second order as a whole, first order with respect to iodine chloride, and first order with respect to hydrogen. The order corresponds to exponents of the concentration terms in the differential rate equation. Note that the order cannot be deduced from the net equation.

Any correspondence between stoichiometry and rate law is coincidental and misleading. In the general case, the rate law cannot be inferred even approximately from the observed stoichiometry. A good example of this is provided by the hydrogen-halogen systems. The thermal reactions of hydrogen with iodine and bromine both occur according to the same stoichiometry:

Net equation: $$H_2 + I_2 \longrightarrow 2HI$$

Net equation: $$H_2 + Br_2 \longrightarrow 2HBr$$

The rate of production of HI is described by

Differential rate equation: $$\frac{d[HI]}{dt} = k[H_2][I_2] \tag{22.3}$$

Thus, the $H_2 - I_2$ reaction is second order as a whole, first order in $[H_2]$, and first order in $[I_2]$. The coincidence between the net equation and the rate equation is just that—a coincidence. The rate of production of the halogen acid in the bromine system is not so simply described, having instead the following functional dependence:

Differential rate equation: $$\frac{d[HBr]}{dt} = \frac{k_a[H_2][Br_2]^{1/2}}{k_b + [HBr][Br_2]^{-1}} \tag{22.4}$$

It is not easy to describe the order of this reaction, though it is first order in hydrogen, but the rate equation summarizes the experimental observations. Obviously, different mechanisms must be involved in the HBr and HI systems, since their rate equations are different. This example also illustrates the common observation of fractional dependence on concentration terms.

The essential idea to be retained is that reaction order, which may commonly be nonintegral, need have no obvious relationship to the stoichiometry of the reaction, and may not be expressible as a simple number.

Exercise 22.7

Give the orders for the following net reactions and rate equations: $C_{12}H_{22}O_{11} + H_2O \longrightarrow 2C_6H_{12}O_6$, $d[C_{12}H_{22}O_{11}]/dt = -k[C_{12}H_{22}O_{11}][H^+]$; $2NH_{3(g)} = N_{2(g)} + 3H_{2(g)}$ (on tungsten surface), $d[NH_3]/dt = -k$; $H_2 + Br_2 \longrightarrow 2HBr$, initially $d[HBr]/dt = k[H_2][Br_2]^{1/2}$. *Answer:* First order in $C_{12}H_{22}O_{11}$, first order in hydrogen ion; zero order in any reactant; first order in hydrogen, one-half order in bromine.

REACTION MOLECULARITY

A reaction mechanism that is responsible for the conversion of reactants to products ordinarily consists of a series of simultaneous and/or sequential steps, which may be written as mechanistic equations. These steps may be individually characterized in terms of the number of molecules involved. Each mechanistic step may thus be described in terms of its *molecularity.*

A *unimolecular* step is one in which only a single molecule is involved and results in either a rearrangement or a fragmentation. For example, a process observed in the mass spectrometer is the rearrangement of the benzyl ion to the tropylium ion:

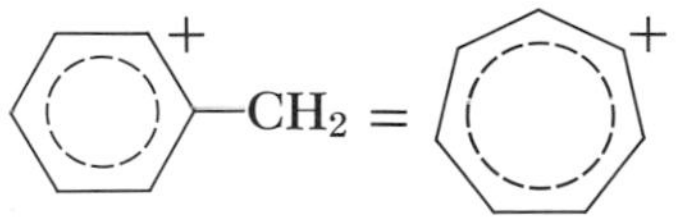

Differential rate equation: $-d[C_6H_5CH_2^+] = k[C_6H_5CH_2]^+$

A *bimolecular* step is one in which two species must come together before a reaction can occur. For example, there are a large number of bimolecular ion-molecule reactions, similar to the following:

Mechanistic equation: $CH_4^{\oplus} + C_2H_6 \longrightarrow CH_5^{\oplus} + C_2H_5$

Differential rate equation: $-\dfrac{d[C_2H_6]}{dt} = k[CH_4^+][C_2H_6]$

Practically all actual chemical reactions—that is, practically all mechanistic steps, as opposed to net reactions—are unimolecular or bimolecular. Thus actual chemical reactions are extremely simple.

Occasionally we find a *termolecular* mechanistic step, apparently involving a simultaneous collision of three species followed by separation of the reaction products. For example,

Mechanistic equation: $2NO + Br_2 \longrightarrow 2NOBr$

Differential rate equation: $\dfrac{d[NOBr]}{dt} = k[NO]^2[Br_2]$

The probability of true termolecular reaction steps in the gas phase is very low. On the basis of a simple calculation of collision frequency, it can be shown that ternary collisions in the gas phase are much rarer (less than $1/10^3$) than binary collisions. It is therefore better to view this reaction and other similar reactions involving nitric oxide as being made up of an equilibrium and a subsequent bimolecular step:

$$NO + Br_2 \underset{k_2}{\overset{k_1}{\rightleftharpoons}} NOBr_2$$

$$NO + NOBr_2 \xrightarrow{k_3} 2NOBr$$

Differential rate equation:

$$\frac{d[NOBr]}{dt} = \frac{k_1k_3}{k_2}[NO]^2[Br_2] = k[NO]^2[Br_2] \qquad (22.5)$$

This mechanism is consistent with our observed rate data. It is also consistent with the fact that the system shows a negative activation energy. That is, as the temperature is raised, the rate of reaction appears to decrease as in Figure 22.1, B. We see that the first step in this mechanism yields an unstable intermediate $NOBr_2$, which may either decompose in the reverse reaction or undergo collision and reaction with a second molecule of NO. As the temperature of the reaction increases, we would expect that the rate of reverse reaction of $NOBr_2$ would increase and that its equilibrium concentration would be reduced, resulting in a decrease in the rate of production of NOBr and hence in an apparently negative activation energy.

Exercise 22.8

Write type equations using A, B, C as reactants to illustrate a unimolecular, a bimolecular, and a termolecular mechanistic step. *Answer:* A = products is unimolecular; A + B = products is bimolecular; A + B + C = products, or A + 2B = products, or 3A = products are all termolecular.

NEGATIVE APPARENT ACTIVATION ENERGIES

We are now in a position to understand the negative activation energies previously mentioned for atom recombination reactions. Consider the recombination of two atoms:

$$I\cdot + I\cdot \longrightarrow I_2$$

At the instant of bond formation, an amount of energy is liberated equal to the bond energy of the molecule. If this energy is not removed in some way, the molecule will simply redissociate. It is for this reason that the reaction is commonly written as

$$I\cdot + I\cdot + M \longrightarrow I_2 + M$$

The relative rate of two- and three-body collisions in a gas is given approximately by the ratio of mean free path to molecular diameter.

$$l/d \cong 10^{-5}/10^{-8} = 10^3 = \frac{\text{number of two-body collisions}}{\text{number of three-body collisions}}$$

As collisions with M become "stickier," recombination becomes more and more likely.

In view of these points and the experimental observation that the rate of recombination diminishes with increasing temperature, we should more properly write the reaction mechanism as

$$I + M \underset{k_2}{\overset{k_1}{\rightleftharpoons}} IM$$

$$IM + I \xrightarrow{k_3} I_2 + M$$

The activation energy for reaction 1 is usually close to zero, as is that for 3, but the activation energy for reaction 2 is always positive. Thus the net, or apparent, activation energy in the "forward" direction is negative, even though there is no actual negative activation energy. Rates that decrease as temperature increases indicate mechanisms involving competing reactions in which the rate of the "forward" reaction increases more slowly with rising temperature than does the rate of some competing reaction.

Although this mechanism is supported by the observed kinetics and energetics, you must remember that it is in no way proved by them. In this particular case further substantiating evidence has been provided by the spectroscopic observation of the unstable complex IM.

Exercise 22.9

What would be the nature of M to make reaction $I + M \longrightarrow IM$ more probable than the reaction $I + I \longrightarrow I_2$, even though both reactions are certainly exothermic? *Answer:* If M is a polyatomic molecule, it may be able to disperse the energy of reaction among its various modes of motion and so achieve stability until further collisions reduce its total energy content to a truly stable level. Or IM might radiate the energy.

MOLECULAR AND FREE RADICAL MECHANISMS

Consider the photochemical gas-phase decomposition of a saturated hydrocarbon such as ethane with radiation of wavelength 1470 Å. This system illustrates a number of techniques in common use by gas kineticists.

An analysis of the distribution of products in this system shows that about 90% of the products consist of hydrogen, ethylene, and acetylene. When we speculate about the mechanistic steps in this reaction, two obvious processes occur to us as sources of hydrogen:

$$(1)\quad C_2H_6 + h\nu \longrightarrow C_2H_4 + H_2 \qquad \text{(molecular mechanism)}$$

or

$$\left.\begin{array}{ll}(2a) & C_2H_6 + h\nu \longrightarrow C_2H_5\cdot + H\cdot \\ (2b) & H\cdot + C_2H_6 \longrightarrow H_2 + C_2H_5\cdot\end{array}\right\} \qquad \text{(free radical mechanism)}$$

Mechanism 1 represents a molecular elimination of hydrogen; mechanism 2 is a free radical process involving subsequent hydrogen abstraction (*b*) from ethane by a hydrogen atom produced in the primary process (*a*). How can we determine whether one or both of these processes contribute to the over-all decomposition? Two approaches are now in common use. In an elegant experiment of Okabe and McNesby in 1961, it was determined that process 1 is by far the most important. Their experiment consisted of measuring the rate of production of isotopically substituted hydrogens from the photochemical decomposition of a mixture of C_2H_6 and C_2D_6 in equal amounts. If process 2 were important, we would expect a considerable yield of HD in addition to substantial amounts of H_2 and D_2. In fact, the following distribution was obtained:

H_2, 58.1% HD, 3.3% D_2, 38.5%

The other technique in common use which permits the kineticist to distinguish between molecular and free radical mechanisms in the gas phase is the

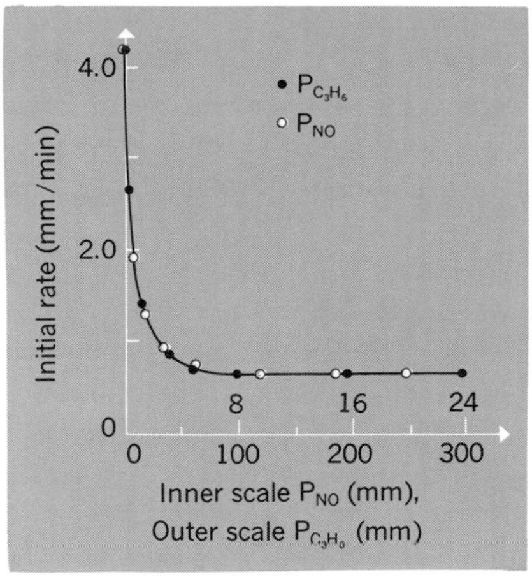

Figure 22.8 Effect of added free radical scavengers, nitric oxide and propylene, on the thermal unimolecular decomposition of 100 mm of *n*-pentane at 530°C. [F. J. Stubbs and C. N. Hinshelwood, *Proc. Roy. Soc., A*, **200,** 458 (1950).]

addition of trace quantities of free radical scavengers. These are materials which exhibit a very small activation energy when they react with free radicals. They remove the free radicals and decrease the yield of products formed through a free radical mechanism. The two scavengers in most common use are nitric oxide and ethylene. They are particularly effective in removing hydrogen atoms:

$$H\cdot + NO\cdot \longrightarrow HNO$$
$$H\cdot + C_2H_4 \longrightarrow C_2H_5\cdot$$

In the ethane system, the addition of NO has little effect on the rate of production of hydrogen, thus confirming the basically molecular nature of the mechanism. The complete details of the mechanism for the photochemical decomposition of ethane, however, are not completely understood at present.

A further example of the use of free radical scavengers is shown in Figure 22.8, which demonstrates the effectiveness of nitric oxide in eliminating the free radical processes in the thermal decomposition of *n*-pentane. If enough scavenger is used, the initial rate of decomposition can be reduced to a low value, which remains unchanged if further scavenger is added. The interpretation of this result is that there are at least two mechanisms participating in this system, one of which is probably a free radical mechanism; the other is molecular.

Exercise 22.10

Which is the faster, the free radical or the molecular mechanism of the thermal $C_2H_6 = C_2H_4 + H_2$ reaction? *Answer:* Figure 22.8 shows that, at least initially, the free radical mechanism for C_7H_{16} is about ten times as fast as the thermal molecular mechanism. It is likely that the C_2H_6 thermal reaction is similar. The greater slowness of the thermal molecular mechanism is consistent with the great molecular contortions needed to produce H_2 in one step from C_2H_6. Photochemical excitation, as contrasted with thermal excitation, forms excited electron states involving antibonding orbitals and possibly wide deviations from the geometry of the ground state. These new geometries often enhance the likelihood of splitting out stable molecular products, rather than the free radicals most common in thermal reactions.

IONIC MECHANISMS

As you found out in Chapter 17, especially in Problem 17.14, the likelihood of forming ions thermally in a gas is so small as to be negligible except at the highest temperatures. Thus ionic mechanisms in the gas phase are normally undetectable. This is not true in condensed phases.

Interactions between ions and the surrounding molecules can be strong enough in condensed phases to make the ions stable relative to the corresponding neutral molecules. In fact, many substances exist in their own pure condensed phases primarily as ions. This becomes more and more probable as the difference in relative electronegativity increases (Figure 14.4). Thus, compounds of a metallic and a nonmetallic element may be ionic in the pure condensed phases and also in solution in solvents such as water.

We have already pointed out in the discussion of Table 22.2 that in many cases reactions between ions of opposite charge occur every time the ions collide. Such reactions may be very rapid and their rate completely controlled by the rate of diffusion of the ions—they are said to have diffusion-controlled rates.

The rate of reaction between an ion and a neutral molecule, and especially between two ions of like charge, is normally much slower, partly because of the high repulsive forces acting. Consider the reaction

$$2Ce^{+4} + Tl^{+1} = 2Ce^{+3} + Tl^{+3}, \qquad \mathcal{E}^0 = 0.196 \tag{22.6}$$

This is a very slow reaction, as you would predict from the like positive charges on the reactants and the very high charge on the Ce^{+4}. But the rate of this and of many other ionic reactions is slowed by an additional limitation—only some oxidation states can be easily achieved. Others are energetically unavailable and do not readily form the intermediate compounds necessary to carry out the reaction. In the reaction of (22.6), because of the high energy required to form Ce^{+2} and Tl^{+2} respectively, neither of the following steps is energetically feasible:

$$Ce^{+4} + Tl^{+} \longrightarrow Ce^{+3} + Tl^{+2}$$
$$Ce^{+4} + Tl^{+} \longrightarrow Ce^{+2} + Tl^{+3}$$

Since the termolecular reaction of Equation (22.6) is most unlikely, there is no mechanism by which this reaction can proceed rapidly. But introduction of Mn^{++} ions leads to a much more rapid reaction. The ionic repulsions are still there, but readily attainable intermediates can now form, as in the following mechanism, which fits the experimental data:

$$Ce^{+4} + Mn^{+2} \longrightarrow Ce^{+3} + Mn^{+3}$$
$$Ce^{+4} + Mn^{+3} \longrightarrow Ce^{+3} + Mn^{+4}$$
$$Tl^{+1} + Mn^{+4} \longrightarrow Tl^{+3} + Mn^{+2}$$
$$\text{Net:}\quad 2Ce^{+4} + Tl^{+1} \longrightarrow 2Ce^{+3} + Tl^{+3}$$

Almost all precipitation reactions (and similar reactions in which ions merely come together without redox occurring) are fast, as indicated in Table 22.2. The slowness with which some precipitates form is seldom due to a slow rate of formation of electrically neutral aggregates but rather to a slow nucleation rate of a relatively complicated crystal structure or to the slow rate of the subsequent diffusion steps in which further growth occurs. It is the slow nucleation (initial formation) of crystals that accounts for the phenomenon of supersaturation found in many precipitation reactions.

Exercise 22.11

Suggest a mechanism by which scratching the inside of a container initiates precipitation from a supersaturated solution. *Answer:* A wide variety of surfaces are exposed along the scratch. If one of them approximately matches the crystal structure of the potential crystal, nucleation may occur and crystal growth proceed. Alternatively the high rate of energy dissipation along the scratched surface may provide ΔE_{act} for a slow initial step and initiate crystallization.

FROM RATE DATA TO RATE LAWS

Perhaps the simplest way to determine the relationship of rate to concentration of a given reactant, A, is to start with a system in which that particular reactant is present in lower concentration than all other species. During the reaction, the concentration of the reactant of interest, A, will decrease but all other concentrations will remain essentially unchanged. Thus any change in rate will be due solely to the change in concentration of the reactant being studied:

$$\frac{d[\text{products}]}{dt} = k[\text{A}]^m$$

The method may be repeated for each possible reactant to give the total rate law. Since this method treats each reactant separately, keeping all other variables essentially constant, it is called the isolation method.

Another method of determining the relationships of concentrations to rate is called the initial-rate method. Consider a reaction that is typical of some of the systems we would call complex—those systems in which the rate law is not the same as the stoichiometry. Let us take the reaction between nitric oxide and hydrogen. Some data available on the system are given in Table 22.3. Note that, since the rates change with composition of the system, initial rates are given (that is, the limiting rate as $t \longrightarrow 0$).

The stoichiometry of the reaction is given as

$$2\text{NO} + 2\text{H}_2 \longrightarrow \text{N}_2 + 2\text{H}_2\text{O}$$

All products are gases above 100°C, so the reaction can be followed quite simply by manometric techniques.

One observation can be made immediately about the form of the mechanism. Since tetramolecular collisions in the gas phase will have a prohibitively low frequency, the mechanism cannot be simply related to the stoichiometry. We can determine the order of the reaction by holding the concentration of one reactant constant while varying the other. Let us consider the order of the reaction with respect to hydrogen first. To determine this, the initial rate of the reaction is observed at varying hydrogen concentrations and fixed nitric oxide concentrations as in the last three lines of Table 22.3. Setting the lowest hydrogen pressure equal to 1.00, we compute the two other relative hydrogen pressures:

$$\frac{205}{147} = 1.39, \qquad \frac{289}{147} = 1.97$$

Setting the lowest measured rate corresponding to the lowest hydrogen pressure equal to 1.00, we compute the relative rates of reaction for the two other hydrogen pressures:

$$\frac{110}{79} = 1.39, \qquad \frac{160}{79} = 2.02$$

It is clear that the rate is proportional to the first power of the hydrogen concentration. Thus the reaction is first order in hydrogen. A similar manipulation of the data for fixed hydrogen concentration and variable nitric oxide concentration reveals that the rate depends on the second power of the nitric oxide concentration. Thus the rate law must have the form

$$\text{rate of reaction} = k[\text{NO}]^2[\text{H}_2] = -\frac{d[\text{NO}]}{dt} = -\frac{d[\text{H}_2]}{dt} = 2\frac{d[\text{N}_2]}{dt} = \frac{d[\text{H}_2\text{O}]}{dt} \tag{22.7}$$

Confirmation of this conclusion is provided by considering the constancy of the values of k that can be derived for various concentrations. These data are presented in the last column of Table 22.3.

Many reactions involving gases are not homogeneous—that is, they do not occur in the gas phase—and so are termed heterogeneous. Their presence is tested by varying the surface-to-volume ratio of the reaction vessel to see whether this has a pronounced effect upon the rate of reaction. Variation of surface can be readily achieved by packing the vessel with glass tubes or glass powder. In the H_2—NO system, such an experiment reveals that the mechanism is mainly homogeneous, but that a wall reaction also occurs and leads to inconstancy in the k's calculated in Table 22.3.

Table 22.3 Rate data for the reaction of hydrogen with nitric oxide at 826°C. Rate = $k[H_2][NO]^2$.

Hydrogen pressure (mm Hg)	Nitric oxide pressure (mm Hg)	Initial reaction rate (mm/100 sec)	k[a] [from Eq. (22.7)] ($mm^{-2}\ sec^{-1}$)
400	152	25	$2.71 \cdot 10^{-7}$
400	300	103	$2.86 \cdot 10^{-7}$
400	359	150	$2.91 \cdot 10^{-7}$
300	232	45	$2.79 \cdot 10^{-7}$
300	310	92	$3.19 \cdot 10^{-7}$
300	400	174	$3.63 \cdot 10^{-7}$
289	400	160	$3.46 \cdot 10^{-7}$
205	400	110	$3.37 \cdot 10^{-7}$
147	400	79	$3.35 \cdot 10^{-7}$

SOURCE: C. N. Hinshelwood and T. E. Green, *J. Chem. Soc.*, **129**, 730 (1926).
[a] The variation in k is due to a competing wall reaction involving the NO.

Exercise 22.12

Synthesize data in a table like Table 22.3 for a system whose rate equation is known to be

$$-\frac{d[A]}{dt} = k[A][B]$$

Answer:

p_A (mm)	p_B (mm)	Initial rate (mm/100 sec)	
400	200	100	
400	300	150	
400	400	200	$k = 1.3 \cdot 10^{-5}\ \text{mm}^{-1}\ \text{sec}^{-1}$
300	400	150	
200	400	100	

MECHANISTIC EVIDENCE FROM TRACER EXPERIMENTS

Tracer applications can also give evidence concerning mechanisms, independent of rate measurements. We have, for example, the esterification of benzoic acid with methyl alcohol:

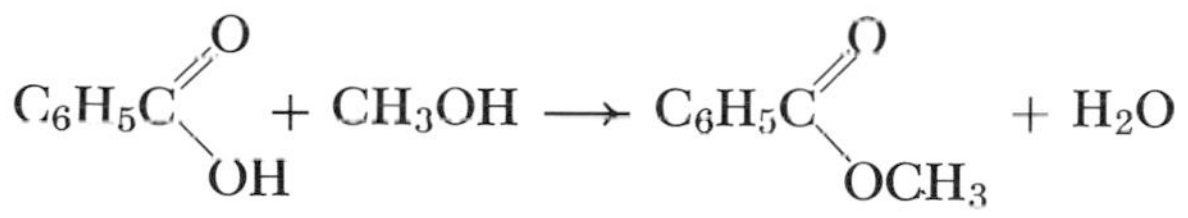

We may logically ask whether the oxygen that winds up in the water molecule is one that belonged originally to the methyl alcohol or to the benzoic acid. Rate data alone give no evidence on this point. But if we carry out the experiment using methyl alcohol, in which the oxygen contains a small percentage of oxygen 18, we find that no oxygen-18 appears in the water, thus proving that the oxygen of the water comes from the acid. Definitive experiments of this type are numerous.

RATE-DETERMINING STEPS AND REACTIVE INTERMEDIATES

The usual reason the rate law is substantially different from the net stoichiometry is that more than one mechanistic step is involved. The sum of all the simple steps then gives the net equation. It is commonly true that one of these steps will be substantially slower than any of the others. When this is the case, the rate of the over-all reaction will be determined by this single slow step. We call such a step the rate-determining step. Normally such systems have simple (usually second-order) rate laws from which the equation for the rate-determining step (usually bimolecular) may be deduced. For example, the reaction between hydrogen and iodine monochloride proceeds in the gas phase according to the following stoichiometry:

Net equation: $$2ICl + H_2 \longrightarrow 2HCl + I_2$$

However, the rate law has the form

Differential rate equation: $$\text{rate} = k[ICl][H_2]$$

This strongly suggests that the rate-determining step in this mechanism is a slow bimolecular reaction between ICl and H_2. In fact, the kinetic data on this system have been explained in terms of a two-step mechanism:

Mechanistic equations: $$ICl + H_2 \xrightarrow{\text{slow}} HI + HCl \qquad \text{(the rate-determining step)}$$

$$ICl + HI \xrightarrow{\text{fast}} HCl + I_2 \qquad \text{(a subsequent fast reaction)}$$

Similarly, the first order experimental rate law

$$\frac{d[C_7H_7^+]}{dt} = k[C_6H_5CH_2^+]$$

suggests $C_6H_5CH_2^+ \xrightarrow{\text{slow}} C_7H_7^+$.

Consider the net reaction in aqueous solution:

$$3I^- + S_2O_8^= = 2SO_4^= + I_3^-$$

The experimental differential rate equation $d[I_3^-]/dt = k[I^-][S_2O_8^=]$ suggests the

Rate-determining step: $$I^- + S_2O_8^= \xrightarrow{\text{slow}} IS_2O_8^{\equiv}$$

It is reasonable that this reaction between ions of like charge would be slow.

The intermediate compound, $IS_2O_8^{\equiv}$, is not very stable and so does not exist for long periods of time, but its structure is a reasonable one, probably

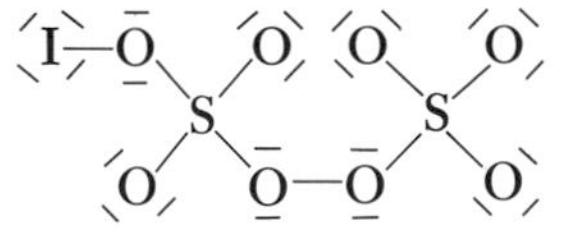

with five pairs of electrons on iodine, as in I_3^- and similar species. The likelihood of forming this structure on collision is high, since there are six identical exposed oxygens. Reactive intermediates must, in general, have probable geometrical and electron structures.

The fact that the stoichiometric coefficient of the iodide ion (3) exceeds the iodide order (1) means there must be additional mechanistic steps after the slow rate-determining step. Possible further steps could be

$$IS_2O_8^{\equiv} \xrightarrow{\text{fast}} 2SO_4^= + I^+$$

$$I^+ + I^- \xrightarrow{\text{fast}} I_2$$

$$I_2 + I^- \xrightarrow{\text{fast}} I_3^-$$

which sum to give the experimental net reaction. We would expect that each of the last three reactions might be fast, consistent with the electrical forces involved.

On the other hand, the complicated experimental rate law

$$\frac{d[HBr]}{dt} = \frac{k_a[H_2][Br_2]^{1/2}}{k_b + [HBr][Br_2]^{-1}}$$

suggests a complicated mechanism with no single rate-determining step.

Exercise 22.13

Suggest an equation for the rate-determining step in the net reaction, $5HBr + HBrO_3 = 3Br_2 + 3H_2O$, when the differential rate equation is: $d[Br_2]/dt = k[H^+]^2[Br^-][BrO_3^-]$. *Answer:* Although the rate equation is fourth order, the slow mechanistic step is most likely bimolecular. Thus, if there are equilibria such as $H^+ + Br^- \rightleftarrows HBr$ and $H^+ + BrO_3^- \rightleftarrows HBrO_3$, the slow step could be $HBr + HBrO_3 \longrightarrow$ products [possibly $\cdot Br + \cdot BrO(OH)_2$]. This suggestion fits all the available data. Following steps would then be fast. Try to invent a complete mechanism.

A more complicated problem arises in the isotopic exchange reaction

$$Cr^{*+++}{}_{(aq)} + CrO_4{}^{=}{}_{(aq)} = CrO_4{}^{*=}{}_{(aq)} + Cr^{+++}{}_{(aq)}$$

which we shall write, for simplicity,

$$Cr(III)^* + Cr(VI) = Cr(VI)^* + Cr(III)$$

At constant acidity the experimental rate equation is

$$\text{forward rate} = k[Cr(III)]^{4/3}[Cr(VI)]^{2/3}$$

Since the rate-determining step can involve only integral numbers of atoms and the intermediate formed must contain integral numbers of atoms, this rate law suggests an intermediate step involving a single Cr(III) and some other species whose concentration is proportional to $[Cr(III)]^{1/3}[Cr(VI)]^{2/3}$. The following mechanism is consistent with these ideas:

$$Cr(III)^* + 2Cr(VI) \underset{k_2}{\overset{k_1}{\rightleftarrows}} 3Cr(V)(\text{one}^*) \text{ rapid equilibrium, } K = \frac{k_1}{k_2} = \frac{[Cr(V)]^3}{[Cr(III)][Cr(VI)]^2}$$

$$Cr(V) + Cr(III)^* \xrightarrow{k_3} Cr \cdot Cr^*(\text{ave IV}) \longrightarrow Cr(III) + Cr(V)^*, \text{ slow}$$

$$Cr(V)^* + Cr(VI) \longrightarrow Cr(VI)^* + Cr(V), \text{ fast}$$

From the first of these mechanistic equations we get

$$[Cr(V)] = K^{1/3}[Cr(III)^*]^{1/3}[Cr(VI)]^{2/3}$$

Thus the

$$\text{forward rate} = k_3[Cr(V)][Cr(III)^*] = k_3[Cr(III)^*]^{4/3}[Cr(VI)]^{2/3}$$

The rate here would be immeasurably slow except for the high degree of solvation by the water, which produces ions such as $Cr(H_2O)_6{}^{+++}$ and $CrO_4{}^{=}$. In these large ions the charge densities are low and the sign of the net charge on the Cr(VI) species reversed, so the rates are readily measurable. But these solvent interactions do not appear in the rate law, and its form gives no direct evidence of their occurrence.

In most cases, as in those discussed so far, reaction rate is limited by a single slow step involving the formation of a reactive intermediate [like $IS_2O_8^=$ or Cr · Cr* (ave IV)]. The formula of the reactive intermediate (and the reactants in the rate-determining step) can often be deduced from examination of the experimental rate law.

FORMULATION OF A MECHANISM FOR THE H_2—NO SYSTEM

The experimental rate data in the NO—H_2 system can be expressed in the form

$$\text{rate} = k[NO]^2[H_2] \tag{22.8}$$

We might consider that such an expression predicts that the mechanism may consist of a single termolecular reaction between NO and H_2. However, our previous information would suggest that we first consider a sequence of bimolecular steps (because of their greater frequency of occurrence), only one of which would be slow. We may make the reasonable suggestion that the over-all reaction can be described in three steps:

1. $$NO + H_2 \underset{k_{-1}}{\overset{k_1}{\rightleftarrows}} NOH_2 \tag{22.9}$$

2. $$NOH_2 + NO \xrightarrow{k_2} N_2 + H_2O_2 \tag{22.10}$$

3. $$H_2O_2 + H_2 \xrightarrow{k_3} 2H_2O \tag{22.11}$$

Net: $$2NO + 2H_2 = N_2 + 2H_2O$$

We observe that this sequence of reactions (*a*) gives the observed over-all stoichiometry, (*b*) consists of only bimolecular steps, and (*c*) involves as intermediates two species, NOH_2 and H_2O_2, neither of which is found in the final products. Criterion *a* is, of course, mandatory.

Let us comment on each of the molecules noted in *c*. The molecule NOH_2 is not a stable chemical species and we may think of it as only a transient associated complex. Because of this we must consider the reverse reaction to its formation. It is quite possible for any such molecule to undergo a unimolecular dissociation to NO and H_2 (with a low E_{act}) before it has the chance to collide with a second molecule of NO to give the products $N_2 + H_2O_2$. We are justified in neglecting the reverse of reaction (22.10), since it would be a bimolecular reaction involving collision of H_2O_2 and N_2, almost surely with considerable activation energy. Also, the competing reaction of H_2O_2 with H_2 should be much faster both because the activation energy is lower and because the initial concentration of H_2 is greater than that of N_2. We must now determine whether this suggested mechanism is capable of yielding the observed rate law. We may write the rate law in a differential fashion either in terms of disappearance of reactants or appearance of products:

$$\text{rate} = \frac{d[N_2]}{dt} = \frac{1}{2}\frac{d[H_2O]}{dt} = -\frac{1}{2}\frac{d[NO]}{dt} = -\frac{1}{2}\frac{d[H_2]}{dt}$$

Consider the rate of formation of N_2 in reaction (22.10):

$$\frac{d[N_2]}{dt} = k_2[NOH_2][NO] \qquad (22.12)$$

Since NOH_2 is a highly reactive, unstable species, its concentration is difficult to determine. However, we have assumed it to be in equilibrium with NO and H_2, as in the reaction represented by the first equation. Thus

$$\frac{[NOH_2]}{[NO][H_2]} = K = \frac{k_1}{k_{-1}}$$

$$[NOH_2] = \frac{k_1}{k_{-1}}[NO][H_2]$$

Substituting in (22.12), we get

$$\frac{d[N_2]}{dt} = \frac{k_2k_1}{k_{-1}}[NO]^2[H_2]$$

in complete agreement with the experimental rate equation (22.8).

The same result is obtained if we set up the rate expressions in terms of $d[NO]/dt$, but what about the other possibilities given above? What about $d[H_2O]/dt$, for example? In terms of the rate of formation of the product molecule water we have

$$\frac{d[H_2O]}{dt} = 2k_3[H_2O_2][H_2] \qquad (22.13)$$

Although the hydrogen concentration is a readily measurable quantity, that of the intermediate H_2O_2 is not. We must have some measure of the H_2O_2 concentration, and we obtain it through the approximation of the *steady state.*

THE STEADY-STATE APPROXIMATION

The principle of the steady-state approximation was first suggested in 1919–1920 by Christiansen, Herzfeld, and Polanyi. They recognized that in many reactions in gas or condensed phases, relatively small concentrations of reactive intermediates (free radicals, atoms, or unstable molecules) were present. According to this principle, for reactions of the usual speed (half-times of the order of 100 sec or longer), a quasi-equilibrium concentration of these intermediates is established by the time any measurements are made. The concentration of these intermediates is thus maintained at a constant and small level by production and removal in other reactions. The approximation involved is that of setting the rate of change in their concentrations equal to zero. Thus, in the NO—H_2 system, since NOH_2 and H_2O_2 are not found in the final products, we may make the assumption that during the course of the reaction they are present in steady and low concentrations, and so apply the steady-state approximation to them (see Figure 22.9).

For H_2O_2, subtracting the rate of consumption in Equation (22.11) from the rate of production in Equation (22.10) yields

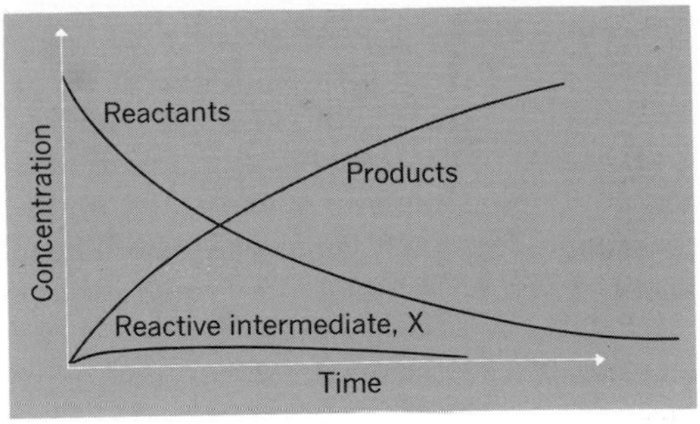

Figure 22.9 Conceptual basis of the steady-state approximation. The rates of change in concentration of principal reactants will be appreciable over most of the reaction time. However, the rate of change of concentration of a reactive intermediate, X, will be small over most of the reaction time, since its concentration is initially zero, is finally zero, and is never high at any time. Thus, $d[X]/dt \cong 0$ at all times (except possibly at the very start of the reaction). The smaller the concentration of X, the better the steady-state approximation holds.

$$\frac{d[H_2O_2]}{dt} = k_2[NOH_2][NO] - k_3[H_2O_2][H_2]$$

By the steady-state approximation, $d[H_2O_2]/dt = 0$, so we obtain

$$[H_2O_2] = \frac{k_2}{k_3}\frac{[NO]}{[H_2]}[NOH_2] \tag{22.14}$$

We may obtain an expression for the NOH_2 concentration in a similar way:

$$\frac{d[NOH_2]}{dt} = k_1[NO][H_2] - k_{-1}[NOH_2] - k_2[NOH_2][NO] \tag{22.15}$$

$$[NOH_2] = \frac{k_1[NO][H_2]}{[k_{-1} + k_2[NO]]} \tag{22.16}$$

Now we may insert expression (22.16) into (22.14) to obtain an expression for the steady-state concentration of H_2O_2, and then insert this in the rate expression (22.13). This yields

$$\frac{d[H_2O]}{dt} = \frac{2k_1k_2[NO]^2[H_2]}{k_{-1} + k_2[NO]} \tag{22.17}$$

Thus if reaction (22.10) is slow compared to the reverse of reaction (22.9) and we can say that $k_2[NO] \ll k_{-1}$, we may write the rate of reaction in complete agreement with the experimental rate law (22.8):

$$\text{rate} = \frac{2k_1k_2}{k_{-1}}[NO]^2[H_2] \tag{22.18}$$

Note that the assumption $k_2[NO] \ll k_{-1}$ in this development is exactly the same as the assumption that NO, H_2, and NOH_2 are in equilibrium in the earlier development. The equilibrium could only exist if reaction (22.10) was slow compared to the reverse reaction (22.9).

It should be noted that the apparent reasonableness of the assumption and the consequent agreement of our predicted rate law with the experimental rate do not prove our mechanism. There may be other mechanisms that would equally well fit the data. For example, we should consider what predictions can be made on the basis of the following mechanisms, as in Equations (22.9) to (22.11):

1′. $NO + H_2 \rightleftharpoons NOH_2$

2′. $NOH_2 + H_2 \longrightarrow H_2O + NH_2$

3′. $NH_2 + NO \longrightarrow N_2 + H_2O$

or

$$1''. \quad NO + NO \rightleftharpoons N_2O_2$$
$$2''. \quad N_2O_2 + H_2 \longrightarrow H_2O + N_2O$$
$$3''. \quad N_2O + H_2 \longrightarrow H_2O + N_2$$

Exercise 22.14

Does the "primed" mechanism above satisfy the experimental data? *Answer:* Use the steady-state approximation:

$$\frac{d[H_2O]}{dt} = k_3'[NH_2][NO] + k_2'[NOH_2][H_2]$$

$$\frac{d[NH_2]}{dt} = 0 = k_2'[NOH_2][H_2] - k_3'[NH_2][NO], \text{ or } [NH_2] = \frac{k_2'}{k_3'}[NOH_2][H_2]/[NO]$$

$$\frac{d[NOH_2]}{dt} = 0 = k_1'[NO][H_2] - k_{-1}'[NOH_2] - k_2'[NOH_2][H_2], \text{ or}$$

$$[NOH_2] = \frac{k_1'[NO][H_2]}{k_{-1}' + k_2'[H_2]}$$

Substituting gives

$$\frac{d[H_2O]}{dt} = \frac{2k_1'k_2'[H_2]^2[NO]}{k_1' + k_2'[H_2]}$$

which does not agree with the experimental rate equation (22.8) no matter what the relative values of the k's may be.

RATE LAWS FOR SIMPLE AND COMPLEX REACTIONS

Although the experimental differential rate law does not establish any particular mechanism, it may provide valuable insight into possible mechanisms and, of course, it always describes the relationship between concentrations and time. It is often more convenient to have the rate law in an integrated rather than differential form. Though many rate laws cannot be readily integrated, a few can; fortunately, these few cover many common chemical systems. Let us try integrating a few. (Note that the dimensions of k vary as the order of the reaction varies.)

FIRST-ORDER RATE LAWS

A common rate law is the

FIRST ORDER RATE LAW:
$$\frac{-d[A]}{dt} = k[A] \tag{22.19}$$

This suggests (but certainly does not prove) the rate-determining step

$$A \longrightarrow \text{products}$$

Such a rate law is characteristic of nuclear radioactivity, for example, suggesting that each nucleus decomposes quite independently of all others. This is consistent with all other evidence. Equation (22.19) may be integrated directly to give $\ln \{[A_1]/[A_2]\} = k(t_2 - t_1)$.

It is also common to set $[A] = a - x$, where a is the concentration of A at $t = 0$ and x is the amount which has reacted in the interval 0 to t. We then get

$$\frac{-d(a-x)}{dt} = k(a-x) = \frac{dx}{dt}$$

This integrates, between the limits $t = 0$, $x = 0$, and t, x to give the

INTEGRATED FIRST ORDER RATE LAW

$$\ln \frac{a}{a-x} = kt$$

or

$$\frac{a-x}{a} = e^{-kt} \tag{22.20}$$

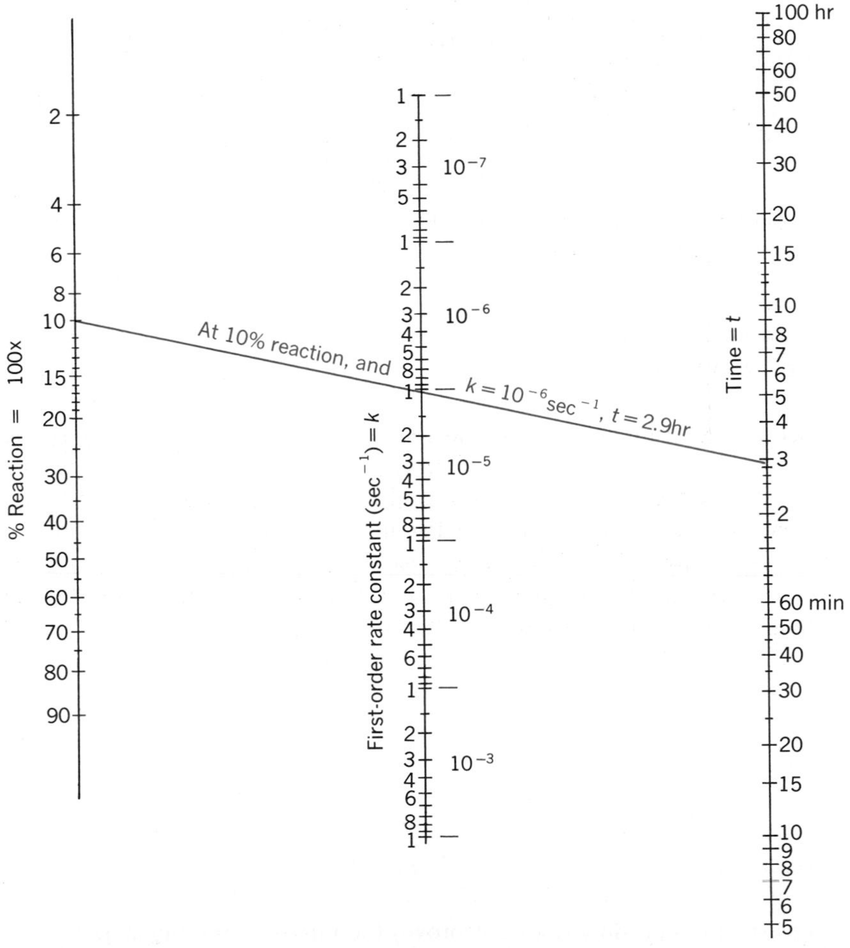

Figure 22.10 Nomograph for first-order reactions. Connect the two known values with a straight line. The desired value is at the intersection of this line with the third vertical. [S. G. Smith and I. D. R. Stevens, *J. Chem. Ed.*, **38,** 574 (1961).]

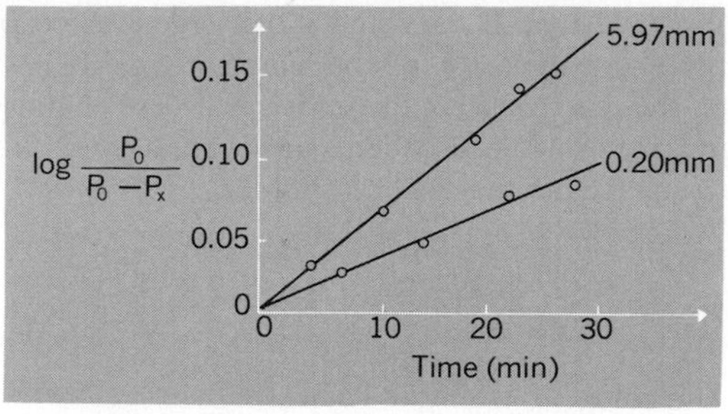

Figure 22.11 Rate data for the thermal decomposition of cyclobutene at 150.4°C. [W. P. Hauser and W. D. Walters, *J. Phys. Chem.*, **67**, 1328 (1963). Copyright 1963 by the American Chemical Society.]

It is obvious from this relationship that the change with time of the concentration of species A will be exponential. Figure 22.10 is a nomograph for rapid solution of Equation (22.20). Given any two of the three values $100x/a$, k, and t, the third is determined by drawing a straight line between the other two and noting its intersection on the desired scale.

A technique for evaluation of first-order rate data is the graphical plotting of $\ln(a - x)$, or $\ln(\text{A})$ versus t. A linear relationship confirms the first order and provides the rate constant k as the slope. Figure 22.11 illustrates the appearance of such a plot.

A quantity of considerable usefulness is the half-life, τ, of a reaction, or that period of time required to convert half of the original concentration to product. For a first-order reaction, this interval can be shown to be

$$\tau = \frac{0.693}{k} = \text{constant for any one reaction} \qquad (22.21)$$

Since the half-life is not dependent upon the initial concentration, it will take just as long to carry out the reaction from 0 to 50% conversion as from 50 to 75% conversion. This test of constant half-life (or any other fractional life) can frequently be made by inspection of untreated rate data to establish or rule out first-order behavior at the outset.

Another example of a system whose over-all rate of reaction is first order is the thermal isomerization of cyclopropane:

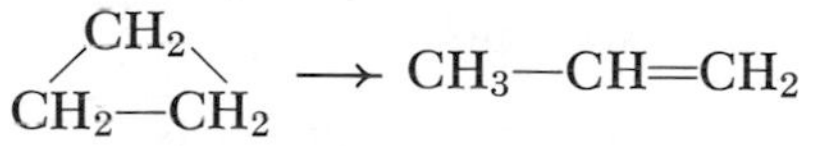

For this reaction $k = 1.5 \cdot 10^{15} e^{65,000/RT}$ sec^{-1} at pressures of the order of 1 atm and temperatures near 500°C. This indicates that the slow step is probably the breaking of the triangular structure into a "linear" one.

Exercise 22.15

J. Walker* gives the following data on the base hydrolysis of methyl acetate when the initial concentrations of base and ester are the same.

t (min)	3	4	5	6	7	8	10	12	15	18	21	25
% hydrolysis	26.0	31.7	36.6	41.1	45.0	48.1	53.6	58.4	63.7	68.1	71.2	74.6

* *Proc. Roy. Soc. London*, **A78**, 157 (1906).

Assume there is no appreciable back reaction. Is the reaction first order? Use two methods. *Answer:* Visual inspection shows the half-life is not constant (nor are any of the other fractional lives). Thus the reaction is not first order. Nor does plotting ln (100 − % hydrolysis) versus t give a straight line. Reaction is not first order over-all. Figure 22.10 can also be used to show the reaction is not first order.

SECOND-ORDER RATE LAWS

A second-order rate law might have the form

$$-d[\mathrm{A}]/dt = k[\mathrm{A}]^2$$

or

$$-d(a - x)/dt = k(a - x)^2 = dx/dt$$

suggesting a rate-determining step such as

$$\mathrm{A} + \mathrm{A} \longrightarrow \text{products}$$

A collisional activation of A by another A could be possible, or a reaction such as $HI + HI \longrightarrow H_2 + I_2$ or $2C_2H_5\cdot \longrightarrow n\text{—}C_4H_{10}$.

The integrated forms can be written down as

$$\left[\frac{1}{[\mathrm{A}_2]} - \frac{1}{[\mathrm{A}_1]}\right] = k(t_2 - t_1)$$

and

$$\frac{x}{a(a - x)} = kt \qquad \text{or} \qquad \frac{1}{t} = a^2k\left(\frac{1}{x}\right) - ak \tag{22.22}$$

with

$$\tau = 1/ka$$

Note that it now takes twice as long to go from 50 to 75% reaction as from 0 to 50%. A plot of $1/[\mathrm{A}]$ versus t, or a plot of $1/x$ versus $1/t$, which gives a straight line, indicates second-order kinetics with respect to [A].

Another common form of second-order experimental rate equation is

$$-d[\mathrm{A}]/dt = k[\mathrm{A}][\mathrm{B}] \tag{22.23}$$

suggesting a rate-determining step such as

$$\mathrm{A} + \mathrm{B} \longrightarrow \text{products}$$

An example is

$$CH_3COCH_3 + H^+ \longrightarrow CH_3COHCH_3^{\oplus}$$

Equation (22.23) cannot be integrated unless we know [B] as a function of [A] or as a function of x. If A and B are both initial reactants, the stoichiometric equation gives this relationship. Thus, if the net reaction is

$$\mathrm{A} + n\mathrm{B} = \text{products}$$

we get, from $d[\mathrm{A}]/dt = k[\mathrm{A}][\mathrm{B}]$,

$$-d(a - x)/dt = k(a - x)(b - nx)$$

since [B] decreases n times as fast as [A] in the net reaction.

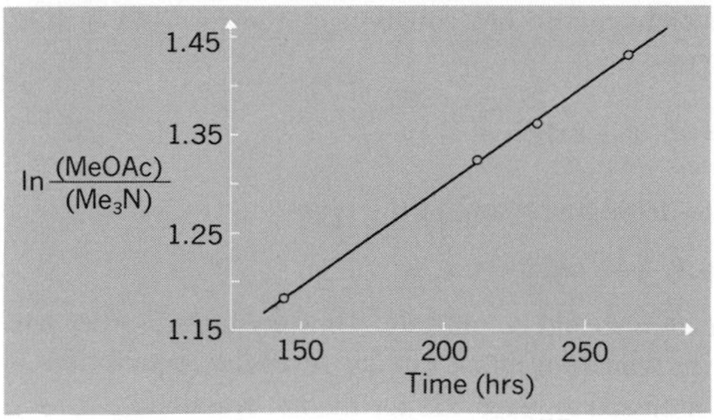

Figure 22.12 Rate data for the methyl acetate-trimethylamine system. [L. P. Hammett and H. L. Pfluger, *J. Am. Chem. Soc.*, **55**, 4079 (1933). Copyright 1933 by the American Chemical Society.]

Definite integration by partial fractions between the usual limits, if $na \neq b$, gives

$$\frac{1}{na - b} \ln \frac{b(a - x)}{a(b - nx)} = kt = \frac{1}{na - b} \ln \frac{b}{a} \frac{[A]}{[B]} \tag{22.24}$$

A plot of $\ln\{[A]/[B]\}$ versus t should give a straight line. If $na = b$, Equation (22.24) becomes indeterminate.

Equation (22.24) probably describes more kinetic experiments than any other rate law, consistent with the frequent occurrence of bimolecular rate-determining steps. (But remember that the bimolecular law does not prove that there is a bimolecular rate-determining step.)

If $n = 1$ and $a \neq b$, we then get the integrated rate law

$$\frac{1}{a - b} \ln \frac{b(a - x)}{a(b - x)} = kt = \frac{1}{a - b} \ln \frac{b}{a} \frac{[A]}{[B]} \tag{22.25}$$

Note that τ is no longer a simple function, since $a \neq b$. If $a = b$, we again get an indeterminate form for Equation (22.25), but Equation (22.22) then provides a suitable integrated form. Figure 22.12 shows a typical plot of $\ln\{[A]/[B]\}$. Even though it is known from other data that the mechanism is not a simple, bimolecular, one-step process, Figure 22.12 supports the second-order description of the net reaction

$$CH_3COOCH_3 + (CH_3)_3N \longrightarrow N(CH_3)_4^+ + CH_3COO^-$$

Exercise 22.16

Are the data in Exercise 22.15 consistent with a second-order mechanism? *Answer:* Visual inspection of the half-life indicates second order is close (first half-life $\cong$ 9 min; second half-life $\cong$ 17 min). Furthermore, plotting $1/t$ versus $1/x$ [Equation (22.22)] gives a straight line consistent with second order over-all. Note $x = (100 - \%$ hydrolysis) assuming there is no appreciable back reaction. Rate law is $d[\text{alcohol}]/dt = k[\text{ester}][OH^-]$.

THIRD-ORDER RATE LAWS

Third-order rate laws are rare, but are usually of the form

$$-d[A]/dt = k[A]^2[B]$$

All known examples correspond to a stoichiometric net equation of the form 2A + B = products. In terms of a, b, and x, this gives

$$\frac{-d(a-x)}{dt} = k_1(a-2x)^2(b-x) = \frac{dx}{dt} \tag{22.26}$$

These rate laws are consistent with a rate-determining step of the type

$$2A + B \longrightarrow \text{products}$$

but we have already indicated that such steps should be unlikely. Thus these third-order rate laws more often indicate a mechanism in which an initial rapidly reversible equilibrium is followed by a slow bimolecular step, as discussed on page 558 for the net reaction

$$2NO + 2H_2 = N_2 + 2H_2O.$$

Equation (22.26) may just as well be written in the form

$$\frac{-d(a-x')}{dt} = k_2(a-x')^2\left(b-\frac{x'}{2}\right) = \frac{dx'}{dt}$$

which integrates to

$$k_2t = \frac{2}{(a-2b)^2}\left[\frac{x'(2b-a)}{a(a-x')} + \ln\frac{2b(a-x')}{a(2b-x')}\right] \tag{22.28}$$

Note that $x' = 2x$ and that $k_1 = k_2/2$. This emphasizes the fact that rate constants should always be associated with rate equations, not just with net equations. Otherwise the meaning of k may be ambiguous.

COMPLEX RATE LAWS

Many systems are known in which more than one mechanistic step makes its presence felt in the rate law. Consider, for example, the experimental rate law already mentioned for the net thermochemical reaction $H_2 + Br_2 = 2HBr$:

$$\frac{d[HBr]}{dt} = \frac{k_a[H_2][Br_2]^{1/2}}{k_b + [HBr][Br_2]^{-1}} \tag{22.29}$$

We have already pointed out that this rate law indicates a complicated mechanism, with no single rate-determining step. What else might be deduced? If there were no denominator, the rate law would be

$$\frac{d[HBr]}{dt} = k_a[H_2][Br_2]^{1/2}$$

This suggests a mechanistic step of the form

$$H_2 + Br \xrightarrow{k_3} \text{products (possibly} \longrightarrow HBr + H)$$

preceded by the equilibrium

$$M^* + Br_2 \underset{k_2}{\overset{k_1}{\rightleftarrows}} 2Br + M$$

These two steps together give

$$[Br] = \left[\frac{k_1[Br_2][M^*]}{k_2[M]}\right]^{1/2}$$

and

$$\frac{d[\text{products}]}{dt} = k_3[H_2][Br] = k_3k_1^{1/2}k_2^{-1/2}[H_2][Br_2]^{1/2}\left\{\frac{[M^*]}{[M]}\right\}^{1/2}$$

where $\{[M^*]/[M]\}$ represents the fraction of molecules having enough energy to dissociate Br_2 into 2Br upon collision. In general, half-powers in rate equations indicate an equilibrium step involving splitting of a molecule prior to a later, slower step.

Equation (22.29) indicates that the rate is decreased by HBr, since HBr appears in the denominator. This suggests that HBr reacts with some intermediate in the mechanism, thus tending to reverse the reaction. We have already seen that Br and H are two possible intermediates. Thus the [HBr] term in the denominator suggests we consider as possible steps the reactions

$$HBr + H \longrightarrow H_2 + Br$$

$$HBr + Br \longrightarrow H + Br_2$$

The effect of the $[Br_2]$ in the denominator of (22.29) is not so apparent. Such terms are usually interpreted by trying various mechanistic schemes until one, and hopefully only one, gives the experimental rate law. We then accept this scheme as the most likely mechanism.

Trial of many mechanisms has revealed only one that gives the experimental rate law in Equation (22.29). The presumed mechanism involves a free radical chain and is consistent with the deductions we have just made.

1. Chain-initiating reaction: $M^* + Br_2 \xrightarrow{k_1} 2Br + M$

2. Chain-terminating reaction: $M + Br + Br \xrightarrow{k_2} Br_2 + M^*$

3 and 4. Chain reactions: $\begin{cases} Br + H_2 \xrightarrow{k_3} HBr + H \\ H + Br_2 \xrightarrow{k_4} HBr + Br \end{cases}$

5. Chain-inhibiting reaction: $HBr + H \xrightarrow{k_5} H_2 + Br$

We can evaluate the rate of formation of HBr in terms of these five reactions:

$$\frac{d[HBr]}{dt} = k_3[H_2][Br] + k_4[H][Br_2] - k_5[HBr][H] \qquad (22.30)$$

Applying the steady-state approximation to [H] and [Br] gives

$$\frac{d[H]}{dt} = 0 = k_3[Br][H_2] - k_4[H][Br_2] - k_5[Br][H]$$

$$[H] = \frac{k_3[Br][H_2]}{k_4[Br_2] + k_5[HBr]} \qquad (22.31)$$

$$\frac{d[Br]}{dt} = 0 = 2k_1[Br_2][M^*] - 2k_2[Br]^2[M] - k_3[Br][H_2] + k_4[H][Br_2] + k_5[HBr][H] \qquad (22.32)$$

Substituting (22.31) into (22.32) we get

$$[\mathrm{Br}] = \left[\frac{k_1}{k_2}[\mathrm{Br_2}]\right]^{1/2} = \left[\frac{k_1}{k_2}\frac{[\mathrm{Br_2}][\mathrm{M^*}]}{[\mathrm{M}]}\right]^{1/2} \tag{22.33}$$

Substituting (22.33) into (22.31) gives

$$[\mathrm{H}] = \frac{k_1{}^{1/2}k_2{}^{-1/2}k_3[\mathrm{Br}]^{1/2}[\mathrm{H_2}]}{k_4[\mathrm{Br_2}] + k_5[\mathrm{HBr}]} \tag{22.34}$$

If we now substitute (22.33) and (22.34) into (22.30), we get

$$\frac{d[\mathrm{HBr}]}{dt} = \frac{2k_1{}^{1/2}k_2{}^{-1/2}k_3k_4k_5{}^{-1}[\mathrm{H_2}][\mathrm{Br_2}]^{1/2}\{[\mathrm{M^*}]/[\mathrm{M}]\}^{1/2}}{k_4k_5{}^{-1} + [\mathrm{HBr}][\mathrm{Br_2}]^{-1}} \tag{22.35}$$

which exactly matches the experimental law written in Equation (22.29). Note that $\{[M^*]/[M]\}$ is a constant at any temperature representing the fraction of molecules with enough energy to dissociate Br_2 upon collision.

Since this is the only mechanism known to give the rate law and since this mechanism fits all other experimental data on the system, we presume it is the predominating series of steps by which equilibrium between H_2, Br_2, and HBr is established. Equation (22.35) is so complicated that it is usually used in the differential rather than the integrated form.

In general, complicated rate equations are "solved" (or matched to possible mechanisms) by assuming certain mechanisms and comparing the resulting differential rate equations with the experimental ones. Usually the differential rate equation will be too complicated to integrate. In such cases numerical methods may be used to check the rate data with the theoretical rate equation.

Any actual total mechanism will usually consist of a combination of consecutive, opposing, and concurrent reactions. Figure 22.13 illustrates the effect of consecutive radioactive decays.

CONCURRENT REACTIONS

Reaction schemes in which a substance disappears by more than one simultaneous path are known as concurrent reactions. In the simplest possible case, in which a

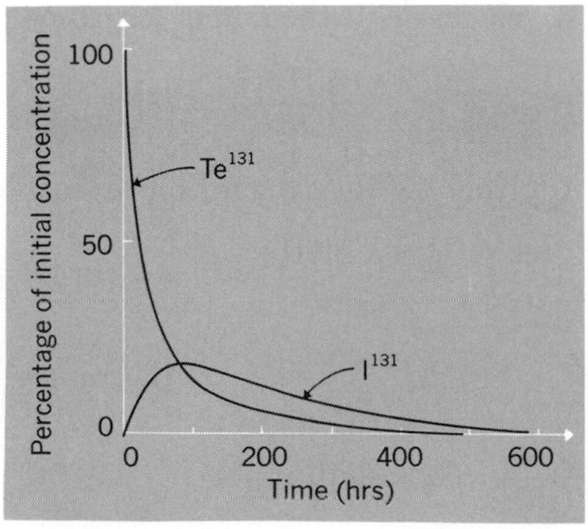

Figure 22.13 Concentration distribution of isotopes during the successive beta decay of tellurium-131.

material disappears by two concurrent first-order processes, we may write the symbolic reaction sequence

$$A \xrightarrow{k_1} B$$

$$A \xrightarrow{k_2} C$$

and a straightforward kinetic analysis provides the integrated rate law

$$\ln \frac{a}{a - x} = (k_1 + k_2)t \tag{22.36}$$

This type of kinetics is frequently observed in a sequence of reactions of varying order undergoing competition for a single reactant. Complications for the organic chemist arise from synthetic procedures that produce undesirable side products in addition to that single product whose synthesis was desired. The thermal decomposition of *n*-pentane discussed on page 551 follows Equation (22.36). For the net reaction $H_2C{-}CH_2$ (bridged by O) $+ H^+ + Cl^- = CH_2OHCH_2Cl$, the differential rate equation is

$$\frac{-d[C_2H_4O]}{dt} = k_1[C_2H_4O] + k_2[C_2H_4O][Cl^-] + k_3[C_2H_4O][H^+] + k_4[C_2H_4O][H^+][Cl^-]$$

which suggests that there are four different, independent, but concurrent mechanisms for the reaction.

SMOG FORMATION

Very extensive work has been done on the kinetics of atmospheric pollution and the resulting smog. The four sets of reactions in Table 22.4 constitute the best cur-

Table 22.4 A possible mechanism for photochemical smog formation.

1. Light absorption	$NO_2 + h\nu = NO + O$ (SO_2 and SO_3 are other light absorbers)
2. Atomic oxygen chain	(*a*) $O + R \longrightarrow R\cdot + RCHO$[a]
	(*b*) $R\cdot + O_2 \longrightarrow RO_2\cdot$
	(*c*) $RO_2\cdot + NO \longrightarrow RO\cdot + NO_2$ — Net (b)–(d): $NO + O_2 = NO_2 + O$
	(*d*) $RO\cdot \longrightarrow R\cdot + O$
3. Ozone chain[a]	(*a*) $O + O_2 \longrightarrow O_3$[a]
	(*b*) $O_3 + R \longrightarrow RCO_2\cdot + RCHO$[a] (not balanced)
	(*c*) $RCO_2\cdot + NO \longrightarrow RCO\cdot + NO_2$
	(*d*) $RCO\cdot + NO_2 + O_2 \longrightarrow RC(=O){-}O{-}O{-}NO_2$ (probably two steps)
4. Chain termination	(*a*) $O + NO_2 \longrightarrow NO + O_2$
	(*b*) $O_3 + NO \longrightarrow NO_2 + O_2$
	(*c*) $RO\cdot + NO_2 \longrightarrow RONO_2$

[a] These four reactions produce the ozone, aldehydes, and compound X (acyl peroxynitrate) that are the main irritants in photochemical smog. The over-all process can be described as the photochemical initiation of the oxidation of gaseous hydrocarbon residues to noxious chemicals.

rent interpretation of photochemical smog formation. The light-absorbing reactant NO_2 comes from $N_2 + O_2 = 2NO$ in engines and other combustion processes, followed by $NO + \frac{1}{2}O_2 = NO_2$ in the atmosphere. (Oxides of sulfur, SO_2 and SO_3, from oil and coal combustion also act as chain initiators.) R represents hydrocarbons, mainly from spilled or incompletely burned fuels. Over half of these come from transport vehicles (mainly automobiles), about one-third from industrial processes, the balance from households. General atmospheric pollution, including smog, amounts to about 130 million tons of contaminants introduced per year and causes about 11 billion dollars in property damage annually in the United States. The kinetics of the problem are reasonably well understood. It would seem appropriate to act on that knowledge.

THE ATMOSPHERE

Photochemistry, rates, and mechanisms are also of great importance in analysis of the upper atmosphere (Figure 22.14). Composition, temperature, and pressure data have been obtained from balloon and rocket flights and from photochemical observations. The partial pressure of any species may be determined by multiplying the total pressure at the desired altitude by the relative concentration of the species. All the following have been discovered, or confirmed, by kinetic measurements.

1. There is some sedimentation of gases in the atmosphere because of differences in molecular weight.
2. The temperature rises when radiant energy is being absorbed in a photochemical process.
3. Pressure falls almost logarithmically with height at first, then more slowly.
4. Ionic and electron processes become common at high altitudes.
5. Monatomic species become more common at high altitudes.

It should be clear that the atmosphere is not an equilibrium system and that all of these effects become comprehensible only in terms of kinetic ideas.

SUMMARY

The experimental study of reaction kinetics consists in determining the rate at which reaction occurs and interpreting that rate in terms of a set of mechanistic steps. The first step in any experimental study is to find some property of the system whose change is proportional in a reproducible and stoichiometric way to the change in concentration of some species involved in the reaction. Titration, spectroscopy (especially UV-visible and NMR), shock tubes, index of refraction, pressure, and density are typical of the measurements which can be used to follow reaction rates.

Temperature and concentration of species present are the principal variables which affect reaction rates. It is normal to hold all but one of these constant in a series of experiments and determine the effect upon the rate of changing that

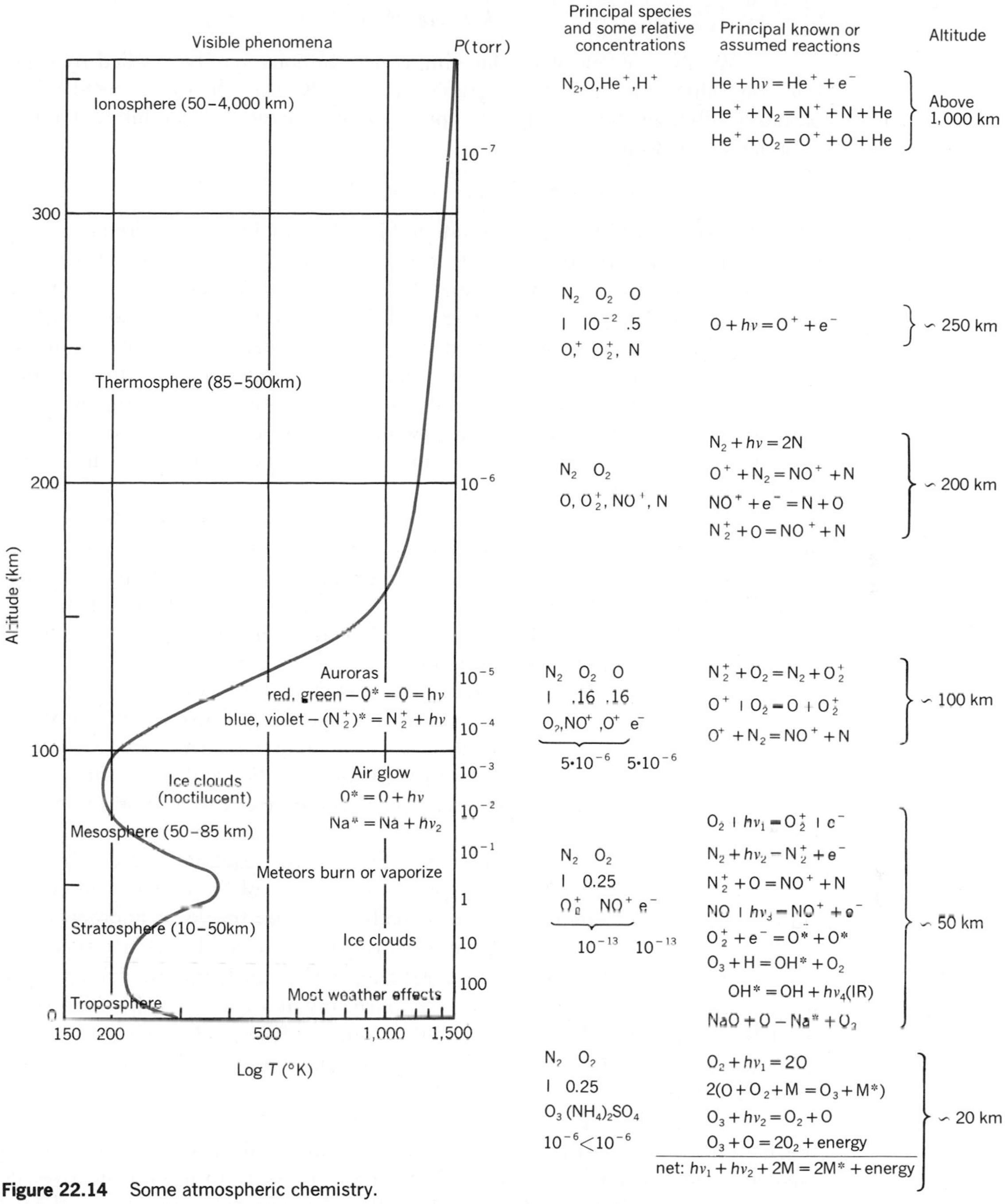

Figure 22.14 Some atmospheric chemistry.

one variable. The effect of temperature is often marked, so that temperature control is important to valid measurements. In many cases, the temperature effect may be correlated with rate in terms of an activation energy such that the rate constant, k, at unit concentrations is given by the relationship

$$k = Ae^{-\Delta E_{\text{act}}/RT}$$

Variation of rate with changing concentrations may be studied by using isolation, initial rate, half-life, or graphical methods. The effect of concentrations on rate is often given at constant temperature by an experimental differential rate equation of the form

$$\text{rate} = k[\text{A}]^m[\text{B}]^n[\text{C}]^o = Ae^{-\Delta E_{\text{act}}/RT}\,[\text{A}]^m[\text{B}]^n[\text{C}]^o$$

which may or may not be directly integrable. The exponents m, n, and o may be positive or negative, fractional or integral, and are known as the order of the reaction with respect to the corresponding A, B, and C species. Possible mechanisms are then assumed and their concurrence with the experimental rate law checked.

When a reaction is first order with respect to each of two species, or second order with respect to one (and only these species appear in the rate equation), it is very likely that the mechanism is limited by a rate-determining step involving a collision between the corresponding two molecules. They then form a reactive intermediate whose formula is the sum of the formulas of the species in the experimental rate equation.

Negative orders and fractional order in the experimental rate equation, however, indicate the existence of additional steps preceding the rate-determining step in the mechanism. Over-all orders greater than three also indicate steps preceding the rate-determining step. Orders which are less than the stoichiometric coefficient of the corresponding species in the net equation indicate additional steps following the rate-determining step.

The great majority of actual mechanistic steps are bimolecular (involve the collision between only two molecules), not counting possible interactions with the solvent. The reactive intermediates are most commonly formed from species at least one of which is present in relatively high concentration and in collisions which are geometrically and electrically probable. Because mechanisms tend to proceed with the minimum expenditure of energy, the weak bonds tend to break and the strong ones to form or remain unchanged. Bimolecular reactions that give a single molecule are rare, especially in the gas phase, because of the difficulty of getting rid of the energy of bond formation. Usually one bond breaks as another forms. Isotopic effects and tracer studies supply insights into possible mechanisms.

Any acceptable mechanism must sum to the stoichiometric net equation; must contain only species which are geometrically and electronically reasonable; must be consistent with all the energetic, isotopic effect, and tracer studies; and must lead to a theoretical differential rate equation identical with the one obtained experimentally.

The theoretical differential rate equation is obtained from the assumed mechanism by solving the set of stoichiometric mechanistic steps for the rate of change of one of the stable species. It is often necessary to use the steady-state assumption to obtain a straightforward solution. Only by coincidence does the net equation show a direct correlation with the rate equation.

In the majority of cases studied so far, it has been possible to find one and only one mechanism that fits all the experimental data. But there is no such thing as a proved mechanism, no matter how good the experimental data may be. There is always the possibility that there is another as yet undiscovered mechanism which would also fit the data. However, the extent of uncertainty in interpreting reaction kinetics is decreasing very rapidly, and even such complicated changes as those found in biological cycles, cells, organs, and even individuals and societies are beginning to be understood at the molecular level.

The most basic characteristic of the contemporary world is the fact of change.—Nathan M. Pusey.

PROBLEMS

22.1. Predict the shape of the curve for Figure 22.1, A, as the temperature becomes very high, and justify your prediction.

22.2. A substance decomposes according to the following competitive paths:

$$A \xrightarrow{k_1} B$$

$$A \xrightarrow{k_2} C$$

If $k_1/k_2 = 10$ at 10°C and 0.1 at 40°C, what is the difference in activation energy for the two processses? (About 30 kcal.) Which has the higher activation energy?

22.3. Examine the mechanism for the I^-—$S_2O_8^=$ reaction (p. 556). Rationalize the statement that each of the fast steps is indeed faster than the presumed rate-determining step.

22.4. Calculate ΔE_{act} for a reaction whose rate doubles in going from 0.00 to 10.00°C; in going from 90 to 100°C. (About 10 kcal.)

22.5. Flour in bulk is very difficult to burn, though many housewives seem to prove the contrary all too often in their ovens. How do you then account for the very great explosions which occur in the dusty flour mills?

22.6. How does using a pressure cooker accelerate the cooking of foods?

22.7. Outline how you would try to determine the kinetic order of the reaction

$$(CH_3CO_2)_2C_2H_{4(g)} = (CH_3CO)_2O_{(g)} + CH_3CHO_{(g)}$$

What data would you obtain and what would you do with them? What are the most likely complications which would have to be considered?

22.8. In each of the following, x and y are variables; the other terms are constants. What function of x and what function of y would you plot in each case to give a straight-line reaction? Show why you are using these functions.

$$ax = by + c$$

$$x = Ae^{-y/RT}$$

$$xy = ax + by$$

22.9. For each of the following net reactions and accompanying differential rate equations, postulate a mechanism and a reactive intermediate that fits both the rate equation and the net equation and is chemically reasonable. Derive the integrated rate equation for system *a*.

(*a*) $(CH_3)_2CO + I_2 \xrightarrow{H^+} CH_3COCH_2I + H^+ + I^-$,
$-d[I_2]/dt = k[(CH_3)_2CO][H^+]$.
(*b*) $CH_3COOC_2H_5 + OH^- = CH_3COO^- + C_2H_5OH$,
$-d[OH^-]/dt = k[OH^-][CH_3COOC_2H_5]$.
(*c*) $Br_{2(g)} \overset{N_2}{=} 2Br$, $\quad d[Br]/dt = k_1[Br_2]^2 + k_2[Br_2][N_2]$.
(*d*) $H_2O_2 + 2H^+ + 2I^- = 2H_2O + I_2$,
$-d[H_2O_2]/dt = k_1[H_2O_2][I^-]\{1 + k_2[H^+]\}$.
(*e*) $OCl^-_{(aq)} + I^-_{(aq)} = OI^-_{(aq)} + Cl^-_{(aq)}$, $\quad$ rate $= k[OCl^-][I^-]/[OH^-]$.
(*f*) $H_3AsO_{4(aq)} + 3I^-_{(aq)} + 2H^+_{(aq)} = H_3AsO_{3(aq)} + I_3{}^-_{(aq)} + H_2O$,
rate $= k[H_3AsO_4][I^-][H^+]$.
(*g*) $H_3AsO_{3(aq)} + I_3{}^-_{(aq)} + H_2O = H_3AsO_{4(aq)} + 3I^-_{(aq)} + 2H^+_{(aq)}$,
rate $= k[H_3AsO_3][I_3{}^-]/[I^-]^2[H^+]$.
(*h*) $C_6H_5NH_2 + 2CH_3CO_3H$(peroxyacetic acid)
$= C_6H_5NO + 2CH_3CO_2H + H_2O$, $\quad$ rate $= k[C_6H_5NH_2][CH_3CO_3H]$.

22.10. P. C. Moews, Jr. and R. H. Petrucci [*J. Chem. Ed.*, **41,** 549–551 (1964)] discuss the reaction

$$S_2O_8{}^{2-} + 3I^- = 2SO_4{}^{2-} + I_3{}^-$$

They measure the time, *t*, for a constant small increment, *dx*, of the reaction to occur as a function of the initial concentrations of $S_2O_8{}^{2-}$ and I (where $x = [SO_4{}^=]$ or $[I_3{}^-]$). Data are good to ±5%.

	Molarity		
Experiment	$S_2O_8{}^{2-}$	I^-	*t* (sec)
1	0.077	0.077	21
2	0.038	0.077	44
3	0.019	0.077	91
4	0.077	0.038	42
5	0.077	0.019	79

(*a*) Determine the rate equation—that is, the order of the reaction with respect to each of the reactants. (*b*) What is the probable formula of the activated complex in the rate-determining step? (*c*) Suggest a possible mechanism for the over-all reaction. Indicate the rate-determining step. (*d*) Give the reasons why you chose the step you did as rate-determining rather than any of the others.

22.11. The following data are given by W. van Pee and J-C. Jungers [*Bull. Soc. Chim. France*, **1**, 158 (1967)] for the reaction in hexanol-1:

$$NH_2CONH_2 \xrightarrow{k_1} NH_3 + HNCO$$

T (°C)	131.5	139.5	147.5	160.5
k_1 (min^{-1})	$2.44 \cdot 10^{-3}$	$5.00 \cdot 10^{-3}$	$10.52 \cdot 10^{-3}$	$31.50 \cdot 10^{-3}$

Calculate ΔE_{act}. [$\Delta E_{act} \cong 30$ kcal mole^{-1}]

22.12. (*a*) Find the order of the rate law which fits the following experimental data:

$$2N_2O_5 = 4NO_2 + O_2 \quad \text{(gas phase)}$$

Concentration of N_2O_5 (10^{-3} mole/liter)	5.00	4.20	3.53	2.96	2.48
t (min)	0	4	8	12	16

(*b*) How many minutes does it take the reaction to go one-quarter of the way toward completion? (About 10 min.)

22.13. The age of water and of whiskey may be determined by measuring the radioactive tritium (H_1^3) content. (Tritium is formed in nature by cosmic radiation.) Calculate the age of a suspected counterfeit whiskey sample which is 0.10 as radioactive as a freshly prepared sample. The half-life of tritium is 12.5 years. (Age $\cong$ 40 years.)

22.14. How would you apply the isolation method in studying the rate of the H_2—NO reaction? Invent some "synthetic" data which would be consistent with the established mechanism.

22.15. Suggest three or four methods for minimizing photochemical smog problems.

22.16. If the temperature of the upper atmosphere is 1500°K, how can "space walks" be accomplished?

22.17. Suppose you found an experimental rate law of the form

$$dx/dt = k(a - x)(b - x)(c - x)$$

Suggest a reasonable mechanistic interpretation of the law.

II

22.18. The following data were obtained by Ramsperger and Waddington [*J. Am. Chem. Soc.*, **55**, 214 (1933)] for the thermal decomposition of trichloromethyl chloroformate at 290°C:

$$ClCOOCCl_3 \longrightarrow 2COCl_2$$

t (sec)	0	63	181	334	513	760	1164
p (cm)	1.576	1.712	1.888	2.087	2.279	2.484	2.708

What is the order of the reaction? What is the rate constant for the reaction? ($k \cong 10^{-5}$, you specify units.)

22.19. Hypophosphites decompose as follows:

$$H_2PO_2^- + OH^- \longrightarrow HPO_3^= + H_2$$

In a certain experiment 19.5 cc of H_2 (STP) were generated in 20 min when the concentration of $H_2PO_2^-$ was 0.50 *F* and that of OH^- was 1.28 *F*. A second experiment yielded 25.0 cc of H_2 (STP) in 50 min when the concentrations of $H_2PO_2^-$ and OH^- were 0.25 *F* and 1.28 *F*. A third experiment yielded 135.0 cc of H_2 (STP) in 30.0 min when the concentrations of $H_2PO_2^-$ and OH^- were 0.25 *F* and 3.94 *F*. What is the order of the reaction with respect to $H_2PO_2^-$ and with respect to OH^-?

22.20. The initial rates of the reaction described in Figure 22.8 are given below from Stubbs and Hinshelwood [*Proc. Roy. Soc.*, A, **200**, 458 (1950)]. What information can you get from these data alone? Be as quantitative as possible. The data are for the initial rate of reaction of n—C_5H_{12} as a function of T, p_O, and p_{NO}. ($\Delta E \cong$ 10 kcal.)

p_{NO}	p_O at 530°		p_O at 550°	
	100	250	100	250
0	4.20	13.2	9.8	29.2
2.0	1.24	6.7	4.7	20.6
5.0	0.73	4.4	3.1	16.0
10.0	0.58	3.3	2.3	10.7
20.0	0.58	3.3	2.3	7.6

22.21. John H. Sullivan [*J. Chem. Phys.*, **46**, 73 (1967)] has shown that the rate constants of the photochemical reaction between H_2 and I_2 and the high temperature reaction between H_2 and I_2 are both described by the equation $k = 6.6 \cdot 10^7 e^{-5310/RT}$ l^2 mole^{-2} sec^{-1}.

(*a*) What is the activation energy for the rate-determining step in these reactions?
(*b*) What is the likelihood that each of these two reactions proceeds by the same mechanism?

22.22. Show that the following mechanisms all agree with the experimental rate equation (22.3) for the H_2 reaction with I_2 [J. H. Sullivan, *J. Chem. Phys.*, **46**, 73 (1967)]. Which mechanism seems more likely? Add the information that the rate data for the thermal and photochemical reactions are identical and again select the most likely mechanism.

I. $H_{2(g)} + I_{2(g)} \longrightarrow 2HI.$

II(*a*). $I_{2(g)} \underset{k_2}{\overset{k_1}{\rightleftarrows}} 2I\cdot_{(g)}.$

(*b*). $M + \cdot I_{(g)} + H_{2(g)} \underset{k_4}{\overset{k_3}{\rightleftarrows}} H_2I\cdot_{(g)} + M^*.$

(*c*). $H_2I\cdot_{(g)} + I\cdot_{(g)} \xrightarrow[\text{slow}]{k_5} 2HI_{(g)}.$

III(*a*). $I_{2(g)} \rightleftarrows 2I\cdot_{(g)}.$

(*b*). $2I\cdot_{(g)} + H_{2(g)} \longrightarrow 2HI_{(g)}.$

22.23. (*a*) Set up the rate expression, $d[D]/dt$, for the following mechanism:

$$A \underset{k_2}{\overset{k_1}{\rightleftarrows}} B, \qquad B + C \xrightarrow{k_3} D$$

(*b*) Show that this reaction may be first order at high pressures and second order at low pressures.

22.24. The thermal decomposition of ozone has been studied by Jahn [*Z. Anorg. Chem.*, **48**, 260 (1906)], who found the rate of disappearance of ozone to be second order in ozone and inversely proportional to the first power of the oxygen concentration according to the stoichiometry

$$2O_3 \longrightarrow 3O_2$$

Show that the following mechanism is in agreement with these observations at low ozone concentrations:

$$O_3 \underset{k_{-1}}{\overset{k_1}{\rightleftarrows}} O_2 + O \qquad O + O_3 \xrightarrow{k_2} 2O_2$$

22.25. The gas-phase reaction between sulfur dioxide and hydrogen, to produce sulfur and water, gives the following time increments, Δt, for a constant small amount of reaction $\Delta[H_2]$. Data are good to $\pm 5\%$.

	Initial pressure (mm)		t
Expt.	*Sulfur dioxide*	*Hydrogen*	Δt *(arbitrary units)*
a	24	99	37
b	51	101	18
c	100	99	9
d	101	52	19
e	100	25	35

(*a*) Write the equation for the net reaction.
(*b*) Determine the order of the reaction with respect to each reactant and write the differential rate equation.
(*c*) What is the probable formula of the activated complex in the rate-determining step?
(*d*) Suggest a possible mechanism for the over-all reaction. Indicate the rate-determining step.
(*e*) Give the reasons why the step you chose, rather than any of the other steps, is rate-determining.

22.26. The experimental rate law for the reaction

$$2Fe^{+++} + 2I^- \longrightarrow 2Fe^{++} + I_2$$

is found to be

$$-\frac{d[Fe^{+++}]}{dt} = \frac{k[Fe^{+++}]^2[I^-]^2}{[Fe^{+++}] + k'[Fe^{++}]}$$

This rate law should suggest to you how the reaction may proceed. Show that the following mechanism is consistent with the rate law.

$$Fe^{+++} + I^- \underset{k_{-1}}{\overset{k_1}{\rightleftharpoons}} FeI^{++} \qquad \text{fast}$$

$$FeI^{++} + I^- \underset{k_{-2}}{\overset{k_2}{\rightleftharpoons}} Fe^{++} + I_2^- \qquad \text{slow}$$

$$I_2^- + Fe^{+++} \xrightarrow{k_3} Fe^{++} + I_2 \qquad \text{slow}$$

22.27. Dukes [*J. Am. Chem. Soc.*, **82**, 9 (1960)] has studied the oxidation of plutonium(III) by nitrous acid in acid solutions. The stoichiometry of the reaction is

$$Pu(III) + H^+ + HNO_2 \longrightarrow Pu(IV) + NO + H_2O$$

One of the mechanisms proposed for the reaction is

$$HNO_2 + H^+ = NO^+ + H_2O \qquad \text{rapid equilibrium}$$

$$NO^+ + Pu(III) \longrightarrow NO + Pu(IV) \qquad \text{slow}$$

Derive the rate law that is consistent with this mechanism.

22.28. The first-order decomposition of hydrogen peroxide, formula H_2O_2, into water and oxygen is followed by titrating the unreacted H_2O_2 with acidified permanganate solution.
(*a*) Write an equation for the decomposition.
(*b*) Write an equation for the reaction with the permanganate.
(*c*) The data on p. 578 were obtained. How would you go about determining the rate constant, k, for the decomposition reaction? (You need not determine k.) What dimensions would it have?

t (min)	0	5	10	20	30	50
ml of permanganate solution for fixed amount of H_2O_2 solution	46.1	37.1	29.8	19.6	12.3	5.0

22.29. The reaction represented by the equation

$$*Fe^{++} + Fe^{+++} = *Fe^{+++} + Fe^{++}$$

where * means radioactive, can be studied by mixing radioactive Fe^{++} with non-radioactive Fe^{+++}. The rate of appearance of radioactive Fe^{+++} is then measured. The rate proves to be second order over-all, first order in the concentration of Fe^{++}, and first order in the concentration of Fe^{+++}: $k = 4.0\ F^{-1}\ \text{sec}^{-1}$.

(*a*) Calculate the rate of formation of radioactive Fe^{+++} if the concentrations of Fe^{+++} and radioactive Fe^{++} are initially 0.01 F and 10^{-15} F respectively. (Rate $\cong 10^{-17}\ F\ \text{sec}^{-1}$.)

(*b*) How many ions of radioactive Fe^{+++} are being formed per second under the conditions in *a*? (About 10^7 ions $\text{sec}^{-1}\ l^{-1}$.)

(*c*) What is a possible mechanistic step for this reaction?

22.30. The rate of recombination of bromine atoms in the presence of added inert gases has been measured in a flash photolysis experiment by Givens and Willard [*J. Am. Chem. Soc.*, **81**, 4773 (1959)]:

$[Br_2]/[Ar] = 0.021$

k ($\text{liter}^2\ \text{moles}^{-2}\ \text{sec}^{-1}$) · (each times 10^{-9})	5.6	5.0	3.3	3.1
T (°C)	30	63	112	154

$[Br_2]/[CO_2] = 0.0083$

k · (each times 10^{-9})	9.3	8.1	5.8	4.9
T	30	51	84	110

Determine the activation energy for each of these reactions. How do you account for the sign of the activation energy? Which gas appears to be the more effective in stabilizing the bromine molecule? How do you account for this? ($\Delta E_{act} \cong$ 10–20 kcal.)

22.31. The decomposition of N_2O_5 dissolved in CCl_4 has been studied by Eyring and Daniels [*J. Am. Chem. Soc.*, **52**, 1472 (1930)]. The following data are typical.

Net equation: $$2N_2O_5 = 2N_2O_4 + O_2$$

t (min)	0	82	162	409	604	1129	1721	1929	3399	∞
$[N_2O_5]$ (moles/liter)	5.33	5.04	4.78	4.06	3.36	2.37	1.57	1.36	0.53	0

The reaction is either first or second order in $[N_2O_5]$. Decide which it is. What does the order for the reaction indicate about possible mechanisms for this reaction? Write an appropriate expression (rate equation) for the rate of disappearance of N_2O_5 based on your conclusions.

22.32. The rate constant k for the third-order reaction expressed in $\text{liter}^2\ \text{moles}^{-2}\ \text{sec}^{-1}$ for the reaction $2NO + O_2 \longrightarrow 2NO_2$ at 600°K is $6.63 \cdot 10^5$; at 645°K it is $6.52 \cdot 10^5$. For the reverse second-order reaction, k is 83.9 and 407 at these two temperatures. (*a*) Calculate the equilibrium constants at the two temperatures. (*b*) Calculate the activation energy for the forward and reverse reactions. (*c*) What is the heat of the reaction at constant volume? ($K_{eq} \cong 10^3$, $\Delta E_f \cong 0$ kcal mole^{-1}.)

III

22.33. The thermal decomposition of acetaldehyde vapor has been interpreted in terms of the mechanism

$$CH_3CHO \xrightarrow{k_1} CH_3\cdot + CHO\cdot$$

$$CH_3\cdot + CH_3CHO \xrightarrow{k_2} CH_4 + CH_3CO\cdot$$

$$CH_3CO\cdot \xrightarrow{k_3} CH_3\cdot + CO$$

$$2CH_3CO\cdot \xrightarrow{k_4} CH_3COCOCH_3$$

What will be the dependence of the rate of production of CO on acetaldehyde pressure? How will the experimental activation energy be related to the activation energies of each of the individual steps?

22.34. The photochemical chlorination of chloroform in the gas phase has been found to obey the rate law

$$\frac{d}{dt}[CCl_4] = kI_{abs}{}^{1/2}[CHCl_3]$$

for the reaction with the stoichiometry

$$Cl_2 + CHCl_3 = CCl_4 + HCl$$

where I_{abs} is the absorbed intensity and appears in the initial step:

$$h\nu + Cl_2 \xrightarrow{k_2} 2Cl\cdot, \qquad \text{rate} = k'I_{incident}[Cl_2] = k''I_{abs}$$

Suggest a mechanism which is in agreement with the observed kinetics.

22.35. Thermal decomposition of gaseous hydrocarbons (as in the industrial production of gasoline) leads to net reactions of which that for ethane may be considered typical:

$$H_3C\text{—}CH_3 = H_2C\text{=}CH_2 + H_2 + \text{minor products}$$

The mechanistic steps appear to be

$$H_3C\text{—}CH_3 \xrightarrow[k_1]{\text{heat}} 2H_3C\cdot$$

$$H_3C\cdot + H_3C\text{—}CH_3 \xrightarrow[k_2]{} CH_4 + H_3C\text{—}CH_2\cdot$$

$$H_3C\text{—}CH_2\cdot \xrightarrow[k_3]{} H_2C\text{=}CH_2 + H\cdot$$

$$H\cdot + H_3C\text{—}CH_3 \xrightarrow[k_4]{} H_2 + H_3C\text{—}CH_2$$

$$2CH_3\text{—}CH_2\cdot \xrightarrow[k_5]{} H_3C\text{—}CH_3 + H_2C\text{=}CH_2$$

$$2CH_3\text{—}CH_2\cdot \xrightarrow[k_6]{} CH_3CH_2CH_2CH_3$$

Will the over-all rate equal, exceed, or be less than the rate of the first reaction? Identify the chain-initiating, chain-propagating, and chain-terminating steps and show that the over-all rate constant is given by

$$k_{overall} = k_3\left(\frac{k_1}{k_5 + k_6}\right)^{1/2}$$

See page 1092 for a list of references and readings in the recent chemical literature related to the material in this chapter.

CHAPTER 23

The Theoretical Basis of Chemical Kinetics

STEPHEN V. FILSETH

The basic process by which molecules become activated is by collision, usually with one another (thermal activation) or with a photon (photochemical activation).

With thoughtful devotion to detail and careful analysis of the data, meaningful values for rate constants and ΔE_{act} can be extracted from kinetic experiments. We seek now to show how this type of information can be translated into an expanded appreciation of how chemical reactions occur. We shall describe the principles and practice of the present state of theoretical treatments of reaction rate data. We begin with what might be thought the simplest of systems—vapor-phase unimolecular reactions. The theory of unimolecular reactions is far from complete, however, and can currently be best described as a continuing international research project.

THE LINDEMANN HYPOTHESIS

We have seen in Chapter 22 that most actual chemical reactions (as opposed to over-all mechanisms) follow either first- or second-order rate laws. Let's look into possible correlations at the molecular level. Lindemann suggested that reactions might not immediately follow a collisional event in which a molecule received an activation energy sufficient to permit its reaction. The idea of an interval that is longer than vibrational frequencies, during which the molecular energy would concentrate in a small volume of the molecule (perhaps one bond) and give reaction, has proved central to many subsequent theoretical approaches. During this interval and before decomposition, it might be that the energized molecule would undergo a collision with another unenergized molecule. In this collision it is likely that the energy will be redistributed in such a fashion that neither molecule now possesses the requisite amount of energy for reaction. Under these circumstances, we can distinguish two possibilities.

1. The reactant concentration is so high that collisional deactivation of reactant molecules is much more prevalent than the competing, slower dissociation. This gives an approximately steady concentration of energized molecules maintained by collisional activation and deactivation. From this steady-state concentration of energized molecules, a small fraction will continue to react, a fraction which will depend upon the concentration of the energized molecules and thus on the first power of the concentration.

2. The reactant concentration is so low that the interval between collisions is long enough to permit the reaction of most molecules that reach the energized state. Thus, the rate will tend toward second order—the rate at which bimolecular collisions supply excited molecules.

These considerations indicate that the only distinction between unimolecular and bimolecular reactions of pure gases is the duration, or lifetime, of the excited state relative to the two competing processes: reaction and collisional deactivation.

We may treat this situation quantitatively by considering the symbolic reaction mechanism,

$$A + A \xrightarrow{k_1} A^* + A$$

where A^* represents an activated molecule—one with enough energy to undergo reaction. This step can be followed by

$$A^* + A \xrightarrow{k_{-1}} A + A$$

$$A^* \xrightarrow{k_2} \text{products}$$

We may invoke the steady-state assumption to treat this as

$$\frac{d}{dt}[A^*] = k_1[A]^2 - k_{-1}[A^*][A] - k_2[A^*] = 0 \tag{23.1}$$

We next obtain the steady-state concentration of activated molecules as

$$[A^*] = \frac{k_1[A]^2}{k_{-1}[A] + k_2} \tag{23.2}$$

The rate of formation of products is thus

$$\frac{d}{dt}[\text{products}] = k_2[A^*] = \frac{k_1 k_2 [A]^2}{k_{-1}[A] + k_2} \tag{23.3}$$

At sufficiently high pressures we may expect that $k_{-1}[A] \gg k_2$, because of the large value of [A]. In this event we can neglect k_2, and we obtain

$$\frac{d}{dt}[\text{products}] = \frac{k_1 k_2}{k_{-1}}[A] = k_\infty[A] \tag{23.4}$$

The reaction will appear to be first order at the limit of infinite pressure.

On the other hand, as we proceed to the limit of very low pressures, [A] becomes small and we may expect that $k_{-1}[A] \ll k_2$. We can express the rate as

$$\frac{d}{dt}[\text{products}] = k_1[\text{A}]^2 \tag{23.5}$$

and the reaction will appear to be second order. Such a shift from first- to second-order rate law with decreasing pressure has been observed in many systems.

Exercise 23.1

Which of the following mechanisms is most likely to show second-order kinetics? (*a*) $Br_2 \longrightarrow 2\ Br$; (*b*) $O^{18} \longrightarrow e^- + F^{18}$. *Answer:* Nuclear reactions, as in *b*, are unaffected by molecular collisions except at very high T ($>10^6$ degrees) and are first order at lower T. Br_2 needs energy to break the Br—Br bond, as from a molecular collision which gives second order.

THE COLLISION THEORY

According to the Lindemann scheme, both first- and second-order gas phase reactions are initiated by a molecular collision. Thus, if we knew the frequency of collisions for any system, we would have a measure of its maximum possible rate of reaction. Consider the random motions of molecules moving through a gas with a velocity v. Any molecule, of diameter d, will effectively sweep out a volume in the form of a cylinder of diameter $2d$, such that it will collide with other molecules lying within the cylinder. In 1 second, the volume of the cylinder will be $v\pi d^2$. If there are n molecules per cm^3, we can write

$$z = n\pi v d^2 \tag{23.6}$$

for the collision frequency of one molecule. This derivation assumes that the molecule of interest has a fixed velocity v and that the gas through which it moves is composed entirely of stationary molecules. A more realistic treatment of the collision frequency problem would recognize that the desired quantity is the frequency of collisions of molecules having a Maxwell-Boltzmann distribution of velocities, with the molecules of a gas having the same distribution of velocities. Such a treatment for a single component gas yields

$$z = \sqrt{2}\, n\pi d^2 \bar{v} \tag{23.7}$$

where $\bar{v}$ is the mean velocity of the molecules in the gas. We may generalize for a gas that contains two different types of molecules and, inserting the expression for the mean velocity of a molecule with a Maxwell-Boltzmann energy distribution given in Figure 8-12, obtain

$$z_{12} = n_1 n_2 \pi \left(\frac{d_1 + d_2}{2}\right)^2 \left(\frac{8kT}{\pi} \frac{m_1 + m_2}{m_1 m_2}\right)^{1/2} \tag{23.8}$$

where d, n, and m represent the molecular diameter, concentration, and mass, respectively, of the two components of the system. (Watch units and dimensions if you use this equation!)

Thus we can equate the rate of a bimolecular reaction with the product of the frequency of collisions and the fraction of molecules at a given temperature that possess an energy in excess of the activation energy, ΔE_{act}. We know that this latter factor is given by the Boltzmann factor $e^{-\Delta E_{act}/RT}$, and we can express our rate as

$$\text{rate} = z_{12} e^{-\Delta E_{act}/RT} = k n_1 n_2 \tag{23.9}$$

We may now express the pre-exponential factor A in the Arrhenius expression for a rate constant, $k_1 = Ae^{-\Delta E_{act}/RT}$, as

$$\frac{z_{12}}{n_1 n_2} = A = \pi[(d_1 + d_2)/2]^2 \left(\frac{8kT}{\pi} \frac{m_1 + m_2}{m_1 m_2}\right)^{1/2} \text{cm}^3\ \text{mole}^{-1}\ \text{sec}^{-1} \tag{23.10}$$

In this expression, $\pi[(d_1 + d_2)/2]^2$ is referred to as the *collision cross section.* This formulation of the Arrhenius A factor is referred to as the collision frequency pre-exponential factor and, for typical molecules at room temperature, it has a value of 10^{13} to 10^{14} cm^3 mole^{-1} sec^{-1}. Experiment shows that although in many cases these factors are in agreement with rate data, there is also a large body of systems for which they are not. No reasonable modifications of the simple collision model seem capable of accounting for this latter group of systems, and it is evident that the simple collision theory is of only limited usefulness. In particular, some unimolecular systems have been studied in which the measured rates exceed the predictions. We shall not study the current interpretation of these deviations in detail, but they rely on two general concepts: (1) the probability of reaction upon collision depends on the orientation of the molecules, and/or (2) vibrational and/or rotational energy (as well as translational) may be transferred. We shall introduce the factor P to cover these effects and write

$$k = \text{rate constant} = P z_{12} e^{-E_{act}/RT} = Ae^{-E_{act}/RT} \tag{23.11}$$

Exercise 23.2

What happens if T increases according to the simple collision theory of reaction rates? *Answer:* (1) The collision rate increases as $T^{1/2}$, increasing the rate. (2) The availability of activation energy increases as $e^{-1/T}$, increasing the rate much more than (1). The principal effect is, then, on the Boltzmann distribution of kinetic energy.

INERT GAS EFFECT—THE TRANSFER OF THERMAL ENERGY

Since the basic process by which molecules become activated is collision, we would expect that all molecules, so long as they are thermally stable, should be capable of producing the activated molecule for a unimolecular reaction. The relative efficiencies of some gases in transferring energy in some typical unimolecular reactions are given in Table 23.1. These data should give some insight into the nature of P in Equation (23.11).

We can treat the process that involves a foreign gas by introducing an extra energization step in the following way:

$$\text{A} + \text{M} \underset{k_{-1}'}{\overset{k_1'}{\rightleftarrows}} \text{A}^* + \text{M}$$

$$\text{A} + \text{A} \underset{k_{-1}}{\overset{k_1}{\rightleftarrows}} \text{A}^* + \text{A}$$

$$\text{A}^* \xrightarrow{k_2} \text{products}$$

Table 23.1 Efficiencies of several inert gases in some unimolecular reactions.

Inert gas	Isomerization of cyclopropane[a]	Isomerization of cyclobutane[b]	Decomposition of azomethane[c]
Reactant	1.00	1.00	1.00
Ne	—	0.097	—
Ar	0.05	0.17	—
He	0.06	0.076	0.07
N_2	0.06	0.18	0.21
CO	0.07	—	0.13
H_2	0.24	0.28	—
CH_4	0.27	0.50	0.20
O_2	—	—	0.37
H_2O	0.79	0.47	0.46
$C_6H_5CH_3$	1.60	1.50	—

[a] H. O. Pritchard, R. G. Sowden, and A. F. Trotman-Dickenson, *Proc. Roy. Soc., A*, **217**, 563 (1953).
[b] H. O. Pritchard, R. G. Sowden, and A. F. Trotman-Dickenson, *Proc. Roy, Soc., A*, **218**, 416 (1953).
[c] D. V. Sickman and O. K. Rice, *J. Chem. Phys.*, **4**, 608 (1936).

We may write a steady-state equation for A* as

$$\frac{d[A^*]}{dt} = k_1[A]^2 - k_{-1}[A^*][A] + k_1'[A][M] - k_{-1}'[A^*][M] - k_2[A^*] = 0 \quad (23.12)$$

which yields

$$[A^*] = \frac{k_1[A]^2 + k_1'[A][M]}{k_{-1}[A] + k_{-1}'[M] + k_2} \quad (23.13)$$

The data in Table 23.2 have been obtained in the form of the relative effectiveness of energy transfer—by a study of rates of reaction at varying concentrations of A and M (see p. 568 on concurrent reactions). The data on many systems can be approximately generalized in the following way. The monatomic and diatomic gases are relatively ineffective, and the effectiveness of the polyatomic molecules depends upon their complexity. Molecules possessing many degrees of freedom, or normal modes, which can conceptually acquire energy in a variety of ways, are more effective than fairly simple molecules. This type of generalization would suggest to us that transfer must be by an essentially collisional redistribution of kinetic and vibrational energy and gives the second interpretation of P in Equation (23.11). We might expect a somewhat different behavior to be involved for the transfer of electronic energy, which we shall explore in the next section.

Table 23.2 Quenching cross-section data for Hg 6($^3P_1$) atoms.

Compound	CH_4	N_2	C_2H_6	H_2	O_2	H_2S	NO	C_2H_4	C_6H_6	$C_2(CH_3)_4$	CCl_4	C_2HCl_3
Cross section (Å^2)	0.06	0.19	0.42	6.01	13.9	23	24.7	26	42	43	46	52

Exercise 23.3

Arrange the following nonreacting gases in order of their probable effectiveness, at equal P and T, on the gas phase unimolecular reaction, $N_2O_4 \longrightarrow 2NO_2$: CO_2, Kr, N_2. *Answer:* The most effective gas will probably have most "degrees of freedom" $= U = 3N$. For CO_2, $U = 9$; Kr, $U = 3$; N_2, $U = 6$. Thus order of increasingly effective transfer of energy and increasing rate should be Kr, N_2, CO_2.

FLUORESCENCE QUENCHING—THE TRANSFER OF ELECTRONIC ENERGY

One of the most informative fields of gas kinetics is the study of photochemically sensitized reactions. The sensitizer most commonly employed is an electronically excited Hg atom, which is produced from the ground state atom by absorption of radiation of wavelength 2537 Å:

$$\text{Hg } 6(^1S_0) + 2537 \text{ Å} \longrightarrow \text{Hg } 6(^3P_1)$$

[The symbols following the Hg are called term symbols and identify the electronic energy state of the atom. The only part of the symbolism you may find currently useful is the left superscript, which is always one more than the number of unpaired electrons. Thus, $^3P_1$ indicates two unpaired electrons, $^1S_0$ indicates none.] Following this excitation, the fluorescent or reverse process will occur unless the excitation energy of the mercury atom is removed by interaction with some other species, as in

$$\text{Hg } 6(^3P_1) + \text{M} \longrightarrow \text{Hg } 6(^1S_0) + \text{M}^*$$

where the molecule M has acquired an additional 112 kcal/mole, the energy of the 2537 Å ultraviolet light. The efficiencies for removal of this excitation energy by some of the more common systems studied are shown in Table 23.2.

These data are given in terms of a quantity known as the quenching cross section, which is expressed as an area and is a measure of the effective collision theory area presented by the quencher to a Hg atom during an encounter. The higher the cross section, the greater the effectiveness of the particular gas in removing the excitation energy. We see that the relative complexity of the molecule or the number of vibrational degrees of freedom it possesses does not seem to be the determining factor in the transfer of the electronic energy of the mercury atom. Note for example the relative cross sections for ethane and ethylene. This behavior is essentially electronic in nature as compared with the mechanism of vibrational quenching described in the previous section. This leads us to conclude that the primary interaction between Hg $6(^3P_1)$ atoms and quenching molecules takes place according to the following patterns—that is, to π bonds and unshared pairs of electrons.

Olefins: $R_2C{=}CR_2 \leftarrow Hg^*$

Halogenated compounds: $R{-}\overline{\underline{Cl}}| \longleftarrow Hg^*$

Carbonyl-containing compounds: $R{-}C({=}O){-}R$, with $O \leftarrow Hg^*$

Now what is the effect upon the quenching molecule of the energy received from the mercury atom? Since 112 kcal/mole is an amount of energy in excess of some bond strengths, we may expect that a frequent effect may be the rupture of a bond within the molecule. Two general types of behavior are observed.

Immediate decomposition. In this case, the molecule decomposes in a period of time that is short compared with the collision frequencies, and thus the process is most conveniently written as

$$\mathrm{Hg}\ 6(^3P_1) + \mathrm{R{-}H} \longrightarrow \mathrm{R}\cdot + \mathrm{H}\cdot + \mathrm{Hg}\ 6(^1S_0)$$

Examples of this type of reaction are found in many compounds containing single carbon-hydrogen bonds but having few other distinguishing characteristics. With ethane the principal products consist of hydrogen formed in the following abstraction reaction,

$$\mathrm{H}\cdot + C_2H_6 \longrightarrow H_2 + C_2H_5\cdot$$

and ethylene and *n*-butane formed through disproportionation and combination of $C_2H_5\cdot$:

$$C_2H_5\cdot + C_2H_5\cdot \longrightarrow C_2H_4 + C_2H_6$$

or

$$\longrightarrow C_4H_{10}$$

Delayed reaction. In this case, the electronic state of the quenching gas is long-lived compared to collision frequencies and we have the prospect of observing a concentration dependence just as we did for thermal unimolecular reactions. The most familiar examples of this type of decomposition can be found among molecules containing a double bond (π bond). The following mechanism with ethylene is consistent with observed rate data:

$$C_2H_4 + \mathrm{Hg}\ 6(^3P_1) \longrightarrow C_2H_4^* + \mathrm{Hg}\ 6(^1S_0)$$
$$C_2H_4^* \longrightarrow C_2H_2 + H_2$$

ABSOLUTE REACTION RATE THEORY (ARRT)

In this development of the basic theory of Eyring and others, we shall follow the somewhat simplified scheme of Laidler. We picture any reaction as involving the transmission of the reactants across a potential barrier whose height is determined by the activation energy of the reaction. In this picture it is necessary for the reactants to come together to form an "activated state" in the sense of the following reaction,

$$\mathrm{A} + \mathrm{B} \longrightarrow (\mathrm{AB})^{\ddagger} \longrightarrow \text{products}$$

where the superscript double dagger refers to the activated complex. This activated complex need not be a bound molecule, though it may be weakly so. Thus, for example, we may picture a reaction as illustrated in Figure 23.1.

A more quantitatively correct model of passage through the activated complex or transition state has been given in the form of multi-dimensional potential energy diagrams. Although these diagrams are prohibitively complex for all

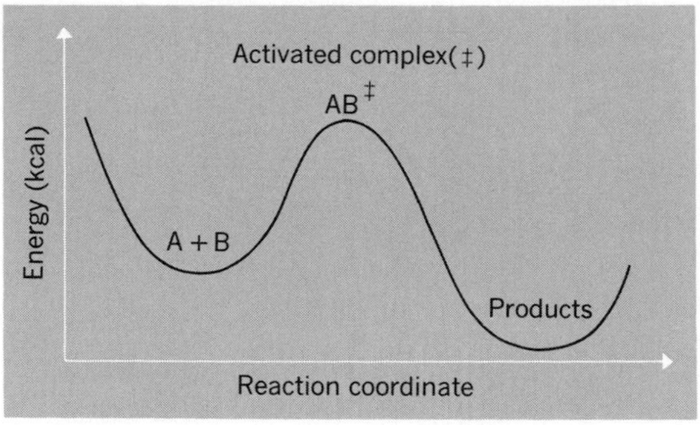

Figure 23.1 Activated complex picture of a generalized bimolecular reaction.

but the simplest cases, some useful feeling for the path of reaction can be obtained from the simple ones.

Consider the simple exchange reaction

$$H + H_2 \longrightarrow H_2 + H$$

which may be represented in transition state theory as

$$H + H_2 \longrightarrow [H\cdots\cdot H\cdots\cdot H]^{\ddagger} \longrightarrow H_2 + H$$

We may represent the potential energy of the system as a function of internuclear separation by plotting potential energy as a function of the two interatomic distances. Such a diagram is shown in Figure 23.2, and a contour map of the same diagram appears as Figure 23.3. Calculations on this simple system indicate that there are two valleys, corresponding to the potential wells of the two separate molecules. These valleys meet at a col, or saddle point, which corresponds to the transition state through which the reactants must pass as an activated complex.

Let us consider again the general reaction

$$A + B \underset{k_2}{\overset{k_1}{\rightleftharpoons}} (AB)^{\ddagger} \underset{k_4}{\overset{k_3}{\rightleftharpoons}} C + D \tag{23.14}$$

When the reaction has proceeded to equilibrium, we may say that the concentration of $(AB)^{\ddagger}$ is in equilibrium with both reactants and products. A main assumption of absolute reaction rate theory states that, even in the absence of a reverse

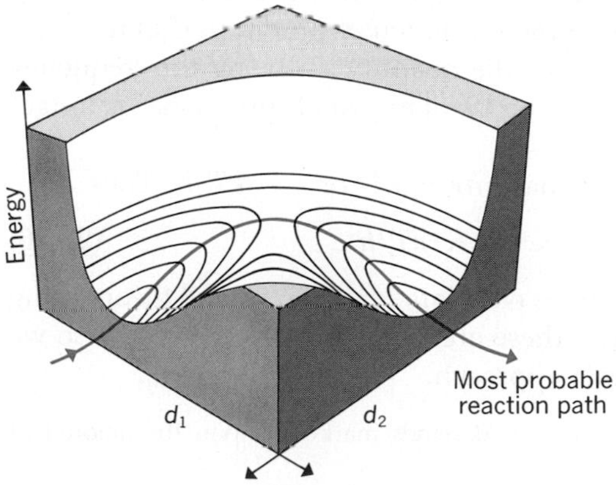

Figure 23.2 Variation of potential energy with interatomic distance in the system $H \cdot \underset{d_1}{\cdot\cdot} \cdot H \cdot \underset{d_2}{\cdot\cdot} \cdot H$.

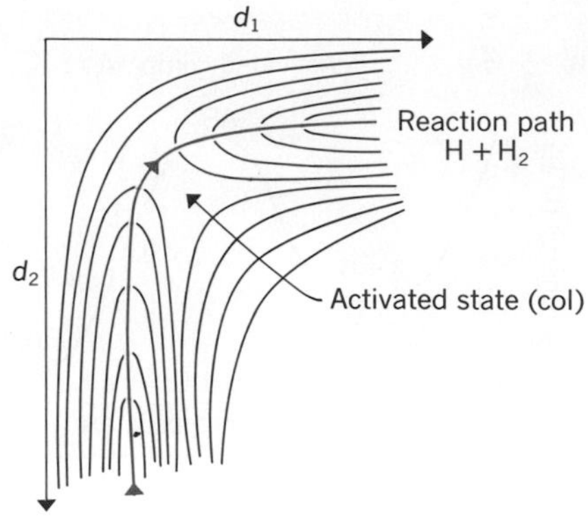

Figure 23.3 Energy contour map for the H—H$_2$ system.

reaction, we can still calculate the concentration of the activated complex as though there were an equilibrium between reactants and the molecules in the activated complex. In this hypothesis, we identify the rate of entrance into the transition state with the rate of reaction:

$$A + B \xrightarrow{k_1} AB^{\ddagger} \xrightarrow{k_3} \text{products}$$

$$\frac{d[AB^{\ddagger}]}{dt} = k_1[A][B] = -k_3[AB^{\ddagger}]$$

Once having reached the state of activated complex, the reactants normally proceed on to products. The "equilibrium" concentration of $AB^{\ddagger}$ is reached when its rate of formation from reactants and its rate of decomposition into products are equal. Note that this formulation exactly matches a steady-state assumption with regard to $[AB^{\ddagger}]$.

The "equilibrium" between reactants and activated complexes in Equation (23.14) gives

$$K^{\ddagger} = \frac{[AB]^{\ddagger}}{[A][B]} = \frac{k_1}{k_3}, \; k_1 = k_3K^{\ddagger} \tag{23.15}$$

If the activated complex consists of $n_a + n_b$ atoms, then we may expect that of the possible $[3(n_a + n_b) - 6]$ normal modes of vibration, one will be much "looser" than the others—corresponding to that mode which eventually is involved in rupture of the activated complex with the formation of products. Call its vibrational frequency ν. We now recognize that the quantity ν—being the frequency of vibration in the normal mode, which upon breaking yields products—is in fact the rate constant, k_3, of decomposition.

For a fully excited oscillator we have $h\nu = kT$, or $\nu = kT/h$. Thus

$$k_1 = k_3K^{\ddagger} = \nu K^{\ddagger} = K^{\ddagger}kT/h \tag{23.16}$$

In principal a value of $K^{\ddagger}$, hence k_1, may be calculated from statistical theory using molar partition functions. In most cases these are very difficult to evaluate so we shall use the alternative thermodynamic approach.

The concentration of the various species depends markedly upon the amount of

Table 23.3 Comparison of experimental and calculated mass spectra from 2,3-dithiabutane, H_3CSSCH_3.

Ion	Percentage abundance	
	Statistical theory	Measured
$CH_3S_2^+$	15.1	16.2
$C_2H_5S^+$	4.6	4.5
CH_4S^+	4.4	3.5
CH_3S^+	9.1	7.1
CH_2S^+	11.2	11.0

SOURCE: Calculations of B. G. Holrock *in* R. W. Kiser, *Introduction to Mass Spectrometry and its Applications*, Prentice-Hall, (1965).

energy contained within the molecule. For example, above an energy of about 3 *ev* the ion $C_2H_5^+$ undergoes the decomposition

$$C_2H_5^+ \longrightarrow C_2H_3^+ + H_2$$

Clearly such a reaction is characterized by an activation energy, and the problem of predicting these curves is essentially a kinetic problem. Absolute reaction rate theory has been applied to this problem by Rosenstock and others. In certain favorable cases, the results are encouraging, as demonstrated by Table 23.3.

THERMODYNAMIC DESCRIPTION OF REACTION RATE

From Equation (23.16) we get

$$k_1 = \left(\frac{kT}{h}\right)K^{\ddagger} \qquad (23.17)$$

in which, we must remember, the k appearing in kT is the Boltzmann constant and not a rate constant. We may then write $K^{\ddagger}$ in terms of $\Delta G^{\ddagger}$ as $\Delta G^{\ddagger} = -RT \ln K^{\ddagger}$ [following Equation (20.11)]. We then have

$$k_1 = \left(\frac{kT}{h}\right)e^{-\Delta G^{\ddagger}/RT} \qquad (23.18)$$

and if we express the free energy in terms of enthalpy and entropy terms, $\Delta G^{\ddagger} = \Delta H^{\ddagger} - T\,\Delta S^{\ddagger}$, we have

$$k_1 = \left(\frac{kT}{h}\right)e^{\Delta S^{\ddagger}/R}e^{-\Delta H^{\ddagger}/RT} \qquad (23.19)$$

We may convert this expression into one that involves the experimental activation energy ϵ in the following way. Since $K^{\ddagger}$ is a concentration equilibrium constant, we may write [from thermodynamics; Equation (29.21)]

$$\frac{d \ln K^{\ddagger}}{dT} = \frac{\Delta E^{\ddagger}}{RT^2} \qquad (23.20)$$

Differentiating the logarithmic form of (23.17) gives

$$\frac{d\ln k_1}{dT} = \frac{1}{T} + \frac{d\ln K^{\ddagger}}{dT} = \frac{1}{T} + \frac{\Delta E^{\ddagger}}{RT^2} = \frac{RT + \Delta E^{\ddagger}}{RT^2} \tag{23.21}$$

Differentiating the Arrhenius form, equation (23.11), gives

$$\frac{d\ln k_1}{dT} = \frac{\Delta E_{\text{act}}}{RT^2} \tag{23.22}$$

and thus we may write

$$\Delta E^{\ddagger} + RT = \Delta E_{\text{act}} \tag{23.23}$$

We may also write

$$\Delta H^{\ddagger} = \Delta E^{\ddagger} + P\,\Delta V^{\ddagger} \tag{23.24}$$

and thus

$$\epsilon = \Delta H^{\ddagger} - P\,\Delta V^{\ddagger} + RT \tag{23.25}$$

For a typical bimolecular reaction, $P\,\Delta V^{\ddagger} = \Delta nRT = 1 \cdot RT = RT$. Thus $\epsilon = \Delta H^{\ddagger}$ for such reactions. In general, $-P\,\Delta V^{\ddagger} + RT \cong -\Delta nRT + RT = RT(1 - \Delta n)$. For most conditions of interest, $RT = 2 \cdot T < 1$ kcal and $(1 - \Delta n)$ is between 1 and -1. Since ϵ is often of the order of 10 kcal, $(-P\,\Delta V^{\ddagger} + RT)$ may usually be neglected and $\epsilon \cong \Delta E^{\ddagger}$. Thus, for most reactions,

$$\Delta E^{\ddagger} \cong \Delta H^{\ddagger} = \epsilon \equiv \Delta E_{\text{act}} \tag{23.26}$$

which should clarify and relate these manifold symbols for the energy required to activate a system.

For a bimolecular reaction we get, from Equation (23.19) and $\Delta H^{\ddagger} = \Delta E_{\text{act}}$,

$$k_1 = \left(\frac{kT}{h}\right) e^{\Delta S^{\ddagger}/R} e^{-\Delta E_{\text{act}}/RT}$$

$$A = \left(\frac{kT}{h}\right) e^{\Delta S^{\ddagger}/R}$$

For a unimolecular reaction, using equation 23.25, where $\Delta V^{\ddagger}$ is zero, so that $e^{P\,\Delta V} = e$, we may write the rate equation, if RT is small, as

$$k_1 = e\left(\frac{kT}{h}\right) e^{\Delta S^{\ddagger}/R} e^{-\epsilon/RT} \tag{23.27}$$

We may identify term by term with the Arrhenius formulation of reaction rates (p. 583) to obtain

$$A = e\left(\frac{kT}{h}\right) e^{\Delta S^{\ddagger}/R} \tag{23.28}$$

We now have a new formulation of the Arrhenius pre-exponential factor, which involves $\Delta S^{\ddagger}$, the change in entropy upon passage from reactants into the activated complex. $\Delta S^{\ddagger}$ is related to the probability of the activated state forming and having the appropriate geometry to allow: (1) the energy to flow into the bonds that must rupture, and (2) the atoms to rearrange to give the product molecules.

Exercise 23.4

Can you design an experiment to test the suggestion that $\Delta S^{\ddagger}$ may profitably be considered as two terms: (1) a $\Delta S_P^{\ddagger}$ which measures collision probability, and (2) a $\Delta S_O^{\ddagger}$ which measures the likelihood of favorable orientation on collision? *Answer:* No such experiment has apparently been done definitively. Perhaps very careful measurements on the H–D system would give some insight. The collision rate of H_2 and D_2 will be different from that of HD with HD due to the m_1m_2 term in μ (8 versus 9). On the other hand, every H_2–D_2 collision which leads to reaction produces 2HD, while half the HD–HD collisions should produce 2HD and half should produce H_2 and D_2. Hopefully, any experimentally observed difference in $\Delta S^{\ddagger}$ might be checked against these two predictions. Current experiments which measure reaction probabilities between crossed beams of oriented molecules may also provide information.

ARRHENIUS PRE-EXPONENTIAL FACTORS FOR UNIMOLECULAR REACTIONS

The Arrhenius factors for unimolecular reactions have a wide range of values. We may attempt some interpretation for A factors as low as 10^{10} sec^{-1} and those as

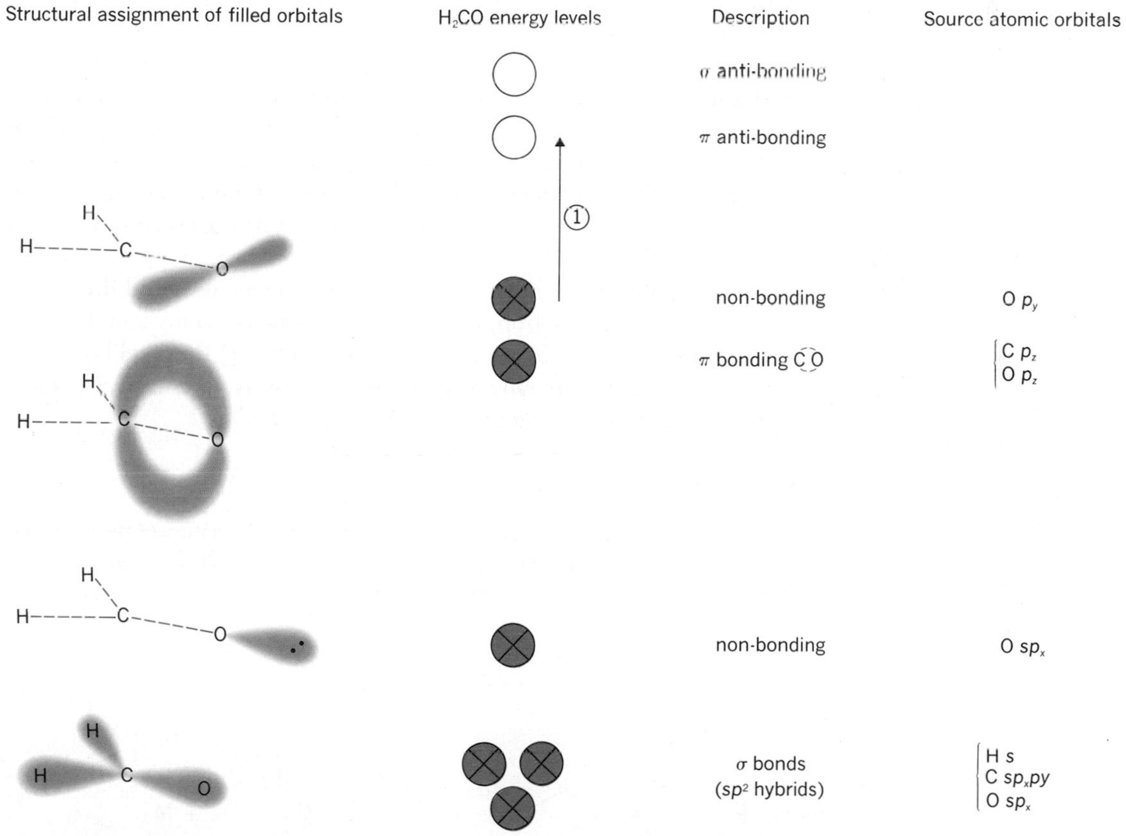

Figure 23.4 Molecular orbital energy level diagram for formaldehyde. [H. H. Jaffe and M. Orchin, *Theory and Applications of Ultraviolet Spectroscopy*, Wiley, 1962.]

high as 10^{17} sec^{-1}. We shall describe those A factors lying between $10^{11.5}$ and $10^{14.5}$ sec^{-1} as normal (they agree with predictions from collision theory) and those outside this range as abnormal. These numerical limits on A can be translated into limits on $\Delta S^{\ddagger}$, using Equation (23.28). If this is done, we conclude that if the entropy of activation lies within the range of ± 7 eu, then the Arrhenius factor will be normal. If $\Delta S^{\ddagger}$ is less than -7 eu, passage into the activated complex is evidently accompanied by a considerable decrease in entropy, indicating that the activated complex has considerably less freedom of motion than did the molecule in the reactant state. The thermal decompositions of many esters have a large negative entropy of activation which has been interpreted as a result of a transition state involving a cyclic intermediate:

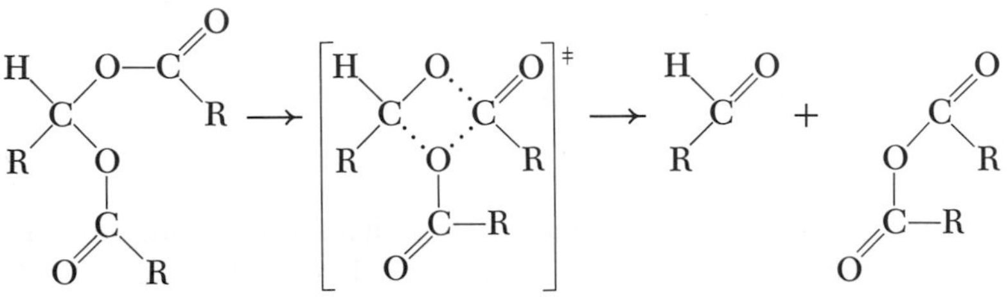

It has been shown that many reactions of this type have low Arrhenius factors in the range of $10^{9.2}$ to $10^{11.1}$ sec^{-1}.

If $\Delta S^{\ddagger}$ exceeds 7 eu, the transition state is much looser than the initial state. A natural and representative example is the unimolecular isomerization of cyclopropane to propylene, whose A factor is $10^{15.17}$. We might suggest that there is greater freedom of motion in the activated complex in the C—C bond, which must rupture to provide the rearrangement. A similar interpretation would account for the variation of A in Table 22.1 between *t*-butyl hydrocarbons and *t*-butyl halides.

Thus, there is a necessary relationship between mechanism and the values of the Arrhenius factors for a reaction, consistent with our previous idea that the $\Delta S^{\ddagger}$ term may be thought of as covering two main effects: (1) the likelihood of a molecular collision, and (2) the likelihood that the collision is geometrically (electrically) favorable for forming the activated state.

Exercise 23.5

Assuming that the equations below correctly represent the formation of the activated complex, in which would you expect $\Delta S^{\ddagger}$ to be abnormally low, normal, and abnormally high? Give reasons. Remember 3D!

(*a*) $H_2 + I \longrightarrow H\text{—}H\text{—}I$

(*b*) $M^* +$ 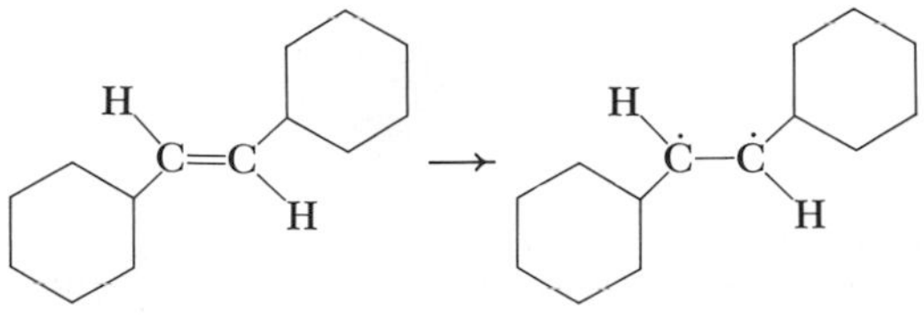 $+ M$

(c) H_2 + 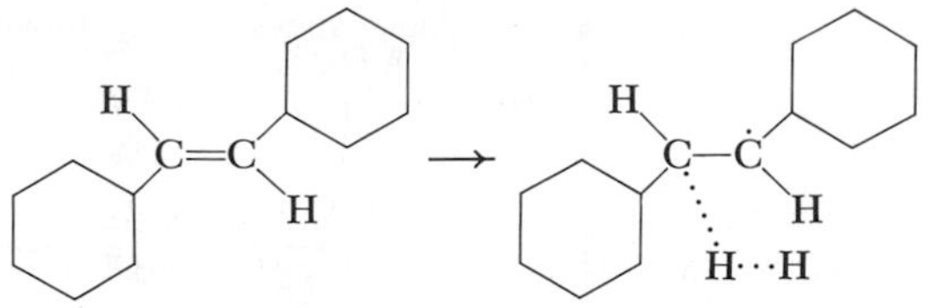

Answer: (*a*) Simple, symmetric molecules with few apparent geometrical restrictions, $\Delta S^{\ddagger}$ and A probably in normal range. (*b*) Few if any geometrical restrictions to collision. Any collision may be expected to impart energy, giving a "loose" activated state. $\Delta S^{\ddagger}$ probably slightly high. (*c*) In two dimensions this looks like a "crowded" and unlikely collision. But reaction is probably between H_2 and the π orbital of carbon, which is perpendicular to the plane of the molecule. Thus there are few geometric restrictions and $\Delta S^{\ddagger}$ is probably in the normal range, since gain in looseness of large molecule is offset by loss of freedom of H_2. The value of A probably is normal.

ENERGY DISTRIBUTION AFTER DIRECT PHOTON EXCITATION IN GAS-PHASE REACTIONS

We have previously described the transfer of electronic energy in photosensitized reactions (pp. 585–586). Here we will concern ourselves with the dissipation of energy that is received directly by photon excitation. As an illustrative example, consider the absorption of ultraviolet light by molecules containing the carbonyl group >C=O; we shall choose formaldehyde. From Chapter 17 we recall that we may represent the lower energy levels available to the formaldehyde molecule in terms of the molecular orbital energy-level diagram shown in Figure 23.4.

The lowest-energy light that may be absorbed by formaldehyde would correspond to the transition labeled (1) in Figure 23.4. This corresponds to the excitation of an electron residing in a nonbonding p orbital on the oxygen into a vacant antibonding π orbital between the oxygen and the carbon. This transition is referred to as $\pi_a \longleftarrow n$ transition, in which the subscript a indicates the antibonding character of the π orbital. This transition occurs in formaldehyde at about 2700 Å, and is of low intensity because of the different symmetry of the two orbitals involved. Other transitions observed in the ultraviolet absorption spectrum of formaldehyde are $\sigma \longleftarrow n$, $\pi_a \longleftarrow \pi_b$, $\sigma \longleftarrow \pi_b$, as you should be able to predict. (The higher energy state is listed first, the arrow indicates the direction of the transition.)

The kinetic study of photochemical reactions is concerned with the redistribution of energy which follows the initial act of absorption. The several processes that may occur are illustrated in Figure 23.5, which superimposes the vibrational energy levels upon the various schematic electronic energy levels. We may note that, other than for the ground state of the molecule, we have pairs of excited states. These result from the unpairing of an electron pair, which occurs when a single electron is transferred to an excited state by a photon absorption. Whenever we have two unpaired electrons, we may have two electronic states—called a singlet if the electron spins are opposed, and a triplet if the two spins are parallel. Of these two states, the triplet (designated T) will usually have the lower energy. The various

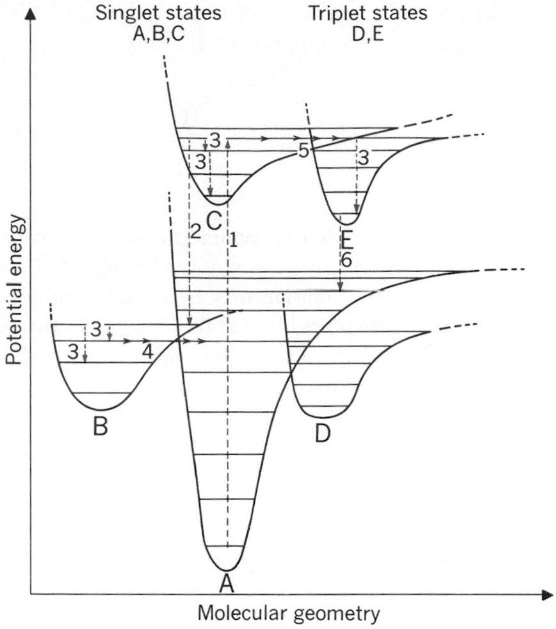

Figure 23.5 Schematic energy-level diagram for a diatomic molecule. Three singlet electronic states are shown—A, B, C; two triplet states are shown—D, E. Note that all radiative transfers occur at constant molecular geometry as stated in the Franck-Condon principle. Rotational states are not indicated. In a real system it would be most unusual for an excited state (like B) to be bound more tightly than the ground state (A).

processes subsequent to the initial act of absorption are indicated numerically in Figure 23.5 and described below.

1. The initial absorption from the ground-state singlet may lead to any of several excited singlet states (A $\longrightarrow$ B, A $\longrightarrow$ C), depending upon the energy of the light. Direct absorption to an excited triplet state is normally a "forbidden" process and in practice is either weak or not observed.
2. The radiative loss of energy between singlets (such as C $\longrightarrow$ B) is referred to as fluorescence. Frequently fluorescence is observed to occur within a period of about 10^{-8} seconds following excitation. This period of time is long compared to vibration frequencies and collision times, and thus competing processes such as internal conversion or dissociation or reaction may remove the excitation energy before it can be radiated through fluorescence.
3. If formed in a vibrationally excited level of an electronically excited state, the excess vibrational energy may be thermally degraded through collisions.
4. A process such as B $\longrightarrow$ A has been called internal conversion and involves a nonradiative conversion of electronic energy into vibrational energy by some mechanism(s) only incompletely understood.
5. A process (such as C $\longrightarrow$ E) that leads to the population of excited triplet states from singlet states (or the converse) is called intersystem crossing. It is a nonradiative process, which depends upon proper overlap of potential energy surfaces and an absence of competing processes.
6. Once formed, an excited triplet state may undergo (*a*) transition either by radiation or internal conversion to the lowest triplet state and/or (*b*) undergo a radiative process called phosphorescence, leading to the ground-state singlet. Since *b* is a radiative process involving a change of multiplic-

ity, we may expect it to be slow. Experimentally we observe that phosphorescent emission half-times are often of the order of seconds or longer.

Exercise 23.6

How is the design of a fluorescent lamp coating related to the discussion in this section? *Answer:* A short half-life should be used so that the light goes out when voltage is reduced to zero. Phosphorescence should be held to a minimum. A fluorescence over the whole visible range excited by the mercury UV emission requires properly spaced energy levels. Thus singlet-singlet transitions absorbing in the UV but emitting as high a percent as possible to give a "flat" visible spectrum would be best. There should be as little internal conversion as possible to heat, so as to be more efficient than a tungsten bulb.

REACTIONS IN CONDENSED PHASES

Although reactions in condensed phases, especially solutions, have provided a greater amount of kinetic data than reactions in the gas phase, the theoretical situation of the first is less satisfactory. The reason for this is the greater complexity involved in a quantitative discussion of the effects when molecules are always close to other molecules. An unambiguous comparison of reactions in the gas phase and in condensed phases requires that the system studied react according to the same mechanism in both phases.

The rate data for the thermal dissociation of dicyclopentadiene and the monomer dimerization given in Table 23.4 illustrate a system in which the changes are very small in going from gas to liquid phase.

Table 23.4 Dimerization of cyclopentadiene and dissociation of the dimer.

	$k_{\text{dimerization}}$	$k_{\text{dissociation}}$
Pure gas	$10^{6.1}\ e^{-16,700/RT}$	$10^{13.1}\ e^{-35,000/RT}$
Pure liquid	$10^{5.7}\ e^{-16,000/RT}$	$10^{13.0}\ e^{-34,500/RT}$

SOURCE: A. Wasserman, *Monatsh*, **83**, 543 (1952).

Few systems have actually been studied in both the solution and gas phases, and our remarks about reactions in solution will be largely restricted to a discussion of various solvent effects and a comparison between reactions in varying liquid media. The lack of acceptable quantitative models will not prevent us from gaining an appreciation of the nature of these effects. We may expect that the nature of any solvent will have a pronounced effect upon the course of the reaction. We shall discuss solid-phase reactions later in Chapter 32, but you should be able to anticipate most of the differences between liquid and solid phases.

Exercise 23.7

Rationalize the observation in Table 23.4 that the activation energies are less in the liquid than in the gas phase. *Answer:* Since the molecules are already close together, there is less energy differences between a pair of "neighboring" molecules and a pair of molecules in the activated complex in the liquid than in the gas phase.

THE CAGE EFFECT

This effect is also sometimes called the Franck-Rabinovitch effect and is a result of the essentially continual collisions and dense packing that exists in a liquid as compared with a gas. As an example we may choose the photochemical decomposition of ethyl iodide:

$$C_2H_5I + h\nu \longrightarrow C_2H_5\cdot + I\cdot$$

This reaction is known to occur with unit quantum efficiency in the gas phase. That is, each molecule that absorbs a quantum of light is dissociated and the fragments appear finally, following secondary reactions, as stable products. In solution, the quantum yield may drop from unity to less than one-tenth, depending upon temperature. It seems likely that although bond rupture occurs for every absorbed photon, the fragments are constrained to remain in close proximity to each other by a "cage" of solvent molecules and will often eventually recombine, thus diminishing the rate of formation of products.

Exercise 23.8

Which would probably have the greater cage effect as a solvent—C_2H_5OH or glycerine, $CH_2OHCHOHCH_2OH$? *Answer:* The two solvents are similar in functional groups (hydroxy hydrocarbons), but glycerine has more OH groups per molecule and thus will have more intermolecular hydrogen bonds than will ethanol. This will give a more viscous solution with more rigid cages. Glycerine's cage effect should be larger than that in ethanol.

Exercise 23.9

Would you expect the reaction, $Co(S)_6^{+++} + 6NH_3 \longrightarrow Co(NH_3)_6^{+++} + 6S$ (where S = solvent) to proceed more rapidly in H_2O or C_2H_5OH as solvent? *Answer:* H_2O is a more polar molecule ($\mu = 1.85$) than C_2H_5OH ($\mu = 1.70$). The reactant species $Co(S)_6^{+++}$ will be more tightly bound if $S = H_2O$; thus the activation energy for $S = H_2O$ should be higher than for $S = C_2H_5OH$. Furthermore, $Co(S)_6^{+++}$ probably interacts much more strongly with H_2O as a solvent, further slowing the rate in H_2O.

SOLVOLYSIS REACTIONS

Since the solvent is ordinarily present in enormous excess (in hydrolysis reactions the concentration of water is typically of the order of 55 molar), it is difficult to tell kinetically if the solvent is involved in the rate-determining step. For example, the hydrolysis of alkyl halides may be written as

$$RX + H_2O \longrightarrow ROH + HX$$

and we may write the rate expression as

$$\frac{d}{dt}[HX] = k[RX][H_2O] \tag{23.29}$$

However, since the concentration of water is constant (within experimental uncertainty) during the reaction, the observed rate constant will in fact include the concentration of water and the reaction will appear to be first order. That reactions of this type occur can be inferred from the strong dependence of rate upon the solvent ionizing power.

In addition to the special effects mentioned above, one also observes the influence of viscosity in very fast reactions.

Exercise 23.10

What is a probable mechanism for the net reaction $C_{12}H_{22}O_{11}$ (sucrose) + H_2O = $C_6H_{12}O_6$ (glucose) + $C_6H_{12}O_6$ (fructose)? The rate equation is $d[\text{product}]/dt = k[\text{sucrose}][H^+]$. *Answer:* There is probably a fast equilibrium between sucrose and H^+ followed by a slow reaction with H_2O, followed by release of H^+ by the products. It is very unlikely that the reaction with H^+ is slow; H^+ in aqueous solutions has high mobility. The involvement of H_2O in the slow step does not show up in the rate law, due to the unchanging concentration of H_2O.

CHAIN REACTIONS

If one prepares in the dark an equimolar mixture of hydrogen and chlorine and then exposes it to the light output of a normal photographic flashbulb, a violent explosion occurs. A similar experiment carried out with an equimolar mixture of hydrogen and iodine gives only a moderate rate of reaction even when high-intensity continuous illumination is provided. How may we interpret these two effects?

The apparent color of both iodine and chlorine and the colorless nature of gaseous hydrogen suggests that the light is probably absorbed by the halogen (though H_2 may absorb in the UV). We guess that the elementary process is

$$X_2 + h\nu \longrightarrow 2X\cdot$$

followed by

$$X\cdot + H_2 \longrightarrow HX + H\cdot$$

and

$$H\cdot + X_2 \longrightarrow HX + X\cdot$$

This type of mechanism can explain explosions as free radical chain reactions. The second reaction is exothermic for chlorine and endothermic for iodine (see Table 14.8), though the two ΔS values will be similar. Thus chlorine can, and does, explode by a free radical chain, whereas iodine follows a nonchain mechanism, as in Problem 22.22.

The over-all chlorine chain mechanism is:

Chain initiation: $h\nu + Cl_2 \longrightarrow 2Cl\cdot$

Chain propagation: $\begin{cases} Cl\cdot + H_2 \longrightarrow HCl + H\cdot \\ H\cdot + Cl_2 \longrightarrow Cl\cdot + HCl \end{cases}$ and so on $\longrightarrow$

In the absence of other reactions which remove the chlorine and hydrogen atoms, one quantum of light is sufficient to convert all the reactants to products, since each reaction regenerates a free radical and continues the chain. Under certain circumstances a yield of 10^6 molecules has been obtained per quantum of absorbed light. Reactions which are self-propagating are referred to as chain reactions.

As shown by Rice and Herzfeld in 1934, complex free radical chain reactions can frequently lead to deceptively simple rate laws. Consider the decomposition of acetaldehyde:

Chain initiation: $CH_3CHO \xrightarrow{k_1} CH_3\cdot + CHO\cdot$

Chain propagation:

$$\begin{cases} CH_3\cdot + CH_3CHO \xrightarrow{k_2} CH_4 + CH_3CO\cdot \\ CH_3CO\cdot \xrightarrow{k_3} CH_3\cdot + CO \\ CHO\cdot \xrightarrow{k_4} H\cdot + CO \\ H\cdot + CH_3CHO \xrightarrow{k_5} H_2 + CH_3CO\cdot \end{cases}$$

Chain termination: $2CH_3\cdot \xrightarrow{k_6} C_2H_6$

Such a mechanism can be shown to yield the rate law,

$$-\frac{d}{dt}[CH_3CHO] = 2k_2\left(\frac{k_1}{k_6}\right)^{1/2}[CH_3CHO]^{3/2} = k[CH_3CHO]^{3/2} \quad (23.30)$$

The three-halves order of this reaction has been verified experimentally by Laidler and others. The reaction is more complex than even the above mechanism indicates, however, since the addition of various inert gases leads to a decrease in rate and an increase in order. This effect cannot be predicted on the basis of the above mechanism.

Chain termination involving net removal of free radicals may occur homogeneously throughout the reaction vessel and/or it may occur heterogeneously on the walls of the vessel. In the latter process a radical is adsorbed on an active site of the reaction vessel and undergoes recombination when another radical collides with it. The heterogeneous process becomes more important as the pressure is decreased, since its frequency changes only as the first power of the concentration and the homogeneous process changes as the second power.

A great many chain reactions, in particular the oxidation of hydrocarbons (as in gasoline engines), are described as branched chain reactions. In these reactions there is on the average more than one chain carrier produced in each chain propagation step. For example,

$$\dot{\underset{\cdot}{O}} + CH_4 \longrightarrow CH_3\cdot + \cdot OH$$

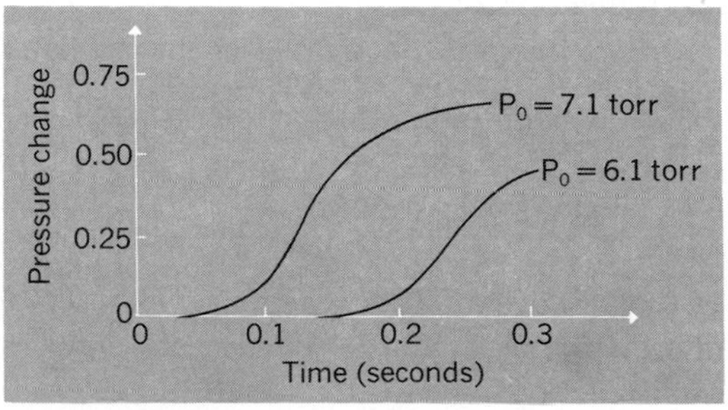

Figure 23.6 Combustion of a mixture of hydrogen and oxygen at 485° C. [A. A. Kovalshii, *Phys. Z. Sow.*, **4**, 723 (1933).]

A characteristic property of these reactions is an induction period at the beginning of the reaction when the rate is low (and in some reactions immeasurably low). This behavior is illustrated in Figure 23.6. In many cases these induction effects reflect the slow buildup of an intermediate, which may then catalyze the decomposition or serve as a particularly effective chain carrier. Such reactions are said to be autocatalytic: Problem 22.16, *a* provides another example.

Exercise 23.11

Suggest a mechanistic role for $Pb(C_2H_5)_4$, lead tetraethyl, in minimizing knock in an internal combustion engine. *Answer:* Knock accompanies too rapid, or too early, reaction of the fuel and oxygen. The mechanism certainly involves free radicals produced during the oxidation. Remember that O_2 itself is a diradical (two unpaired electrons per molecule). If $Pb(C_2H_5)_4$ decomposes at reaction temperatures, $C_2H_5{:}$ will be produced. These free radicals may terminate some of the oxidation chain reactions, thus slowing down the combustion and minimizing knock. The details of fuel combustion are still not known, so complicated is the mechanism.

CATALYSIS

Many reactions that are thermodynamically favorable are found to occur at inconveniently low rates. In some of these the addition of certain materials can result in a higher rate without altering the over-all stoichiometry. The substances are catalysts. Thus, for example, the hydrolysis of sucrose occurs at a very low rate in pure water, but the addition of small amounts of acid gives much more rapid reaction:

$$H_2O + C_{12}H_{22}O_{11} \xrightarrow{H^+} C_6H_{12}O_6 + C_6H_{12}O_6$$

This is an example of homogeneous catalysis, since the reaction occurs in but a single phase.

Another example, is the gas-phase thermal decomposition of acetaldehyde vapor accelerated by the presence of small amounts of iodine. The mechanism presumably will involve iodine atoms, as

$$\begin{aligned} I_2 &\longrightarrow 2I\cdot \\ I\cdot + CH_3CHO &\longrightarrow HI + CH_3CO\cdot \\ CH_3CO\cdot &\longrightarrow CH_3\cdot + CO \\ CH_3\cdot + I_2 &\longrightarrow CH_3I + I\cdot \\ CH_3\cdot + HI &\longrightarrow CH_4 + I\cdot \\ \hline \text{Net: } CH_3CHO &\longrightarrow CH_4 + CO \end{aligned}$$

The iodine is eventually reformed by recombination of iodine atoms and illustrates another general property of catalysis—the catalyst is regenerated.

There are many examples of heterogeneous catalysis in which the reaction occurs at the surface of a solid catalyst. One of the more familiar illustrations is the catalytic cracking step in the refinement of crude oil. We have already given several others. Some idea of the practical importance of catalysts is obtained from the fact that, using synthetic heterogeneous catalysts alone, the United States produces annually about $30 billion of materials that would not otherwise be available.

A catalyst has been defined by Bell as a substance that appears in the rate equation at a higher power than its coefficient as a reactant in the stoichiometric equation for the reaction. (See Problem 22.9 for examples.)

We may inquire into the general role of a catalyst. Consider the acetaldehyde system mentioned above. In the uncatalyzed decomposition, we may write the transition state for the initial process as

$$CH_3\text{—}CHO \longrightarrow (CH_3\text{—}CHO)^{\ddagger} \longrightarrow CH_3\cdot + CHO\cdot$$

This process requires the breaking of the C—C bond and is to be compared with a possible transition state for the similar process in the catalyzed reaction,

$$I\cdot + CH_3CHO \longrightarrow \left(\begin{array}{c} CH_3\text{—}CO \\ \quad\ \ | \\ \quad\ \ H\cdots I \end{array}\right)^{\ddagger} \longrightarrow HI + CH_3CO\cdot$$

In this case, the reaction yields the stable molecule HI. We can expect a more stable (lower $\Delta E^{\ddagger}$) species in the transition state in the catalyzed reaction. The endothermicity of the first step in the uncatalyzed reaction will be about 75 kcal/mole. In the catalyzed reaction it may only be 5–10 kcal/mole. Catalysts also can affect $\Delta S^{\ddagger}$ by changing orientational probabilities, but as a general rule, a catalyst is effective because it provides a new path for the reaction—one with lower activation energy.

We may treat such a situation quantitatively. We write a schematic reaction sequence as

$$A \xrightarrow{k_1} B \qquad \text{uncatalyzed reaction, } \frac{d[B]}{dt} = k_1[A]$$

$$A + C \underset{k_{-2}}{\overset{k_2}{\rightleftharpoons}} D \qquad \text{catalyzed formation of an intermediate}$$

$$D \xrightarrow{k_3} B + C$$

For the catalyzed rate of appearance of product B, we may write

$$\frac{d}{dt}[B] = k_3[D] \tag{23.31}$$

and we may set up the steady-state expression for the concentration of D as

$$\frac{d}{dt}[D] = k_2[A][C] - k_{-2}[D] - k_3[D] = 0 \tag{23.32}$$

and thus

$$[D] = \frac{k_2[A][C]}{k_{-2} + k_3} \tag{23.33}$$

and we have for the catalyzed reaction

$$\frac{d}{dt}[B] = \frac{k_2k_3[A][C]}{k_{-2} + k_3} \tag{23.34}$$

The total rate is:

$$\frac{d[B]}{dt} = k_1[B] + \frac{k_2k_3[A][C]}{k_{-2} + k_3}$$

The catalyzed mechanism is different but the final product must be the same. The over-all rate is bound to be faster since two mechanisms are possible, and it may be much faster indeed.

Exercise 23.12

Compare the Bell definition of a catalyst with the following one: "A catalyst is a reactant affecting the rate of reaction and regenerated during the net reaction." *Answer:* The Bell definition is more operational since it does not require a detailed knowledge of the mechanism. Furthermore, "regeneration" is difficult to apply unambiguously in such cases as autocatalysis, where the concentration of the catalyst changes with time.

ACID-BASE CATALYSIS

An important class of reactions are those catalyzed by *acids* and *bases*. In aqueous systems the effective catalysts are usually H_3O^+ and OH^-. In some cases a reaction will be catalyzed by both acids and bases, and we can represent the rate constant for such a system as summed for three different mechanisms, each proceeding through a different activated complex,

$$k_1 = k_0 + k_{H^+}[H^+] + k_{OH^-}[OH^-] \qquad (23.35)$$

where k_0 is the rate constant for the uncatalyzed reaction. Some of the situations likely to arise are illustrated in Figure 23.7.

We may think of the mechanism of such reactions in terms of movement of the electrons as influenced by H^+ and/or OH^-. For example, in the hydrolysis of ethyl acetate we may write the three mechanisms in the following ways.

slow:

$$H_3-C\overset{O-C_2H_5}{\underset{O\delta^-}{\overset{\delta^+}{\Big|}}} \xrightarrow{H_2O} H_3-C\overset{O-C_2H_5}{\underset{O\quad H}{\Big|}}:\ddot{O}-H \longrightarrow$$

$$H_3-C\overset{\ddot{O}-H^+}{\underset{O}{\overset{H}{\Big|}}} + OC_2H_5^- \longrightarrow H_3-C\overset{O-H}{\underset{O}{\Big|}} + HOC_2H_5$$

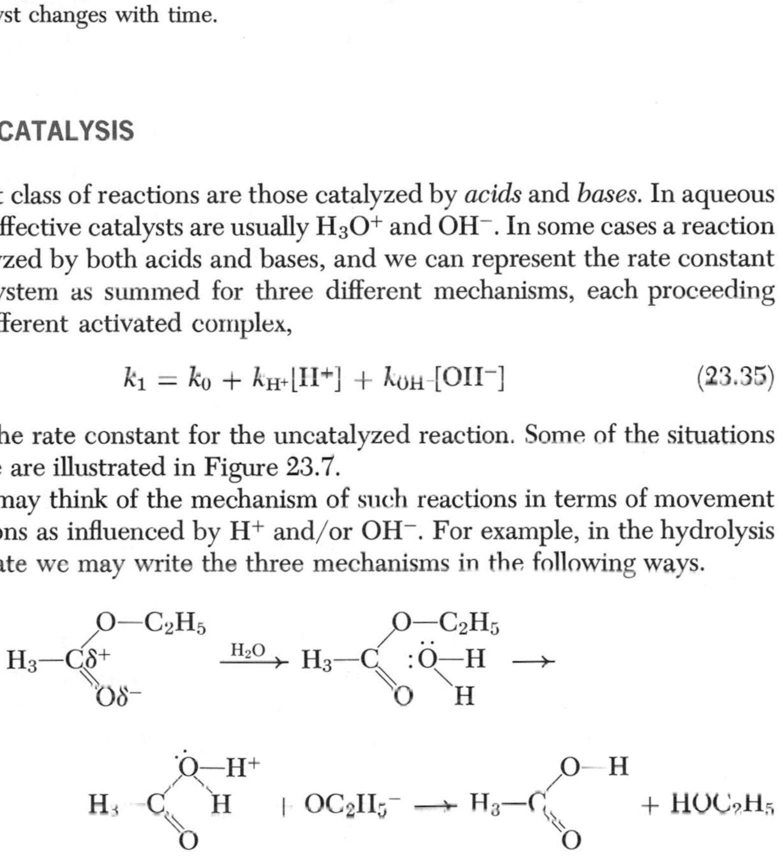

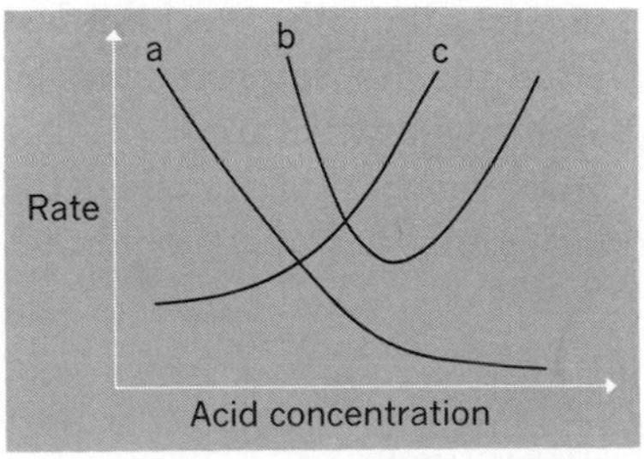

Rate

Acid concentration

Figure 23.7 Variation of rate in an acid-base catalyzed reaction. **(A)** Strongly catalyzed by base, weakly catalyzed by water, no appreciable catalysis by acid. **(B)** Strongly catalyzed by base, less catalyzed by water, strongly catalyzed by acid. **(C)** No appreciable catalysis by base, little catalyzed by water, strongly catalyzed by acid.

moderate:

$$H_3-C\overset{\delta+}{\underset{O\delta^-}{\overset{O-C_2H_5}{|}}} \xrightarrow{H_3O^+} H_3-C\overset{\delta+}{\underset{O}{\overset{O-C_2H_5}{|}}} \xrightarrow{H_2O}$$

$$\overset{H^+}{\underset{H\quad H}{O}}$$

$$H_3-C\overset{O-C_2H_5}{\underset{O-H^+}{|}} \longleftarrow :\ddot{O}H_2 \longrightarrow H_3-C\overset{\ddot{O}^+-H}{\underset{O-H^+}{\overset{|}{|}}}H + OC_2H_5^-$$

$$\downarrow H^+$$

$$\downarrow -2H^+ \qquad HOC_2H_5$$

$$H_3-C\overset{O-H^+}{\underset{O}{|}}$$

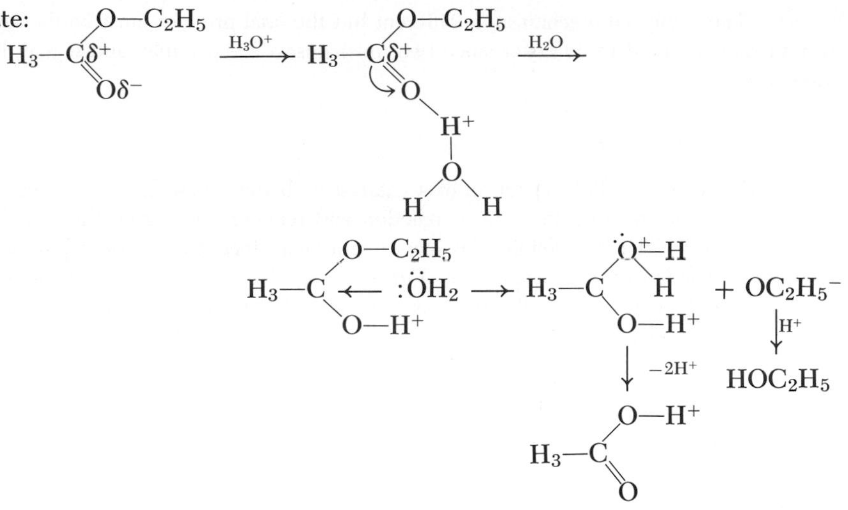

fastest:

$$H_3-C\overset{\delta+}{\underset{O\delta^-}{\overset{O-C_2H_5}{|}}} \xrightarrow{OH^-} H_3-C\overset{O-C_2H_5}{\underset{O}{|}}\ \overset{\ominus}{:}\ddot{O}-H \longrightarrow$$

$$H_3-C\overset{O-H}{\underset{O}{|}} + OC_2H_5^-$$

$$\downarrow H_2O$$

$$HOC_2H_5 + OH^-$$

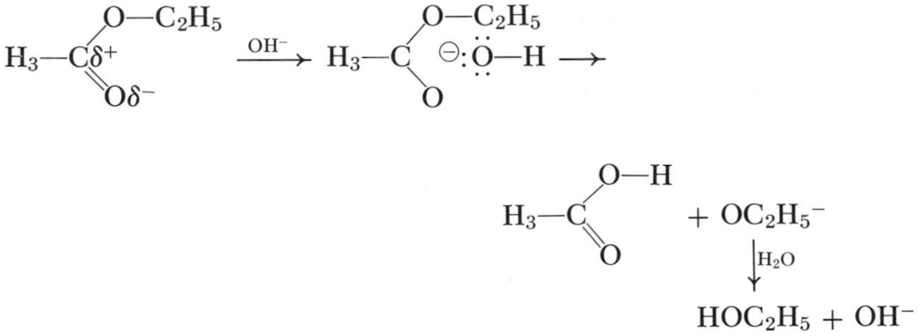

ENZYMES

An example of specific catalysis is provided by studies of *enzyme catalysis.* The understanding of these biological catalysts is progressing rapidly. Enzymes contain many groups of varying acidity. For many enzymes the catalytic rate is found to pass through a maximum as pH varies. This is interpreted in terms of a mechanism such as

$$EH_2^{(n+1)+} \rightleftarrows EH^{n+} \rightleftarrows E^{(n-1)+}$$

where these are three forms of the enzyme in various stages of protonation. It is assumed that, although all may interact with the reactant, only the center enzyme is capable of catalyzing the reaction. Some enzymes will catalyze only a single reaction, such as the urease-catalyzed hydrolysis of urea, but others exhibit less specificity. The principal difficulty that has restricted the full interpretation of these reactions is the lack of a detailed knowledge of enzyme structure.

One enzyme which has been investigated is α-chymotrypsin, for which the following quantitative data on one of its reaction mechanisms have been obtained.

$$EH + R-\overset{O}{\overset{\parallel}{C}}-OCH_3 \underset{K_1 = 1.18 \cdot 10^{-3}M}{\rightleftarrows} EH \cdot R\overset{O}{\overset{\parallel}{C}}OCH_3 \underset{k_{-2} = 32.5\ M^{-1}\ \text{sec}^{-1}}{\overset{k_2 = 857\ \text{sec}^{-1}}{\rightleftarrows}} ER\overset{O}{\overset{\parallel}{C}} + CH_3OH$$

$$\mathrm{ER\overset{\overset{\displaystyle O}{\|}}{C}} + \mathrm{H_2O} \underset{}{\overset{k_3\,=\,0.84\,M^{-1}\,\mathrm{sec}^{-1}}{\rightleftarrows}} \mathrm{EHR\overset{\overset{\displaystyle O}{\|}}{C}OH} \underset{K_4\,=\,(1.18\cdot 10^{-3}M)^{-1}}{\rightleftarrows} \mathrm{EH} + \mathrm{R\overset{\overset{\displaystyle O}{\|}}{C}OH}$$

$$\text{Net:}\quad \mathrm{R{-}\overset{\overset{\displaystyle O}{\|}}{C}{-}OCH_3} + \mathrm{H_2O} = \mathrm{R{-}\overset{\overset{\displaystyle O}{\|}}{C}{-}OH} + \mathrm{CH_3OH}$$

where EH $=$ α-chymotrypsin and $\mathrm{R\overset{\overset{\displaystyle O}{\|}}{C}OCH_3}$ $=$ 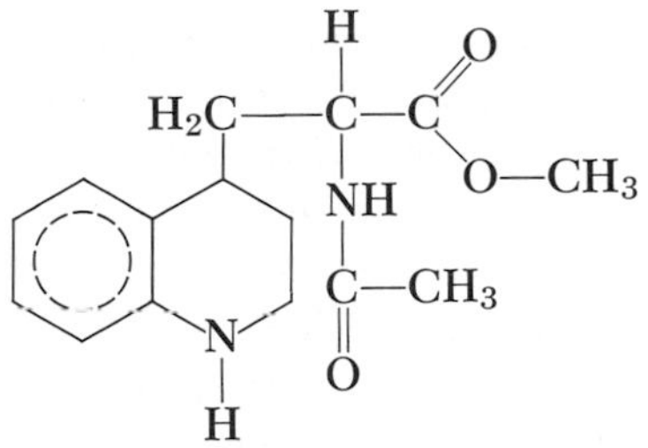

The K values are equilibrium constants; the k values are rate constants. Detailed studies, including use of D_2O as a solvent, indicate that a main determinant of the rate of the slow steps is the rate of transfer of hydrogen ions, but the geometry of the intermediate complex is unknown. This statement will not be true much longer.

Since there are probably hundreds of enzymes in living systems, and since almost all physiological reactions have rates determined by enzymic catalysis, it is clear that any detailed comprehension of the chemistry of living systems must await the study of a great deal of presently unknown chemical kinetics. We shall discuss enzymes further in Chapter 40.

SUMMARY

The theoretical interpretation of rates and mechanisms of chemical reactions (indeed of change in general) always involves a model of the encounter of the reacting species and an interchange of mass and energy between the species. Since bimolecular encounters are always more likely than ones of higher order, most theories emphasize them. All theories use the idea of an activated complex acting as an intermediate between reactants and products. Lindemann theory postulates that if forward reaction of the activated complex occurs more rapidly than back reaction, second-order kinetics are observed (for example, in the limit of very low pressures in gas reactions). Conversely, if back reaction is more rapid than forward reaction, first-order gas-phase kinetics are seen (for example, in the limit of high pressures).

The detailed interpretation of activation energy involves models which describe the relative contribution of translational energies (thermal energies) and internal energies (rotational, vibrational, electronic, but especially vibrational) to the formation of the activated complex.

Collision theory interprets rates in terms of (1) the likelihood of a collision calculated from the kinetic theory of gases, and (2) the availability of activation energy, $e^{-\Delta E_{\mathrm{act}}/RT}$. Agreement with observation however, is obtained only if a probability factor is added. It cannot be calculated from collision theory but can be related to the likelihood of a collision producing a geometrical arrangement favorable to forming the activated state.

Absolute reaction rate theory retains the idea of available activation energy as $e^{-\epsilon/kT}$, and determines reaction probability in terms of a ratio of partition functions and a frequency of vibration along the bond direction which yields products. Thermodynamic rate theory also retains the exponential factor in the form $e^{-\Delta H^{\ddagger}/RT}$, but treats the probability term as an entropy of activation $\Delta S^{\ddagger}$ and the same frequency factor, kT/h, found in absolute reaction rate theory. For practical purposes it is customary to equate the activation energies of all three theories to ΔE_{act}, the experimentally observed Arrhenius activation energy.

Gas-phase reactions, chain reactions, and reactions in condensed phases may all be interpreted in terms of a combination of activation energy, collision, and probability factors. Application of these ideas to particular systems such as explosions, acid-base catalysis, and enzymes leads to reasonable structural and energetic correlations of rate and mechanism with other molecular properties.

False facts are highly injurious to the progress of science, for they often endure long; but false views, if supported by some evidence, do little harm, for everyone takes a salutory pleasure in proving their falseness.—Charles Darwin, The Descent of Man (1871).

PROBLEMS

23.1. What effect would you expect each of the following gases to have upon the rate of the following reactions in the gas phase at elevated temperatures when added to a constant volume reaction vessel: Gases: Ar, NO, N_2, CH_4, I_2.
Reactions:

(*a*) $\begin{matrix} H_2C-CH_2 \\ | \quad\quad | \\ H_2C-CH_2 \end{matrix} \longrightarrow 2C_2H_4$

(*b*) $H\cdot + CH_4 \longrightarrow H_2 + \cdot CH_3$

(*c*) $CH_3\overset{\overset{O}{\|}}{C}CH_3 \longrightarrow C_2H_6, CO, CH_4, H_2$

(*d*) $C_2H_4{}^* \longrightarrow C_2H_2 + H_2$

23.2. The hydrolysis of cyanamide has been studied at 30°C in solutions of varying acidity. The reaction which is acid-catalyzed is apparently first order:

$$NH_2CN + H_2O \longrightarrow (NH_2)_2CO$$

Determine the apparent order with respect to hydrogen ion in this system [M. T. Sullivan and M. C. Kilpatrick, *J. Am. Chem. Soc.*, **67**, 1815 (1945)].

temperature = 30.0°C $[NH_2CN] = 0.045$ molar

k (sec^{-1}) · 10^5	0.47	1.28	5.68	8.63	12.89
[HCl]	0.096	0.247	0.982	1.61	2.07

23.3. The enzyme alcohol dehydrogenase converts ethylene glycol to poisonous oxalate ion and ethanol to acetate ion according to the mechanism of Problem 23.16. The value of $k_1/k_2 = K$, for the equilibrium $E + S = ES$, is much less for ethylene glycol than for ethanol. Use this fact to rationalize the treatment of ethylene glycol poisoning by intravenous feeding of ethanol. The treatment halves the fatality rate, and of course, keeps the recipient drunk throughout the process.

23.4. Sketch the "potential energy versus reaction coordinate" curve for the reaction $CD + E = C + DE$ between the molecules CD (bond energy 100 kcal mole^{-1}) and DE (bond energy 70 kcal mole^{-1}). Is the reaction endothermic or exothermic? How much?

23.5. Hydrogen peroxide decomposes spontaneously, but slowly. Addition of acetanilide, $(C_6H_5NHCOCH_3)$, in trace amounts greatly reduces the rate of decomposition. Can you suggest a mechanism for this interaction?

23.6. The photochemical decomposition of hydrogen iodide results in the decomposition of two molecules of HI per photon absorbed. The following mechanisms are suggested.

$$\text{I}\quad\begin{cases} h\nu + HI = II\cdot + I\cdot & +71\text{ kcal} \\ I\cdot + HI = I_2 + H\cdot & +35\text{ kcal} \\ H\cdot + H\cdot + M = H_2 + M & -104\text{ kcal} \end{cases}\qquad \Delta H$$

or

$$\text{II}\quad\begin{cases} h\nu + HI = H\cdot + I\cdot & +71\text{ kcal} \\ H\cdot + HI = H_2 + I\cdot & -33\text{ kcal} \\ I\cdot + I\cdot + N = I_2 + N & -36\text{ kcal} \end{cases}$$

(*a*) Which mechanism is more likely? (*b*) Calculate ΔH for the over-all decomposition reaction.

23.7. Prutton and Maron state, "The primary light absorption process should be practically temperature independent. Again, since secondary reactions in photochemical processes are thermal in character, these should have temperature coefficients akin to those of ordinary reactions. However, most secondary reactions in photochemical processes involve interaction between atoms or free radicals, or of these with molecules. For such reactions the energy of activation is usually small or even zero."

(*a*) Why should the "primary light absorption process be practically temperature independent," whereas the primary thermal processes are not? Be specific in terms of the changes which occur in these two types of primary processes and the prerequisites which must be satisfied before the changes can occur.

(*b*) Why should the secondary processes in photochemical reactions between "atoms or free radicals, or of these with molecules" have small, or zero, activation energies? Be specific in terms of the nature of activation energies and the processes that they represent.

23.8. The following partial mechanism has been suggested [M. H. J. Wijnen, *J. Chem. Phys.*, **27**, 710 (1957)] to account for the kinetics of the photochemical decomposition of methyl acetate:

$$CH_3CO\cdot \longrightarrow \cdot CH_3 + CO \qquad 2$$
$$\cdot CH_3 + CH_3O\cdot \longrightarrow CH_4 + CH_2O \qquad 3$$
$$\longrightarrow CH_3OCH_3 \qquad 4$$
$$2CH_3O\cdot \longrightarrow CH_3OH + CH_2O \qquad 5$$
$$2CH_3\cdot \longrightarrow C_2H_6 \qquad 6$$
$$\cdot CH_3 + CH_3COOCH_3 \longrightarrow CH_4 + \cdot CH_2COOCH_3 \qquad 7$$

Show that a plot of $R_{CH_4}/[R_{C_2H_6}{}^{1/2}[MeOAc]]$ as ordinate versus $R_{CH_3OCH_3}/[R_{C_2H_6}{}^{1/2}[MeOAc]]$ as abscissa should provide a straight line, with intercept on the ordinate equal to $k_7/k_6{}^{1/2}$ and slope k_3/k_4, where R means rate.

23.9. The mechanism of sun-tanning is initiated by the absorption of the 0.2% of solar radiation lying in the 2900–3132 Å range. The earth's atmosphere cuts off radiation beyond 2900 Å and the burning efficiency drops from 100% at 2967 Å to 2% at 3132 Å. Outline a research project to discover an effective ointment to protect against sunburn. Many commercial ointments contain *o*- or *p*-amino benzoates or titanium dioxide. Suggest mechanisms by which these substances might work.

23.10. Outline a possible mechanism for the combination of hydrogen and oxygen to give water as a final stable product, such that no more than one chemical bond is broken in any single step of the mechanism and no more than two molecules collide to react in any single step. Do these seem reasonable restrictions which might apply in a good many chemical reactions?

23.11. Sketch a simple potential energy diagram (*PE* versus *d*) for molecular HBr and indicate on it the following types of transitions. Give one sentence in each case which states your reasons for drawing the transition as you did, and another sentence describing the difference between the original and final state of the molecule. (*a*) A transition involving rotation only. (*b*) A vibrational transition. (*c*) An electronic transition.

23.12. The experimental rate law for the thermal reaction of carbon monoxide and chlorine to give phosgene is observed as:

$$\frac{d[COCl_2]}{dt} = k[CO][Cl_2]^{3/2}$$

The following mechanism is suggested:

$$Cl_2 \underset{k_{-1}}{\overset{k_1}{\rightleftharpoons}} 2Cl\cdot$$

$$Cl\cdot + CO \underset{k_{-2}}{\overset{k_2}{\rightleftharpoons}} COCl\cdot$$

$$COCl\cdot + Cl_2 \xrightarrow{k_3} COCl_2 + Cl\cdot$$

(*a*) If this mechanism is correct, would you expect a long reaction chain, quantum efficiency greater than 10, or a short chain, less than 10?

(*b*) Is the suggested mechanism consistent with the observed rate law?

II

23.13. The quantum yield for the formation of HBr in the photochemical reaction of H_2 with Br_2 is given as

$$\Phi = \frac{\text{rate}_{\text{HBr}}}{I_{\text{abs}}} = \frac{A[\text{H}_2]I_{\text{abs}}^{-1/2}}{\{1 + B[\text{HBr}]/[\text{Br}_2]\}}$$

$$h\nu + \text{Br}_2 \xrightarrow{1} 2\text{Br}\cdot$$

$$\cdot\text{Br} + \text{H}_2 \xrightarrow{2} \text{HBr} + \text{H}\cdot$$

$$\text{H}\cdot + \text{Br}_2 \xrightarrow{3} \text{HBr} + \text{Br}\cdot$$

$$\text{HBr} + \text{H}\cdot \xrightarrow{4} \text{H}_2 + \text{Br}\cdot$$

$$\text{M} + \text{Br}\cdot + \text{Br}\cdot \xrightarrow{5} \text{Br}_2 + \text{M}$$

Show that the indicated mechanism for this reaction is in agreement with this rate law and identify the constants A and B in terms of rate constants for elementary steps in the mechanism.

23.14. The presence of argon greatly accelerates the recombination of iodine atoms in the net reaction $\text{I}\cdot + \text{I}\cdot = \text{I}_2$. Suggest three possible mechanisms for this catalysis and comment on their relative probability. Suggest experiments which might distinguish between the three possibilities.

23.15. The apparent cross section (effective molecular area) for the gas-phase reaction

$$\text{A}^+ + \text{BC} \longrightarrow \text{AB}^+ + \text{C}$$

is several hundred square angstroms. Comment on the probable nature of a "collision" and the forces acting.

23.16. Derive the differential rate equation for the reaction scheme (originally suggested by Michaelis and Menten)

$$\text{E} + \text{S} \underset{k_2}{\overset{k_1}{\rightleftharpoons}} \text{ES} \xrightarrow{k_3} \text{E} + \text{product}$$

in which E = enzyme, S = substrate, ES = intermediate molecule. How does the over-all rate depend on $[\text{E}]_{\text{tot}}$, where $[\text{E}]_{\text{tot}} = [\text{E}] + [\text{ES}]$: (*a*) at values of $[\text{S}] \ll [\text{E}]_{\text{tot}}$; (*b*) at values of $[\text{S}] \gg [\text{E}]_{\text{tot}}$?

III

23.17. The first mechanistic step in the gas-phase pyrolysis (thermal decomposition) of methane is usually given as

$$\text{CH}_4 \xrightarrow{k} \text{CH}_3\cdot + \text{H}\cdot, \qquad d[\text{CH}_3]/dt = k[\text{CH}_4]$$

This step implies that the rate of production of methyl radicals is proportional to the number of molecules of methane present—entirely reasonable. However, it also suggests that normal molecules have enough energy built into them so that they can dissociate with nothing being done to them—not very reasonable.

(*a*) Devise a collision mechanism—involving activated molecules, an activation step, a decomposition step, and a deactivation step—that yields the above rate law upon the application of a steady-state treatment. (Methane is the only gas present.) Show that your process yields the rate law given above and clearly indicate any assumptions that are necessary.

(*b*) Write chemical equations for the reactions appropriate to the listed enthalpies of formation:

	ΔH_{298} formation
$CH_{4(g)}$	17.89 kcal/mole
$\cdot CH_{3(g)}$	32.0 kcal/mole
$H\cdot_{(g)}$	52.0 kcal/mole

(*c*) Use the data in *b* to estimate the minimum activation energy for the process shown in the equation. Explain. ($\Delta E_{act} \cong 60$ kcal mole^{-1}.)

23.18. The following rate constants for the inversion of sucrose have been reported by a group of freshman students. Use these data to obtain a "best value" for the activation energy of the reaction. How would you grade each student? ($\Delta E_{act} \cong 20$ kcal mole^{-1}.)

	T °C	k (min^{-1})		T °C	k (min^{-1})
Ashenfelter	22–23	1.04	Simmons	26.7	1.38
White	23	1.09	Stevens, K.	26.6–28.4	1.98
Pellinen	23.1	1.24	Naumann	27–30	1.907
Latham	22.5–28.2	2.85	Williams	27.5	1.89
Trapp	26	1.49	Crossman	28–29	2.22
Stevens, R.	26	1.6	VanHecke	29.5	1.99
Leppo	26–27	1.61	Squibb	31	2.8
Pope	26.6	2.53	Davis	31–32.5	2.35

See page 1092 for a list of references and readings in the recent chemical literature related to the material in this chapter.

CHAPTER 24

Some Simple Reactions of Carbon Compounds

PHILIP C. MYHRE

If most nucleophilic displacement reactions occur either by sequential breaking, then making, of bonds, or by synchronous making and breaking of bonds, we should expect two different sets of kinetic, structural, and stereochemical results.

Synthesis is the organic chemist's stock in trade. In this chapter we shall examine some of the recurring problems of synthesis by exploring in detail a few of the many reactions of carbon compounds.

It may first be well, however, to recall that organic chemistry is an "old" branch of chemistry. The study of carbon compounds, which developed and flourished in the late nineteenth and early twentieth centuries, was based on a few very simple but exceedingly productive ideas: the quadrivalence of carbon, the phenomena of catenation and multiple bonding, and the existence of stereoisomers resulting from tetrahedral coordination about carbon. Utilizing these concepts as well as considerable manipulative skill, chemists were able to characterize large numbers of compounds of carbon, and many syntheses, some of great complexity, were effected. Much of this was done long before there were any electronic theories of bonding.

The most complete compendium of organic compounds—Beilstein's *Handbuch der Organischen Chemie*—was designed to catalog the compounds of carbon reported in the chemical literature. First published in 1881 in two volumes, the fourth edition, which surveys the literature up to 1910, was published in 1939 by the German Chemical Society—in twenty-nine volumes! Even lengthier supplements have since been compiled, spanning the periods from 1910–1919 (*Erstes Ergänzungswerk*), 1920–1929, (*Zweites Ergänzungswerk*), and 1930–1949 (*Drittes Ergänzungswerk*). The last supplement is not yet complete. An official guide of 246 pages has been published to facilitate the use of the *Handbuch*, and supplements now fill some sixty feet of library shelving. Several guidebooks to the guide are also available.

Organic compounds and reactions can be codified in ways similar to those used in Beilstein. There is great value in doing so, even though profitable utilization of this information frequently requires a more compact format, which has been made possible by increased understanding of how reactions occur. As indicated in this text, our understanding of chemical reactions is far from complete, and there is no immediate fear that problems of importance will be exhausted. Yet even incomplete understanding has greatly facilitated the problems of synthesis. Our recently acquired ability to synthesize very complex materials—steroids, proteins, chlorophylls—is some evidence of this.

With these thoughts in mind, let us consider some simple reactions of carbon compounds, assuming that the problems, methodology, and generalizations found and used in the study of these few reactions will be applicable to many others. A mixture of jigsaw puzzles, each with many missing pieces, is a reasonable analogy to the data presented the chemist who desires a detailed picture of a reaction. Bits and pieces of information are scattered throughout the literature. The chemist must assemble the data, select those pertinent to the problem at hand, evaluate them, and merge them into a coherent pattern. There will always be a number of missing data; some experimental data will not be valid; and there will be data which are not obviously incorrect but which do not appear to be accommodated by the developing pattern. If a pattern is recognizable, one can hopefully design an experiment that will fill out the basic form and may eventually permit extension into unexplored areas. Let us try a few simple problems.

REACTIONS OF ALKANES

The alternative name for alkanes—paraffins (L. *para, affinis,* little affinity)—implies that alkanes are relatively inert. Alkanes are inert toward many reagents—for instance, most acids and bases—but we are all familiar with the exothermic and oftentimes explosive nature of reactions of alkanes, such as natural gas or gasoline, with oxygen. [See Table 24.1 and note the approximate constancy of ΔH per gram as the alkane formulas approach the limiting formula $(CH_2)_n$.]

The first step in the partial oxidation of alkanes is, with very few exceptions, a slower reaction than the later steps; thus the initial products tend to be rapidly oxidized further. This, rather than unfavorable equilibrium, represents the real barrier to direct synthesis of partly oxidized compounds from alkanes.

Exercise 24.1

Rationalize the fact that the first members of the alkane series are more (rather than less) exothermic with oxygen per gram than the later members. *Answer:* The ratio of H to C drops as the series progresses. It is the "extra" H's on the terminal carbons that make the initial reactants more exothermic. Note that $\Delta(\Delta H)$ in Table 24.1 becomes constant and equal to the combustion of a CH_2 group at 156.2 ± 0.2 kcal $(CH_2)^{-1}$.

Table 24.1 Heats of combustion of alkanes in oxygen.

$$C_nH_{2n+2(g)} + (\tfrac{3}{2}n + \tfrac{1}{2})O_{2(g)} \longrightarrow nCO_{2(g)} + (n+1)H_2O_{(l)}$$

Hydrocarbon			$\Delta(\Delta H^0)$		
Name	Formula	$-\Delta H^0$ (kcal/mole)	per CH_2 group	ΔH^0 (kcal/gram)	Hydrogen (percent by wt.)
Methane	CH_4	212.8		−13.3	25.1
			160.0		
Ethane	C_2H_6	372.8		−12.4	20.1
			157.8		
Propane	C_3H_8	530.6		−12.2	18.3
			157.4		
Isobutane	C_4H_{10}	688.0		−11.9	17.3
			157.2		
n-Pentane	C_5H_{12}	845.2		−11.6	16.8
			149.8		
n-Hexane	C_6H_{14}	995.0		−11.6	16.4
			156.3		
n-Heptane	C_7H_{16}	1151.3		−11.5	16.1
			156.2		
n-Octane	C_8H_{18}	1307.2		−11.5	15.9
			156.3		
n-Decane	$C_{10}H_{22}$	1620.1		−11.4	15.6
			156.5		
n-Hexadecane	$C_{16}H_{34}$	2559		−11.3	15.1
			156.0		
n-Eicosane	$C_{20}H_{42}$	3183		−11.3	15.0

HALOGENATION OF ALKANES

The halogenation of alkanes is a reaction formally analogous to oxidation. Experiments show that this *substitution reaction* is quite general and may be formulated as

$$-\overset{|}{\underset{|}{C}}-H + X_2 \longrightarrow -\overset{|}{\underset{|}{C}}-X + H-X \qquad (24.1)$$

where X = F, Cl, Br, I. Given this information, the questions of interest to a chemist, and the approximate order in which they are answered, are these.

1. What conditions are necessary for reaction?
2. What side reactions or limitations exist?
3. What specific compounds or structural types can be usefully synthesized by this reaction?
4. What is the detailed mechanism of the reaction?

A mixture of chlorine and a simple alkane—methane, ethane, propane—is unreactive if stored in the dark at room temperature. However, irradiation of the mixture with ultraviolet light (frequently about 3650 Å) or heating to about 300°C results in a very violent, exothermic reaction. As shown in Figure 24.1, the rate can vary from explosion, to burning, to "slow" reaction, depending on the mole ratios of chlorine to the alkane.

Examination of products resulting from a reaction of equimolar amounts of chlorine and methane reveals the presence not only of hydrogen chloride and chloromethane (CH_3Cl, b.p. − 24°C) but also of smaller amounts of dichloromethane (CH_2Cl_2, b.p. 40°C) and trichloromethane (chloroform, $CHCl_3$, b.p. 61°C), together with trace amounts of tetrachloromethane (CCl_4, b.p. 77°C) and hexachloroethane (CCl_3CCl_3, b.p. 187°C). Thus

Figure 24.1 Relationship of mole ratio to rate of reaction between chorine and propane:
(a) a stoichiometric ratio for the reaction

$$4Cl_{2(g)} + C_3H_{8(g)} = 3C_{(c)} + 8HCl_{(g)}$$

(b) a stoichiometric ratio for the reaction

$$10Cl_{2(g)} + C_3H_{8(g)} = 3CCl_{4(g)} + 8HCl_{(g)}$$

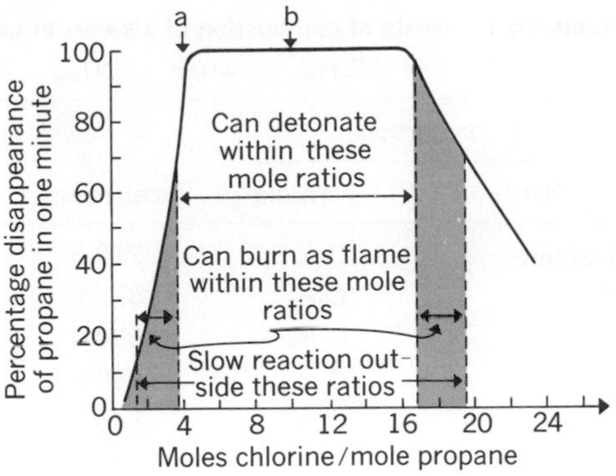

$$CH_4 + Cl_2 \xrightarrow[\text{or heat } (\sim 300°)]{h\nu(\sim 3600\ \text{Å})} HCl + \{CH_3Cl + CH_2Cl_2 + CHCl_3 + CCl_4 + CCl_3CCl_3\} \quad (24.2)$$

Further experimentation establishes that the di- and polychloralkanes arise from successive substitution steps such as

$$\begin{aligned} CH_4 + Cl_2 &= CH_3Cl + HCl \\ CH_3Cl + Cl_2 &= CH_2Cl_2 + HCl \end{aligned} \quad (24.3)$$

and so on.

This result points out immediately a synthetic limitation of this reaction. The intermediate products can undergo reaction at rates that are competitive with the rate of the initial reaction. If we wish to make monochloromethane efficiently by this procedure, it is necessary to design the reaction system in a manner that maximizes both yield and ease of isolation. One way, of course, would be to conduct the chlorination with a large excess of methane, so that the concentration of alkane reactant remains high throughout the reaction. Since the rate depends upon the concentration of reactants as well as the specific rate constant, we would anticipate chloromethane as the only chloroalkane product of significance. The boiling points of methane (−162°C) and chloromethane (−24°C) are sufficiently different that low-temperature distillation would easily separate product from unconsumed reactant. Finally, recycling the unconsumed reactant permits efficient use of all the reactant.

Examination of reactions of the other halogens with methane reveals great differences in the rates of reaction as well as in the positions of equilibrium. If we make use of average bond enthalpy data (Table 13.5), the enthalpy of reaction can be computed and we can make some predictions concerning the position of equilibrium. The entropy changes for the reactions

$$-\overset{|}{\underset{|}{C}}-H + X_2 \rightleftharpoons -\overset{|}{\underset{|}{C}}-X + H-X,$$

$$\begin{array}{lcccccl} X = & F & Cl & Br & I & & \\ \Delta H^0_{298°} = & -104 & -25 & -8 & +7 & \text{kcal mole}^{-1} & (24.4) \end{array}$$

are small (no change in number of moles of gases) and so the enthalpies of reaction (24.4) are reasonable estimates of ΔG^0. We see that fluorination and chlorination must give "complete" conversion to products. For bromination, we estimate that more than 99% of reactants would be converted to "products." However, the equilibrium in the iodination reaction gives less than 1% conversion to "products."

As the large negative enthalpy of reaction would indicate, direct fluorination of alkanes proceeds with almost uncontrollable violence. Certain techniques, such as high dilution of reactants with inert gas and efficient heat-exchanging apparatus, permit the fluorination of some simple alkanes, but even with these extensive precautions considerable carbon-carbon bond cleavage occurs when fluorinations of alkanes containing several carbon atoms are attempted. In short, direct fluorination, like direct oxidation, is such an exothermic reaction that it does not represent a very practical means of *partial* fluorination. Partial fluorination and partial oxidation require more circuitous synthetic procedures (Figure 21.27).

Exercise 24.2

Gas-phase nitrations of alkanes usually proceed rapidly to give good yields: $RH + HONO_2 = RNO_2 + H_2O$. What can you deduce from this fact? *Answer:* The rapid rate indicates relatively low values of activation energy and entropy. The good yields indicate rather large negative values of ΔG^0, probably due to exothermic values for ΔH, since ΔS^0 is probably small. These conclusions are all consistent with the known shapes, polarities, and bond energies of the reactants.

SELECTIVITY IN HALOGENATION REACTIONS

A question of considerable importance to the synthetic chemist is that of product distribution. Monohalogenation of alkanes is illustrative of this. An isomeric mixture of products would be anticipated if the alkane reactant contains different kinds of hydrogen. Methane and ethane contain only one kind of hydrogen and will yield only one kind of monochloroalkane. The possible isomers of the various C_1 through C_5 alkanes and their reported distribution upon vapor phase chlorination at 300°C is given in Table 24.2.

The data in Table 24.2 indicate that all possible isomeric chloroalkanes can be obtained by chlorination of the appropriate alkane. We also note that the isomer distribution is not random. For example, chlorination of isobutane affords about 66% isobutyl chloride and 33% *t*-butyl chloride, not the statistically predicted 90% and 10%. Examination of all these data shows that there is a positional selectivity or discrimination. Hydrogen attached to tertiary carbon appears to be more readily replaced than hydrogen at a secondary carbon, which in turn is more readily replaced than hydrogen at a primary carbon. We will return to a discussion of the possible significance of these observations.

It should also be apparent from the data in Table 24.2 that a chemist desiring a unique chloralkane product would use direct chlorination procedures only when the reactant alkane contains one kind of hydrogen or when the difference in selectivity is so large that one isomer is formed in overwhelming amount. If really pressed, he might choose the direct halogenation procedure, which would yield a variety of products if a feasible chemical or physical means of separating

Table 24.2 Monochloralkanes resulting from halogenation of some simple alkanes and relative yield. The products are listed in order of decreasing yield.

Alkane	Products	
CH_4 methane	CH_3Cl chloromethane (methyl chloride), b.p. −24°C	
$CH_3—CH_3$ ethane	$CH_3—CH_2—Cl$ chloroethane (ethyl chloride), b.p. 12°C	
$CH_3—CH_2—CH_3$ propane	$CH_3—CH(Cl)—CH_3$ 2-chloropropane (isopropyl chloride) 52%, b.p. 78.5°C	$CH_3—CH_2—CH_2Cl$ 1-chloropropane (*n*-propyl chloride) 48%, b.p. 47°C
$CH_3—CH_2—CH_2—CH_3$ *n*-butane	$CH_3—CH(Cl)—CH_2—CH_3$ 2-chlorobutane (*sec*-butyl chloride) 68%, b.p. 68°C	$CH_3—CH_2—CH_2—CH_2Cl$ 1-chlorobutane (*n*-butyl chloride) 32%, b.p. 78.5°C
$CH_3—C(CH_3)_2—H$ 2-methylpropane (isobutane)	$CH_3—CH(CH_3)—CH_2Cl$ 1-chloro-2-methylpropane (isobutyl chloride) 67%, b.p. 69°C	$CH_3—C(CH_3)_2—Cl$ 2-chloro-2-methylpropane (*t*-butyl chloride) 33%, b.p. 51°C
$CH_3—CH_2—CH_2—CH_2—CH_3$ *n*-pentane	$CH_3—CH_2—CH_2—CH(Cl)—CH_3$ 2-chloropentane 49%, b.p. 97°C	$CH_3—CH_2—CH(Cl)—CH_2—CH_3$ 3-chloropentane 27%, b.p. 97°C
	$CH_3—CH_2—CH_2—CH_2—CH_2Cl$ 1-chloropentane (*n*-amyl chloride) 24%, b.p. 108°C	
$(CH_3)_2CH—CH_2—CH_3$ 2-methylbutane (isopentane)	$(ClCH_2)(CH_3)CH—CH_2—CH_3$ 1-chloro-2-methylbutane 33.5%, b.p. 100°C	$(CH_3)_2CH—CH(Cl)—CH_3$ 2-chloro-3-methylpropane 28%, b.p. 93°C
	$(CH_3)_2CCl—CH_2—CH_3$ 2-chloro-2-methylbutane (*t*-amyl chloride) 22%, b.p. 86°C	$(CH_3)_2CH—CH_2—CH_2Cl$ 1-chloro-3-methylbutane 16.5%, b.p. 99°C
$CH_3—C(CH_3)_2—CH_3$ 2,2-dimethylpropane, or neopentane	$CH_3—C(CH_3)_2—CH_2Cl$ 1-chloro-2,2-dimethylpropane (neopentyl chloride), b.p. 84°C	

SOURCE: Data reported by Hass, McBee, and Weber, *Ind. Eng. Chem.*, **28,** 333 (1936). More recent work indicates that the distillation analyses used to obtain these data are probably not completely reliable.

products could be devised. A summary of some synthetically useful chlorinations and brominations, with yield data and physical constants, is given in Table 24.3. Note that the substitution of reagents such as sulfuryl chloride (SO_2Cl_2) and N-bromosuccinimide for molecular chlorine and bromine often facilitates laboratory synthesis. Later discussion should establish that these reagents function in a manner that is mechanistically similar to that of the molecular halogens.

Table 24.3 Direct halogenations of preparative value and percentage yields. Note the frequent use of photochemical reactions.

1. 

cyclopropane — chlorocyclopropane ~75% (b.p. 44°C) (b.p. 77°C) (b.p. 87°C)

2. $CH_3—CF_2—CH_3 + Cl_2 \xrightarrow{h\nu} CH_3—CF_2—CH_2Cl + CH_3—CF_2—CCl_3$

55% (b.p. 55°C) (b.p. 101°C)

3. $CH_3—C(CH_3)_2—Cl + SO_2Cl_2 \xrightarrow{\text{benzoyl peroxide}} CH_3—C(CH_3)(CH_2—Cl)—Cl$

t-butyl chloride — 1,2-dichloro-2-methylpropane 46% (b.p. 107°C)

4. 

cyclopentane (b.p. 49°C) — chlorocyclopentane (b.p. 114°C) — dichlorocyclopentanes (b.p. 80°C/50 mm)

5. 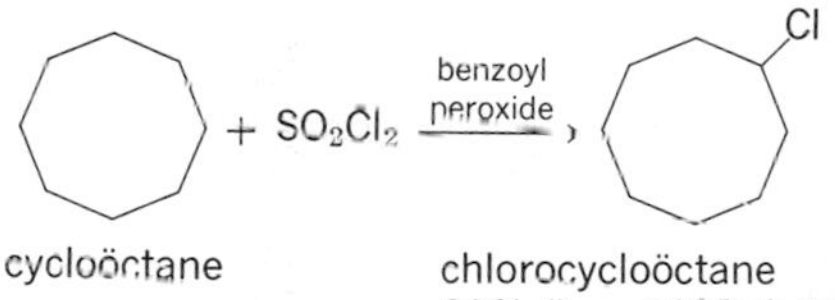

cycloöctane — chlorocycloöctane 83% (b.p. 30°C/0.25 mm)

6. 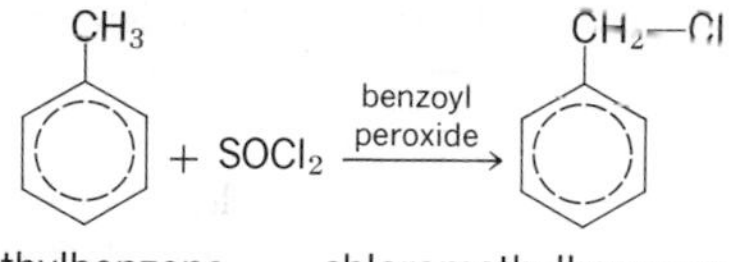

methylbenzene (toluene) — chloromethylbenzene (benzyl chloride) 75% (b.p. 97°C/62 mm) (only monochlorinated product)

7. 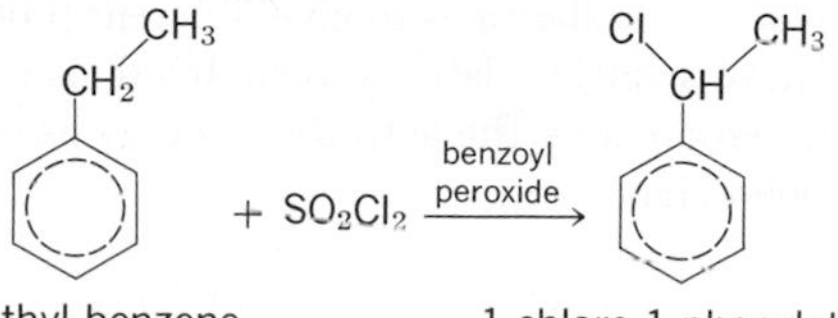

ethyl benzene — 1-chloro-1-phenylethane 85% (b.p. 91°C/30 mm)

Table 24.3   contd.

8. CH₃—C(CH₃)(CH₃)—H + Br₂ $\xrightarrow{h\nu}$ CH₃—C(CH₃)(CH₃)—Br + CH₃—C(CH₂Br)(CH₃)—Br 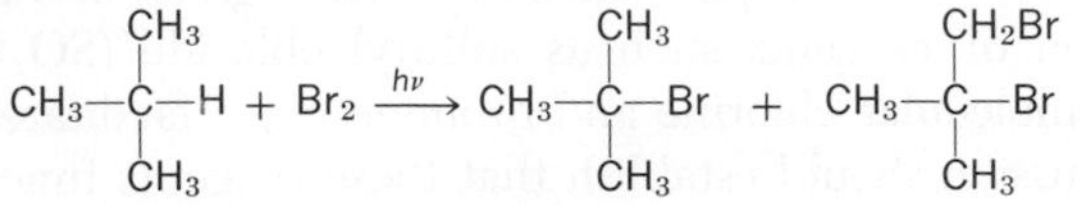

isobutane   t-butyl bromide   1,2-dibromo-2-methylpropane
                             60% (b.p. 73°C)   (b.p. 83°C/100 mm)

9. + Br₂ $\xrightarrow{h\nu}$ Br 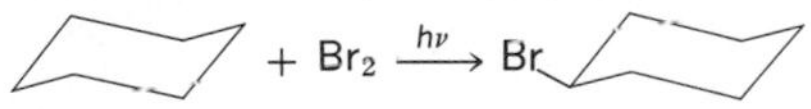

cyclohexane   bromocyclohexane
                   "100%" (b.p. 52°C/13 mm)

10. (CH₃)(CH₃)CH—CH₂—CH₂—CH₃ + Br₂ $\xrightarrow{h\nu}$ Br—C(CH₃)(CH₃)—CH₂—CH₂—CH₃ 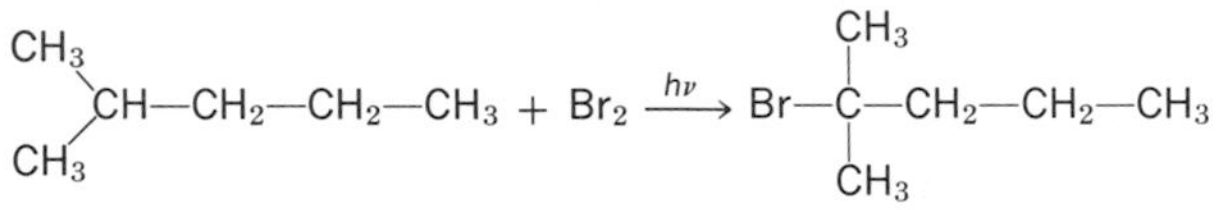

2-methylpentane   2-bromo-2-methylpentane
                                   90% (b.p. 92°C/40 mm)

11. CH₃—C(CH₃)(CH₃)—C(CH₃)(CH₃)—H + Br₂ $\xrightarrow{h\nu}$ CH₃—C(CH₃)(CH₃)—C(CH₃)(CH₃)—Br 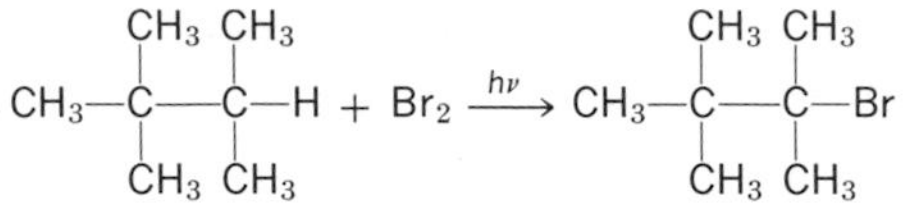

2,2,3-trimethylbutane   2-bromo-2,3,3-trimethylbutane
                                 96% (b.p. 150°C)

12. 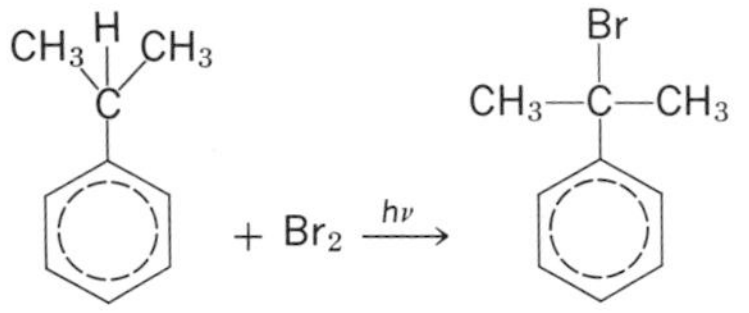

isopropylbenzene   2-bromo-2-phenylpropane
(cumene)   (cumyl bromide) 73%

13. 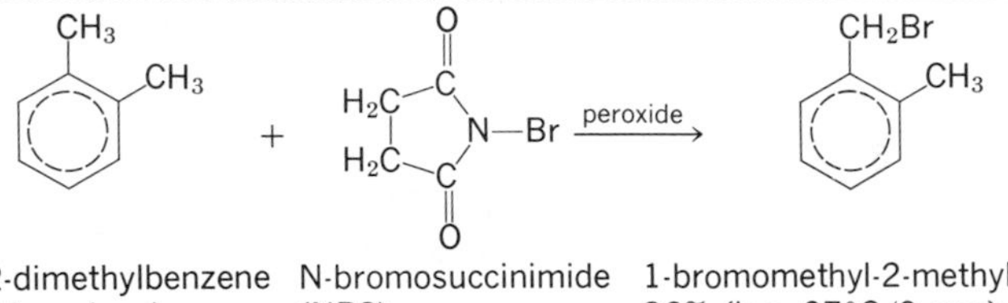

1,2-dimethylbenzene   N-bromosuccinimide   1-bromomethyl-2-methylbenzene
(ortho-xylene)   (NBS)   86% (b.p. 97°C/9 mm)

Exercise 24.3

Rationalize the fact that reactions of carbon compounds seldom give 100% "yields," whereas many "inorganic" reactions are quantitatively stoichiometric. *Answer:* Most carbon compounds contain several geometrically different bonds of similar bond activation energy which react at similar rates to give different products. Most common inorganic compounds have a single relatively weak bond (as between two ions) so that the products are determined by the activation energy associated with changes in this bond, and this bond alone.

INDUSTRIAL CHLORINATION

Sometimes isomeric purity is not important. Large quantities of isopentane and *n*-pentane are chlorinated industrially to yield a mixture of chloropentanes, which can be converted to a mixture of alcohols, "Pentasol," and sold as a useful solvent. Amines and mercaptans (thioalcohols) of industrial utility can also be made:

$$C_5H_{12} + Cl_2 \longrightarrow C_5H_{11}Cl + HCl$$

$$C_5H_{11}Cl \begin{cases} + NaOH \longrightarrow C_5H_{11}OH + NaCl \\ + 2NH_3 \longrightarrow C_5H_{11}NH_2 + NH_4Cl \\ + NaSH \longrightarrow C_5H_{11}SH + NaCl \end{cases} \tag{24.5}$$

A plant layout suitable for chlorination of pentane is shown in Figure 24.2. It may be noted that flow rates through the reactor are of the order of 60 mph to prevent propagation of the reaction flame backward to the mixer.

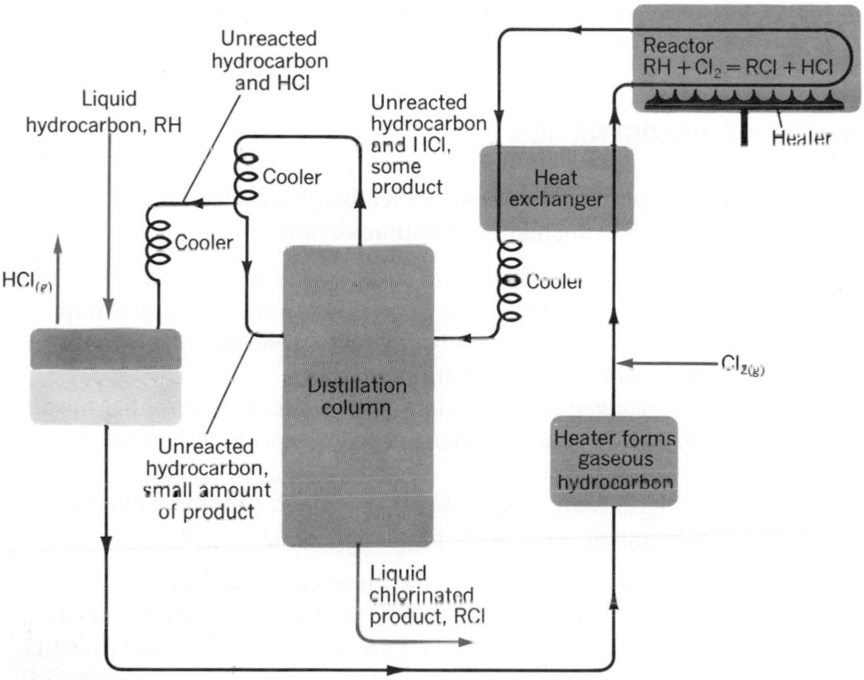

Figure 24.2 Plant layout for chlorination of pentane and other paraffin hydrocarbons.
Net reaction: $RH_{(l)} + Cl_{2(g)} = RCl_{(l)} + HCl_{(g)}$

Some other commercially important products made by direct chlorination procedures include chloromethane, a refrigerant, and an intermediate in synthesis; chloroethane, a general anesthetic and synthetic intermediate [as in making tetraethyl lead, $(C_2H_5)_4Pb$]; hexachlorocyclopentadiene (C_5Cl_6), a precursor to the insecticides Chlordane, Aldrin, and Dieldrin.

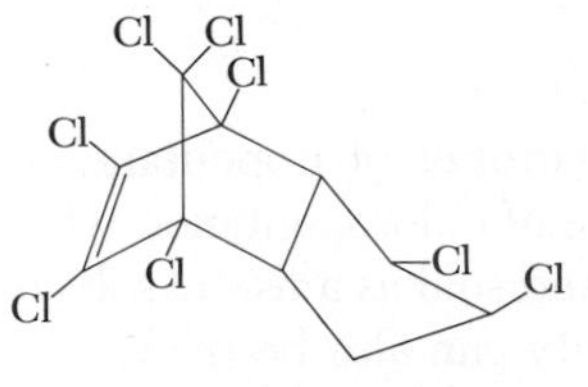

Chlordane

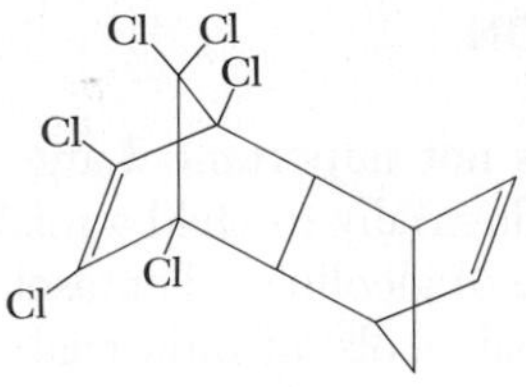

Aldrin

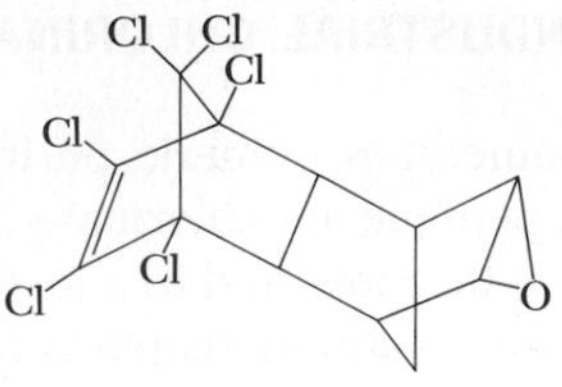

Dieldrin

Exercise 24.4

Compare the velocity of flow through the chlorination reactor with the velocity of sound in chlorine. Should there be any relationship? *Answer:* Velocity of sound in air $\cong$ 1100 ft sec^{-1} at room temperature. $(mv^2)_{\text{air}} = (mv^2)_{\text{Cl}_2}$, $v_{\text{Cl}_2}/v_{\text{air}} = \sqrt{\frac{28}{71}} \cong$ 0.6 or velocity of sound in $Cl_2 = 0.6 \cdot 1100$ ft sec$^{-1} \cdot (\frac{1}{5000}$ miles ft$^{-1}) \cdot 4000$ sec hr$^{-1} \cong$ 500 mph compared to flow velocity of 60 mph. Both heat and sound propagate by molecular collision and at about the same rate but the amount of heat propagating backward in this fairly slow reaction, when the forward flow rate is 60 mph, is too little to initiate this reaction. Very fast reactions (most thermal explosions) propagate at velocities near those of sound and thus could be carried out under "controlled" conditions only at very high flow rates.

MECHANISM OF HALOGENATION

Let's consider possible step-by-step sequences leading from reactants to products. We have quite a bit of experimental information already.

1. Alkanes and molecular halogen are inert unless reaction is initiated by irradiation with light or very strong heating. Activation energy is required.
2. The reaction is not notably sensitive to phase changes; that is, halogenations proceed equally well in gas or liquid phases.
3. Substitution of halogen is not random. The order of preferential substitution is tertiary carbon > secondary carbon > primary carbon. Rate of reaction varies.
4. Product distributions are temperature-dependent, yielding a more statistical or random distribution with increasing temperature.

Further investigation shows that photochlorination (chlorination induced by irradiation) is an efficient reaction. For every photon of light absorbed by the system, several thousand molecules of product are formed. We say that the quantum yield is high. Experiments also establish that the rate of reaction and the quantum yield are markedly reduced by introduction of radical scavengers (see Chapter 22) and that the rate of chlorinations carried out at elevated temperatures without irradiation is greatly increased by the introduction of radical initiators such as tetraethyl lead.

These data seem most consistent with a free-radical chain process. The first step in such a process must be an initiation step, generating a radical, probably the dissociation of a chlorine molecule,

$$\text{Chain initiation:} \quad Cl_2 \xrightarrow{k_1} 2Cl\cdot \tag{24.6}$$

The necessary energy for bond dissociation (58 kcal mole^{-1}) can be furnished by strong heating or absorption of light ($h\nu > D$). An alternative initiation step, the dissociation of a carbon-hydrogen bond, appears much less likely, since much higher energies would be required to break this stronger bond (90–100 kcal mole^{-1}). Even more compelling is the fact that alkanes, unlike Cl_2, do not absorb light in the near ultraviolet. Consequently no mechanism of direct photodissociation of alkanes is available.

Following dissociation, a cyclic sequence of steps leading to product could be proposed:

$$
\text{Chain-propagating steps} \left\{
\begin{array}{l}
-\overset{|}{\underset{|}{C}}-H + Cl\cdot \xrightarrow{k_2} -\overset{|}{\underset{|}{C}}\cdot + H-Cl \\[2em]
-\overset{|}{\underset{|}{C}}\cdot + Cl_2 \xrightarrow{k_3} -\overset{|}{\underset{|}{C}}-Cl + Cl\cdot
\end{array}
\right.
\tag{24.7}
$$

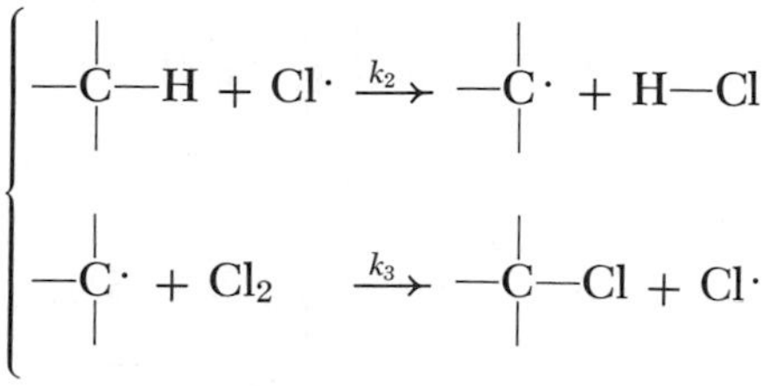

The sequence shown would account for the high quantum yields observed, since each turn around the cycle furnishes another chlorine atom.

Radical recombinations, hydrogen abstractions, and disproportionations can compete for chlorine atoms and alkyl radicals and so terminate the chains.

$$
\text{Chain-terminating steps} \left\{
\begin{array}{l}
\left.
\begin{array}{l}
Cl\cdot + Cl\cdot + M \longrightarrow Cl_2 + M^* \\[1.5em]
Cl\cdot + \cdot\overset{|}{\underset{|}{C}}- + M \longrightarrow Cl-\overset{|}{\underset{|}{C}}- + M^* \\[1.5em]
-\overset{|}{\underset{|}{C}}\cdot + \cdot\overset{|}{\underset{|}{C}}- + M \longrightarrow -\overset{|}{\underset{|}{C}}-\overset{|}{\underset{|}{C}}- + M^*
\end{array}
\right\} \text{radical recombinations} \\[4em]
\left.
\begin{array}{l}
Cl\cdot + -\overset{|}{\underset{\underset{H}{|}}{C}}-\overset{|}{\underset{|}{C}}\cdot \longrightarrow HCl + \hspace{-0.3em}\diagup\hspace{-0.5em}C{=}C\hspace{-0.5em}\diagup
\end{array}
\right\} \text{hydrogen atom abstraction} \\[2.5em]
\left.
\begin{array}{l}
-\overset{|}{\underset{|}{C}}\cdot + -\overset{|}{\underset{\underset{H}{|}}{C}}\hspace{-0.3em}\overset{|}{\underset{|}{C}}\cdot \longrightarrow -\overset{|}{\underset{|}{C}}-H + \hspace{-0.3em}\diagup\hspace{-0.5em}C{=}C\hspace{-0.5em}\diagup
\end{array}
\right\} \text{disproportionation}
\end{array}
\right.
$$

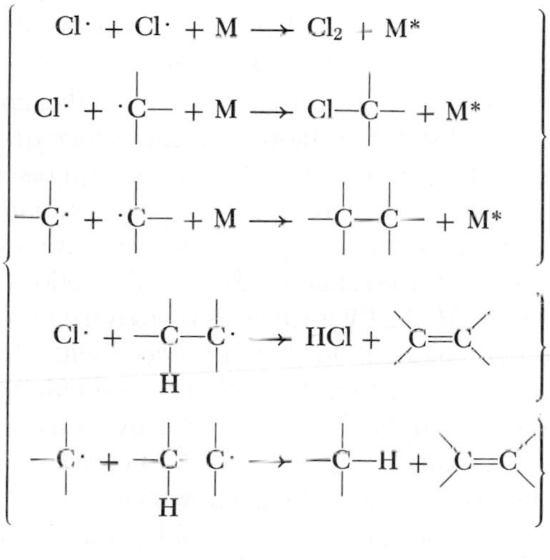

$$\tag{24.8}$$

There is no guarantee that this sequence of steps is the exclusive or even the main path to products, but detailed investigations lead to the conclusion that the mechanism outlined is generally applicable to halogenations of alkanes.

Exercise 24.5

Suggest a possible mechanism for the nitration of alkanes discussed in Exercise 24.2. *Answer:* Assuming a similarity to chlorination, we would get (*a*) $HONO_2 \xrightarrow{\text{heat}}$ $HO\cdot + \cdot NO_2$, both reasonable free radicals, (*b*) $RH + \cdot OH \longrightarrow R\cdot + H_2O$, (*c*) $R\cdot + \cdot NO_2 \longrightarrow RNO_2$, (*d*) possibly also a chain $R\cdot + HONO_2 \longrightarrow RNO_2 + \cdot OH$, and so on.

ENTHALPY CHANGES AND MECHANISTIC STEPS

A convenient way of inspecting the mechanism outlined—and also alternative mechanisms—is by evaluating the enthalpies of the individual steps. Again, making use of average bond enthalpy data (Table 14.8), we obtain the following estimates of enthalpies of reaction for the chain-propagating steps, indicating that only F_2 and Cl_2 are apt to react by this mechanism.

	Estimated ΔH^0 (kcal mole^{-1}) X = F	Cl	Br	I
$-\overset{|}{\underset{|}{C}}-H + X\cdot \longrightarrow -\overset{|}{\underset{|}{C}}\cdot + H-X$	-31	$+1$	$+17$	$+33$
$-\overset{|}{\underset{|}{C}}\cdot + X-X \longrightarrow -\overset{|}{\underset{|}{C}}-X + X\cdot$	-67	-21	-20	-21
Net: $-\overset{|}{\underset{|}{C}}-H + X-X \longrightarrow -\overset{|}{\underset{|}{C}}-X + H-X$	-98	-20	-3	$+12$

(24.9)

(Note that we assume an average carbon-hydrogen bond energy at this point. We will shift to more realistic estimates of actual bond energies of specific carbon-hydrogen bonds in later discussions.) What is assumed about ΔS^0, if these ΔH^0 values are used to evaluate possible mechanisms?

The results shown in equations (24.9) may be diagramed as in Figure 24.3, in which we see different states of the reaction sequence nestled in potential wells of as yet unspecified height. Further discussion requires some estimate of the barriers between the potential wells. A crude approximation could be obtained by setting the barrier or activation energy equal to zero for all reaction steps that are exothermic, and equal to the estimated ΔH^0 for all reactions that are endothermic. (Remember that $\Delta H \cong \Delta E$ if ΔPV is small, as is often true.) If we make this assumption, we conclude that chlorination should proceed with almost every collision of reactant species and thus afford a product that is randomly substituted. In contrast, the first step in bromination should require an activation energy of *at least* 17 kcal mole^{-1} and reaction would then proceed with minimal activation energy to yield product. Fluorination is a veritable Niagara, evolving great quantities of energy as reactants cascade to products; iodination would require a stiff upstream fight only to fall into a final product state of higher energy than reactants.

Exercise 24.6

Sketch a figure like 24.3 for a two-step mechanism in which $\Delta H_1 = -20$ kcal, $\Delta H_2 = 10$ kcal. Comment on the probable rate and equilibrium. *Answer:* Assume ΔS effects are negligible. If all activation energies (above actual ΔH's) are small, then the system will tend rapidly to come to an equilibrium in which the middle state predominates, especially if the system is closed rather than isolated. In an isolated system more of the final state will be achieved as a means of "storing" the energy released in step I. Your diagram should show an enthalpy minimum for the middle state with a final state 10 kcal lower than the initial state.

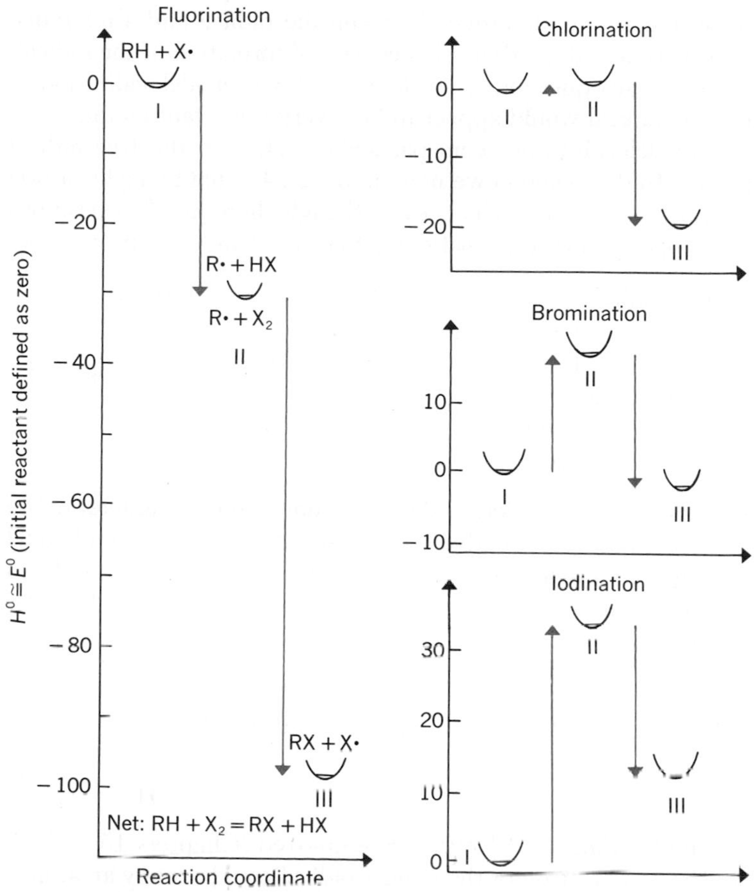

Figure 24.3 Estimated enthalpies of reaction for halogenation of hydrocarbons. I ⟶ II represents RH + X· ⟶ R· + HX; II ⟶ III represents R· + X_2 ⟶ RX + X·; I ⟶ III represents RH + X_2 ⟶ RX + HX.

FREE RADICAL STABILITY AND DELOCALIZATION OF ELECTRONS

We have examined the halogenation reaction at length, but a question important to the synthetic chemist remains unanswered. How can we explain the observed relationships between structure and reactivity in terms of our theories of chemical bonding? We know that the stability of a radical will directly affect rate of reaction, if the transition state has radical character, but we are faced with the problem of accounting for the experimentally observed stability order of radicals:

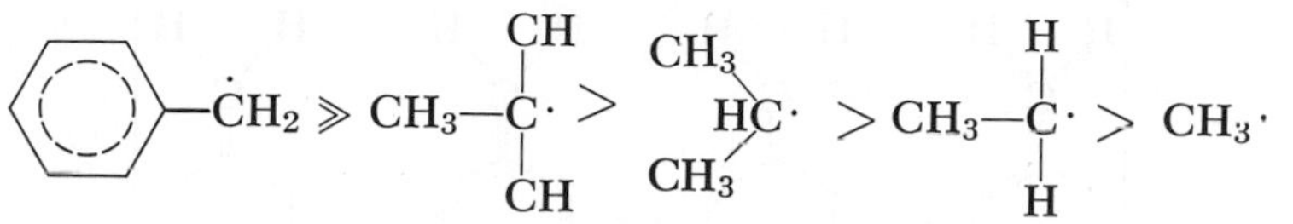

benzyl > tertiary > secondary > primary > methyl

By stability we mean the energy difference between the radical and a reference state (in this case the parent hydrocarbon); hence ease of formation of the radical. The complete answer to this question is not known. However, delocalization of the odd electron in the radical would appear to be a very important factor.

The effects of delocalization seem particularly clear in the free radical chlorination of toluene. In this reaction we note in Table 24.3 that benzyl chloride is the exclusive monochlorination product, even though there are five positions (three different ones—*o*, *m*, *p*) on the aromatic ring that could undergo substitution.

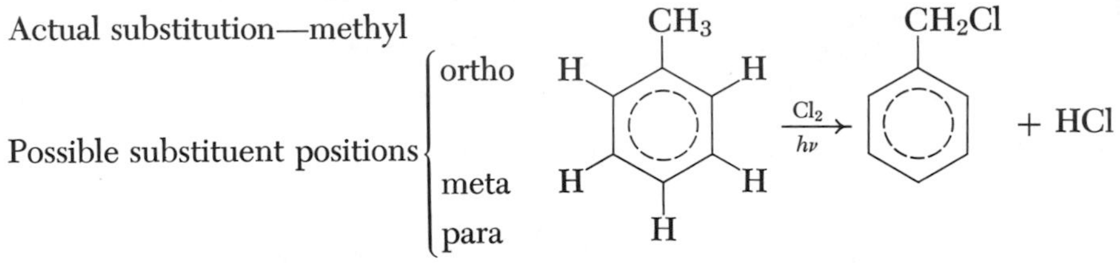

The experimental result would be anticipated if we assume radical character in the transition state and note that the respective bond dissociation energies of a benzyl C—H bond ($C_6H_5CH_2$—H) and a phenyl (C_6H_5—H) C—H bond are 85 and 103 kcal mole^{-1}. However, the question at present is why a benzyl radical ($C_6H_5\dot{C}H_2$) should be more stable (easier to form) than a phenyl radical 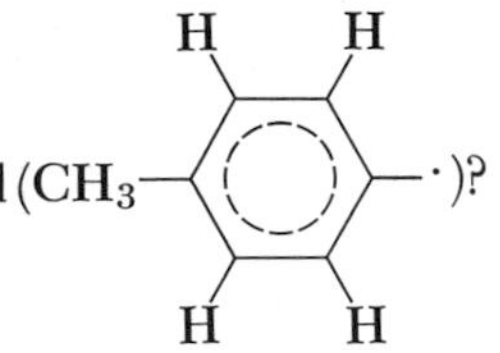?

An examination of the bonding model normally employed (Chapters 15 and 17) reveals an answer. The odd electron of the benzyl radical could occupy an atomic *p*-orbital of the methyl carbon. This atomic orbital can overlap and hence interact with the π-molecular orbitals (made from the combination of six atomic *p*-orbitals of the ring carbons). As a result of this interaction, the unpaired electron has a probability distribution that includes the ring as well as the methyl carbon:

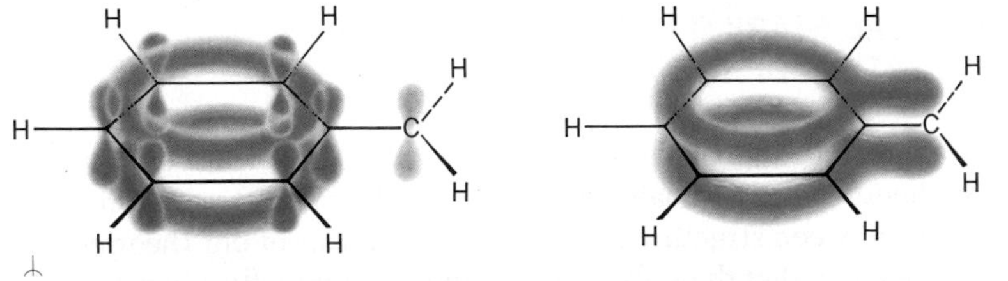

A more detailed picture may be obtained by examining the localized valence bond resonance structures which contribute to the resonance hybrid:

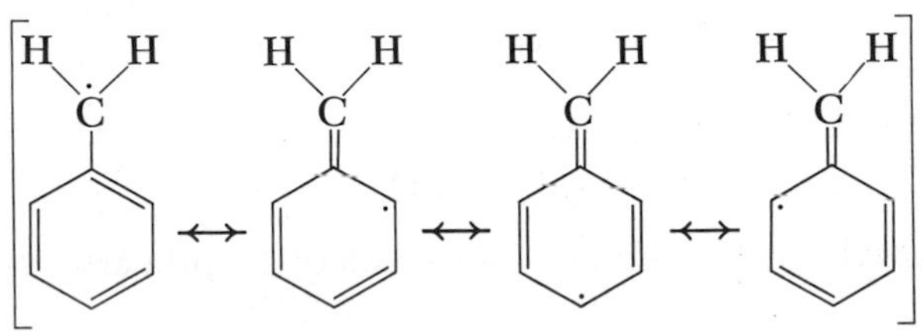

These contributing structures are formally generated by moving electrons about the ring, maintaining the normal quadrivalence of carbon. This model predicts partial radical character only on the *ortho* and *para* carbons. What experiments could be devised to test this result?

Let us now compare the benzyl radical with one of the three possible phenyl radicals that could be formed by cleavage of a phenyl C—H bond:

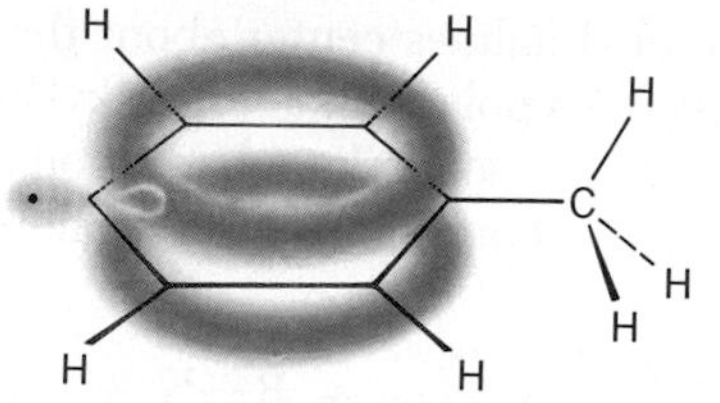

The unpaired electron of the phenyl radical would occupy an sp^2 orbital of carbon. These orbital axes are at right angles to the π-molecular orbitals, and effective overlap is not possible. The odd electron is *localized;* it cannot be spread out through the ring or be delocalized by way of the π-cloud. As a result, we would consider this radical to be much less stable than the benzyl radical. Thus the phenyl—H bond is harder to break than the benzyl—H bond.

Extension of this type of explanation to explain the stability order of alkyl radicals (tertiary > secondary > primary > methyl) is possible. However, general agreement on the mode of delocalization has not been reached. Rather than discuss the various views at length, we will simply state that *some* delocalization of an electron to carbons next to the electron-bearing carbon is possible, and that the extent of delocalization is directly related to the number of carbon bonds attached to carbon bearing the unpaired electron.

Exercise 24.7

Discuss the stability of the $SO_4^{=}$ ion with respect to its slow rate of reduction and with respect to the strength of HSO_4^- and H_2SO_4 as acids. *Answer:* Sulfur and oxygen each have six valence electrons. These $5 \cdot 6 = 30$ electrons plus the two giving the charge to the ion give a total of 32 valence electrons in $SO_4^{=}$. This is sufficient to give a single bond between S and each O plus three unshared electron pairs per oxygen, 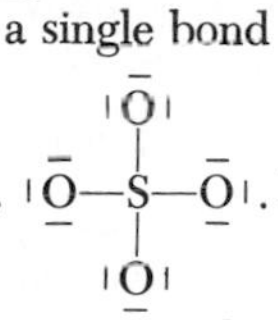. But sulfur has additional empty orbitals, such as $3d$, so π bonding also occurs, as shown by the short bonds observed in $SO_4^{=}$ ions (observed, 1.51 Å; single bond, 1.70 Å). This allows delocalization of the "unshared pairs" on the oxygens stabilizing the ion more and more as it becomes more symmetrical. Thus H_2SO_4 and HSO_4^- are relatively strong acids (due to increasing delocalization) in the series $H_2SO_4 \longrightarrow HSO_4^- \longrightarrow SO_4^{=}$. Rate of reaction decreases in the same order and for the same reason.

SOME REACTIONS OF ALKYL HALIDES

Alkyl halides are considerably more reactive than alkanes, but there are many similarities in the physical and chemical properties of these two classes of carbon compounds. For example, both alkanes and alkyl halides are very weak bases. Recall that chloride ion is also a weak base, enhanced by the negative charge.) Although other compounds of carbon will undergo protonation and hence dissolve in cold concentrated sulfuric acid, alkanes and most alkyl halides are insoluble in this very strong acid. Thus sulfuric acid extraction represents a useful means of removing alkenes, arenes, and impurities that contain oxygen and nitrogen (all more powerful bases than are the halides) from alkanes and many alkyl halides.

Most reactions of alkyl halides center about the carbon-halogen bond, as we might anticipate in view of its polar character. Alkyl halides will undergo a type of reaction (frequently called a nucleophilic substitution or a nucleophilic displacement) that can be symbolically represented in the following way:

$$\mathrm{N}\odot + \mathrm{R{-}L} \longrightarrow \mathrm{R{-}N} + \mathrm{:L}$$

Table 24.4 Some nucleophilic displacement reactions.

$$\left(\begin{array}{l} \mathrm{R{-}Br} + \mathrm{:M{-}H} = \mathrm{HBr} + \mathrm{R{-}M} \\ \mathrm{R{-}Br} + \mathrm{:M^-} \quad = \mathrm{Br^-} + \mathrm{R{-}M} \end{array}\right)$$

Alkyl halide	Nucleophile		Products	Functional type formed
$CH_3{-}Br$ +	$H{-}\ddot{O}{-}H$	$\longrightarrow$	$H{-}Br + CH_3{-}OH$	alcohol
$CH_3{-}Br$ +	$:\ddot{O}{-}H^-$	$\longrightarrow$	$Br^- + CH_3OH$	alcohol
$CH_3{-}Br$ +	$:\ddot{O}{-}R^-$	$\longrightarrow$	$Br^- + CH_3{-}\ddot{O}{-}R$	ether
$CH_3{-}Br$ +	$:C{\equiv}C{-}R$	$\longrightarrow$	$Br^- + CH_3{-}C{\equiv}C{-}R$	alkyne
$CH_3{-}Br$ +	$^-O_2C{-}R$	$\longrightarrow$	$Br^- + CH_3{-}O{-}C(=O){-}R$	ester
$CH_3{-}Br$ +	I^-	$\longrightarrow$	$Br^- + CH_3{-}I$	alkyl halide
$CH_3{-}Br$ +	$:NH_3$	$\longrightarrow$	$HBr + CH_3{-}\ddot{N}H_2$	primary amine
$CH_3{-}Br$ +	$:NH_2R$	$\longrightarrow$	$HBr + CH_3{-}\ddot{N}HR$	secondary amine
$CH_3{-}Br$ +	$:NHR_2$	$\longrightarrow$	$HBr + CH_3{-}\ddot{N}R_2$	tertiary amine
$CH_3{-}Br$ +	$:\ddot{S}H^-$	$\longrightarrow$	$Br^- + CH_3{-}SH$	(mercaptan) thio alcohol
$CH_3{-}Br$ +	$:\ddot{S}{-}R^-$	$\longrightarrow$	$Br^- + CH_3{-}\ddot{S}{-}R$	thio ether
$CH_3{-}Br$ +		$\xrightarrow{AlCl_3}$	HBr + 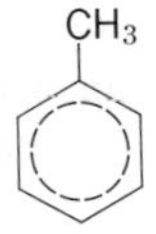	alkylbenzene
$CH_3{-}Br$ +	$:\bar{C}H(COOR)_2$	$\longrightarrow$	$Br^- + CH_3{-}CH(COOR)_2$	alkylmalonic ester

where N represents a nucleophile ("nucleus loving") and L represents a leaving group (in our discussion, a halide ion). A nucleophile may be defined as any reagent with an electron pair available for the formation of a new bond—that is, a Lewis base. Reagents familiar to us as strong or moderately strong bases such as hydroxide ion ($:\ddot{O}H^-$), acetate ion ($CH_3-C\overset{O^-}{\underset{O}{\langle}}$), and ammonia ($:NH_3$) are nucleophiles. However, other reagents which are weak bases, such as iodide ion ($:\ddot{X}:^-$), isobutylene [$(CH_3)_2C{=}CH_2$], and benzene, are also nucleophiles. Investigation reveals that the correlation of "nucleophilicity" with polarizability (see p. 348) is better than the correlation of nucleophilicity with basicity. For the present, however, we can most conveniently think of a nucleophile as being a Lewis base (see p. 430).

Nucleophilic displacement reactions, particularly those involving alkyl halides, represent one of the most important classes of organic reactions. Table 24.4 gives some indication of their scope. It should be clear from an examination of this table that an understanding of this type of reaction opens the door to a large area of synthetic chemistry. We will examine a few specific nucleophilic displacements to gain some insight concerning this general reaction type.

Exercise 24.8

Suggest some nucleophiles in addition to those listed in Table 24.4 and write a type equation for their reaction with an alkyl iodide. *Answer:* Nucleophiles normally have at least one unshared pair of electrons and high polarizability (large size, small effective nuclear charge, weak attraction for valence electrons). Thus large negative ions which are not greatly stabilized by electron delocalization will usually be good nucleophiles. ClO_4^- and $SO_4^=$ would not be good due to electron delocalizations, but $S^=$, BCl_4^-, and NH_2^- would be good. Type equation: $RI + :X^{-n} = RX^{1-n} + I^-$.

SOLVOLYSIS REACTIONS OF ALKYL HALIDES

The reaction of alkyl bromides with water leads to the formation of the corresponding alcohol, although alkene formation is often an important side reaction.

$$CH_3{-}Br + H_2O \longrightarrow \underset{\text{methanol}}{CH_3OH} + HBr$$

$$CH_3CH_2{-}Br + H_2O \longrightarrow \underset{\text{ethanol}}{CH_3{-}CH_2{-}OH} + HBr$$

$$\begin{matrix} CH_3 \\ CH_3 \end{matrix}\!\!>\!CH{-}Br + H_2O \longrightarrow \underset{\text{isopropanol}}{\begin{matrix} CH_3 \\ CH_3 \end{matrix}\!\!>\!CH{-}OH} + HBr$$

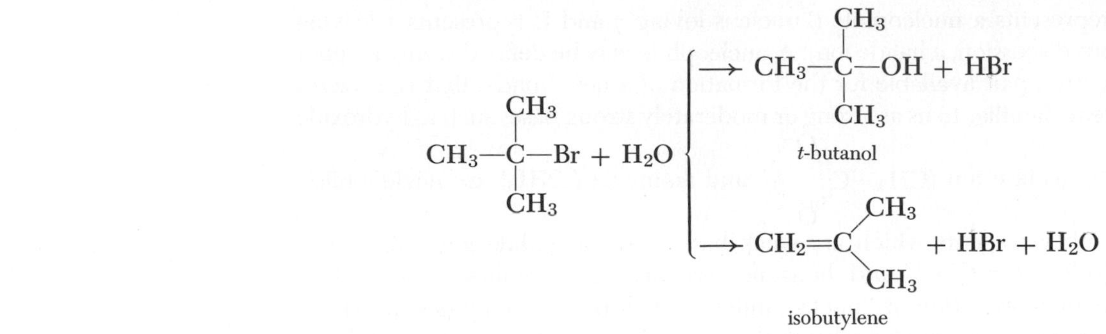

$$CH_3-\underset{\underset{\textstyle CH_3}{|}}{\overset{\overset{\textstyle CH_3}{|}}{C}}-Br + H_2O \begin{cases} \longrightarrow CH_3-\underset{\underset{\textstyle CH_3}{|}}{\overset{\overset{\textstyle CH_3}{|}}{C}}-OH + HBr \\ \qquad\qquad t\text{-butanol} \\ \\ \longrightarrow CH_2{=}C\overset{\overset{\textstyle CH_3}{\diagup}}{\underset{\underset{\textstyle CH_3}{\diagdown}}{}} + HBr + H_2O \end{cases}$$

isobutylene

This type of reaction is called a *solvolysis reaction,* since one of the reagents is the solvent. Kinetic studies reveal that alkyl halides react quite slowly with water. It is found, however, that the rates of reaction are rather remarkable functions of alkyl group structure. For example, the relative rate data shown in Table 24.5 show that *t*-butyl bromide undergoes solvolysis at a rate 10^5 times as fast as isopropyl bromide.

The use of aqueous solutions containing hydroxide ion (as added sodium hydroxide) greatly increases the rate of formation of methanol, ethanol, and iso-propanol. An investigation of the rate of reaction of methyl bromide and ethyl bromide in aqueous solutions containing hydroxide ion reveals a rate law of the form

$$\frac{d[\text{ROH}]}{dt} = k[\text{RBr}][\text{OH}^-]$$

In contrast, it is found that the rate of formation of *t*-butyl alcohol from *t*-butyl bromide is not appreciably altered by conducting the reaction in basic solutions. The rate law remains

$$\frac{d[(CH_3)_3COH]}{dt} = k[(CH_3)_3CBr]$$

Thus the results of these hydrolysis reactions confront us with the dual problems of accounting for variations of both rate and rate law with variations of structure.

NUCLEOPHILIC DISPLACEMENT BY HALIDE ION

Another nucleophilic displacement reaction which we might explore involves the replacement of one halide by another:

$$I^- + R-X \rightleftarrows R-I + X^-$$

This reaction represents a useful method of synthesizing alkyl iodides from alkyl

Table 24.5 Relative rates of solvolysis of alkyl bromides at 50°C.

$$(R-X + H_2O \longrightarrow R-OH + HBr)$$

R	CH_3-	CH_3CH_2-	$(CH_3)_2CH-$	$(CH_3)_3C-$
Relative rate	1.05	1.00	11.6	$1.2 \cdot 10^6$

Table 24.6 Relative rates of nucleophilic displacement by iodide ion.
($R{-}Br + I^- \longrightarrow R{-}I + Br^-$)

R	$CH_3{-}$	$CH_3{-}CH_2{-}$	$(CH_3)_2CH{-}$	$(CH_3)_3C{-}$
Relative rate	145	1	0.0078	0.00051
R	$CH_3CH_2{-}$	$CH_3CH_2CH_2{-}$	$(CH_3)_2CH{-}CH_2{-}$	$(CH_3)_3C{-}CH_2{-}$
Relative rate	1	0.82	0.036	0.000012

SOURCE: Data of L. Fowden, E. D. Hughes, and C. K. Ingold, *J. Chem. Soc.*, 3187 (1955).

chlorides or bromides. (Recall that alkyl iodides could not be synthesized by direct halogenation procedures.) Experiments show that the reaction with iodide ion proceeds with a measurable rate if alkyl halides have the halogen substituent at a primary or secondary carbon. *Tert*-alkyl halides react so slowly that they cannot be utilized. Relative rates for a reaction of this type are shown in Table 24.6.

The rate law for displacement reactions of this type is found to be first order in both alkyl halide and iodide ion:

$$\frac{-d[\mathrm{RBr}]}{dt} = k[\mathrm{RBr}][\mathrm{I}^-]$$

The use of radioactive iodide ion ($^{131}I^-$) enables one to measure the rate of the symmetrical reaction

$$*I^- + R{-}I \longrightarrow R{-}I* + I^-$$

This can be accomplished by periodically withdrawing an aliquot of reaction solution, isolating the alkyl iodide, and counting the material to determine the amount of incorporated iodine-131.

A kinetic study of a symmetrical exchange reaction of considerable interest has been performed utilizing iodine-131 and the optically active compound (−)-2-iodooctane. The experiments consisted of following simultaneously the rate of incorporation of iodine-131 and the rate of loss of optical activity (racemization). Optical activity need not be lost in this reaction, but if it is, there are at least two ways in which the racemization could occur.

Alternative 1.—Racemization (production of equal quantities of the two optically isomeric products) could result if *either* a "right-handed" or "left-handed" isomer could be formed *each* time displacement took place.

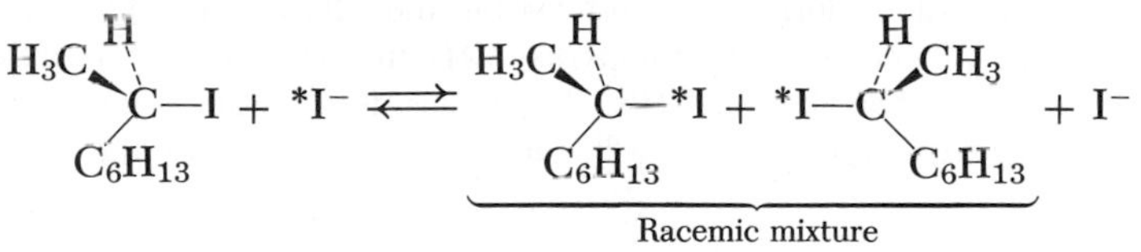

Under this mechanism the rate of inversion would equal half the rate of incorporation of I^{131}.

Alternative 2.—Racemization could also occur in a symmetrical reaction in which an inversion of configuration accompanied every displacement.

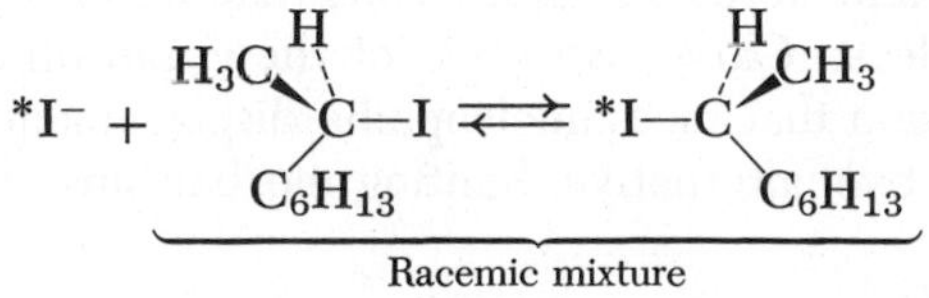

Here the rate of inversion equals the rate of incorporation of I^{131}.

Experiments show quite conclusively that the initial rate of inversion is exactly equal to the initial rate of incorporation of iodine-131. Thus one concludes that, for this type of nucleophilic displacement, *every displacement proceeds with inversion of configuration* as in alternative 2.

If this condition prevails for reactions which are not symmetrical, the use of optically active reactants would dictate optically active products with *inverted configurations*. Many examples of this are known. For example, (−)-2-bromooctane undergoes reaction with hydroxide ion to yield the optically active alcohol of opposite configuration.

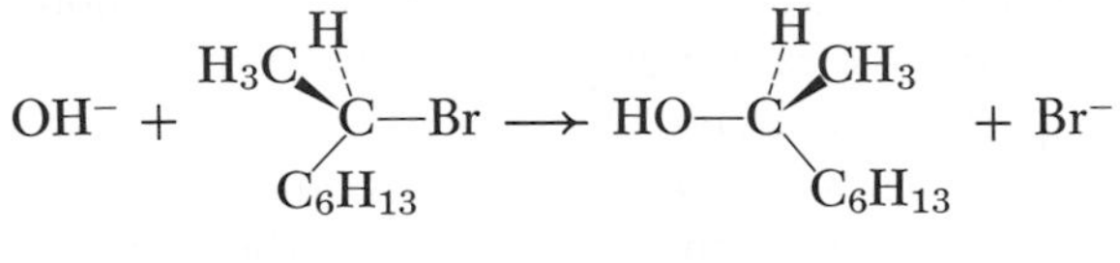

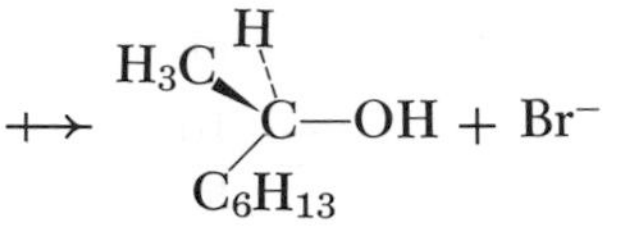

(Not formed)

However, we find once again that the stereochemical result of a nucleophilic displacement depends upon the structure of the alkyl halide. Optically active 1-chloro-1-phenylethane undergoes solvolysis in aqueous media to yield an alcohol which is not optically active but mainly a racemic mixture.

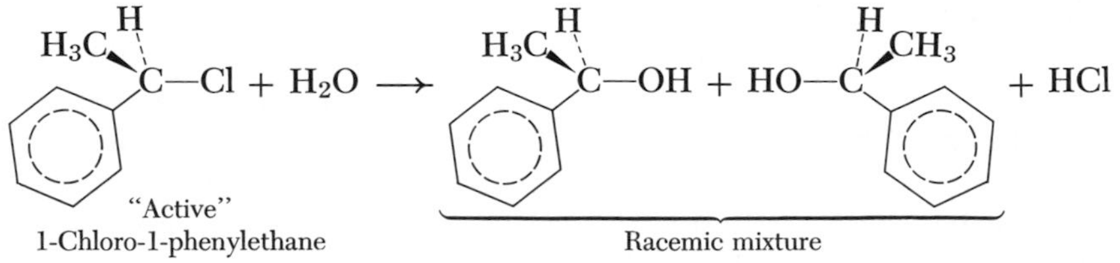

"Active"
1-Chloro-1-phenylethane

Racemic mixture

Exercise 24.9

Suggest an interpretation of the relative rate data in Table 24.6. *Answer:* The following sections will explore this more fully, but the following two ideas might suggest themselves: (*a*) perhaps bulky groups (like CH_3) impair the formation of the activated complex more than the small H's; (*b*) perhaps, if inversion is involved, the larger masses, having larger inertia, will not invert as rapidly as the very low mass hydrogens.

MECHANISTIC INTERPRETATION OF NUCLEOPHILIC DISPLACEMENT REACTIONS

The structural, kinetic, and stereochemical results that we have described appear conflicting, to say the least. Close inspection of these and other data, however, have led to the conclusion that most nucleophilic displacement reactions can be understood in terms of two, alternative, limiting mechanisms, whose basic difference is that of timing. That is, the reaction may occur either by sequential breaking and making of bonds or by synchronous making and breaking of bonds leading us to predict two different sets of kinetic, structural, and stereochemical results. Let us explore these two mechanistic possibilities and compare our predictions with the results of experiment.

THE SYNCHRONOUS, OR CONCERTED, MECHANISM OF NUCLEOPHILIC DISPLACEMENT—S_N2 REACTIONS

If we consider a synchronous mechanism in which the nucleophile starts to bond to carbon as the leaving group starts to break its bond to carbon, bonding theory as well as electrostatics would lead us to predict that the most energetically favorable process would be one in which the nucleophile attacks carbon "backside" with respect to the leaving group:

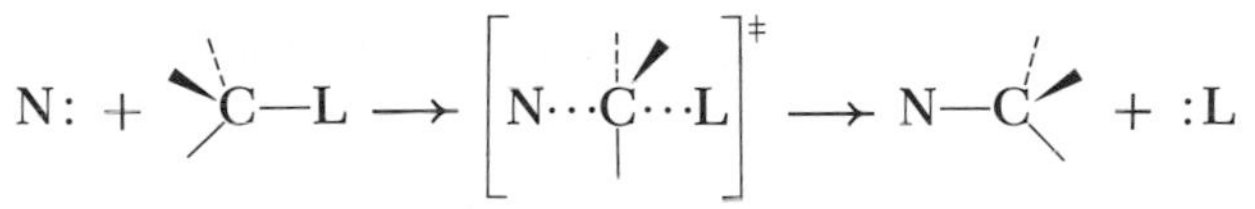

The bonding model invoked would imply that tetrahedral carbon with bonds formed from four sp^3 hybridized orbitals would undergo rehybridization as the reaction proceeds, reaching approximately sp^2 hybridization in the transition state where both the nucleophile and the leaving group are partially bonded to carbon by way of the remaining p-orbital of carbon. Remember the small "backside" lobe of the bonding p-orbital suggested in Figures 15.1 and 15.2. This could allow overlap with N to begin before overlap with L ceased.

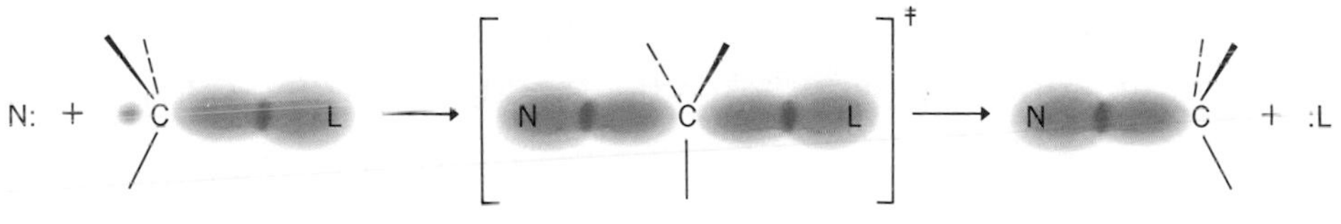

It should be clear that such a process would result in inversion of the configuration about carbon each time a displacement occurs. In addition, we would predict a first-order rate law in each reactant. Finally we would expect that the rate of this backside displacement process would be markedly affected by the size and shape of the groups attached to the carbon undergoing substitution. That is, large groups attached to carbon undergoing reaction should cause significant repulsion to backside attack by the nucleophile, with a resulting retardation of reaction rate. Thus, the reactivity order shown in Figure 24.4 would be predicted for the indicated series of primary alkyl halides.

The predicted sensitivity of backside displacement reactions to steric effects implies an important synthetic limitation. Reactions that proceed by this mechanism cannot be effectively applied to *tert*-alkyl halides. Secondary alkyl

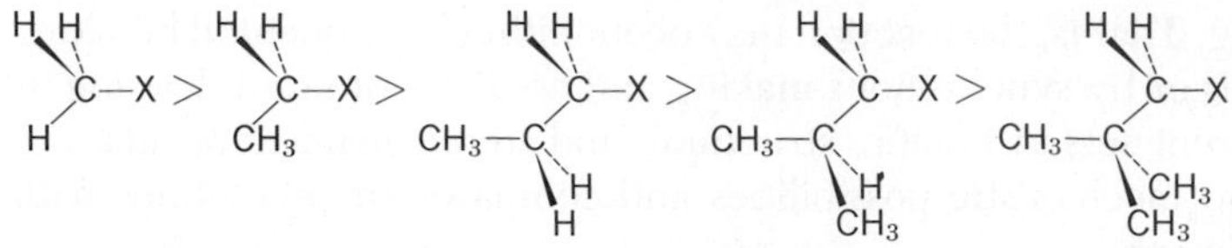

Figure 24.4 A series of alkyl halides, showing progressively greater hindrance to backside displacement. Compare ordering with the data in Table 24.6. Note that relatively free rotation around the C–C σ bonds permits different orientations of the alkyl groups attached to the carbon undergoing displacement.

halides react much more slowly than primary alkyl halides, and even primary alkyl halides can be subject to severe steric rate retardation.

What happens to secondary and tertiary alkyl halides when they are subjected to reactions favoring this concerted displacement process? Do they simply remain in the reaction mixture as unreacted starting material? Oftentimes not, particularly when the attacking nucleophile is strongly basic: when it is, elimination side reactions become the predominant mode of reaction. For example, a standard procedure for the preparation of alkyl ethers (R—Ö—R) involves displacement of a halide ion by an alkoxide ion (R—Ö:⁻).

Alcohols, like water, can react with an alkali metal. Thus,

$$H-\ddot{O}-H + Na^0 \longrightarrow Na^+OH^- + \tfrac{1}{2}H_{2(g)}$$

$$CH_3-\ddot{O}-H + Na^0 \longrightarrow Na^+\overset{\ominus}{O}CH_3 + \tfrac{1}{2}H_{2(g)}$$

Alkoxides, like hydroxides, are very strong bases:

$$CH_3-\ddot{O}:^- + H^+ \rightleftharpoons CH_3-\ddot{O}-H, \qquad K_{eq} = \frac{[CH_3OH]}{[H^+][CH_3O^-]} \approx 1 \cdot 10^{18}$$

Reaction of sodium methoxide with a series of alkyl bromides is found to give the following products:

$$CH_3-O^- + CH_3CH_2-CH_2-CH_2-Br \xrightarrow[\text{reflux}]{CH_3OH} CH_3-O-CH_2-CH_2-CH_2-CH_3 + Br^-$$

methyl *n*-butyl ether

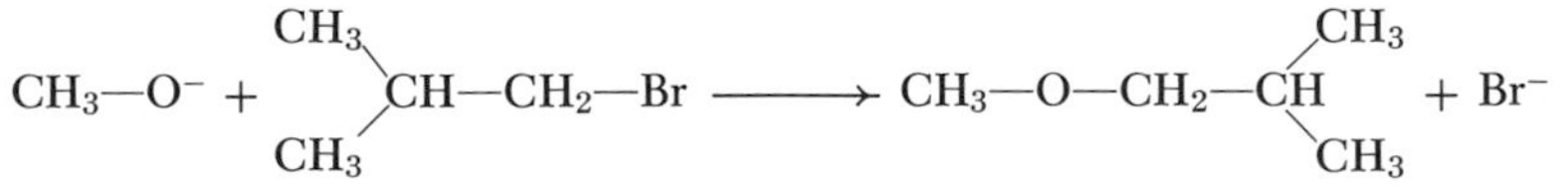

methyl isobutyl ether

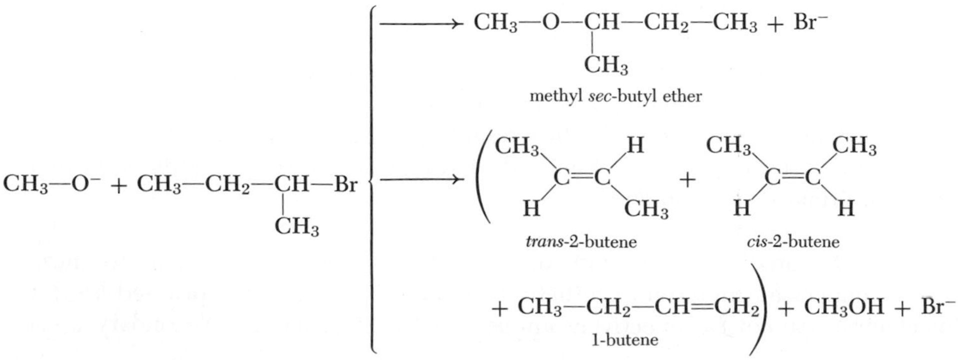

$$CH_3{-}O^- + CH_3{-}\underset{CH_3}{\overset{CH_3}{|}}{C}{-}Br \longrightarrow \underset{\text{2-methylpropene}}{CH_2{=}C(CH_3)_2} + CH_3OH + Br^- \tag{24.10}$$

The reasons for the occurrence of a process resulting in elimination of hydrogen bromide must be associated with two factors: steric hindrance to backside attack and basicity of the nucleophile. If the nucleophile's path of approach to the carbon bearing the halide ion is blocked or partially blocked, an alternative process—proton abstraction from an adjacent carbon—could become competitive or perhaps the major path of reaction (see Figure 24.5).

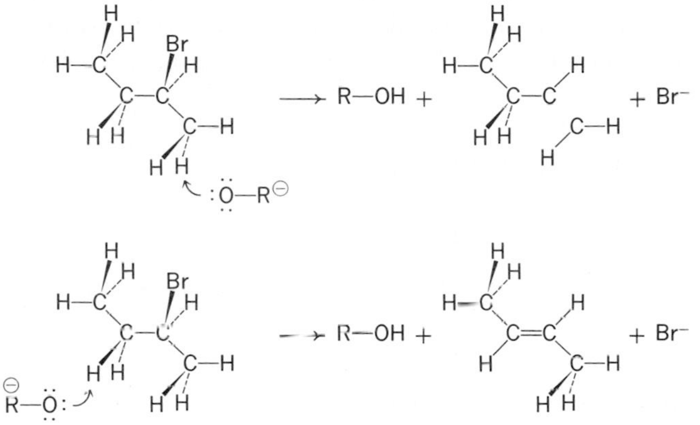

Figure 24.5 Two possible elimination reactions yielding 1-butene and *trans*-2-butene. The arrows designate the direction of electron flow in the making and breaking of bonds.

The possibility of competitive elimination reactions must always be considered in the design of syntheses involving nucleophilic displacement reactions. Note that we could greatly improve the yield of methyl *sec*-butyl ether compared to Equation (24.10) (or of methyl *t*-butyl ether) if we "invert" the alkoxide and halide reactants and elect to use as the reactants the alkoxide salts of *sec*-butyl alcohol (and *t*-butyl alcohol) together with a methyl halide such as methyl iodide:

$$\begin{array}{c}CH_3\\ \quad\diagdown\\ \quad CH{-}O^-\\ \quad\diagup\\ CH_3{-}CH_2\end{array} + CH_3{-}I \longrightarrow \begin{array}{c}CH_3\\ \quad\diagdown\\ \quad CH{-}O{-}CH_3\\ \quad\diagup\\ CH_3{-}CH_2\end{array} + I^-$$

$$(CH_3)_3C{-}O^- + CH_3{-}I \longrightarrow (CH_3)_3C{-}O{-}CH_3 + I^-$$

The reasons for this should be clear; methyl iodide is free of steric congestion and, equally important, it cannot undergo elimination because there are no other carbon atoms in the molecule.

In summary, the concerted nucleophilic displacement mechanism which we have employed to rationalize certain experimental observations should have the following characteristics.

1. A rate law of the form, rate $= k$ [alkyl halide][nucleophile].
2. Inversion of configuration about carbon accompanying every displacement.
3. Marked sensitivity of reaction rate to bulky groups around the reaction site.

4. Competitive elimination reactions, particularly when the nucleophile is a strong proton acceptor.

Note also that, by recognizing this mechanism, we can design more efficient synthetic procedures. It is clear, however, that we cannot explain all of our observations in terms of this mechanism alone.

THE IONIZATION MECHANISM OF NUCLEOPHILIC DISPLACEMENT—S_N1 REACTIONS

If we consider an alternative mode of nucleophilic displacement—one in which the bond between the leaving group and carbon breaks *before* the new bond forms—we would expect rather different structural, kinetic, stereochemical, and solvent effects:

$$\text{R—L} \underset{k_{-1}}{\overset{k_1}{\rightleftharpoons}} \text{R}^+ + :\text{L}$$

$$\text{R}^+ + :\text{N} \xrightarrow{k_2} \text{R—N}$$

The general rate law for such a mechanism [applying the steady-state assumption to (R^+)] should have the form

$$\text{rate} = \frac{-d[\text{RL}]}{dt} = k_2[\text{R}^+][:\text{N}]$$

$$= \frac{k_1k_2[\text{RL}][:\text{N}]}{k_{-1}[:\text{L}] + k_2[:\text{N}]}$$

If

$$k_2[\text{N}:] \gg k_{-1}[:\text{L}]$$

then we have

$$\text{rate} = k_1[\text{RL}]$$

The latter situation might be expected to prevail in solvolysis reactions if the nucleophile is in large excess and N: is more nucleophilic than L:. However, it should be realized that solvolysis reaction conditions do not permit discrimination between the bimolecular synchronous process and the ionization mechanism, since the rate laws for both reactions under these conditions would appear to be first order. In fact, it is frequently quite difficult to discriminate between the concerted and ionization mechanisms by direct kinetic experiment. A resolution of this problem may frequently be obtained by study of the rate of reaction as a function of excess leaving group (:L) in the reacting solution. One would anticipate a rate retardation and a change from clean first-order kinetics if an ionization mechanism is operative but no appreciable change in rate or rate law should be observed as the concentration of L: varies, if the reaction takes place by a concerted process.

The ionization mechanism of nucleophilic displacement is frequently called the S_N1 (substitution nucleophilic unimolecular) mechanism, in contrast to the concerted process (S_N2). In our discussion of the ionization mechanism we could anticipate the following characteristics.

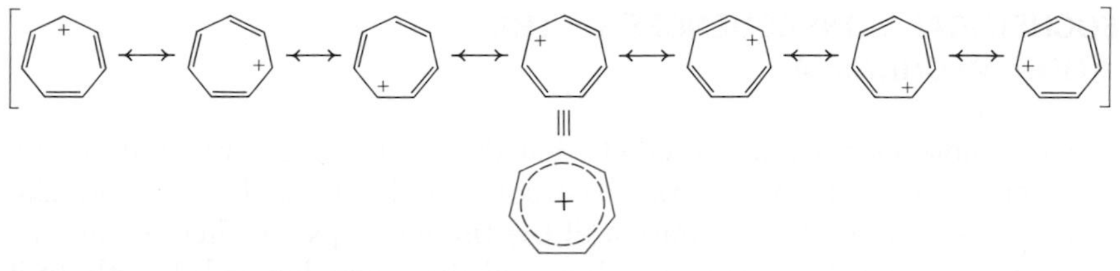

Figure 24.6 Contributing resonance structures of cycloheptatrienylium ion. Hydrogens not shown.

1. A rate law of the form, rate $= \dfrac{k[\mathrm{RL}]}{k'[\mathrm{L}]/[\mathrm{N}] + 1}$.
2. An alkyl group reactivity order, benzyl > tertiary > secondary > primary.
3. Racemization of configuration.
4. Marked sensitivity of the rate to the polarity of the solvent.

Perhaps the most striking feature of the ionization mechanism is the postulate concerning the existence of an alkyl cation (carbonium ion) as a reactive intermediate in view of the moderately high ionization energy of carbon (see Table 3.1). We would anticipate that the stability of electron-deficient alkyl cations, as with alkyl radicals, would be strongly dependent upon their structures. The ability to delocalize positive charge is of crucial importance.

In this regard we should note that one of the most stable carbonium ions known, cycloheptatrienylium ion (tropenium or tropylium ion), has its positive charge equally distributed on seven carbon atoms (Figure 24.6).

The previous discussion of the effects of structure on stability of alkyl radicals can be transferred without substantial change to a discussion of alkyl cation stabilities. Thus we would anticipate a stability order for alkyl cations, as

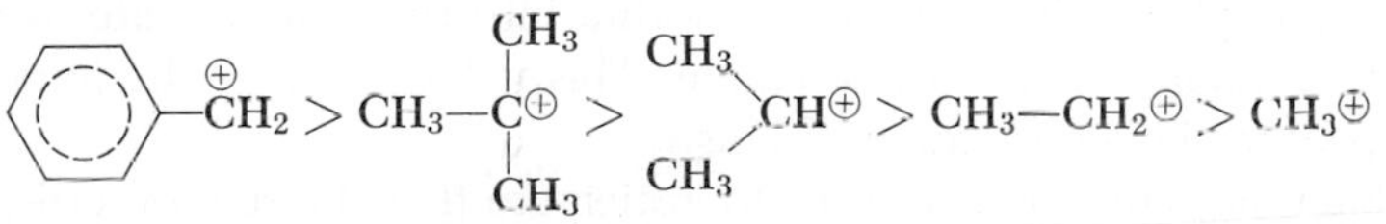

The benzyl cation is presumably stabilized by delocalization of charge by way of the π orbitals of the molecule. The alkyl cations have differential stabilities due, in part, to inductive electron release through the carbon-carbon bonds or possibly by a process called hyperconjugation:

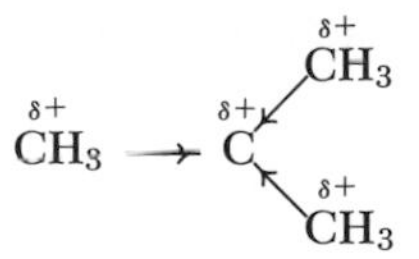

inductive model of alkyl cation stabilization

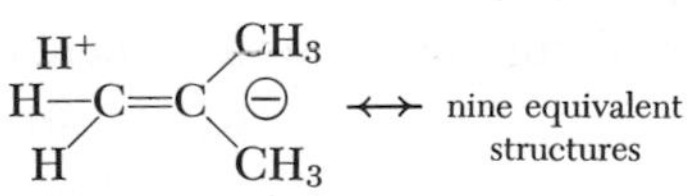

hyperconjugation model of alkyl cation stabilization

Both these terms describe the relative availability of adjacent electron clouds. High availability stabilizes the cation by delocalizing the positive charge. As indicated in earlier discussions (see p. 621), the relative importance of these two modes of delocalization are the subject of rather heated debate and discussion. Nevertheless, there appears to be little question concerning the factual correctness of the indicated stability order.

STEREOCHEMICAL CONSEQUENCES OF THE IONIZATION MECHANISM

Our model of molecular bonding predicts that the most stable configuration of a carbonium ion is one in which the cationic carbon is sp^2 hybridized. This hybridization permits maximum spatial separation of the three groups attached to cationic carbon and implies that the cationic carbon and the atoms bonded directly to it lie in a plane:

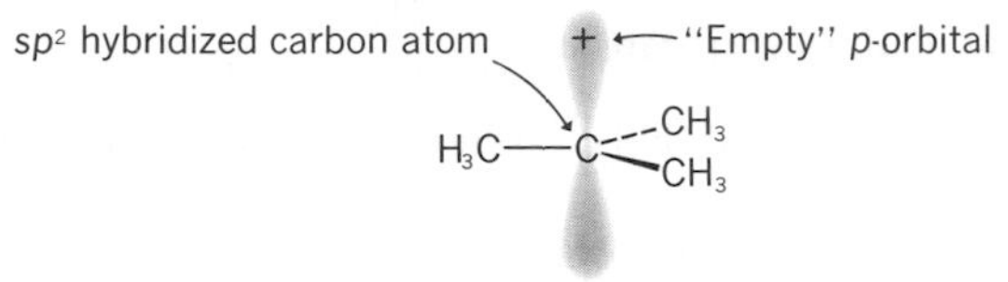

t-Butyl cation
(trimethyl carbonium ion)

If an optically active alkyl halide undergoes nucleophilic displacement by an ionization mechanism, we must expect a racemic product, since the attacking nucleophile can approach the cation equally well from above or below the planar ion (Figure 24.7).

THE EFFECT OF SOLVENT ON DISPLACEMENT REACTIONS

All the ionic displacement reactions discussed occur in solution but not (with very few exceptions) in the vapor phase. This observation reflects the interaction of ionic species, whether reactants or intermediates, with solvent. Stabilization of ions by solvation is crucial. (Review problems 17.14 and 17.21 to contrast the energy required for gas phase dissociation of chlorine into two chlorine atoms compared to a chlorine anion and a chlorine cation. This will emphasize the important role solvents play in the stabilization of ions.)

Such considerations lead us to anticipate that the rate of a displacement reaction proceeding by an ionization process would strongly depend upon the polarity of the solvent. We must recognize that our argument is based upon a model of the transition state. Specifically, we are assuming that the transition state looks very much like a separated carbonium ion and halide ion. If we can safely assume that the transition state is very similar in energy to the reactive intermediates as shown in Figure 24.8, our arguments have validity.

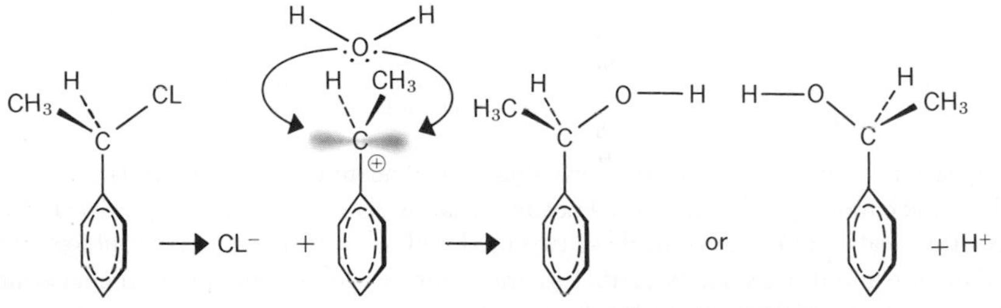

Figure 24.7 Racemization is the predicted result of the ionization mechanism.

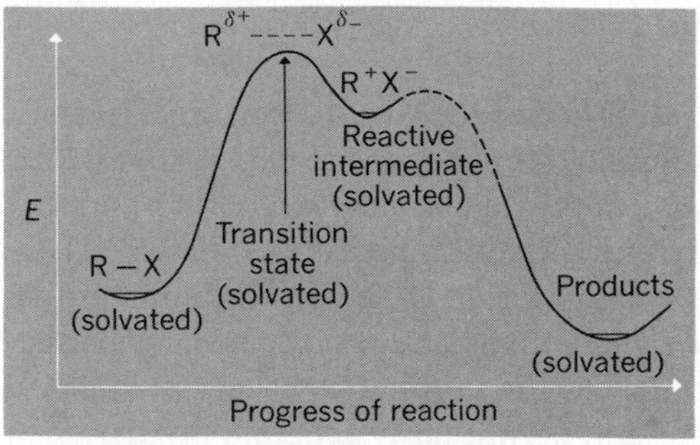

Figure 24.8 Transition state and reactive intermediate of similar energy in an ionization process.

Often specific solvation is of great importance. Methods by which we can "force" a reaction to take an ionization reaction path include the use of very polar solvents as well as the use of specific solvating or coordinating species in the solvent. The use of silver ion is a good example:

$$R—X + Ag^{\oplus} \longrightarrow \left[\overset{\delta+}{R}\cdots Cl\cdots \overset{\delta+}{Ag}\right] \longrightarrow R^{\oplus} + AgCl\,(s)$$

The rate at which this precipitation reaction proceeds is frequently used to discriminate between alkyl halides of varying structure. Other so-called "electrophilic" catalysts (Lewis acids) are particularly useful in promoting the reaction between alkyl halides and the nucleophile, benzene

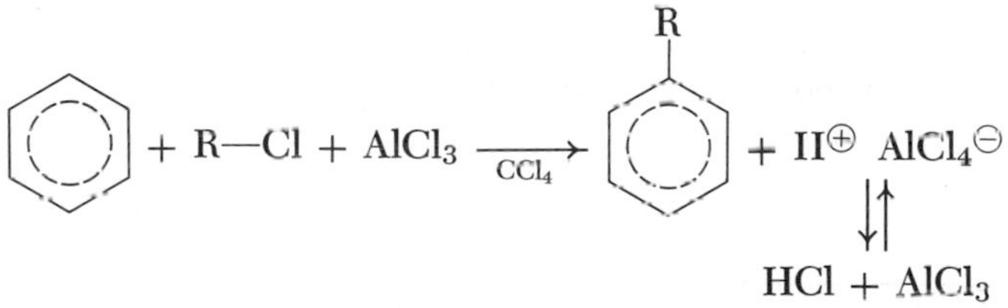

Reactions of this type must normally be conducted in solvents that are nonpolar in order to facilitate solubility of the reagents. Full or partial ionization of the alkyl halide in such media is made possible by the strong Lewis acid, aluminum chloride. As a result, the relatively weak nucleophile, benzene, can attack the electron-deficient alkyl group, leading to the formation of an alkyl benzene.

It is reasonable to inquire concerning the role of solvation in concerted displacement reactions. The answer depends upon the nature of the reactants.

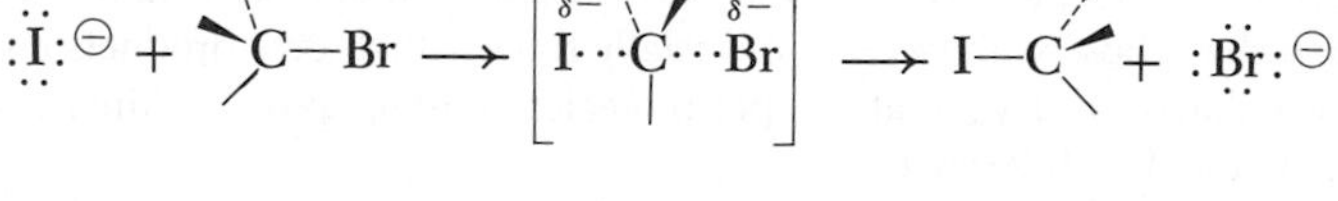

The transition state for a concerted displacement, implies some dispersal of negative charge in S_N2 compared with S_N1 reactions. This dispersal of charge should result in a lower solvation effect for S_N2 reactions. In short, the rate of an S_N2 reaction should not be highly dependent upon the polarity of the solvent.

SUMMARY

In our discussion of the predicted characteristics of the two limiting mechanisms, S_N1 and S_N2, we have made numerous implicit applications to real systems. It is important to emphasize that it is what we observe that is of major concern and that the models or constructs we devise to explain or understand these observations are just that—models and constructs. Their validity lies in their usefulness in correlation and prediction. It is true that the synchronous and ionic mechanisms suggested for nucleophilic substitution do enable the correlation of a vast body of important reactions of carbon compounds and permit fairly accurate prediction of untried experiments. It would be overly optimistic to expect that all reactions classifiable as nucleophilic displacement reactions fit snugly into either the S_N1 or S_N2 mechanistic category. Indeed, there are numerous specific examples that fall into the fuzzy gray area between these two limiting mechanisms. This is to be expected, since the feature that distinguishes the two reaction paths is simply one of timing.

The noblest lesson [Darwin] left to the world is this,—which to him amounted to a profound, almost religious conviction,— that every fact in nature, no matter how insignificant, every stripe of color, every tint of flowers, the length of an orchid's nectary, unusual height in a plant, all the infinite variety of apparently insignificant things, is full of significance. For him it was a historical record, the revelation of a cause, the lurking place of a principle.—F. Cramer, The Method of Darwin. A Study in Scientific Method, *A. C. McClurg and Co., Chicago, 1896.*

PROBLEMS

24.1. Estimate values of ΔS^0 and ΔG^0 for a few of the reactions in Table 24.1, both per mole and per gram. Comment on any trends. $[\Delta S^0_m = 22m + 21 - S^0(C_mH_{2m+2}) \cong 10(m - 1).]$

24.2. Reactions of alkanes with chlorine are generally more rapid and more easily controlled than those with oxygen, especially those which give products containing only a few chlorine or oxygen atoms per molecule. Discuss possible kinetic and energetic reasons for this difference.

24.3. How many tons of chlorine and of C_5H_{12} must be used to produce 10 tons of monochlorinated product? (About 6 tons Cl_2.)

24.4. Predict the reactivity of 1-chlorobicyclo[2.2.1]heptane to nucleophilic displacement by either a concerted or an ionization process.

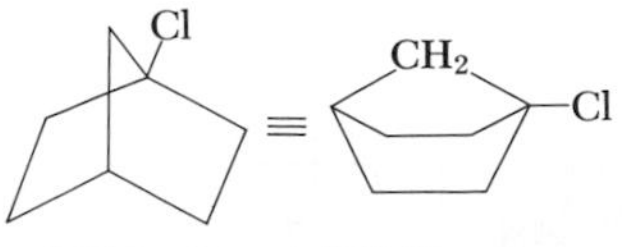

1-Chlorobicyclo[2.2.1]heptane

24.5. Treatment of many alcohols with an *excess* of a hydrogen halide results in the formation of an alkyl halide

$$CH_3{-}CH_2{-}CH_2{-}CH_2{-}OH + HBr \longrightarrow CH_3{-}CH_2{-}CH_2{-}CH_2{-}Br + H_2O$$

n-butyl alcohol

In terms of the principle of microscopic reversibility, write a sequence of steps for this reaction. What would be the expected rate law?

24.6. Carbon skeleton rearrangement frequently accompanies nucleophilic displacement reactions of primary alkyl halides proceeding by an ionization mechanism. The example shown is typical.

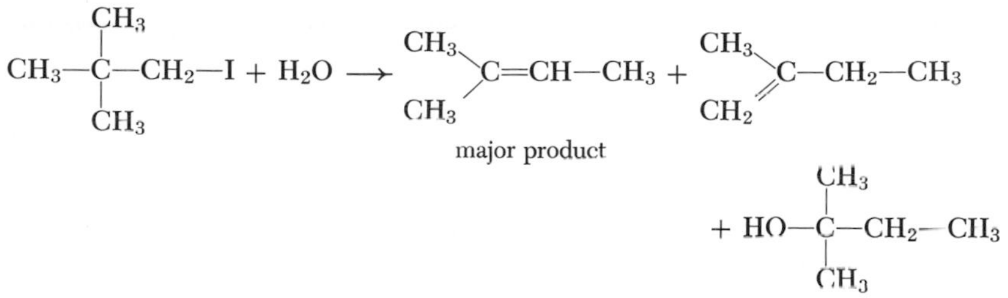

Can you give a structural explanation of these results?

24.7. Estimate the heat of combustion of n-C_9H_{20}. List the uncertainty in your estimate. ($\Delta H^0 \cong 1500$ kcal mole^{-1}.)

24.8. Why bother to put a heat exchanger in the plant represented in Figure 24.2?

24.9. Account for the two different rate laws on page 627 in terms of possible mechanisms.

II

24.10. Calculate ΔH^0 for each of the propagation steps of the sequence

$$Cl_2 \xrightarrow{h\nu} 2Cl\cdot$$
$$CH_4 + Cl \longrightarrow CH_3Cl + H\cdot$$
$$Cl_2 + H\cdot \longrightarrow HCl + Cl\cdot$$

Discuss the feasibility of this mechanism with respect to other possible mechanisms.

24.11. Name and draw condensed structural formulas of the products obtained upon monochlorination of 2,2-dimethylbutane at 300°C. Estimate the percentage yield of each product. (4-chloro 2,2-dimethyl butane $\cong$ 20%.)

24.12. A separation procedure applicable to the isolation of 1-chloro-2,2-dimethylbutane from the mixture (Problem 24.11) involves reaction of the mixture of chloroalkanes with sodium ethoxide [$(CH_3CH_2O^-)(Na^+)$] in ethanol solvent at about 80°C, followed by distillation of the resulting reaction products. Can you explain why this procedure might be effective?

See page 1093 for a list of references and readings in the recent chemical literature related to the material in this chapter.

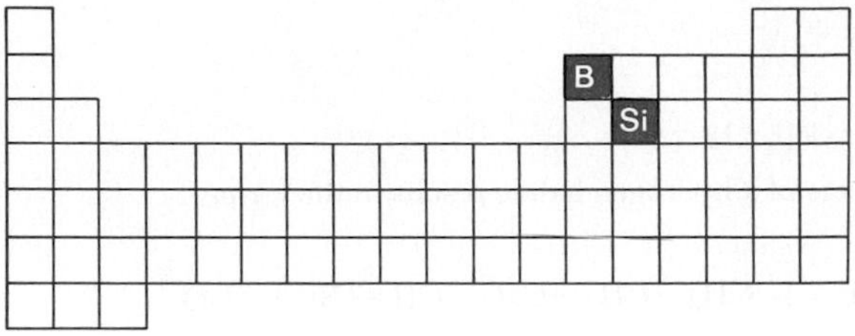

CHAPTER 25

Silicon and Boron

KENNETH M. HARMON

In the periodic table boron lies above aluminum, between beryllium and carbon, and is diagonally related to silicon. It has a very cosmopolitan set of properties; under various chemical conditions boron can show behavior like any one of its neighbors, or sometimes like several of them at once.

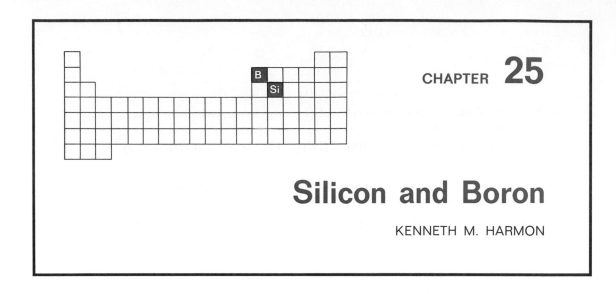

Because of their diagonal proximity in the periodic table, silicon and boron might be expected to be chemically very similar. They do have much in common: the pure elements are rather similar, both appear in nature as oxides, and both form unstable hydrides and volatile, moisture-sensitive halides. Nevertheless, the differences between them are often great, and their relationship is casual; one might say that although they hold hands from time to time, they by no means go steady.

ELEMENTARY SILICON

With a few rare exceptions, silicon is found in nature as the oxide, known as *silica* (SiO_2), or as metallic salts of silicon-oxygen anions, known as *silicates.* Between them, these two materials make up over 75% of the weight of the crust of the earth; among the elements, only oxygen occurs in greater abundance than silicon on this planet (see Table 18.2).

Elementary silicon is produced by heating silica with carbon at high temperatures in an electric furnace:

$$SiO_{2(c)} + C_{(c)} = Si_{(c)} + CO_{2(g)}$$

Elementary silicon is a crystalline solid with a melting point of 1410°C and a highly metallic luster, but it is not a metal; the silicon atoms are bonded together in a macromolecular, tetrahedral array identical with the diamond lattice. Silicon is a *semiconductor*—that is, a substance whose electrical conductivity increases exponentially with temperature (see p. 389). The conductivity of silicon is also extremely sensitive to the presence of trace impurities, particularly at room temperatures; the natural conductivity of the pure element is vanishingly small.

Many solid-state electronic devices are prepared by *doping* pure silicon with trace amounts of known impurities, and for this process ultrapure silicon is required as the starting material. It is prepared by the reduction of silicon tetrachloride with hydrogen at elevated temperatures:

$$SiCl_{4(g)} + 2H_{2(g)} = Si_{(c)} + 4HCl_{(g)}$$

The $SiCl_4$ itself is first rendered ultrapure by preparative gas chromatography (see Chapter 36). The final purification to give less than 10^{-9} atom percentage of impurities is accomplished by zone melting (see Chapter 35).

Addition of small amounts of a Group V element such as As leads to substitution of silicon atoms by arsenic in the silicon crystal lattice. However, As has five valence electrons whereas only four are needed to bond the arsenic in the lattice. Thus there is an electron left over, which sits in a lattice interstice ready to conduct electricity. The lattice is said to be *n*-doped, for negative. Similarly, adding gallium leads to *p*-doping (positive), since Ga has only three valence electrons, thus attracting an electron from somewhere else in the lattice and leaving a positive "hole" in some orbital which can conduct electricity by moving from one bonding site to another throughout the crystal.

Exercise 25.1

What kind of a semiconductor—*p* or *n*—would each of the following give: Sb in Ge, In in Si, Se in Ge? *Answer:* If the doping element has more valence electrons than the host lattices, *n*-type will be produced. Conversely, *p*-types are produced when the doping element has fewer valence electrons than the host lattice. Apply to the given systems.

CHEMISTRY OF SILICON

Silicon lies directly beneath carbon in the periodic table, and one might expect that the two elements would form the same type of compounds. This is not realized; simple silicon compounds bear some structural but little chemical similarity to carbon compounds, and there are no known silicon analogues for the vast majority of complex organic compounds. Three factors are mainly responsible for these differences. (1) The silicon atom, with a covalent radius of 1.17, is larger than carbon, which has a covalent radius of 0.77. (2) The nuclear charge of silicon is shielded by an additional shell of electrons, which reduces the electronegativity to 1.8, compared to 2.5 for carbon. (3) The electronic structure of silicon is (Ne, $3s^2$, $3p^2$, $3d^0$); thus, unlike carbon, silicon has more than four possible bonding orbitals in its outer shell. The nature of the effects of these three factors on the chemistry of silicon will be considered in the discussion of some representative compounds.

The normal covalency of silicon is four. Unlike the higher members of

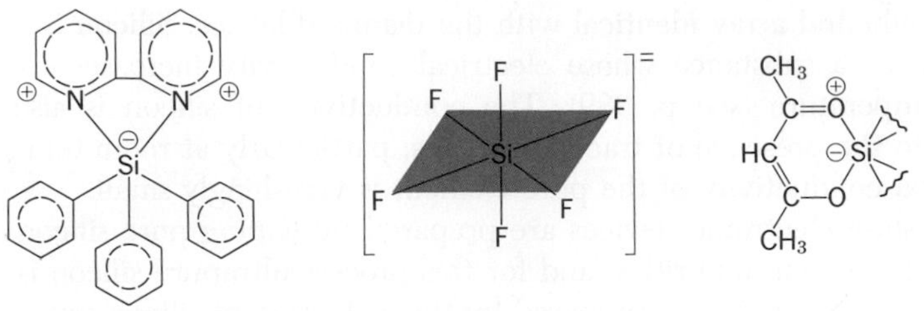

Figure 25.1 Silicon compounds of high coordination number.

the fourth period—germanium, tin, and lead—silicon does not readily form a series of divalent compounds. In general, higher coordination, as in Figure 25.1, is found only in combinations with the most electronegative elements; the $SiCl_6^=$ anion, for example, is unknown.

Exercise 25.2

Describe the probable atomic orbital hybridization in $SiF_6^=$. What geometry should this give? *Answer:* Six orbitals of silicon would be $3s$, $3p^3$, $3d^2$, or sp^3d^2 hybridization, which is octahedral (Table 15.2). Gillespie theory also predicts octahedral coordination.

SILICON HYDRIDES

Unlike carbon, which forms a literally unlimited number of binary compounds with hydrogen, silicon forms only a few hydrides, and these are of very limited stability. Indeed, they are all pyrophoric—that is, they ignite spontaneously in air—and thus can exist only in a controlled atmosphere.

The known silicon hydrides, or *silanes,* are produced by the action of mineral acid on the substance magnesium silicide (approximately Mg_2Si), which is formed by the reduction of silica with magnesium metal. (A similar reaction—the production of traces of silane by reaction of ferric silicide—produces the musty odor often noted when acids are poured down cast iron drains.) A mixture is obtained, containing about 40% silane (SiH_4), 30% disilane (Si_2H_6), 15% trisilane (Si_3H_8), and 10% tetrasilane (Si_4H_{10}). The remaining 5% consists of higher hydrides and is mostly penta- and hexasilanes. The structures of the silanes are similar to the hydrocarbons with the analogous formulas; thus disilane is $H_3Si—SiH_3$ and trisilane is $H_3Si—SiH_2—SiH_3$. With the perfection of the methods of gas chromatography it has been possible to separate the higher silanes according to their skeleton isomers. The physical properties of some silanes are contrasted with those of the analogous hydrocarbons in Table 25.1.

SILICON HALIDES

Silicon reacts exothermically with halogens to form the halides, as

$$Si_{(c)} + 2Cl_{2(g)} = SiCl_{4(l)}$$

Table 25.1 Some properties of silanes and alkanes.

Compound	Formula	Melting point (°C)	Boiling point (°C)	Density (g/cm³)
Methane	CH_4	−182.7	−161.3	0.415 (−164°)
Silane	SiH_4	−185	−111.9	0.68 (−185°)
Ethane	C_2H_6	−172	−88.7	0.546 (−88°)
Disilane	Si_2H_6	−132.5	−14.5	0.686 (−25°)
Propane	C_3H_8	−189.9	−44	0.585 (−44°)
Trisilane	Si_3H_8	−117.4	52.9	0.743 (0°)
n-Butane	C_4H_{10}	−135	−0.5	0.602 (−0.8°)
n-Tetrasilane	Si_4H_{10}	−84.3	107.4	0.825 (0°)

These reactions afford a convenient route to the chloride, bromide, and iodide, but the reaction with fluorine is too violent to be useful. Tetrafluorosilane is prepared by the reaction of silica with hydrofluoric acid:

$$SiO_{2(c)} + 4HF_{(aq)} = SiF_{4(g)} + 2H_2O_{(l)}$$

Hydrofluoric acid is used commercially to etch markings on glass. It must therefore always be handled in polyethylene or copper vessels in the laboratory, as it will attack conventional glass laboratory apparatus. All silicon halides, except the fluoride, hydrolize rapidly in water, as in Figure 25.2.

Exercise 25.3

Suggest a mechanism for the observed hydrolysis of carbon tetrachloride in bright sunlight, whereas it is stable toward hydrolysis under usual laboratory conditions. *Answer:* The UV light probably provides the necessary activation energy (CCl_4 does not absorb in the visible), perhaps to give $CCl_4 + h\nu = \cdot CCl_3 + \cdot Cl$; $\cdot CCl_3 + H_2O$ = products, such as $COCl_2 + HCl + H\cdot$; $M + H\cdot + Cl\cdot = HCl + M^*$. Possible net reaction: $CCl_4 + H_2O = COCl_2 + 2HCl$.

SILICON OXIDES

The bulk of the silicon used by man is used in the form of oxides. Cement, bricks, mortar, granite, sand, gravel, glass, clay, and porcelain are only a few examples of important materials composed largely of silicon oxides. Silicon materials, indeed, are the chemicals which, by tonnage, are most used by man.

Oxides of silicon can be divided into two main types: (1) the neutral oxide called *silica,* and (2) the salts of oxyanions of silicon known as *silicates.*

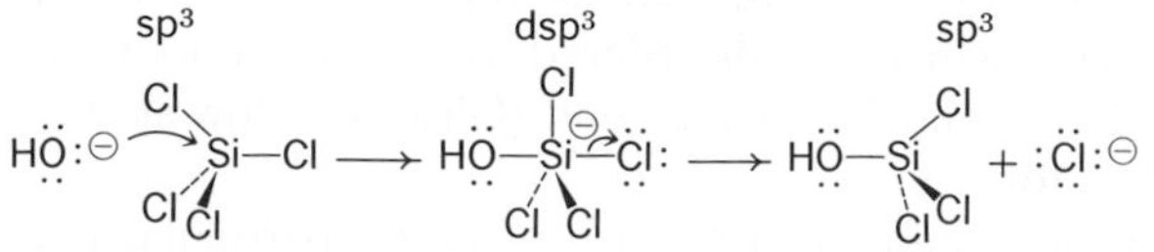

Figure 25.2 First step in hydrolysis of a silicon halide.

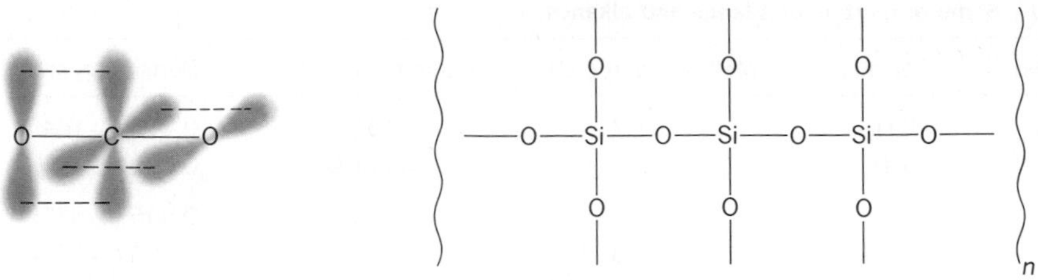

Molecular CO_2 Cross-linked spiral chains in $(SiO_2)_n$

Figure 25.3 Structures of CO_2 and SiO_2.

SILICA

The normal oxide of silicon is SiO_2; a divalent oxide, SiO, corresponding to carbon monoxide, CO, is not known except in the gas phase at high temperature. Silicon dioxide, or silica, bears little resemblance to carbon dioxide. Carbon dioxide is an acid gas that sublimes from the solid (at 1 atm pressure) at $-78°C$; silica is a remarkably hard, chemically resistant, crystalline substance that does not melt until 1710°C. It is hard to find a more marked difference between two substances having similar formulas and prepared from atoms so close to each other in the periodic table.

The difference between the two oxides arises from the fact that silicon fails to form double bonds of the sigma-pi type (see p. 336) with second-row elements—apparently because the silicon atom is too large to allow significant overlap of $2p$ and $3p$ orbitals. Carbon dioxide is a monomolecular species with two oxygens double-bonded to a single carbon. Silicon dioxide, which must contain only single bonds, is a macromolecular species, with each silicon attached to four oxygens and each oxygen attached to two silicons (Figure 25.3).

Silica occurs naturally in the form of *quartz,* which is a major constituent of granite and is found in many other rocks in combination with other minerals. Most sand is composed of tiny grains of quartz that have been formed as rocks are broken down by erosion or freezing. Well-formed crystals of silica are often found in nature; some of these, probably deposited from very hot aqueous solutions, attain a large size and are as clear as the finest man-made crystal.

By far the largest use for purified silica is in the form of glass. When silica is melted it forms a very viscous, tacky material, and only at extreme temperatures does it exhibit the free-flowing properties of a liquid. The process of melting results in a significant loss of ordering within the crystalline material but does not supply enough energy to break all (or even many) of the silicon-oxygen bonds. Thus the melt is still a highly polymerized material (remember sulfur). As this melt cools, it becomes more and more viscous, and if the rate of cooling is fairly rapid the residual chains and fragments of the original crystalline lattice will not have time to move about within their sluggish environment to reform the crystal. Instead, the mass hardens into a glass, which is a disordered, really liquid, material that has become too viscous to flow under its own weight. (Glass will flow slowly, however, under sufficient applied force.)

Pure silica glass is used for a number of special purposes, particularly in optical parts of scientific instruments in which transmission of ultraviolet light or extreme resistance to heat shock are important. For most purposes, however, pure silica glass is too expensive and too difficult to work with—it begins to soften only at about 1400°C. The two main types of commercial glass are *lime glass* (or *soft glass*) and *borosilicate glass,* of which *Pyrex* and *Kimax* are two well-known examples.

Soft glass is produced in much the largest quantity, and is one of the cheapest and most useful substances available; it has been prepared in various modifications since long before the birth of Christ. It is made by melting together a mixture of sand (silica), limestone (calcium carbonate), and soda ash (sodium carbonate). Carbon dioxide is expelled by heating, and the resulting melt—a solution of silicon, calcium, and sodium oxides in each other in a weight ratio of about 73–10–17—has a much lower softening point (about 600°C) than pure silica, and thus can be handled much more easily. Soft glass is quite susceptible to attack by basic reagents and is sensitive to thermal shock.

Borosilicate glass, however, prepared from a melt of silicon, boron, aluminum, sodium, and potassium oxides (in a weight ratio of about 80–13–2–4–0.4), is much more resistant to chemicals and can be heated or cooled much more rapidly, without cracking, than soft glass: it begins to soften at about 800°C. It is widely used for laboratory and scientific apparatus and for such household and industrial goods as baking ware and chemically resistant plumbing fixtures.

Exercise 25.4

Suggest an interpretation at the atomic level for the greater resistance of borosilicate glass to thermal shock compared to soft glass. *Answer:* The greatest change in composition is substitution of B and Al, oxidation state +3, for Ca^{++} and Na^{+}. It seems reasonable that the +3 B and Al would form stronger, less "stretchable," more covalent bonds, thus reducing the coefficient of thermal expansion and increasing resistance to thermal shock.

SILICATES

The silicates are a highly diverse group of materials comprising the bulk of the soils, clays, rocks, minerals, and gemstones found in the crust of the earth. They are formed from variously sized and arranged bits of the silica lattice, and they have a higher ratio of oxygen to silicon than does silica. This excess of oxygen introduces negative charge into the material, and metal ions must be present within the structure of a silicate to maintain electrical neutrality. The study of silicates is really a branch of science in its own right; we will, in this brief introduction, only try to outline the major types of silicate salts known, to indicate the structures of the oxyanions present, and to give an example or so of each type.

The various types of silicon oxyanions are shown in Figure 25.4. In every type each silicon atom is surrounded by a tetrahedral arrangement of four oxygen atoms. The larger condensed anions are formed by two or more silicons, sharing oxygens. Since any two specific silicon atoms never share more than one atom of oxygen, we can think of the tetrahedral units about silicon atoms as being joined by sharing a *tetrahedral apex* but never a tetrahedral edge or face. (This lack of

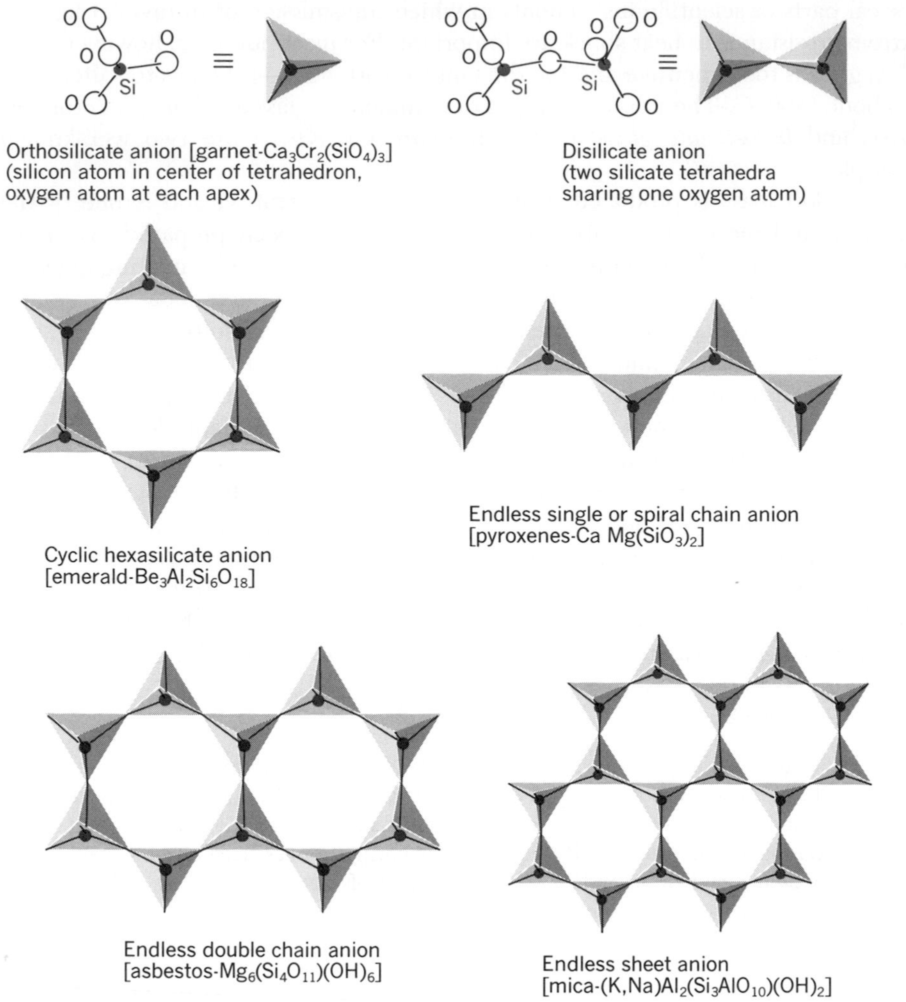

Figure 25.4 Silicate anion structures, and examples. The positive ions sit in the interstices of the silicate tetrahedra.

edge- or face-sharing is presumably due to the mutual repulsion of the +4 silicons.) All of the silicates consist basically of a lattice array of oxygen atoms, within which there are void spaces into which small metal atoms may fit to balance the negative charge.

The simplest type of anion is found in the *orthosilicates:* a single silicon atom is surrounded by four oxygens. This anion is found in zircon, $ZrSiO_4$, and in the garnets, $M_3{}^aM_2{}^b(SiO_4)_3$, where M^a can be Ca^{++}, Mg^{++}, Mn^{++}, or Fe^{++}, and M^b is Al^{+++}, Cr^{+++}, or Fe^{+++}. The garnets are very hard and find extensive use as industrial abrasives.

The *disilicate ion,* $Si_2O_7{}^{-6}$, is formed by a single shared oxygen between two silicon atoms. It is found in scandium silicate or thortveitite, $Sc_2Si_2O_7$, but is generally rare. A more common type of small anion is formed by condensation of three or six tetrahedra to form the cyclic *trisilicate* or cyclic *hexasilicate* anions.

The cyclic hexasilicate anion is found in $Be_3Al_2Si_6O_{18}$, one form of which is the jewel emerald.

The other common forms of silicate anions are highly condensed species such as endless single chains, endless double chains, endless sheets, or endless three-dimensional networks. Silicates with the chain anions tend to be fibrous; a familiar example is asbestos, a double chain silicate with the formula $Mg_6(Si_4O_{11})(OH)_6$. The silicates with anions of the sheet type tend to cleave easily in one plane, as the forces binding sheet to sheet are much less than the forces within a single sheet; the best-known example is mica, $(Na,K)Al_2(Si_3AlO_{10})(OH)_2$. Finally, there are silicates in which the structure is an endless three-dimensional network; this arrangement leads to very hard minerals such as ultramarine, $Na_8(Si_6Al_6O_{24})(S_2)$.

Exercise 25.5

Mica cleaves more easily under water than in air. Why? *Answer:* Mica consists of very extended, two-dimensional, negatively charged silicate sheets bound to one another by intermediate positive ions. Water, as it does with all ions, aquates the separating sheets, reducing the coulombic forces and easing the separation. The molecules in air are much less effective at reducing interionic forces.

GEOCHEMISTRY OF SILICATES

Not only do silicates show a regular progression of structures from discrete ions, SiO_4^{-4}, through linear combinations and planes, to the three dimensional structure of SiO_2 as the Si-O ratio varies from $\frac{1}{4}$ to $\frac{1}{2}$; silicates also exhibit an enormous variety of compositions due to ionic substitution reactions. Thus Al^{+++} is about the same size and is isoelectronic with Si^{+4}. Substitution of Al^{+++} for Si^{+4} is common, but this reduces the positive charge of the crystal one unit for each such substitution. This may be counterbalanced by simultaneous substitution of Cl^- for $O^=$ (similar size and isoelectronic in valence electrons), or by addition of an M^+ ion (such as Na^+, K^+) in an octahedral hole in the silicate structure. Similarly, substitution of two Si^{+4} by two Al^{+3} can be counterbalanced by addition of one Mg^{++} ion in an octahedral (or tetrahedral) hole in the silicate lattice. Clearly an infinite variety of substitutional compositions is possible, accounting for the wide range of silicates found in nature. The actual number is limited by the fact that some substitutional lattices are more stable than others (ΔG minimizes) so that many silicates have relatively constant composition.

Depending on the ratio of alkali metal ions to silicon atoms, the acid-base properties of the silicates vary greatly. Pure SiO_2 is acidic with respect to water. For example,

$$SiO_{2(c)} + 2H_2O_{(l)} = H^+{}_{(aq)} + H_3SiO_4^-{}_{(aq)}$$

Pure Na_2SiO_3 is basic, as in

$$Na_2SiO_{3(c)} + 2H_2O_{(l)} = 2Na^+{}_{(aq)} + H_3SiO_4^-{}_{(aq)} + OH^-{}_{(aq)}$$

The variation in acidity resulting from these variable compositions has great effect on the geochemical reactions inside the earth and on the weathering reactions at its surface. In fact, much of silicate chemistry is readily interpreted in terms of acid-base theory and simple structural theory. The plus four state is so stable with respect either to oxidation or reduction that redox reactions involving silicon are almost unknown in natural silicates. The silicates are rather good solvents for many minerals, solvents in which acid-base reactions or redox of other elements occur.

SILICONES

A third class of silicon-oxygen compounds of considerable industrial importance is the *silicones*. When an alkyl halide—for example, chloromethane—reacts with a heated alloy of silicon and copper, alkyl halosilanes are formed:

$$2CH_3Cl_{(g)} + Si(Cu)_{(c)} = (CH_3)_2SiCl_{2(l)} + Cu_{(c)}$$

The copper is a catalyst, and alkyl copper compounds have been shown to be intermediates in the reaction:

$$CH_3Cl + Cu = CH_3CuCl$$

$$2CH_3CuCl + Si = (CH_3)_2SiCl_2 + 2Cu$$

When the alkyl chlorosilanes react with water, a dihydroxy compound known as a *silanol* is formed; for example, dimethyldichlorosilane gives dimethylsilanol:

$$(CH_3)_2SiCl_{2(l)} + 2H_2O_{(l)} = (CH_3)_2Si(OH)_{2(aq)} + 2HCl_{(aq)}$$

These silanols lose water rapidly to yield compounds that were named *silicones*, since it was at first thought that they contained a silicon-oxygen double bond and thus resembled *ketones*. Actually they contain macromolecular species in which a repeating series of silicon-oxygen bonds forms the backbone of a polymer (Figure 25.5). Modifications of these chains, and control of the degree of polymer formation leads to a wide variety of commercial silicon products.

OCCURRENCE OF BORON

Boron, like silicon, is found almost exclusively as the oxide or salts of the oxide in nature. Unlike silicon, it is a relatively rare element and constitutes only a small portion of the earth's crust. Major deposits of boron oxides are found in India and California. Large deposits of the boron containing minerals *kernite* and *borax* are found in the deserts of southern California, particularly in the Mojave desert and in Death Valley. Commercial recovery from these beds is a large industry today and provides the raw material for a wide diversity of boron chemicals.

Elementary boron can be produced cheaply by heating boric oxide with powdered magnesium:

$$B_2O_{3(c)} + 3Mg_{(c)} = 2B_{(c)} + 3MgO_{(c)}$$

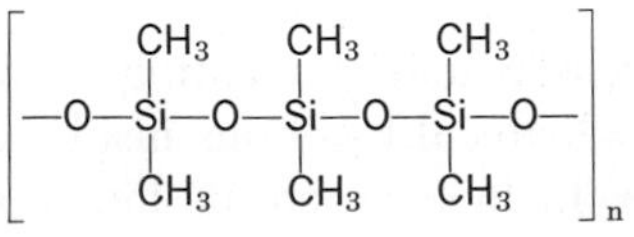

Figure 25.5 A silicone polymer chain.

The material is not crystalline and cannot be rendered pure. However, boron of greater than 99.5% purity is prepared by reducing a boron trihalide with hydrogen on a hot tantalum filament at high temperature:

$$2BBr_{3(g)} + 3H_{2(g)} = 2B_{(c)} + 6HBr_{(g)}$$

Boron obtained in this manner is a gray, brittle solid with a melting point of about 2300°C. Broken surfaces of the material appear black, and thin flakes of the crystal transmit some light. Boron, like silicon, is a semiconductor.

Exercise 25.6

Suggest a method of synthesizing pure BBr_3 to be used in the preparation of pure $B_{(c)}$. *Answer:* An apparent way would be to take impure boron (from Mg reduction of B_2O_3) and pass Br_2 over it, producing BBr_3, which would be purified by distillation. A better actual method is to pass BF_3 through Al_2Br_6, producing nonvolatile AlF_3 and gaseous BBr_3, which may be further purified by distillation. BF_3 may be prepared by heating together B_2O_3, H_2SO_4, and NaF.

CHEMISTRY OF BORON

In the periodic table boron lies above aluminum, between beryllium and carbon, and, as we noted before, is diagonally related to silicon. It has a very cosmopolitan set of properties; under various chemical conditions boron can behave like any one of its neighbors, or sometimes like several of them at once. However, boron has certain properties—in particular the formation of electron-deficient cage compounds—which it exhibits to a greater extent than any other element. It is possible that the next fifty to one hundred years will see the chemistry of boron develop a complexity rivaling that of carbon chemistry today.

Boron, like carbon, has four orbitals available to it for bonding. The ionization energies of the atom are high (the first is 191 kcal mole^{-1} and the next two are higher yet), and monatomic boron ions are unknown in condensed phases. The normal oxidation state of boron is +3, with the boron forming three sp^2 hybrid covalent bonds to give planar molecules; however, boron may have a coordination number of four in certain sp^3 hybridized anions and complexes, and even of five or six in the electron-deficient cage compounds to be discussed later.

In discussing the chemical and structural properties of boron compounds it is convenient to divide them into two major divisions: (1) compounds in which boron is bonded only to other elements, and (2) compounds containing boron-boron bonds.

DIBORANE

The compound *borane*, BH_3, can exist only transiently or as a complex with a Lewis base, for example H_3BNH_3. Molecules of borane apparently dimerize spontaneously when they come in contact with each other to form *diborane*, B_2H_6. Diborane is a colorless gas with a foul odor, and is extremely toxic. It has both a positive

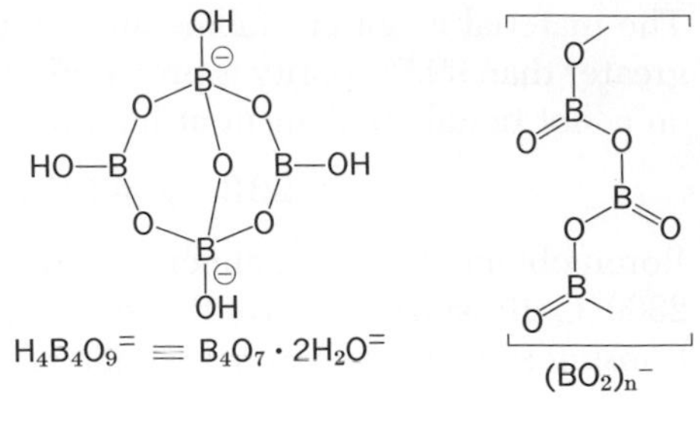

Figure 25.6 Two oxyanions of boron.

enthalpy and a positive free energy of formation; hence it cannot be synthesized directly from the elements. The reaction

$$B_2H_{6(g)} + 3O_{2(g)} = 2B_2O_{3(c)} + 3H_2O_{(g)}$$

takes place violently and spontaneously on exposure of diborane to air.

Diborane will react with Lewis bases such as amines (p. 431) to give *amineborane* complexes:

$$2R_3N\!:_{(g)} + B_2H_{6(g)} = 2R_3\overset{\oplus}{N}\text{—}\overset{\ominus}{B}H_{3(l)}$$

These can serve as convenient sources of diborane in chemical reactions, since they can be stored or shipped in safety.

Exercise 25.7

Suggest a method of regenerating B_2H_6 from R_3NBH_3. *Answer:* Add a stronger acid than BH_3, say HCl, to give $R_3NH^+Cl^-_{(c)}$ plus free $B_2H_{6(g)}$.

BORON OXIDES

The main natural sources of boron are the minerals borax, $Na_2B_4O_7(H_2O)_{10}$, and kernite, $Na_2B_4O_7(H_2O)_4$. These contain hydrated forms of the $B_4O_5(OH)_4^{=}$ anion (Figure 25.6). Some borate salts contain polymeric anions; for instance, calcium metaborate, CaB_2O_4, contains an infinite chain as shown in Figure 25.6. Boron oxide itself, B_2O_3, can exist in a crystalline, three-dimensional lattice in which each boron is surrounded by four oxygens. When the material is melted, it cools to form a glass in which there are infinite, random sheets in which each boron is surrounded by three oxygens. Since this bonding leaves the central 2*p* orbital of the boron at least partially empty (there is some resonance overlap with the unshared electrons on the oxygens), boron oxide is slightly acidic; the melt readily dissolves basic oxides, a fact of importance in glassmaking (see p. 642).

Boron oxide dissolves in water to form boric acid:

$$B_2O_{3(c)} + 3H_2O_{(l)} = 2B(OH)_{3(aq)}$$

Boric acid is a very weak acid and acts like a Lewis acid rather than a Brönsted

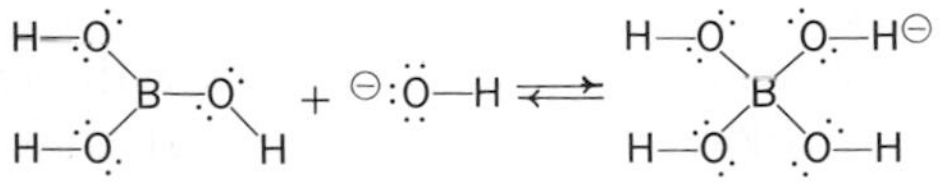

Figure 25.7 Reaction of boric acid with base.

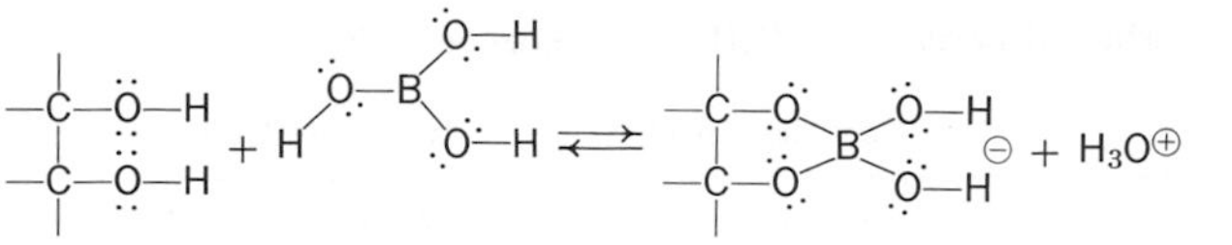

Figure 25.8 Reaction of boric acid and a 1.2-diol.

acid. In basic solution it does not act as a proton donor, as does nitric acid, for example; instead, a hydroxide ion adds to the empty $2p$ orbital of the boron atom to form a $B(OH)_4^-$ complex ion (Figure 25.7). Boric acid does not give a good end point on titration with base. It can be titrated, however, in the presence of certain 1,2-diols (difunctional alcohols in which the two hydroxyl groups are on adjacent carbons), which react with boric acid to give the hydronium salt of a complex borate anion (Figure 25.8). The hydronium ion titrates as a strong acid.

BORON-NITROGEN COMPOUNDS

We can touch only briefly on the wide field of boron-nitrogen chemistry. One interesting example is *borazine*, $B_3N_3H_6$, which is prepared by heating ammonium chloride with boron chloride, followed by a sodium borohydride reduction step:

$$3NH_4^+Cl^-_{(c)} + 3BCl_{3(g)} = B_3N_3Cl_3H_{3(c)} + 9HCl_{(g)}$$

$$4B_3N_3Cl_3H_{3(ether)} + 12BH^-_{4(ether)} = 4B_3N_3H_{6(ether)} + 12Cl^-_{(c)} + 6B_2H_6$$

Borazine (sometimes called *borazole*) is a cyclic compound of the structure shown in Figure 25.9. In appearance it resembles benzene, with which it is isoelectronic, with the atoms lying at the vertices of a regular hexagon. Like benzene, it is an aromatic molecule and derives considerable stability from electron delocalization. The boron-nitrogen bond length is 1.44 Å, which is intermediate in length between a boron-nitrogen single bond (1.54 Å) and double bond (1.36 Å). In the delocalized resonance forms, however, there is a separation of charge, which involves coulombic work; thus the form with the lone electron pairs localized on nitrogen makes a significant contribution to the resonance hybrid of borazine. The similarity of benzene and borazine is reflected in some of the physical properties, as shown in Table 25.2. The chemical difference between these two molecules is considerable, however; borazine is much more reactive than benzene with a wide range of chemical reagents, and decomposes slowly in contact with water or the atmosphere.

Thermal decomposition of any compound with a 1:1 ratio of boron to nitrogen—for example, $F_3B—NH_2$—yields *boron nitride,* a material with the formula $(BN)_n$. Boron nitride is related to borazine in the same way that graphite (p. 386) is related to benzene; it consists of infinite sheets of units like those in borazine (Figure 25.10), and these sheets are stacked together to form the crystal.

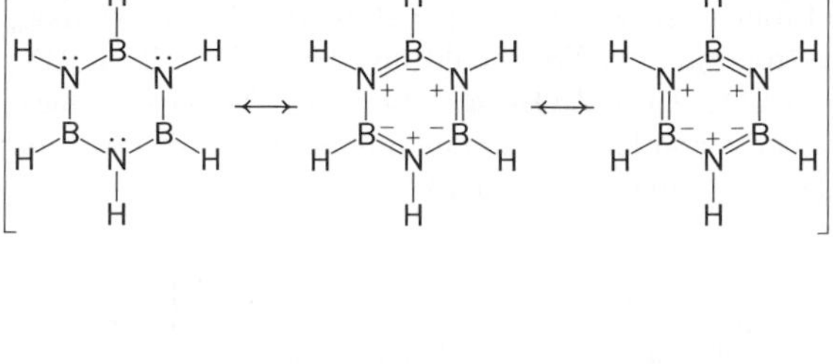

Figure 25.9 Structure of and resonance in borazine.

Table 25.2 Some properties of borazine, $B_3N_3H_6$, and benzene, C_6H_6.

Property	Borazine, $B_3N_3H_6$	Benzene, C_6H_6
Molecular weight	80.50	78.11
Melting point	−58°C	5.5°C
Boiling point	63°C	80°C
Density	0.8614 (5.0°)	0.8787 (15°)
Bond angle in ring	120°	120°
Ring single bond (theory)	1.56 Å	1.54 Å
Ring double bond (theory)	1.36 Å	1.33 Å
Ring bonds observed (all alike)	1.44 Å	1.40 Å

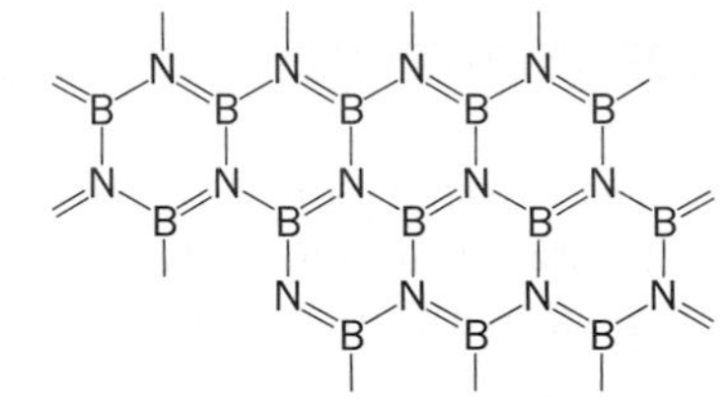

Figure 25.10 Structure of boron nitride.

In graphite the sheets are staggered, so that the center of the rings in one layer are over a bond in the next layer, but in boron nitride the centers of the rings are directly over each other in each layer; however, the arrangement of borons and nitrogens are reversed in alternate layers, so that each of the nitrogens in the second layer is over a boron in the first layer and each boron in the second layer is over a nitrogen in the first layer. Thus the interaction of the electrical charges on the atoms due to bond polarity is maximized; this coulombic force holds the layers of boron nitride together much more tightly than those of graphite. Boron nitride is a very hard, crystalline material that melts at over 3000°C. It is almost completely inert chemically even at extreme temperatures, but under very high temperature and pressure, it changes to another allotropic form called *borazon,* which has a structure like that of diamond (p. 385). In borazon each boron is bonded to four nitrogens, and each nitrogen to four borons. The borons each carry a full (−) charge and the nitrogens a full (+) charge. Borazon is the hardest material known; it can scratch diamond, and it is stable at a much higher temperature than diamond.

Exercise 25.8

Silicon carbide is also a hard substance with a crystal structure like that of borazon or diamond. Suggest some other formulas which should have similar hardness. *Answer:* Criteria are: average of four valence electrons per atom, tetrahedral bonding, and small differences in electronegativity. We should investigate TiC, TiSi, AlN, SiGe. Actually many oxides—Al_2O_3, TiO_2, ZrO_2—are also hard. These oxides have $CN = 6$ or 8, pack very efficiently, and have maximum interatomic attractions and minimum interionic repulsions. See Tables 18.7 and 16.4.

BORON HYDRIDES

The carbon hydrides, or hydrocarbons, abound in nature, and the early rise of organic chemistry attests to their ready availability. There are no boron hydrides found naturally, and the first ones to be synthesized—for instance, diborane—were so unstable and reactive that it was felt the field of boron hydride chemistry would be extremely limited. Today, however, some thirty to fifty boron hydride compounds are known; with isomers and substituted compounds included, the number reaches into the hundreds. What is more, many of these compounds are thermally stable, some more stable than any known organic compound. The field of boron hydride chemistry is off to a fast start and may well in time rival the chemistry of the carbon hydrides.

It is an interesting thing that this host of substances—many perfectly capable of existence anywhere on earth—could never have existed on this planet without human involvement in their creation. The compounds may be stable, but the *intermediates* in their formation are instantly destroyed by oxygen or water vapor. It is possible that on a planet with a reducing atmosphere the dominant chemistry could be that of the boron hydrides.

The formulas of a number of boron hydrides and some of their properties are listed in Table 25.3. In these hydrides the bonds from boron to the external hydrogens are thought to be ordinary two-electron, two-orbital bonds. The bridge hydrogens each combine a hydrogen 1*s* orbital with two boron orbitals (from different borons) to form a bridging three-center bond. The boron-boron bonds are almost always a resonating network of three-center bonds; only tetraborane has a normal boron-boron bond.

A few examples may illustrate the type of bonding believed to exist. In diborane each boron is sp^3-hybridized, with two orbitals in normal bonds and two in hydrogen bridge bonds. In tetraborane, again, each boron is sp^3; the two central borons each contribute an orbital to a normal boron-boron bond, an orbital to a normal boron-hydrogen bond, and two orbitals to hydrogen bridge bonds. The two apex borons each have two normal boron-hydrogen bonds and two hydrogen bridge bonds. In pentaborane-(9) the four basal borons are considered to be sp^2, with one of the three sp^2 bonds in a normal boron-hydrogen bond and two in hydrogen bridge bonds. The remaining 2*p* orbital of each of these four borons points toward the apex boron. The apex boron is considered to be sp^2-hybridized, with one sp^2 orbital directed outward toward the external hydrogen to form a normal boron-hydrogen bond and each of the other two directed toward a boron on oppo-

Table 25.3 Properties of some boron hydrides.

Compound	Formula	Appearance	Melting point (°C)	Boiling point (°C)
Diborane	B_2H_6	Colorless gas	−165.5	−92.5
Tetraborane	B_4H_{10}	Colorless gas	−120.8	16
Pentaborane (9)	B_5H_9	Colorless liquid	−46.8	58.4
Hexaborane	B_6H_{10}	Colorless liquid	−65	decomposes
Decaborane	$B_{10}H_{14}$	White crystals	99.5	213

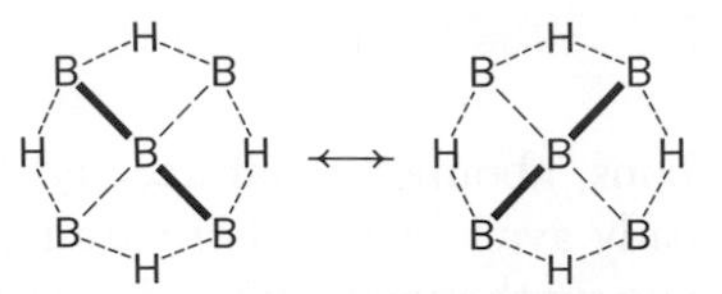

Figure 25.11 Resonance in B_5H_9; apical H's not shown.

site corners of the square base. The remaining $2p$ orbital of the apex boron lies over the other two basal borons. The four orbits of the basal borons and the three orbits of the apex boron combine to form a set of three bonding orbitals—two two-electron, two-orbital bonds and one two-electron, three-orbital bond—which resonate between two major forms (Figure 25.11).

You will quickly realize that valence bond descriptions of this type become unwieldy, if not actually meaningless, as we consider the higher boron hydrides. A person wanting an excellent review of boron bonding and a discussion of the molecular orbital description of these hybrides is referred to *Boron Hydrides* by W. N. Lipscomb (New York, Benjamin, 1963). Some interesting recently discovered borane ions are shown in Figure 25.12.

SUMMARY

The chemistry of silicon and boron shows many analogies consistent with the diagonal relationship of the elements in the periodic table. Silicon is one of the most common elements and its chemistry contributes in a major fashion to a wide variety of geochemical systems. Study of these silicate systems has contributed greatly to our knowledge of structure and structural variables, especially with respect to variations due to changes in composition and to substitutional reactions in solids.

Boron is a rare element. But contemporary chemists show great interest in the boron hydrides and related compounds because of the common occurrence in such systems of bridging hydrogen bonds and other types of multicenter bonds.

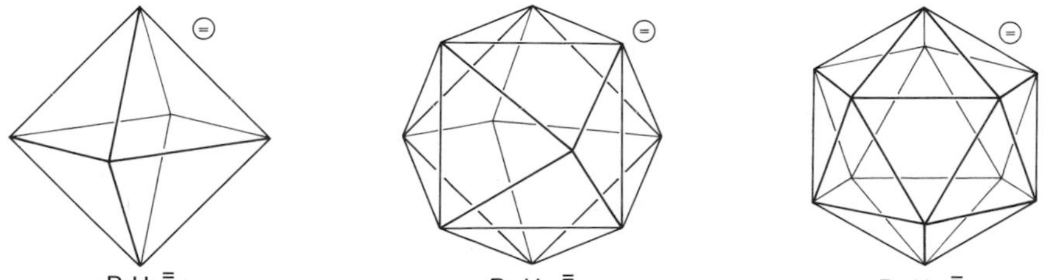

$B_6H_6^=$ $B_{10}H_{10}^=$ $B_{12}H_{12}^=$

Figure 25.12 Borane anions. There is a B—H unit at each vertex.

It is the greatest discovery in method which science has made that the apparently trivial, the merely curious, may be clues to an understanding of the deepest principles of Nature.
—*G. P. Thomson,* The Inspiration of Science, *Oxford University Press, New York, 1961.*

PROBLEMS

25.1. Sketch a zone melting furnace assembly. Why does the liquid section remain between the two crystalline sections rather than dropping out?

25.2. Write equations for the following reactions.
(*a*) Tetrasilane, Si_4H_{10}, burns in air.
(*b*) Trimethylsilyl chloride, $(CH_3)_3SiCl$, reacts with water.
(*c*) Pentaborane is burned in air.
(*d*) Boron bromide reacts with trimethylamine.
(*e*) Borazine, $B_3N_3H_6$, is thermally decomposed.

25.3. Arrange the following four complexes in the order of degree of dissociation (in order of strength of the B—N bond): triethylamine-borane, ammonia-borane, triethylamine-triethylborane, ammonia-triethylborane. Justify your order.

25.4. When two different boron halides are mixed the following scrambling process can occur:

$$BX_3 + BY_3 = BX_3 + BX_2Y + BY_2X + BY_3$$

Assume the scrambling is statistical. What are the product ratios? In the exceptional case of boron iodide and boron fluoride, no trace of scrambled products can be detected in mixtures of the two halides. The explanation is not known, but several possibilities exist. Can you outline several, and support your arguments?

25.5. Rationalize these two facts: (1) ordinary glass can be cut much more easily under water than in air; (2) glass fibers 0.00025 inches in diameter have tensile strengths in air of about 550,000 psi, but this figure increases appreciably in a vacuum.

25.6. The rate of crack propagation through glass in an atmosphere of N_2 has been found to depend strongly on the pressure of water vapor in the ambient gas [S. Wiederhorn, NBS Technical Note 293, pp. 18–19 (1966)]. Would you guess that the rate is increased or decreased by the presence of water vapor? Suggest a possible mechanism for the effect.

25.7. You have worked with glass. What criterion have you as to whether it is a pure substance or a solution?

25.8. Kernite, $Na_2B_4O_7 \cdot 4H_2O$, can be shipped to its destination and there treated with water to form borax, $Na_2B_4O_7 \cdot 10H_2O$. What saving in freight costs results from doing this, instead of converting it to borax before shipping? (About 30%.)

25.9. Suggest a chemical means of distinguishing *cis*-1,2-cyclopentandiol from *trans*-1,2-cyclopentandiol.

25.10. Silicones prepared from dialkylsilandiols are usually liquids; however, if some monoalkylsilantriol is added to the polymerizing mixture, greases or solids are obtained. Can you account for this?

25.11. All of the listed properties of benzene and borazine are similar except the melting point. How can you account for this difference?

II

25.12. Consider the following compounds:

C_4H_4NH

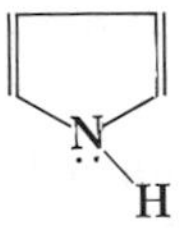

pyrrole

C_4H_4S

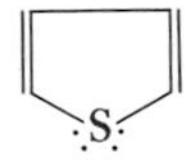

thiophene

C_4H_4Si

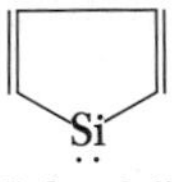

"silenole"

Pyrrole is slightly aromatic (that is, has a cyclic resonance system like benzene), is soluble in water, and boils at 131°C; thiophene, on the other hand, is highly aromatic (much resonance interaction), is not soluble in water, and boils at 78°C. Both show aromatic substitution reactions. Account for the differences in the properties of these two compounds in terms of their electronic structures. What properties would you predict for the hypothetical silenole? What kind of reactions should it show?

See page 1093 for a list of references and readings in the recent chemical literature related to the material in this chapter.

PART 5

Thermodynamics

WHY DO NET REACTIONS OCCUR?

CHAPTER 26

Thermodynamic Functions

The seven thermodynamic functions have a common property which makes them most useful in describing chemical systems; each is independent of the history of the system and the change in any one of the functions is independent of how the change is accomplished. They are all state functions.

In past chapters we have found it convenient to describe chemical systems in terms of T, P, V, and n (number of moles), and we have described energy changes in systems in these terms plus the functions q and w. In using these six variables, certain generally useful functions came to light: E, H, S, and C. These functions belong to the set of thermodynamic functions, and in this chapter we shall discuss some of their interrelationships, experimental measurements, and uses.

GENERAL VARIABLES

The units usually chosen as fundamental in any system (c.g.s., mks, English, and so on) are length (l), mass (m), and time (t). Appendix II gives some other variables in terms of these units. It is very common, for convenience, to add two additional units to this list: temperature, T, and electric charge, Q. This is true even though l, m, and t are sufficient, as Appendix I shows.

However, an equally useful set of variables for work in chemistry is temperature, T; pressure, P; volume, V; and number of moles, n. All of these are defined on absolute scales such that zero values mean the absence of the quality measured by that variable. This gives absolute temperatures, absolute pressures, absolute volumes, and absolute numbers of moles.

Table 26.1 Six common thermodynamic variables.

Function	Formal dimensions	Defining equation	Conditions or descriptions
P	$ml^{-1}t^{-2}$	$P = \frac{F}{A}$	force per unit area
V	l^3	V = three dimensional space available to system	
n	mole	$n = \frac{\text{number of molecules}}{N_0}$	N_0 = Avogadro's number
T	T	$T_{\text{triple point } H_2O} = 273.16°K$	triple point of water
		$T = \frac{PV}{nR}$	any ideal gas
w	ml^2t^{-2}	$w = \text{force} \cdot \text{distance} = \int F\,dl = \int \frac{F}{A} A\,dl$	
		$w = \int P_{\text{ext}}\,dV$ (assumes no other kind of work except expansion-compression)	work done by system on external surroundings, hence P_{ext}
q	ml^2t^{-2}	q = number of calories of heat entering system	

Two additional variables occur so often that they are also given special symbols: w for work, and q for heat.

These six symbols are central in all modern treatments of the energetics of chemical systems, especially from the standpoint of thermodynamics. Table 26.1 summarizes these six functions and their definitions.

THE FOUR LAWS OF THERMODYNAMICS

Early thermodynamicists postulated three laws, then added a fourth (now called the zeroth law) to make the set complete. We have already used them all, but we will repeat them here.

ZEROTH LAW: If $T_1 = T_2$ and $T_2 = T_3$, then $T_1 = T_3$. (26.1)

Two systems in thermal equilibrium with a third system are in equilibrium with one another. [We shall not discuss constrained equilibria, so that it follows from the zeroth law that all unconstrained equilibria are isothermal. It is also true that they are isobaric (constant pressure) and that each species has a constant chemical potential throughout the system.]

FIRST LAW: $$dE = dq - dw. \quad (26.2)$$

The change in internal energy, E, in any system is the difference between the heat entering the system, dq, and the work done by the system, dw (see Chapter 7). The internal energy of any isolated system is constant, since then $dq = 0 = dw$.

SECOND LAW: $$dS = dq_{\text{rev}}/T. \quad (26.3)$$

The change in entropy, S, during any change in a system is equal to the heat entering the system when the change is performed reversibly, dq_{rev} (sometimes merely written q_{rev}), divided by the absolute T. A reversible process is one which is performed under minute, or differential, driving forces, so that the system is essentially at equilibrium at all times. In all actual processes the entropy of an isolated system always increases,

THIRD LAW:

$$S^0_{0°\mathrm{K}} = 0, \qquad (26.4)$$

for any pure crystalline material. It is impossible ever to attain, by a finite series of steps, a condition of zero entropy.
It is impossible ever to attain, by a finite series of steps, a condition of zero entropy.

For each of the above laws we have given a statement, followed by what appears to be amplification or even a corollary. But the initial statement actually includes all corollaries. These four laws are a sufficient basis for all thermodynamic relationships, just as Euclid's postulates are sufficient for Euclidean geometry, and Newton's laws are sufficient for Newtonian mechanics. Thermodynamics, however, unlike Euclidean geometry or Newtonian mechanics, does not currently seem to be just one of several postulate systems with which one can study the relationships of energy and matter.

Though the four laws might, of course, be displaced at any time by a more inclusive set of postulates, and though alternate postulates may someday be developed, such alternates are not now available. The four laws of thermodynamics are as well established, as widely accepted, and as free from experimental anomalies as any known scientific laws. They are, therefore, very powerful. In this chapter we shall explore some of the reasons for their power.

It is important to remember that exact thermodynamics deals only with equilibrium systems (zeroth law), and that the other three laws may or may not need to be applied explicitly for a thermodynamic treatment of a given system. In general, the zeroth law is most often applied, the first law next most often, the second law almost as often, and the third law least.

THERMODYNAMIC FUNCTIONS

The six variables—P, V, T, n, q, and w—are quite sufficient to express all the thermodynamic relations we have developed, but, as is often true when one manipulates variables mathematically, certain combinations of these variables recur over and over. When this happens, it is common to define a new variable, or function, of simpler form. Thus the first law of thermodynamics substitutes dE for $dq—dw$ and the second law substitutes dS for dq_{rev}/T. Neither dE nor dS is introduced *de novo:* each is merely introduced to simplify the symbolism.

In a similar fashion we have already introduced several other thermodynamic functions, summarized in Table 26.2. Only one of these is new here: $A = E - TS$, where A is the Helmholtz free energy. Like internal energy, A is of greatest use in constant-volume systems. We shall find little use for A in this book, which deals mainly with constant-pressure systems.

The seven functions listed in Table 26.2 (E, S, H, G, A, C_P, and C_V) and the six variables listed in Table 26.1 (P, V, n, T, q, and w) give the symbols of greatest use in the thermodynamic description of chemical systems.

Table 26.2 Definitions of standard thermodynamic functions.

Name	Function	Definition	Differential form
Internal energy	E	$dE = dq - dw$	see definition
Entropy	S	$dS = dq_{\text{rev}}/T$	see definition
Enthalpy	H	$H = E + PV$	$dH = dE + d(PV) = dE + P\,dV + V\,dP$
Gibbs free energy	G	$G = H - TS$	$dG = dH - d(TS) = dH - T\,dS - S\,dT$
Helmholtz free energy	A	$A = E - TS$	$dA = dE - d(TS) = dE - T\,dS - S\,dT$
Heat capacity at constant pressure	C_P	$C_P = \left(\frac{\partial H}{\partial T}\right)_P$	see definition
Heat capacity at constant volume	C_V	$C_V = \left(\frac{\partial E}{\partial T}\right)_V$	see definition

STATE FUNCTIONS

The seven thermodynamic functions have a common property which makes them most useful in describing chemical systems: each is independent of the history of the system and the change in any one of the functions is independent of how the change is accomplished. They are all state functions.

Consider a more common pair of variables h and w. The change in height between the bottom and top of a mountain is independent of the path followed in reaching the top of the mountain. But the work required to scale the mountain is not independent of path. In this example, h is a state function independent of path, w is not a state function; q is not a state function either, since heat absorbed is also a function of path. But if a chemical system is moved from the bottom to the top of the mountain in many different ways, $\Delta E = \int mg\,dh$ will always be the same so long as the system is the same at the bottom of the mountain each time it is there and is the same at the top of the mountain each time it is there; $\Delta E = mg(h_2 - h_1)$, as in the derivation of the barometric formula on page 167. The E is a state function; its change depends only on the change in state functions—not on how the change was accomplished.

State functions, such as E, S, H, G, and A, have another valuable property: they give exact, or perfect, differentials. Exact differentials can be integrated between limits without regard for the actual changes that occur as the system moves from one limiting condition to the other. Thus integration of thermodynamic functions is often possible if only the limiting conditions are known, thanks to the exact nature of the differentials. Again, q and w do not give exact differentials, and great care must be taken in treating functions expressed in terms of q and w, since one must know the path of the change before any integration (for example) is attempted.

A useful mathematical property of exact differentials is much used in thermodynamics. If $dL = M\,dx + N\,dy$, and dL is an exact differential, then

$$\left(\frac{\partial M}{\partial y}\right)_x = \left(\frac{\partial N}{\partial x}\right)_y \tag{26.5}$$

We shall use this equation often and you will find it useful in solving problems. Learn it—and, of course, its conditions.

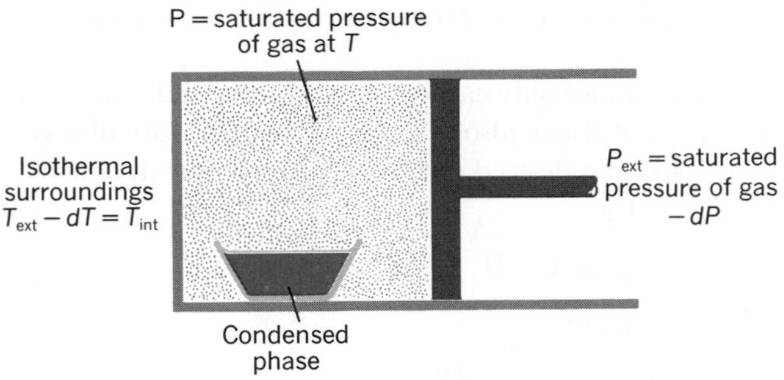

Figure 26.1 Isothermal, isobaric evaporation of a condensed phase carried out under equilibrium conditions—that is, carried out reversibly. $dq_{rev} = dq_P = dH_{vap} = T\,dS_{vap}$. Note that the external T is differentially greater than the internal T, so net vaporization slowly occurs, and the internal volume increases so slowly that no more than a differential pressure drop occurs across the piston.

REVERSIBLE PROCESSES

It should be clear to you now that q and w are dependent on path. They do not give exact differentials. (We also discussed this problem on p. 222.) Let us look at q and w more thoroughly.

The easier term is q, since we have already developed the idea and stated, as the second law,* that

$$dS = \frac{dq_{rev}}{T} \qquad \text{or} \qquad dq_{rev} = T\,dS \tag{26.6}$$

Thus, in general, dq is the heat entering a system during a change. During a reversible change, $dq_{rev} = T\,dS$.

One possible reversible change might be the slow isothermal evaporation of a condensed phase to give a gas, with the process carried out very close to equilibrium conditions. This could be done as in Figure 26.1, for example. The process illustrated in Figure 26.1 is being carried out reversibly at constant T and P. All driving forces—dT and dP—are differential. The piston is frictionless. Thus $dq_{rev} = dq_P = d(\Delta H)_{vap}$ from Equation (7.5).

From the second law, $dq_{rev} = T\,dS = T\,dS_{vap}$. Thus $d(\Delta H)_{vap} = T\,d(\Delta S)_{vap}$, or $\Delta H_{vap} = T\,\Delta S_{vap}$ at constant T and with $P = p^0$.

But ΔH, T, and ΔS are state functions. Thus, for any vaporization process, $\Delta H_{vap} = T\,\Delta S_{vap}$, reversible or not, as long as the same condensed state is being converted to the same gaseous state (constant T and P). Thus ΔH, or ΔS, for a system vaporizing into a vacuum (a highly irreversible process) is exactly the same as ΔH or ΔS for the same system and process carried out reversibly as in Figure 26.1, as long as T and P are the same before and after the reaction.

Hence the invention of a reversible process allows us to obtain a perfectly

---

*The second law is sometimes written as $dS = dq_{rev}/T$, and sometimes as $dS = q_{rev}/T$. Thus we sometimes indicate differential quantities of heat as dq, and sometimes as q. The same ambiguity, dw and w, exists for work. Historically this is because q and w are not state functions, and dq and dw are not exact differentials. In this book we use dq and dw only to emphasize reversible values. Otherwise, and most commonly, q and w will be used for both large and differential quantities.

general relationship, $\Delta H_{\text{vap}} = T\,\Delta S_{\text{vap}}$, composed only of readily measurable state functions.

Heat, q, entering a system cannot only cause phase changes, $\Delta H_{\text{phase change}}$, and chemical reaction, $\Delta H_{\text{reaction}}$, but it can also change the temperature of a system. Suppose, again, we accomplish the desired change reversibly, say at constant pressure. Then, since $(\partial H/\partial T)_P = C_P$,

$$dq_{\text{rev}} = dq_P = dH_{\text{heating}} = C_P\,dT, \qquad \text{all at constant } P$$

Again we get only state functions:

$$dH_{\text{heating}} = C_P\,dT$$

or

$$\Delta H_{\text{heating}} = \int_{T_1}^{T_2} C_P\,dT$$

Now consider w. There are many kinds of work—gravitational, electric, magnetic, and others—depending on the force field in which the work is done. We shall restrict ourselves to work against an external pressure, so-called $P\,dV$ work. Limiting ourselves in this way gives

$$dw = P_{\text{external}}\,dV$$

This problem was also discussed in Chapter 7. We must use P_{external}, since w is defined as work done *by* the system, and this work will always be done on the surroundings external to the system. The work will be done reversibly if $P_{\text{internal}} - P_{\text{external}} = dP$. That is, if the internal pressure is differentially greater than the external pressure, the system will do work reversibly on the surroundings. Then

$$dw_{\text{rev}} = P_{\text{ext}}\,dV \tag{26.7}$$

which is often merely written $w = P\,dV$, but *you must remember the limiting conditions* for reversible work: $P = P_{\text{ext}}$, and $P_{\text{int}} - P_{\text{ext}} = dP$. For example, if $P_{\text{ext}} = 0$, as in expansion of an ideal gas into a vacuum, $w = \int P_{\text{ext}}\,dV = 0$. But note that P_{int} was always positive. Note also that, since $dw = P_{\text{ext}}\,dV$, we get the maximum work done if P_{ext} is a maximum at all times. P_{ext} will be a maximum if $P_{\text{int}} - P_{\text{ext}} = dP$, which is the condition for reversibility. Thus in this, as in all processes,

$$w_{\text{max}} = w_{\text{rev}} \tag{26.8}$$

The reversible work is always the maximum obtainable work; irreversible processes always produce less work.

MAXWELL'S RELATIONS

Substituting $dq_{\text{rev}} = T\,dS$ from the second law, (26.2), and $w_{\text{rev}} = P\,dV$ from (26.7) into the first law, we obtain

$$dE = T\,dS - P\,dV$$

This equation involves only state functions thus applies equally to reversible and to irreversible processes. Application of the condition for an exact differential equation (26.5), gives a

FIRST MAXWELL EQUATION:

$$\left(\frac{\partial T}{\partial V}\right)_S = -\left(\frac{\partial P}{\partial S}\right)_V \tag{26.9}$$

Equation (26.9) states that for *any* system the rate of change of the temperature with volume at constant entropy equals the negative of the rate of change of pressure with entropy at constant volume. Or, inverting,

$$\left(\frac{\partial V}{\partial T}\right)_S = -\left(\frac{\partial S}{\partial P}\right)_V$$

This form may look a little more interesting, since it allows the calculation of the rate of change of entropy with pressure at constant volume from a knowledge of the rate of change of volume with temperature at constant entropy. And, most important, the equation is perfectly general; it applies to all known systems. The equation may still seem exotic and not very immediately useful, but let us continue.

From the first law, $dE = dq - dw = dq_{\text{rev}} - dw_{\text{rev}} = T\,dS - P\,dV$. By definition, $H = E + PV$ and $dH = dE + d(PV) = dE + P\,dV + V\,dP$. Thus

$$\begin{aligned} dH &= T\,dS - P\,dV + P\,dV + V\,dP \\ &= T\,dS + V\,dP \end{aligned}$$

(Note that $V\,dP$ is *not* the same as $P\,dV$: $P\,dV$ is work, but $V\,dP$ has no simple interpretation or name.) Applying Equation (26.5) again, we get a

SECOND MAXWELL EQUATION:

$$\left(\frac{\partial T}{\partial P}\right)_S = \left(\frac{\partial V}{\partial S}\right)_P \quad \text{or} \quad \left(\frac{\partial P}{\partial T}\right)_S = \left(\frac{\partial S}{\partial V}\right)_P \tag{26.10}$$

Now we have an equation that relates the rate of change of entropy with volume at constant P to the rate of change of P with T at constant S. Again the equation may be interesting, but we have no immediate use for it. You should, however, at least be intrigued at the ability of thermodynamics to generate new relationships with little effort.

If we start again with the first law, $dE = dq - dw = dq_{\text{rev}} - dw_{\text{rev}}$, we may obtain

$$\begin{aligned} dE &= T\,dS - P\,dV \\ dH &= dE + d(PV) = T\,dS - P\,dV + V\,dP + P\,dV \\ dH &= T\,dS + V\,dP \end{aligned}$$

By definition,

$$G = H - TS \quad \text{or} \quad dG = dH - d\,TS = dH - T\,dS - S\,dT$$

or

$$\begin{aligned} dG &= T\,dS + V\,dP - T\,dS - S\,dT \\ &= V\,dP - S\,dT \end{aligned}$$

Applying Equation (26.5) once more, we get a

THIRD MAXWELL EQUATION:

$$\left(\frac{\partial V}{\partial T}\right)_P = -\left(\frac{\partial S}{\partial P}\right)_T \tag{26.11}$$

Examination shows this equation to be more understandable than the other two: $(\partial V/\partial T)_P$ is a straightforward, readily measured term—the rate of change of volume with T at constant P—and it equals the negative of the rate of change of entropy with P at constant T. This gives us a way to calculate the entropy associated with any change in P, at constant T, for any system for which V is known as a function of T, at constant P.

Consider an ideal gas, $PV = nRT$, $(\partial V/\partial T)_P = nR/P$:

$$-\left(\frac{\partial S}{\partial P}\right)_T = \left(\frac{\partial V}{\partial T}\right)_P = \frac{nR}{P}$$

At constant T,

$$dS = -\frac{nR}{P}\,dP$$

$$\int dS = \Delta S = -nR\int\frac{dP}{P} = -nR\int d\ln P = -nR\ln\frac{P_2}{P_1}$$

$$\Delta S = nR\ln\frac{P_1}{P_2} \tag{26.12}$$

This equation, directly related to Equation (10.2), which we derived earlier for the volume change of an ideal gas at constant T, is merely a special case of the very general third Maxwell relation.

The last Maxwell relation may now be quickly obtained. We have found that

$$dE = T\,dS - P\,dV$$

and, by definition,

$$A = E - TS \qquad \text{or} \qquad dA = dE - d(TS) = dE - T\,dS - S\,dT$$

Therefore

$$\begin{aligned} dA &= T\,dS - P\,dV - T\,dS - S\,dT \\ &= -P\,dV - S\,dT \end{aligned}$$

Applying Equation (26.5), we get a

FOURTH MAXWELL EQUATION: $$\left(\frac{\partial P}{\partial T}\right)_V = \left(\frac{\partial S}{\partial V}\right)_T$$

This gives us a general equation for the change in the entropy of a system as a function of V, at constant T, in terms of the readily measured $(\partial P/\partial T)_V$.

These four derivations are summarized in Table 26.3.

Exercise 26.1

Calculate the entropy of an ideal gas as a function of volume at constant T, using the Maxwell relations. *Answer:* $(\partial S/\partial V)_T = (\partial P/\partial T)_V = (\partial \frac{nRT}{V}/\partial T)_V = nR/V$, $dS = nR\,dV/V = nR d \ln, V$, $(S_2 - S_1) = nR \ln (V_2/V_1)$.

Table 26.3 Derivation of the Maxwell relations. (Remember the limitations to processes involving only $P\,dV$ work and constant n.)

Definition		Maxwell relations (from Euler conditions)
$dw_{rev} = P\,dV$		
$dq_{rev} = T\,dS$		
$dE = dq - dw$	$dE = T\,dS - P\,dV$	$(\partial T/\partial V)_S = -(\partial P/\partial S)_V$
$H = E + PV$	$dH = T\,dS + V\,dP$	$(\partial T/\partial P)_S = (\partial V/\partial S)_P$
$G = H - TS$	$dG = -S\,dT + V\,dP$	$-(\partial S/\partial P)_T = (\partial V/\partial T)_P$
$A = E - TS$	$dA = -S\,dT - P\,dV$	$(\partial S/\partial V)_T = (\partial P/\partial T)_V$

EQUILIBRIUM CONDITIONS

The equations derived in the previous section and summarized in the central column of Table 26.3 provide valuable insights into the conditions that must be satisfied at equilibrium.

Consider the general equation $dE = T\,dS - P\,dV$ as applied to an isolated equilibrium system at constant volume. For any small shift from equilibrium such that

$$dE = 0, \qquad dV = 0$$

it must also be true that

$$T\,dS = 0 \quad \text{and} \quad dS = 0$$

Thus, for any small shift in an isolated system at constant volume which has come to equilibrium, $dS = 0$. Since dS for all spontaneous changes is positive in an isolated system of constant volume, the entropy of the system is a maximum at equilibrium where $dS = 0$. The general condition for equilibrium in isolated systems of constant volume is that the entropy be a maximum, and ΔS is positive for all total real processes.

The universe is often treated as an isolated system of constant volume. Thus the universe, according to thermodynamics, is headed toward an equilibrium state of maximum entropy. (See the Clausius statement: Appendix III, Number 20.) If, on the other hand, the universe is expanding, it is then headed toward a state of indefinitely large entropy; that is, the maximum occurs at infinite volume.

The two other equations

$$dG = -S\,dT + V\,dP$$

and

$$dA = -S\,dT - P\,dV$$

are readily applicable under two very common laboratory conditions. The first says that $dG = 0$ in an equilibrium closed system at constant T and P, and the second says that $dA = 0$ in an equilibrium closed system at constant T and V. Both G and A go to minimum values under these respective conditions. Thus the Gibbs free energy, G, of a closed equilibrium system at constant T and P is a minimum.

Table 26.4 Some equilibrium conditions (only $P\,dV$ work) for closed systems.

From	At equilibrium
$dE = T\,dS - P\,dV$	At constant E and V, S is a maximum
$dH = T\,dS + V\,dP$	At constant H and P, S is a maximum
$dG = -S\,dT + V\,dP$	At constant T and P, G is a minimum (S_{univ} is a maximum)
$dA = -S\,dT + P\,dV$	At constant T and V, A is a minimum (S_{univ} is a maximum)

This was discussed on page 229, where it was pointed out that for a closed system at constant T and P, $\Delta G/T = -\Delta S_{universe}$, a useful way of typifying or characterizing free energy changes. These equilibrium conditions are summarized in Table 26.4.

RELATION OF S, E, H, C_P, C_V, G, AND A TO q AND w

We have stated above that the seven thermodynamic functions are merely different forms of the six variables—P, V, n, T, q, and w. Let us summarize these relations here.

We have already been acquainted with these relations for S, E, H, C_P, and C_V. They are the following.

General functions:

$$dS = dq_{rev}/T \qquad \text{Second law [Eq. (26.3)]}$$

$$\Delta E = q_V \qquad \text{[Eq. (7.3)]}$$

$$\Delta H = q_P \qquad \text{[Eq. (7.5)]}$$

For processes involving change in temperature:

$$C_V = \left(\frac{\partial E}{\partial T}\right)_V \quad \text{or} \quad C_V\,dT = dq_V \qquad \text{[Eq. (7.4)]}$$

$$C_P = \left(\frac{\partial H}{\partial T}\right)_P \quad \text{or} \quad C_P\,dT = dq_P \qquad \text{[Eq. (7.7)]}$$

Thus all these functions are directly related to q, the heat gained by a system. The C_V and C_P are related to the amount of heat, q, required to change the temperature of a system. The ΔS is related to the amount of heat entering the system as a function of the temperature of the system.

Now let us look at G:

$$\begin{aligned} G &= H - TS = E + PV - TS \\ dG &= dE + d(PV) - d(TS) = dq_{rev} - dw_{rev} + d(PV) - d(TS) \\ &= T\,dS - dw_{rev} + P\,dV + V\,dP - T\,dS - S\,dT \\ &= -dw_{rev} + P\,dV + V\,dP - S\,dT \end{aligned}$$

At constant T and P,

$$dG = -dw_{rev} + P\,dV$$

or

$$-dG = dw_{rev} - P\,dV = dw_{max} - P\,dV \tag{26.13}$$

Thus the change in G is a work term; dG equals minus the total work done by the system plus the $P\,dV$ work done by the system. (Or $-dG$ equals the total work done by the system minus the $P\,dV$ work done by the system.) If there is no $P\,dV$ work at constant T and P, $dG = -dw_{\text{rev}}$. The reversible work is also the maximum work, Equation (26.8), and so $-dG$ represents the maximum work, less the $P\,dV$ work, that a system can perform at constant T and P. The G is a work function, and its negative change represents the maximum work the system can deliver at constant T and P, other than $P\,dV$ work.

Now consider A:

$$\begin{aligned} A &= E - TS \\ dA &= dE - d(TS) = dq_{\text{rev}} - dw_{\text{rev}} - T\,dS - S\,dT \\ &= T\,dS - dw_{\text{rev}} - T\,dS - S\,dT \\ &= -dw_{\text{rev}} - S\,dT \end{aligned}$$

At constant T,

$$dA = -dw_{\text{rev}} \qquad (26.14)$$

or

$$-dA = dw_{\text{rev}} = dw_{\text{max}}$$

Thus $-dA$ is the maximum, or reversible, work a system can do at constant temperature. Like G, A is a work function, though it is called the Helmholtz free energy. Free energy changes represent the maximum energy available to do work.

We therefore see that the seven thermodynamic functions are all invented to convert q and w into state functions, so that we can unambiguously express changes involving q and w in terms of quantities whose changes are independent of the path of the change. Table 26.5 summarizes these relationships. Note that all the variables except n are explicitly involved, and n can be explicitly involved by converting to molar values—for example, $\bar{S}$, $\bar{E}$, $\bar{H}$, etc. Thus $n\,d\bar{E} = dq_V$, $-n\,d\bar{G} = dw_{\text{rev}} - nP\,d\bar{V}$, etc.

Exercise 26.2

Calculate the maximum work available when steam condenses isothermally to water at 1 atm and 373°K. *Answer:* $dw_{\text{max}} = -dG + P\,dV$. At 373°K and 1 atm, $dG = 0$ for condensation of water, since this is an equilibrium state. So $dw_{\text{max}} = P\,dV = P(V_l - V_g) \cong -PV_g \cong -P \cdot (nRT/P) = -nRT = -1.99 \cdot 373n = -744$ cal mole^{-1}. Thus 744 cal mole^{-1} of work are done on the system.

Table 26.5 Relationships between thermodynamic functions and q and w.

	Limitations
1. $dS = dq_{\text{rev}}/T$	none (second law)
2. $dE = dq_V$	constant volume
3. $dH = dq_P$	constant pressure
4. $-dG = dw_{\text{rev}} - P\,dV$	constant temperature and pressure
5. $-dA = dw_{\text{rev}}$	constant temperature
6. $C_V\,dT = dq_V$	change in temperature at constant volume
7. $C_P\,dT = dq_P$	change in temperature at constant pressure

THE SECOND LAW—INTERCONVERTIBILITY OF q AND w

We now see that E, H, G, A, C_P, C_V are straightforward changes of variable that allow us to describe q and w in terms of state functions. Each is strongly dependent on the idea that $dE = dq - dw$, the first law, with which you have been familiar for a long time. They also depend on the second law, $dS = dq_{\text{rev}}/T$. How was this function ever invented?

Examination of the zeroth and first laws shows that they are very good for describing an equilibrium system which is conserving energy. But conserved functions, like energy, cannot of themselves predict or correlate changes. Yet we see changes involving energy flows, for example, continually occurring. The total heat does not change but its distribution does.

Furthermore, net heat always flows spontaneously from high to low temperature, never the reverse. In general, heat flows from systems or regions where it is concentrated—high temperature, high pressure, high concentration of particles, high potential energy—to systems or regions where the energy is less concentrated—low temperature, low pressure, low concentration of particles, low potential energy. We observe that energy tends to spread out among the available quantum levels and throughout the available space. Entropy is used to describe and measure this tendency of energy to diffuse from systems or regions of high energy concentration to regions of low energy concentration. Since we have never observed a violation of this principle, we assume we shall find a law that will quantitatively state the tendency of energy to diffuse—the second law. The general ideas, and the concept of entropy, were first suggested by Clausius about 1850.

Consider a setup of two constant-temperature reservoirs at T_1 and T_2. If $T_1 > T_2$, net heat will flow from reservoir (1) to reservoir (2). Suppose that we now interpose a system into which the heat, q_1, from reservoir (1) will flow, and that the system will then do work w on the surroundings, although the system itself will remain unchanged, $\Delta E_{\text{sys}} = 0$.

The system could be a dynamo generating electricity, or a paddle wheel turning under falling water and lifting an external weight, or any other device for converting heat into work. It could, for example, be a chemical reaction which

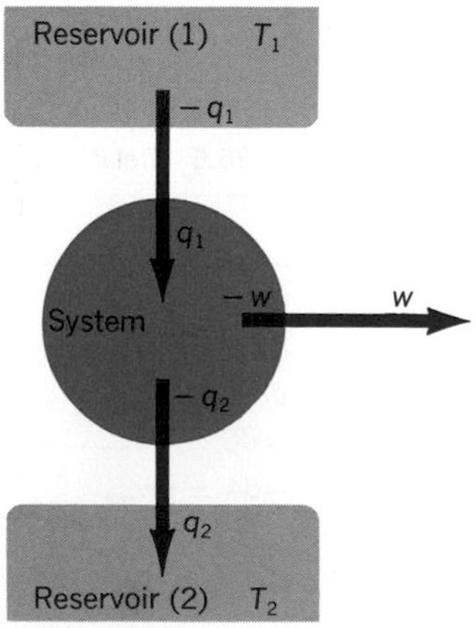

Figure 26.2 A system for converting q to w.

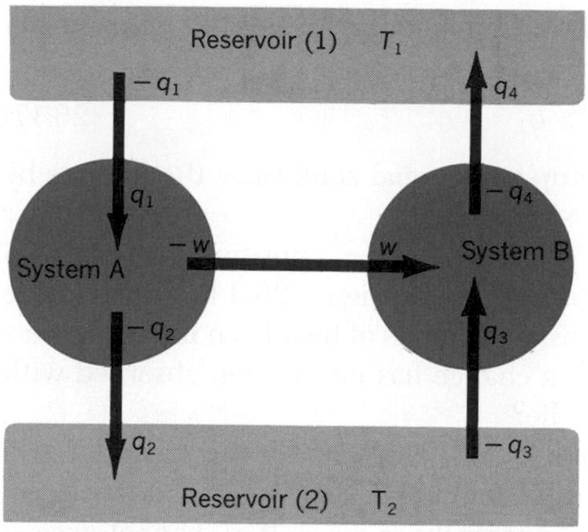

Figure 26.3 Two coupled working systems.

could absorb some heat, do some work, and then return to its original condition by discharging heat, q, to the reservoir of lower T. Figure 26.2 summarizes the q and w terms. Note that $\Delta E_{sys} = 0$, since it experiences no net change. Note that heat of amount q_1 is gained by the system, heat of amount q_2 is lost by the system, while the work done on the system is $-w$, the negative of the work done on the surroundings.

We define efficiency, e, of conversion of heat to work as

$$e = \frac{w}{q_1} \text{ (or, since } w = q_1 - q_2\text{,)}$$

$$= \frac{q_1 - q_2}{q_1} = \frac{\text{(heat absorbed by system)—(heat lost by system)}}{\text{(heat absorbed by system)}}$$

$$= 1 - \frac{q_2}{q_1} \tag{26.15}$$

Now consider two different systems between the reservoirs, as in Figure 26.3. Systems A and B are coupled so that the work done by A is now completely done on B and is used to transfer q_3 units of heat from reservoir 2 and deliver q_4 units to reservoir 1.

Suppose that we can find a system more efficient than system A at interconverting q and w, and use it as a heat pump for system B. Then the work provided by A will be used by B to pump heat from reservoir 2 to reservoir 1 more efficiently than A used heat in generating w. In the equations

$$e_A = 1 - \frac{q_2}{q_1}, \qquad e_B = 1 - \frac{q_3}{q_4}$$

if $e_B > e_A$, then $1 - (q_3/q_4) > 1 - (q_2/q_1)$, or

$$\frac{q_3}{q_4} < \frac{q_2}{q_1} \tag{26.16}$$

Since system B is more efficient at interconverting q and w, a given amount of w in system B should move a larger amount of q than could be done in A were it to run backwards as a heat pump. Thus, in general, $q_3 > q_2$ and hence, from Equation (26.16),

$$q_4 > q_1 \tag{26.17}$$

Now the total work, dw, in the entire setup must equal zero, since the w done by system A exactly equals the w done on system B.

Thus $q_{tot} = q_4 - q_1 = -(q_2 - q_3) = q_3 - q_2 =$ a positive amount [from Equation (26.17)]. The total effect of the changes in Figure 26.3 has been (since the central systems are unchanged) to transfer q_{tot} units of heat from the cold reservoir (2) to the hot reservoir (1). But such a change has never been observed with zero work. Where does our error in logic lie?

The only assumption in the discussion of Figure 26.3 is that system B can pump heat more effectively than A could if running backwards—that is, $q_3 > q_2$. Apparently this assumption is incorrect. Apparently, if $dw = 0$, q_3 cannot exceed q_2, since q_4 cannot exceed q_1.

Now the efficiency of A can vary all the way from 0, when $q_2 = q_1$ and no work is done, to a maximum when the maximum work, w_{max}, is done. System A will produce w_{max} when A operates reversibly. If A then delivers w_{max} to B, B can pump $w_{max} + q_3 = q_4$ units of heat into reservoir 1. But we have just shown that q_4 cannot exceed q_1 and q_3 cannot exceed q_2 if $dw = 0$. Even if B operates reversibly (that is, at maximum efficiency), no more heat can enter reservoir 1 as q_4 than left as q_1. But, under these reversible conditions $q_1 = q_4$ and $q_2 = q_3$.

We may summarize: (*a*) no system can be more efficient than a reversible system; (*b*) all reversible systems are equally efficient; (*c*) under conditions of reversibility exactly as much heat flows from reservoir 2 to reservoir 1 as flows from reservoir 1 to reservoir 2—there is no net heat flow under reversible conditions; (*d*) under all irreversible conditions there is net flow of heat from the hot reservoir (1) to the cold reservoir (2), $|q_1| > |q_4|$; (*e*) it is impossible to convert heat completely into work (q_2 cannot be zero), but it is possible to convert work completely into heat (as in system B operating reversibly).

Notice that the changes discussed (Figures 26.2 and 26.3) are very general. Nothing whatever is specified about the nature of systems A and B. It is only required that they can react in a cycle such that the final condition is identical with the initial condition. Any system can meet this requirement. Furthermore, nothing is said about the nature of the reservoirs, except that they are isothermal. They could be masses with high total heat capacities, such as the oceans or the atmosphere. Or they could be chemical systems reacting at constant temperature. Or they could be systems undergoing phase changes which keep the temperature fixed, such as an ice bath. Or the reservoir could be any other constant-temperature system—a living system, for example, or even a human being. The discussion is perfectly general. Therefore the conclusions are also general. Until someone finds a system in which net heat flows from a cold to a hot system with no other change occurring, we accept the idea that the entropy of the universe (or any isolated system at constant volume) increases during every actual change. The ability of an isolated system of constant volume to do work continually decreases. If the isolated system is increasing in volume, its ability to do work decreases even faster, since its energy is becoming less and less concentrated due to the expansion.

Figure 26.3 can be quickly generalized even further if we remember that mass and energy (or heat) are interconvertible and thus are two different forms of the same quantity. Just as we never observe a process whose only result is a net flow of "heat" from a region where it is dilute (low temperature) to a region where it is concentrated (high temperature), so we never observe a process whose only result is a net flow of "mass" from a region where it is dilute (such as a dilute solution or a low-pressure gas) to a region where it is concentrated (a concentrated solution or a high-pressure gas). Mass-energy always tends to diffuse or spread out, as described by the second law of thermodynamics; q/T for any total real process is always positive.

KELVIN TEMPERATURE

William Thomson (Lord Kelvin) decided to tie this efficiency to the temperatures of the two reservoirs by using efficiency to define the temperature. He assumed that e is a function of the two temperatures for any reversible cycles independent of the interconversion systems used:

$$e = \varphi(T_1, T_2) = \left(\frac{q_1 - q_2}{q_1}\right)_{\text{rev}} = 1 - \left(\frac{q_2}{q_1}\right)_{\text{rev}}$$

If

$$1 - \left(\frac{q_2}{q_1}\right)_{\text{rev}} = \varphi(T_1, T_2)$$

then

$$\left(\frac{q_2}{q_1}\right)_{\text{rev}} = \varphi'(T_1, T_2)$$

and for another system

$$\left(\frac{q_3}{q_2}\right)_{\text{rev}} = \varphi'(T_2, T_3)$$

But these two systems in tandem must be equivalent to a third system such that

$$\left(\frac{q_3}{q_1}\right)_{\text{rev}} = \varphi'(T_1, T_3)$$

Thus

$$\frac{(q_3/q_1)_{\text{rev}}}{(q_2/q_1)_{\text{rev}}} = \frac{\varphi'(T_1, T_3)}{\varphi'(T_1, T_2)}$$

or

$$\left(\frac{q_3}{q_2}\right)_{\text{rev}} = \frac{\varphi'(T_1, T_3)}{\varphi'(T_1, T_2)} = \varphi'(T_2, T_3) \tag{26.18}$$

Equation (26.18) is satisfied if

$$\varphi'(T_1, T_2) = \frac{\varphi''(T_1)}{\varphi''(T_2)}$$

and so forth. Then

$$\left(\frac{q_1}{q_2}\right)_{\text{rev}} = \frac{\varphi''(T_1)}{\varphi''(T_2)}$$

for a reversible system operating between T_1 and T_2.

Kelvin decided to choose the simplest function possible and defined T_1 and T_2 as

$$\varphi''(T_1) = T_1, \qquad \varphi''(T_2) = T_2$$

Then

$$\left(\frac{q_1}{q_2}\right)_{\text{rev}} = \frac{T_1}{T_2} \tag{26.19}$$

so that the ratio of the heat changes in the two reservoirs during a reversible change equals the ratio of their Kelvin temperatures. The ideal gas scale is defined so that it gives essentially the same values of T. See Chapter 6. Ideal gas temperatures and Kelvin temperatures are interchangeable.

From the relation $(q_1/q_2)_{\text{rev}} = T_1/T_2$, we can get $(q_2/q_1)_{\text{rev}} = T_2/T_1$ or

$$1 - \left(\frac{q_2}{q_1}\right)_{\text{rev}} = 1 - \frac{T_2}{T_1}$$

$$\left(\frac{q_1 - q_2}{q_1}\right)_{\text{rev}} = \frac{T_1 - T_2}{T_1} = e = \frac{w_{\text{max}}}{(q_1)_{\text{rev}}}$$

Thus the efficiency of reversible conversion of q to w may be represented in terms of either the values of q_{rev} or the values of the Kelvin, or ideal gas, temperatures of the reservoirs.

Exercise 26.3

What fraction of the heat of combustion of gasoline can be used to drive an automobile? *Answer:* $e = w/(q_1)_{\text{rev}} = (T_1 - T_2)/T_1$ = thermodynamic efficiency. Cars typically operate with $T_2 \cong 350°\text{K}$, just below the boiling point of water and $T_1 \cong 1000°\text{K}$ the achievable flame temperature. Thus $e = (1000 - 350)/1000 = 0.65$. Using these optimistic assumptions, a car uses about 65% of the heat of combustion of the gasoline. The actual figure is less.

THE SECOND LAW AND ENERGY FLOW

From Kelvin's definition of T, $(q_1/q_2)_{\text{rev}} = T_1/T_2$ as in (26.19), we get $(q_1)_{\text{rev}}/T_1 = (q_2)_{\text{rev}}/T_2$. That is, q_{rev}/T is conserved in a reversible change. We recognize that $q_{\text{rev}}/T = \Delta S$. Hence the entropy function, S, is intimately related with problems of energy flow. For a reversible process, since $(q_1)_{\text{rev}}/T_1 = (q_2)_{\text{rev}}/T_2$, $\Delta S_1 = \Delta S_2$, $\Delta S_{\text{total}} = \Delta S_1 - \Delta S_2 = 0$.

But all real processes proceed under finite driving forces and are irreversible. Real processes produce less work than reversible processes. Thus, for a given q_1, since w is less for the irreversible process than the reversible process, q_2 is greater for the irreversible than for the reversible process.

Reversible: $(q_1 - q_2)_{\text{rev}} = w_{\text{max}}, \dfrac{(q_1)_{\text{rev}}}{T_1} = \dfrac{(q_2)_{\text{rev}}}{T_2} = \Delta S_1 = \Delta S_2, \Delta S_{\text{tot}} = 0$

Irreversible: $q_1 - q_2' = w'$. Since $w' < w_{\text{max}}, q_2' > q_2$

$$q_1/T_1 < q_2'/T_2,\ \Delta S_1 < \Delta S_2,\ \Delta S_2 - \Delta S_1 = \Delta S_{\text{tot}} = +$$

All real processes (all of which are irreversible) occur with an increase in total entropy.

The entropy function therefore falls out of a general discussion of the flow of energy and the interconversion of q and w. For reversible systems, S is conserved: $\Delta S = 0$. But for all real systems, $\Delta S_{\text{tot}} = +$ for a spontaneous change. The entropy function can give us especially valuable guidance in predicting the direction of change in any isolated system of constant volume.

If $\Delta S_{\text{tot}} = 0$, the system is at equilibrium (reversible change).

If $\Delta S_{\text{tot}} = +$, the change will proceed spontaneously.

If $\Delta S_{\mathrm{tot}} = -$, the change will proceed spontaneously in the direction reverse, or opposite, to that proposed.

SUMMARY

The thermodynamic functions—S, E, H, G, A, C_P, and C_V—can all be expressed in terms of the experimentally accessible variables P, V, n, T, q, and w. The functions are introduced to obtain numerical values that are independent of path: E, H, C_P, and C_V are primarily related to the total heat, q, in a system; G and A are primarily related to the maximum available work, w_{max}, and S is related to the tendency of mass-energy to diffuse and to the interconversion of q and w.

Manipulation of the thermodynamic functions can lead to new functions, including several that describe equilibrium states under different sets of conditions.

The second law, $dS = dq_{\mathrm{rev}}/T$, provides quick guidance to the possible direction of change in any isolated system of constant volume.

One word characterizes the most strenuous of the efforts for the advancement of science that I have made perseveringly during fifty-five years, and that word is FAILURE. I know no more of electric and magnetic forces or of the relation between either, electricity and ponderable matter, or of chemical affinity, than I knew and tried to teach to my students of natural philosophy fifty years ago in my first session as Professor. —*Lord Kelvin, quoted in S. P. Thompson,* The Life of William Thomson, *Macmillan, London, 1910.*

The educated person must be taught that it is not a disgrace to fail and that he must analyze every failure to find its cause He must learn to fail intelligently. For failing is one of the greatest arts in the world.—C. F. Kettering.

PROBLEMS

(In each of the following, where applicable, draw a figure to define the system.)

26.1. What advantages have liquid-filled thermometers over gas-filled ones?

26.2. Derive an expression for the entropy of an ideal gas and of a van der Waals gas as a function of volume during an isothermal process.

26.3. Prove that, for an ideal gas, $(\partial H/\partial V)_T = 0$ and $(\partial C_V/\partial V)_T = 0$.

26.4. Discuss the following natural phenomena in terms of how closely they approximate reversible processes: zinc dissolves in $HCl_{(aq)}$, water evaporates from the ocean, an electric battery sits on a shelf, a potentiometer is used to measure the voltage of an electric cell, wood burns in a fireplace, gasoline propels a car, iron rusts.

26.5. Compare the dimensions of entropy and heat capacity; of Gibbs free energy and entropy and enthalpy.

26.6. Calculate the work involved in reversibly compressing 1 mole of an ideal gas from 1 atm to 5 atm at 27°C. ($w \cong -1000$ cal.)

26.7. Most liquids can be cooled below their equilibrium melting point. Such liquids are said to be undercooled (or supercooled). Undercooled liquids often form crystals spontaneously even though in an isolated system (such as an insulated box). How can you rationalize this spontaneous occurrence with the fact that crystals have *lower* entropy than the liquid they are in equilibrium with?

26.8. A bomb calorimetry experiment at 18°C provides the following ΔE's for the combustion reactions:

$$C_2H_{2(g)} + \tfrac{5}{2}O_2 \longrightarrow 2CO_2 + H_2O, \qquad \Delta E = -311.5 \text{ kcal/mole}$$

$$C_6H_{6(l)} + \tfrac{15}{2}O_2 \longrightarrow 6CO_2 + 3H_2O, \qquad \Delta E = -787.5 \text{ kcal/mole}$$

Calculate ΔE and ΔH for the following reaction at 18°C:

$$3C_2H_{2(g)} \longrightarrow C_6H_{6(l)} \qquad [\Delta E \cong 150,\ \Delta H \cong 150 - 2 \text{ kcal (mole } C_6H_6)^{-1}.]$$

26.9. The Reaumur and Centigrade temperature scales both use 0° for the melting point of ice, but the Reaumur calls the boiling point of water 80° and the Centigrade calls it 100°. A Reaumur thermometer is seen to read 64°. What is the Centigrade temperature? ($t \cong 80$°C.)

26.10. Indicate for the following processes whether the indicated quantities will be positive (+), negative (−), or zero (0). All quantities apply to the system. Draw a figure to define the system in each case. (*a*) Expansion of an ideal gas into a vacuum at constant temperature, closed system: w, ΔE, ΔH. (*b*) Reversible compression of one mole of steam to liquid water at 100°C and 1 atm pressure, closed system: ΔE, ΔG, ΔS. (*c*) One mole of an ideal gas expands reversibly at constant temperature from 10 atm to 1 atm, closed system: w, ΔE, ΔH, ΔG. (*d*) Melting 10 g of ice at −5°C in 50 g of water at 20°C, isolated system: ΔS, ΔH. (*e*) A massless partition separating two ideal gases from one another in a thermostatted container is removed, closed system: q_{rev}, ΔS, ΔG.

26.11. At what surrounding temperature does the thermodynamic efficiency of a human being acting as a heat engine become zero? Can a person do any work above this temperature? Give your reasons. Is there any insight here into the problem of people in the tropics? In the zone of the Arctic Circle?

26.12. Most human beings have optimal over-all efficiency at about 70°F. What decreases efficiency at higher temperatures? What decreases efficiency at lower temperatures? What would be your rationalization of the location of past centers of civilizations?

II

26.13. Even the most optimistic estimates of hydrocarbon fuel reserves (some say less than 100 years) indicate that they are sufficient for no more than 1000 years. Suppose the deuterium were extracted, and the fusion reaction to give helium became feasible. What time span of energy demand could then be filled? Assume the deuterium in the oceans becomes available and estimate the "total available fusion energy" in terms of time span supply. Comment briefly on the implications your figures hold for society. (Total deuterium $\cong 10^8$ years.)

26.14. If a human being weighing 180 lb and generating 1500 kcal per day operated adiabatically, what would be the rise in his body temperature in one day? Calculate the entropy change in the human if he operated isothermally and reversibly. Assume $w = 0$. How does this entropy change fit in with the second law of thermodynamics? ($\Delta T \cong 20°\text{K}$.)

26.15. A 0.1-g sample of gaseous C_8H_{18} and a stoichiometric amount of pure oxygen are enclosed in an insulated piston. Reaction occurs at a constant pressure of 10 atm. What is the equilibrium condition that must be satisfied in this system? Estimate the approximate equilibrium temperature and volume. ($T \cong 4 \cdot 10^3$ °K if reaction is stoichiometric. It isn't.)

26.16. Calculate the thermodynamic efficiency for converting energy into work of a system operating between 37°C and 20°C. Compare with a system using the same amount of energy but operating between 500°C and 100°C. Given a limited supply of fuel, which system would you use to accomplish work? Suggest two common systems which fit the comparison you have just made. ($e \cong 5\%$ and 50%.)

26.17. Calculate the maximum work a human being acting as a heat engine could do on 3000 kcal day^{-1} (the average United States value) in a surrounding temperature of 20°C, in a surrounding temperature of 0°C, and in a surrounding temperature of 40°C. Convert each of these work terms into the number of kilograms of bricks the human could lift to a height of 1 meter in a day. Comment on the comparisons between your thermodynamic calculations and your past experience. Rationalize any apparent discrepancies. A human can do no lifting at all on less than about 1000 kcal per day per square meter of body surface. Why?

26.18. One mole of an ideal monatomic gas ($C_V = \frac{3}{2}R$) initially at 10 atm pressure and 25°C was expanded adiabatically and irreversibly to 1 atm. In this process, the work done was 15 liter atm. Calculate ΔS for this process. [$\Delta S \cong 2$ cal (mole °K)$^{-1}$.]

See page 1093 for a list of references and readings in the recent chemical literature related to the material in this chapter.

CHAPTER 27

Calculation of Thermodynamic Functions

A very serious problem would result if thermodynamic properties of every chemical reaction had to be determined by separate experiments. We already know several million compounds, and the number of reactions between them is astronomical. Fortunately, it is sufficient to know the properties of the compounds—no mean task in itself.

With the four laws as a basis of development, thermodynamics provides (1) a wealth of exact equations which define equilibrium states under many sets of conditions, (2) new insights into the relationships among the experimentally determined variables, (3) means of using equations of state to calculate heat and work terms, and (4) guidance in choosing the best methods of calculating numerical quantities related to chemical equilibria and in deciding what experimental data are needed. Chapter 26 examined 1 and 2. This chapter will explore 3 and 4. Specifically, it will explore how each of the thermodynamic functions—E, H, S, and G—vary with P, V, and T, and how these variations may be calculated from calorimetric and (in Chapter 28) spectroscopic data.

CALCULATION OF ΔE

According to the

FIRST LAW: $$\Delta E = q - w$$

Thus ΔE may be calculated for any process for which q and w are known. If we consider only $P\,dV$ work, we obtain

$$\Delta E = q - \int P\,dV$$

which at constant volume becomes

$$\Delta E = q_V$$

Thus ΔE is an especially useful term in constant-volume processes, since it merely equals the heat gained by the system at constant volume.

Typical changes measured in a bomb calorimeter include heats of phase change at constant V, heats of combustion in O_2, F_2, or Cl_2, heats of hydrogenation [$C_2H_{4(g)} + H_{2(g)} = C_2H_{6(g)}$], and other reactions involving gases. Most bomb calorimeters are used for changes involving gases, since the bomb allows us to operate at high concentrations of gas (giving generally high rates of reaction) and since there might be large $P\,dV$ terms if the reactions were carried out at constant pressure.

Not all changes in E, of course, involve chemical reactions or phase changes. We may, for example, merely have heating or cooling, without reaction. Consider the total differentiation of E with respect to T and V:

$$dE = \left(\frac{\partial E}{\partial T}\right)_V dT + \left(\frac{\partial E}{\partial V}\right)_T dV$$

(Taking a total differential is a common step in deriving thermodynamic formulas. Bear it in mind if you have to do some derivations.)

Since, at constant volume, $(\partial E/\partial T)_V = C_V$ and $(\partial E/\partial V)_T\,dV = 0$, we get $dE = C_V\,dT$ for heating and cooling effects at constant volume:

$$\int dE = \Delta E = \int C_V\,dT$$

The term C_V may be constant, in which case $\Delta E = C_V(T_2 - T_1) = C_V\,\Delta T$. But in general C_V is a function of T. An analytical expression of $C_V = \varphi(T)$ (usually of the form: $C_V = a + bT + cT^{-2}$) may be available for mathematical integration. Or it may be necessary to plot C_V against T and perform a graphical integration by counting squares, by using a planimeter, by cutting out and weighing the desired area of the graph, or by some other technique of determining area.

In general, there are three types of changes in the internal energy—reactions, phase changes, heating. The total change is

$$\Delta E = \Sigma\,\Delta E_{\text{reaction}} + \Sigma\,\Delta E_{\text{phase changes}} + \int_{T_1}^{T_2} C_V\,dT$$

or the sum of all the separate changes.

Exercise 27.1

Calculate the energy required to heat 100 g of helium from 400°K to 1000°K at constant volume. *Answer:* $\Delta E = q_V = \int C_V\,dT = C_V(T_2 - T_1) = \frac{3}{2}nR(T_2 - T_1) =$ (3/2)(100/4.00)1.99(1000 − 400) = 45,000 calories.

CALCULATION OF ΔH

Chemists work with systems at constant pressure more commonly than at constant volume. Since $\Delta H = q_P$ [Equation (7.5)], ΔH is a more commonly used function than ΔE. The values of ΔE, as obtained in a bomb calorimeter, for instance, may be readily changed to ΔH values by applying the fundamental definition of H:

$$H = E + PV$$
$$dH = dE + d(PV)$$

For reactions in a condensed phase, $d(PV)$ is usually small; thus $\Delta H = \Delta E$ to a good approximation. For a reaction involving ideal gases, $d(PV) = d(nRT)$. At constant T this gives

$$d(PV) = d(nRT) = RT\,dn$$

or

$$\begin{aligned} dH &= dE + RT\,dn \\ \Delta H &= \Delta E + RT\,\Delta n \end{aligned} \tag{27.1}$$

where Δn represents the change in number of moles of ideal gas during the isothermal reaction. If $\Delta n = 0$, then $\Delta H = \Delta E$.

Reactions need not be performed in a bomb calorimeter. They may be performed in a constant-pressure calorimeter—for example, a Dewar vessel open to the atmosphere as in Figure 27.1. The experiments are carried out as in the bomb. Here

$$\Delta H = q_P$$

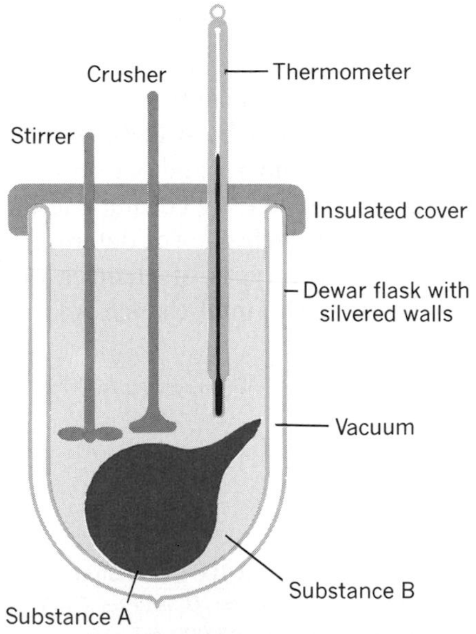

Figure 27.1, A Constant-pressure calorimeter. Substance A is sealed in a thin-walled bulb and allowed to come to thermal equilibrium with substance B and the calorimeter. The thin-walled bulb is then crushed and the temperature change accompanying the reaction of substance A with substance B is noted. Knowledge of the total heat capacity of calorimeter and contents and of the number of moles of reactant then allows the calculation of $\Delta\overline{H}$ for the reaction between the two substances. A and B might be aqueous solutions of $AgNO_3$ and NaCl.

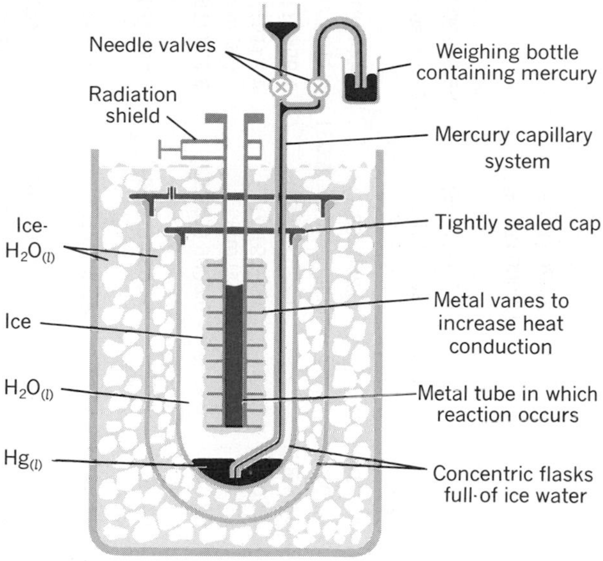

B

Figure 27.1, B A constant-pressure calorimeter operating at $T = 0°$ C, the ice point. Ice is frozen onto the metal vanes of a central tube by placing liquid nitrogen in the tube while it is immersed in water. The excess liquid nitrogen is poured out and the ice-encased tube allowed to come to equilibrium with water at the ice point (0° C). A thermal change is then carried out in the metal tube—phase change or reaction—and the change in volume of the inner ice bath is measured by the change in weight of the mercury in the weighing bottle at the top. This change in weight is proportional to the value of q_P. (Why?) How would you calculate q_P?

and ΔH is the heat actually gained by the system in the calorimeter. Enthalpy changes (commonly, and loosely, called heat changes or heat content changes) are then equal to the observed heats of reaction, q_P. Enthalpies of reaction, ΔH_{reac}, and enthalpies of phase change, ΔH_{pc}, may be readily measured in this way.

For a heating or cooling process we have, from Chapter 7, $\int dH = H_2 - H_1 = \Delta H = \int C_P\, dT$. The C_P is generally a function of T and, especially for gases, many analytical expressions of $C_P = \varphi(T)$ are known. For condensed phases, graphical integration must often be performed. Table 27.1 lists constants for some substances for one common form of analytical expression. The other common forms involve log T, T^2, or T^{-1} terms—all readily integrable functions. Table 27.1 also contains other thermodynamic data we shall refer to shortly.

Thus, for processes involving heating or cooling, using the equations in Table 27.1, we obtain

$$\begin{aligned}\Delta H\Big|_{T_1}^{T_2} &= \int_{T_1}^{T_2} C_P\, dT = \int (a + bT + cT^{-2})\, dT \\ &= \int a\, dT + \int bT\, dT + \int cT^{-2}\, dT \\ &= a(T_2 - T_1) + \frac{b}{2}\left(T_2^2 - T_1^2\right) - c\left(\frac{1}{T_2} - \frac{1}{T_1}\right)\end{aligned}$$

Thus ΔH for any general change is the sum of the enthalpies of reactions, plus the sum of the enthalpies of phase changes, plus the sum of the integrals of $C_P\, dT$:

Table 27.1 Values for some molar thermodynamic functions.

	cal mole^{-1}, °K^{-1} = $\bar{C}_P = a + b \cdot 10^{-3}T + c \cdot 10^5 T^{-2}$				298°K, 1 atm			1 atm	
Substance	a	b	c	Range (°K)	$\Delta\bar{H}^0_{form}$ (kcal mole^{-1})	$\Delta\bar{G}^0_{form}$ (kcal mole^{-1})	$\bar{S}^0$ (cal deg^{-1} mole^{-1})	$\Delta\bar{H}_{fus}$(m.p.) (kcal mole^{-1}, °K)	$\Delta\bar{H}_{vap}$(b.p.) (kcal mole^{-1}, °K)
$Al_{(c)}$	4.94	2.96	—	298–932	0	0	6.769	2.570 (931.7)	67.950 (2600)
$Al_{(g)}$	4.97	0.12	—	298–5000	78.000	68.300	39.304		
$Al_2O_{3(c)}$	27.49	2.82	−8.38	298–1800	−400.400	−378.078	12.174	26.000 (2313)	
$B_2H_{6(g)}$	13.68	18.60	−5.27	298–1500	7.530	19.776	55.334	1.06 (107.7)	3.45 (180.63)
$BO_{(g)}$	6.89	1.08	−0.21	298–2500	5.744	−1.028	48.607		
$Ca_{(\alpha c)}$	5.25	3.44	—	298–713	0	0	9.95	$(\alpha - \beta)$0.270 (713)	
$Ca_{(\beta c)}$	2.68	6.80	—	713–1123				2.070 (1123)	
$CaO_{(c)}$	11.67	1.08	−1.56	298–2000	−151.790	−144.4	9.5	12.000 (2873)	
$CaO_{(g)}$	8.70	0.16	−0.74	298–2000					
$CaCl_{2(c)}$	17.18	3.04	−0.60	298–1055	−190.4	−179.3	27.2	6.780 (1055)	55.0 (2300)
$C_{(graphite)}$	4.03	1.14	−2.04	298–2500	0	0	1.359	(subl. 1 atm, 4620)	170.89 (subl. 298)
$C_{(diamond)}$	2.27	3.06	−1.54	298–1200	0.4533	0.6930	0.568		
$CO_{(g)}$	6.79	0.98	−0.11	298–2500	−26.417	−32.783	47.214	0.200 (68.1)	1.444 (81.66)
$CO_{2(g)}$	10.57	2.10	−2.06	298–2500	−94.054	−94.265	51.072	sublimes $\Delta H = 6.031$ kcal (194.7)	
$CH_{4(g)}$	5.65	11.44	−0.46	298–1500	−17.895	−12.145	44.490	0.225 (90.68)	1.955 (111.67)
$C_2H_{2(g)}$	12.13	3.84	−2.46	298–2000	54.190	49.993	48.004	0.9 (191.7) 900 mm	4.2 (191.7) 900 mm
$C_2H_{4(g)}$[a]	2.706	29.160	$-90.59 \cdot 10^{-7}T^2$	273–1500	12.496	16.281	52.447	0.8008 (103.97)	3.237 (169.45)
$C_2H_{6(g)}$[a]	2.195	38.282	$-110.01 \cdot 10^{-7}T^2$	273–1500	−20.236	−7.860	54.85	0.6834 (89.89)	3.517 (184.53)
$C_6H_{6(g)}$[a]	−0.283	77.936	$-262.96 \cdot 10^{-7}T^2$	273–1500	19.280	30.989	64.34	2.35 (278.7)	7.35 (353.3)
$Cl_{2(g)}$	8.85	0.16	−0.68	298–3000	0	0	53.289	1.531 (172.16)	4.878 (239.1)
$F_{2(g)}$	8.26	0.60	−0.84	298–2500	0	0	48.447	.122 (53.54)	1.562 (85.0)
$H_{2(g)}$	6.52	0.78	0.12	298–3000	0	0	31.208	.028 (13.96)	.216 (20.39)
$H_2O_{(g)}$	7.30	2.46	—	298–2750	−57.798	−54.636	45.106		
$H_2O_{(l)}$	18.04	—	—	298–373	−68.317	−56.688	16.75	1.436 (273.16)	9.770 (373.16)
$H_2O_{2(l)}$	12.81	28.00	—	298–450	−44.88	−28.78	26.2	2.920 (272.5)	10.53 (425)
$HCl_{(g)}$	6.27	1.24	0.30	298–2000	−21.970	−22.685	44.645	.476 (158.9)	3.860 (188.1)

$HCN_{(g)}$	9.41	2.70	−1.44	298–2500	31.200	28.704	48.213	.040 (170.4)	6.027 (298.8)
$HF_{(g)}$	6.55	0.72	0.17	298–4000	−64.800	−65.301	41.509	1.094 (190.1)	1.800 (293.1)
$HNO_{3(g)}$					−32.28	−17.87	63.64		
$K_{(c)}$	1.34	19.40	—	298–336.4	0	0	15.3	.554 (336.7)	18.530 (1030)
$K_{(l)}$	7.06	.70	—	336.4–1100	0.546				
$K_2O_{(c)}$	18.53	—	—	298	−86.400	−75.64	20.3		
$KCl_{(c)}$	9.89	5.20	0.77	298–1043	−104.175	−97.592	19.76	6.100 (1043)	38.840 (1680)
$N_{2(g)}$	6.66	1.02	—	298–2500	0	0	45.77	0.172 (63.78)	1.335 (77.36)
$NH_{3(g)}$	7.11	6.00	−0.37	298–2000	−11.02	−3.94	45.97	1.35 (195.40)	5.58 (239.73)
$NO_{(g)}$	7.03	0.92	−0.14	298–2500	21.59	20.69	50.347	0.55 (109.5)	3.293 (121.4)
$NO_{2(g)}$	10.07	2.28	−1.67	298–2000	8.011	12.354	57.323		
$N_2O_{4(g)}$	20.05	9.50	−3.56	298–1000	2.274	23.485	72.636	3.502 (261.96)	9.101 (294)
$O_{2(g)}$	7.16	1.00	−0.40	298–3000	0	0	49.004	.106 (54.36)	1.630 (90.19)
$O_{3(g)}$	11.23	1.92	−2.16	298–1500	34.100	38.997	57.080		2.59 (162.65)
$S_{8(g)}$	42.54	1.04	−5.04	298–1000	24.510	11.919	103.280	2.360 (392)	20. (717.76) [equilib ⟶ g]
$SO_{2(g)}$	11.04	1.88	−1.84	298–2000	−70.947	−71.741	59.298	2.060 (200)	5.955 (263.14)
$SO_{3(g)}$	13.90	6.10	−3.22	293–1500	−94.45	−88.545	61.342	2.060 (290)	9.99 (316.5)

SOURCE: Columns 2–5 from K. K. Kelley, U.S. Bureau of Mines Bulletin 584 (1960); columns 6–10 mostly from Wicks and Block, U.S. Bureau of mines Bulletin 605 (1963) or *JANAF Thermochemical Data*, Midland, Mich., Dow Chemical Co., 1960– .

[a]The heat-capacity equations for gaseous C_2H_4, C_2H_6, and C_6H_6 have their first two terms in the same form as those of other substances, but the third term differs.

$$\Delta H_{\text{tot}} = \Sigma\, \Delta H_{\text{reac}} + \Sigma\, \Delta H_{\text{pc}} + \Sigma \int C_P\, dT \qquad (27.2)$$

Exercise 27.2

Calculate the heat required to melt one ton of aluminum. *Answer:* Assume constant pressure, initial $T = 300°\text{K}$, final $T = 932°\text{K}$. $\Delta H = q_P = n[\int C_P\, dT + \Delta H_{\text{fus}}] = n[\int(4.94 + 2.96 \cdot 10^{-3}T)\, dT + \Delta H_{\text{fus}}] = n[4.94(T_2 - T_1) + 1.48 \cdot 10^{-3}(T_2{}^2 - T_1{}^2) + \Delta H_{\text{fus}}] = [2000 \cdot 454/(27.0 \cdot 1000)][4.94(932 - 300) + 1.48 \cdot 10^{-3}(932^2 - 300^2) + 2570] = 216$ kcal.

VARIATION OF H WITH P

It may be shown that $(\partial H/\partial P)_T = V(1 - \alpha T)$ and $(\partial H/\partial V)_T = (\alpha T - 1)/\beta$, where $\alpha = (1/V)(\partial V/\partial T)_P$, the volume coefficient of thermal expansion, and $\beta = -(1/V)(\partial V/\partial P)_T$, the volume coefficient of compressibility. For ideal gases both $(\partial H/\partial P)_T$ and $(\partial H/\partial V)_T$ equal zero, and they are small for all systems except at large pressures. We shall assume ΔH is independent of P and V.

Exercise 27.3

Calculate the heat generated in changing the pressure from 1 to 1000 atm at constant temperature for a liquid having a volume coefficient of thermal expansion of $10^{-4}\,°\text{K}^{-1}$. *Answer:* Assume α constant, and ΔV negligible compared to V. $(\partial H/\partial P)_T = V(1 - \alpha T)$, $\Delta H = \int V(1 - \alpha T)\, dP = V(1 - \alpha T)(P_2 - P_1) = V(1 - 10^{-4} \cdot 300)(1000 - 1) = 0.97$ liter atm per liter of volume $= 23$ cal per liter of volume.

VARIATION OF H WITH T—USE OF THE BRIDGMAN TABLE

This leaves the variation of H with T to be studied. From Equation (7.7),

$$\left(\frac{\partial H}{\partial T}\right)_P = C_P$$

Since H is relatively independent of P and V, we might assume that $(\partial H/\partial T)_V = C_P$ also. The actual value is

$$\begin{aligned}\left(\frac{\partial H}{\partial T}\right)_V &= C_P + T\left(\frac{\partial V}{\partial T}\right)_P^2\left(\frac{\partial P}{\partial V}\right)_T - V\left(\frac{\partial V}{\partial T}\right)_P\left(\frac{\partial P}{\partial V}\right)_T \\ &= C_P - \frac{TV\alpha^2}{\beta} + \frac{V\alpha}{\beta} = C_P - \frac{(T\alpha - 1)V\alpha}{\beta} \\ &= C_P + \frac{(1 - \alpha T)V\alpha}{\beta} \qquad (27.3)\end{aligned}$$

where the last term is ordinarily small. Thus we shall ordinarily assume that $(\partial H/\partial T)_V = C_P$.

Presumably we could derive Equation (27.3) for $(\partial H/\partial T)_V$ from the four laws and the definitions of the thermodynamic functions, but the derivation would no doubt be a long one. P. W. Bridgman greatly simplified the cataloging of thermodynamic partial differential equations when he constructed the tabulation shown in Table 27.2. This table makes it easy

Table 27.2 **For the derivation of thermodynamic formulas any partial derivative may be treated as the ratio of two terms. These terms are given below. Note that the most common variables in addition to P, V, and T are C_P, $(\partial V/\partial T)_P = \alpha V$, and $(\partial V/\partial P)_T = \beta V$, three of the most readily available types of data. S is the only other variable used—also often tabulated.**

$$(\partial T)_P = -(\partial P)_T = 1$$
$$(\partial V)_P = -(\partial P)_V = (\partial V/\partial T)_P$$
$$(\partial S)_P = -(\partial P)_S = C_P/T$$
$$(\partial E)_P = -(\partial P)_E = C_P - P(\partial V/\partial T)_P$$
$$(\partial H)_P = -(\partial P)_H = C_P$$
$$(\partial G)_P = -(\partial P)_G = -S$$
$$(\partial A)_P = -(\partial P)_A = -[S + P(\partial V/\partial T)_P]$$

$$(\partial V)_T = -(\partial T)_V = -(\partial V/\partial P)_T$$
$$(\partial S)_T = -(\partial T)_S = (\partial V/\partial T)_P$$
$$(\partial E)_T = -(\partial T)_E = T(\partial V/\partial T)_P + P(\partial V/\partial P)_T$$
$$(\partial H)_T = -(\partial T)_H = -V + T(\partial V/\partial T)_P$$
$$(\partial G)_T = -(\partial T)_G = -V$$
$$(\partial A)_T = -(\partial T)_A = P(\partial V/\partial P)_T$$

$$(\partial S)_V = -(\partial V)_S = (1/T)[C_P(\partial V/\partial P)_T + T(\partial V/\partial T)_P^2]$$
$$(\partial E)_V = -(\partial V)_E = C_P(\partial V/\partial P)_T + T(\partial V/\partial T)_P^2$$
$$(\partial H)_V = -(\partial V)_H = C_P(\partial V/\partial P)_T + T(\partial V/\partial T)_P^2 - V(\partial V/\partial T)_P$$
$$(\partial G)_V = -(\partial V)_G = -[V(\partial V/\partial T)_P + S(\partial V/\partial P)_T]$$
$$(\partial A)_V = -(\partial V)_A = -S(\partial V/\partial P)_T$$

$$(\partial E)_S = -(\partial S)_E = (P/T)[C_P(\partial V/\partial P)_T + T(\partial V/\partial T)_P^2]$$
$$(\partial H)_S = -(\partial S)_H = -VC_P/T$$
$$(\partial G)_S = -(\partial S)_G = -(1/T)[VC_P - ST(\partial V/\partial T)_P]$$
$$(\partial A)_S = -(\partial S)_A = (1/T)(P[C_P(\partial V/\partial P)_T + T(\partial V/\partial T)_P^2] + ST(\partial V/\partial T)_P)$$

$$(\partial H)_E = -(\partial E)_H = -V[C_P - P(\partial V/\partial T)_P] - P[C_P(\partial V/\partial P)_T + T(\partial V/\partial T)_P^2]$$
$$(\partial G)_E = -(\partial E)_G = -V[C_P - P(\partial V/\partial T)_P] + S[T(\partial V/\partial T)_P + P(\partial V/\partial P)_T]$$
$$(\partial A)_E = -(\partial E)_A = P[C_P(\partial V/\partial P)_T + T(\partial V/\partial T)_P^2]$$

$$(\partial G)_H = -(\partial H)_G = -V(C_P + S) + TS(\partial V/\partial T)_P$$
$$(\partial A)_H = -(\partial H)_A = -[S + P(\partial V/\partial T)_P][V - T(\partial V/\partial T)_P] + P(\partial V/\partial P)_T$$
$$(\partial A)_G = -(\partial G)_A = -S[V + P(\partial V/\partial P)_T] - PV(\partial V/\partial T)_P$$

SOURCE: P. W. Bridgman, *Phys. Rev.*, **3**, 273 (1914).

to write down any of the common partial derivatives of the thermodynamic functions by setting down the appropriate partial derivatives and then constructing the right side of the equation from Table 27.2. [Try obtaining Equation (27.3) in this way.]

We shall use Table 27.2 from time to time instead of a derivation. However, if you are asked to perform a derivation on a test or problem, it is *not* sufficient to use Table 27.2. You may wish to use the table to check your result, but all your derivations are to start from the four laws and the definitions of the thermodynamic functions, and are to show each step from then on. You should already have noted some of the powerful mathematical devices for chemical work: using the properties of a perfect differential [equations (26.5) and (26.9)], taking total derivatives (pp. 677 and 691), substituting from Maxwell's equations [equation (27.8) and p. 690], plus the standard substitutions from the first and second laws.

VARIATIONS IN H

Table 27.3 summarizes the variation of H with P, V, and T. As can be seen, we need generally concern ourselves only with the variation of H with T, $dH = C_P\,dT$, regardless of variations in P or V.

Exercise 27.4

Calculate the ΔH_{vap} of water as a function of T. Data in Table 27.1. *Answer:* For water, $dH_l = (C_P)_l\,dT$; for gas, $dH_g = (C_P)_g\,dT$; for vaporization, $\Delta H_{\text{vap}} = H_g - H_l$ or $d(\Delta H_{\text{vap}}) = dH_g - dH_l = (C_P)_g\,dT - (C_P)_l\,dT$. Then $d(\Delta H_{\text{vap}}) = [(C_P)_g - (C_P)_l]\,dT = \Delta C_P\,dT$, or $(\Delta H_{\text{vap}})_T - (\Delta H_{\text{vap}})_{373} = \int_{373}^{T} \Delta C_P\,dT$; $(\Delta H_{\text{vap}})_T = (\Delta H_{\text{vap}})_{373} + \int(7.30 + 2.46 \cdot 10^{-3}T - 18.04)\,dT = 9770 - 10.74(T - 373) + 1.23 \cdot 10^{-3}(T^2 - 373^2) = [13{,}610 - 10.74T + 1.23 \cdot 10^{-3}T^2]$ cal mole^{-1}.

HEATS OF REACTION

A very serious problem would result if the thermodynamic properties of every chemical reaction had to be determined by separate experiments. We already know several million compounds, and the number of reactions among them is astronomical. Fortunately it is sufficient to know the properties of the compounds—no mean task in itself. This great simplification is included in the first law. During any change in a closed system the total energy change is the difference between the sum of the internal energies of the products and the sum of internal energies of the reactants. The same thing is true of enthalpy. Thus, for any reaction

$$\text{aA} + \text{bB} + \text{cC} = \text{dD} + \text{fF}$$

$$\Delta H = \text{enthalpy gained by system} = q_P$$

$$\Delta H_{\text{tot}} = \text{d}\overline{H}_{\text{D}} + \text{f}\overline{H}_{\text{F}} - \text{a}\overline{H}_{\text{A}} - \text{b}\overline{H}_{\text{B}} - \text{c}\overline{H}_{\text{C}}$$

$$\Delta H_{\text{tot}} = \sum_i n_i \overline{H}_{i(\text{products } i)} - \sum_j n_j \overline{H}_{j(\text{reactants } j)}$$

The values of $\overline{H}_i$ are called the molar heats of formation of each substance i under the conditions of the reaction. We have showed that values of H are relatively insensitive to variations in P and V at constant T. Thus determination of

Table 27.3 ***H* as a function of *P*, *V*, and *T*.**

Exact	Approximate (most systems)	Ideal gas (exactly)	ΔH
$(\partial H/\partial P)_T = V(1 - \alpha T)$	$= 0$	$= 0$	$\Delta H \cong 0$, if P varies
$(\partial H/\partial V)_T = (\alpha T - 1)/\beta$	$= 0$	$= 0$	$\Delta H \cong 0$, if V varies
$(\partial H/\partial T)_P = C_P$	$= C_P$ (exactly)	$= C_P$	$\Delta H = \int C_P\,dT$, const. P
$(\partial H/\partial T)_V = C_P + (1 - \alpha T)V\alpha/\beta$	$= C_P$	$= C_P$	$\Delta H \cong \int C_P\,dT$, const. V

$\overline{H}_{\text{formation}}$ is greatly simplified. Only the temperature need be carefully controlled.

We define the heat of formation of any substance at any temperature as the enthalpy change when the elements react to give that substance. Careful work requires a standard pressure—it is usually 1 atm. The common standard temperature is $25°C = 298.15°K$, and most values of standard heats of formation, ΔH_f^0, are tabulated for this temperature. The above definition of heat of formation includes an implicit definition: the standard heats of formation, ΔH_f^0, of all the elements are defined as zero at 298.15°K and 1 atm pressure.

Consider the following experiments. When H_2 and Cl_2 react in the standard state so that the initial and final conditions are both at 298.15°K and 1 atm, we find that $q_P = \Delta H = -22.062$ kcal mole^{-1}. Thus

$$\tfrac{1}{2}H_{2(g)} + \tfrac{1}{2}Cl_{2(g)} = HCl_{(g)}, \qquad \Delta H = -22.062 \text{ kcal mole}^{-1}$$
$$n\,\Delta\overline{H}_f \qquad 0 \qquad 0 \qquad -22.062$$

The standard heat of formation of $HCl_{(g)}$ is -22.062 kcal mole^{-1} at 298.15°K. The standard heats of formation of H_2 and Cl_2 at 298.15°K are zero, by definition. Similarly,

$$Na_{(c)} + \tfrac{1}{2}Cl_{2(g)} = NaCl_{(c)}, \qquad \Delta H = -98.232 \text{ kcal mole}^{-1}$$
$$n\,\Delta\overline{H}_f \qquad 0 \qquad 0 \qquad -98.232$$

From these two reactions the heat of a third reaction can be predicted:

$$Na_{(c)} + HCl_{(g)} = H_{2(g)} + NaCl_{(c)}$$
$$n\,\Delta\overline{H}_f \qquad 0 \qquad -22.062 \qquad 0 \qquad -98.232$$

or

$$\Delta H_{\text{reac}} = -98.232 - (-22.062) = -76.170 \text{ kcal mole}^{-1}$$

Thus tabulation of experimentally determined standard heats of formation of all known compounds would allow the calculation of ΔH_{reac} of all possible reactions. Table 27.1 tabulates a minute fraction of the known values of enthalpies of formation at 298°K. (Actually many tabulations are at 298°K but we shall not be concerned with the small differences between 298, 298.15, or 298.16°K as standards. They can all be made consistent, of course, if C_P is known, see Table 27.3.)

The data in Table 27.1 allow us to calculate $\Delta H_{298°K}$ for any reaction involving the species in that table and the elements. Remember that $\Delta H_{\text{formation}}$ of all elements is 0 at 298°K by definition. We shall use ΔH_f to represent enthalpy of formation, and assume $\Delta H_f = \Delta H_f{}^0$ as long as T is constant. In general

$$\Delta H_{\text{reac}} = \sum_i n_i\,\Delta\overline{H}_{f(\text{products } i)} - \sum_j n_j\,\Delta\overline{H}_{f(\text{reactants } j)}$$

Exercise 27.5

Calculate and comment on the heat of reaction at 298°K for $Al_2O_{3(c)} + 3H_{2(g)} = 2Al_{(c)} + 3H_2O_{(l)}$. *Answer:* $\Delta H^0 = 2\,\Delta H_f^0{}_{Al} + 3\,\Delta H_f^0{}_{H_2O(l)} - \Delta H_f^0{}_{Al_2O_3(c)} - 3\,\Delta H_f^0{}_{H_2(g)} = 0 + 3(-57.8) - (-400.9) - 0 = 227.0$ kcal, an endothermic reaction. Since ΔS^0 is probably negative, ΔG^0 will be positive and this is a most unlikely reaction in the standard state.

VARIATION OF ΔH_{reac} WITH TEMPERATURE, PRESSURE, AND VOLUME

The values of ΔH_{reac} are assumed to be constant at all values of P and V, but they do vary appreciably with T. We have frequently used the relation

$$dH = C_P\,dT$$

For a reaction, if there are no phase changes among reactants or products as T varies, this becomes the differential form of the

KIRCHHOFF EQUATION: $$d(\Delta H_{\text{reac}}) = \Delta C_P\,dT$$

where

$$\begin{aligned}
\Delta C_P &= \sum_i n_i\overline{C}_{P(\text{products } i)} - \sum_j n_j\overline{C}_{P(\text{reactants } j)} \\
&= \sum_i (n_i a_i + n_i b_i T + n_i c_i T^{-2}) - \sum_j (n_j a_j + n_j b_j T + n_j c_j T^{-2}) \\
&= (\Delta a + \Delta b T + \Delta c T^{-2}) \\
d\,\Delta H &= \Delta C_P\,dT \\
\int_{298}^{T} d\,\Delta H &= \int_{298}^{T} \Delta C_P\,dT \\
\Delta H_T - \Delta H_{298} &= \int_{298}^{T} \Delta C_P\,dT = \int_{298}^{T} (\Delta a + \Delta b T + \Delta c T^{-2})\,dT
\end{aligned}$$

$$\begin{aligned}
\Delta H_T &= \Delta H_{298} + \int_{298}^{T} \Delta a\,dT + \int_{298}^{T} \Delta b T\,dT + \int_{298}^{T} \Delta c T^{-2}\,dT \\
&= \Delta H_{298} + \Delta a(T - 298) + \frac{\Delta b}{2}(T^2 - 298^2) - \Delta c\left(\frac{1}{T} - \frac{1}{298}\right)
\end{aligned}$$

which becomes the integrated form of the

KIRCHOFF EQUATION:

$$\Delta H_T = \Delta H_{298} + \Delta a(T - 298) + \frac{\Delta b}{2}(T^2 - 298^2) + \Delta c\left(\frac{1}{298} - \frac{1}{T}\right) \qquad (27.4)$$

Thus, to calculate ΔH_T at any temperature T for any reaction, we need the value of ΔH_{298} for the reaction and the heat capacity equations for each reactant and each product. From the C_P equations we can calculate Δa, Δb, and Δc for the reaction.

Consider the $\frac{1}{2}H_2 + \frac{1}{2}Cl_2 = HCl$ reaction:

$$\tfrac{1}{2}H_{2(g)} + \tfrac{1}{2}Cl_{2(g)} = HCl_{(g)}, \qquad \Delta H = -22.062 \text{ kcal mole}^{-1}$$

From Table 27.1 we get

$$\begin{array}{lll}
C_P(\text{HCl}) & & 6.27 + 1.24 \cdot 10^{-3}T + 0.30 \cdot 10^5 T^{-2} \\
C_P(\frac{1}{2}H_2) & = 3.26 + 0.39 \cdot 10^{-3}T + 0.06 \cdot 10^5 T^{-2} & \\
C_P(\frac{1}{2}Cl_2) & = 4.43 + 0.08 \cdot 10^{-3}T - 0.34 \cdot 10^5 T^{-2} & \\
\hline
\Sigma C_{P(\text{reactants})} & = 7.69 + 0.47 \cdot 10^{-3}T - 0.28 \cdot 10^5 T^{-2} & \\
 & & \text{or } -7.69 - 0.47 \cdot 10^{-3}T + 0.28 \cdot 10^5 T^{-2} \\
\Delta C_P & = & \overline{-1.42 + 0.77 \cdot 10^{-3}T + 0.58 \cdot 10^5 T^{-2}}
\end{array}$$

Thus, for the reaction $\frac{1}{2}H_{2(g)} + \frac{1}{2}Cl_{2(g)} = HCl_{(g)}$, we obtain

$$\Delta C_P = -1.42 + 0.77 \cdot 10^{-3}T + 0.58 \cdot 10^5 T^{-2}$$
$$= \Delta a + \Delta b T + \Delta c T^{-2}$$

From Equation (27.4) the heat of this reaction at T is given by

$$\Delta H_T = -22{,}062 - 1.42(T - 298) + \frac{0.77}{2} \cdot 10^{-3}(T^2 - 298^2) + 0.58 \cdot 10^5\left(\frac{1}{298} - \frac{1}{T}\right)$$

The numerical terms may be collected into a single term to give

$$\Delta H_T = -21{,}539 - 1.42T + 0.39 \cdot 10^{-3}T^2 + 0.58 \cdot 10^5 T^{-2}$$

This equation is valid in the range 298–2000°K. The C_P equation for HCl is not valid at higher temperatures. Note that ΔH and ΔC_P must be expressed in the same units if they are to be added. In this example we have used cal mole^{-1}.

You can now calculate ΔH_f and ΔH_{reac} at any value of T for any changes involving only the species listed in Table 27.1. Reference to standard tabulations allows the calculation of ΔH as a function of T for thousands of compounds and hundreds of thousands of reactions. Such calculations are essential to the control and comprehension of all chemical processes—for example, industrial design of plants, rocket theory and practice, chemical synthesis. ΔH is valuable in and of itself but these calculations also are integral to the determination of ΔG and of equilibrium constants under conditions where they cannot be accurately measured directly—as in a rocket nozzle or under stellar conditions.

ADIABATIC REACTIONS

Reactions may be carried out under adiabatic conditions, $q = 0$, as well as under isothermal conditions. For an adiabatic reaction at constant pressure, $q_P = 0 = \Delta H$. Thus the ΔH that would have been lost or gained by the system in an isothermal change must now be involved in heating or cooling the system. Consider Figure 27.2 for a process in which ΔH_{298} is negative.

Now what temperature will the system attain, starting at 298°, if the reac-

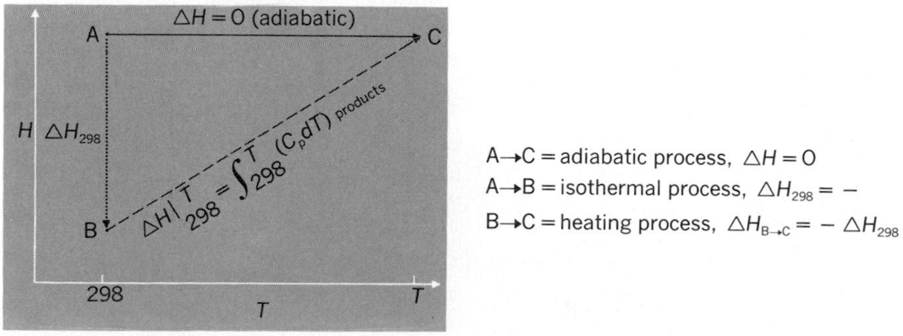

Figure 27.2 Comparison of an isothermal process, here $\Delta H = -$, and an adiabatic process, $\Delta H = 0$, both at constant pressure in the same system.

tion is performed adiabatically at constant pressure—that is, proceeds from A to C at constant H? Since H is a state function, ΔH is independent of path. Since H is constant for the system, any change in H must appear as a change in T of the system. We now invent a path from A to C for which we have data to calculate T. Such a path is A $\longrightarrow$ B $\longrightarrow$ C. A $\longrightarrow$ B is a constant temperature process, $\Delta H = \Delta H_{298}$, $\Delta T = 0$. B $\longrightarrow$ C is a heating process using up ΔH_{298} in heating the system, $\Delta T = T - 298$:

$$\Delta H = \int_{298}^{T} (C_P\, dT)_{\text{products}} + \Delta H_{298} = 0$$

Thus we calculate the temperature to which the products of the reaction can be changed by the heat involved in converting reactants to products at 298°K.

Flames and explosions are examples of very rapid reactions, so rapid in fact that their centers approximate adiabatic conditions. This allows calculation of maximum flame and explosion temperatures from data on the heat of reaction at some measurable temperature and the heat capacities of the reaction products.

In general, for an adiabatic reaction at constant pressure,

$$-\Delta H_{T_1} = \int_{T_1}^{T_2} (C_P\, dT)_{\text{products}} \tag{27.5}$$

Figure 27.2 can be extended to illustrate Equation (27.10), as shown in Figure 27.3, for the case where $|\Delta H_{T_1}| > |\Delta H_{T_2}|$ and ΔH_{T_1} and ΔH_{T_2} are both negative.

CALCULATION OF ΔS

Absolute values of E and H are not known. We deal only with ΔE and ΔH. This is mainly because of the easy interconversion of mass and energy and because of our inability to measure mass with enough accuracy to determine small conversions.

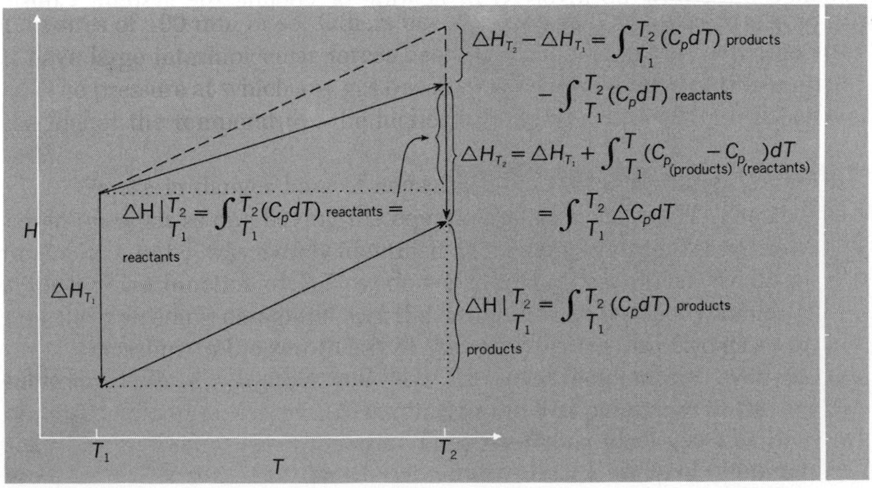

Figure 27.3 Illustration of Kirchhoff relationship used in obtaining Equation (27.10).

The conversion factor c^2 in the Einstein equation $\Delta E = c^2 \Delta m$ is so enormous that tiny conversions of mass produce very large amounts of energy. Thus we are satisfied to define arbitrary standard states (the pure elements at 1 atm and 298°K) as having zero enthalpies and measure all changes with respect to this arbitrary zero. We adopted the same policy in calculating $\mathcal{E}^0$ for any half-reaction in an electric cell.

Entropy functions are different. According to the third law, the entropy of any pure, perfect crystal at 0°K is exactly zero:

THIRD LAW: $$S^0_{0°\text{K}} = 0$$

Thus we can determine and tabulate absolute values of S_T if we can measure ΔS in going from 0°K to T°K. The absolute value of ΔS for any change, then, will be the difference in entropy of the products and reactants. Table 27.1 tabulates values of $\bar{S}^0_{298°}$ for a small fraction of the substances for which values are known. How are these values obtained?

From the second law,

THERMAL SECOND LAW: $$\Delta S = \frac{q_{\text{rev}}}{T}$$

PROBABILITY SECOND LAW: $$\Delta S = k \ln \frac{W_2}{W_1}$$

We shall use both laws, but we discuss the thermal first. Consider pure substances at constant pressure. As in Equation (27.2), for a pure substance, we get

$$\Delta S \Big|_{T_1}^{T_2} = \sum \frac{q_{\text{rev}}}{T} = \sum \frac{q_P}{T} = \sum \frac{\Delta H_{\text{tot}}}{T} = \sum \left(\frac{\Delta H}{T}\right)_{\text{pc}} + \sum \int \frac{C_P\, dT}{T}$$

$$\Delta S \Big|_{T}^{T_2} = \sum \left(\frac{\Delta H}{T}\right)_{\text{pc}} + \sum \int \frac{C_P}{T}\, dT$$

VARIATION OF ENTROPY WITH T

Thus, for constant-pressure processes, with a pure substance,

$$\Delta S = \sum \left(\frac{\Delta H}{T}\right)_{\text{pc}} + \sum \int \frac{C_P}{T}\, dT \qquad (27.6)$$

assuming that each phase change is carried out at a constant value of T (which can be different, of course, for each change). The $\int (C_P/T)\, dT$ terms take care of changing the system from one T to another.

If we have an analytical expression for C_P as a function of T, the evaluation of ΔS is straightforward. Consider heating 2 moles of oxygen from 298°K to 1000°K, assuming that any reaction (such as dissociation) is negligible. There are no phase changes, so

$$\Delta S = \int \frac{C_P}{T}\, dT$$

$$\Delta\bar{S}_{O_2} = \int_{298}^{1000} (7.16 + 1.00 \cdot 10^{-3}T - 0.40 \cdot 10^5 T^{-2}) \frac{dT}{T}$$

$$= \int_{298}^{1000} \left(\frac{7.16}{T} + 1.00 \cdot 10^{-3} - 0.40 \cdot 10^5 T^{-3}\right) dT$$

$$= 7.16 \int_{298}^{1000} \frac{dT}{T} + 1.00 \cdot 10^{-3} \int_{298}^{1000} dT - 0.40 \cdot 10^5 \int_{298}^{1000} \frac{dT}{T^3}$$

$$\Delta\bar{S}_{O_2} = 7.16 \ln \frac{1000}{298} + 1.00 \cdot 10^{-3}(1000 - 298) + \frac{0.40 \cdot 10^5}{2}\left(\frac{1}{1000^2} - \frac{1}{298^2}\right)$$

$$= 7.16 \cdot 1.211 + 1.00 \cdot 10^{-3} \cdot 702 + 0.20 \cdot 10^5(0.10 \cdot 10^{-5} - 1.13 \cdot 10^{-5})$$

$$= 8.66 + 0.702 - 0.21 = 9.15 \text{ cal mole}^{-1} \text{ deg}^{-1}$$

For 2 moles, $\Delta S = 18.30$ cal deg^{-1} when oxygen is heated from 298°K to 1000°K.

For any reversible phase change,

$$\Delta S_{sys} = \left(\frac{\Delta H}{T}\right)_{pc}$$

Thus $\Delta\bar{H}_{fus}$ of $CaCl_{2(c)}$ is 6.780 kcal mole^{-1} at 1055°K, and therefore

$$\Delta\bar{S}_{fus} = \frac{6780}{1055} = 6.42 \text{ cal mole}^{-1} \text{ deg}^{-1}$$

VARIATION OF ENTROPY WITH PRESSURE

Entropy, unlike E and H, is a marked function of P and V. We could write down the relationships, using Table 27.2, but it will be better to run through a derivation, to provide additional experience and background for your own efforts.

From Maxwell's third relation, $(\partial S/\partial P)_T = -(\partial V/\partial T)_P$. At constant T,

$$dS = -\left(\frac{\partial V}{\partial T}\right)_P dP = -V\alpha \, dP$$

For an ideal gas, $V\alpha = nR/P$, $dS = -nR\, dP/P = -nR d \ln P$,

$$\Delta S_T = nR \ln \frac{P_1}{P_2}$$

which we derived before as Equation (26.12).

VARIATION OF ENTROPY WITH VOLUME

Similarly, with varying V and constant T from Maxwell's fourth relation, $(\partial S/\partial V)_T = (\partial P/\partial T)_V$, we get

$$dS = \left(\frac{\partial P}{\partial T}\right)_V dV$$

in which $(\partial P/\partial T)_V$ may be evaluated by taking the total derivative of V with respect to P and T:

$$dV = \left(\frac{\partial V}{\partial P}\right)_T dP + \left(\frac{\partial V}{\partial T}\right)_P dT$$

At constant volume, $dV = 0$ and

$$0 = \left(\frac{\partial V}{\partial P}\right)_T dP + \left(\frac{\partial V}{\partial T}\right)_P dT$$

or

$$-\left(\frac{\partial P}{\partial T}\right)_V = \frac{(\partial V/\partial T)_P}{(\partial V/\partial P)_T}$$

$$\left(\frac{\partial P}{\partial T}\right)_V = \frac{\alpha}{\beta} \qquad (27.7)$$

Thus, at constant T,

$$dS = \frac{\alpha}{\beta}\, dV$$

For an ideal gas, we can substitute values of α and β from the ideal gas laws to get

$$\alpha = \frac{1}{V}\left(\frac{\partial V}{\partial T}\right)_P = \frac{R}{PV}$$

$$\beta = -\frac{1}{V}\left(\frac{\partial V}{\partial P}\right)_T = \frac{RT}{P^2V}$$

$$dS = \frac{R/PV}{RT/P^2V} dV = \frac{P}{T} dV$$

$$= \frac{nR}{V} dV = nRd\ln V$$

$$\Delta S_T = nR \ln \frac{V_2}{V_1}$$

which we derived before as Equation (10.2). Note that the derivation included assumptions about a reversible process. But, since ΔS is a state function, the final equation is not so limited—it relates entropy to volume for any isothermal process in an ideal gas with only $P\,dV$ work. Under these conditions $(V_2/V_1) = (W_2/W_1)$, the ratio of the number of attainable states before and after the volume change.

Thus, for gases, ΔS depends strongly on P and V at constant T. For condensed phases, $\alpha/\beta \cong 0.1$ and dV is small so there are normally only small effects on S. We shall assume them to be negligible.

TROUTON'S RULE

It is observed, based on experimental $(\Delta H_{\text{vap}}/T)$ data, that the molar entropy of vaporization of many substances equals about 21 eu at the normal boiling point of the substance. This rule is named after its discoverer, Trouton. Note that this means that such substances have $(W_2/W_1) \cong 4 \cdot 10^4$ at the normal boiling point for each molecule, assuming they are independent of one another. This can be interpreted to indicate that the $(\overline{V}_g/\overline{V}_l)$ ratio in gas and liquid is $4 \cdot 10^4$ at the boiling point. Thus, for a liquid such as ether boiling to give a gaseous molar volume at 1 atm of 25,000 ml, the free volume in the liquid must be about 0.6 ml; the actual total molar volume of liquid is about 70 ml. Thus only about 1% of the total liquid volume is available to accommodate free molecular motions. This interpretation assumes, of course, that the molecular rotations and vibrations are the same in the liquid and gaseous state.

VARIATION OF ENTROPY WITH TEMPERATURE AND VOLUME

We may derive a more general equation for ΔS if no reactions or phase changes occur; by taking the total derivative of S,

$$dS = \left(\frac{\partial S}{\partial T}\right)_V dT + \left(\frac{\partial S}{\partial V}\right)_T dV$$

or

$$T\,dS = T\left(\frac{\partial S}{\partial T}\right)_V dT + T\left(\frac{\partial S}{\partial V}\right)_T dV$$

but

$$(q_{\mathrm{rev}})_V = (T\,dS)_V = C_V\,dT$$

so

$$T\left(\frac{\partial S}{\partial T}\right)_V = C_V$$

From Maxwell's fourth relation, $(\partial S/\partial V)_T = (\partial P/\partial T)_V$. Thus $T\,dS = C_V\,dT + T(\partial P/\partial T)_V\,dV$ or $dS = C_V\,d\ln T + (\partial P/\partial T)_V\,dV$. This includes both the term for changing temperature and the term for changing volume:

$$\Delta S = \int C_V\,d\ln T + \left(\frac{\partial P}{\partial T}\right)_V dV \tag{27.8}$$

For an ideal gas this becomes

$$\Delta\bar{S} = \int \bar{C}_V\,d\ln T + \int R\frac{d\bar{V}}{\bar{V}} = \int \bar{C}_V\,d\ln T + R\int d\ln \bar{V}$$

$$= \int \bar{C}_V\,d\ln T + R\ln\frac{\bar{V}_2}{\bar{V}_1}$$

If C_V is constant (that is, not a function of T), we get

$$\Delta\bar{S} = \bar{C}_V\ln\frac{T_2}{T_1} + R\ln\frac{\bar{V}_2}{\bar{V}_1} \tag{27.9}$$

The first term represents the ΔS due to a change in T at constant volume. The second term gives ΔS due to a change in volume at constant T. The two together give total ΔS for a process involving both change in T and change in V for an ideal gas with a constant value of C_V, for example, a monatomic gas.

VARIATION OF ENTROPY WITH PRESSURE AND TEMPERATURE

By total differentiation, $dS = (\partial S/\partial P)_T\,dP + (\partial S/\partial T)_P\,dT$. In a manner analogous to that of the preceding section we see that $C_P = T(\partial S/\partial T)_P$ and, from Maxwell's third relation, $-(\partial S/\partial P)_T = (\partial V/\partial T)_P$. Thus $dS = C_P\,d\ln T - (\partial V/\partial T)_P\,dP$.

ENTROPY OF A PURE SUBSTANCE

Let us apply these ideas to the calculation of the entropy of a pure substance. We shall use phosphine, PH_3, since good data are available and provide an interesting insight into the third law. From Equation (27.6),

$$\Delta S = S_T - S_0 = S_T = \int_0^T \frac{C_P}{T}\,dT + \sum\left(\frac{\Delta H}{T}\right)_{\text{pc}}$$

We need heat capacity data from 0°K to T and values of ΔH for each phase change. All of these data for PH_3 have been obtained in calorimetric studies by C. C. Stephenson and W. F. Giauque.* The heat capacity data are plotted in Figure 27.4, which also indicates the observed phase changes. No analytical expressions were derived for C_P as a function of T, so graphical integrations are performed. We may do this in two ways, since

$$\Delta S = \int \frac{C_P}{T}\,dT = \int C_P\,d\ln T = 2.303\int C_P\,d\log T \tag{27.10}$$

Therefore we may either plot (C_P/T) against T or C_P against $\ln T$ (or $\log T$) in doing the integration. A plot of (C_P/T) versus T is preferred for two main rea-

* *J. Chem. Phys.*, **5**, 149–158 (1937).

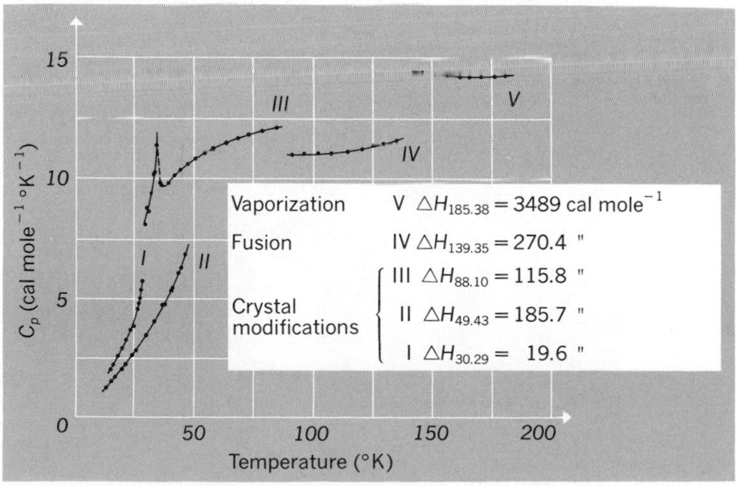

Figure 27.4. Heat capacity in calories per degree per mole of phosphine. [C. C. Stephenson and W. F. Giauque, *J. Chem. Phys.*, **5**, 155 (1937).]

sons: (1) it has a simpler shape to integrate, and (2) there is less of a problem with the limit at $T \longrightarrow 0$. We have $\ln T \longrightarrow -\infty$ as $T \longrightarrow 0$, but $(C_P/T) \longrightarrow 0$ as $T \longrightarrow 0$. Both curves are shown in Figure 27.5.

In both Figure 27.4 and Figure 27.5 we note two C_P curves below $T = 49.43°K$. This occurs because there are two crystal forms of PH_3 in this range. According to the third law, each form should have zero entropy at 0°K. Since there is only one crystal form above 49.43°K, we should get the same entropy above 49.43°K when calculating for either low-temperature curve, assuming that $S = 0$ at 0°K for both substances. If we do get the same entropy, our confidence in the third law is increased.

One problem remains. How do we extrapolate from the lowest experimental temperature, here 15.80°K, to 0°K? One way to do it is graphically. This will work reasonably well on the (C_P/T) versus T curve, but may give trouble on the C_P versus $\ln T$ curve. The other way, and the one which is almost universally used, is to rely on a generalization put forward by Debye. He studied many low-temperature heat-capacity curves and presented the theory that at low temperatures

$$C_V = \frac{12R\pi^4}{5\theta_D{}^3} T^3 = aT^3$$

where R is the gas constant and θ_D is a characteristic temperature for each substance—the Debye temperature. At these low temperatures $C_P = C_V$ for all practical purposes, so we get from the

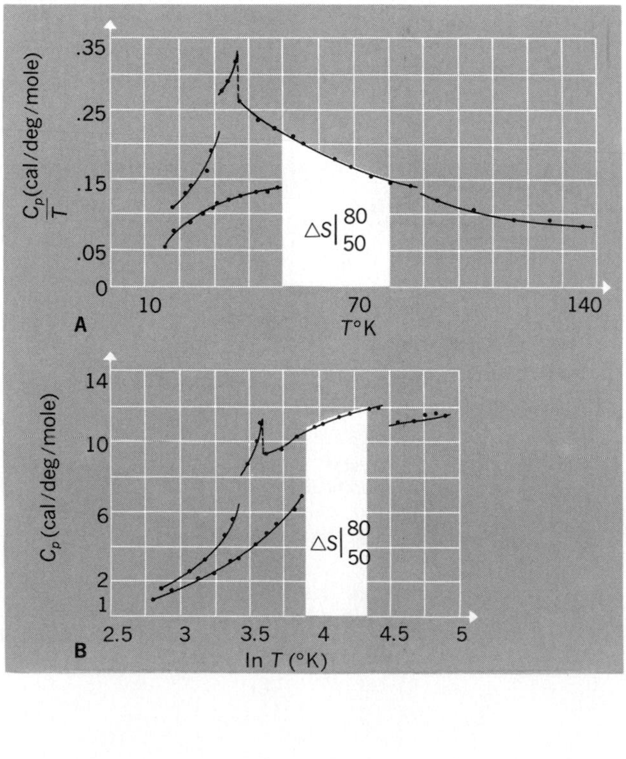

Figure 27.5 Graphs for integration of $\bar{C}_P$ versus T data to give $\Delta\bar{S}|_0^T$ for phosphine, PH_3.

DEBYE EQUATION:

$$S_T - S_0 = \Delta S = \int_0^T \frac{C_V\,dT}{T} = \int_0^T \frac{aT^3\,dT}{T} = \int_0^T aT^2\,dT$$

$$\Delta S \Big|_0^T = \tfrac{1}{3}aT^3 = \tfrac{1}{3}(C_V)_T = \tfrac{1}{3}(C_P)_T \qquad (27.11)$$

Thus the Debye law states that the entropy of any pure substance at low temperatures equals one-third of its heat capacity. The generalization usually works (up to 20°K or so), but it should always be checked against the available data.

Now we can calculate S_{298} of phosphine, using the Debye equation at low temperatures, $\int (C_P/T)\,dT$ over all other ranges of T, and $\Delta H/T$ at each phase change. The results of these calculations are shown in Table 27.4, as given by Stephenson and Giauque.

Many of the values for S_{298} in Table 27.1 were obtained from similar treatment of data on heat capacities and heats of transition for the compounds listed.

Note the agreement, in Table 27.4, between the values of $\bar{S}_{49.43°K}$ for the two forms—excellent confirmation of the third law of thermodynamics. The "spike" in the curve for Form I at 35°K probably indicates the onset of molecular rotation in this crystal in this range of temperatures. Relatively free rotation of the PH_3 molecules (at least around one axis) probably occurs in the crystal of Form I at 40°K and above. Form II apparently never rotates appreciably until after its transition to Form I at 49.43°K.

Exercise 27.6

Calculate the change in entropy if 100 g of calcium, initially at 27°C, are melted. *Answer:* See Table 27.1 for data. $\Delta S^0 = n[\int C_P\,dT/T + \Sigma\,\Delta H_{pc}/T] = (100/40.0)$ $[\int_{300}^{713}(5.25 + 3.44 \cdot 10^{-3}T)\,dT/T + 270/713 + \int_{713}^{1123}(2.68 + 6.80 \cdot 10^{-3}T)\,dT/T +$

Table 27.4 Calculation of the entropy of PH_3 (all data in cal mole^{-1} °K^{-1}).

		Form I		Form II
Form I	0–15°K, Debye function	0.495		
	15–30.29° graphical	2.185		
	30.29° transition, $\Delta\bar{H} = 19.6$	0.647		
	30.29–49.43° graphical	4.800		
Form II	0–15°K, Debye function			0.338
	15–49.43°K graphical			4.041
	49.43° transition, $\Delta\bar{H} = 185.7$			3.757
	$\bar{S}_{49.43°K}$	8.13 →	8.14	← 8.14
	49.43–88.10° graphical		6.705	
	88.10° transition, $\Delta\bar{H} = 115.8$		1.314	
	88.10–139.35° graphical		5.194	
	139.35° fusion, $\Delta\bar{H}_{fus} = 270.4$		1.940	
	139.35–185.38° graphical		4.140	
	185.38° vaporization, $\Delta\bar{H}_{vap} = 3489$		18.82	
	$\bar{S}_{185.38°K}$		46.25 cal mole^{-1} deg^{-1} (±0.1)	

SOURCE: C. C. Stephenson and W. F. Giauque, *J. Chem. Phys.*, **5**, 155 (1937).

2070/1123] = 100/40.0[5.25 ln (713/300) + 3.44 · 10^{-3}(713 − 300) + 270/713 + 2.68 ln (1123/713) + 6.80 · 10^{-3}(1123 − 713) + 2070/1123] = 2.50[4.45 + 1.42 + 0.38 + 1.31 + 3.06 + 1.84] eu = 31.2 eu, a large positive value, as you probably anticipated.

Exercise 27.7

Calculate and comment on the entropy change for converting $CO_{(g)}$ into $CH_{4(g)}$ at 298°K by treatment with H_2. *Answer:* Net equation: $CO_{(g)} + 3H_{2(g)} = CH_{4(g)} + H_2O_{(l)}$, ΔS^0 will probably be negative (4 moles gas ⟶ 1 mole gas + 1 mole liquid). ΔS^0 (from Table 27.1) = 44.490 + 16.75 − 47.214 − 3 · 31.208 = −79.60 eu (cal °K^{-1}), as anticipated. From the entropy standpoint this is an unlikely reaction.

ENTROPY CHANGE DURING REACTION

The values of S_{298} tabulated for pure substances at standard pressure may be used to calculate ΔS of reaction, since

$$\Delta S^0_{\text{reac}} = \sum_i n_i \bar{S}^0_{(\text{products } i)} - \sum_j n_j \bar{S}^0_{(\text{reactants } j)} \tag{27.12}$$

This assumes, however, that we wish the entropy change to start with pure separated reactants and end with pure separated products; hence the superscript zeros, which indicate that the standard states are important. There is also an entropy of mixing term when the reactants intermix [see Equation (10.4)] and an entropy of mixing of the products which must be considered if we are interested in anything other than the pure, separated materials. Furthermore, since S is sensitive to pressure and volume variations, we must remember that all substances, especially gases, are presumed to be at one atmosphere, as indicated by the superscript zero, S^0. The H and E are not very sensitive to P or V and we are often somewhat cavalier about neglecting the difference between ΔE^0 and ΔE and between ΔH^0 and ΔH. Cavalier or not, you should remember the difference—the superscript zero refers to substances in a specified standard state. Usually the standard state is the pure substance at 298°K and 1 atm. For substances in solution, the standard state is usually a 1 F solution. But we shall discuss solution chemistry at greater lengths later.

Just as we could calculate ΔH_{reac} as a function of T from a knowledge of ΔH_{298}, and of C_P as a function of T, so can we calculate ΔS^0_{reac} as a function of T at constant P, assuming no phase changes over the interval in T. The variation due to any changes in P can then be calculated separately:

$$dS = \frac{C_P\,dT}{T} \quad \text{or} \quad dS = C_P\,d\ln T$$

$$d\,\Delta S = \frac{\Delta C_P\,dT}{T}$$

$$\Delta S_T - \Delta S_{298} = \int_{298}^{T} \frac{\Delta C_P\,dT}{T} = \int_{298}^{T} \frac{\Delta C_P}{T}\,dT \tag{27.13}$$

The treatment is exactly analogous to that for ΔH as a function of T (p. 686).

CALCULATION OF ΔG

The term, $-\Delta G$, you will remember from Equation (26.13) and the preceding discussion, represents the maximum work obtainable from any isothermal, reversible process less any $P\,dV$ work. Thus ΔG is a very useful and important term in evaluating changes in chemical systems. From the fundamental definition $G = H - TS$, we get the differential form $dG = dH - dTS$ or, at constant T, $dG = dH - T\,dS$. In general, $dG = dH - T\,dS - S\,dT$ or $\Delta G = \Delta H - T\,\Delta S - S\,\Delta T$. It should be clear that we can calculate ΔG by substitution, using our available methods of calculating ΔH and S. But there are easier methods than simple substitution of ΔH and ΔS values. Let us explore them:

$$\begin{aligned} dG &= dH - T\,dS - S\,dT \\ &= dE + d(PV) - T\,dS - S\,dT \\ &= dq_{\text{rev}} - dw_{\text{rev}} + P\,dV + V\,dP - T\,dS - S\,dT \end{aligned}$$

If we consider $P\,dV$ work only, then

$$\begin{aligned} dG &= T\,dS - P\,dV + P\,dV + V\,dP - T\,dS - S\,dT \\ &= V\,dP - S\,dT \end{aligned} \tag{27.14}$$

VARIATION OF FREE ENERGY WITH P AND V

In a process at constant T, from (27.14),

$$dG = V\,dP \qquad \text{or} \qquad \left(\frac{\partial G}{\partial P}\right)_T = V$$

$$\Delta G = \int V\,dP \tag{27.15}$$

and for an ideal gas

$$\Delta G = n\int \frac{RT\,dP}{P} = nRT\ln\frac{P_2}{P_1} \tag{27.16}$$

Thus ΔG, like ΔS, is sensitive to changes in P. In fact, since $(\partial H/\partial P)_T = 0$,

$$\Delta G = -T\,\Delta S$$

for any change in pressure of an ideal gas at constant T. This result is also obtainable by comparing Equation (26.12) with Equation (27.16).

From Table 27.2 we can see very quickly that

$$\left(\frac{\partial G}{\partial V}\right)_T = \frac{V}{(\partial V/\partial P)_T} = -\frac{1}{\beta}$$

and for an ideal gas

$$\left(\frac{\partial G}{\partial V}\right)_T = \frac{V}{nRT/P^2} = P \tag{27.17}$$

As with entropy, ΔG is sensitive to variations in V or P.

EFFECT OF TOTAL P ON EQUILIBRIUM VAPOR PRESSURE

An interesting problem associated with the variation of G with P arises when one considers the variation in equilibrium vapor pressure of a substance as the applied pressure changes. For example, how does the vapor pressure of a condensed phase, α, vary if it is placed in a steel bomb under 100 atm of pressure of a gas insoluble in α? Now, from (27.15), $dG = V\,dP$. But if the α phase and the gas stay in equilibrium, ΔG for the phase change remains zero during any change in total pressure. Thus

$$d\overline{G}_{(\alpha)} = (\overline{V}\,dP)_\alpha = d\overline{G}_{(g)} = (\overline{V}\,dP)_g$$

or, since condensed phases are almost incompressible, $\overline{V}_\alpha\,dP = (V\,dP)_{(g)}$. If the equilibrium gas acts ideally, we get

$$\overline{V}_\alpha\,dP = RT d\ln p$$

or

$$\frac{d\ln p}{dP} = \frac{\overline{V}_\alpha}{RT}$$

which gives (upon integration if $\overline{V}_\alpha$ and T are constant)

$$\ln\frac{p_2}{p_1} = \frac{\overline{V}_\alpha}{RT}[P_2 - P_1]$$

We see that equilibrium vapor pressures depend on total P but since $\overline{V}_\alpha$ is small the effect is seldom large. For example, for H_2O, $\overline{V}_\alpha = 18$ ml at the usual pressures, then

$$\log\frac{p_2}{p_1} = \frac{0.018 \text{ liter mole}^{-1}}{2.303\cdot 0.082 \text{ liter atm mole}^{-1}\,{}^\circ\text{K}^{-1}\cdot 300^\circ\text{K}}[100 - 0] \text{ atm}$$

$$= 0.031, \qquad \frac{p_2}{p_1} = 1.07$$

Thus, increasing the total applied pressure to 100 atm increases the vapor pressure of water by 7%.

VARIATION OF FREE ENERGY WITH T

Going back to Equation (27.14) again, we obtain, for a constant-pressure process,

$$dG = -S\,dT$$

or

$$\left(\frac{\partial G}{\partial T}\right)_P = -S = \frac{G - H}{T}$$

and

$$\left(\frac{\partial\,\Delta G}{\partial T}\right)_P = -\Delta S = \frac{\Delta G - \Delta H}{T} \tag{27.18}$$

Equation (27.18) is completely consistent with our conclusion in Chapter 1 that the sign of ΔS determines the change of ΔG with changing T. If ΔS is positive, ΔG becomes more and more negative as T increases. But we have already discovered that the equilibrium constant, K, is related to ΔG^0 by the equation $\Delta G^0 = -RT\ln K$, or $(\Delta G^0/T) = -R\ln K$. Thus both ΔG^0 and T help determine the magnitude of K, but the sign of ΔG^0 determines whether K is greater or less than 1. Let us examine this relationship by differentiating $\Delta G/T$ with respect to T at constant P:

$$\left(\frac{\partial}{\partial T}\frac{\Delta G}{T}\right)_P = \frac{1}{T}\left(\frac{\partial\,\Delta G}{\partial T}\right)_P - \frac{\Delta G}{T^2} = -\frac{\Delta S}{T} - \frac{\Delta G}{T^2} \tag{27.19}$$

Thus, at sufficiently high T, the $(\Delta S/T)$ term is always greater than the $(\Delta G/T^2)$ term, so ΔS determines equilibrium at high T, as discussed in Chapter 10. But Equation (27.19) can be further simplified. Substituting (27.18) gives the

GIBBS-HELMHOLTZ EQUATIONS:

$$\left(\frac{\partial(\Delta G/T)}{\partial T}\right)_P = \left(\frac{1}{T}\,\frac{\Delta G - \Delta H}{T}\right) - \frac{\Delta G}{T^2} = -\frac{\Delta H}{T^2}$$

$$\left(\frac{\partial(\Delta G/T)}{\partial(1/T)}\right)_P = \Delta H \tag{27.20}$$

or

$$\left(\frac{\partial(\Delta G^0/T)}{\partial(1/T)}\right)_P = \Delta H^0 \tag{27.21}$$

Equations (27.18), (27.20), and (27.21) are much used in chemistry; they are all forms of the *Gibbs-Helmholtz equations.* Since we have discovered how to calculate ΔH as a function of T [see Equation (27.4)], it is clear we can also calculate ΔG as a function of T, using Equation (27.18) and/or the Gibbs-Helmholtz equations as guides. Figure 27.6 summarizes some properties of thermodynamic functions.

Exercise 27.8

Equations (27.18) and (27.21) show that the variation of ΔG with temperature is determined by ΔS, and that the variation of $(\Delta G/T)$ with temperature is determined by ΔH. Which, ΔS or ΔH, is more simply related to any shift in equilibrium state as T increases? *Answer:* At constant T, $\Delta G = \Delta H - T\Delta S$ and ΔG can be used to determine the direction of reaction. But, as pointed out in Chapter 10, $(\Delta G/T)_{sys} = (\Delta H/T)_{sys} - \Delta S_{sys} = -(\Delta S)_{univ}$. From the second law we know that it is the magnitude of $(\Delta S)_{univ}$ which determines the distance from equilibrium. Thus $(\Delta G/T)$

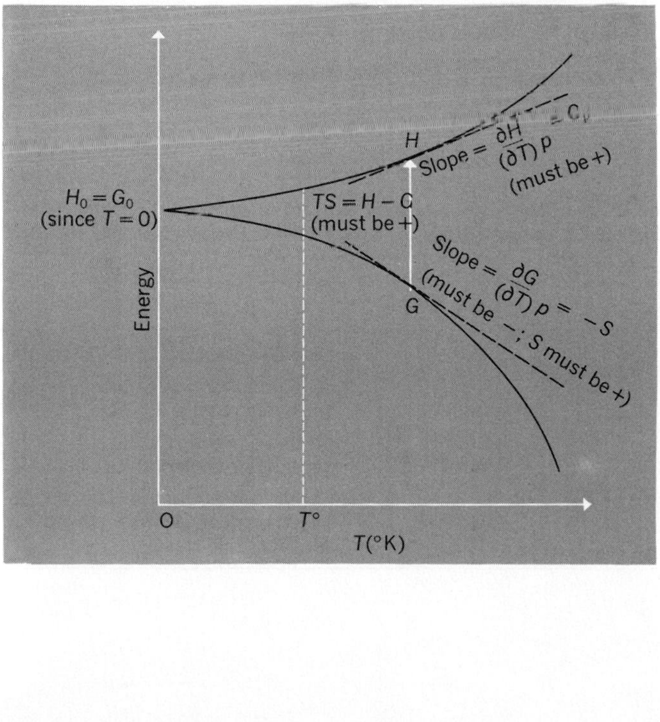

Figure. 27.6 Some thermodynamic functions of a pure substance as a function of T at constant P. The standard state may be at any temperature, $T°$, but usually is either at 0° K or 298.15° K. For elements in their standard states, $H° = 0$ by definition.

allows us to correlate both changes in ΔG and changes in T. If $(\Delta G/T)$ becomes more negative [$\Delta G = -$ from Equation (27.21)], then $(\Delta S)_{\text{univ}}$ will become more positive and net reaction will occur as the equation is written. Thus since $\partial(\Delta G/T)/\partial(1/T) = \Delta H$, it is the sign of ΔH, not of ΔS, which is most simply related to equilibrium shifts with change in T. Note that this is consistent with Le Châtelier's principle that endothermic reactions become more likely as T rises.

From our defining equation $G = H - TS$ we can write the differential form

$$dG = dH - T\,dS - S\,dT$$

or, at constant T,

$$dG = dH - T\,dS$$

or in increment form

$$\Delta G = \Delta H - T\,\Delta S \tag{27.22}$$

This equation is limited to closed systems at constant T and is usually applied at constant P. It is one of the most useful equations in all chemical thermodynamics. First, it applies to the most common set of conditions—a closed system at constant T. Second, it allows direct prediction of reaction direction if merely the signs of ΔH and ΔS are known (see pp. 46, 228, and Table 27.5). Note that (a) the most likely reactions at low T are all exothermic, (b) the most likely reactions at high T can be either exothermic or endothermic, (c) the sign and magnitude of ΔH completely determines the likelihood of reaction at low T, (d) the sign of ΔS completely determines the likelihood of reaction at high T. Thus at low T enthalpy is usually the more important factor, but at high T entropy is always the deciding factor in determining the likelihood of change, as shown in Equation (27.22).

Remember from Chapter 9 that Equation (27.22) may also be written

$$-\frac{\Delta G}{T} = -\frac{\Delta H}{T} + \Delta S$$

for a closed system at constant T and P. This is identical, term by term, to

$$\Delta S_{\text{univ}} = \Delta S_{\text{surroundings}} + \Delta S_{\text{sys}}$$

relating ΔG and ΔH for a closed system at constant T and P to values of ΔS.

Table 27.5 Effect of signs of ΔH and ΔS on ΔG—tendency to react at constant T, P, and mass—assuming that ΔH and ΔS do not change sign as T varies. (Remember: the sign of T is always +.)

Type	ΔH	ΔS	$\Delta G = \Delta H - T\,\Delta S$	Conclusion
1	− (exothermic)	+	−	A probable reaction at all values of T
2	− (exothermic)	−	− at low T + at high T	A probable reaction at low T, an improbable reaction at high T
3	+ (endothermic)	+	− at high T + at low T	A probable reaction at high T, an improbable reaction at low T
4	+ (endothermic)	−	+	An improbable reaction at all T (reverse reaction is more probable at all T)

FREE ENERGY CHANGE DURING REACTION

The general equation, at constant T, P, and mass,

$$\Delta G = \Delta H - T\,\Delta S$$

allows us to calculate ΔG of reaction at any T if we know ΔH and ΔS at that T. Thus values of $\Delta\overline{H}_f$ and $\overline{S}$ from Table 27.1 could be used to calculate $\Delta\overline{G}_f$. But it is even simpler to tabulate values for $\Delta\overline{G}_f$ of the compounds, as is also done in Table 27.1. Then

$$\Delta G_{\text{reac}} = \sum_i n_i\,\Delta\overline{G}_{\text{f(products } i)} - \sum_j n_j\,\Delta\overline{G}_{\text{f(reactants } j)} \tag{27.23}$$

in a manner exactly analogous to that used in calculating ΔH and ΔS. Since ΔG is a strong function of P, like S but unlike ΔH, we tabulate values of ΔG_f^0, the free energy of formation of substances in their standard states (usually 298°K and 1 atm), and generally calculate

$$\Delta G^0_{\text{reac}} = \sum_i n_i\,\Delta\overline{G}^0_{\text{f(product } i)} - \sum_j n_j\,\Delta\overline{G}^0_{\text{f(reactant } j)} \tag{27.24}$$

(It should be evident, from the equation $\Delta G = \Delta H - T\,\Delta S$, that the fact that ΔH is insensitive to variations in P although ΔS is sensitive to such variations assures us that ΔG will also be sensitive to variations in P.)

Exercise 27.9

Is the reaction $2NO_{2(g)} = N_2O_{4(g)}$ spontaneous in the standard state? *Answer:* From Table 27.1, $\Delta G^0 = 23.485 - 2 \cdot 12.354 = -1.223$ kcal, a small negative value, so the reaction occurs as written in the standard state, but not to any great extent. Thus, at equilibrium, at 298°K, $p_{N_2O_4} > p_{NO_2}$ at a total pressure of about 2 atm. At lower total pressure, NO_2 will become more common. At higher T, since $\Delta H^0 = 2.274 - 2 \cdot 8.011 = -13.748$ kcal, NO_2 will also become more common. Thus high pressure and low temperature favor N_2O_4, as Le Châtelier's principle states.

THERMODYNAMIC FUNCTIONS OF A PURE SUBSTANCE

Figure 27.6 presents some thermodynamic relationships at constant P. It is perfectly general for all pure substances and should give you a mental picture to simplify the mathematical ones. By definition $G = H - TS$; therefore at $T = 0$, $G_0 = H_0$. C_P is always positive. Since $(\partial H/\partial T)_P = C_P$, H must increase as T increases. Similarly $(\partial G/\partial T)_P = -S$ and, since S is always positive, G must decrease as T increases. The increase of H and decrease of G with rising T is consistent with the fact that TS must increase as T increases. TS must increase faster than T since S always increases with T.

For some pure substances, such as the noble gases, C_P is constant as T rises. Then H will rise at a constant rate. But S increases with T for all substances, thus the G curve will always have an increasingly negative slope as T rises. In general, C_P is less than S, so at any given T the absolute value of the slope of the H curve is less than that of the G curve.

Table 27.6 Thermodynamic data for hydrocarbon formation at 25°C and 1 atm.

Compound	Formula	ΔH_f^0 (kcal/mole)	ΔS_f^0 (cal/deg mole)	ΔG_f^0 (kcal/mole)	
Methane	$CH_{4(g)}$	−17.89	−19.3	−12.14	
Ethane	$C_2H_{6(g)}$	−20.24	−41.5	−7.86	
Propane	$C_3H_{8(g)}$	−24.80	−64.4	−5.61	Stable
n-Butane	$C_4H_{10(g)}$	−29.81	−87.4	−3.75	
n-Pentane	$C_5H_{12(g)}$	−35.00	−110.8	−1.96	
n-Hexane	$C_6H_{14(g)}$	−39.96	−134.5	+0.05	
n-Heptane	$C_7H_{16(g)}$	−44.89	−157.6	+2.09	
n-Octane	$C_8H_{18(g)}$	−49.82	−181.0	+4.14	Unstable
n-Nonane	$C_9H_{20(g)}$	−54.74	−204.3	+6.18	
n-Decane	$C_{10}H_{22(g)}$	−59.67	−227.7	+8.23	

SOURCE: N.B.S. Circular 461.

COMPOUND FORMATION

Table 27.6 contains data which clearly outline the importance of considering free energy changes rather than changes in enthalpy or entropy alone in predicting compound formation. The formation of gaseous hydrocarbons becomes more and more exothermic with respect to the elements as additional CH_2 groups form. On the other hand, their entropies of formation become more and more negative, tending to offset the enthalpy term. Thus gaseous normal hydrocarbons up to C_4H_{10} are stable with respect to the elements at 298°K and 1 atm, but C_5H_{12} and above are unstable, both with respect to the elements and with respect to the lower hydrocarbons. This is one of the thermodynamic bases for the cracking reactions which produce gasoline and other hydrocarbons of low molecular weight from crude oil.

SUMMARY

The thermodynamic functions ΔH, ΔS, and ΔG may all be evaluated for heating processes, for phase changes, and for chemical reactions from suitable calorimetric data. Their evaluation as a function of T for heating processes requires only C_P data. Their evaluation as a function of T for phase changes and/or reactions requires a determination of ΔH for the process at some known temperature plus C_P data. To evaluate ΔG^0 for a reaction as a function of T, one must determine the value of K at some known T. Thus the fundamental thermodynamic experimental data must include heat capacities, heats of phase changes and reactions, and equilibrium constants. The variations of ΔH, ΔS, and ΔG with P and V are calculable if values of α and β are available.

Pure logical thinking cannot yield us any knowledge of the empirical world.—A. Einstein, Essays in Science (1934).

PROBLEMS

27.1. Consider a typical chemical reaction (gas phase in the present instance) such as

$$Cl_2 + H_2 \longrightarrow 2HCl$$

Explain the enthalpy change of this reaction in terms of molecular structure.

27.2. Would you expect the isothermal molar enthalpy changes during chemical reactions to be (*a*) relatively independent of, or (*b*) strongly dependent on, the pressures of the reactants and products?

27.3. Calculate q, w, ΔE, ΔH, ΔS, ΔG, and ΔA for the conversion of 1.00 mole of gaseous water to liquid at 100°C and 1.00 atm pressure. [$q \cong 10$ kcal mole^{-1}, $w \cong -0.7$ kcal mole^{-1}.]

27.4. Hildebrand's rule states that $\Delta H_{vap} = 27$ for any liquid vaporizing to give a gas concentration of 0.0050 moles per liter. Typical variations in the "constant" are N_2 27.6, Cl_2 27.8, CCl_4 27.0, C_6H_5F 27.4, Hg 26.2, Zn 26.4, but H_2O 32.0, NH_3 32.4, C_2H_5OH 33.4. Can you rationalize these figures and suggest why Hildebrand's "constant" is better behaved than Trouton's "constant"? Trouton's "constant" for the same systems is 21.

27.5. Calculate the quantities indicated below for the reversible isothermal compression of one mole of an ideal gas from 1 atm to 5 atm at 27°C: q, w, ΔE, ΔH, ΔS, ΔG, ΔA. ($w \cong -1$ kcal mole^{-1}.)

27.6. Addition of 1 liter of 1 *M* H_2SO_4 to 1 liter of 1 *M* $Ba(OH)_2$ causes an evolution of 32,000 calories. Write the equation for the reaction which occurs. How does this heat of reaction correlate with those on the heat of formation of H_2O? Is $BaSO_4$ more soluble in hot or in cold water?

27.7. A solution of sodium acetate to which phenolphthalein has been added is colorless until heated. It then becomes pink. Interpret this in terms of the equation for the net reaction for the equilibrium in the sodium acetate solution.

27.8. Calculate the heat of vaporization of water at 50°C. $C_{P(H_2O(l))} = 18$ cal mole^{-1} °K^{-1} and is constant. ($\Delta H_{vap} \cong 10$ kcal mole^{-1}.)

27.9. ΔH^0_{298} for $SO_{3(g)} = -94.45$ kcal/mole. The following reaction is one of the steps in the commercial production of sulfuric acid:

$$2SO_2 + O_2 \longrightarrow 2SO_3$$

(*a*) What is the equilibrium constant expression for the above reaction? (*b*) What experimental conditions would you suggest for maximizing the yield of SO_3? Give reasons. (*c*) Is it possible to produce SO_3 when the products and reactants are all in the standard state? ($\Delta G^0 \cong -30$ kcal mole^{-1}.)

27.10. Construct a figure similar to Figure 27.3 for a process in which $\Delta H_{298} = +$ and $\Delta H_{298} < \Delta H_T$.

27.11. Equation (27.1) indicates that T decreases in an adiabatic reversible expansion of an ideal gas? A decrease in T usually indicates a decrease in S, yet for a reversible adiabatic process, $q_{rev} = 0$ and $\Delta S = q_{rev}/T = 0$. How then does ΔS remain zero?

II

27.12. The equilibrium vapor pressure of ice at $-10°C$ is 1.950 mm and that of supercooled water at the same temperature is 2.149 mm. Calculate ΔG and ΔS accompanying the change of 1 mole of supercooled water at $-10°C$ to ice at $-10°C$ and the same (total) pressure. ($\Delta G \cong -40$ cal mole^{-1}.)

27.13. Calculate $\Delta\bar{S}_{fus}$ and $\Delta\bar{S}_{vap}$ for a representative sample of the substances in Table 27.1. Are there any regularities? How do you account for the relative sizes of $\Delta\bar{S}_{fus}$ and $\Delta\bar{S}_{vap}$? How do you account for any other regularities? Can you predict a set of conditions for which $\Delta\bar{S}_{vap}$ might be constant regardless of the liquid-gas system?

27.14. Calculate $\Delta\bar{H}^0$, $\Delta\bar{S}^0$, and $\Delta\bar{G}^0$ at 298°K for each of the following reactions. Which reactions will proceed as written, in the standard state at 298°K? at 1000°K? Guess answers before using any numerical data. (*b*. $\Delta G^0 \cong 40$ kcal.)
(*a*) $N_{2(g)} + O_{2(g)} = 2NO_{(g)}$.
(*b*) $2CH_{4(g)} = C_2H_{2(g)} + 3H_{2(g)}$.
(*c*) $\frac{3}{2}O_{2(g)} = O_{3(g)}$.
(*d*) $SO_{2(g)} + \frac{1}{2}O_{2(g)} = SO_{3(g)}$.

27.15. Show that the process $H_2O_{(l,\,5°C)} \longrightarrow H_2O_{(c,\,5°C)}$ is not a spontaneous process in an isolated system containing, in addition to the water, a thermostat at 5°C. The heat of fusion of water is 79.7 cal/g at 0°C and the specific heats for water and ice may be taken as 1 cal/deg g and 0.5 cal/deg g respectively. Diagram the system. ($\Delta G \cong$ 0.01 cal g^{-1}.)

27.16. How much heat is required to convert 1 mole of liquid water at 25°C to 1 mole of gaseous water at 500°C? Assume constant P. ($\Delta H \cong 15$ kcal mole^{-1}.)

27.17. An evacuated glass tube contained powdered quartz and a sealed ampoule with 2.7382 g of $H_2S_{2(l)}$. The tube was immersed in a calorimeter. When the ampoule was broken, the quartz catalyzed the decomposition of H_2S_2 to orthorhombic sulfur and H_2S (partly liquid and partly vapor). The temperature rose 0.153°C. The heat capacity of the calorimeter was 1060 cal/deg. The average temperature was 17°C and the volume of gaseous H_2S was 14.4 ml. The vapor pressure of liquid H_2S at this temperature is 16.3 atm, and its heat of vaporization is given as $\Delta H = 6.25 - 8.30 \cdot 10^{-3}T$ kcal/mole. From these data, find ΔE for the reaction

$$H_2S_{2(l)} \longrightarrow H_2S_{(l)} + S_{(orthorhombic)}$$

[$\Delta E \cong 5$ kcal (mole $H_2S_2)^{-1}$.]

27.18. Calculate $\bar{S}^0$ at the highest T for each substance for which smoothed data are given. Calculate $\bar{H}^0 - \bar{H}^0_0$. (*a*) AsH_3 [*J. Am. Chem. Soc.*, **77**, 2154 (1955)], (*b*) C_2N_2 [*Ibid*, **61**, 2940 (1939)], (*c*) HNO_3 [*Ibid*, **64**, 48 (1942)]. Comment on the entropies of PH_3 and AsH_3 at 100°K. Which should be higher? T is in °K, C_P in cal mole^{-1} °K^{-1}.

(a) T/C_P										
T	15	20	25	30	35	40	50	60	80	100
C_P	2.795	4.370	6.078	8.100	10.406	10.748	11.350	11.676	12.016	12.207

(b) T/C_P											
T	15	20	25	30	40	50	70	100	150	200	245 (m.p.)
C_P	0.86	1.76	2.82	3.78	5.57	7.02	9.13	11.41	14.47	17.45	20.65

(c) T/C_P	15	20	25	30	40	50	70	100	150	200	231.5 (m.p.)
	0.677	1.238	1.934	2.740	4.468	5.855	7.988	10.06	12.37	14.70	16.76

[$S^0_{100} \cong 20$ cal (mole°K^{-1}) for AsH_3.]

III

27.19. Calculate the minimum amount of heat required in the synthesis of 100 tons of $HCN_{(g)}$ according to the reaction

$$NH_{3(g)} + CO_{(g)} = HCN_{(g)} + H_2O_{(g)}$$

($g \cong 10^5$ kcal.)

27.20. Select a synthesis reaction of your own and repeat for it the calculations of Problem 27.19.

27.21. Using the following data, calculate the molar entropy of gaseous isobutene at 25°C.

$\bar{S}_{90°K} = 10.81$ cal/deg mole
Freezing point = −140.7°C
Boiling point = −6°C
$\Delta H_{fus} = 25.22$ cal/g
$\Delta H_{vap} = 96.5$ cal/g
C_P (gas) in range of 226–298°K = 20 cal/deg mole

Specific Heat

T (°K)	92.9	105.5	118.9	139.2	166.1	179.8	210.2	252.9
C_P (cal/g °K)	0.2498	0.2749	0.3056	0.4547	0.4621	0.4681	0.4860	0.5172

[$S^0_{298} \cong 70$ cal (mole°K)$^{-1}$.]

27.22. Compare ΔH^0_{298} for the following, and calculate the maximum flame temperature in each case. Estimate, before performing the detailed calculations, the magnitude of the maximum flame temperatures. (*a*) H_2 burns in air. (*b*) H_2 burns in pure oxygen. (*c*) CH_4 burns in air. (*d*) B_2H_6 burns in oxygen to BO. (*e*) C_2H_2 burns in oxygen. (*f*) H_2 burns in fluorine. (*Hint:* Assume that ΔH^0_{298} heats the products adiabatically to the maximum flame temperature T.) (*a*. $T_{max} \cong 3000$°K.)

27.23. Calculate the maximum adiabatic flame temperature when ethane is burned with twice the amount of air necessary to give exactly complete combustion. Carry out an estimate of the numerical answer to the closest 100°C. [$T \cong 1000$°K.]

See page 1093 for a list of references and readings in the recent chemical literature related to the material in this chapter.

CHAPTER **28**

Thermodynamic Functions from Molecular Data

The knowledge of certain molecular properties, such as molecular weight, temperature, symmetry number, moment of inertia, vibrational frequencies, and electronic energies, allows the calculation of the total free energy of any molecule acting as an ideal gas.

The observant student will note that, in the preceding chapter, the thermodynamic quantities were evaluated from calorimetric data: heat capacities, heats associated with phase changes and reactions, and experimentally determined equilibrium constants. These data are obtained on macroscopic specimens, since the temperature effects must be large enough to register on available thermometric devices. But energy changes may also be recorded in spectra, and we have already pointed out that thermodynamic data can be obtained from considerations of molecular properties. Let us summarize the relations obtained so far.

For translational motion in an ideal gas (using classical theory, $RT \gg \Delta\bar{E}$):

$$\text{Eq. (6.19)} \qquad \bar{E} = \tfrac{3}{2}RT$$

$$\text{Eq. (7.9)} \qquad \bar{C}_V = \tfrac{3}{2}R$$

$$\text{Eq. (7.8)} \qquad \bar{C}_P = \bar{C}_V + R = \tfrac{5}{2}R$$

For vibrational motion (using quantum theory, especially when $RT \leq \Delta\bar{E}$, or $kT \leq h\nu$):

$$\text{Eq. (8.13)} \qquad (\bar{E} - \bar{E}_0)_{\text{vib}} = \frac{RTx}{e^x - 1}, \qquad x = \frac{h\nu}{kT}$$

$$\text{Eq. (8.16)} \qquad \bar{C}_V = \frac{Rx^2e^2}{(e^x - 1)^2}$$

$$\text{Eq. (10.21)} \qquad \bar{S}_V = \frac{Rx}{e^x - 1} - R\ln(1 - e^{-x})$$

PARTITION FUNCTIONS

Consider the case of a mole of a substance, in thermal equilibrium. Each molecule can exchange energy with all the others and move among known molecular energy levels of energy ϵ_i above the ground state $\epsilon_0 = 0$, each level having a statistical weight g_i. Assuming that the Boltzmann equation holds, the relative probability that a molecule will attain the ith energy state is $g_i e^{-\epsilon_i/kT}$. The total molar energy is $\bar{E} = \Sigma_i n_i \epsilon_i = N_0 \bar{\epsilon}$ where $\bar{\epsilon}$ is the average energy per molecule. The energy contribution of each possible state of the molecule over a long period of time is then its energy ϵ_i times the relative probability of the state being attained, or $g_i \epsilon_i e^{-\epsilon_i/kT}$, and the total energy of all possible states of the system is $\Sigma_i g_i \epsilon_i e^{-\epsilon_i/kT}$. The sums of the relative probabilities of all states, each having a relative probability of $g_i e^{-\epsilon_i/kT}$, is $\Sigma_i g_i e^{-\epsilon_i/kT}$. Thus the average energy of a molecule $\bar{\epsilon}$, is the sum of the energies of all possible states, divided by the sum of the states, or

$$\bar{\epsilon} = \frac{\sum_i g_i \epsilon_i e^{-\epsilon_i/kT}}{\sum_i g_i e^{-\epsilon_i/kT}} = \frac{\sum_i g_i \epsilon_i e^{-\epsilon_i/kT}}{Z} \tag{28.1}$$

where Z is called the molecular partition function or sum of the molecular states. For N_0 noninteracting and distinguishable particles the molar partition function, Q, is

$$Q = Z^{N_0} \tag{28.2}$$

In actual experiments we cannot see the particles; they are indistinguishable. Under these conditions we find $Q = Z^{N_0}/N_0!$. (For this conversion Stirling's approximation for $N!$, when N is large, is useful. It is $\ln N! = N \ln N - N$.)

Equation (28.1) can be made even simpler by differentiating Z with respect to T and noting that

$$\left(\frac{\partial Z}{\partial T}\right)_V = \frac{1}{kT^2}\sum_i g_i \epsilon_i e^{-\epsilon_i/kT}$$

$$\frac{1}{Z}\left(\frac{\partial Z}{\partial T}\right)_V = \frac{1}{kT^2}\,\frac{\sum_i g_i \epsilon_i e^{-\epsilon_i/kT}}{Z} = \frac{\bar{\epsilon}}{kT^2}$$

or

$$\bar{\epsilon} = \frac{kT^2}{Z}\left(\frac{\partial Z}{\partial T}\right)_V = kT^2\left(\frac{\partial \ln Z}{\partial T}\right)_V$$

or

$$\bar{E} = N_0\bar{\epsilon} = RT^2\left(\frac{\partial \ln Z}{\partial T}\right)_V \tag{28.3}$$

STANDARD STATES

A knowledge of Z over the available energy states allows the evaluation of the internal energy as a function of T. The solution of Equation (28.3) will give a constant of integration which we will call $\bar{E}^0$, the energy in some standard state. If we choose the same standard state we have been using, we will define $\bar{E}^0$ as 0 for all pure elements at 298°K and 1 atm pressure, and give it the symbol $\bar{E}^0_{298}$. All other values of $\overline{E}^0$ will then be compared to the elements as 0 in their standard states.

Another common standard state is the pure elements at 0°K. The symbol for E^0 in this standard state is E_0^0. Similarly, values for H_0^0 and G_0^0 are much used. It is important when combining data from various sources to check that all are using the same standard state. Otherwise the calculations will be in error by the values $E_{298}^0 - E_0^0$, $H_{298}^0 - H_0^0$, $G_{298}^0 - G_0^0$, and so on. More and more tables are also becoming available to perform the conversion from one standard state to another quickly and easily. We shall continue to concentrate on 298°K and 1 atm pressure as standard.

THERMODYNAMIC FUNCTIONS FROM PARTITION FUNCTIONS

From the value of $\overline{E}$ in Equation (28.3) we can quickly evaluate the other thermodynamic variables. All turn out to be functions of Z and its variation with V and/or T:

$$\overline{C}_V = \left(\frac{\partial \overline{E}}{\partial T}\right)_V = \frac{\partial}{\partial T} RT^2\left(\frac{\partial \ln Z}{\partial T}\right)_V = \frac{R}{T^2}\left(\frac{\partial^2 \ln Z}{\partial (1/T)^2}\right)_V \tag{28.4}$$

For change in T only,

$$\overline{S} - \overline{S}_0 = \int_0^T \frac{\overline{C}_V}{T}\, dT = \int_0^T \frac{1}{T}\frac{\partial}{\partial T} RT^2\left(\frac{\partial \ln Z}{\partial T}\right)_V dT$$

which can be simplified, using the third law, to

$$\overline{S} = R\frac{\partial T \ln Z}{\partial T}$$

or to

$$\overline{S} = \frac{\overline{E}}{T} + R\ln\frac{Z}{N_0} + R \tag{28.5}$$

In a similar fashion, using the thermodynamic relationship of Tables 26.2 and 26.3, we obtain the results summarized in Table 28.1.

Table 28.1 shows that evaluation of the partition function Z and its change with T and V would allow the calculation of all thermodynamic quantities. Z is solely a function of the quantized energy states and their statistical weights. Thus a knowledge of the possible energy states of a system, the statistical weight of each

Table 28.1 Thermodynamic functions in terms of the molecular partition function, $Z = \Sigma_i g_i e^{-\epsilon_i/kT}$, V, and T.

$P = RT(\partial \ln Z/\partial \overline{V})_T$
$\overline{C}_V = (R/T^2)(\partial^2 \ln Z/\partial(1/T)^2)_V$
$E = RT^2(\partial \ln Z/\partial T)_V$
$\overline{H} = RT^2(\partial \ln Z/\partial T)_V + RT\overline{V}(\partial \ln Z/\partial \overline{V})_T$
$\overline{S} = RT(\partial \ln Z/\partial T)_V + R \ln Z + R[1 - \ln N_0]$
$\overline{G} = -RT \ln Z + RT\overline{V}(\partial \ln Z/\partial \overline{V})_T - RT[1 - \ln N_0]$
$\overline{A} = -RT \ln Z - RT[1 - \ln N_0]$

one, and the change in distribution among the states with varying T and V would give all the thermodynamic functions.

We solved this problem for the vibration of a diatomic, harmonic oscillator (on p. 197 and following) and obtained $\overline{E} - \overline{E}_0$ for the system in terms of ν, the frequency of vibration, and T [see Equation (8.13)].

But not all systems are so easily solved. In general, it has not been possible to determine exact partition functions for condensed states. This is consistent with our discussion of spectra in Chapters 3 and 8. The principal source of detailed information on energy levels is the spectrum of a substance. Gases give sharp lines, allowing unambiguous identification of the energy states, ϵ, and their statistical weights, g (from intensity measurements). Condensed phases give "smeared" or continuous spectra. Molecular interactions are large because of the small distances and because the interactions vary with time, owing to random molecular motions. Thus the energy states are difficult, even impossible, to identify; they can only be calculated approximately. Thermodynamic functions for condensed states are normally calculated from calorimetric and similar macroscopic measurements.

In ideal gases there are no intermolecular forces. Many real gases approximate ideality (as shown in Chapter 6), especially at low pressures and high temperatures. This has allowed exact evaluation of the partition function of an ideal gas from theoretical considerations. The thermodynamic functions calculated from ideal gas partition functions (using experimental spectral data) agree completely with the thermodynamic values obtained from thermal and other macroscopic measurements. Let us look at some of the results.

STATISTICAL THERMODYNAMIC FUNCTIONS FOR IDEAL GASES

We shall not evaluate the partition function of an ideal gas from first principles based on quantum mechanics, statistical theory, and kinetic theory, but merely enumerate some of the results.

One important assumption must be stated first. It was also inherent in the introduction to absolute reaction rate theory on page 586. It is that energy states can be classified as translational, rotational, vibrational, electronic, and nuclear and that there is no interaction between these states. We already know, from the discussion of rotational stretching (p. 195), that this assumption is not quite true. Actually the rotational stretching, which increases with J, does affect vibrational frequencies, ν. But such cross-effects are usually small, and the assumption of separability of energy states is a good approximation to the actual experimental situation.

If energy states are separable, we can calculate partition functions for each kind of separable state, and from these we can calculate thermodynamic functions for each kind of state. The functions for the total system then will be the sum of the separate contributions. For example,

$$S_{tot} = S_{trans} + S_{rot} + S_{vib} + S_{elec} + S_{nuc} + \cdots$$

Full calculations involve mathematical formulations we have not developed—especially solutions of the Schrödinger equation [Equation (4.7)]—but the total molar partition function, Q, in terms of separable translation, rotation, vibration, and electronic energy levels, turns out to be

$$Q = \frac{1}{N!} Z_{\text{trans}}^{N} \cdot Z_{\text{rot}}^{N} \cdot Z_{\text{vib}}^{N} \cdot Z_{\text{elec}}^{N} \tag{28.6}$$

$$= \frac{1}{N!} Z_{\text{trans}}^{N} \cdot Z_{\text{int}}^{N}$$

Each of the Z terms is the molecular partition function for the molecular energy described. In general,

$$Z = \sum_{i} g_i e^{-\epsilon_i/kT} \tag{28.7}$$

representing the sum over all molecular states, i, each of energy ϵ_i and statistical weight g_i. The term $1/N!$ must be included to prevent counting the N identical molecules present more than once for each molecule in determining translational properties. The Z_{int} represents the total internal partition function—rotation, vibration, electronic, nuclear, etc.—which is independent of V (for an ideal gas with zero intermolecular forces) but depends on T. The $[1 - \ln N_0]$ terms in Table 28.1 come from the $N!$ term in Z_{trans} using the Stirling formula. They should not be included in calculations involving only internal partition functions. Also note that $(\partial \ln Z_{\text{int}}/\partial V) = 0$ for each internal partition function.

Calculation from statistical and wave mechanics for translating particles shows that

$$Z_{\text{trans}} = V\left(\frac{2\pi mkT}{h^2}\right)^{3/2}$$

then

$$Q = \frac{1}{N!} V^N \left(\frac{2\pi mkT}{h^2}\right)^{3N/2} Z_{\text{int}}^{N} \tag{28.8}$$

From Table 28.1,

$$P = kT\left(\frac{\partial \ln Q}{\partial V}\right)_T = \frac{kT}{Q}\left(\frac{\partial Q}{\partial V}\right)_T$$

Substituting (28.18) and remembering that Z_{int} is independent of V, we get

$$P = \frac{kT\left\{\partial\left[\frac{1}{N!} V^N \left(\frac{2\pi mkT}{h^2}\right)^{3N/2} Z_{\text{int}}^{N}\right]\Big/\partial V\right\}_T}{\frac{1}{N!} V^N \left(\frac{2\pi mkT}{h^2}\right)^{3N/2} Z_{\text{int}}^{N}} = kT\left(\frac{\partial \ln V^N}{\partial V}\right)_T = \frac{NkT}{V} = \frac{RT}{\overline{V}}$$

or

$$P\overline{V} = RT$$

which is the ideal gas equation derived from statistical thermodynamics. Our theories are at least consistent.

The rotational partition function for a diatomic molecule, $Z_{\text{rot}} = \Sigma$(rotational states), is readily calculated from our model in Chapter 8. Since $g_{\text{rot}} = 2J + 1$ and $\epsilon_{\text{rot}} = J(J + 1)h^2/8\pi^2 I$, therefore, from Equation (28.7),

$$Z_{\text{rot}} = \sum_{J} (2J + 1)\exp\left[\frac{-J(J + 1)h^2}{8\pi^2 IkT}\right]$$

Let us assume there are enough states, closely enough spaced to replace the sum with an integral. Then

$$Z_{\text{rot}} = \int_0^\infty (2J+1)\exp\left[\frac{-J(J+1)h^2}{8\pi^2 IkT}\right] dJ = \int_0^\infty \exp\left[\frac{-J(J+1)h^2}{8\pi^2 I\, dT}\right] d(J^2+J)$$

$$= \int_0^\infty e^{-ax}\, dx = -\frac{1}{a}e^{-ax}\Big|_0^\infty = -\frac{1}{a}(e^{-a\infty} - e^{-a\cdot 0}) = \frac{1}{a} = \frac{8\pi^2 IkT}{h^2}$$

The corresponding equation for Z_{rot} in Table 28.2 contains a σ which is discussed below.

THERMODYNAMIC FUNCTIONS FROM MOLECULAR PROPERTIES

In a similar fashion, the equations in Table 28.2 may be derived. Many of the equations for thermodynamic functions contain several universal constants—for example, the entropy equations. Thus it is common to find these equations written with all such constants evaluated:

Table 28.2 Evaluation of some thermodynamic functions from partition functions.

Function	Translational[a]	Rotational	Vibrational[b] (each vibration)	Electronic[c]
Z	$V\left(\frac{2\pi mkT}{h^2}\right)^{3/2}$	linear $\frac{8\pi^2 IkT}{\sigma h^2}$; nonlinear rigid $\frac{8\pi^2(8\pi^2 I_1 I_2 I_3)^{1/2}(kT)^{3/2}}{\sigma h^3}$	$\frac{e^{-x/2}}{(1-e^{-x})}$	$\sum_i g_i e^{-\epsilon_i/kT}$
P	RT/V	0	0	0
$\bar{C}_V$	$\frac{3}{2}R$		$\frac{Rx^2e^x}{(e^x-1)^2}$	
$\bar{E} - E_0$	$\frac{3}{2}RT$	RT	$\frac{RTx}{e^x-1}$	
$\bar{H} - \bar{H}_0$	$\frac{5}{2}RT$			
$\bar{S}$	$R\ln\frac{e^{5/2}V}{Nh^3}(2\pi mkT)^{3/2}$	linear $R\ln\frac{8\pi^2 IkeT}{h^2\sigma}$	$R\left[\frac{x}{e^x-1} - \ln(1-e^{-x})\right]$	
$\bar{A} - \bar{A}_0$		$-RT\ln\frac{8\pi^2 IkT}{h^2}$	$\frac{Nh\nu_0}{2} + RT\ln(1-e^{-x})$	
$\bar{G} - \bar{G}_0$	$-RT\left[\ln\frac{VM^{3/2}T^{3/2}}{n} + \ln\frac{(2\pi k)^{3/2}}{h^3N^{5/2}}\right]$			

[a] The $1/N!$ of Equations (28.6) and (28.8) is used in calculating translational functions.
[b] A separate thermodynamic value must be evaluated for each vibrational state (each value of x). The total contribution of all vibrations to the total thermodynamic function is the sum of these individual terms.
[c] Electronic Z's usually have only two terms, so they are summed directly, but Z_{elec} may interact strongly with other Z's, so simple calculations should be accepted with great caution.

$$\bar{S}_{trans} = 6.8645 \log M + 11.4408 \log T - 4.5756 \log P - 2.315 \quad (28.9)$$

$$\bar{S}_{rot} = 4.5756 \log IT/\sigma + 177.41 \text{ for rigid linear molecules} \quad (28.10)$$

$$\bar{S}_{rot} = \tfrac{3}{2}R \ln T + \tfrac{1}{2}R \ln I_1I_2I_3 - R \ln \sigma + 267.62 \text{ for rigid nonlinear molecules} \quad (28.11)$$

The symmetry number, σ, equals the number of indistinguishable ways a given molecule can be oriented in space when it is rotated about its center of mass. Homonuclear diatomic molecules, X_2, have $\sigma = 2$, since an end-for-end rotation produces two indistinguishable forms. For heteronuclear diatomic molecules, including molecules like HD and Cl^{35}—Cl^{37}, which merely differ in nuclei, $\sigma = 1$, since all possible orientations are distinguishable. Table 28.3 illustrates some symmetry numbers.

Exercise 28.1

What is the effect of increasing molecular weight (*a*) on the translational entropy, (*b*) on the rotational entropy, (*c*) on the vibrational entropy? *Answer:* (*a*) The translational entropy increases with the logarithm of the molecular weight. (*b*) The rotational entropy increases with the logarithm of $I = \mu d^2$, where μ is the reduced mass which often increases with molecular weight (but depends on the weight distribution in the molecule). (*c*) The vibrational entropy is a complicated function of $h\nu/kT$, decreasing as $h\nu/kT$ increases. Since ν normally decreases as mass increases, the vibrational entropy also tends to increase as molecular weight increases, but again the effect depends upon the distribution of the mass.

Table 28.3 Symmetry numbers, σ.

	σ	Type of molecule
	1	All linear molecules lacking end-for-end symmetry—for example, HCl, Br^{79}—Br^{80}, D—C≡C—H, Br—Hg—Cl, S=C=O, N=N=O
	2	All linear molecules with end-for-end symmetry—for example, all homonuclear diatomics, H—C≡C—H, Cl—Hg—Hg—Cl, etc. Others such as 

Other examples

Molecule	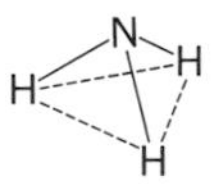	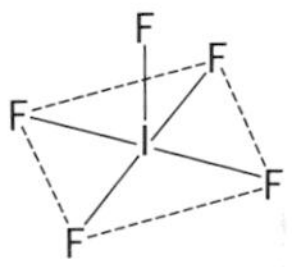	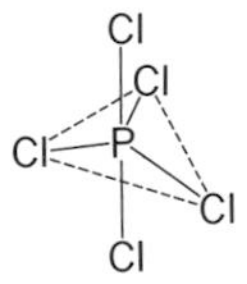	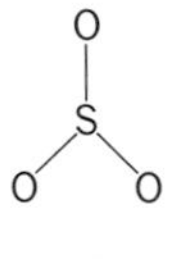
σ	3	4	6	6
Molecule	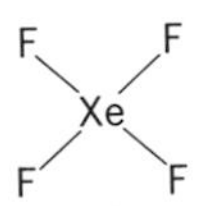	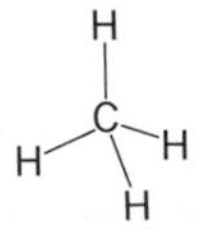	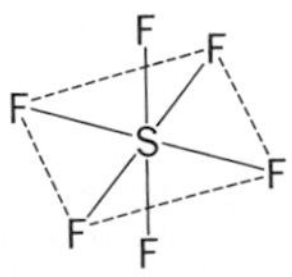	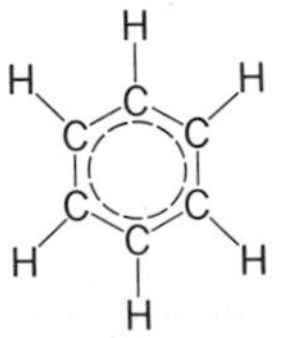
σ	8	12	12	12

TABULATED VALUES OF $h\nu/kT$ FUNCTIONS

The evaluation of thermodynamic functions for vibrational motions can be laborious because of the exponential terms involved. However, examination of Table 28.2 shows that all these functions may be expressed in terms of $x = h\nu/kT$. The original use of such functions was suggested by Einstein in his theory of heat capacity, so the functions are sometimes called Einstein functions. Extensive tables have been prepared by H. L. Johnston, L. Cavedoff, and J. Belzer.* Table 28.4 summarizes these data at larger intervals and in the form of dimensionless numbers whose values are insensitive to changes in the "best" values of the physical constants (see Appendix I). Remember that the total contribution to the thermodynamic functions is the sum of all contributions, one from each vibration. Thus, a diatomic molecule has only one vibration, a linear molecule has $U = 3n - 5$ [Equation (8.9)]. A nonlinear, triatomic molecule has $U = 3 \cdot 3 - 6 = 3$ separate vibrations contributing to its thermodynamic functions [see Equation 8.10)], and so it will have three vibrations contributing to its entropy of vibration. For any molecule $U = \Sigma_n g_n$ = number of vibrational contributions to $\overline{S}_{\text{vib}}$ from all of n vibrational states.

Exercise 28.2

Calculate the entropy of PH_3 from molecular data and compare with the value in Table 27.4. PH distance = 1.42 Å, HPH angles = 93.5°, $I_1I_2I_3 = 330 \cdot 1^{-120}$ g cm^2, $3 \cdot 4 - 6 = 6$ vibrational frequencies at ν_1 2327 (1), ν_2 991 (1), ν_3 2421 (2), ν_4 1121 (2) cm^{-1}. Parenthetical figures give number of vibrations at that frequency. *Answer:* $S_{\text{tot}} = S_{\text{trans}} + S_{\text{rot}} + S_{\text{vib}} = [6.86 \log M + 11.44 \log T - 4.58 \log P - 2.315] + [\frac{3}{2}R \ln T + \frac{1}{2}R \ln I_1I_2I_3 - R \ln \sigma + 267.62] + \Sigma[Rx(e^x - 1) - \ln(1 - e^{-x})]$. If we now substitute the values $M = 34.0$, $T = 185.4$°K, $P = 1$ atm, $\sigma = 3$, $x = h\nu/kT = 7.75 \cdot 10^{-3}\nu^{-1}$, etc. for each ν, we get an entropy of 46.39 cal per mole degree compared to the value in Table 27.4 of 46.25 eu. The difference between these two values, 0.14 eu, is completely accounted for by gas imperfections in phosphine; thus there is perfect agreement between the spectroscopic value of the entropy and the calorimetric value of the entropy. Note there is essentially zero entropy of vibration at this T.

THE FREE ENERGY FUNCTION

There is another method, simpler than those discussed so far, for performing many calculations. Part of its simplicity is due to the existence of tabulated data, but the existence of the tables is testimony to the value of the method. To illustrate it,

$$G = H - TS$$

$$G_T = H_T - TS_T$$

$$\frac{G_T}{T} = \frac{H_T}{T} - S_T$$

$$\frac{G_T - H_{298}}{T} = \frac{H_T - H_{298}}{T} - (S_T - S_{298}) - S_{298}$$

---

* *Contributions to the Thermodynamic Functions by a Planck-Einstein Oscillator in One Degree of Freedom* (NAVEXOS P-646) Washington, Office of Naval Research, 1949.

Table 28.4 **Harmonic-oscillator functions. (Note that it is not necessary to specify G^0 and H^0 since vibrational functions are independent of pressure and state; they depend only on T.) $x = h\nu/kT$.**

x	$-(G - H_0)/RT$ $-\ln(1 - e^{-x})$	$(H - H_0)/RT$ $x/(e^x - 1)$	C_V/R $x^2e^x/(e^x - 1)^2$
0.0	∞	1.0000	1.0000
0.1	2.3522	0.9508	0.9992
0.2	1.7078	0.9033	0.9967
0.3	1.3502	0.8575	0.9925
0.4	1.1096	0.8133	0.9868
0.5	0.9328	0.7708	0.9794
0.6	0.7959	0.7298	0.9705
0.7	0.6863	0.6905	0.9602
0.8	0.5966	0.6528	0.9483
0.9	0.5218	0.6166	0.9352
1.0	0.4587	0.5820	0.9207
1.1	0.4048	0.5489	0.9050
1.2	0.3584	0.5172	0.8882
1.3	0.3182	0.4870	0.8703
1.4	0.2832	0.4582	0.8515
1.5	0.2525	0.4308	0.8318
1.6	0.2255	0.4048	0.8114
1.7	0.2017	0.3800	0.7904
1.8	0.1807	0.3565	0.7687
1.9	0.1620	0.3342	0.7466
2.0	0.1454	0.3130	0.7241
2.2	0.1174	0.2741	0.6783
2.4	0.0951	0.2394	0.6320
2.6	0.0772	0.2086	0.5859
2.8	0.0627	0.1813	0.5405
3.0	0.0511	0.1572	0.4963
3.2	0.0416	0.1360	0.4536
3.4	0.0340	0.1174	0.4129
3.6	0.0277	0.1011	0.3743
3.8	0.0226	0.0870	0.3380
4.0	0.0185	0.0746	0.3041
4.2	0.0151	0.0639	0.2726
4.4	0.0124	0.0547	0.2436
4.6	0.0101	0.0467	0.2170
4.8	0.0083	0.0398	0.1928
5.0	0.0068	0.0339	0.1707
5.2	0.0055	0.0288	0.1508
5.4	0.0045	0.0245	0.1329
5.6	0.0037	0.0208	0.1168
5.8	0.0030	0.0176	0.1025
6.0	0.0025	0.0149	0.0897
6.5	0.0015	0.0098	0.0637
7.0	0.0009	0.0064	0.0448
7.5	0.0006	0.0042	0.0312
8.0	0.0003	0.0027	0.0215
8.5	0.0002	0.0017	0.0147
9.0	0.0001	0.0011	0.0100
9.5	0.0001	0.0007	0.0068
10.0	0.0000	0.0004	0.0045

Values of $(G_T^0 - H_{298}^0)/T$, called the free energy function; $(H_T^0 - H_{298}^0)/T$, called the enthalpy function; and $S_T^0 - S_{298}^0$ as well as S_{298}^0 are tabulated for many substances, or can be calculated from calorimetric or spectroscopic data. [Some tables tabulate $(G_T^0 - H_0^0)/T$ and $(H_T^0 - H_0^0)/T$, based on a standard state of 0°K, but values of $H_{298}^0 - H_0^0$ are available to convert values from one set of tables into terms consistent with the other tables. We shall use 298°K as standard.]

The free energy function, $(G_T^0 - H_{298}^0)/T$, is selected for tabulation partly because it varies only slowly with, and is often almost linear in, T. Thus it is easy to have a compact table of $(G_T^0 - H_{298}^0)/T$ versus T and obtain intermediate results by interpolation. Figure 28.1 demonstrates this. Furthermore, the free energy function, unlike the values of ΔG_T^0 obtained from expressions like Equation (27.21), depends only on properties of a single substance. Finally, the free energy function is useful and easy to manipulate:

$$\begin{aligned}\frac{\Delta G_T^0}{T} &= \frac{\Delta G_T^0}{T} - \frac{\Delta H_{298}^0}{T} + \frac{\Delta H_{298}}{T} \\ &= \frac{\Delta G_T^0 - \Delta H_{298}^0}{T} + \frac{\Delta H_{298}^0}{T} \\ &= \Delta\,\frac{G_T^0 - H_{298}^0}{T} + \frac{\Delta H_{298}^0}{T}\end{aligned}$$

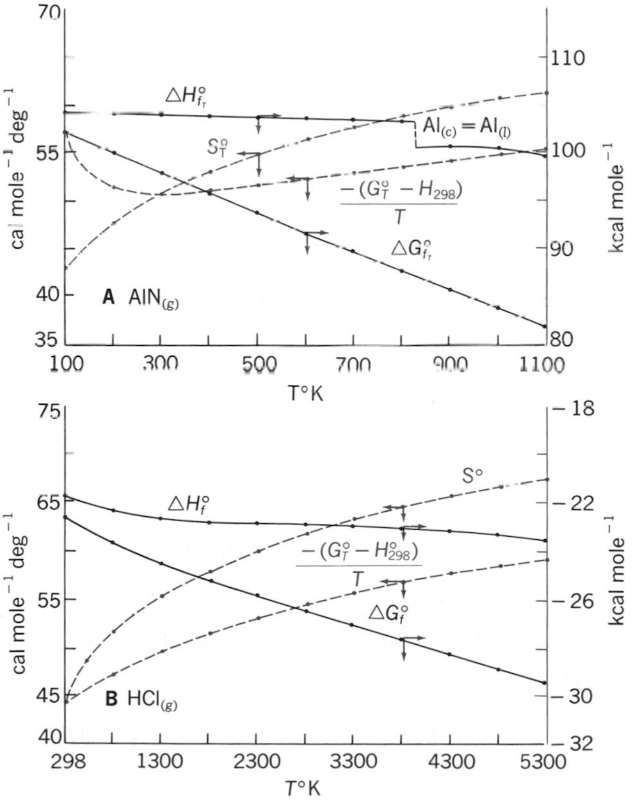

Figure 28.1 G_T^0, H_T^0, S_T^0, and $[(G_T^0 - H_{298}^0)/T]$ versus T.

Table 28.5 Free energy functions from *JANAF Thermochemical Data*. Functions for most substances are tabulated in the complete *JANAF* tables to 6000°K at 100° intervals, H^0_{298} values are given in Table 27.1.

Substance	$-(G^0_T - H^0_{298})/T$ (cal mole^{-1} °K^{-1}) at nine temperatures								
	298	400	500	1000	1500	2000	3000	4000	6000
$Al_{(c)}$	6.769	7.001	7.449	10.008	12.223	14.125	—	—	—
$Al_{(g)}$	39.304	39.503	39.878	41.864	43.395	44.583	46.357	47.666	49.569
$Al_2O_{3(\alpha c)}$	12.174	12.972	14.598	24.434	32.839	39.716	50.508	—	—
$B_2H_{6(g)}$	55.334	55.905	57.108	65.377	73.566	80.817	92.800	102.314	116.918
$C_{(graphite)}$	1.359	1.450	1.646	3.020	4.348	5.490	7.325	8.756	10.924
$CO_{(g)}$	47.214	47.488	48.006	50.845	53.158	55.026	57.917	60.117	63.381
$CO_{2(g)}$	51.072	51.434	52.148	56.359	59.984	62.974	67.670	71.278	76.672
$CH_{4(g)}$	44.490	44.837	45.533	50.016	54.387	58.306	64.905	70.251	78.536
$C_2H_{2(g)}$	48.004	48.438	49.303	54.466	58.977	62.772	68.884	73.699	81.067
C_2H_4	52.447	52.887	53.796	59.822	65.632	70.749	79.229	86.014	96.435
$Cl_{2(g)}$	53.289	53.612	54.231	57.623	60.310	62.423	65.617	68.010	71.540
$F_{2(g)}$	48.447	48.746	49.324	52.553	55.167	57.248	60.427	62.825	66.378
H_2	31.208	31.480	31.995	34.758	36.937	38.678	41.395	43.502	46.721
$H_2O_{(g)}$	45.106	45.422	46.026	49.382	52.196	54.548	58.354	61.379	66.044
$HCl_{(g)}$	44.645	44.919	45.435	48.220	50.456	52.262	55.076	57.236	60.474
$HCN_{(g)}$	48.213	48.561	49.244	53.216	56.625	59.467	63.997	67.537	72.915
$HF_{(g)}$	41.509	41.782	42.298	45.059	47.234	48.974	51.679	53.764	56.908
$HNO_{3(g)}$	63.663	64.194	65.269	71.917	77.819	82.746	90.547	96.573	105.593
$N_{2(g)}$	45.770	46.043	46.561	49.378	51.665	53.513	56.376	58.559	61.802
$NH_{3(g)}$	45.967	46.303	46.958	50.854	54.368	57.420	62.468	66.568	72.893
$NO_{(g)}$	50.347	50.627	51.157	54.064	56.432	58.340	61.282	63.513	66.812
$NO_{2(g)}$	57.323	57.681	58.382	62.498	66.014	68.891	73.362	76.762	81.789
$N_2O_{4(g)}$	72.636	73.394	74.907	84.028	91.938	98.443	108.586	116.318	127.767
$O_{2(g)}$	49.004	49.282	49.812	52.765	55.185	57.136	60.157	62.476	65.970
$O_{3(g)}$	57.080	57.462	58.217	62.648	66.386	69.413	74.084	77.623	82.856
$S_{8(g)}$	103.280	104.791	107.712	123.880	136.752	146.874	162.128	173.462	189.940
$SO_{2(g)}$	59.298	59.683	60.437	64.825	68.524	71.528	76.175	79.705	84.939
$SO_{3(g)}$	61.342	61.846	62.856	69.020	74.447	78.980	86.237	91.981	100.955

SOURCE: *JANAF Thermochemical Data*, Midland, Mich., Dow Chemical Co., 1960– .

(There are corresponding equations involving H^0_0.) Thus ΔG_T at any T can be obtained from ΔH^0_{298} and tables of the free energy functions of each of the reactants and products. Some values of the free energy function are tabulated in Table 28.5. In almost every case these are calculated from spectroscopic data using equations similar to those in Table 28.2.

The free energy functions for linear molecules may be written in terms of molecular properties as:

$$\left(\frac{\overline{G}_T - \overline{H}_0}{T}\right)_{\text{trans}} = -6.8645 \log M - 11.4408 \log T + 4.5756 \log P + 7.283$$

$$\left(\frac{\overline{G}_T - \overline{H}_0}{T}\right)_{\text{rot}} = 4.5756\ (\log \sigma - \log I - \log T) + 6.336$$

$$\left(\frac{\overline{G}_T - \overline{H}_0}{T}\right)_{\text{vib}} = 4.5756 \sum_i \log\,(1 - e^{-x_i}) \qquad \text{[for each vibration]}$$

$$\left(\frac{\overline{G}_T - \overline{H}_0}{T}\right)_{\text{elec}} = -4.5756 \log Z_{\text{elec}}$$

Note that H_0^0, the standard enthalpy at 0°K, is used here.

Thus, a knowledge of M, the molecular weight in atomic weight units; T, the Kelvin temperature; σ, the symmetry number; I, the moment of inertia in atomic weight units per Ångstrom^2; $x = h\nu/kT$, dimensionless, or ν, each vibration frequency in sec^{-1}; and ϵ_i, the energy spacing of each electronic state (in the same units as kT), allows the calculation of the total free energy of any linear molecule acting as an ideal gas. You will remember from Chapters 3 and 8 that I, ν, and ϵ_{elec} are available for many substances from spectroscopic data. The values of thermodynamic functions calculated from such spectroscopic data agree, within experimental uncertainty, with those calculated from thermal data. Thus spectroscopic data are now used with confidence to extend thermodynamic calculations to conditions not accessible to calorimetric measurements. An especially productive field is high-temperature chemistry—as in stellar atmospheres, rocket propulsion, or high-temperature industrial processes.

These values, combined with those in Table 27.1, provide data on a large number of possible reactions.

For example, let us calculate ΔG_{1000}^0 for the reaction

	$Al_2O_{3(\alpha c)}$	=	$2Al_{(g)}$	+	$\frac{3}{2}O_{2(g)}$
$\frac{G_{1000}^0 - H_{298}^0}{1000}$ (cal mole^{-1} °K^{-1})	24.434		$-2 \cdot 41.864$		$-\frac{3}{2} \cdot 52.765$
H_{298}^0 (kcal mole^{-1} °K^{-1})	-400.4		78.0		0

$$\Delta\frac{G_{1000}^0 - H_{298}^0}{1000}$$
$$= -2 \cdot 41.864 - \tfrac{3}{2} \cdot 52.765 + 24.434 = -138.54 \text{ cal mole}^{-1}\ {}^\circ\text{K}^{-1}$$

$$\Delta H_{298}^0 = (78.0 + 0 + 400.4)1000 = 478{,}400 \text{ cal mole}^{-1}\ {}^\circ\text{K}^{-1}$$

$$\Delta G_{1000}^0/1000 = -138.54 + \frac{478{,}400}{1000} = 339.9 \text{ cal mole}^{-1}\ {}^\circ\text{K}^{-1}$$

$$\Delta G_{1000}^0 = 339{,}900 \text{ cal mole}^{-1}\ {}^\circ\text{K}^{-1} = 339.9 \text{ kcal mole}^{-1}\ {}^\circ\text{K}^{-1}$$

This is a very large positive value for ΔG_{1000}^0, and indicates that $Al_2O_{3(\alpha c)}$ is very stable indeed with respect to decomposition into $Al_{(g)}$ and $O_{2(g)}$ at 1000°K.

Let us repeat the calculation, using data directly from the JANAF tables, for the reaction at the highest T for which data are available, 3500°K. Since Al_2O_3 melts at 2315°K, we calculate for liquid aluminum oxide.

	$Al_2O_{3(l)}$	=	$2Al_{(g)}$	+	$\frac{3}{2}O_{2(g)}$	at 3500°K
$G^0_{3500} - H^0_{298}/3500$ (cal mole^{-1} °K^{-1})	-66.791		$-2 \cdot 47.054$		$-\frac{3}{2} \cdot 61.383$	
H^0_{298} (kcal mole^{-1} °K^{-1})	-373.356		78.0		0	

$$\Delta(G^0_{3500} - H_{298}/3500) - 2 \cdot 47.054 - \tfrac{3}{2} \cdot 61.383 + 66.791$$
$$= -119.392 \text{ cal mole}^{-1} \text{ °K}^{-1}$$

$$\Delta H^0_{298} = 78.0 + 0 + 373.356 = 451.4 \text{ kcal mole}^{-1} \text{ °K}^{-1}$$

$$\Delta G^0_{3500}/3500 = -119.392 + \frac{451.400}{3500} = -9.579$$

$$\Delta G^0_{3500} = -33{,}530 \text{ cal mole}^{-1} \text{ °K}^{-1} = -33.53 \text{ kcal mole}^{-1} \text{ °K}^{-1}$$

Thus, at 3500°K, liquid Al_2O_3 will be readily dissociated into $Al_{(g)}$ and $O_{2(g)}$. We can predict this with great confidence, even though the experiment has probably never been performed. [Note that we have not considered dissociation into other possible products—$O_{(g)}$, for example, which will almost certainly be present at this T.]

The value of using the free energy function and its tabulated values rather than integrating the Gibbs-Helmholtz equation (27.21) should be obvious.

The JANAF tables contain values of C^0_P, S^0, $(G^0_T - H^0_{298})/T$, $H^0_T - H^0_{298}$, ΔH^0_{form}, ΔG^0_{form}, and log K_P for temperatures from 0°K to 6000°K for about 1000 substances. The tables are in looseleaf form, and the number of items is continually increasing. They also give some molecular constant data, and data on electronic, rotational, and vibrational states for gases.

We shall, in the next chapter, explore the relationship of K_P to the thermodynamic functions.

SUMMARY

Calorimetric data on heat capacities, heats of transition and heats of reaction, and/or spectral data on rotational, vibrational, and electronic states, can be used to calculate values of C, E, H, S, G, and A for pure substances. The experimental calorimetric and spectral data are often tabulated, as are the calculated values of the thermodynamic functions. Special combinations of the functions, such as the free energy function $(G^0_T - H^0_{298})/T$, are also tabulated to make the task of calculating the changes of thermodynamic functions during reactions especially easy.

Thermodynamic data can be calculated and tabulated for pure substances and then used to calculate changes that would take place during reactions that have never been observed in the laboratory. Such calculations can enormously decrease the number of laboratory experiments that must be performed, and they also permit design calculations to be made with great confidence even under conditions previously unknown. Thermodynamic calculations can indicate the likelihood that a projected reaction will be successful (for example, $\Delta G = -$) without carrying out the reaction under the proposed conditions. We shall explore this more carefully in the next chapter.

"Looking back . . . over the long labyrinth path which finally led to the discovery [of the quantum theory], I am vividly reminded of Goethe's saying that men will always be making mistakes as long as they are striving after something."
—*M. Planck*, Scientific Autobiography, (1949).

PROBLEMS

28.1. Which makes the greatest contribution to the entropy of SO_2 at 298°K—rotation, translation, vibration, or electronic states? Which has the highest molar entropy under STP—He, Ne, Ar, or Kr?

28.2. The standard heat of formation of $H_2Te_{(g)}$ is 23.8 kcal mole^{-1}. Its standard free energy of formation is unknown. Use data from Tables 18.1 and 27.1 and an estimate of the standard entropy of H_2Se to determine whether H_2Te is stable in the standard state with respect to decomposition into the elements. ($\Delta G_f^0 \cong 20$ kcal mole^{-1}.)

II

28.3. Calculate the total vibrational entropy for the following gases at 300°K, and at 1000°K. Estimate, before doing any calculations, which should be larger in each consecutive pair.

(*a*) HCl, $\nu = 8.65 \cdot 10^{13}$ sec^{-1}. ($S_{100} \cong 0$, $S_{1000} \simeq 0.2$ eu for vibration.)
(*b*) H_2O, $\nu_1 = 10.97 \cdot 10^{13}$, $\nu_2 = 4.79 \cdot 10^{13}$, $\nu_3 = 11.27 \cdot 10^{13}$.
(*c*) CH_4, $\nu_1 = 8.74 \cdot 10^{13}$, $\nu_2 = 4.56 \cdot 10^{13}$, $\nu_3 = 9.06 \cdot 10^{13}$, $\nu_4 = 3.92 \cdot 10^{13}$.
$g_1 = 1$ $\quad g_2 = 2$ $\quad g_3 = 3$ $\quad g_4 = 3$
(*d*) H_2, $\nu = 12.48 \cdot 10^{13}$.
(*e*) Cl_2, $\nu = 1.67 \cdot 10^{13}$.

28.4. Calculate ΔS^0_{1000} for the reaction $N_{2(g)} + O_{2(g)} \longrightarrow 2NO_{(g)}$. [$\Delta S^0_{1000} = 6$ cal (mole°K)$^{-1}$.]

28.5. Calculate S^0_{rot} for one or more diatomic molecules at 50°K, 300°K, and 1000°K. Comment on the results.

28.6. Use the data in Problem 28.3 to calculate ΔS_{vib} for the reaction $H_2 + Cl_2 = 2HCl$ and comment on the value of ΔS_{vib}. Compare with ΔS^0. Comment on the relative sizes. Estimate ΔS_{vib} before you do any calculations.

28.7. It should not be surprising that from Equation (7.18) we may obtain

$$Z_{rot} = \sum_J (2J + 1)\exp[-J(J + 1)h^2/8\pi^2IkT]$$

(*a*) Justify the above statement of Z, symbol by symbol, in terms of the general equation for a molecular partition function.
(*b*) If the rotational spacings are small compared to kT at the temperature of interest, then $g\ dg = (2J + 1)\ dJ = d(J^2 + J)$ and we can replace the above sum expression for Z_{rot} by the integral

$$Z_{rot} = \int_0^\infty e^{-(J^2+J)hB/kT}\, d(J^2 + J)$$

Integrate this expression.

III

28.8. Calculate $S^0_{298.1}$ for CCl_4. $I = 510 \cdot 10^{-40}$, $\nu_1(1) = 440$, $\nu_2(2) = 238$, $\nu_3(3) = 791$, $\nu_4(3) = 311$. [$S^0_{298(g)} \cong 70$ cal (mole °K)$^{-1}$.]

28.9. Which of the following seems most feasible as a method of synthesizing HCN? Consider reaction both at 298°K and at 1000°K.

(*a*) $NH_{3(g)} + CO_{(g)} = HCN_{(g)} + H_2O_{(g)}$.

(*b*) $NO_{(g)} + CH_{4(g)} = HCN_{(g)} + \frac{1}{2}H_{2(g)} + H_2O_{(g)}$.

(*c*) $\frac{1}{2}H_{2(g)} + C_{(\text{graph})} + \frac{1}{2}N_{2(g)} = HCN_{(g)}$.

(*d*) $\frac{1}{2}H_2O_{(g)} + \frac{7}{4}C_{(\text{graph})} + NO_{(g)} = HCN_{(g)} + \frac{3}{4}CO_2$.

28.10. As a physical chemist you have been asked to determine the thermodynamic properties of bromine, specifically those relating to the reaction (at 298°K):

$$Br_2 \text{ (liq, } P = 1 \text{ atm)} \longrightarrow Br_2 \text{ (gas, 1 atm)}$$

(*a*) Exactly what physical measurements (experiments) would you make to determine ΔH^0_{298}, ΔG^0_{298}, and ΔS^0_{298}? Explain any assumptions necessary to evaluate the constants from the experimental data.

(*b*) Using free energy function and enthalpy data, work backward and evaluate the parameters you would have measured in the experiments described in your answers to *a*. Note that ΔH^0 is *not* zero.

(*c*) Is $\Delta S^0_{298} = (\Delta H^0_{298}/298)$? If not, why not? Under what circumstances could the standard enthalpy be used to calculate the entropy change? Calculate the entropy changes around the path implied in your answer to the question of the previous sentence. [Use $\Delta G^0_{298} = 751$ cal, if you have been unable to answer *b*.]

28.11. Calculate some of the functions which are missing in Table 28.2, such as $\overline{C}_{V\text{rot}}$, $\overline{H}_{\text{rot}}$, $\overline{H}_{\text{vib}}$, and others.

See page 1093 for a list of references and readings in the recent chemical literature related to the material in this chapter.

CHAPTER 29

Equilibrium Constant Calculations

The factors that determine values of heat capacities, enthalpy, entropy, and free energy are, of course, functions of position in the periodic table. The thermodynamic functions are related to atomic and molecular energy levels, to radius ratios and other size effects, and to masses.

One of the main tasks of a chemist is to find feasible methods for synthesizing desired substances. All the reactions employed in such methods must involve a shift toward equilibrium conditions, and a major problem is thus to predict equilibrium conditions and the means of achieving them. Table 26.4 lists some equilibrium conditions for various types of systems and restraints. Because the most common chemical restraint is constant pressure and the next most common is constant temperature, we shall spend most of our time discussing equilibrium problems in a closed system of constant pressure and constant temperature. Table 26.4 shows that the Gibbs free energy, G, tends to a minimum under these conditions. Thus a common problem for a chemist is to determine ΔG for a reaction and attempt to make it as large a negative value as possible.

A large negative value of ΔG does not ensure that a reaction will occur, of course. The rate may be too slow or there may be a competing or concurrent reaction which prevents accumulation of the desired product. But calculations that give a large positive value of ΔG are clear proof that the reaction is not feasible and need not even be tried in the laboratory.

THE CHEMICAL POTENTIAL

At equilibrium the Gibbs free energy of a closed system of constant T and P is at a minimum. No net flows of heat or species occur. No work can be done by the system. Thus the transfer of an infinitesimal amount of component A from one place in the system to another involves no work or change in free energy either of the system or the component. The molar free energy of each component is the same everywhere in the system. At any two sites, α and β, $\overline{G}_A$ is the same:

$$(\overline{G}_A)_\alpha = (\overline{G}_A)_\beta \tag{29.1}$$

Many terms have been invented to describe this situation. Since no net chemical reactions are occurring, there is no net tendency for one species to react to give another species or to move from one region to another. The *escaping tendency* of a given species is the same everywhere in the system.

Or the system may be viewed in terms of its potential to react. Since there is no net tendency to react, the *chemical potential* of each species must be the same everywhere in the system.

Or the system may be viewed in terms of the reactivity, or activity, of the species. Since no net reactions are occurring, the *activity* of each species must be constant throughout the system.

These three terms—escaping tendency, chemical potential, and activity—are not synonymous, but each represents the tendency of a species to react. One additional term is also commonly used—*fugacity*. Let us investigate these terms.

Escaping tendency is the most descriptive of the terms. The phrase is easy to use qualitatively: for example, the escaping tendency of protons increases as the concentration increases, or the escaping tendency of a gas always increases as temperature increases. The escaping tendency of a species, then, is a measure of its tendency to leave, or escape, the condition in which it finds itself. An increase either in concentration or in temperature always increases escaping tendency. Quantitatively,

$$\text{escaping tendency} = \text{fugacity} = f$$

Chemical potential, μ, like other potentials, refers to the possibility of doing work, reminding us of free energy, also a work function. The chemical potential, μ, is defined as the molar free energy:*

$$\mu_A = \overline{G}_A \tag{29.2}$$

This is not much of a gain, since we have merely substituted one name and symbol for another (and a Greek symbol at that). The only real advantage turns out to be that chemical potential is a more descriptive phrase to most people than molar free energy. Thus we shall commonly use chemical potential, μ, in our discussions, remembering that it is identical with the molar free energy and measures the tendency of the species to react. Large positive values of the chemical potential mean highly reactive species.

Large values of the activity, a, also mean highly reactive species, but

*The chemical potential is actually defined in terms of the partial molar free energy:

$$\mu_i = \left(\frac{\partial G}{\partial n_i}\right)_{T,P,n_1,n_2\ldots}$$

For pure substances $\mu = \overline{G}$, but, in solutions, the partial molar free energy of the ith component, μ_i equals the rate of change of G for the system as n_i varies, all other variables staying constant. For the purpose of this course it is sufficient to consider μ_i as the free energy contributed to the system by one mole of component i.

activity is defined in a logarithmic relationship to the chemical potential:

$$G_A = G_A^0 + nRT \ln a_A \tag{29.3}$$

$$\mu_A = \mu_A^0 + RT \ln a_A \tag{29.4}$$

In the standard state $\mu_A = \mu_A^0$, so a_A must then equal 1. The activity is, thus, defined as unity in the standard state. The activity can have no dimensions as it is used in Equation (29.3). Activity, a, is dimensionless; its relationship to fugacity is

$$a = \frac{f}{f^0}$$

where the fugacity could have any of the usual dimensions used to measure concentration—molarity, mole fraction, pressure, and others. These concentration units are all related, since pressure may be calculated from molarity or other concentration units, using Henry's Law and Raoult's Law for solutions or Dalton's Law for gases.

The important thing is that, in evaluating a, the measure of concentration be in the same units as were used when f^0 and μ_A were determined. Since $a = f/f^0$, a can have the same numerical magnitude as f since f^0 most often has a numerical value of unity (1 atm, 1 M, and so on). In practice, we substitute in formulas for the activity, a, the numerical values for pressures and concentrations—actually we are always substituting dimensionless ratios. This is illustrated by Equations (29.5):

$$a = \begin{cases} \dfrac{f}{f^0} & \text{in general} \\[2ex] \dfrac{p}{p^0} = p & \text{for ideal gases, standard state 1 atm} \\[2ex] \dfrac{M}{M^0} = M & \text{for ideal solutions, standard state 1 } M \text{ solutions} \\[2ex] \dfrac{Xp^0}{1 \cdot p^0} = X & \text{for ideal solutions, standard state pure solvent} \end{cases} \tag{29.5}$$

Using the usual standard states, this means that pressure units are used for gases, molarity for substances in solution in condensed phases, and all pure condensed phases have an activity of 1 (since $f = f^0$ for the pure phase).

EQUILIBRIUM CONSTANTS AND ACTIVITIES

Consider the type reaction

$$aA + bB = cC + dD$$

$$\Delta G = c\overline{G}_C + d\overline{G}_D - a\overline{G}_A - b\overline{G}_B$$

Substituting the values of $\overline{G}$ for each species, using Equation (29.3) at constant temperature, we obtain

$$\Delta G = \Delta G^0 + RT \ln \frac{a_C{}^c a_D{}^d}{a_A{}^a a_B{}^b} \tag{29.6}$$

Equation (29.6) involves no assumptions as to ideal systems. It only requires that T remain constant. It allows the calculation of ΔG for any process under any conditions if ΔG^0 and the experimental activities are shown, as long as T remains constant.

At equilibrium $\Delta G = 0$ and we get

$$\Delta G^0 = -RT \ln \left[\frac{a_C{}^c a_D{}^d}{a_A{}^a a_B{}^b}\right]_{eq} = -RT \ln K_{th} \tag{29.7}$$

This gives a general proof of the relationship between Gibbs free energy and the equilibrium constant. The thermodynamic equilibrium constant, K_{th}, can always be evaluated if ΔG^0 or the equilibrium activities can be determined.

In general, activities are not equal to concentrations but are related by the defining equation

$$a = \gamma c \tag{29.8}$$

where γ is called the activity coefficient. Since a is dimensionless, γ has units the reciprocal of those of c. Thus one must be careful to match γ values with corresponding values of c, not just any measure of concentration. In all ideal systems $\gamma = 1$ and $a = c$ numerically. In other systems γ may be more or less than 1, depending on the type and strength of the molecular interactions causing deviations from ideality.

Substitution in Equation (29.7) gives

$$\Delta G^0 = -RT \ln \left[\frac{(\gamma_C c_C)^c (\gamma_D c_D)^d}{(\gamma_A c_A)^a (\gamma_B c_B)^b}\right]_{eq}$$

$$= -RT \ln \left[\frac{c_C{}^c c_D{}^d}{c_A{}^a c_B{}^b}\right]_{eq} \left[\frac{\gamma_C{}^c \gamma_D{}^d}{\gamma_A{}^a \gamma_B{}^b}\right]_{eq}$$

Since in ideal systems all γ's equal unity, for ideal systems and a standard state of unit concentrations we get

$$\Delta G^0 = -RT \ln \left[\frac{c_C{}^c c_D{}^d}{c_A{}^a c_B{}^b}\right]_{eq}$$

$$= -RT \ln K_c \tag{29.9}$$

This equation is often reasonably applicable even in nonideal systems, since the real requirement for its use is that

$$\frac{\gamma_C{}^c \gamma_D{}^d}{\gamma_A{}^a \gamma_B{}^b} = 1.$$

and this equation can be satisfied even if all the γ's deviate from unity, so long as their deviations tend to cancel out. This cancellation is especially likely if $c + d = a + b$, since the values of γ often tend to change by similar amounts as conditions in the system vary.

In this course we shall almost always assume that concentrations and pressures may be used in equilibrium calculations (that is, all values of $\gamma = 1$), so we need not concern ourselves with activity coefficients and values of the thermodynamic equilibrium constant, K_{th}.

Thus, for gas phase reactions (p in atmospheres),

$$K = K_p = \frac{p_C{}^c p_D{}^d}{p_A{}^a p_B{}^b}$$

and for condensed solution phases (c in moles per liter),

$$K = K_c = \frac{c_C{}^c c_D{}^d}{c_A{}^a c_B{}^b}$$

For reactions involving both gases and solutions, both pressures and concentrations are used. For example,

$$Ce^{++++}{}_{(aq)} + \tfrac{1}{2}H_{2(g)} = Ce^{+++}{}_{(aq)} + H^+{}_{(aq)}$$

$$K = \frac{[Ce^{+++}][H^+]}{[Ce^{++++}][p_{H_2}]^{1/2}}$$

where the aqueous concentrations would be expressed in moles per liter and the hydrogen pressure in atmospheres. Of course, gas concentrations in moles per liter may also be used to give

$$K_c = \frac{[Ce^{+++}][H^+]}{[Ce^{++++}][H_2]^{1/2}}$$

Exercise 29.1

What error is introduced into the equilibrium calculations for the Ce^{++++}—H_2 reaction if ideal solutions are assumed when actually all the activity coefficients are 0.50? *Answer:* $[\gamma_{Ce^{++++}} \cdot \gamma_{H^+}/\gamma_{Ce^{+++}}(\gamma_{H_2})^{1/2}] = 0.50^{1/2} = 0.70$, leading to a 30% error in K.

STANDARD STATES, FREE ENERGY CHANGES, AND K

We have mentioned from time to time the existence of various conventions regarding standard states, but have adhered in practice to the standard state based on pure elements at 1 atm and 298°K. This state works eminently well in studying reactions between gases or between pure substances. It is not as convenient in dealing with reactions in condensed solution phases, and especially in aqueous solutions. This standard state would be very convenient if the solvent used in making a solution served only as an inert diluent for the reacting species, but this is seldom the case. Strong interactions occur between solvent and solute: the solvent, especially water with ionic species, is far from acting as an inert diluent, and notice must thus be taken of solvent effects.

We shall discuss these solvent effects briefly later and mention here only that they lead to the definition of additional standard states. Two common types are (1) infinitely dilute solutions—that is, solutions so dilute that the solute particles act independently of one another and have properties that are linearly proportional to their concentrations (remember the colligative properties), (2) approximately 1-molar solutions, in which the ions are acting as they would in an infinitely dilute solution. In this book, although we are dealing with chemical equilibrium, we shall generally neglect solvent-solute interactions and assume that all solutions are ideal. Our standard state then becomes a 1-molar solution at 298°K.

In general, therefore, we may write

$$\Delta G^0 = -RT \ln K \tag{29.10}$$

The values of K are calculated by using standard-state units—pressure in atmospheres for all gases and concentrations in moles per liter of solution for all solutes in solution. The concentrations of all pure condensed phases, such as pure solids, are not specifically evaluated, but are included in K, since the concentrations remain constant throughout the reaction, as discussed in Table 19.3.

You may ask how Equation (29.10) can possibly be correct dimensionally, since K normally has dimensions and a logarithmic term must be dimensionless. The answer is that Equation (29.10) is derived from an equation like (29.6). In (29.6) there are two logarithmic terms [see Equation (29.7) for ΔG^0 as a log term] of complementary dimensions such that their ratio is dimensionless. One term is found to equal zero, and disappears explicitly from the equation. Its dimensions do not disappear, though they are not explicitly present. Thus, dimensionally, Equation (29.10) should be written

$$\Delta G^0 = -RT \ln K + RT \ln K'$$
$$= -RT \ln \frac{K}{K'} = -RT \ln K$$

since $K' = 1$. The dimensions of K and K' are identical.

$$K' = \left[\frac{\prod_i [\text{prod}]_i^{n_i}}{\prod_j [\text{reac}]_j^{n_j}} \right]_{\text{std. state}} = 1 \tag{29.11}$$

K_p AND K_c

Since G^0 is defined in terms of a standard state based on pressures of gases, K in the equation $\Delta G^0 = -RT \ln K$ is also based on pressures in the gas phase. But we often express gas concentrations in moles per liter rather than in pressure units.

Thus for the reaction $N_2 + 3H_2 = 2NH_3$,

$$K = K_p = \frac{p_{NH_3}{}^2}{p_{N_2} p_{H_2}{}^3}$$
$$K_c = \frac{M_{NH_3}{}^2}{M_{N_2} \cdot M_{H_2}{}^3}$$

How are these values of K related?

If we assume ideal gas behavior, we get

$$p = \frac{nRT}{V} = MRT$$

$$M = \frac{p}{RT} \text{ moles per liter}$$

$$K_c = \frac{(p_{NH_3}/RT)^2}{(p_{N_2}/RT)(p_{H_2}/RT)^3}$$

$$= \frac{p_{NH_3}{}^2}{p_{N_2}p_{H_2}{}^3}\frac{(RT)^4}{(RT)^2} = K_p(RT)^{4-2}$$

$$= K_p(RT)^{-\Delta n} = K(RT)^{-\Delta n} \qquad (29.12)$$

Equation (29.12) is a general relationship for reactions involving ideal gases, where Δn = change in number of moles of gas during the net reaction.

Exercise 29.2

Calculate the ratio of K_c/K_p at 300°K for the Haber process. *Answer:* $N_2 + 3H_2 = 2NH_3$, $\Delta n = -2$, $K_c/K_p = (RT)^{-\Delta n} = (RT)^2 = (0.082 \cdot 300)^2 = 613$ liter² atm² mole⁻² $= 613$ (atm/M)². Note that R should not be expressed in cal mole^{-1} °K^{-1} here if the dimensions are to be meaningful.

STANDARD EMF AND *K*

We showed in Equation (26.14) that, at constant T,

$$dA = -w_{rev}$$

For an electrochemical cell operating at voltage $\mathcal{E}$ and passing $n\mathcal{F}$ coulombs of electricity, the electrical work done by the cell is

$$w_{elec} = \mathcal{F}\mathcal{E}\, dn$$

There may also be $P\,dV$ work done by the cell, $w = P\,dV$, so if the cell operates reversibly and produces maximum work,

$$dA = -P\,dV - \mathcal{F}\mathcal{E}\,dn = -w_{rev}$$

or

$$\mathcal{F}\mathcal{E}\,dn = w_{rev} - P\,dV$$

But Equation (26.13) showed that, when both T and P are constant,

$$-dG = w_{rev} - P\,dV$$

so

$$-dG = \mathcal{F}\mathcal{E}\,dn$$

or

$$\Delta G = -n\mathcal{F}\mathcal{E} \qquad (29.13)$$

and

$$\Delta G^0 = -n\mathcal{F}\mathcal{E}^0$$

since $\mathcal{E}^0$ and G^0 both refer to the reaction in the standard state. [For $\mathcal{E}^0$ values see Table 20.2.]

Thus, from Equation (29.10),

$$\Delta G^0 = -RT\ln K = -n\mathcal{F}\mathcal{E}^0$$

and

$$\mathcal{E}^0 = \frac{RT}{n\mathcal{F}}\ln K \qquad (29.14)$$

Equation (29.14) has already been introduced in Equation (20.3).

From (29.6), $\Delta G = \Delta G^0 + RT \ln [(a_C{}^c a_D{}^d)/(a_A{}^a a_B{}^b)]$ for a typical reaction. Substituting from (29.13) gives the

NERNST EQUATION:
$$\mathcal{E} = \mathcal{E}^0 - \frac{RT}{n\mathcal{F}} \ln \frac{a_C{}^c a_D{}^d}{a_A{}^a a_B{}^b} \tag{29.15}$$

$$= \frac{RT}{n\mathcal{F}} \ln K - \frac{RT}{n\mathcal{F}} \ln \frac{\prod_i [\text{prod}]_i{}^{n_i}}{\prod_j [\text{reac}]_j{}^{n_j}} \tag{29.16}$$

$$\mathcal{E} = \frac{RT}{n\mathcal{F}} \ln K - \frac{RT}{n\mathcal{F}} \ln Q = \frac{RT}{n\mathcal{F}} \ln \frac{K}{Q}$$

Thus the voltage, $\mathcal{E}$, corresponding to any particular concentrations of reactants and products, is related to $\mathcal{E}^0$ or K, and $\ln(\Pi_i/\Pi_j) = \ln Q$, where the logarithmic term has the form of the equilibrium constant but contains values of the concentrations for which $\mathcal{E}$ is desired. We shall call Q the activity quotient.

At $T = 298°\text{K}$, Equation (29.15) becomes

$$\mathcal{E} = \mathcal{E}^0 - \frac{0.0592}{n} \log \frac{a_C{}^c a_D{}^d}{a_A{}^a a_B{}^b} = \mathcal{E}^0 - \frac{0.0592}{n} \log Q \tag{29.17}$$

Exercise 29.3

Calculate the voltage of an electric cell at equilibrium. *Answer:*

$$\mathcal{E} = \mathcal{E}^0 - \frac{0.0592}{n} \log \left[\frac{\prod_i [\text{prod}]_i{}^{n_i}}{\prod_j [\text{prod}]_j{}^{n_j}} \right].$$

But, at equilibrium,

$$\mathcal{E}^0 = -\frac{0.0592}{n} \log K = -\frac{0.0592}{n} \log \left[\frac{\prod_i [\text{prod}]_i{}^{n_i}}{\prod_j [\text{prod}]_j{}^{n_j}} \right]$$

so $\mathcal{E} = 0$ at equilibrium, and the cell can deliver no voltage and, of course, no current.

ΔS AND ΔH FROM VALUES OF $\mathcal{E}$

Measurement of $\mathcal{E}$ as a function of T gives a method of calculating ΔS and ΔH for a cell reaction. From Equation (27.18),

$$\Delta S = -\left(\frac{\partial\, \Delta G}{\partial T}\right)_P$$

Then, from (29.13),

$$\Delta S = \left(\frac{\partial n\mathcal{F}\mathcal{E}}{\partial T}\right)_P$$

$$= n\mathcal{F}\left(\frac{\partial \mathcal{E}}{\partial T}\right)_P \tag{29.18}$$

The entropy change of the electrochemical cell reaction is related to the rate of change of the cell voltage with temperature. Furthermore,

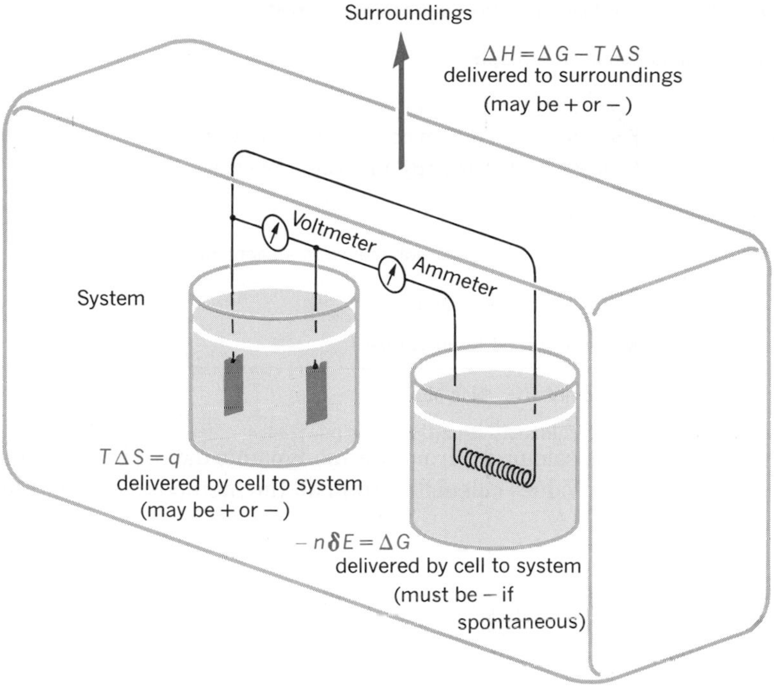

Figure 29.1 $T\,\Delta S$, ΔG, and ΔH for an electric cell-resistor closed system operating at constant T and P. (See also Exercise 32.13.)

$$\begin{aligned}\Delta H &= \Delta G + T\,\Delta S\\ &= -n\mathcal{F}\mathcal{E} + Tn\mathcal{F}\left(\frac{\partial \mathcal{E}}{\partial T}\right)_P\\ &= -n\mathcal{F}\left[\mathcal{E} - T\left(\frac{\partial \mathcal{E}}{\partial T}\right)_P\right]\end{aligned} \tag{29.19}$$

Thus, measurements on cell voltages allow ready calculation of values for ΔH, ΔS, ΔG, and K for the cell reaction.

Figure 29.1 illustrates another relationship between ΔH, ΔS, T, and ΔG for a system containing an operating electric cell. The maximum work the cell can deliver outside itself (assuming no $P\,dV$ work) is $\Delta G = -n\mathcal{F}\mathcal{E}$, which can be converted to heat, q_{max}, by using an electric heater outside the cell. During this process the cell itself has an entropy change ΔS, which generates $q = T\,dS$ within the cell. Assuming constant T and P we get $q_P = \Delta H = \Delta G + T\,\Delta S = q_{cell} + q_{heater}$. Thus a calorimetric measurement of q in the cell gives ΔS_{cell}, a voltmeter measurement and a knowledge of n give q for the heater from $q = \Delta G = -n\mathcal{F}\mathcal{E}$, and the sum of these two terms gives ΔH for the system, cell plus heater, as shown in Figure 29.1. Or a calorimetric measurement of ΔH and a determination of n and $\mathcal{E}$ allows calculation of ΔS.

CALCULATION OF *K*, THE EQUILIBRIUM CONSTANT

Much of Chapters 19 and 20 was used to show how equilibrium constants could be calculated from analytical data on acid-base, precipitation, and redox equilibria.

Table 29.1 Some methods of evaluating *K*, the equilibrium constant.

I. Analytical data and the net equation (Chapter 19)	
$aA + bB = cC + dD$	
$K = \left[\frac{[C]^c[D]^d}{[A]^a[B]^b}\right]_{eq}$	Evaluate *a*, *b*, *c*, *d* from equation for net reaction Evaluate [*C*], [*D*], [*A*], [*B*] by analysis of equilibrium systems
II. Electrochemical cells (Chapter 20)	
$\ln K = n\mathcal{F}\mathcal{E}^0/RT$	Measure *n*, *T*, and $\mathcal{E}^0$ (voltage when all activities are unity)
III. Thermal and spectroscopic data (Chapters 27 and 28)	
$\Delta G^0 = -RT \ln K$	Measure ΔG^0 at temperature *T*

We now see that *K* can also be calculated from thermodynamic data. The methods are summarized in Table 29.1. Values calculated from all the methods agree within the experimental uncertainty.

VARIATIONS IN *K*, THE EQUILIBRIUM CONSTANT

The equilibrium constant for a reaction is independent of changes in *n*, *V*, or *P* for an isothermal system. (This is only strictly true: (1) if all gases behave ideally, (2) the interactions with the solvent remain unchanged, and (3) initially pure liquid and solid phases remain pure. Otherwise the reactivities of the species are changed by interactions with neighboring molecules and the degree of interaction varies with the concentrations of the species.) You might conjecture how *K* can be independent of *P* even though *G* depends on *P* and

$$\Delta G^0 = -RT \ln K$$

Exercise 29.4

Does ΔG^0 depend on *P*? *Answer:* No. ΔG^0 depends only on the standard state, which has a defined *P*; therefore ΔG^0 is not a function of *P* as long as the same standard state is used.

K does vary with *T*. Equation (27.27) gives the

GIBBS-HELMHOLTZ EQUATION:

$$\left(\frac{\partial(\Delta G/T)}{\partial(1/T)}\right)_P = \Delta H$$

or

$$\left(\frac{\partial(\Delta G^0/T)}{\partial(1/T)}\right)_P = \Delta H^0$$

Since

$$\Delta G^0 = -RT \ln K$$

then

$$\frac{\Delta G^0}{T} = -R \ln K$$

and we get the

VAN'T HOFF EQUATION:
$$\frac{\partial \ln K}{\partial(1/T)} = -\frac{\Delta H^0}{R} \tag{29.20}$$

Thus a plot of ln K versus $1/T$ gives a line of slope $(-\Delta H^0/R)$. Figure 29.2 shows some plotted data. The nearly straight lines in these plots are consistent with the idea that ΔH^0 is almost independent of T for most systems.

For K_c, with ideal gases, we get from Equation (29.12)

$$\left(\frac{\partial \ln K_c}{\partial(1/T)}\right)_P = \left(\frac{\partial \ln (K)(RT)^{-\Delta n}}{\partial(1/T)}\right)_P = \left(\frac{\partial \ln K}{\partial(1/T)}\right)_P + \Delta n\left(\frac{\partial \ln RT}{\partial T/T^2}\right)_P$$
$$= \frac{-\Delta H^0}{R} + \Delta n T = \frac{-(\Delta H^0 - \Delta n RT)}{R}$$

or from Equation (27.1),

$$\left(\frac{\partial \ln K_c}{\partial(1/T)}\right)_P = \frac{-\Delta E^0}{R} \tag{29.21}$$

An analytic expression for K as a function of T can be readily derived from heat capacity data, a single value of ΔH, and a single value of K, by integrating Equation (29.20) using the Kirchhoff equation (27.4).

Exercise 29.5

Use the data in Table 27.1 to calculate K at 298°K and estimate K at 1000°K for the reaction $CO + \frac{1}{2}O_2 = CO_2$. *Answer:* At 298°K, $\Delta G^0 = -RT \ln K = -94{,}265 + 32{,}783 = -61{,}482$; $\log K = 61{,}482/1365$; $K = 10^{45.04}$. $\Delta H^0_{298} = -94.054 + 26.417 = -67.637$ kcal. Assume that ΔH^0 is independent of T. Then $[\partial \ln K/$

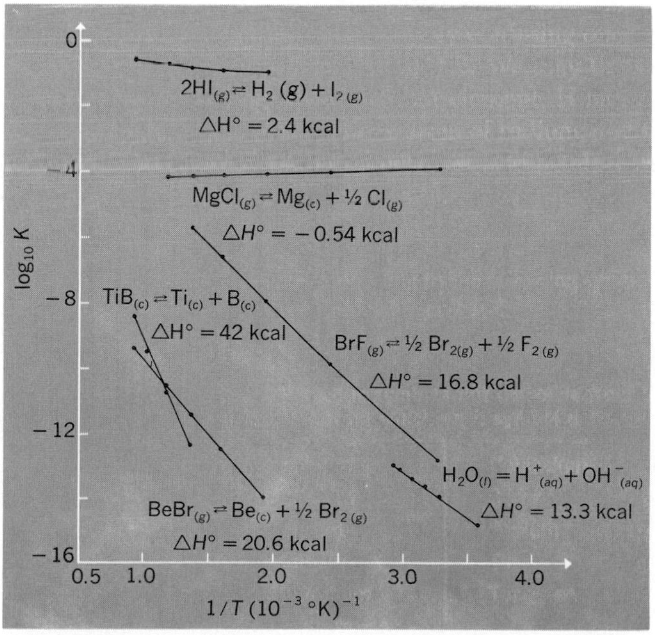

Figure 29.2 Calculation of $\Delta \overline{H}^0$ from log K as a function of T [see Equation (29.20)].

$\partial(1/T)] = +67{,}637/1.989$; $\log(K_{1000}/K_{298}) = (67{,}637/4.575)[1/1000) - (1/298)]$. $K_{1000}/10^{45.04} = 10^{-34.82}$, $K_{1000} = 10^{10.22}$. (You should have predicted the decrease in K with increasing T from the sign of ΔH^0, and also that K would still be large at 1000°K.)

THE HABER PROCESS

K is a function of T as shown in the preceding section, but is not usually a strong function of P, as outlined on page 698. Activity coefficients that deviate greatly from unity do cause important effects at high P. Figure 29.3 shows some actual data on ammonia synthesis. You may wish to use data from the figure to calculate values of K as a function of T and to estimate deviations from ideality as P increases.

Exercise 29.6

Ammonia plants commonly operate in such a way that only 10% conversion to NH_3 occurs when the stoichiometric mixture of N_2 and H_2 passes over the catalyst. Rationalize this in the light of Figure 29.3. *Answer:* Even the best available catalyst gives only slow rates at readily attainable values of P and T. It is more economical to use a high rate of flow over the catalyst, condense out the NH_3 formed, and recycle the gases than it is to use a lower rate of flow and obtain a higher yield per pass. The critical number in industry is output per hour, which equals rate of flow times fraction converted. Output per hour of NH_3 is maximized at high flow rates.

VARIATION IN THE FREE ENERGY FUNCTION

The free energy function (p. 713) may be written

$$\Delta \frac{G_T^0 - H_{298}^0}{T} = \frac{\Delta G_T^0}{T} - \frac{\Delta H_{298}^0}{T}$$

$$= -R \ln K - \frac{\Delta H_{298}^0}{T} \qquad (29.22)$$

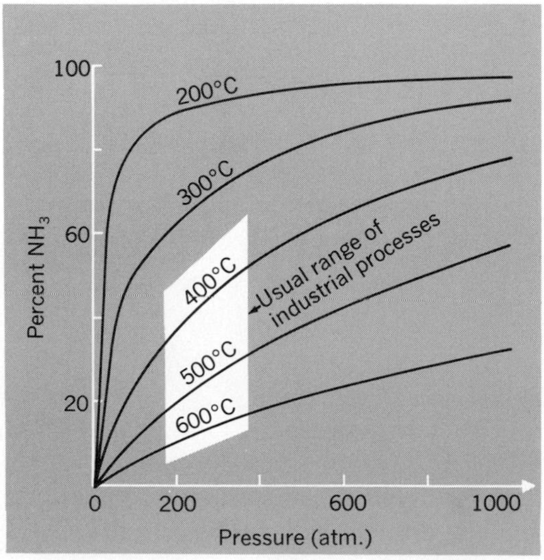

Figure 29.3 Some data on the Haber process.

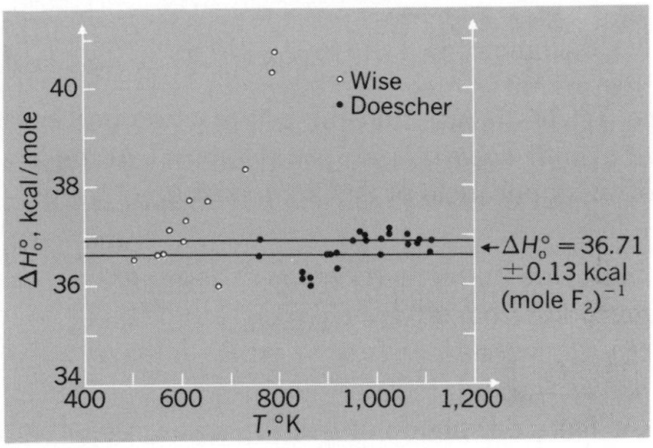

Figure 29.4 Use of Equation (20.21) to calculate ΔH_0^0 for $F_{2(g)} = 2F_{(g)}$. [Stamper and Barrow, *Trans. Faraday Soc.*, **54,** 1592 (1958).]

If the free energy functions of the reactants or products are known, one can calculate a value for ΔH_{298}^0 from each experimental value of *K*. This is considerably preferable to the slope method of Equation (29.20), which essentially gives only one value of ΔH^0 (often less accurate) for the reaction from a whole set of equilibrium measurements.

Figure 29.4 shows the use of the free energy function in calculating ΔH_0^0 for the reaction $F_{2(g)} = 2F_{(g)}$, using spectroscopic data to evaluate $(G_T^0 - H_0^0)/T$ and the direct dissociation constant measurements of Doescher (1952) and of Wise (1954) to evaluate *K* in Equation (29.22). Using only their data, one would obtain single values of ΔH_0^0 by using Equation (29.20). Equation (29.21) gives several dozen values of ΔH_0^0, shows their consistency or lack thereof, and indicates that Wise had a serious temperature-dependent error in his work. (Note the use of 0°K here as a standard state rather than 298°K.)

HANDLING EXPERIMENTAL DATA

R. G. Bates and V. E. Bower* measured the cell reaction

$$\tfrac{1}{2}H_{2(g)} + AgCl_{(c)} = Ag_{(c)} + H^+_{(aq)} + Cl^-_{(aq)}$$

at 5° intervals in 0.1 *M* HCl. They expressed their results as

$$\mathcal{E} = 0.35510 - 0.3422 \cdot 10^{-4}t - 3.2347 \cdot 10^{-6}t^2 + 6.314 \cdot 10^{-9}t^3$$

where $t =$ °C. The value of $\mathcal{E}^0$ can be obtained from Table 20.2. How much thermodynamic data can you get from these measurements?

From Table 20.2 we can calculate $\mathcal{E}^0$:

$$\begin{array}{llr} (19) & AgCl_{(c)} + e^- = Ag_{(c)} + Cl^-, & \mathcal{E}^0 = 0.2223 \\ (-14) & \tfrac{1}{2}H_{2(g)} = e^- + H^+, & \mathcal{E}^0 = 0.0000 \\ \hline & AgCl_{(c)} + \tfrac{1}{2}H_{2(g)} = Ag_{(c)} + H^+_{(aq)} + Cl^-_{(aq)}, & \mathcal{E}^0 = 0.2223 \text{ at } 298°K \end{array}$$

From Equation (29.13),

$$\begin{aligned} \Delta G^0 &= -n\mathcal{F}\mathcal{E}^0 \\ &= -1\ \text{eq} \cdot 23.053 \frac{\text{kcal}}{\text{eq} \cdot \text{volt}} \cdot 0.2223\ \text{volt} \\ &= -5.14\ \text{kcal} = -w_{max} + P\,dV = -w_{rev} + P\,dV \end{aligned}$$

J. Res. Natl. Bur. Stand. (U.S.), **53**, 283(1954).

$$w_{max} = w_{rev} = +5.14 \text{ kcal} + P\,dV = 5.14 + RT\,\Delta n$$
$$= 5.14 + 1.99 \cdot 10^{-3} \cdot 298 \cdot (-\tfrac{1}{2}) = 4.84 \text{ kcal}$$

Thus gaseous hydrogen can reduce $AgCl_{(c)}$ to $Ag_{(c)}$ and the cell reaction proceeds as written if all species are present at unit activity. ($[H^+] = [Cl^-] = 1\ M$, $p_{H_2} =$ 1 atm.) It can perform 4.84 kcal of work per mole of $AgCl_{(c)}$ reacting.

From Equation (29.14),

$$\log K_{298} = \frac{n\mathfrak{F}\mathcal{E}^0}{2.303\ RT} = (1/0.0592)0.2223 = \frac{0.2223}{0.0592} = 3.76$$

$$K_{298} = 5.6 \cdot 10^3 = \frac{[H^+][Cl^-]}{p_{H_2}{}^{1/2}}$$

(Note the odd dimensions of K, M^2 atm$^{-1/2}$.)

Knowing K, we could calculate values of concentrations for various equilibrium states. For example, if $[H^+] = [Cl^-] = 0.1\ M$ (assuming γ's are all unity),

$$(p_{H_2}{}^{1/2})_{eq} = \frac{[H^+][Cl^-]}{5.6 \cdot 10^3} = \frac{10^{-2}}{5.6 \cdot 10^3} = 1.8 \cdot 10^{-6} \text{ atm}^{1/2}$$

$$(p_{H_2})_{eq} = 3.2 \cdot 10^{-12} \text{ atm}$$

Since one mole of gas disappears in the net reaction, we would guess that ΔS would be negative. Let us see. From Equation (29.18),

$$\Delta S = n\mathfrak{F}\left(\frac{\partial \mathcal{E}}{\partial T}\right)_P$$

But

$$dt = dT$$

and therefore

$$\Delta S = n\mathfrak{F}[\partial(0.35510 - 0.3422 \cdot 10^{-4}t - 3.2347 \cdot 10^{-6}t^2 + 6.314 \cdot 10^{-9}t^3)/\partial T]$$
$$= n\mathfrak{F}[-0.3422 \cdot 10^{-4} - 2 \cdot 3.2347 \cdot 10^{-6}t + 3 \cdot 6.314 \cdot 10^{-9}t^2]$$

If $T = 298$, then $t = 25$, and

$$\Delta S_{298} = 1 \text{ eq} \cdot 23.053 \frac{\text{kcal}}{\text{eq} \cdot \text{volt}}[-0.3422 \cdot 10^{-4} - 6.4694 \cdot 10^{-6} \cdot 25 + 18.942 \cdot 10^{-9} \cdot 25^2](\text{volts})\ {}^\circ\text{K}^{-1}$$

$$= 23.053 \frac{\text{kcal}}{{}^\circ\text{K}}[-0.3422 \cdot 10^{-4} - 1.6174 \cdot 10^{-4} + 0.1187 \cdot 10^{-4}]$$

$$= 23.053 \cdot [-1.8409 \cdot 10^{-4}] \frac{\text{kcal}}{{}^\circ\text{K}}$$

$$\Delta S_{298} = -42.5 \cdot 10^{-4} \text{ kcal } {}^\circ\text{K}^{-1} = -4.25 \text{ cal } {}^\circ\text{K}^{-1}$$

which is negative, but smaller than expected (see p. 49). We interpret this to mean that the loss in entropy, when $H_{2(g)}$ dissolves, plus the loss in entropy when the hydrogen ions surround themselves with water (see p. 48), almost equals the gain in entropy due to formation of free $Cl^-_{(aq)}$ in 0.1 M HCl, since these are probably the biggest terms affecting ΔS.

From Equation (29.19), $\Delta H = -n\mathfrak{F}[\mathcal{E} - T(\partial\mathcal{E}/\partial T)_P]$, or

$$\Delta H_{298} = -8405 - 40.75t + 0.0447t^2 + 2.91 \cdot 10^{-4}t^3 \tag{29.23}$$
$$= -9391 \text{ cal at } 298°\text{K in } 0.1\ M \text{ HCl}$$
$$\Delta G_{298} = -n\mathfrak{F}\mathcal{E} = -n(0.35510 - 0.3422 \cdot 10^{-4}t - 3.2347 \cdot 10^{-6}t^2 + 6.314 \cdot 10^{-9}t^3)$$
$$= -1 \text{ (eq)} \cdot 23.053 \text{ (kcal eq}^{-1} \text{ volt}^{-1}) \cdot 0.35238 \text{ (volts)}$$
$$= -8.1234 \text{ kcal} = -8123.4 \text{ cal in } 0.1\ M \text{ HCl}$$

Since $\Delta G = \Delta H - T\,\Delta S$, let us check the above:

$$\Delta G = \Delta H - T\,\Delta S = -9391 + 298 \cdot 4.25 = -9391 + 1267 = -8124 \text{ cal}$$

which, of course, agrees within the uncertainty of the calculations.

From the Kirchhoff equation, $\Delta C_P = (\partial\,\Delta H/\partial T)$ [p. 686] and from Equation (29.23), we obtain

$$\Delta C_P = -40.75 + 0.0849t + 8.73 \cdot 10^{-4}t^2$$
$$= -37.97 \text{ cal mole}^{-1}\ °\text{K}^{-1}$$

This is in excellent agreement with the direct calorimetric value of -38.5 cal mole^{-1} deg^{-1}.

Thus the single value of $\mathcal{E}^0$ and the equation giving the variation of $\mathcal{E}$ as a function of t allow the calculation of ΔG^0, K, ΔG, ΔH, ΔS, ΔC_P, and w_{max}. Each term, upon examination, can provide valuable insight into the reaction and the species involved.

We could also use Equation (29.15) and calculate the actual pressures of hydrogen used by Bates and Bower, knowing that they worked in 0.1 M HCl solutions.

From the Nernst equation (Equation 29.15) we get

$$\mathcal{E} = \mathcal{E}^0 - \frac{RT}{n\mathfrak{F}} \ln \frac{[H^+][Cl^-]}{{p_{H_2}}^{1/2}}$$

At $t = 25°$C,

$$\mathcal{E} = 0.35510 - 0.3422 \cdot 10^{-4}t - 3.2347 \cdot 10^{-6}t^2 + 6.314 \cdot 10^{-9}t^3$$
$$\mathcal{E} = 0.35510 - 0.000854 - 0.002022 + 0.0000925$$
$$= 0.35232 \text{ volts}$$

$$0.35232 = 0.2223 - \frac{0.0592}{1} \log \frac{0.1 \cdot 0.1}{{p_{H_2}}^{1/2}}$$

Assuming the activity coefficients of H^+ and Cl^- are unity,

$$0.1300 = +0.0592 \log \frac{{p_{H_2}}^{1/2}}{10^{-2}}$$

$$\log \frac{{p_{H_2}}^{1/2}}{10^{-2}} = 2.20$$

$${p_{H_2}}^{1/2} = 10^{2.20} \cdot 10^{-2} = 10^{0.20} = 1.6 \text{ atm}$$

In all likelihood Bates and Bower really worked at 1 atm pressure of H_2, in which case we may calculate rough values for an "average" activity coefficient defined as

$$\frac{p_{H_2}{}^{1/2}}{\gamma^2[H^+][Cl^-]} = 2.20 = \frac{1}{\gamma^2 10^{-2}}$$

$$\gamma^2 = 10^{-0.20}$$

$$\gamma = 10^{-0.10} = 0.80$$

Thus, 0.1 *M* HCl acts about the same as an 0.08 *M* solution of ideal HCl would. The activity of the ions is about 80% of their concentration.

The factors that determine values of heat capacities, enthalpy, entropy, and free energy are, of course, functions of position in the periodic table. The thermodynamic functions are related to atomic and molecular energy levels, to radius ratios and other size effects, and to masses. The thermodynamic properties of most simple compounds have now been measured directly, but—as a glance at Figures 29.5, 29.6, and 29.7, will show—good estimates could be made by interpolation, using the atomic number as a guide. The data in Figures 29.6 and 29.7 are the listed thermodynamic quantities per equivalent of the compound; that is, each datum is the molar value divided by the sum of the oxidation states of the cations in one formula. Thus for Na_2O the divisor is 2; for CaO, 2; for Al_2O_3, 6; for $ScCl_3$, 3; for Fe_3O_4, 8; for LiF, 1; and so on.

Exercise 29.7

Can you rationalize the "anomalies" in the entropy curve of the elements at Z = 25, 43, 63, and 75? *Answer:* Elements 25 and 43 have half-full *d* levels in the gas phase plus a full *s* level. The "anomaly" may be due to the greater delocalization of these electrons in the crystal when the *d* shell is half full (25 and 43) compared to enhanced

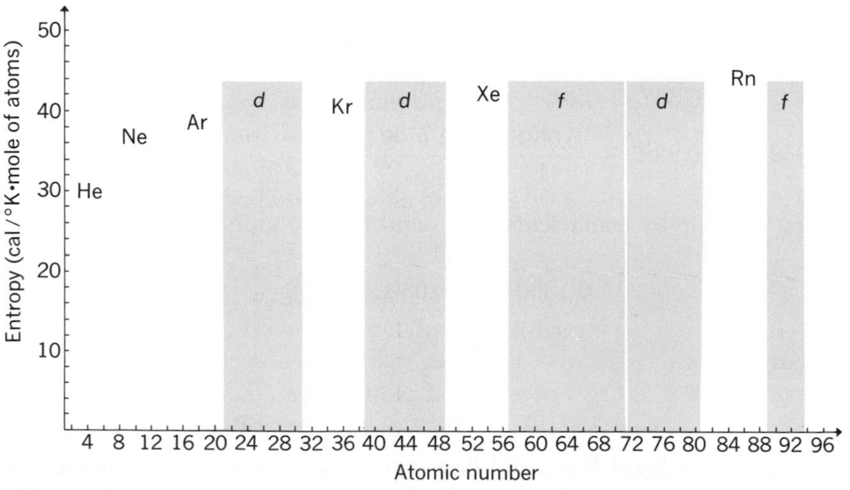

Figure 29.5 Entropies of the elements in their standard state at 298°K and 1 atm pressure (cal/°K · mole of atoms).

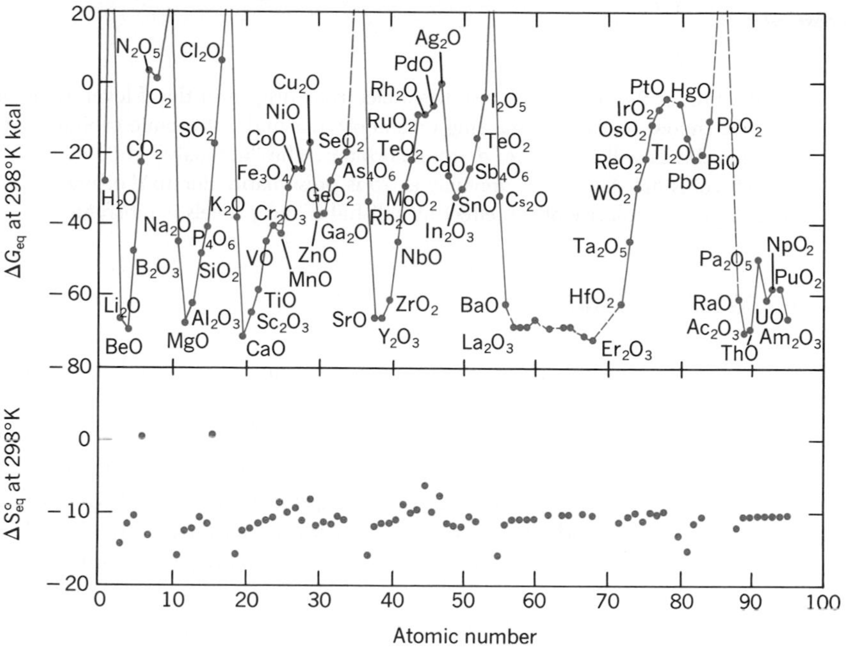

Figure 29.6 Entropies and free energies of formation of some oxides per equivalent. [J. A. Allen, *Energy Changes in Chemistry*, Allyn and Bacon. 1966.]

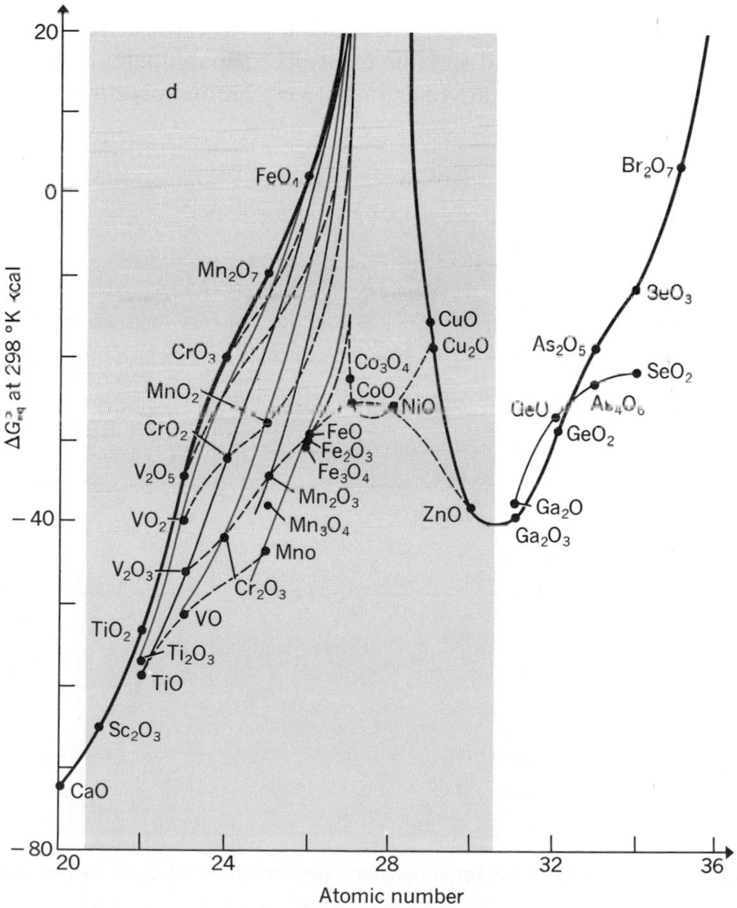

Figure 29.7 Free energies of formation of some oxides per equivalent. [J. A. Allen, *Energy Changes in Chemistry*, Allyn and Bacon, 1966.]

localization at 24 and 42 because the *s* electrons drop into the *d* level. Remember that we should really be discussing crystal orbitals and not atomic orbitals, but the crystal orbitals will stem from *d* atomic orbitals. The "anomaly" at 63 occurs when the *f* level is half filled. The anomaly at 75 is presumably due to *d* orbitals, as at 25 and 43. The regularity of the effect at half-full *d* and *f* levels is satisfying.

FREE ENERGY DIAGRAMS

Calculations of simple equilibria associated with a single net equation are relatively straightforward. But actual systems can react in many ways, and the real equilibrium can be extremely complicated. One method often used to simplify such complicated calculations is shown in Figure 29.8. Originally suggested by Ellingham, these diagrams are a great help to metallurgists, flame specialists, and high-temperature researchers and designers. The diagram involves plotting ΔG^0 as a function of T for all the possible reactions between any given set of reactants. Since G tends to a minimum, the most likely reaction thermodynamically is that which has the most negative value of ΔG. When two lines, representing the same set of reactants, cross, the two reactions are equally likely at the temperature of crossing. At all other temperatures, the lower-lying line represents the more probable reaction.

These diagrams, of course, give no clue as to rates of reaction. Further studies may be required to find suitable catalysts for potentially interesting reactions. But high-lying lines indicate reactions of very limited practical potential and

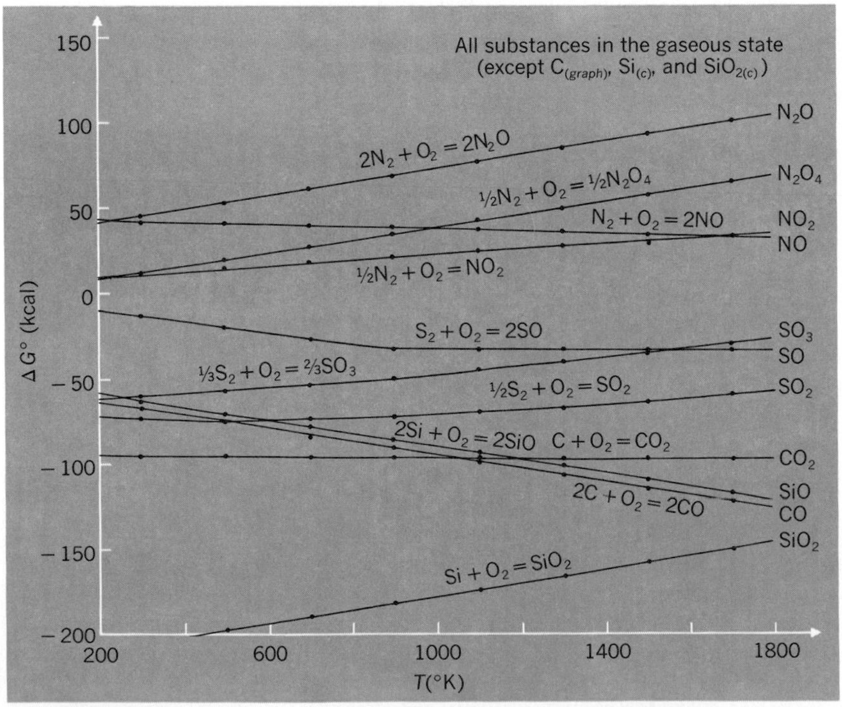

Figure 29.8 ΔG^0 versus T for some reactions (per one mole of O_2 in each case).

low-lying lines indicate reactions of great likelihood. (One must remember that high-lying lines represent reactions that have a great likelihood of proceeding in the direction reverse to that given in the equation.)

For example, as shown in Figure 29.8, C and O_2 tend, below 1000°K, to give mainly CO_2, and, above 1000°K, mainly CO. (Remember the problem of the blast furnace design, discussed on p. 140.)

Exercise 29.8

Under what conditions would N_2 and O_2 react to give an oxide? *Answer:* The gases N_2O, N_2O_4, and NO_2 become more stable with respect to the elements as T falls. Figure 29.8 indicates that N_2O_4 might be stable ($\Delta G = -$) at very low T, but this is doubtful. Furthermore, the rate of reaction would be too slow to make such a synthesis feasible. Gaseous NO, on the other hand, becomes increasingly stable as T rises. The rates would also be high at high T. Such a synthesis can be carried out commercially either in electric arcs or in nuclear piles, either of which can provide the required high temperature.

CHEMICAL FUELS AND ROCKET PROPULSION

A fundamental relationship in rocket propulsion is

$$\begin{aligned} v &= -g \ln (1 - \alpha)\left\{\frac{2}{g}\frac{\gamma}{\gamma - 1}R\frac{T_c}{M}\left[1 - \left(\frac{P_e}{P_c}\right)^{(\gamma-1)/\gamma}\right]\right\}^{1/2} \\ &= -g \ln (1 - \alpha)\{I_{sp}\}^{1/2} \end{aligned}$$

where v is the velocity of the rocket at burnout, g is the acceleration due to gravity, α is the ratio of initial mass of propellant to gross mass of vehicle, γ is the ratio of the specific heats of the gases, R is the gas constant, T_c is the combustion chamber temperature, M is the average molecular weight of the product gases, P_e is the exit (nozzle) pressure, and P_c is the pressure in the combustion chamber; I_{sp} is the specific impulse.

Nozzle design can adjust P_e/P_c, but T_c, M, γ, and α are properties mainly dependent on the fuel system. Desired properties are high-burning temperatures, products of low molecular weight, simple molecular products (more favorable γ—see Table 7.2); all these tend to give high I_{sp} values. The last factor is low mass per calorie emitted on combustion (gives favorable α). Other problems such as reliability, storability, heat transfer, toxicity, and corrosivity must also be considered. What chemicals meet these criteria?

Figure 29.9 shows the heat of combustion with oxygen (per gram of reactants) versus atomic number of the heaviest element in the compound (see also Table 24.1). Charts calculated for fluorine or chlorine as oxidizers are quite similar. The high atomic weight of chlorine makes it a poor choice, but fluorine gives good energetics. Unfortunately, fluorine and its combustion products are toxic; it may be used in the future but we will neglect it here.

The products of high molecular weight, especially in the light of their relatively poor energetics, eliminate from consideration all elements of atomic number higher than nitrogen.

Li, Be, B, and their compounds all produce solid (hence high effective molar weight) products. This leaves H_2 as the best initial choice. Table 29.2 shows how I_{sp} varies with the H_2-O_2 ratio. The stoichiometric 2/1 mole ratio gives maximum T (remember Figure 27.2), but excess H_2 lowers the average molar weight fast enough to give a maximum I_{sp} at a 5.0/1.0 mole ratio of H_2 to O_2.

Table 29.3 gives some data for the optimum I_{sp} systems for various fuels with various oxidizers at $P_c = 20$ atm, $P_e = 1$ atm, and points out some of their advantages and disadvantages.

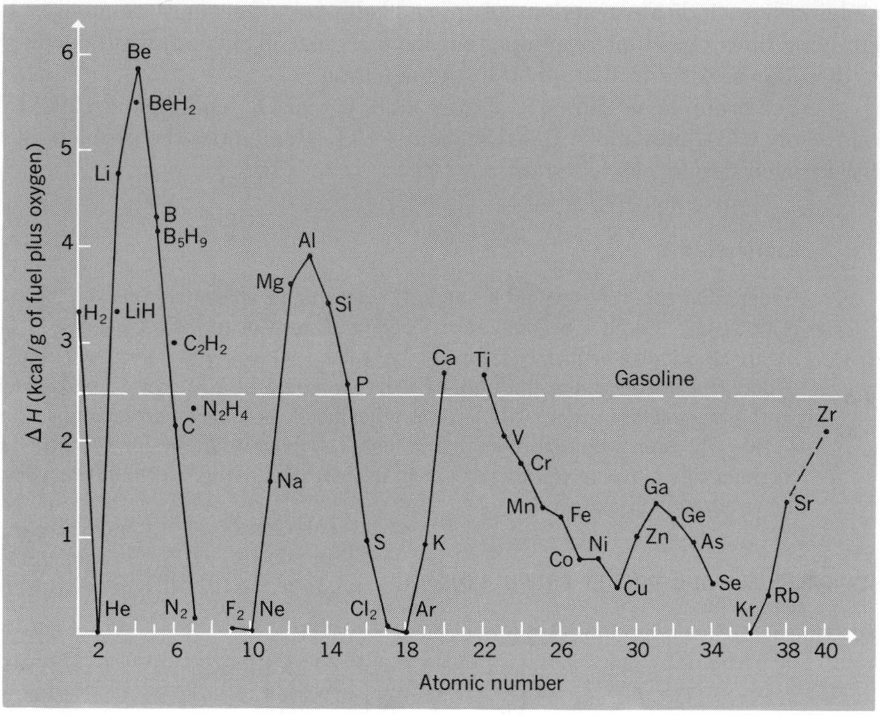

Figure 29.9 Heat of combustion per gram versus atomic number of heaviest element in the fuel.

Examination of Table 29.3 shows that no one system has a clear-cut advantage over all the rest. Currently, solids are best for long-term storage, N_2O_4—N_2H_4 is best for moderately long storage, and H_2—O_2 is best for lifting off large loads. Nuclear fuels will probably be best for very long flights; ion projectors may also find uses for such purposes.

Present designers think it unlikely that anything but chemical fuels will be found for lift-off and that it is also unlikely appreciably better fuel-oxidizer systems will be found. But if a fuel could be found that would liberate He or pure H_2 at 3000°K, a completely new problem would present itself to the delighted rocket designers. Perhaps we will find a helium hydride-lithium hydride complex (HeH^+ LiH_2^-) stable at practical storage temperatures. (Estimate the I_{sp} that such a fuel might produce.) Or perhaps someone will eventually solve the problem of storing hydrogen atoms so their electron spins are parallel. The resulting H atoms would not then react except in the presence of a catalyst, which would liberate 52 kcal per gram of H_2 at an average molar weight of 2. (Estimate the I_{sp} for this.)

Table 29.2 Burning properties of H_2—O_2 systems at 20 atm.

Mole ratio (H_2/O_2)	1.8/1	2/1	3.2/1	5.0/1	6.5/1
Flame T_c (°K)	3450	3480	3030	2750	2140
Average molecular weight	17	16	11.5	8.6	7
I_{sp} (lb sec/lb)	280	295	338	350	340

Table 29.3 Data on some rocket propellants at $P_c = 20$, $P_e = 1$ atm.

Oxidizer	Fuel	Average density	I_{sp}	T_c	Average Mol. wt.	Advantages	Disadvantages
O_2	H_2	0.43	350	2760	9	I_{sp}, low T and M	low ρ, not storable
	N_2H_4	1.06	280	3230	18		
	Gasoline	0.98	264	3460	22		
	C_2H_5OH	0.99	259	3340	22		
O_3	H_2	0.23	373	2700	9	high I_{sp}, low T and M	O_3 unstable
F_2	H_2	0.32	373	3090	9	high I_{sp}	toxic, corrosive (could be used in second stage)
	NH_3	1.16	306	4260	19		
	N_2H_4	1.30	316	4660	19		highest T
H_2O_2	N_2H_4	1.24	262	2860	19		not storable
	Gasoline	1.28	248	2940	21		
HNO_3	N_2H_4	1.26	255	2880	19		
	$C_6H_5NH_2$	1.39	235	3090	21	highest density	low I_{sp}
	Gasoline	1.30	240	3120	25	cheapest	
N_2O_4	N_2H_4	1.20	263	3010	19	most storable liquid	low I_{sp}
Best current solid propellant			~250			most storable system, least corrosive	low I_{sp}
Best projected solid propellant			~290				

SUMMARY

Exact thermodynamic formulas for treating equilibria involve use of activities and activity coefficients. For many purposes concentrations and partial pressures give sufficiently good values of K. Such values can be calculated from analytical, electromotive-force, thermal, and spectroscopic data. These data may be correlated with the periodic table to give a powerful set of tools in designing new chemical processes. Impossible processes may be eliminated without costly plant construction, and the relative feasibilities of complicated processes can be calculated, using data obtained on much simpler systems.

In advancing to a Science of Cause in any subject, the labour and the struggle is, not to analyze the phenomena according to any preconceived and already familiar ideas, but to form distinctly new conceptions, such as do really carry us to a more intimate view of the processes of nature.—W. Whewell,
The Philosophy of the Inductive Sciences (1882).

PROBLEMS

29.1. JANAF (as in Table 28.5) stands for Joint Army, Navy, Air Force. What military interest is there in tables of free energy functions?

29.2. At what temperature will NO_2 and N_2O_4 be present each at atmospheric pressure and in equilibrium with one another? ($T \cong 300°K$.)

29.3. What compound is produced if silicon and oxygen are heated together at 1000°K? Does the equilibrium partial pressure of oxygen over SiO_2 increase or decrease as T rises? How do you account for this? ($SiO_{2(g)}$, p_{O_2} increases.)

29.4. A. T. Larson and R. L. Dodge [*J. Am. Chem. Soc.*, **45,** 2926 (1923)] report the data below for the gas-phase reaction $N_2 + 3H_2 = 2NH_3$. What additional thermodynamic data can be obtained from these values? Perform two or three typical calculations.

T (°K)	598	648	673	773
$K_{P(atm)}$	0.0401	0.0181	0.0129	0.00381

[$\Delta\mathcal{H}^0 \cong -10$ kcal (mole NH_3)$^{-1}$.]

29.5. The following data were found in a research article [P. Delahay et al., Amer. Pet. Inst. Preprint, Los Angeles, Calif., May 12, 1958]. Are they internally consistent for the reaction given? Delahay et al. cite Gmelin's *Handbuch der Anorganischen Chemie* [Part B-1, p. 6, Verlagchemie, g.m.b.h. Leipzig-Berlin (1953)] as the primary source.

$$H_2S_{(g)} = H_{2(g)} + \tfrac{1}{2}S_{2(g)}$$

T (°K)	298	400	600	800	1000
K	$2.1 \cdot 10^{-3}$	$1.2 \cdot 10^{-9}$	$6.5 \cdot 10^{-6}$	$5.1 \cdot 10^{-4}$	$7.3 \cdot 10^{-3}$
Fraction of H_2S dissociated at $P_{tot} = 1$ atm	$4.4 \cdot 10^{-9}$	$1.4 \cdot 10^{-6}$	$4.3 \cdot 10^{-4}$	$8.0 \cdot 10^{-3}$	$4.7 \cdot 10^{-2}$

29.6. One gram of phosphorus is burned in air and gives 2.291 g of an oxide. This quantity of the oxide is found to react with exactly 0.872 g of H_2O to give 3.163 g of a compound of phosphorus, hydrogen, and oxygen. Determine the empirical formula of the oxide and of the other compound. ($H_{<3}PO_{<4}$.)

29.7. A. K. Covington, R. A. Robinson, and R. G. Bates [*J. Phys. Chem.*, **70,** 3820 (1960)] have determined pK values for heavy water, D_2O, as given below and compared to present values of pK for ordinary water, H_2O. Which is larger, ΔH^0 for H_2O or D_2O? Which is the stronger acid?

t (°C)	10	20	25	30	40	50
pK_{H_2O}	14.533	14.167	13.996	13.832	13.536	13.262
pK_{D_2O}	15.439	15.049	14.869	14.699	14.385	14.103

29.8. Why is H_2O_2 listed as a nonstorable oxidizer in Table 29.3? It is on sale and is safely kept in many homes. Did you ever look at the stopper in such a bottle? ($K_p \cong 10^{20}$ atm.)

II

29.9. Use the data in Table 28.5 to test the probability of some reactions. Calculate values for K at a couple of temperatures and calculate the equilibrium concentrations, making whatever assumptions you may find necessary.

29.10. The critical temperature of water is 374.0°C, the critical pressure is 3184 pounds per square inch (gauge pressure), and the critical volume is 45 ml mole^{-1}. Estimate, under these conditions, (*a*) the concentration of hydrogen ions, (*b*) the concentration of hydroxide ions, (*c*) the concentration of water. What would you predict about the action of water on quartz (pure SiO_2) under these conditions? Is there any relationship to the large quartz crystals found in nature? (pH $\cong$ 4.)

29.11. It is desired to pass carbon monoxide and water vapor at a 2 to 1 mole mix into a reaction vessel at 700°C and 15 atm and to withdraw gas containing carbon dioxide and hydrogen each at 1.5 atm partial pressure. Utilize the appropriate thermodynamic criterion of equilibrium to show quantitatively that this is thermodynamically possible. The equilibrium constant for the reaction

$$CO_{(g)} + H_2O_{(g)} = CO_{2(g)} + H_{2(g)}$$

is 0.71 at 700°C and you may assume the gases to behave ideally.

29.12. Calculate ΔG^0 and the equilibrium constant for the reaction $H_2 + O_2 \rightleftarrows H_2O_2$ at 25°C. At what total pressure would the stoichiometric system be in equilibrium? ($\Delta G \cong -30$ kcal mole^{-1}.)

29.13. If the free energy, ΔG^0, of the reaction

$$Ag^+_{(aq)} + Cl^-_{(aq)} = AgCl_{(c)}$$

is $-13{,}300$ calories/mole at 25°C, and $Ag = Ag^+ + e^-$, $\mathcal{E}^0 = -0.799$ *v*, calculate $\mathcal{E}$ for an electrode made by placing silver metal in a 0.5 *M* Ag^+ solution at 25°C. ($\mathcal{E} \cong -0.8$ volt.)

29.14. Calcium carbonate (limestone) is often heated to form commercial calcium oxide (quicklime). Calculate the temperature required for this reaction under each of the following conditions: (*a*) heated in a stream of gas from the burning of natural gas in air, (*b*) heated electrically in a furnace, (*c*) heated in the open atmosphere. The dissociation pressure as a function of *T* is given here.

T (°C)	600	800	840	880	896	910
p_{CO_2} (torr)	10	180	320	580	760	1000

(*a*: $T \cong 700$°C; *b*: $T \cong 900$°C.)

29.15. Discuss and justify the conditions you would recommend for the commercial accomplishment of the following reaction to give synthesized gasoline:

$$14C_{(c)} + 15H_{2(g)} = C_7H_{14(g)} + C_7H_{16(g)} + 71{,}000 \text{ cal}$$

29.16. Calculate ΔH^0, ΔG^0, and ΔS^0 for the ionization of H_2O and of D_2O at 25°C, using the data in Problem 29.7. Is it a difference in ΔH^0 or ΔS^0 that is the main contributor to the difference in acidity? Interpret your answer in terms of bonding theory? ($\Delta S^0_{298} \cong 17$ cal (mole°K)$^{-1}$ for D_2O.)

29.17. For the cell reaction

$$Ag_{(c)} + \tfrac{1}{2}Cl_{2(g)} = AgCl_{(c)}$$

$d\mathcal{E}^0/dT = -0.000595$ volts °K^{-1} at 298°K and 1 atm. Calculate ΔG^0, *K*, ΔS^0, and ΔH^0 for this reaction. Could silver chloride be made in this fashion? Write the two half-reactions. What is the vapor pressure of chlorine over pure silver chloride at 298°K? ($p_{Cl_2} \cong 10^{-40}$ atm.)

29.18. List the experimental data which must be obtained to determine the entropy of gaseous water at 298°K (*a*) from calorimetric data, (*b*) from spectroscopic data. Do this by writing down the equations for calculating S^0_{298} for gaseous water, thus showing the way in which each set of experimental data enters its appropriate equation.

Do not use experimental numbers, but merely the appropriate letter symbols. Be sure to identify clearly each letter symbol you use in terms of the experimental measurement which leads to its numerical evaluation.

III

29.19. Calculate the equilibrium concentrations in the system

$$N_{2(g)} + O_{2(g)} = 2NO_{(g)}$$

at 298°K, 1000°K, 3000°K, and 5000°K. Design a process for manufacturing NO from the atmosphere. Discuss probable problems and energy requirements. ($K_{1000} \cong 10^{-8}$.)

29.20. Would the cell potential of a strip of zinc immersed in 0.01 *M* zinc sulfate connected to a strip of silver immersed in 0.001 *M* silver nitrate in an appropriately designed cell be larger or smaller than $\mathcal{E}^0$? Calculate $\mathcal{E}$ for the cell. Which electrode is the anode? What is the net reaction that will occur in the cell? What would the cell potential become if 1 *M* HCl were added around the silver electrode? ($\mathcal{E} \cong 1$ volt in 1 *M* HCl.)

29.21. (*a*) Assuming that the reaction in a rocket motor is adiabatic, calculate the temperature of the carbon dioxide and water of the exhaust of the rocket motor if the fuel used is ethane, $C_2H_{6(g)}$. (*b*) In the foregoing part of the problem we have assumed that the entire combustion occurs at 25°C and that the heat all goes to heating the products of combustion. (This assumption is certainly wrong.) Would the actual temperature of the gases be higher or lower than the value obtained above? (*a*: $T \cong$ 5000°K if O_2 is used.)

29.22. (*a*) Estimate $\Delta\overline{H}^0$ and the effect of lowering pressure on the system

$$I_{2(g)} = 2I_{(g)}$$

(*b*) M. L. Perlman and G. K. Rollefson [*J. Chem. Phys.*, 9, 362 (1941)] give the following data:

T (°K)	872	973	1073	1173	1274
K	$1.81 \cdot 10^{-4}$	$1.80 \cdot 10^{-3}$	0.0108	0.0480	0.167

Calculate a "best" value for ΔH^0, and for K at 1000°K. (Compare Table 13.2.) What fraction of the I_2 is dissociated at 1000°K if the total pressure is 1 atm? if the total pressure is 0.01 atm? Account for any difference in percent dissociation. (*c*) Look up appropriate data and calculate the free energy functions for I_2 and I at each temperature. Calculate a best value of $\overline{H}_0^0$.

See page 1093 for a list of references and readings in the recent chemical literature related to the material in this chapter.

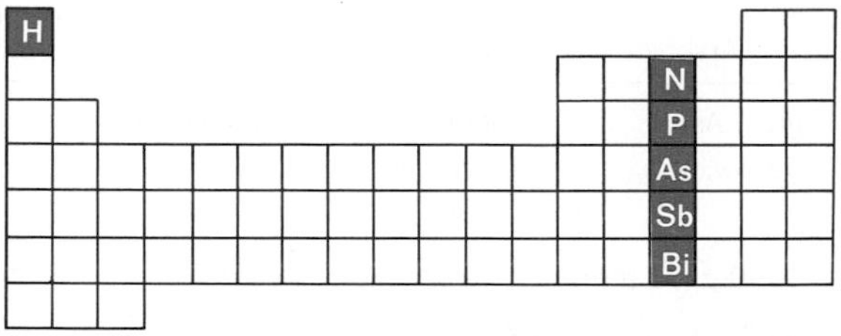

CHAPTER 30

The Nitrogen Family—Group V

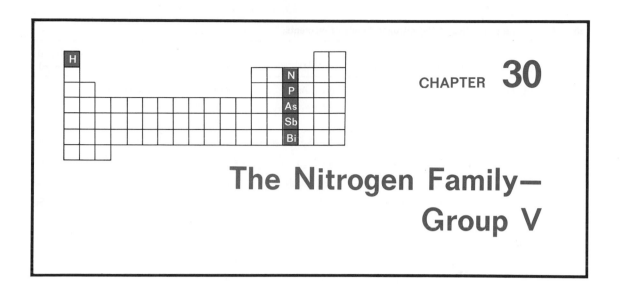

Members of the nitrogen family show an even more varied set of trends than do the chalcogens, with rate effects often dominating over equilibrium effects in determining the products formed.

We have now discussed the chemistry of the noble gas family of elements, of hydrogen, of the halogens, and of the chalcogens. We have also alluded to the chemistry of many other elements—including nitrogen. In this chapter we shall explore more systematically the chemistry of nitrogen and of phosphorus, arsenic, antimony, and bismuth.

SOME FAMILY RELATIONSHIPS

Table 30.1 presents some properties of the nitrogen family of elements. Only some of the properties in Table 30.1 (boiling point, electron structure, I.E., and covalent radius of the gaseous atom) exhibit a simple monotonic trend. We may thus expect (and do find) a much richer variety in the chemistry of this group than in any of the groups studied so far. Remember that most of the properties of the halogens and even of the chalcogens did show monotonic trends.

There is a general increase in metallic nature as Z increases, as would be expected from the decrease in I.E. Similarly, the electrical and thermal conductivities of the comparable crystals (calculated on a per atom basis) generally increase as Z increases. Thus electron mobility in the crystalline element generally increases with Z. This is consistent with increasing delocalization of electrons in moving from nitrogen, represented as $:N{\equiv}N:$, with a *CN* of 1, to Bi, acting as a

Table 30.1 Some properties of the nitrogen family of elements.

Property	Nitrogen	Phosphorus	Arsenic	Antimony	Bismuth	Trend (⟶)
Formula (room *T*)	$N_{2(g)}$	white, $P_{4(c)}$ violet, $P_{(c)}$ black, $P_{(c)}$	gray, $As_{(c)}$ yellow, $As_{4(c)}$	metallic, $Sb_{(c)}$ black, $Sb_{4(c)}$	metallic, $Bi_{(c)}$	
M.p. (°K)	63.18	317.4 (w)	1090(g, 36 atm)	903 (metal)	544.5	max. As
ΔH_m (kcal mole^{-1})	0.172	0.601 (w)	6.62 (g)	4.74 (metal)	2.6	max. As
B.p. (°K)	77.36	553 (w)	886 (subl)	1713 (metal)	1832	increase
ΔH_v (kcal mole^{-1})	1.335	11.880 (w)	30.52 (g) [subl to As_4]	49.45 (metal) [subl to Sb_4]	36.2	max. Sb
S^0_{298} (eu)	45.77	39.28 (w)	8.40 (g)	10.5 (metal)	13.6	min. As
Electron structure, $X_{(g)}$	2;2,3	Ne;2,3	Ar;10;2,3	Kr;10;2,3	Xe;14;10;2,3	
I.E., $X_{(g)}$, (kcal mole^{-1})	335	242	226	199	168	decrease
Covalent radius (Å)	0.726	1.10	1.25	1.45	1.55	increase

relatively metallic crystal, with a *CN* of 6. As a matter of fact, the crystal structures of the metallic forms of As, Sb, and Bi are quite similar, with three close and three slightly more distant neighbors, and all have similar thermal and electrical conductivities, indicating similar degrees of delocalization of the electrons.

The lack of simple monotonic trends in the melting points, boiling points, and ΔH values may be partly rationalized if we look at Figure 5.10, where D values for N_2, P_2, As_2, Sb_2, and Bi_2 are given as 226, 116, 91, 70, and 47 kcal/mole, respectively; note too that the usual gaseous molecules are N_2, P_4, As_4, Sb_4, and Bi, respectively. Figure 5.13 indicates that the liquid elements also tend to contain molecules such as N_2, P_4, and As_4. Thus the low m.p., b.p., ΔH_m, and ΔH_v values for N_2 and white P_4 indicate that only weak intermolecular bonds break during melting and vaporization, $\Delta H_m + \Delta H_v \ll D$. The intramolecular bonds remain unbroken. The consistently higher values for these properties for As, Sb, and Bi indicate a considerably greater degree of breaking of strong bonds during their phase changes, consistent with the changing molecular composition. The D values for As and Sb are rather greater than that for Bi, and thus the ΔH_v and T_{bp} values for As and Sb, although relatively high because of bond breaking, are not as high as if all bonds broke to give monatomic gas, as with Bi. Thus note that for Bi, $\Delta H_m + \Delta H_v \cong D$, but for Sb, $\Delta H_m + \Delta H_v < D$, and for As, $\Delta H_{subl} < D$.

The variations in D are attributed to appreciable occurrence of multiple bonding only in N_2 (:N≡N:). The bonds in P, As, and Sb seem generally similar, but as the bonding electrons get farther and farther from the nuclei (covalent radius increases) they are less and less attracted by two nuclei simultaneously. The Bi—Bi bond is much weaker than the trend in D would have predicted. Similar effects are found in a great deal of the chemistry of the elements from Au through Bi ($Z = 79$ to 83). These bonding effects are attributed to an apparent "inertness" or stability of a pair of 6*s* electrons in this range of Z. In bismuth, the $6s^2$ electrons do not seem to be much involved in bonding compared to the *s* electrons in As and Sb. Thus bismuth typically acts as though it had three valence electrons (the $6p^3$ set) whereas the other elements—N, P, As, Sb—more often appear to have five of their electrons actively engaged in bonding.

OXIDATION STATES

Table 30.2 lists some typical examples of oxidation states of the Group V elements. Other oxidation states ($-\frac{1}{3}$, N_3^-; $+4$ Sb_2S_4; $+1$ H_3PO_2) are known, but we shall not list them here. Thus, with the exception of nitrogen, we shall for the most part concentrate on the -3, $+3$, and $+5$ states. Possible electron structures can be assigned, using VB theory, as in Figure 30.1.

Possible electron structures for most of the simplest nitrogen compounds have already been suggested in Table 17.4. Again all the compounds (except the odd molecules NO and NO_2) can be assigned electron structures having noble gas orbital sets. But remember from our discussion of MO theory that many of the properties of the molecules are not interpretable in terms of VB theory alone. Bond strengths correlate much better with MO theory.

The most common sources of the elements are listed in Figure 5.3. Nitrogen is most commonly found as N_2 in the atmosphere but also as biogenic nitrates in desert areas—KNO_3 (Chile saltpeter) and $NaNO_3$ (Bengal saltpeter). (Why only in desert areas?) Phosphorus is obtained almost solely from $Ca_3(PO_4)_2$ rock. The other elements are found principally as $+3$ sulfides or oxides. Of elements in Group V, only nitrogen is found free in nature, further evidence of the exceptionally stable molecular orbitals and high entropy of $N_{2(g)}$.

Table 30.2 Oxidation states in the nitrogen family.

State	N	P	As	Sb	Bi
-3	NH_3 ammonia	PH_3 phosphine	AsH_3 arsine	SbH_3 stibine	BiH_3 bismuthine
-2	H_2NNH_2 hydrazine				
-1	H_2NOH hydroxylamine				
0	N_2	P_4	As_4	Sb	Bi
$+1$	N_2O nitrous oxide				
$+2$	NO nitric oxide				
$+3$	N_2O_3 nitrogen trioxide	P_4O_6	As_2O_3	Sb_2O_3	Bi_2O_3
$+4$	NO_2 nitrogen dioxide				
$+5$	N_2O_5 nitrogen pentoxide	P_4O_{10}	As_2O_5	Sb_2O_5	Bi_2O_5

$$NH_{3(g)} + H_2O_{(l)} = NH_{3(aq)},\ K_{298°K} \cong 25 \text{ moles liter}^{-1} \text{ atm}^{-1} = \frac{[NH_3]}{p_{NH_3}}$$

$$NH_{3(aq)} + H_2O_{(l)} = NH_4{}^+{}_{(aq)} + OH^-{}_{(aq)},\ K_{298°K} = 1.8 \cdot 10^{-5}\ M = \frac{[NH_4{}^+][OH^-]}{[NH_3]}$$

Thus we see that although ammonia is very soluble in water, the resulting solutions contain only small concentrations of ions. Both of these observations are consistent with the predicted, and observed, high heat of hydration of NH_3, which affects ΔG^0's more than the accompanying entropy loss on solution of the gas or combination of the ions.

Ammonia, $:NH_3$, is a base, a moderately strong and reasonably fast reducing agent, and a complexing agent with cations (or other entities) having vacant bonding orbitals. All of these properties are readily correlated with the exposed nonbonding pair of electrons, the relatively high negative oxidation state, -3 (and hence high negative charge density), and the small size of the molecule (also giving high charge density). Typical reactions are the following.

As a base:

$$H^+{}_{(aq)} + :NH_{3(aq)} = NH_4{}^+{}_{(aq)},\ K = 1.8 \cdot 10^9 = \frac{[NH_4{}^+]}{[H^+][NH_3]}$$

As a reducing agent:

$$\tfrac{1}{3}:NH_{3(aq)} = H^+{}_{(aq)} + \tfrac{1}{6}N_{2(g)} + e^-,\ \mathcal{E}^0 = +0.72,\ K_{1/2} = 1.6 \cdot 10^{12}$$

As a complexing agent:

$$Cu^{++}{}_{(aq)} + 4:NH_{3(aq)} = Cu(NH_3)_4{}^{++}{}_{(aq)},\ K = 1.2 \cdot 10^2 = \frac{[Cu(NH_3)_4{}^{++}]}{[Cu^{++}][NH_3]^4}$$

Note that all the values of K are large, mainly because of ΔH effects associated with the unshared pair of electrons.

Ammonium ion, $NH_4{}^+$, is often confused with ammonia by chemistry students, but the two have quite different properties. Not only is ammonium ion positively charged (ammonia is electrically neutral), but equally important, $NH_4{}^+$, ammonium ion, has no unshared or nonbonding pair of electrons. Thus $NH_4{}^+$ is a weak acid, is a weak and slow reducing agent, and does not form complexes. You should understand that all these properties follow from its symmetrical structure. Typical examples are

$$NH_4{}^+{}_{(aq)} = NH_{3(aq)} + H^+{}_{(aq)}, \qquad K = 5.6 \cdot 10^{-10} = [NH_3][H^+]/[NH_4{}^+]$$

$$\tfrac{1}{3}NH_4{}^+{}_{(aq)} = \tfrac{1}{6}N_{2(g)} + \tfrac{4}{3}H^+ + e^-, \qquad \mathcal{E}^0 = -0.27$$

$$K_{1/2} = 2.8 \cdot 10^{-5}$$

Note that both K's are small (mainly owing to ΔH effects) in contrast to the corresponding K's for NH_3. Rate constants for $NH_4{}^+{}_{(aq)}$ acting as a reducing agent are also small at room temperature.

Ammonium salts [for example, NH_4Cl, $(NH_4)_2SO_4$, NH_4NO_3] are almost all highly soluble in water and completely ionized. (Entropy is almost always an important effect in encouraging solubility of crystals in liquids.) The solubility of the ammonium salts is further enhanced by the low charge density (large size and small charge) which makes it easy for the ionic crystal to lose ions to the solution,

Detailed answers to these questions are still not know
problem further, let us consider an even more startli
Elementary nitrogen, N_2, is almost never a p
reductions of nitrogen compounds. Yet note the $\mathcal{E}^0$ v

$$6H^+_{(aq)} + NO_3{}^-{}_{(aq)} + 5e^- = \tfrac{1}{2}N_{2(g)} + 3H$$
$$4H^+_{(aq)} + NO_{2(g)} + 4e^- = \tfrac{1}{2}N_{2(g)} + 2H$$
$$2H^+_{(aq)} + N_2O_{(g)} + 2e^- = N_{2(g)} + H_2C$$

Again we have evidence of the preponderant role of
solution chemistry of nitrogen compounds. At high
common product. Therefore, the problem seems to
energies required to form N_2, as compared with othe
Common methods of preparing the more co
nitrogen in its various positive oxidation states are giv

Exercise 30.3

Liquid N_2O_4 and N_2H_4 are among the best available li
(see Table 29.3). In what weight ratio should they be r
tion? *Answer:* $N_2O_{4(l)} + 2N_2H_{4(l)} = 3N_{2(g)} + 4H_2O_($
favor reaction. The mole ratio is $\frac{1}{2}$. The weight rati
$2(2 \cdot 14 + 4.1) = \frac{82}{64} \simeq 1.3$.

NITRIC ACID AS A BASE

Many of the major commercial uses of nitric acid dep
acid and an oxidizing agent, but large quantities of nitric
You will note that $HONO_2$ not only has a proton it can

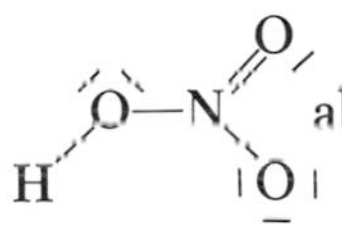 also contains many unshared pairs of elect

act as a Lewis base. For example, it might accept a pro
then dissociate:

$$H^+ + HONO_2 \rightleftharpoons (HO)_2NO^+ \rightleftharpoons H_2$$

There is a great deal of evidence that these reactions d
other strong acids and that $NO_2{}^+$, the nitronium ion, is
in many reactions in which HNO_3 is one of the initial rea
structure of N_2O_5 (Figure 15.14).]
Many carbon compounds, when treated with
HNO_3, form nitro compounds:

$$C_6H_{6(l)} + HNO_{3(l)} + H_2SO_{4(l)} = \underset{\text{nitrobenzene}}{C_6H_5NO_{2(l)}} +$$

the excellent chance for $NH_4{}^+$ ions to form hydrogen bonds to water, and the minimal resulting disturbance of the water structure ($NH_4{}^+$ is tetrahedral, as is H_2O; they are both isoelectronic and are similar in size). Many ammonium salts dissolve with a high positive value of ΔH (reactions are endothermic), and the principal factor leading to the observed high solubility must therefore be an entropy effect. Since dispersion or solution processes alone always tend to increase the entropy, the larger effect in ammonium salts probably arises from their smaller effect on the entropy of the water, as contrasted with other ions (see p. 48).

Exercise 30.2

A crystalline monohydrate of ammonia exists, formula $NH_3 \cdot H_2O$. Does this prove the existence of NH_4OH molecules? *Answer:* Not at all, unless detailed study shows that each NH_3 center is uniquely bonded to one of the surrounding H_2O centers. In all likelihood, the structure is held together by a network of hydrogen bonds in which each ammonia is bonded to several water molecules and each water molecule is bonded to several ammonias.

OXIDES AND ACIDS OF NITROGEN

Air oxidation of ammonia (the synthesized source of most nitrogen compounds) gives nitric oxide, NO, as the usual first product:

$$2NH_{3(g)} + \tfrac{5}{2}O_{2(g)} = 2NO_{(g)} + 3H_2O_{(g)}$$

The nitric oxide can be oxidized by additional air in the presence of water to HNO_3. HNO_3 is also common in the chemistry laboratory as a strong acid, a powerful oxidizing agent, and a generally corrosive chemical. Most syntheses of nitrogen compounds use industrially produced NH_3 or HNO_3 as "starting" materials.

The +5 oxidation state of N in HNO_3 is the maximum observed for the element. Both the molecule and the ion are stabilized by resonance.

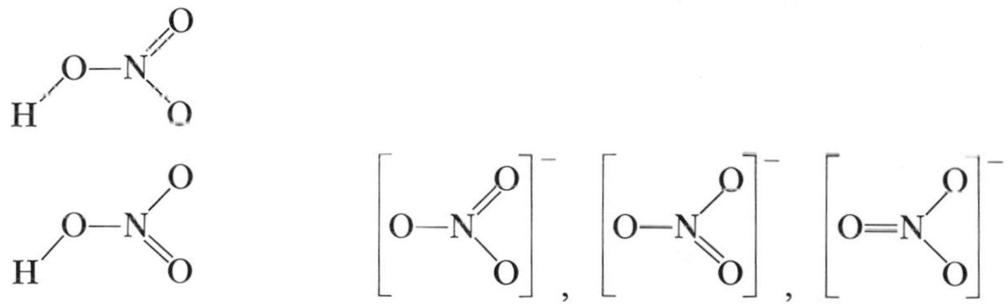

Acid: 2 resonance forms

Ion: 3 resonance forms

The additional resonance stability of the ions (3 forms compared to 2) is one reason HNO_3 ionizes so completely in water (almost 100%). Acids of this strength (degree of ionization) are rare. The slowness with which $NO_3{}^-$ acts as an oxidizing agent may be further evidence of the stabilizing effect of resonance. The rate of oxidation increases rapidly as the acidity of a nitrate solution rises, consistent with the loss of resonance energy. The value of $\mathcal{E}^0$ also rises rapidly, consistent with the presence of H^+ in the half-equation:

$$H_2O + NO_3{}^-{}_{(aq)} + e^- = NO_{2(g)} + 2OH^-{}_{(aq)}, \qquad \mathcal{E}^0 = -0.86$$
$$2H^+_{(aq)} + NO_3{}^-{}_{(aq)} + e^- = NO_{2(g)} + H_2O, \qquad \mathcal{E}^0 = +0.80$$

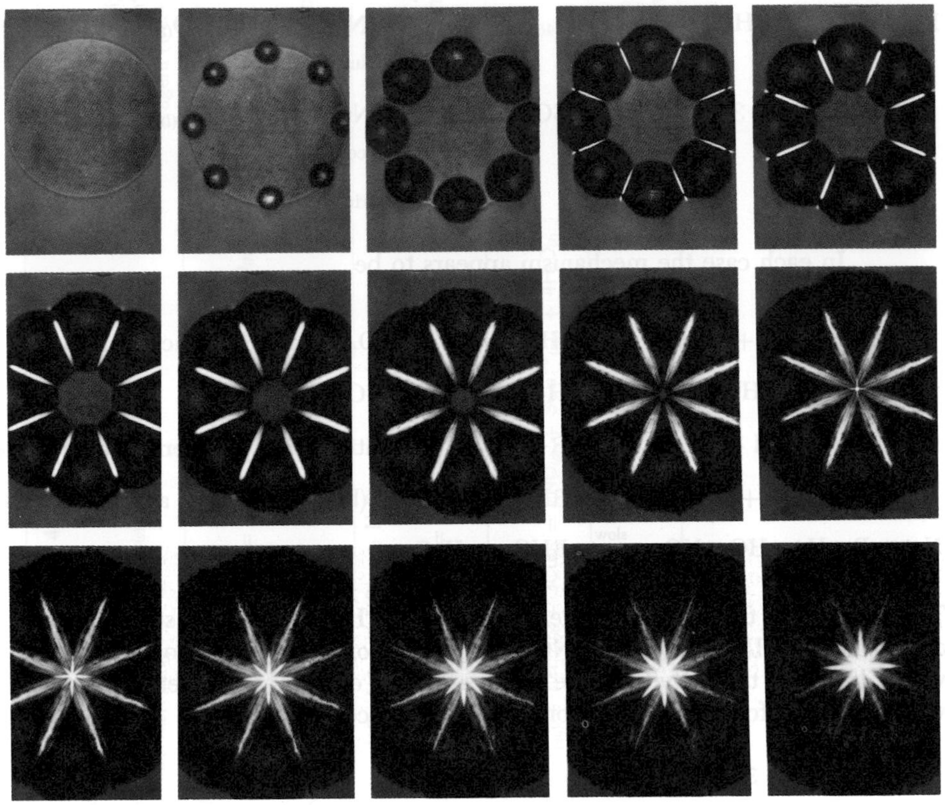

Figure 30.2 Sequential photographs (from upper left to lower right) of eight simultaneous detonations in $C(CH_2ONO_2)_4$. Note the degree with which symmetry is maintained indicating highly reproducible rates. [David D. Abernathy, U.S. Naval Weapons Laboratory, Dahlgren, Va.]

Actually many products are possible, since explosions are not equilibrium reactions. Observation of the two equations would indicate, however, that it is very likely indeed that TNT would give smoke, whereas nitroglycerine might not. Experiment bears this out: the $C_{(s)}$ from the TNT does appear as smoke, but the products from nitroglycerine are colorless gases. Explosives like TNT can be made less smoky by adding compounds of high oxygen content; NH_4NO_3 and NH_4ClO_4 are possible addends.

The two examples cited illustrate the requirements for a good explosive: (*a*) there must be a large increase in volume from reactants to products, (*b*) the reaction must be rapid, (*c*) exothermic reactions are preferred, for they increase both the volume change and the rate of reaction, (*d*) the explosives should be sensitive to shock (to initiate the reaction), but not too sensitive (if they are, they cannot be transported safely). Figure 30.2 shows photographs, taken at one microsecond intervals, of $C(CH_2ONO_2)_4$ in a plastic binder exploding.

Exercise 30.5

Is $C(CH_2ONO_2)_4$ a smoky or smokeless explosive? *Answer:* $C(CH_2ONO_2)_{4(c)} = \frac{1}{2}N_{2(g)} + 4H_2O_{(g)} + 3CO_{2(g)} + 2CO_{(g)}$. There is enough oxygen to convert all the H and C to colorless gaseous oxides. Probably smokeless.

EXPLOSION LIMITS

Figure 30.3 shows the behavior of a stoichiometric (2–1) solution of H_2 and O_2 as P and T are varied while the mixture is sparked. Consider what happens if the initial T is kept constant (for example at 500°C) and the reaction is studied at gradually increasing pressures. Below about 1.4 mm, no explosion occurs; in the pressure range from 1.4 to 50 mm, explosions occur with each spark; from 50 to about 3000 mm, there is no explosion; but above 3000 mm sparking always causes explosions. The first explosion limit, we find experimentally, is highly dependent on the shape, size, and material of the container. Neither of the other limits is. All the limits depend on the gaseous composition, and, of course, on P and T. How do we account for the three explosion limits?

The first explosion limit suggests that wall reactions are important. The limit rises to higher and higher pressures as T (molecular velocity) decreases. Both these experimental effects are consistent with the idea that the first explosion limit is set by the efficiency with which energetic molecules can get to a wall and lose energy before colliding with other molecules. Small dimensions of the container (or added solid packing) favor wall deactivation of the energetic molecules. Lowering the temperature decreases the likelihood of achieving the activation energy during a single collision, and so the gas is "safe" at higher pressures.

The second explosion limit is set by the onset of collisional deactivation in the gas (three-body collisions). This limit rises to higher and higher pressures as T increases, since the activation energy for chain initiation becomes more and more available. But for a given T there is a pressure above which explosion does not occur.

The third explosion limit falls to lower and lower T as the pressure rises, and at this transition the chain is propagated by two additional effects. (1) The explosion, like most, generates radiant energy. At high pressures it becomes more likely that this radiant energy will be reabsorbed before it can escape the container. Radiant energy travels rapidly, so more free radical centers are generated throughout the container. (2) The reaction is now so rapid and the radiant energy level is so high that the temperature of the system rises rapidly, generating a thermal explosion as well as maintaining the former chain—the branching chain. Shock waves may also propagate the explosion in this range.

Another type of explosive limit is also important—the composition limit. For every gaseous solution there are a minimum and a maximum percentage of reducing agent between which the composition must lie if the reaction is to be

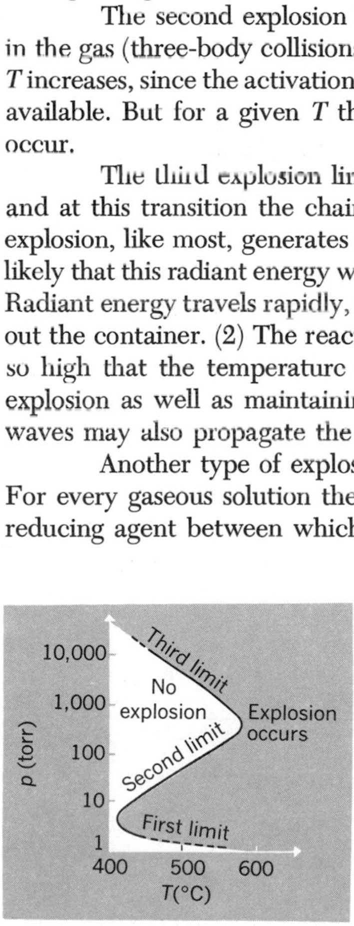

Figure 30.3 Variation of the explosion limit for a stoichiometric gaseous solution of H_2 and O_2 as a function of T and total pressure. Note the three limits characterized by alternately reversing signs of dP/dT for the limit.

Table 30.4 Flammability limits. Percent by volume of reducing agent.

Flammability limits	H_2	CO	CH_4	C_2H_6	C_2H_4	NH_3	$(C_2H_5)_2O$
In air							
Upper	74.	74.	15.	12.4	36.	28.	36.5
Lower	4.0	12.5	5.0	3.0	2.7	15.	1.85
In O_2							
Upper	93.9	93.9	59.2	50.5	79.9	79.0	82.0
Lower	4.65	15.50	5.40	4.10	2.90	13.50	2.10

self-propagating. These may be expressed as explosive limits (composition range in which an explosion occurs) or flammability limits (composition range in which a flowing gas stream will burn). Table 30.4 quotes the flammability limits of some common gaseous solutions. You should seek for regularities in this table and come to an understanding of why there are upper and lower flammability limits and why they vary from system to system.

STANDARD POTENTIAL DIAGRAMS

A very great deal of nitrogen chemistry can be related to redox potentials. These potentials allow the calculation of reaction probabilities in terms of $\mathcal{E}^0$ or $\mathcal{E}$ and ΔG^0 or ΔG. If we consider only the -3, 0, $+1$, $+2$, $+3$, $+4$, and $+5$ states of nitrogen, we see that the half-reactions required to give all relations between the seven states are equal to $6 + 5 + 4 + 3 + 2 + 1 = 21$. If we added the -2, -1, and $-\frac{1}{3}$ states, 45 half-reactions would be required. The values of $\mathcal{E}$ for all of these reactions change with pH. If we wish to add $\mathcal{E}^0$ values for $[OH^-]$ = unit activity, as well as for $[H^+]$ = unit activity, we must tabulate 90 half-reactions.

But for a total of ten oxidation states nine half-reactions (values of $\mathcal{E}^0$) actually suffice to give all the desired relations at any given acidity. Use of the Nernst equation [Equation (29.15)] then allows the calculation of $\mathcal{E}$ (or ΔG) for any other set of concentrations.

Tabulation of nine values of $\mathcal{E}^0$ is simpler than writing 90 half-reactions, or tabulating 90 values of $\mathcal{E}^0$, as shown in Table 30.5. Such tables are often called standard potential diagrams. The compounds are listed in order of oxidation state and the $\mathcal{E}^0$ value for each pair of adjacent oxidation states is given. The listed $\mathcal{E}^0$ values are for the reduction of the left member of each adjacent pair to the right member.

Table 30.5 Standard potential ($\mathcal{E}^0$) diagram for aqueous nitrogen species in 1 *M* H^+ and in 1 *M* OH^-. The species at left is reduced to the species at right in each pair.

In 1*M* H^+

$$NO_3^- \xrightarrow{+0.80} N_2O_4 \xrightarrow{+1.07} HNO_2 \xrightarrow{+1.00} NO \xrightarrow{+1.59} N_2O \xrightarrow{+1.77} N_2 \xrightarrow{-3.09} HN_3 \xrightarrow{-1.26} NH_3OH^+ \xrightarrow{+1.41} N_2H_5^+ \xrightarrow{+1.28} NH_4^+$$

In 1*M* OH^-

$$NO_3^- \xrightarrow{-0.86} N_2O_4 \xrightarrow{+0.88} NO_2^- \xrightarrow{-0.46} NO \xrightarrow{+.076} N_2O \xrightarrow{+0.94} N_2 \xrightarrow{-3.4} N_3^- \xrightarrow{-2.86} NH_2OH \xrightarrow{+0.73} N_2H_4 \xrightarrow{0.15} NH_3$$

Table 30.6 **Standard half-cell reduction potentials for aqueous nitrogen-containing species. Each value of $\mathcal{E}^0$ is for the reduction of the species in the left column to the species heading one of the right columns: for example, $NO_3^- + 10\ H^+ + 8e^- = NH_4^+ + 3H_2O$, $\mathcal{E}^0 = +0.88$ volts; $NO_3^- + 6H_2O + 8e^- = NH_3 + 9\ OH^-$, $\mathcal{E}^0 = -0.12$ volts. (Volts at 25°C.)**

In aqueous 1 *M* H^+

Oxidizing agent	Reducing agent								
	$NH_4^+{}_{(aq)}$	$N_2H_5^+{}_{(aq)}$	$NH_3OH^+{}_{(aq)}$	$HN_{3(aq)}$	$N_{2(g)}$	$N_2O_{(g)}$	$NO_{(g)}$	$HNO_{2(aq)}$	$N_2O_{4(g)}$
$NO_3^-{}_{(aq)}$	+0.88	+0.83	+0.73	+0.10	+1.25	+1.11	+0.96	+0.94	+0.80
$N_2O_{4(g)}$	+0.89	+0.83	+0.71	+1.01	+1.35	+1.02	+1.03	+1.07	
$HNO_{2(aq)}$	+0.86	+0.78	+0.62	+1.00	+1.45	+1.29	+1.00		
$NO_{(g)}$	+0.84	+0.73	+0.50	+1.00	+1.68	+1.59			
$N_2O_{(g)}$	+0.65	+0.44	−0.05	+0.56	+1.77				
$N_{2(g)}$	+0.27	−0.23	−1.87	−3.09					
$HN_{3(aq)}$	+0.69	+0.34	−1.26						
$NH_3OH^+{}_{(aq)}$	+1.36	+1.41							
$N_2H_5^+{}_{(aq)}$	+1.28								

Note that the $\mathcal{E}^0$ values in the diagonal box constitute Table 30.5.

In aqueous 1 *M* OH^-

Oxidizing agent	Reducing agent								
	$NH_{3(aq)}$	$N_2H_{4(aq)}$	$NH_2OH_{(aq)}$	$N_3^-{}_{(aq)}$	$N_{2(g)}$	$N_2O_{(g)}$	$NO_{(g)}$	$NO_2^-{}_{(aq)}$	$N_2O_{4(g)}$
$NO_3^-{}_{(aq)}$	−0.12	−0.15	−0.31	+0.03	+0.26	+0.08	−0.14	+0.01	−0.86
$N_2O_{4(g)}$	−0.02	−0.03	−0.18	+0.23	+0.53	+0.19	+0.20	+0.88	
$NO_2^-{}_{(aq)}$	−0.17	−0.21	−0.45	+0.03	+0.41	+0.15	−0.46		
$NO_{(g)}$	−0.10	−0.15	−0.45	+0.24	+0.84	+0.76			
$N_2O_{(g)}$	−0.32	−0.46	−1.05	−0.15	+0.94				
$N_{2(g)}$	−0.72	−1.16	−3.04	−3.4					
$N_3^-{}_{(aq)}$	−0.41	−0.71	−2.86						
$NH_2OH_{(aq)}$	−0.46	+0.73							
$N_2H_{4(aq)}$	+0.15								

The $\mathcal{E}^0$ values in the diagonal box contain all the information necessary to calculate this whole table.

Table 30.6 is, perhaps, the most useful form in which to present $\mathcal{E}^0$ data. All 90 $\mathcal{E}^0$ values for the ten oxidation states of nitrogen are given in a compact form. Writing the half-reactions is straightforward and they, plus the Nernst Equation (29.15), allow calculation of $\mathcal{E}$ values for all possible concentrations. But you may well ask how all these additional $\mathcal{E}^0$ values are interrelated and calculated from each other and from short tables like 30.5.

Exercise 30.6

Calculate $\mathcal{E}$ for reaction 1 in Table 30.6 if all activities (except H_2O) are reduced to 0.1 from 1. *Answer:*

$$\mathcal{E} = \mathcal{E}^0 - \frac{RT}{n}\ln\left[\prod_i [\text{prod}]_i^{n_i} / \prod_j [\text{prod}]_j^{n_j}\right]$$

$$= 1.77 - \frac{0.0592}{2}\log\,[[N_2]/[N_2O][H_3O^+]^3]$$

$$= 1.77 - 0.0296\log\,(1/10^{-3}) = 1.77 - 0.0888 = 1.68 \text{ volts.}$$

There is a decrease in $\mathcal{E}$ because the concentrations of the reactants are involved to a higher power than are the products.

ADDITION OF $\mathcal{E}^0$ VALUES BY USING ΔG^0

We have seen that ΔG^0 is a state function. Thus ΔG^0 may be calculated for a given process in any available way and the resulting value will be independent of the way used. Let us apply this idea to half-reactions. Let us take the first two on the left in Table 30.5, *a*,

$$NO_3^- + 2H^+ + e^- = \tfrac{1}{2}N_2O_4 + H_2O, \qquad \mathcal{E}^0 = +0.80$$

$$N_2O_4 + 2H^+ + 2e^- = 2HNO_2, \qquad \mathcal{E}^0 = +1.07$$

Note that there are two ways to add these two half-reactions.

One is to proceed as on page 477 et seq. by reversing one of the half-reactions and adding so the electrons drop out. This gives a net equation.

		$\mathcal{E}^0$	$-\Delta G^0/\mathcal{F} = n\mathcal{E}^0$ $(n = 2)$
Oxidation:	$2(\tfrac{1}{2}N_2O_4 + H_2O = NO_3^- + 2H^+ + e^-)$	-0.80	-1.60
Reduction:	$N_2O_4 + 2H^+ + 2e^- = 2HNO_2$	$+1.07$	$+2.14$
Net:	$2N_2O_{4(g)} + 2H_2O_{(l)} = 2HNO_{2(aq)} + 2NO_3^-{}_{(aq)} + 2H^+{}_{(aq)}$	$+0.27$	$+0.54$

Also, since $n = 2$ in all three reactions, $\mathcal{E}^0$ for the net reaction may be found either by adding the $\mathcal{E}^0$ values for the half-reactions or by using the relation $n\mathcal{E}^0 = -\Delta G^0/\mathcal{F}$ [Equation (29.13)]. Since $\mathcal{E}^0$ for this net reaction is +, gaseous N_2O_4 at 1 atm pressure in contact with liquid water must disproportionate spontaneously into aqueous HNO_2, NO_3^-, and H^+, N_2O_4 being unstable in contact with water in the standard state. The Nernst Equation (29.15) and Equation (29.14) could be used, with this value of $\mathcal{E}^0$ to calculate K_{eq}, equilibrium concentrations, and values of $\mathcal{E}$ for all possible equilibrium states in this system. Note that we have calculated $-\Delta G^0/\mathcal{F} = n\mathcal{E}^0$ for each equation. We use $-\Delta G^0/\mathcal{F}$ to avoid continually multiplying and dividing by $\mathcal{F}$. The $n\mathcal{E}^0$ multiplication can, of course, be done easily. Multiplying the upper ($N_2O_4 \longrightarrow NO_3^-$) equation for stoichiometric reasons does not affect $\mathcal{E}^0$ (which is independent of the number of moles of reaction occurring) but does affect $-\Delta G^0/\mathcal{F}$, since ΔG^0 is proportional to number of moles reacting. For each half-reaction and the net reaction, $n = 2$, and

$$n\mathcal{E}^0 = \frac{-\Delta G^0}{\mathcal{F}} \tag{30.1}$$

But we can also add half-reactions to get a new half-reaction. The two half-reactions are written as well as their values of $n\mathcal{E}^0$. Adding the half-reactions gives the new half-reaction, and adding the two values of $n\mathcal{E}^0$ gives the new $n\mathcal{E}^0$.

		$\mathcal{E}^0$	$-\Delta G^0/\mathcal{F} = n\mathcal{E}^0$
Reduction:	$2NO_3^- + 4H^+ + 2e = \cancel{N_2O_4} + 2H_2O$	$+0.80$	1.60
Reduction:	$\cancel{N_2O_4} + 4H^+ + 4e = 2NO + 2H_2O$	$+1.03$	4.12
New half-reaction:	$2NO_3^- + 8H^+ + 6e^- = 2NO + 4H_2O$		6.72

Adding $\mathcal{E}^0$ is not meaningful: the $\mathcal{E}^0$ for the new half-reaction is given by

$$n\mathcal{E}^0 = \frac{-\Delta G^0}{\mathcal{F}} = 6.72 = 6\mathcal{E}^0$$

$$\mathcal{E}^0 = 1.12$$

This value of $\mathcal{E}^0$ for a new half-reaction obtained by adding two half-reactions cannot be obtained merely by adding the $\mathcal{E}^0$ values for the half-reactions, since n for the net reaction is never the same as the individual n's of the half-reactions. Thus one must always add ΔG^0 (or $\Delta G^0/\mathcal{F}$) values and use the relation $\mathcal{E}^0 = \Delta G^0/n\mathcal{F}$ to calculate $\mathcal{E}^0$ for the new half-reaction. When in doubt about adding half-reactions you can always add ΔG^0 (or $\Delta G^0/\mathcal{F}$) values, with complete confidence that the result will be accurate.

The other values in Table 30.6 may be obtained in exactly analogous fashion. Here are a few examples.

		$\mathcal{E}^0$	$-\Delta G^0/\mathcal{F} = n\mathcal{E}^0$
Reduction:	$HNO_2 + H^+ + e^- = \cancel{NO} + H_2O$	1.00	1.00
Reduction:	$\cancel{NO} + H^+ + e^- = \frac{1}{2}N_2O + \frac{1}{2}H_2O$	1.59	1.59
New half-reaction:	$HNO_2 + 2H^+ + 2e^- = \frac{1}{2}N_2O + \frac{3}{2}H_2O$		2.59

$$\mathcal{E}^0 = 1.30 = -\Delta G^0/n\mathcal{F}$$

Note again the agreement with Table 30.6, within ± 0.01 volt. Or many half-reactions can be added.

		$\mathcal{E}^0$	$-\Delta G^0/\mathcal{F} = n\mathcal{E}^0$
Reduction:	$\frac{1}{2}N_2 + \frac{1}{3}H^+ + \frac{1}{3}e^- = \frac{1}{3}\cancel{HN_3}$	-3.09	-1.03
Reduction:	$\frac{1}{3}\cancel{HN_3} + \cancel{H_2O} + \frac{5}{3}H^+ + \frac{2}{3}e^- = \cancel{NH_3OH^+}$	-1.26	-0.84
Reduction:	$\cancel{NH_3OH^+} + \frac{1}{2}H^+ + e^- = \frac{1}{2}\cancel{N_2H_5^+} + \cancel{H_2O}$	$+1.41$	$+1.41$
Reduction:	$\frac{1}{2}\cancel{N_2H_5^+} + \frac{3}{2}H^+ + e^- = NH_4^+$	$+1.28$	$+1.28$
New half-reduction:	$\frac{1}{2}N_2 + 4H^+ + 3e^- = NH_4^+$		$+0.82$

$$\mathcal{E}^0 = +0.27 = \Delta G/n\mathcal{F}$$

Thus any set of half-reactions may be added to give a new half-reaction merely by adjusting coefficients so that all but one of the oxidizing agents and the reducing agents drop out during the addition process. $\mathcal{E}^0$ is calculated by way of $-\Delta G^0/\mathcal{F} = n\mathcal{E}^0$.

STABILITY RANGES AND REDOX

Let us return to the observation that $N_2O_{4(g)}$ is unstable in contact with liquid water with respect to disproportionation into HNO_2, NO_3^-, and H^+ in the standard state. How about the other species in Table 30.5? Let us try them by adjacent pairs.

		$\mathcal{E}^0$
Oxidation:	$HNO_2 = \frac{1}{2}N_2O_4 + H^+ + e^-$	-1.07
Reduction:	$HNO_2 + H^+ + e = NO + H_2O$	1.00
Net:	$2HNO_2 = \frac{1}{2}N_2O_4 + NO + H_2O$	-0.07

HNO_2 in water does not disproportionate to N_2O_4 and NO in the standard state, since $\mathcal{E}^0$ is negative.

		$\mathcal{E}^0$
Oxidation:	$NO + H_2O = HNO_2 + H^+ + e^-$	-1.00
Reduction:	$NO + H^+ + e = \frac{1}{2}N_2O + \frac{1}{2}H_2O$	$+1.59$
Net:	$2NO + \frac{1}{2}H_2O = HNO_2 + \frac{1}{2}N_2O$	$+0.59$

Thus NO in contact with H_2O disproportionates to HNO_2 and N_2O in the standard state since its $\mathcal{E}^0$ is positive.

		$\mathcal{E}^0$
Oxidation:	$N_2O + H_2O = 2NO + 2H^+ + 2e^-$	-1.59
Reduction:	$N_2O + 2H^+ + 2e^- = N_2 + H_2O$	1.77
Net:	$2N_2O = 2NO + N_2$	$+0.18$

N_2O does disproportionate into NO and N_2: $\mathcal{E}^0$ is positive.

If we look at these four examples, $N_2O_4 \longrightarrow NO_3^-$ and HNO_2, $HNO_2 \longrightarrow N_2O_4$ and NO, NO $\longrightarrow HNO_2$ and N_2O, and $N_2O \longrightarrow$ NO and N_2, we find disproportionation occurs whenever the right-hand $\mathcal{E}^0$ in Table 30.5 is more positive than the left-hand one. You should be able to prove this rigorously. Examination of Table 30.5 shows that this means that HNO_2, though it does not disproportionate in the standard state into N_2O_4 and NO, does disproportionate into NO_3^- and N_2 (or into N_2O_4 and N_2). Thus all the positive oxidation states of nitrogen except NO_3^- disproportionate. In every instance the end products are NO_3^- and N_2. This statement is true both in acidic and basic aqueous solutions—only the +5 and 0 states are stable in the standard state.

Just as disproportionation of the central species occurs when the right $\mathcal{E}$ is greater than the left $\mathcal{E}$ for any set of pairs as presented in tables like 30.5, so also, when the left $\mathcal{E}$ is greater than the right $\mathcal{E}$ the extreme set of species react to give the central species. Again you should see that this is rigorously true.

Examination of the negative oxidation states allows us to check these generalizations. Since the redox potentials become increasingly positive from N_2 to $N_2H_5^+$ to NH_4^+ in acid solution and from N_2 to NH_3 in basic solution, only the 0 and −3 states can exist in equilibrium in the standard state.

Note also that N_2 does not disproportionate into NO_3^- and NH_4^+ (or NH_3). Rather, the −3 and +5 states will react to give N_2.

Thus the redox chemistry of nitrogen is simply stated. There are many oxidation states that have slow rates of interconversion, but the only equilibrium states at standard conditions involve either the NO_3^-—N_2 or the N_2—NH_4^+ (or NH_3) systems. All other combinations of oxidation states react to give NO_3^- and N_2 or N_2 and NH_4^+ (or NH_3), depending on the initial oxidation states and the relative amounts of the two initial states.

The great stability of N_2 makes it even more remarkable that it is seldom formed when aqueous nitrogen compounds undergo oxidation or reduction. The effect of the slow rate of formation of N_2 (probably due both to high activation energy and high entropy of activation) is predominant in determining the actual products.

STABILITY RANGES AND pH

We have just determined that NO_3^- is the only + nitrogen containing species (of those listed in Table 30.6) that can exist in equilibrium with N_2 in the standard state. We can also calculate $\mathcal{E}$ as a function of concentration from the

NERNST EQUATION:

$$\mathcal{E} = \mathcal{E}^0 - \frac{RT}{n\mathcal{F}} \ln \frac{a_C{}^c a_D{}^d}{a_A{}^a a_B{}^b}$$

For this system,

(1) $$NO_3^- + 6H^+ + 5e^- = \tfrac{1}{2}N_2 + 3H_2O, \qquad \mathcal{E}_1^0 = 1.25$$

$$\mathcal{E}_1 = 1.25 - \frac{0.0592}{5} \log \frac{p_{N_2}{}^{1/2}}{[NO_3^-][H^+]^6}$$

Suppose we restrict ourselves to studying NO_3^-—N_2 systems in which $p_{N_2} = 1$ and $[NO_3^-] = 1$. Then

$$\mathcal{E}_1 = 1.25 - \frac{0.0592}{5} \log \frac{1}{1[H^+]^6}$$

$$= 1.25 + \frac{0.0592}{5} \log [H^+]^6$$

$$= 1.25 + \frac{6 \cdot 0.0592}{5} \log [H^+]$$

$$\mathcal{E}_1 = 1.25 - \frac{6 \cdot 0.0592}{5} pH \qquad (30.2)$$

Thus $\mathcal{E}_1$ is a linear function of pH.

Similarly, for the system between N_2 and NH_4^+ we get

(2) $$\tfrac{1}{2}N_2 + 4H^+ + 3e^- = NH_4^+, \qquad \mathcal{E}_2^0 = +0.27$$

$$\mathcal{E}_2 = 0.27 - \frac{0.0592}{3} \log \frac{[NH_4^+]}{p_{N_2}{}^{1/2}[H^+]^4}$$

Again we shall consider only systems for which $[NH_4^+] = 1$, $p_{N_2} = 1$. Then

$$\mathcal{E}_2 = 0.27 - \frac{0.0592}{3} \log \frac{1}{[H^+]^4}$$

$$\mathcal{E}_2 = 0.27 - \frac{4 \cdot 0.0592}{3} pH \qquad (30.3)$$

Finally, for the system in basic solutions, where NH_3 is the principal species,

$$(3) \qquad \tfrac{1}{2}N_2 + 3H_2O + 3e^- = NH_3 + 3OH^-, \qquad \mathcal{E}_3^0 = -0.72$$

$$\mathcal{E}_3 = -0.72 - \frac{0.0592}{3}\log\frac{[NH_3][OH^-]^3}{p_{N_2}{}^{1/2}}$$

which, with $[NH_3] = 1$, $p_{N_2} = 1$ gives

$$\mathcal{E}_3 = -0.72 + \frac{3 \cdot 0.0592}{3}pOH = -0.72 + 0.0592 \cdot 14 - 0.0592\, pH$$

$$\mathcal{E}_3 = +0.11 - 0.0592\, pH \tag{30.4}$$

The three equations (30.2), (30.3), and (30.4) give three straight lines which correlate $\mathcal{E}$ and pH for the three possible equilibrium systems in which the activities of the nitrogen-containing species are always unity. These three lines are plotted in Figure 30.4 on pH versus $\mathcal{E}$ coordinates. Note that the slope of each line is given by

$$\text{slope} = -0.0592\frac{(\text{exponent of } [H^+] \text{ in equilibrium expression})}{n} \tag{30.5}$$

As the $\mathcal{E}$ values are for aqueous systems, we restrict the pH range to from 0 (1 M H^+) to 14 (1 M OH^-). Concentrations outside this range are possible, of course, but activity coefficients deviate very widely from unity and the curves are of little use.

Figure 30.4 contains a great deal of information:

1. Of the oxidation states considered in Table 30.5 only N_2—NH_3, N_2—NH_4^+, or NO_3^-—N_2 can exist in thermodynamic equilibrium at the standard state.
2. All other oxidation states listed in Table 30.5 disproportionate either to the 0 and -3 or the $+5$ and 0 equilibrium from their standard states.
3. NH_4^+ (or NH_3) will react with NO_3^- at all pH values in the standard state to give N_2.
4. The relation between $\mathcal{E}$ and pH at equilibrium is given by each solid straight diagonal line.
5. $\mathcal{E}^0$ values in acid solution correspond to $\mathcal{E}$ at $p\text{H} = 0$; see Equations (30.2), (30.3), and (30.4). ($\mathcal{E}_3$ for N_2—NH_3, 0.11, is obtained by extrapolating the equilibrium line to $p\text{H} = 0$.) $\mathcal{E}^0$ for a basic solution is read at pH 14.
6. NH_4^+ and NH_3 are the predominating species respectively in acidic and basic aqueous solutions of -3 nitrogen. If each is to be present at 1 M concentration, the pH must be 9.25, as indicated by the vertical dotted line separating the NH_4^+ and NH_3 fields at that pH. Thus, for the equilibrium $NH_4^+ = NH_3 + H^+$, $K = [NH_3][H^+]/[NH_4^+]$, $pK = 9.25 = -\log K$. Ammonium ion is a weak acid but is stronger than water ($pK = 14$).
7. Within each field (bounded by the solid and/or dotted lines) the indicated species predominate at the pH and $\mathcal{E}$ values covered by that field. The actual equilibrium concentrations of each species at any point may be calculated with the Nernst equation (29.15).

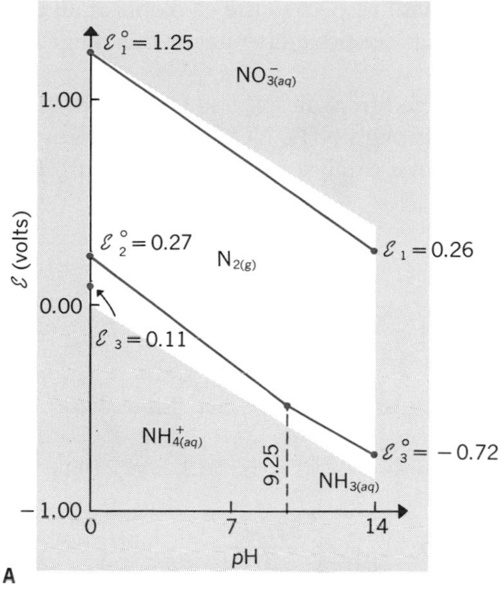

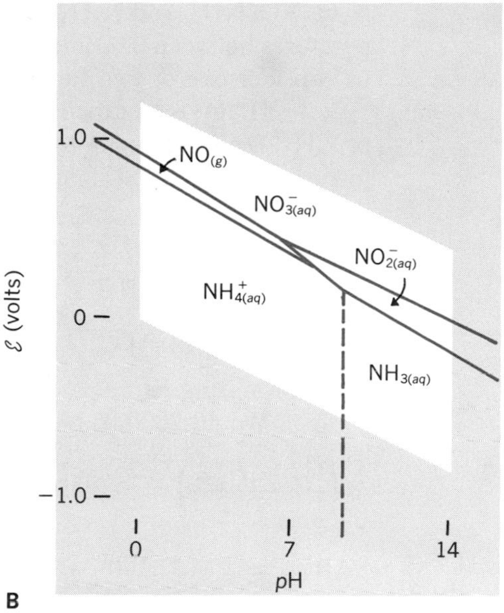

Figure 30.4 pH-potential diagrams for aqueous nitrogen species in the standard state. The potentials are for the reduction of the more positive to the less positive oxidation number. (**A**) Thermodynamically stable species. (**B**) Modification of (**A**) to show formation of $NO_{(g)}$ and $NO^-_{2(aq)}$ two commonly obtained metastable species, rather than $N_{2(g)}$.

8. The $\mathcal{E}$ value necessary to oxidize or reduce any of these species (all concentrations being unity except $[H^+]$) at a given pH to that represented by an adjacent field may be read from the equilibrium line separating the two fields.

These pH-potential diagrams for unit concentration are so compact and present so much information in a highly available form that we shall include them for most of the redox systems discussed from now on. They are gathered in Chapter 38. The set there includes pH-$\mathcal{E}$ diagrams for most of the elements.

Exercise 30.7

Calculate $\mathcal{E}$ for the system in which N_2, NH_3, and NH_4^+ are all present at unit activity in an aqueous system. *Answer:* From Figure 30.4, $\mathcal{E} \cong -0.5$ volts, $p\text{H} = 9.25$. The system is $\frac{1}{2}N_{2(g)} + 4H^+_{(aq)} + 3e^- = NH_4{}^+_{(aq)}$. The exact value of $\mathcal{E}$ can be calculated from $\mathcal{E} = \mathcal{E}^0 - (0.0592/n)\log\{[NH_4{}^+]/[N_2]^{1/2}[H^+]^4\} = 0.27 - 0.0197\log[1/1\cdot(10^{-9.25})^4] = -0.46$ volts.

GAS-PHASE EQUILIBRIA

In addition to aqueous solution data, such as summarized in $\mathcal{E}^0$ values, there are available data for nonaqueous and gaseous systems. Data applicable to equilibrium calculations over a temperature range were given in Tables 27.1 (p. 680) and 28.5 (p. 716) as well as in Figure 29.8 (p. 738). For example, Figure 29.8 shows that

N_2O, NO, NO_2, and N_2O_4 are all unstable with respect to the elements at all temperatures between 0°C and 1800°C as well as considerably outside this range. Let us consider one or two further reactions.

HNO_3 is an expensive chemical formed from air (N_2 and O_2) and H_2 (H_2O or CH_4) by a seemingly roundabout path through NH_3, NO, and NO_2. Why not just pass air ($O_2 + N_2$) and gaseous H_2O over a catalyst and be done with it? Thus at 25°C and 1 atm:

$$H_2O_{(g)} + \tfrac{5}{2}O_{2(g)} + N_{2(g)} = 2HNO_{3(g)}, \qquad K = \frac{p_{HNO_3}{}^2}{p_{H_2O}p_{O_2}{}^{5/2}p_{N_2}}$$

$$\Delta G^0_{298} = 2(-17.87) - (-54.635) = 18.89, \qquad K = 1.6 \cdot 10^{-14}$$

not a promising figure.

Would 2000°K be a more promising temperature? (See Table 28.5.)

$$\Delta\left(\frac{G^0_T - H^0_{298}}{T}\right) = -2(82.746) + 54.548 + \tfrac{5}{2} \cdot 57.136 + 53.513 = 85.409$$

$$\Delta H^0_{298} = 2(-32.100) - (-57.798) = -6.402 \text{ kcal}, \quad \frac{\Delta H^0_{298}}{T} = -3.201 \text{ cal °K}^{-1}$$

$$\frac{\Delta G^0_T}{T} = \Delta\left(\frac{G_T - H^0_{298}}{T}\right) + \frac{\Delta H^0_{298}}{T} = 85.409 - 3.201 = 82.208 \text{ cal °K}^{-1}$$

$$\Delta G^0_{2000} = 164 \text{ kcal}, \; K = 10^{-18}$$

an even less promising figure.

Thus it is pointless to search for a catalyst for the direct conversion of air and water to $HNO_{3(g)}$ unless very high pressures are used, and these are too high to be currently feasible.

PHOSPHORUS

The most common source of phosphorus is $Ca_3(PO_4)_2$. This indicates that the +5 state of phosphorus is the most stable state at the conditions of the earth's surface. $Ca_3(PO_4)_2$ is very insoluble in water, which accounts for the natural occurrence of this compound. The ore can be reduced with carbon (coke) to produce elementary white phosphorus, P_4; silicon dioxide (sand) is added to form a low-melting liquid slag with the CaO, which has a high melting point when pure:

$$Ca_3(PO_4)_{2(c)} + \tfrac{5}{2}C_{(c)} + 3SiO_{2(c)} \longrightarrow \tfrac{1}{2}P_{4(g)} + 3CaSiO_{3(l)} + \tfrac{5}{2}CO_{2(g)}$$

Speculate on a likely mechanism for this reaction, taking into account that all the reactants are solids when added to the reaction chamber.

The P_4 is condensed and stored under water because it catches fire spontaneously in air.

Phosphate rock is the main source of phosphorus fertilizers, which are as important to the growing world population as nitrogen fertilizers. $Ca_3(PO_4)_2$ itself is too insoluble in water to serve as a fertilizer; the rate of uptake by plants is far too slow. But $CaHPO_4$ and $Ca(H_2PO_4)_2$ are more soluble and are good fertilizers. They are formed by treating the mined rock with concentrated H_2SO_4, as in the reaction

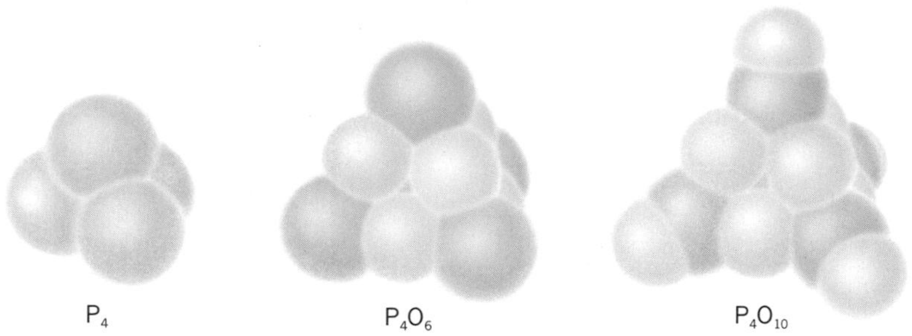

Figure 30.5 Structures of white phosphorus and two oxides.

$$Ca_3(PO_4)_{2(c)} + H_2SO_{4(l)} = 2Ca(HPO_4)_{(c)} + CaSO_{4(c)}$$

Note that this reaction is possible because $PO_4^{\equiv}$ is a stronger base toward H^+ than is $SO_4^=$ under these conditions. $PO_4^{\equiv}$ is also a stronger base than sulfate in aqueous solutions, as you might guess from the higher negative charge density on the $PO_4^{\equiv}$.

Elementary phosphorus burns in a limited supply of air to give

$$2P_{(c)} + \tfrac{3}{2}O_{2(g)} = P_2O_{3(c)}$$

or, if white phosphorus is used, better written as

$$P_{4(c)} + 3O_{2(g)} = P_4O_{6(g)}$$

In excess air the reaction with white phosphorus is

$$P_{4(c)} + 5O_{2(g)} = P_4O_{10(s)}$$

P_4O_6 and P_4O_{10} can be thought of as the tetrahedral phosphorus molecule, with oxygens along the edges of the tetrahedron (P_4O_6) or along the edges and at the apices (P_4O_{10}); see Figure 30.5.

OXIDATION STATES OF PHOSPHORUS

Figure 30.6 summarizes some of the aqueous solution chemistry of phosphorus. The stable oxidation states are -3 (PH_3), $+3$ ($H_2PO_3^-$, $HPO_3^=$), and $+5$ (H_3PO_4, $H_2PO_4^-$, $HPO_4^=$, $PO_4^{\equiv}$). The following conclusions can be read from the figure.

Redox:

1. $\mathcal{E}^0$ tabulated in Table 30.7.
2. The possible aqueous equilibrium standard states are H_3PO_4—PH_3 at high acid, $H_2PO_4^-$—$H_2PO_3^-$ and $H_2PO_3^-$—PH_3 at low acid, $H_2PO_4^-$—$HPO_3^=$ near neutrality, $HPO_4^=$—$HPO_3^=$ in low base, $PO_4^{\equiv}$—$HPO_3^=$ in high base, and HPO_3^-—PH_3 throughout the 6–14 pH range.

Acid strength:

3. The acid strengths decrease as follows (pK's are given): H_3PO_4 (2.15), $H_2PO_3^-$ (6.0), $H_2PO_4^-$ (7.12), $HPO_4^=$ (12.36). H_3PO_3 must be a relatively strong acid ($pK < 2.15$) but disproportionates in acid solution to PH_3 and H_3PO_4.

Figure 30.6 *p*H-potential diagram for aqueous phosphorus species in their standard states.

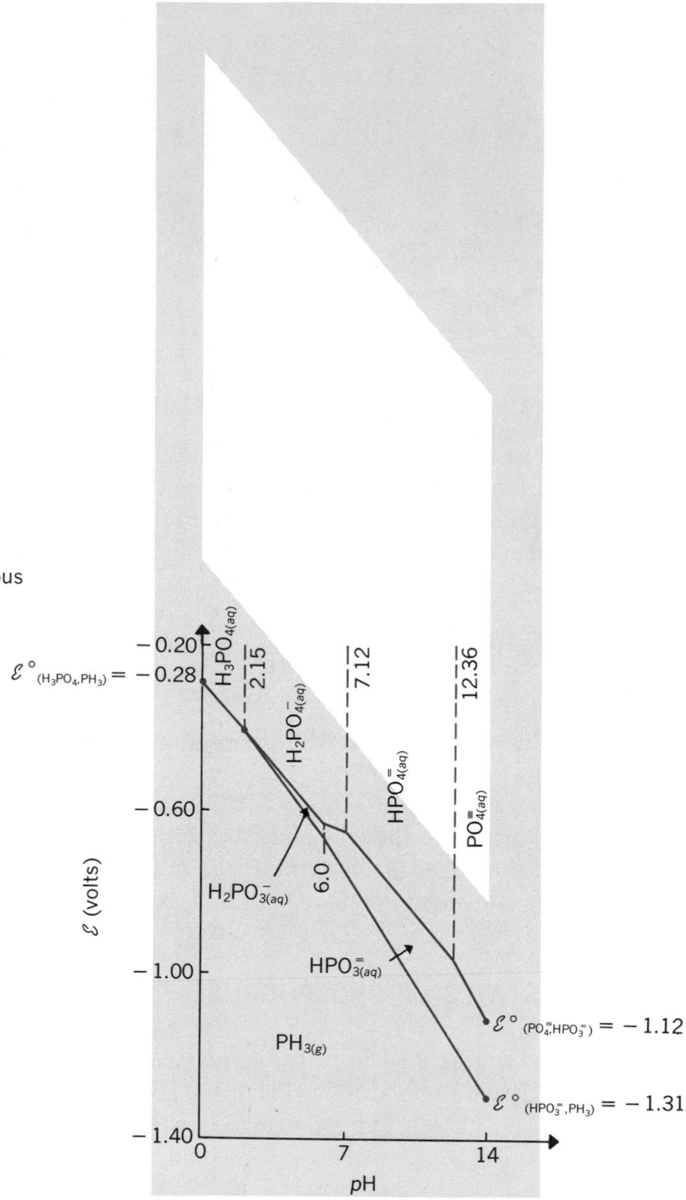

4. $PO_4^{\equiv}$ is the strongest base, $HPO_4^{=}$ is the next strongest, $HPO_3^{=}$ is next, $H_2PO_4^{-}$ is weakest. (Note correlation with negative charge density.)

Examination of Figure 30.6 shows that phosphorus is not thermodynamically stable in contact with aqueous solutions. The data in Table 30.7 show that, in 1 *M* OH^- solution, the following disproportionation occurs:

$$2H_2O + P_{4(c)} + 4OH^-_{(aq)} = 3HPO_3{}^{=}{}_{(aq)} + PH_{3(g)}, \qquad \mathcal{E}^0 = 0.84$$

Table 30.7 $\mathcal{E}^0$ **values for aqueous phosphorus equilibria.**

In aqueous 1 M H^+					
	Reducing agent				
Oxidizing agent	$PH_{3(g)}$	$P_2H_{4(l)}$	$P_{4(c)}$	H_3PO_2	H_3PO_3
H_3PO_4	−0.28	−0.3	−0.41	−0.39	−0.28
H_3PO_3	−0.28	−0.3	−0.50	−0.50	
H_3PO_2	−0.18	−0.2	−0.51		
$P_{4(c)}$	−0.06	−0.1			
$P_2H_{4(l)}$	0.00				
In aqueous 1 M OH^-					
	Reducing agent				
Oxidizing agent	$PH_{3(g)}$	$P_2H_{4(l)}$	$P_{4(c)}$	$H_2PO_2^-$	$HPO_3^{=}$
$PO_4^{\equiv}$	−1.25	−0.3	−1.48	−1.34	−1.12
$HPO_3^{=}$	−1.31	−1.4	−1.73	−1.57	
$H_2PO_2^-$	−1.18	−0.9	−2.05		
$P_{4(c)}$	−0.89	−0.9			
$P_2H_{4(l)}$	−0.8				

In 1 M H^+ solution, from Table 30.7,

$$2P_{4(s)} + 12H_2O = 3H_3PO_{4(aq)} + 5PH_{3(g)}, \qquad \mathcal{E}^0 = 0.35$$

In light of these instabilities with respect to disproportionation, how can phosphorus be collected and stored under water?

SOME PHOSPHORUS COMPOUNDS

You may have noticed in Figure 30.6 that H_3PO_4 can ionize all three hydrogens to form $PO_4^{\equiv}$, but that H_3PO_2 ionizes only one hydrogen to form $H_2PO_2^-$. Structural studies show that the neutral molecules and the ions are

phosphoric acid — phosphate — hypophosphorous acid — hypophosphite

Apparently hydrogens bonded directly to phosphorus are not readily ionized. Phosphorous acid (note the -ous suffix here and in hypophosphorous acid), H_3PO_3, also has one hydrogen that does not ionize; its structure is $HPO(OH)_2$.

Consistent with the ions of +5 phosphorus in Figure 30.6, a series of salts forms; for example, Na_3PO_4 (trisodium phosphate, TSP), Na_2HPO_4 (disodium monohydrogen phosphate), NaH_2PO_4 (monosodium dihydrogen phosphate). When these hydrogen-containing salts are heated, water may be lost and polyphosphates formed:

$$2Na_2HPO_{4(c)} = \underset{\text{sodium pyrophosphate}}{Na_4P_2O_{7(c)}} + H_2O_{(g)}$$

$$NaH_2PO_{4(c)} = \underset{\text{sodium metaphosphate}}{NaPO_{3(c)}} + H_2O_{(g)}$$

The pyrophosphate ion is apparently

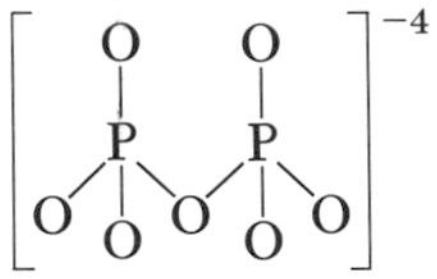

The metaphosphate is not PO_3^- but a complicated polymeric ion, or polyion. One possibility is

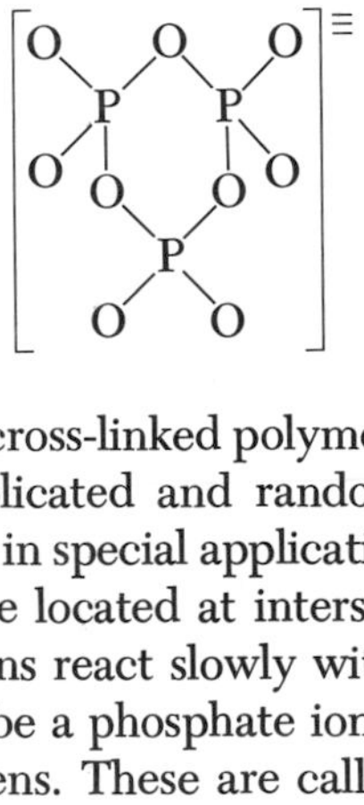

Many other linear and cross-linked polymers are indicated. These polyions form glasses, since their complicated and random pattern make crystallization difficult. Phosphate glass is used in special applications in which silicate glass would be useless. The positive ions are located at interstices in the glass structure.

The phosphorus polyions react slowly with water. The eventual product, as shown in Figure 30.6, must be a phosphate ion containing a single phosphorus atom surrounded by four oxygens. These are called orthophosphates and are the only thermodynamically stable form of +5 phosphorus in water solution.

When phosphorus is heated with sulfur, we get phosphorus trisulfide:

$$4P_{(c)} + 3S_{(c)} = P_4S_{3(c)}$$

This compound is a common incendiary on match heads. Structurally it consists of a phosphorus tetrahedron with sulfur atoms inserted in three of the edges.

BIOCHEMICAL PHOSPHATE

It is widely known that phosphates are an important component of fertilizers for plants but perhaps it is not so widely recognized that they are also essential in foods for animals. Phosphates are important in the structure of bones and teeth, in buffering the body fluids, and in the synthesis of many of the essential biochemicals. All genetic material is held together with phosphate bonds, among others. One of the somewhat simpler essential species in all known living systems, including man, is adenosine triphosphate, ATP. ATP consists of a nitrogenous portion, a carbohydrate portion, and a phosphate portion.

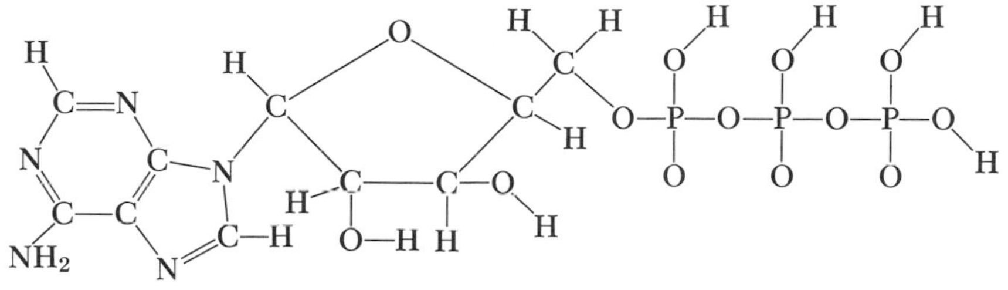

ATP adenosine triphosphate

ATP is a coenzyme that acts together with certain enzymes to catalyze biochemical reactions. A very similar coenzyme is adenosine diphosphate, ADP, which has the same structure as ATP but one less phosphate group. One of the biological uses of ATP is the generation of energy by the hydrolysis of ATP to ADP. There is considerable evidence that this hydrolysis is one of the principal sources of energy in living systems and that the energy may be released as heat, as electricity, as muscle contraction, or in bringing about an endothermic synthesis, depending on the enzyme system involved. We shall discuss the details of these reactions at greater length in Chapter 40, but we may represent at least part of the reaction as follows.

$$\text{Net: ATP} + H_2O = \text{ADP} + H_3PO_4, \qquad \Delta H^0 = -5.0 \text{ kcal}$$

$$\Delta S^0 = 9.4 \text{ eu}$$

$$\Delta G^0 = -7.9 \text{ kcal}$$

(These values are for $\Sigma[\text{ATP}] = \Sigma[\text{ADP}] = \Sigma[PO_4] = 1\ M$, at $p\text{H} = 7$ and 310°K —that is, in the equilibrium mix of the various possible ions at pH 7.)

ARSENIC, ANTIMONY, BISMUTH

Figure 30.7 shows the pH-$\mathcal{E}$ diagram for aqueous arsenic systems. Remember, the slope of each line $= -0.0592$ (exponent of $[H^+]$ in the equilibrium expression)$/n$. Some of the numerical values associated with Figure 30.7 are collected in Table 30.8. Four oxidation states are stable: -3 ($AsH_{3(g)}$); 0 ($As_{(c)}$); $+3$ ($AsO^+_{(aq)}$, $As_4O_{6(c)}$, $AsO_2{}^-_{(aq)}$); and $+5$ ($H_3AsO_{4(aq)}$, $H_2AsO_4{}^-_{(aq)}$, $HAsO_4{}^=_{(aq)}$, $AsO_4{}^{\equiv}_{(aq)}$). Unlike nitrogen and phosphorus, these stable species constitute all the common aqueous species containing arsenic, and consequently rates of reaction for arsenic compounds do not lead to the formation of unstable species. This may well be a result of generally weaker bonds in arsenic compounds, and hence lower activation energies. AsO^+ is the strongest acid in the aqueous arsenic system and $AsO_4{}^{\equiv}$

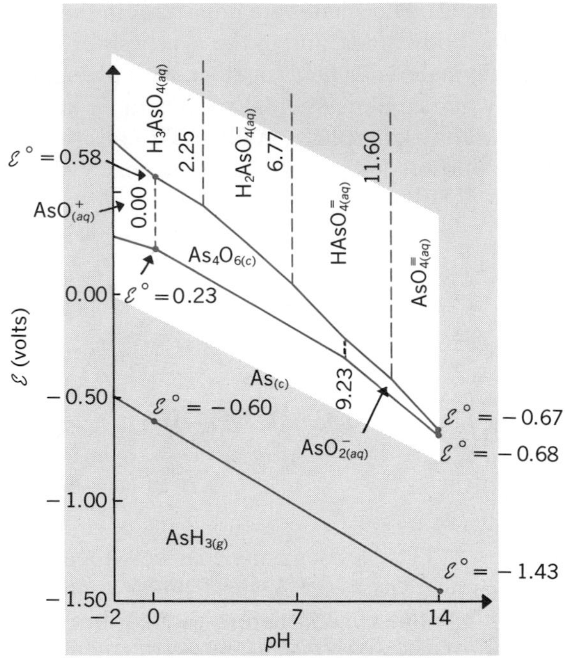

Figure 30.7 *p*H-potential diagram for aqueous arsenic species in their standard states.

is the strongest base. It should not be surprising to find compounds like $(AsO)_3AsO_4$ or $AsAsO_4$.

Such compounds, for example Sb_2O_4, are well known in the antimony system, especially in its compounds with sulfur. Thus Sb_2S_3 is formed when H_2S is bubbled into a +3 Sb solution. The Sb_2S_3 will dissolve in polysulfide, $S^=$ and $S_2^=$, to give $SbS_4^{\equiv}$, from which orange Sb_2S_4 precipitates upon acidification:

Table 30.8 $\mathcal{E}^0$ **values for aqueous arsenic equilibria.**

In aqueous 1 *M* H^+			
Oxidizing agent	Reducing agent		
	$AsH_{3(g)}$	$As_{(c)}$	$As_4O_{6(c)}$
H_3AsO_4	+0.01	+0.37	+0.58
$As_4O_{6(c)}$	−0.18	+0.23	
$As_{(c)}$	−0.60		

In aqueous 1 *M* OH^-			
Oxidizing agent	Reducing agent		
	$AsH_{3(g)}$	$As_{(c)}$	AsO_2^-
$AsO_4^{\equiv}$	−0.96	−0.68	−0.67
AsO_2^-	−1.06	−0.68	
$As_{(c)}$	−1.43		

$$2Sb^{+++}{}_{(aq)} + 3H_2S_{(aq)} = Sb_2S_{3(c)} + 6H^+{}_{(aq)}$$
$$Sb_2S_{3(c)} + 2S_2^{=} + S^{=} = 2SbS_4^{\equiv}$$
$$2SbS_4^{\equiv} + 6H^+ = Sb_2S_{4(c)} + 3H_2S_{(aq)} + S_{(c)}$$

The chemistry of As, Sb, and Bi with sulfur is often used for qualitative analysis of these three elements. The arsenic sulfides (+3 and +5) are yellow, the antimony sulfides (+3 and +4) are orange, and the bismuth sulfide (+3) is black. This trend of darkening color with increasing atomic number is common in the periodic table columns, as shown in Table 30.9. Can you suggest a reason for this darkening in terms of bonding theory? *Hint:* The electrical conductivity generally increases as the color darkens.

Also common is the decrease in stability of the more positive oxidation states with respect to reduction as atomic number increases. Thus +5 is the most common state for phosphorus, arsenic can be either +5 or +3, antimony is mainly found in the +3 state (occasionally +4), and bismuth is most often found as +3 in its compounds (only the strongest oxidizing agents convert bismuth to the +5 state). This trend is attributable partly to the increasing inertness of the pair of *s* electrons as the principal quantum number increases. It is also attributable to the rapidly rising nuclear charge, which makes higher oxidation states more difficult to achieve.

All bismuth isotopes are radioactive, just like the heaviest elements in the chalcogen, halogen, and noble-gas families. But Bi^{209}, the common isotope of bismuth, has a half-life of more than 10^{18} years; it is essentially stable and is relatively common in the laboratory, in industry, and even in the home.

Arsenic, antimony, and bismuth are all poisonous to human beings, and to many other living systems. Their compounds should be handled with care to avoid ingestion.

SUMMARY

Members of the nitrogen family show an even more varied set of trends than do the chalcogens, with rate effects often dominating over equilibrium effects in determining the products formed. Nitrogen is a nonmetal whose aqueous solution chemistry is characterized by only three stable oxidation states, but which has a large number of other kinetically attainable states. Bismuth is quite metallic and has only two relatively stable states, including the element. Phosphorus and arsenic

Table 30.9 Colors of some sulfides in terms of position in the periodic table. Note darkening in columns 2–5.

CuS	ZnS	Ga_2S_3	GeS_2	As_2S_3
black	white	white	white	yellow
Ag_2S	CdS	In_2S_3	SnS_2	Sb_2S_3
black	yellow	yellow	yellow	orange
Au_2S_3	HgS	Tl_2S_3	PbS	Bi_2S_3
black	black	black	black	black

are rather reactive; arsenic has few metastable states and phosphorus has a considerable number.

In general in this family, as in many others, the following changes occur as Z increases. All the trends may be interpreted in terms of increasing Z, increasing atomic size, and more and more closely spaced electronic energy levels.

1. Rates and mechanisms become less determinative of the products of reactions. (Bond strengths get less.)
2. Higher positive oxidation states become less stable. (Covalent bonds to oxygen weaken.)
3. Negative oxidation states become less stable. (Covalent bonds to hydrogen weaken—difference in electronegativity is less.)
4. Acid strength decreases, assuming constant oxidation state. (Positive charge density decreases.)
5. Colored compounds become more common. (Delocalization of electrons increases.)
6. Metallic properties become more pronounced. (Delocalization of electrons increases—more closely spaced orbitals.)

The greatest difficulty of all may be that it is almost impossible for any one individual to collect and to keep in view all at once the now extremely large and very varied mass of both experimental and theoretical evidence, all of which must be most cautiously and critically and simultaneously evaluated if he is to reach sensible conclusions.
—*R. S. Mulliken,* Tetrahedron, **17**, 247 (1962).

PROBLEMS

30.1. Hydrazine in acid solution forms hydrazinium ion, $N_2H_5^+$. Unlike NH_4^+, $N_2H_5^+$ is a fast, rather strong reducing agent. Account for this difference.

$$\tfrac{1}{4}N_2H_5^+ = \tfrac{5}{4}H^+ + \tfrac{1}{4}N_2 + e^-, \qquad \mathcal{E}^0 = 0.23$$

30.2. Can you suggest any connection between the fact that nitrogen and phosphorus are essential to human life, but that arsenic is a poison?

30.3. Account for the color trends in Table 30.9.

30.4. Why are naturally occurring nitrate salts found only in desert areas?

30.5. Suggest a method of preparing pure, solid KNO_3 from a 6 *M* solution of HNO_3.

30.6. A colorless gas is obtained by gently heating a concentrated aqueous solution of ammonium nitrite. Suggest an equation for the reaction.

30.7. A brown gas forms when lead nitrate is gently heated. Suggest an equation for the reaction.

30.8. (*a*) A solution is made up which is one molar in H^+, HNO_2, and $N_2H_5^+$. Write the equation for the net reaction, giving the thermodynamically most stable products, and calculate ΔG^0 for the reaction. Calculate K_{eq} for the reaction. ($\Delta G^0 = -30$ kcal for $n = 1$.)
(*b*) Repeat for one molar OH^-, NO_3^-, and NH_3.
(*c*) Repeat for 1 atm of N_2O_4 gas above an aqueous 1 *M* H^+ solution of N_2O_4.

30.9. N_2O_4 dissolves much more rapidly in basic than in acidic aqueous solutions. Suggest a reason and write appropriate equations.

II

30.10. (*a*) PH_3 is slowly oxidized by excess of a strong oxidizing agent ($\mathcal{E}^0 > 1.0$ volt) in an aqueous 1 *M* NaOH solution. Write the likely half-reaction for the over-all PH_3 half-reaction. Is it likely that any intermediates might form that could be isolated, if the reaction were stopped?
(*b*) Repeat for an aqueous 1 *M* H_2SO_4 solution.
(*c*) Repeat for an aqueous *p*H 7 solution.
(*d*) Repeat for AsH_3 in an aqueous 1 *M* NaOH solution.
(*e*) Repeat for AsH_3 in an aqueous 1 *M* H_2SO_4 solution.
(*f*) Repeat for AsH_3 in an aqueous *p*H 7 solution.
In each case write down what you would see, if anything, if each reaction were carried out in a stoppered glass flask.

30.11. Would NH_2OH probably be a rapid or slow reducing agent?

30.12. Predict probable m.p. and b.p. values for NH_2OH; then check the literature and comment on any discrepancies. Use the isoelectronic principle.

30.13. How do you account for the fact that, in Table 30.6, acidic solutions tend to produce strongly oxidizing half-reactions and basic solutions produce strongly reducing half-reactions?

30.14. Interpret the chemical reactivity of elementary oxygen as contrasted with the chemical inertness of elementary nitrogen in terms of electron structures.

30.15. Would it be safe to store a stoichiometric gaseous solution of hydrogen and oxygen at 500°C and 2 atm pressure? What condition must be met to support an explosion in a stoichiometric $H_2—O_2$ gaseous solution at 1 atm pressure?

III

30.16. Assume that each person in the world eats 500 pounds of food per year and that food contains 5% nitrogen (a maximum value). Why is there a shortage of nitrogen fertilizers?

30.17. Suggest a method by which high-temperature nuclear reactions might be used to fix nitrogen (see Figure 29.8). Calculate the yield per "pass" of the reactants through the hot reactor. How would you cool the products quickly? Why is this necessary?

30.18. At what rate would a 1-g sample of Bi^{209} decompose in units of atoms per second? What do you think is meant by the statement (p. 773) ". . . has a half-life of more than 10^{18} years . . ."? Is this a directly obtained experimental half-life? If not, what other evidence might indicate that Bi^{209} is radioactive? (Rate $\leq 10^{-4}$ atoms sec^{-1} g^{-1}.)

30.19. Use VB and Gillespie theory to predict a probable shape for each of the following: NO_2, NO_2^+, NO_2^-, HO_2, NH_2OH, N_2O_4, CNO^-, OCN^-.

30.20. Red phosphorus and black phosphorus appear to consist of highly polymerized phosphorus atoms, but white phosphorus is known to contain P_4 molecules. White phosphorus is readily soluble in carbon disulfide, but the others are not. White phosphorus flames spontaneously in air, but the others do not. (*a*) Can you interpret these differences? (*b*) Account for the higher entropy per atom in white P_4 compared to red phosphorus. Some thermodynamic properties are given below. (Watch the units!)

	ΔH_f^0	S^0	ΔG_f^0	m.p. (°K)	b.p. (°K)	Density
white $P_{4(c)}$	0	39.28	0	317	554	1.82
red $P_{(c)}$	−4.2	5.45	−2.9	863 (43 atm)		2.34
black $P_{(c)}$	−9.4					2.70
amorphous red P	−1.8					
$P_{4(g)}$	14.08	66.89	5.85			

See page 1093 for a list of references and readings in the recent chemical literature related to the material in this chapter.

PART 6

Structure and Change

HOW DOES STRUCTURE AFFECT PROPERTIES?

CHAPTER 31

Crystals and Symmetry

WILLIAM G. SLY

There are 230, and only 230, ways that symmetry-related objects can arrange in space.

Crystals have always attracted considerable interest because of their beauty, simplicity of form, and symmetry. Many are highly colored and most have sharp edges and well-formed plane faces which sparkle under geometrical conditions of total reflection. These are only the superficial ways in which crystals differ from polycrystalline or amorphous materials.

The basic feature of single crystals that distinguishes them from other solids is anisotropy. That is, crystals have different properties—mechanical, electrical, optical, thermal, piezoelectric, magnetic—when measured in different directions. Crystals often exhibit a high degree of symmetry but they are never isotropic (identical in all directions) in all their properties.

Morphological studies of crystals—of their shape, size, face development, and so on—reveal that every substance tends to form crystals having a characteristic shape and face development. For example, big crystals of a compound are often shaped just like little ones; this is consistent with the fact that they are composed of small subunits, related to one another by linear transformation. A single crystal may be considered to be composed of a large number of identical parallelepipeds (each containing the same arrangement of molecules) stacked together face to face in an ordered way that completely fills space. The anisotropy of the macroscopic and microscopic properties of crystals is a direct consequence of their lattice structure. Molecules also have symmetry, and the way they may pack together to form crystals may be related to the molecular symmetry. We shall first ask if there are limits to the ways in which space can be filled by identical parallelepipeds, and by identical molecules. We certainly hope so!

This chapter will deal primarily with the lattice and symmetry properties of crystals and molecules and with the experimental methods for determining their structure. The many diverse uses of crystals, both in science and industry, and the interesting experimental techniques for measuring their properties must be left for other courses. First we shall discuss some of the symmetry operations.

SYMMETRY ELEMENTS

You no doubt have a general feel for symmetry and use the word to describe objects. Many symmetry operations and combinations of operations are possible, but we shall describe only those applicable to crystals. Table 31.1 lists the symmetry

Table 31.1 Seven types of symmetry elements. Note that $\bar{1}$ and $\bar{2}$ are the center of symmetry and mirror plane, respectively; thus all operations can be depicted as elements of "axial" symmetry.

	Symbolic designation		No.	Description	Example
Point groups and space groups	1		1	Identity operation, 360° rotation about any axis.	
	i ($\bar{1}$)		2	Center of symmetry; converts x, y, z to $-x, -y, -z$.	
	m ($\bar{2}$)		3	Mirror plane, m_y, transforms x, y, z to $x, -y, z$. (Represented by a line on a stereographic projection.)	
	 ⬮	2	4	n-fold rotation axes; a rotation of $360/n$ degrees leaves structure invariant.	
	▲	3			
	■	4			
	⬢	6			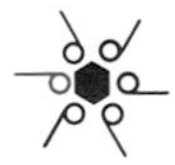
	 ◬	$\bar{3}$	5	n-fold inversion axes; a rotation of $360/n$ degrees followed by the operation i, inversion through the center.	
	◩	$\bar{4}$			
	⬢▼	$\bar{6}$			
Space groups only			6	a, b, c, n glide planes along x, y, z or diagonal (n) axis, respectively.	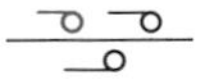
	 ⬯	2_1	7	n-fold screw axis.	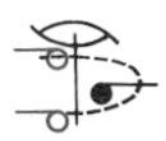
	△	3_1			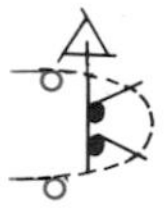
	□	4_1			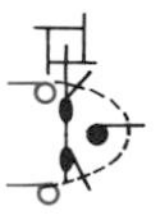
	⬡	6_1			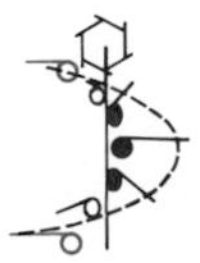

operations needed. We shall define and perform these operations on a completely unsymmetrical figure ⊸, which, when turned over, looks like •–. We shall also use an unsymmetrical comma-shaped figure having one black and one white side (9, ρ). (For convenience, we shall refer to both notations as "commas.")

Consider first those symmetry operations that do not involve linear transformations (translations). There are five types. (1) There is the identity operation, which leaves the system unchanged. All objects have at least this symmetry, 1. (2) The center of symmetry, or inversion, operation, i, involves inverting each point of the object through a center so that x, y, z become $-x$, $-y$, $-z$. (3) Mirror planes and (4) 2-, 3-, 4-, and 6-fold rotation axes are normally easy to see because of past experience with these operations. [We shall discuss later why 5-, 7-, and higher-fold axes are not needed to describe crystals, though they are found in molecules.] (5) Rotation-inversion is a combination operation. Study Table 31.1 to see the results of each type of symmetry operation.

Two further symmetry operations in addition to simple linear transformation, or translation, are found in crystals. (6) There are glide planes, in which symmetry is represented by a translation half-way to the next identical point, followed by a mirror reflection through the glide plane. (7) Screw axes involve a combination rotation and translation. Plant leaves are commonly related by a screw axis, as, of course, are the threads on a machine bolt. Again only 2-, 3-, 4-, and 6-fold axes are found in crystals. If only the nontranslational elements are involved, we say we are dealing with point groups. If translational elements (including glide planes, screw axes) are involved, we say we are dealing with space groups.

LATTICES AND NETS

Let us turn for a moment from unsymmetrical three-dimensional objects such as our "comma" to simple points. Any regularly repeating two-dimensional array of points is called a net. A regular array of points in three dimensions is called a lattice. A crystal is an ordered arrangement of atoms or molecules that can be represented in part by a lattice.

THE SEVEN CRYSTAL SYSTEMS

Typical crystals are rigid structures with flat faces meeting in sharp edges and corners. Each pure substance forms crystals of markedly reproducible symmetry. This observation led Hauy in 1784 to suggest that crystals are composed of parallelepiped building blocks, or unit cells, which pack together to fill all the crystal. His studies indicated that all the unit cells in a given crystal have the same size and shape and that they all have the same orientation in space. Thus any one unit cell can be transposed into any other of the same crystal by simple translation along the three axes shown in Table 31.2.

Defining unit cells as parallelepipeds which can fill all space by translation alone means all lattices must be composed of interpenetrating nets, any pair of axes of the lattice defining one of the nets. There are seven such three-dimensional shapes, or parallelepipeds, called the crystal systems. They are listed in Table 31.2:

Table 31.2 **The seven crystal systems and fourteen Bravais lattices. P = Primitive lattice, one lattice point per unit cell. A, B, C = Lattice centered in one face, two lattice points per cell: A = a lattice point at $[0\ \frac{1}{2}\ \frac{1}{2}]$; B = one at $[\frac{1}{2}\ 0\ \frac{1}{2}]$; C = one at $[\frac{1}{2}\ \frac{1}{2}\ 0]$. I = A body-centered lattice, a point at $[\frac{1}{2}\ \frac{1}{2}\ \frac{1}{2}]$, two lattice points per cell. F = A face-centered lattice, equivalent to A + B + C, four lattice points per cell.**

Crystal system	Bravais lattices (P I C F)	Usual unit cell coordinate axes and angles[a]	Point symmetry of each lattice point	Minimum necessary symmetry
Triclinic	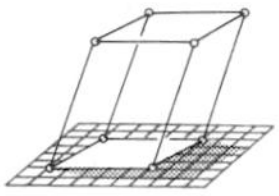	a, b, c, α, β, γ	i	None
Monoclinic	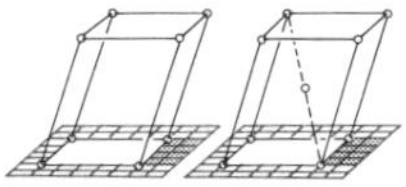	a, b, c, β ($\alpha = \gamma = 90°$)	$\frac{2}{m}$	one 2 (or $\bar{2}$)
Orthorhombic	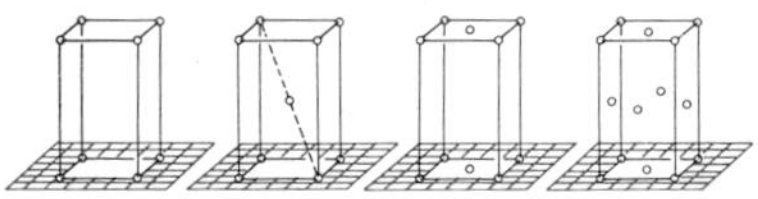	a, b, c ($\alpha = \beta = \gamma = 90°$)	$\frac{2}{m}\,\frac{2}{m}\,\frac{2}{m}$	three 2 (or 2 and two $\bar{2}$)
Trigonal (Rhombohedral)	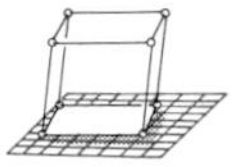	a, α (a = b = c, $\alpha = \beta = \gamma \neq 90°$)	$\bar{3}\,\frac{2}{m}$	one 3 (or $\bar{3}$)
Tetragonal	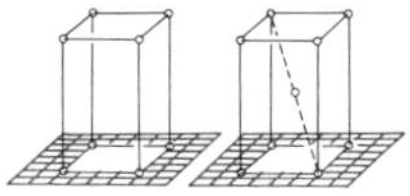	a, c (b = c, $\alpha = \beta = \gamma = 90°$)	$\frac{4}{m}\,\frac{2}{m}\,\frac{2}{m}$	one 4 (or $\bar{4}$)
Hexagonal	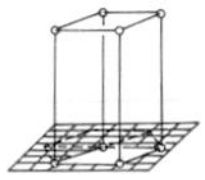	a, c (a = b, $\alpha = \beta = 90°$, $\gamma = 120°$)	$\frac{6}{m}\,\frac{2}{m}\,\frac{2}{m}$	one 6 (or $\bar{6}$)
Cubic	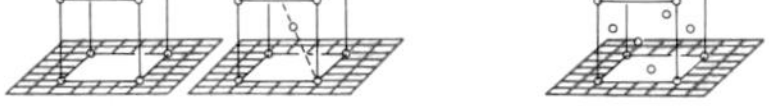	a (a = b = c, $\alpha = \beta = \gamma = 90°$)	$\frac{4}{m}\,\bar{3}\,\frac{2}{m}$	four 3 (or $\bar{3}$)

[a] Lattice angles and lengths: $a \overset{\gamma}{\angle} b \overset{\alpha}{\angle} c \overset{\beta}{\angle} a$ (The angle between a and b is γ, and so on.)

triclinic, monoclinic, orthorhombic, trigonal (or rhombohedral), tetragonal, hexagonal, cubic.

Combining the nontranslational symmetry operations of Table 31.1 with the seven crystal systems shows there are 32, and only 32, ways symmetry-related objects can be arranged in space. If we add the translational symmetry operations, this number rises to 230. There are 230, and only 230, ways symmetry-related objects can arrange in space. This is a hopeful sign, in the face of the millions of known crystals.

Each of the seven crystal systems has a certain minimum required symmetry that must be possessed by any real crystal if it is to be included in that system. Triclinic crystals are characterized by a 1 or $\bar{1}$ axis, monoclinic by a 2 or $\bar{2}$ axis, orthorhombic by three 2 or by a 2 and two $\bar{2}$ axes, trigonal by a 3 or $\bar{3}$ axis, tetragonal by a 4 or $\bar{4}$ axis, hexagonal by a 6 or $\bar{6}$ axis, and cubic by four 3 or $\bar{3}$ axes. Other symmetry elements may, of course, be present, but these minimum symmetry elements must be present to place a crystal in its appropriate system.

If a molecule is placed in any general position inside a unit cell, the internal symmetry of the cell immediately generates (or requires the presence of) n additional symmetry-related molecules. Thus a molecule on one side of a mirror plane requires a mirror-image molecule on the other side of the plane. The maximum multiplication caused by the symmetry is known as the order of that group of symmetry operations.

If the initial molecule or object is itself symmetrical, it may be located on a symmetry element. This may reduce the complexity of the system. Thus a "comma" with a head all one color has a mirror plane and can lie with its mirror plane in the mirror plane of the group. This automatically reduces the number of "commas" by a factor of 2, since the object is now its own image with respect to that mirror operation. Note that this also means that no object can lie in a mirror plane unless it has a mirror plane of its own lying in the mirror plane of the group. Similarly, no rotational axis can go through an object unless that object has a similar axis which coincides exactly with the group axis. Figure 31.1 shows a few examples.

THE FOURTEEN BRAVAIS LATTICES

Upon examining the symmetry axes in various directions through the lattice points of the seven crystal systems, the following results are obtained.

1. Only five kinds of rotational symmetry are possible in lattices: n-fold axes of order 1, 2, 3, 4, and 6. (No axes of 5-, 7-, or higher-fold symmetry will result in a lattice.)
2. Seven different coordinate systems are required to describe all lattices (the seven crystal systems).
3. There are only fourteen different three-dimensional lattices—the Bravais lattices listed in Table 31.2.

All crystals must be describable in part by one of the fourteen Bravais lattices. There are fourteen, and only fourteen, ways in which identical points can form lattices in space.

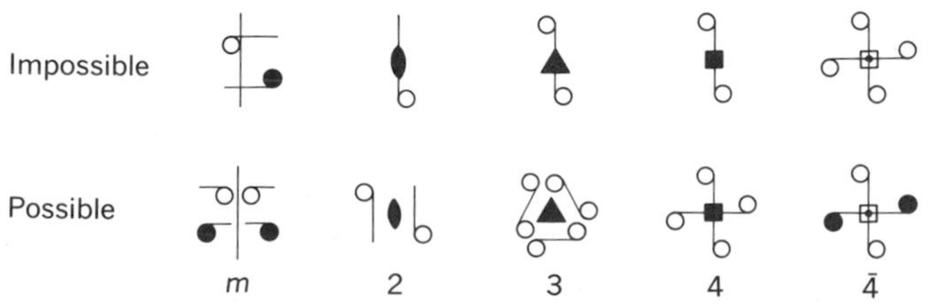

Figure 31.1 Some possible and impossible symmetry relationships.

Figure 31.2 shows four two-dimensional structures in which the molecules are related by symmetry, and where the lattice vectors are chosen in the directions of the symmetry elements. The structure shown in Figure 31.2,A has vertical mirror planes, shown as solid lines. The presence of the mirror plane makes it desirable that the direction $\bar{a}$ be selected as a lattice translation and that one edge of the unit cell parallel this translation. Thus the unprimed and primed cells are both satisfactory but the doubly primed one is not.

UNIT CELLS AND TRANSLATIONAL SYMMETRY

The cells shown in Figure 31.2,A illustrate that there is no unique origin for the lattice nor any unique unit cell within a crystal; the only requirement is that the chosen set of translational vectors be in the appropriate direction and have correct dimensions. The usual choice is the cell of highest symmetry and smallest volume.

The implication is that we are free to slide the lattice throughout the unit cell with the assurance that whatever is found at one lattice point (a carbon atom, an oxygen atom, the midpoint of a C—H bond, or nothing at all) will be found at all other lattice points within the domain over which the crystal is sufficiently perfect to be described by the particular orientation of the lattice.

The structure shown in 31.2,B is similar to that of 31.2,A but the symmetry element is now a glide plane (dashed line). Molecule 1 is transformed to 2 by reflection followed by a translation of $\bar{b}/2$. Glide planes and screw axes are far more often found in crystals than are mirror planes because of the better packing produced by the translations. Notice that the structure shown in 31.2,B is compressed along $\bar{a}$ but that the nearest contact distances between adjacent molecules are approximately the same as those in 31.2,A. Structure 31.2,C has a two-fold symmetry axis normal to the plane of the figure at every lattice point. The symmetry operation, which carries molecule 1 into 2, fixes the origin of the lattice but there is no symmetry element that requires orthogonal axes within the plane. Finally, Figure 31.2,D is a structure which has the full symmetry possessed by the rectangular lattice. Note also that structure 31.2,C is composed entirely of right-handed molecules, but that 31.2,A, 31.2,B, and 31.2,D contain equal numbers of left- and right-handed molecules, consistent with the glide and mirror planes.

Since translation of the unit cell can reproduce the whole crystal, the stoichiometry of the unit cell must be identical with that of the bulk material. For example, the NaCl lattice consists of two interpenetrating face-centered lattices, one of sodium ions and one of chloride ions. The unit cell can be chosen to consist of a cube with one ion at the center, and $\frac{1}{4}$ of the same type of ion along each of the twelve edges for a total of $1 + 12 \cdot \frac{1}{4} = 4$. This means there must be a total of 4 of the other ions in the cell also. These "four" are found as half ions in the center of each of the six faces, and $\frac{1}{8}$ ions at each of the 8 corners for a total of $6 \cdot \frac{1}{2} + 8 \cdot \frac{1}{8} = 4$. Thus the content of the NaCl unit cell is 4 each of sodium and chloride ions, as shown in Figure 31.3.

Exercise 31.1

Measure the unit cells in Figure 31.2,A and B, and show why glide planes tend to occur in crystals containing molecules of low symmetry. *Answer:* Unit edge cell $\bar{b}$ is the same in both but $\bar{a}$ is about 20% shorter in 31.2,B. Thus the unit cell in 31.2,B

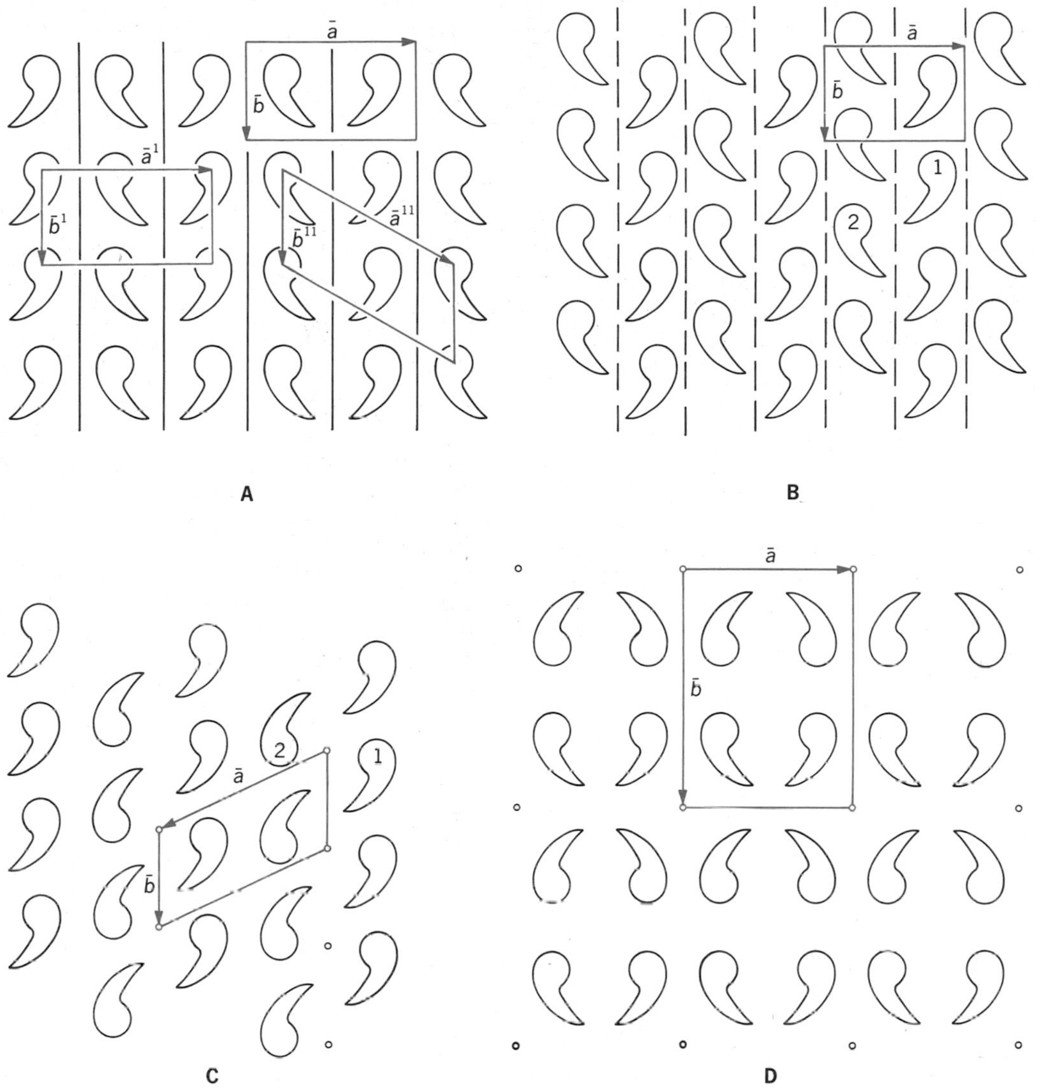

Figure 31.2 Some possible unit cells in two-dimensional structures which have symmetry. (**A**) Vertical mirror planes (solid lines). (**B**) Vertical glide planes (dashed lines). (**C**) two-fold axes. (**D**) Two-fold axes and mirror planes. All the symmetry elements are perpendicular to the plane of the figure.

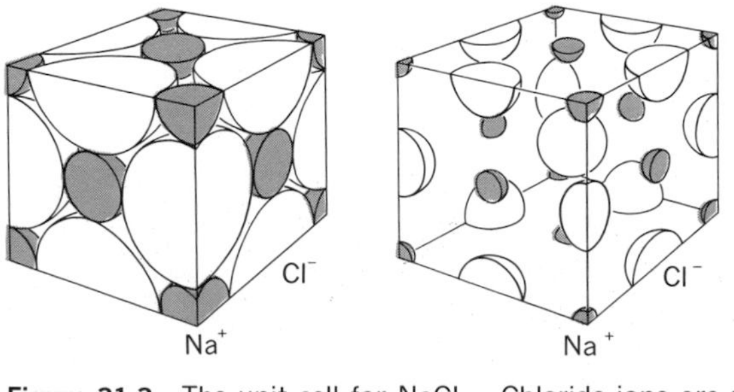

Figure 31.3 The unit cell for $NaCl_{(c)}$. Chloride ions are shown at each edge, another is at the center. Sodium ions are at each corner and each face center. Unit cell content totals 4 (NaCl) $= [12 \cdot \frac{1}{4} + 1]\,(Cl^-) + [8 \cdot \frac{1}{8} + 6 \cdot \frac{1}{2}]\,(Na^+)$.

is about 20% smaller even though the internuclear distances of closest approach remain unchanged. It seems reasonable that most unsymmetrical molecules will "fit" better if they glide slightly with respect to one another. This would bring hollows over bumps, for example.

CRYSTAL FACES; MILLER INDICES

Accurate measurements of the interfacial angles of crystals (goniometry) lead to two important rules about crystals. First, the interfacial angles found on all crystals of a substance are the same regardless of the size of the crystals (constancy of interfacial angles). Second, the faces of crystals can be indexed with sets of small integers (Miller indices) which account for the angles between the various faces on the assumption that they are parallel to lattice planes (the law of rational indices). These two observations formed the first experimental evidence for the periodic nature of crystals.

The idea that crystal faces are parallel to lattice planes provides a ready explanation for the constancy of interfacial angles. If a particular set of faces tends to form on a crystal—presumably because of minimum surface free energy—then a bigger crystal would tend to be bounded by the same faces for the same reasons. See Figure 31.4, which is much simplified, since any crystal big enough to measure will consist of many hundreds or thousands of unit cells. It is not, however, true in every case that thermodynamics completely governs the formation of faces on a crystal; it may well be that the morphology is a result of the rate and mechanism of the growth process.

Identification of planes by Miller indices is shown in Figures 31.4 and 31.5. There are three dimensionless indices (h, k, l) corresponding to the intersections (x, y, z) of the plane with the three crystallographic axes, defined by the unit vectors $\bar{a}, \bar{b}, \bar{c}$. Any plane in a unit cell is defined such that $h = \bar{a}/x, k = \bar{b}/y, l = \bar{c}/z$. Thus the plane cutting through the three vertices adjacent to the origin of a unit cell (that is, intersecting at $x = \bar{a}$, $y = \bar{b}$, $z = \bar{c}$) would be the (111) plane. A plane intersecting at $x = \bar{a}/2$, $y = \bar{b}/3$, and $z = \bar{c}/0$ (meaning it is parallel to c) would be the (320) plane as in Figure 31.4.

The faces that bound real crystals turn out to have small Miller indices. A simple, ex post facto rationalization can be given for these small integers found

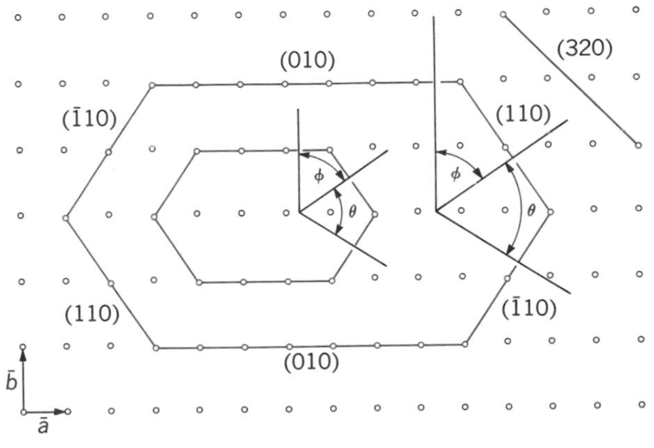

Figure 31.4 Two-dimensional illustration of the law of constant interfacial angles and the similarity in appearance of big and small crystals. A 3 2 0 plane is also indicated.

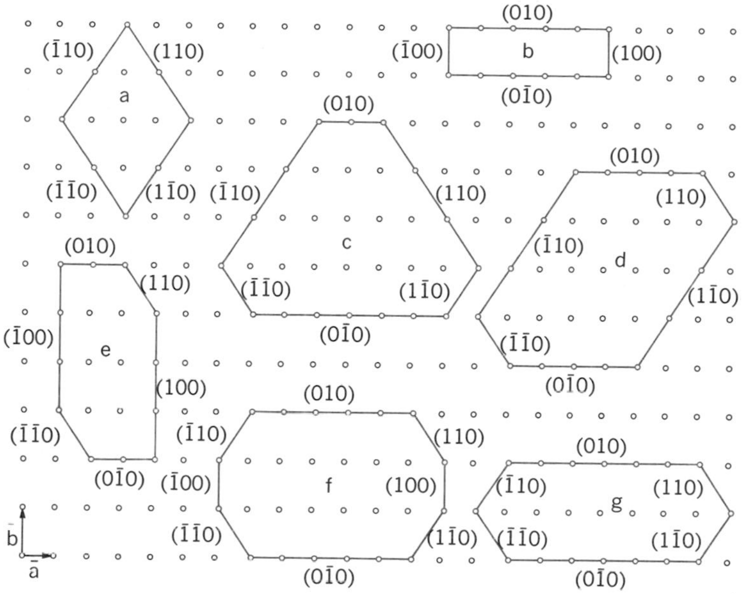

Figure 31.5 A two-dimensional rectangular lattice with typical prism crystal shapes shown in projection. Note that no index for any of the faces is greater than 1.

for the indices of crystal faces. Low values for the indices mean that the equivalent lattice plane has a high density of lattice points per unit area, which implies a high density of molecules—a "smooth" surface in which each molecule is surrounded and held by its closely packed neighbors and thus not readily influenced by external forces. [Compare the point density in the (320) plane of Figure 31.4 with that of a (010) or (110) plane.]

Empirical evidence can be cited in support of this argument. Crystals with a single, long, unit-cell axis tend to form plates with the long axis normal to the plate, and thus the major faces of the crystal are planes containing the short lattice translations. Similarly, crystals with a single, short, unit-cell axis tend to be needles; for example, 11,13-di-*cis*-vitamin A (a long, thin molecule) forms tetragonal needles (unit cell $16.7 \times 16.7 \times 6.70$ Å^3); the needle axis (by symmetry) has the 6.7 Å periodicity, and the molecular axes are probably roughly perpendicular to the direction of crystal growth. The main faces, on the sides of the needles, contain the short lattice translation—a high density of lattice points. In general it is found that crystals have linear dimensions like the reciprocal of the lattice parameters.

Figure 31.5 shows some typical face developments of crystal prisms projected on a two-dimensional rectangular lattice. The wide variety of shapes, quite typical for the prism cross-sections of orthorhombic crystals, are all formed from faces with no index larger than 1. Note the different shapes for crystals *c*, *d*, and *g*, although all are formed from identical faces. Such different extents of face development in real crystals would suggest that they were of different crystal class. However, the method of growth often produces such variations in shape for crystals with identical structures. From a completely indexed set of crystal faces it is usually possible to fix the point symmetry of the crystal and to determine the lattice angles and the axial ratios of the unit cell. Axial ratios determined from morphological studies are often quite accurate, especially from some of the well-formed crystals of naturally occurring minerals.

Exercise 31.2

Write down the Miller indices of the plane that is parallel to the square face of a tetragonal lattice but is half-way between the two square faces. *Answer:* According to Table 31.2 the c axis is the unique axis in a tetragonal crystal. Thus the plane intersects c at $z = \overline{c}/2$ and is parallel to a and b (intersects them at $x = \overline{a}/0$, $y = \overline{b}/0$). Thus $h = \overline{a}/(\overline{a}/0) = 0$, $k = \overline{b}/(\overline{b}/0) = 0$, $l = \overline{c}/(\overline{c}/2) = 2$. Thus this plane has Miller indices of (002). Draw the unit cell to clarify the geometrical relations.

DIFFRACTION FROM A LATTICE

Electromagnetic radiation can be considered as a wave motion of regular period or frequency, just as a lattice is an array of points in space with regular period or frequency. Thus the moving waves can interact with the stationary lattice if their frequencies (wavelength and atomic vibrations) are about the same. Atoms are a few angstroms in diameter, the corresponding wavelengths of electromagnetic radiation are found in the X-ray region (see Figure 8.2). Von Laue was the first to suggest that X-rays should be diffracted by crystals and quickly showed that diffraction could occur when X-rays impinged on a crystal.

THE BRAGG EQUATION

A typical diffractometer for detecting X-ray diffraction (Figure 31.10) will have about 5 million substantially independent orientations for the crystal and the detector. Yet, so rigorous are the diffraction conditions that diffraction will usually be observed for less than 5000 of these, very specifically defined by the crystal lattice (Laue equations) and described by the

BRAGG EQUATION: $$n\lambda = 2d_{hkl} \sin \theta_{hkl,n} \tag{31.1}$$

where λ is the wavelength of the radiation, n is the order of diffraction (an integer), d_{hkl} is the interplanar spacing of the diffracting planes (hkl), $\theta_{hkl,n}$ is the angle of diffraction (and incidence) for the nth-order diffraction from the planes, and the integers h, k, and l, are the Miller indices of the diffracting set of planes.

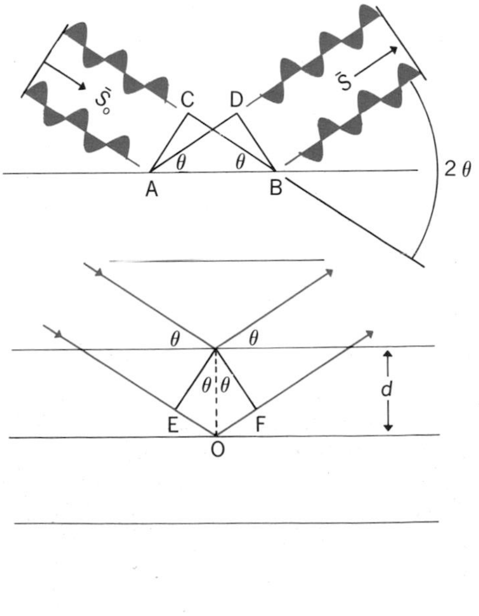

Figure 31.6 Lattice-plane diffraction geometry: "spectral reflection" plus Bragg scattering, $n\lambda = 2d \sin \theta$; $CB = AD$ for all distances AB, and $EO + OF = n\lambda$. (Second-order diffraction is illustrated: $EO = OF = \lambda$, $n = 2$.)

Figure 31.6 illustrates Bragg's relation for second-order diffraction from a set of lattice planes. Since the angle of incidence and diffraction are identical, CB = AD irrespective of the separation AB; all points in any given lattice plane diffract together. Furthermore, Equation (31.1) requires EO + OF = $n\lambda$; thus all points in parallel lattice planes of separation d scatter in phase when the Bragg condition is satisfied.

The experimental observation that diffraction from a crystal occurs only at certain angles, and always with a geometry equivalent to total optical reflection from planes, is direct evidence that crystals can be described in terms of a three-dimensional lattice. The shape and size of the unit cell determine the crystal orientation and 2θ values for which diffraction is possible. In practice we use diffraction data (2θ values and crystal orientation angles) to obtain the crystal-lattice parameters.

Exercise 31.3

Calculate the distance between the lattice planes which give first-order diffraction at an angle of 26.42° with molybdenum X-rays of wavelength 0.710 Å. *Answer:* $n\lambda = 2d \sin\theta$, $n = 1$, $\lambda = 0.710$ Å, $\sin 26.42° = 0.445$, $d = 1 \cdot 0.710$ Å$/2 \cdot 0.445 =$ 0.799 Å.

SYMMETRY AND DIFFRACTION

We shall discuss X-ray diffraction here, although similar descriptions would apply to diffraction of electrons, neutrons, and other forms of radiation, since any moving particle has a wavelength given by the

DE BROGLIE RELATIONSHIP: $\lambda = h/p$

where h = Planck's constant and p = momentum.

The previous section discussed the geometrical conditions for diffraction from a lattice and showed that the crystal lattice, or unit cell, governs where diffraction will be possible. What is observed at the allowed diffraction points (or directions) is, among other things, a function of the kind and arrangement of scattering material (atoms, nuclei, electrons, or others) within the unit cell. For present purposes it will be sufficient to point out that the intensity observed for any measurement may be anything from zero (exactly, or just too small to measure) to a relatively large number.

Moreover, diffraction patterns must exhibit all of the point symmetry possessed by the crystal. If a given symmetry element leaves the crystal invariant it also must leave the diffraction pattern invariant; that is, Bragg's condition must be satisfied at the same value of 2θ and the diffracted intensities must be identical.

Exercise 31.4

Calculate the wavelength (a) of an electron traveling at $6 \cdot 10^8$ cm sec^{-1}, and (b) of a 2-g bullet traveling at about the velocity of sound ($3 \cdot 10^4$ cm sec^{-1}). *Answer:* (a) $\lambda = h/p = h/mv = 6.63 \cdot 10^{-27}$ erg · sec · molecule^{-1}/$9.11 \cdot 10^{-28}$ g molecule^{-1} · $6 \cdot 10^8$ cm sec^{-1} = $1.2 \cdot 10^{-8}$ cm; (b) $\lambda = 6.63 \cdot 10^{-27}$ erg sec molecule^{-1}/2 g · 3 ·

10^4 cm sec^{-1} = $1.2 \cdot 10^{-23}$ cm. Note that the electron wavelength corresponds to atomic dimensions, so diffraction conditions would give readily measurable values of sin θ.

POWDER TECHNIQUES

The simplest diffraction technique consists of passing radiation, usually X-rays, through a sample containing minute crystals. The sample, for instance, may be a finely ground powder or a microcrystalline wire. If the microcrystals are randomly oriented with respect to the incident beam of X-rays, some of them by pure chance will be oriented with planes satisfying the Bragg relation and diffraction will occur. This chance of favorable orientation may be increased by rotating and/or translating the sample so that additional orientations are obtained. Figure 31.7 shows some powder patterns. Since all possible orientations and hence all possible diffractions occur, the number of observed diffraction angles, 2θ, equals the total number of diffracting planes. For some crystals this is a very large number, say 5000. For other crystals fewer lines are obtained. Powder patterns are often called Debye-Scherrer patterns.

CUBIC CRYSTALS AND POWDER PATTERNS

Powder patterns for cubic crystals often have few lines as shown in Figure 31.7. The KCl pattern is a series of regularly spaced lines, and some of the others shown are only slightly more complicated. Even cubic crystals can give complicated patterns, however, if they contain many atoms in a unit cell, as do the alums, which have four $M'M'''(SO_4)_2 \cdot 12H_2O$ units per cell. But let us consider some of the simple cubic patterns.

It may be shown that the interplanar spacing, d, for the hkl planes of a cubic crystal of unit cell dimensions a is given by

$$d = \frac{a}{(h^2 + k^2 + l^2)^{1/2}}$$

For a simple cubic lattice all planes are present; however, there is no sum of squares which equals 7. Thus $h^2 + k^2 + l^2$ can equal 1, 2, 3, 4, 5, 6, 8, 9, etc., but not 7. Thus simple cubic lattices can give a set of regularly spaced lines [remember that $\sin\theta = n\lambda/(2d) = (n\lambda/2a)(h^2 + k^2 + l^2)^{1/2}$] with the seventh line missing. This is exactly what is observed in powdered KCl a result which amazed the first experimenters because they had thought that KCl consisted of KCl molecules or, perhaps, K^+ and Cl^-, which are not identical. But $K^+ + Cl^-$ are isoelectronic (18 electrons each). X-rays are scattered by electrons, not by ionic charge, and therefore, to X-rays, K^+ and Cl^- are almost identical species; the alternating structure, actually composed of two interpenetrating face-centered lattices, acts as a simple cubic structure composed of identical atoms.

Tungsten powder gives a more complicated line pattern. If we assume a cubic structure, we find lines corresponding to $a = 3.16$ Å and $(h^2 + k^2 + l^2)$ equal to 2, 4, 6, 8, 10, ... For copper the corresponding values are $a = 3.62$ Å

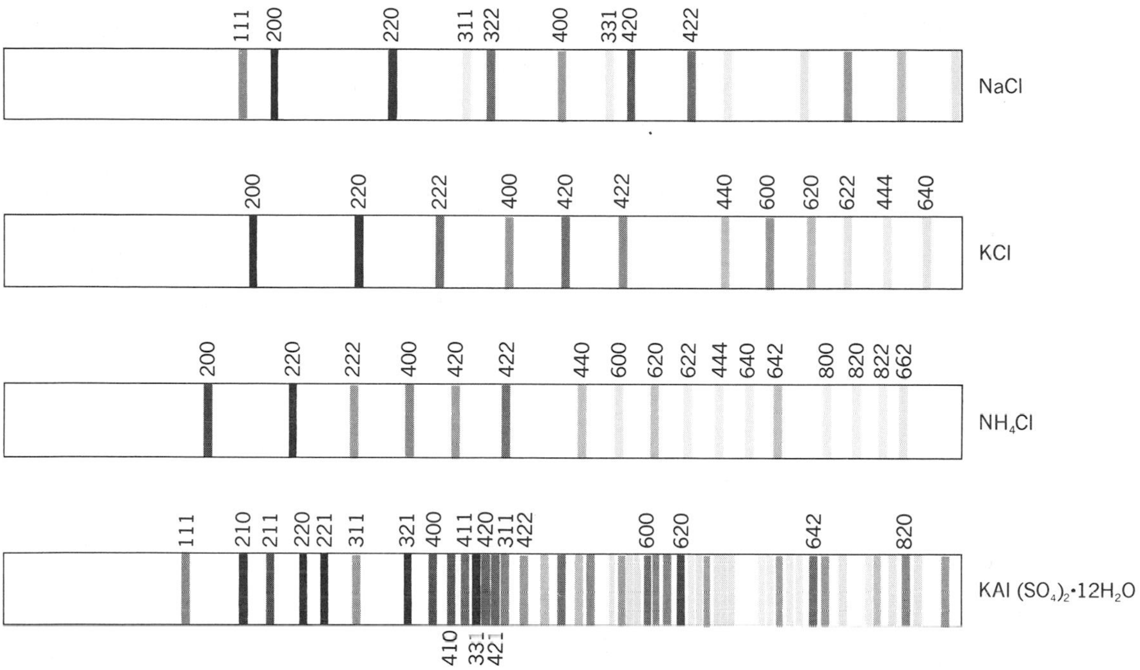

Figure 31.7 Indexed X-ray diffractions from some powdered cubic crystals (Debye-Scherrer patterns). The linear scale for the alum photo is compressed twice as much as the others. [S. Powers and C. Reich.]

and $(h^2 + k^2 + l^2) = 3, 4, 8, 11, 12, \ldots$. The resolution of this problem is shown in Figure 31.8. The centered cubic lattices have planes (200), half way between the 100 planes. Thus these planes constructively interfere and prevent any diffraction from occurring due to the 100 planes. No diffraction is found for $h^2 + k^2 + l^2 = 1$; the first line is missing. For face-centered lattices the same effect occurs with the 110 planes. Again there is an interleaving set (220), which destructively interferes so the $h^2 + k^2 + l^2 = 2$ line is missing, though 110 diffraction is observed in both the simple and body-centered case. In the body-centered cubic, interleaving occurs for the 111 set so the line at $h^2 + k^2 + l^2 = 3$ is missing. Table 31.3 summarizes the effects for the first few lines of each type of cubic lattice.

In the early days of X-ray diffraction the patterns could be obtained and the Bragg relation had been suggested, but the wavelength of X-rays was not known. However, the size of atoms could be estimated from atomic weight data, crystal densities, and Avogadro's number. Knowing the nature of the cubic structure allowed calculation of d and hence of the unknown λ.

Going back to the KCl lattice we see that, though the lines can be explained in terms of a simple cubic system, they actually occur not at $h^2 + k^2 + l^2$ equal to 1, 2, 3, 4, 5, 6, 8, ..., but equal to 4, 8, 12, 16, 20, 24, 32, ... The sin 2θ ratios are the same but the unit cell length, a, must be calculated from the second set of indices. This resolved an early problem in which the a values for $KCl_{(c)}$ were inconsistent with Avogadro's number, atomic weights, and density data—the indexing of the lines had been incorrect.

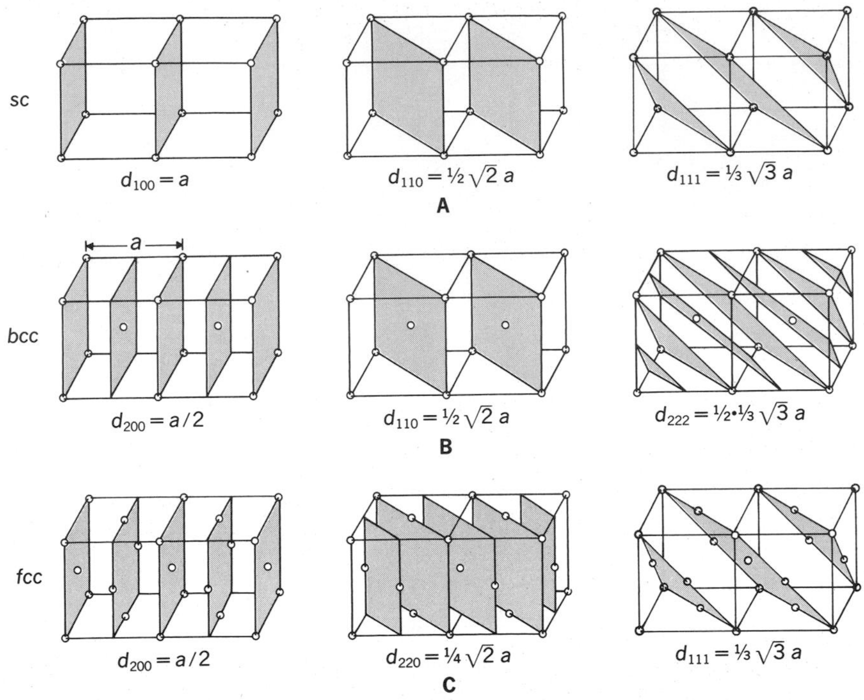

Figure 31.8 Some lattices showing the origin of systematic absences in diffraction patterns.

The NaCl pattern has lines at $h^2 + k^2 + l^2 = 3, 4, 8, \ldots$, as does that of metallic copper, but the line intensities vary in a fashion different from those for copper. This is because all copper atoms are alike and the line intensity is mainly determined by the number of copper atoms in a given diffracting layer. But Na^+ and Cl^- have 10 and 18 electrons, respectively; thus diffraction for various planes

Table 31.3 Some theoretical and experimental powder diffraction patterns showing systematic absences.

hkl	100	110	111	200	210	211	220	221 300	310	
$h^2 + k^2 + l^2$	1	2	3	4	5	6	8	9	10	15,23,28 also missing
Theoretical										
Simple cubic	100	110	111	200	210	211	220	221 300	310	
Body-centered cubic		110		200		211	220		310	
Face-centered cubic			111	200			220		310	
Experimental										
NaCl			111	200			220			2 interpenetrating *fcc*
KCl	200	220	222	400	420	422	440	422 600	620	pseudo sc, 2 interpenetrating *fcc*
NH_4Cl	100	110	111	200	210	211	220	221 300	310	2 interpenetrating sc

gives varying intensities depending on the kinds of atoms that have contributed, sometimes constructively as with 200 planes, sometimes destructively as with 111 planes. Remember the disappearance of the 111 diffraction in KCl, where the atoms are isoelectronic.

Powder patterns are very useful for cubic crystals and even for tetragonal crystals, but are of limited use in deducing structures of lower symmetry. They are, however, of great use in identifying crystalline phases, since the powder pattern is characteristic of the phase regardless of the presence of other phases. Thus large sets of standard powder patterns exist, and the presence in a sample of any substance whose pattern is in the set can be checked by comparing its powder pattern with the standard set. Occurrence of the same lines identifies the presence of the known substance in the unknown systems.

FIELD ION MICROSCOPY

Further evidence for structural symmetry is obtained by field ion microscopy as illustrated in Figure 31.9. The figure reproduces a photograph of the points of impact of helium ions accelerated from a high-voltage platinum tip and traveling in a linearly radiating array to a surrounding film. Each bright spot represents an atom on the platinum tip at which helium gas is ionized. Thus the figure is a much magnified portrait of the tip. One 4-fold, two 2-fold, and four 3-fold axes are readily apparent, plus areas of close-packed and of square-packed atoms consistent with all other evidence that platinum is face-centered cubic.

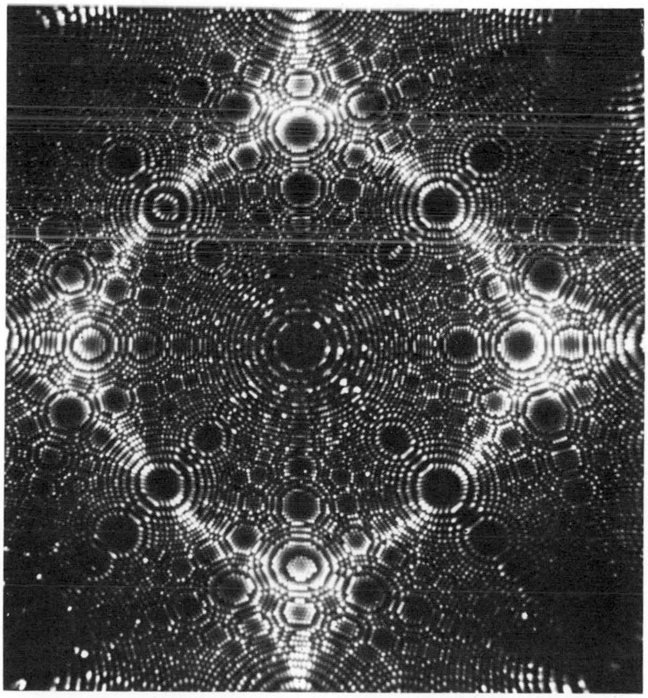

Figure 31.9 Field ion photomicrograph of a platinum tip (taken at 16° K using He gas at a pressure of 5μ and 22 kilovolts). [Courtesy R. W. Newman, Univ. of Florida.]

CRYSTAL ROTATION AND OSCILLATION TECHNIQUES

Single crystals can give information much more directly than powder patterns because only one crystal is diffracting and its orientation can be reproducibly controlled; this controls the number of diffractions observed and simplifies the observation of symmetry. The diffraction symmetry can be discovered and confirmed by the analysis of point-by-point data obtained from a diffractometer such as that illustrated in Figure 31.10. However, several other experimental techniques using film detectors, moving crystals, and so on, have proved to be easier and more reliable methods of determining the symmetry of diffraction patterns and thus the correct crystal class and lattice. We shall discuss photographs obtained by one of these methods.

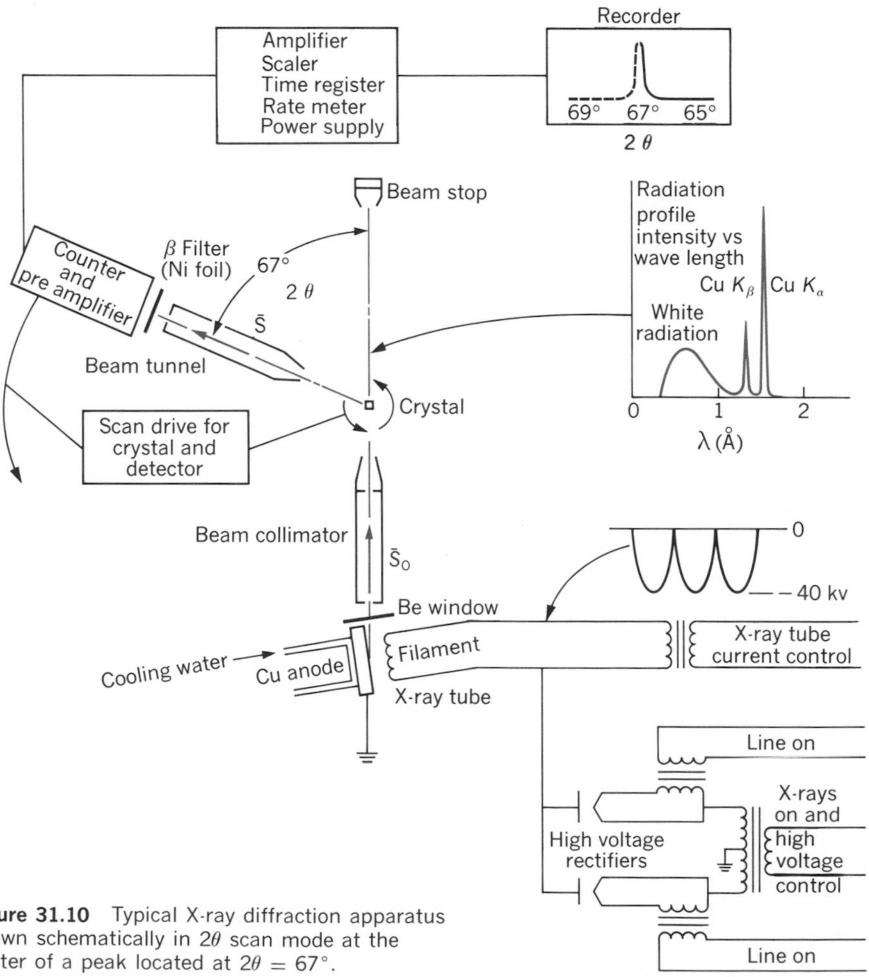

Figure 31.10 Typical X-ray diffraction apparatus shown schematically in 2θ scan mode at the center of a peak located at $2\theta = 67°$.

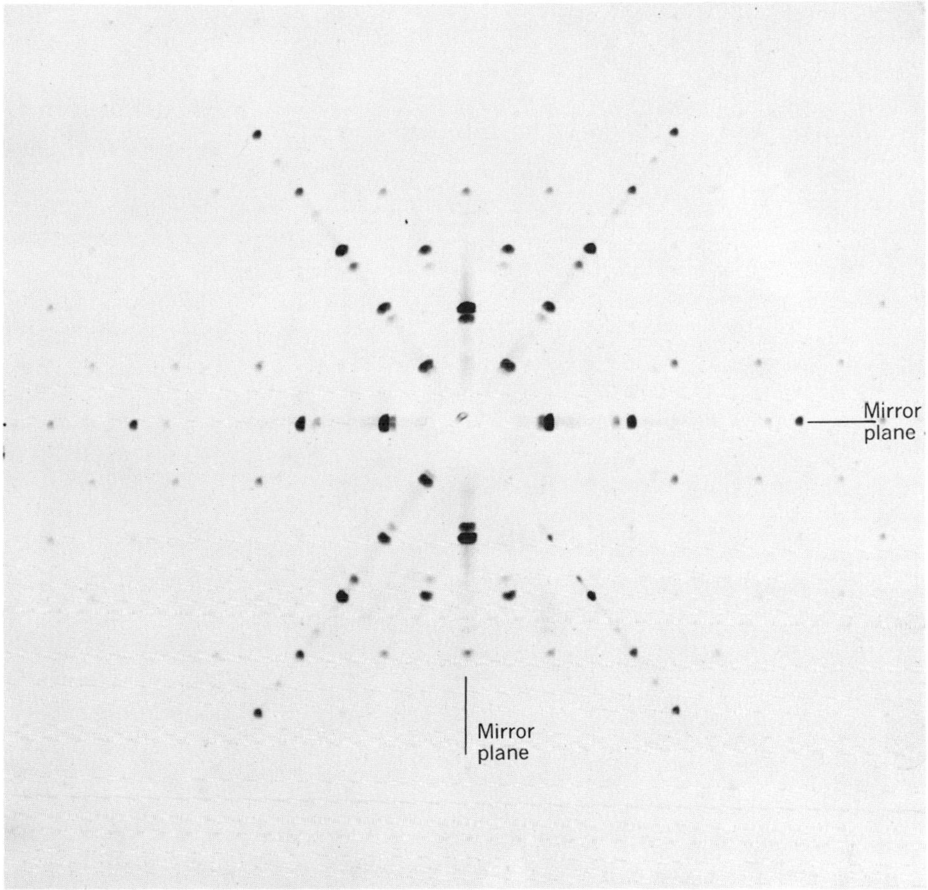

Figure 31.11 X-ray precession photograph for the $hk0$ net of *trans*-vitamin A acetate. 60mm spacing, $\mu = 30°$, unfiltered Cu radiation (β peaks present). Axial angle $= 90°$ between $\bar{a}$ and $\bar{b}$, spots related by two perpendicular mirror planes. Crystal symmetry monoclinic or higher.

SYMMETRY FROM PRECESSION PHOTOGRAPHS

Figure 31.11 is a diffraction photograph from a precession camera for a crystal of *trans*-vitamin A acetate. We will not discuss the details of precession X-ray cameras, but simply point out that the precession method gives an undistorted picture of the (reciprocal) crystal lattice, and diffraction symmetry is exactly that present in the photographs. Figure 31.11 shows the $hk0$ net of the crystal. The $\bar{a}$ and $\bar{b}$ axes are 90° apart, with reflections in equivalent groups of four related by two mirror planes. There must be a 2-fold axis about either $\bar{a}$ or $\bar{b}$ perpendicular to a mirror plane. The crystal class must be monoclinic or higher.

Figure 31.12 is the $h0l$ net for the same crystal (note that the $h00$ reflections appear on both photographs). The $\bar{a}$ and $\bar{c}$ axial angle is 90° but Figure 31.12 shows no symmetry apart from $I_{(h0l)} = I_{\bar{h}0\bar{l}}$. Now it is a general characteristic of all diffraction patterns to follow

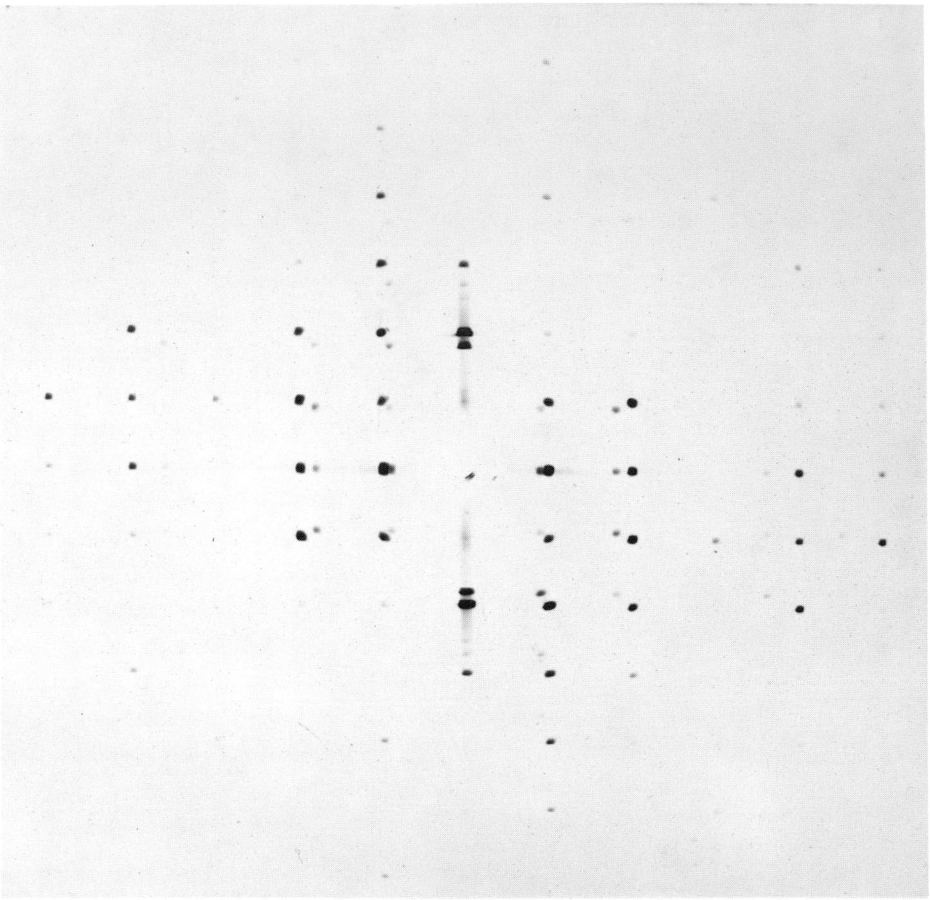

Figure 31.12 X-ray precession photograph for the *h0l* net of *trans*-vitamin A acetate. Same conditions as Figure 31.30. No symmetry apart from $I_{h0l} = I_{\bar{h}0\bar{l}}$, there is an axial angle of 90° between $\bar{a}$ and $\bar{c}$, but $\bar{a}$ and $\bar{c}$ are not symmetry axes.

FRIEDEL'S LAW: $$I_{hkl} = I_{\bar{h}\bar{k}\bar{l}}$$

Thus this matching of intensities does not indicate symmetry in the crystal. There is no symmetry about the *a* or *c* axis. Thus, from Figure 31.11, *b* is a 2-fold axis. Thus, *trans*-vitamin A acetate is a monoclinic crystal.

Note that the lattice of Figure 31.12 is orthogonal (axial angles appear to be 90°), but that once again it is not the dimensions or shape of the lattice that make a crystal orthorhombic but the symmetry of the structure. Figure 31.12 does not have double mirror symmetry, so the crystals are not orthorhombic. (The angle between *a* and *c* is reported to be 90°8′ and the 8′ is barely discernible in Figure 31.12.)

DIFFRACTION INTENSITIES

The intensity observed for any diffraction peak will depend on a number of factors along with the kind and arrangement of scattering material within the unit cell. For example, we would expect the measured diffraction intensity from an X-ray diffractometer, such as that illustrated in Figure 31.10, to be a function of the following.

1. Energy in the incident beam.
2. Volume of the crystal.
3. Scattering efficiency of electrons for the wavelength radiation used.
4. Detector efficiency and counter response.
5. Geometry of the experiment (2θ value).
6. Absorption by the crystal, air, counter windows, and so on.
7. Scan rate, exposure time.

The "integrated intensity" for X-ray diffraction, after background correction and neglecting absorption, is given by the following expression, valid for the geometry shown in Figure 31.10:

$$\text{Integrated intensity} = \frac{Vn^2\lambda^3}{\sin 2\theta}\left(\frac{e^2}{mc^2}\right)^2 (F)^2 \frac{(1 + \cos^2 2\theta)}{2}$$

where V is the volume of the crystal, n is the number of unit cells per unit volume, λ is the wavelength of the radiation, e/mc^2 is the scattering for an electron (e = electron charge, m = electron mass, c = velocity of light), and F is a complex quantity called the structure factor amplitude. $|F|$ is the number of electrons in each unit cell which scatter in the direction 2θ. (θ = Bragg angle, $\bar{S} \cdot \bar{S}_0 = \cos 2\theta$, as in Figure 31.10.) For any given crystal, this becomes $I = K(F)^2(1 + \cos^2 2\theta)/\sin 2\theta$. Thus, in any single experiment, intensity varies with $(F)^2$ and θ only. Calculation of θ and $(F)^2$ is easy but unfortunately one needs F. Taking the square root of F^2, often a complex number, gives many possible answers, only one of which is correct. This is known as the "phase problem." The phase problem is clearly very serious if the sign of F is unknown for any appreciable number of θ values.

THE PHASE PROBLEM

The electron density, $\rho_{(xyz)}$, at any point (xyz) in the unit cell may be expressed in terms of F_{hkl}, the Miller indices (hkl), and the phase angle, α_{hkl}, associated with each particular diffraction amplitude.

$$\rho_{(xyz)} = \frac{1}{V}\sum_{h}\sum_{k}\sum_{l}{}_{-\infty}^{\infty}|F_{hkl}| \cos[2\pi(hx + ky + lz) - \alpha_{hkl}] \qquad (31.2)$$

Equation (31.2) illustrates the "phase problem."

Although F_{hkl} values are known from experiment, α_{hkl} are quantities not available from the laboratory and they are necessary in order to obtain molecular parameters from the observed structure factor amplitudes.

The science (or art) of molecular structure analysis is concerned with ways of obtaining approximate values for α_{hkl} or—what is the same thing—approximate values for the atomic coordinates (crystal structure) so that we can refine the model through electron density maps or through least-squares refinement to increase the agreement between observed and calculated values of $|F_{hkl}|$. Electron density maps give the probabilities of finding electrons as a function of x, y, z in the unit cell. The nuclei are assumed to be centered inside the regions of high electron density (see Figure 31.14, p. 801).

INFORMATION AVAILABLE FROM DIFFRACTION DATA

It would take us too far afield to discuss the methods used to solve the phase problem, but we shall emphasize the kind of results obtained from crystal structure analysis and give a few examples. If the phase problem can be solved, we obtain the unit cell locations for all atoms and some information about vibrational amplitudes. From the atomic positions and the unit cell dimensions, all bond lengths, bond angles, torsion angles, molecular planes, and intra- and intermolecular non-bonded interactions can be calculated, along with their standard errors.

We can discuss any symmetry exhibited by the molecule and the significance of any observed departure from ideal structures. From the thermal parameters it is possible in some cases to separate the motion into components of lattice vibration plus rigid body rotation and possibly intramolecular vibration. The experimental techniques for collecting diffraction data have improved to the extent that significant analyses of vibrational motion are increasingly possible.

CRYSTAL SYMMETRY AND MOLECULAR SYMMETRY

Finally, we consider the important question of the comparison (or correlation) of crystal symmetry with the symmetry of the molecules which constitute the structure. Before we consider possible answers to this question we need to go back to the problem of symmetry in general. Benzene, C_6H_6, requires $3 \times 12 = 36$ general coordinates to describe the positions of all of its atoms. However, we know there is a large set of symmetry elements for each molecule: one 6-fold axis, six 2-fold axes, seven mirror planes, and a center of symmetry. The order of the group is 24 ($6 \times 2 \times 2$) and we have only six carbon atoms, so each must lie on axes or planes of symmetry such that the site symmetry for each atom is of order $4 = 24/6$; likewise for the hydrogen atoms. In this case both types of atoms must lie on 2-fold axes that contain two mirror planes.

Furthermore, use of symmetry requires only eight numbers to locate completely the positions of all twelve atoms: three to locate the center of symmetry, three to describe the direction and orientation of the 6-fold axis, one to define the distance from the origin to a carbon atom, and another to locate a hydrogen atom.

Because of symmetry the definition of a benzene molecule has been reduced from a problem of 36 parameters (three coordinates for each of twelve atoms) to a problem of just eight or, if we do not care about the orientation or location of the molecule, to one of just two (C—C and C—H distances).

In an exactly analogous fashion the number of parameters necessary to define the methane molecule, with tetrahedral (cubic) symmetry, becomes seven; or for a free molecule just one, the C—H distance. In this molecule the carbon atom must lie at the origin and the hydrogens lie on the 3-fold axes.

So what does all this have to do with crystals and molecular symmetry? The answer is—a very great deal!

UNIT CELL SYMMETRY AND MOLECULAR POSITION

Just as point symmetry reduces the number of variables necessary to define a molecule, so the symmetry elements of space groups reduce the volume of the unit cell that requires investigation to deduce the total arrangement.

Consider a crystal which has physical properties consistent with a mirror plane, a 2-fold axis, a center of symmetry, and, like any other closed group, an identity operation. The order is 4. If we locate (or know) the position of one atom, the symmetry elements of the space group locate a total of four equivalent atoms. Thus we need only locate atoms in one quarter of the total volume of the unit cell, "the asymmetric unit," with the full assurance that the symmetry elements of the space group and the lattice translations will generate the rest of the structure. The importance of the number, Z, of molecules contained within a unit cell now becomes apparent. (Z is readily determined from the lattice parameters, the molecular weight, and the density of the crystals, as in the following exercise.)

Exercise 31.5

$Na_2Cr_2O_7 \cdot 2H_2O$ has a density of 2.52 g cm^{-3} and is monoclinic, with unit cell dimensions $a = 6.05$, $b = 10.5$, $c = 12.6$ Å, $\beta = 94.9°$. How many $Na_2Cr_2O_7 \cdot 2H_2O$ units per unit cell? *Answer:* F wt = 298 g mole^{-1}. Units/unit cell = Z.

$$Z = \frac{[abc \sin(180 - \beta)](\text{Å}^3/\text{unit cell})\rho(\text{g cm}^{-3})10^{-24}(\text{cm}^3\ \text{Å}^{-3})6.02 \cdot 10^{23}(\text{units mole}^{-1})}{298\ \text{g mole}^{-1}}$$

$= 4.06 = 4$ units per unit cell. The total uncertainty is 1.5%.

If our cell contains eight molecules, we will have to locate all of the atoms of two entire molecules to solve the crystal structure. If it contains only two molecules, we need only locate the atoms of one-half of one molecule. In this case, the molecule must lie on some symmetry element within the crystal—that is, a center of symmetry, a mirror plane, or a 2-fold axis—and hence the *molecule* is required to have some of the symmetry possessed by the structure.

In general, the molecules which constitute a crystal structure will be *required* to have some of the symmetry possessed by the crystal if, and only if, the number of molecules per unit cell is less than the order of the space group. Does this mean that a molecule of high symmetry cannot exist in a crystal which does not have equivalent symmetry? Not at all! It could exist at any general point and be reproduced by the symmetry up to the full order of the group. But it is one thing for a molecule "incidentally" to have symmetry in a crystal and quite another for it to be *required* to have symmetry in order to be present at all at the special points. The former case reduces the crystallographer's task very little, but the latter may greatly simplify the solution of a particular structure problem as well as our description of the resulting molecular arrangement by reducing the effective order of the group by a factor equivalent to the order of the symmetry element on which the molecule lies.

In conclusion let us consider the structures of some more-or-less representative molecules and compounds and see what can be deduced from space-group order and unit-cell content.

BENZENE

C_6H_6 crystallizes in the orthorhombic system with four molecules in a unit cell of a space group of order 8. The molecules are required to have a center of symmetry only, since the order is reduced only by a factor of two by the unit cell content. The molecular arrangement has much lower symmetry than that possessed by the molecule.

METHANE

CH_4 has four molecules in a space group of order 12 or 24 (uncertain assignment of space group). In this crystal the arrangement makes use of and requires much (or all) of the symmetry of the free molecule, since the order is greatly reduced by the small unit cell content.

VITAMIN A

Two of the crystals described previously in the chapter were *trans*-vitamin A and 11-13-di-*cis*-vitamin A, whose structural formulas are shown in Figure 31.13.

Neither of these molecules possesses any symmetry (the cyclohexene ring is not planar). *Trans*-vitamin A is triclinic with 6 molecules per unit cell (space group unknown, maximum symmetry is an inversion). The 11-13-di-*cis*-vitamin A crystallizes in a tetragonal structure containing four molecules in the unit cell with at least a 4-fold axis. All the molecules are related by symmetry. Neither structure is known, but there is clearly a gross difference in the complexity of the molecular arrangements despite the similarity of the two molecules.

BROMATES

Let us look at an ionic system. Sodium bromate belongs to the cubic system with the unit cell containing four molecules such that the BrO_3^- ion is required to have a 3-fold axis of symmetry. (Since cubic requires four 3-fold axes, and there are four BrO_3^- ions, they must lie on the axes with their own 3-fold axes on the cell 3-fold axes.) Silver bromate, on the other hand, is tetragonal with eight molecules in a unit cell. The structure here is such that it merely requires the bromate ion to have mirror symmetry. It is likely, but not required, that the BrO_3^- has very close to the same symmetry in both crystals, a 3-fold axis containing three mirror planes.

MOLECULAR STRUCTURE DATA FROM CRYSTAL ANALYSIS

A full-scale analysis of all the symmetry and intensity data usually yields a three-dimensional set of electron contours for the unit cell. The electron density contours

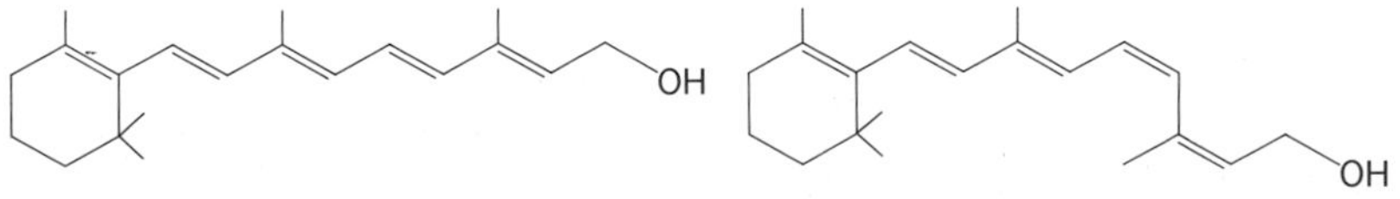

trans-vitamin A   11-13-di-*cis*-vitamin A

Figure 31.13 Two forms of vitamin A.

Figure 31.14 Electron density map through one of the benzene rings of dicobalt hexacarbonyl diphenyl acetylene. The carbon nuclei are at the center of the electron density contours.

and the known symmetry are used to position atomic nuclei in the cell, to deduce bond distances and bond angles, and to estimate thermal motions and molecular potential energy fields. Figure 31.14 shows a part of the electron contour map for crystals of monoclinic dicobalt hexacarbonyl diphenyl acetylene. The structure was solved from film intensities by three-dimensional Patterson (F^2) and electron density maps followed by three-dimensional least-squares refinement. The unit cell with dimensions $a = 16.01$ Å, $b = 15.94$ Å, $c = 8.015$ Å, $\beta = 107.6°$ contains four molecules. The lattice is end-centered and the only symmetry elements are glide planes. Thus only one molecule in the cell had to be located. A second was related to it by the c-glide, a third by the end-centering, and the fourth by c-glide to the third. The relative positions of the two sets of two molecules had to be determined from the electron density maps. Figure 31.14 shows an electron density section through one of the benzene rings of the molecule, and Figure 31.15 shows the structure projected along the $\bar{c}$-axis onto the plane of $\bar{a}$ and $\bar{b}$. The molecule is just one of a number of recently prepared compounds which contain metal-metal and metal-alkyne (or alkene) bonds. Covalent and ionic organo-metallic compounds constitute a very fruitful field of current chemistry.

Di-dihydroazulenium-azulene perchlorate (see Figure 31.16) forms monoclinic crystals, with a 2-fold axis perpendicular to a glide plane, containing four molecules in the unit cell with dimensions $a = 26.32$ Å, $b = 10.20$ Å, $c = 9.97$ Å, $\beta = 93.59°$. The structure was analyzed with diffractometer data and solved by the application of direct methods (statistical probabilities). Refinement was carried out by three-dimensional Fourier and Difference-Fourier maps, and three-dimensional least-squares. The unit cell is centered (order 8), requiring the azulenium-azulene ions to be in special 2-fold positions, which turn out to be the 2-fold axes present in the unit cell. Thus it was only necessary to calculate positions for half of one of the molecules. The other half was given by the 2-fold molecular axis, a second molecule by the c-glide, the third molecule by the centered unit cell, and the fourth by the c-glide acting on the centered molecule. Screw axes tie the entire structure together, as shown in Figure 31.18. (The alternative of a molecular center of symmetry is incompatible with the suggested structure for the ion, but the method of solution required no assumptions with regard to the configuration or

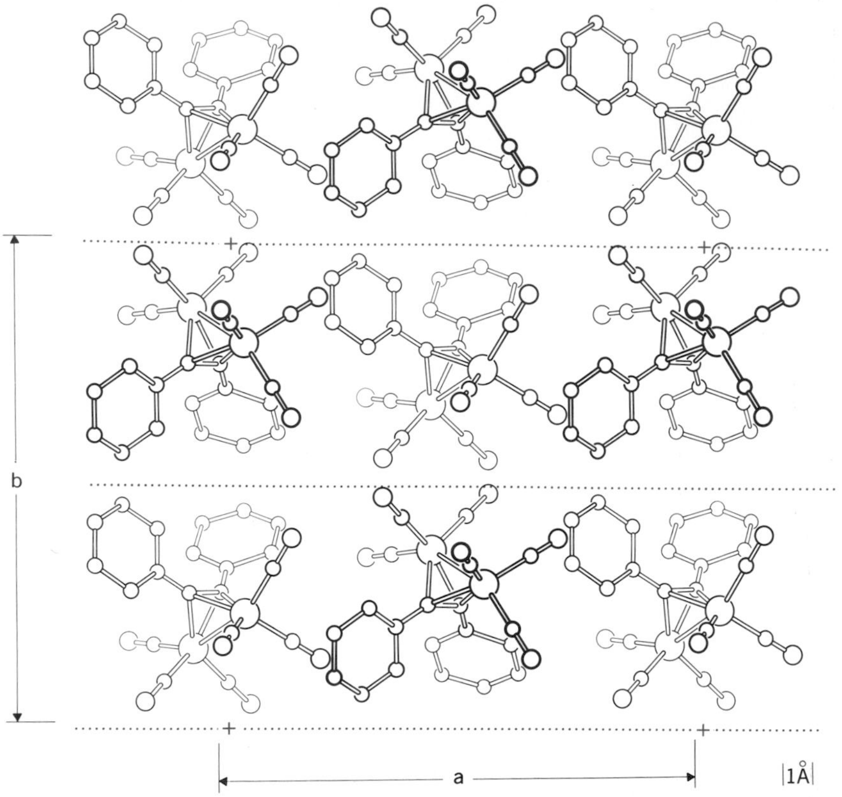

Figure 31.15 Projection along [0 0 1] ontø (0 0 1) of the structure of dicobalt hexacarbonyl diphenyl acetylene. The dotted lines are the c-glide planes present in the c centered unit cell. There are four molecules in the unit cell.

conformation of the molecule.) Note that because there are eight perchlorate ions in the unit cell they may be, and are, in general positions.

Figure 31.17 shows sections from a Fourier projection along the $\bar{b}$ axis onto the *ac* plane. Peaks are illustrated for the chlorine atom and the carbon atoms of the dihydroazulenium ion. The intermolecular arrangement is shown in Figure 31.18, and the bond lengths and angles are given in Figure 31.19. The structure of this substance has helped clarify the mechanism of electrophylic reactions involving azulene and azulenium ion (protonated azulene), since it is the end product for such reactions.

Figure 31.16 Di-dihydroazulenium-azulene perchlorate.

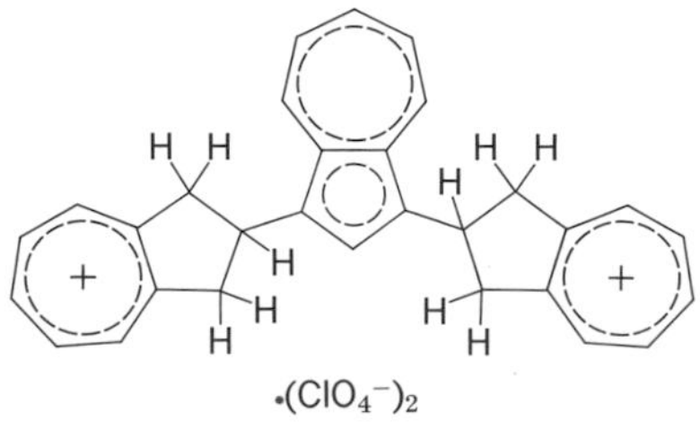

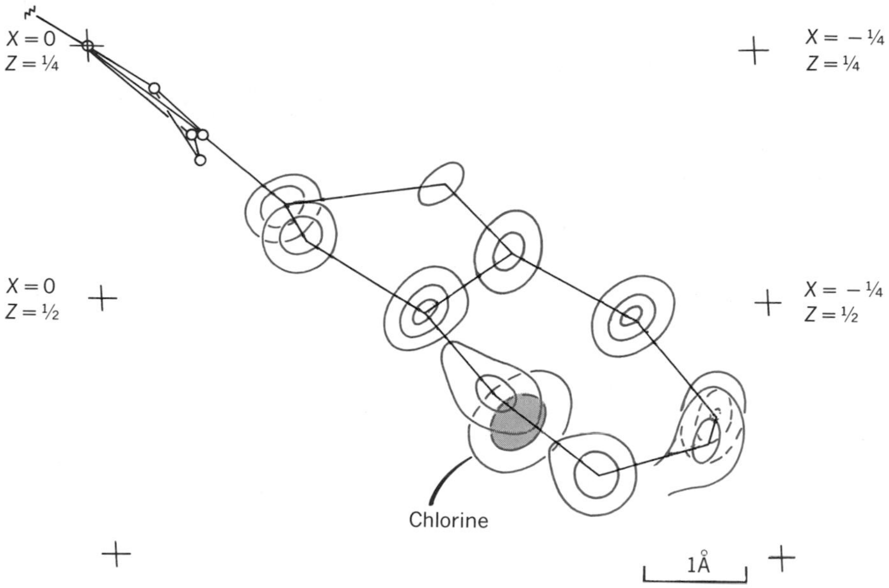

Figure 31.17 Sections from a Fourier projection onto the *ac* plane. Peaks are shown for the chlorine atom and all carbon atoms of the dihydroazulenium ion.

SYMMETRY AND MOLECULAR VIBRATIONS

Symmetry arguments are not only useful for locating atoms and molecules in a crystal but also for understanding their vibrations and electronic states. For example, the symmetry of a molecular electronic orbital must match that of the bonded atoms. We shall not discuss this further than we have already in Chapter 17, but shall discuss vibrational behavior.

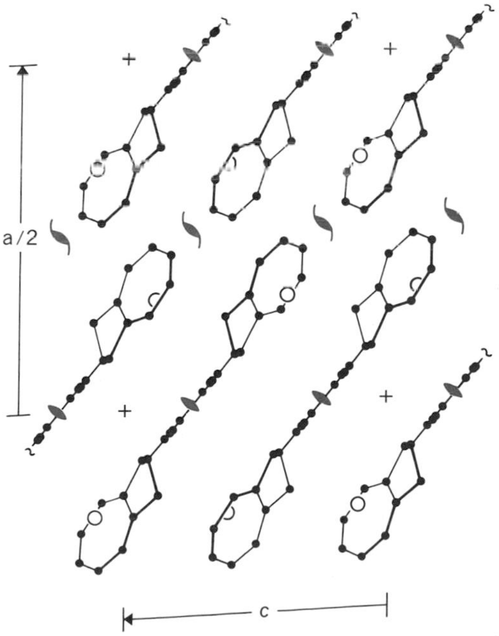

Figure 31.18 The *b*-axis projection of the structure of di-(dihydroazulenium)-azulene perchlorate. Note the correspondence of the two-fold axis of the molecule and the two-fold axis of the unit cell. Only the chlorine atom of each ClO_4^- is shown.

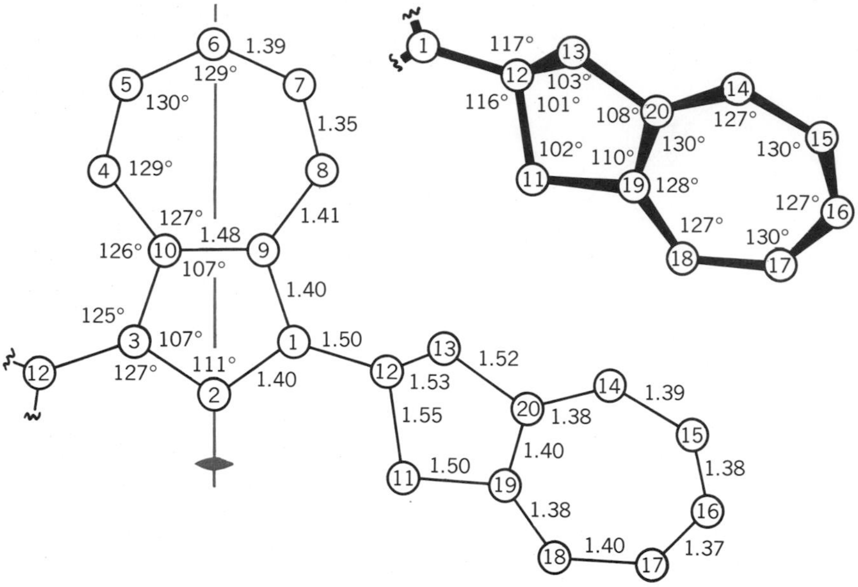

Figure 31.19 Bond lengths and angles in di-(dihydroazulenium)-azulene.

It should be clear from the fundamental definition of vibration—as a motion which leaves the center of mass unchanged but has a restoring force—that a diatomic molecule has a single vibration; the two nuclei move back and forth along their line of centers. The same conclusion is reached if we realize that three coordinates are required to locate any nucleus in space. Thus a diatomic molecule requires six coordinates for its complete description: three of these can be translational coordinates and two rotational coordinates, leaving one vibrational coordinate. In general, as shown in Chapter 8, the total number of vibrations of any nuclear system is $3n - 6$ for nonlinear molecules and $3n - 5$ for linear molecules. To a first approximation, the vibrations are simple harmonic motions with frequencies characteristic of the masses of the atoms and strengths of the bonds involved, as discussed in Chapter 8.

Water, a bent triatomic molecule, must have $3 \cdot 3 - 6 = 3$ vibrations. This means that any actual vibrational pattern of a water molecule may be analyzed in terms of contributions of three simple harmonic motions called the normal modes of motion. In general, since different distortions of the bonds are involved, the three modes and the corresponding frequencies (called ν_1, ν_2, ν_3) will be different. Analysis of the mechanics of motion (technically called normal coordinate analysis) shows that any bent triatomic molecule will vibrate in the three modes shown in Figure 31.20. In the same way any linear triatomic molecule, which

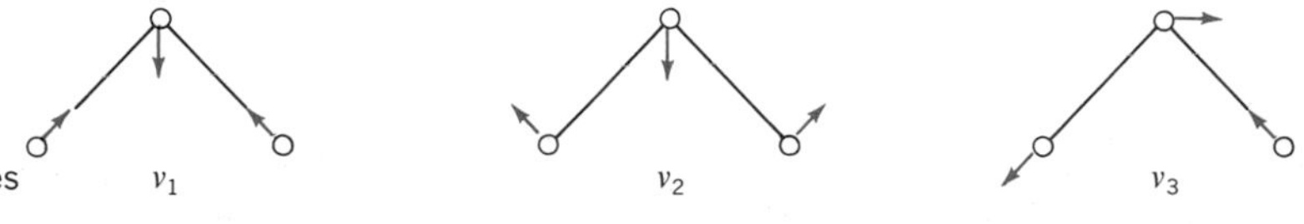

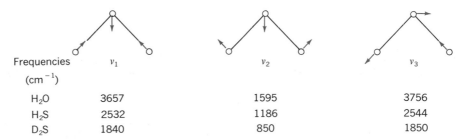

Frequencies (cm^{-1})	ν_1	ν_2	ν_3
H_2O	3657	1595	3756
H_2S	2532	1186	2544
D_2S	1840	850	1850

Figure 31.20 Normal modes of motion in a nonlinear triatomic molecule such as H_2O.

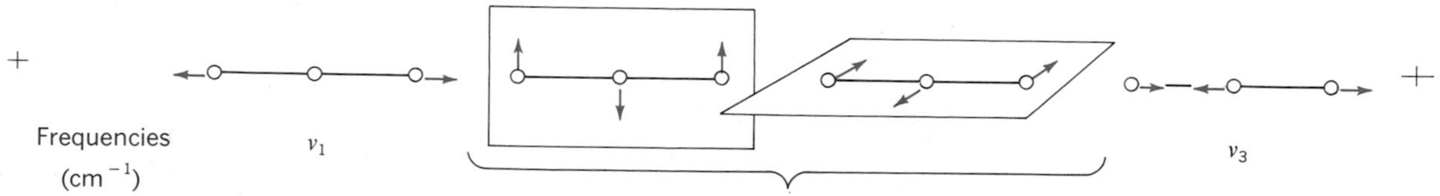

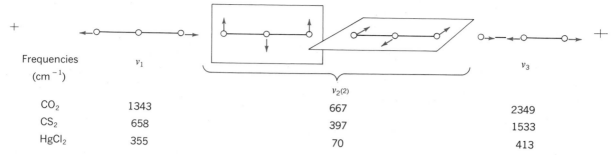

Frequencies (cm^{-1})	ν_1	$\nu_2(2)$	ν_3
CO_2	1343	667	2349
CS_2	658	397	1533
$HgCl_2$	355	70	413

Figure 31.21 Normal modes of motion in a linear triatomic molecule such as O=C=O.

must have $3 \cdot 3 - 5 = 4$ modes, vibrates in the same patterns as illustrated for CO_2 in Figure 31.21. The experimentally observed frequencies for H_2O and CO_2 and some similar molecules are given in the figures.

DEGENERATE MODES OF VIBRATION

Note that, from symmetry, the three water modes (ν_1, ν_2, ν_3) are all different and that their frequencies are also different. With CO_2, two of the vibrations (ν_3) have the same symmetry (one mode along the x- and one along the y-axis) and experimentally they have the same frequency, 667 cm^{-1}. Such a mode is said to be degenerate. When, as in CO_2, there are two identically symmetrical modes, the vibration is said to be doubly degenerate. It should be clear that there are three normal modes of motion in CO_2, one doubly degenerate, and thus three frequencies [again called ν_1, $\nu_2(2)$, ν_3]. In the ν_1 mode the C is stationary and the O's move in and out along the long axis, z, of the molecule. In ν_2 the C moves in opposition to the two O's perpendicular to z. In the ν_3 mode the C moves in opposition to the two O's along the z axis. All modes may be excited (but infrared excites only ν_2 and ν_3, as discussed in Chapter 8). To a good approximation they remain simple harmonic even in the excited states. They may be excited singly or together and the actual atomic motions are describable in terms of various combinations of the three modes in various excited states. Adding ν_1 and ν_3 for CO_2 modes always gives reciprocal atomic motions along z. But adding the two components of ν_2 gives atomic motions perpendicular to z. The net effect of exciting ν_2 is that the atoms move on ellipses whose planes are perpendicular to z. In the special case of equal excitation of both ν_2 components, the atoms move on circles perpendicular to z, and the vibration becomes a rotation!

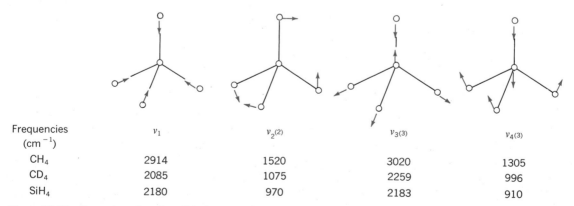

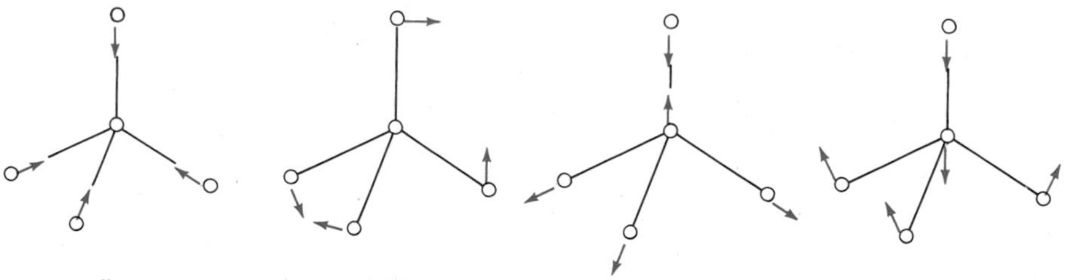

Frequencies (cm^{-1})	ν_1	$\nu_2(2)$	$\nu_3(3)$	$\nu_4(3)$
CH_4	2914	1520	3020	1305
CD_4	2085	1075	2259	996
SiH_4	2180	970	2183	910

Figure 31.22 Normal modes of motion in a tetrahedral molecule such as CH_4.

Triply degenerate modes are also known. For example, tetrahedral molecules have four 3-fold axes plus six 2-fold axes plus an inversion plus four mirror planes. We should not be surprised if this high symmetry were to lead to degeneracy. It does, as shown in Figure 31.22. A tetrahedral mode should have $3 \cdot 5 - 6 = 9$ vibrations, but only 4 different ones are actually found by a normal coordinate analysis, and also experimentally, for tetrahedral molecules. The ν_1 mode is highly symmetric and simple. It is called the breathing mode. The outer atoms move in phase linearly in and out along the bonds, the inner atom being stationary. The ν_2 mode is doubly degenerate. In each of these, every atom moves in phase around an ellipse whose axial lengths depend on the degree of excitation. The ν_3 and ν_4 modes are triply degenerate. The atoms now move on the surface of an ellipsoid of revolution whose axes are again determined by the relative excitations of the three components. All tetrahedral molecules will show the same frequency pattern but the values of the frequencies will be determined by bond strengths and atomic masses. It is interesting to note that ν_1 and ν_3 are mainly bond stretching modes, whereas ν_2 and ν_4 are mainly bond bending, and hence are at lower frequencies than ν_1 and ν_3. Similar separation occurs with other symmetries.

SUMMARY

The external forms of crystals must be consistent with the internal symmetry, but it is the internal symmetry which provides the most direct clues to molecular arrangements, intermolecular forces, and detailed bond distances and angles. Since crystals are composed of repeating three-dimensional patterns, symmetry theory provides powerful methods for the analysis of crystals.

The symmetry operations are identity; rotational axes of 2, 3, 4, 6; inversion axes of $\bar{3}$, $\bar{4}$, $\bar{6}$; mirror planes; glide planes; and screw axes. These combine to give the 32 point groups and the 230 space groups.

Diffraction (usually of X-rays, but also of electrons and neutrons) gives direct insight into the unit-cell dimensions, the interplanar distances, and some of the internal symmetry of the crystal. Detailed analysis of the intensity of the diffraction pattern gives further evidence on symmetry and, if the phase problem can be solved, interatomic distances. In favorable cases these average distances are calculable to ± 0.001 Å and additional insights may be obtained into the nature of thermal motions and the potential energy surfaces for vibration.

Techniques have been developed that allow routine analysis of most unit cells of monoclinic or higher symmetry that contain molecules with up to 100 atoms each. Careful work even allows analysis of complicated substances like hemoglobin or myoglobin, containing about 1,000 atoms not counting hydrogen, and the resolution of the structures at the 1.4 to 2 Å level.

It should be clear that such detailed knowledge allows great insight into the synthesis and properties of complicated substances, and provides otherwise unavailable information on the nature and analysis of biological systems.

Symmetry arguments are also indispensable to the interpretation of internal molecular structure and forces as evidenced in molecular vibrations, electronic states, and molecular interactions with other molecules and with electromagnetic radiation.

The mathematician's playing with the roots of equations, a play which had no practical motivations and almost no possibilities of practical applications, led to the recognition of the importance of symmetry and groups. [But] the importance of symmetry was recognized before mathematicians invented the theory of groups. In 1794 William Blake wrote:

Tiger, Tiger, burning bright
In the forests of the night,
What immortal hand or eye
Could frame thy fearful symmetry?

I can now answer my original question, What are the mathematicians doing? They are trying to make precise the intuitions of poets.—*Bernard Friedman,* Science, **154**, 362 (1966).

PROBLEMS

31.1. Plot curves $y = \cos x$ and $y = |\cos|\, x$ in rectangular coordinates; considering them as symmetrical graphs, indicate for each all symmetry and/or translation necessary to generate all others and also leave each of the figures invariant. What are these elements?

31.2. For the symmetrical figure shown below find the lattice and all symmetry elements that are present. Indicate all symmetry elements also for the lattice used to generate the structure.

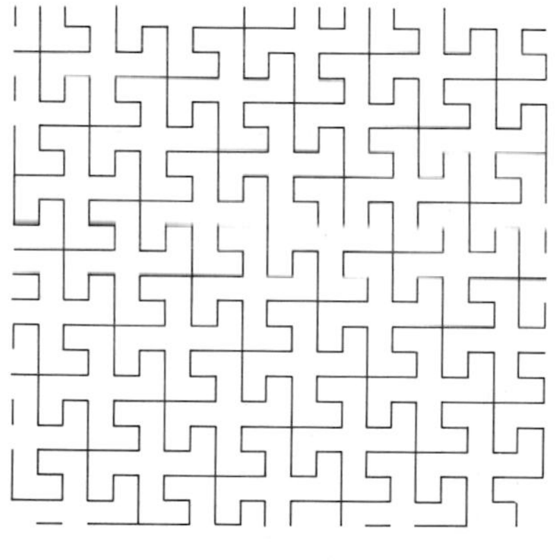

31.3. An X-ray investigation of tropenium molybdenum tricarbonyl fluoroborate $[C_7H_7^+Mo(CO)_3BF_4^-]$ gave an orthorhombic unit cell with the dimensions $a =$ 13.07 Å, $b =$ 16.43 Å, $c =$ 11.78 Å. The density was found to be 1.92 g/cc. How many molecules are contained in the unit cell? ($n = 8$.)

31.4. A rough structural determination shows that solid carbon dioxide is cubic. Discuss very briefly why one can deduce that the carbon dioxide molecules are not lined up in rows, with all their molecular axes parallel to one set of cube edges.

31.5. Solid NaCN, at low temperatures, is tetragonal. At higher temperatures it becomes cubic, having exactly the same structure as sodium chloride. Account for this effect of temperature on the structure.

31.6. Tungsten (W) has a body-centered cubic structure; its density is 19.3 g/cm^3. Calculate the length of a side of the tungsten unit cell. ($a \cong 3$ Å.)

31.7. Below is a table of properties of NaCl and BaO crystals. Although the two crystals have identical structures and essentially equivalent internuclear distances and molar densities, they have radically different melting points and hardnesses [mineral hardness is measured on a scale from very soft (talc) equal to zero, to very hard (diamond) equal to ten]. Explain this difference.

	Molar density moles/cm^3	Internuclear distance Å	Melting point °C	Hardness
NaCl	0.037	2.79	801	2.5
BaO	0.037	2.74	1923	5.5

31.8. Is it possible to have a cubic unit cell containing a single $NaNO_3$ unit?

31.9. What would be the minimum content of NH_4^+ ions in a cubic unit cell? (1 NH_4^+.)

31.10. Elementary vanadium is found to have a cubic unit cell containing two atoms. What is its crystal structure?

31.11. Copper and nickel dissolve in one another in all proportions, forming solid solutions with a closest-packed structure. However, when zinc is added to copper, a closest-packed solid solution (called α) appears over only a small composition range; if too much zinc is added, a body-centered cubic solid solution (called β and having zinc and copper in almost equal amounts) appears. Explain this difference in behavior. (Metallic radii for these elements are, Cu, 1.28 Å; Zn, 1.37 Å; and Ni, 1.25 Å.)

II

31.12. Which of the following are possible modes of vibration? All vectors are in the plane of the paper. Which are the same mode? How would you describe each of the other motions?

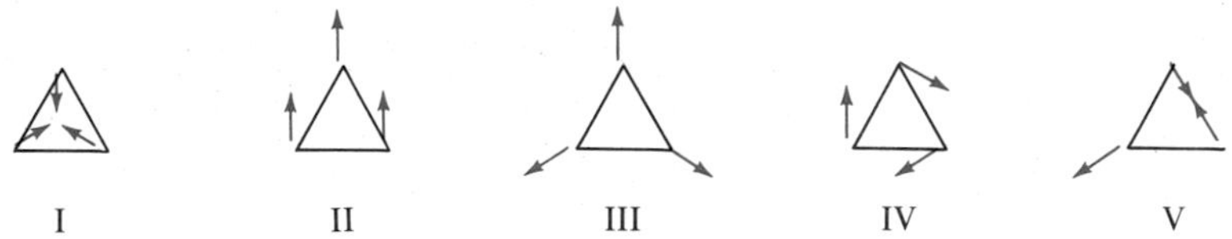

I II III IV V

31.13. Zinc blende has sulfide ions at each corner and in the center of each face of the cubic unit cell. The zinc ions are at $\frac{1}{4}, \frac{1}{4}, \frac{1}{4}$; $\frac{1}{4}, \frac{3}{4}, \frac{3}{4}$; $\frac{3}{4}, \frac{3}{4}, \frac{1}{4}$; and $\frac{3}{4}, \frac{1}{4}, \frac{3}{4}$. The numbers represent fractions of the unit-cell edges, always in the same order, which give the coordinates of the center of each atom. To what crystal system would you now assign zinc sulfide? Sketch a unit cell showing only the zinc ions. What is the formula of zinc blende? Calculate the density in terms of the unit-cell dimensions a, b, c. ($\rho \cong 400/a^3$.)

31.14. The substances Kr, Cu, and I$^-$ (in most alkali iodides) all crystallize in a face-centered cubic (fcc) lattice as shown by their X-ray powder patterns. (Only certain lines corresponding to fcc patterns are present.) The unit cell edges, a_0, are calculated from the same patterns. Use the data given in the table below to calculate, as often as is possible, the "size" (diameter) of the atoms or ions present. If it is not possible to calculate the diameter, say why. Assume spherical shapes for all atoms and ions. Assume the cations are in the octahedral holes in the I$^-$ fcc lattice. Be sure to show your methods of calculation. ($d_{Cu} \cong 3$ Å $\cong d_{Kr}$.)

Substance	Kr	Cu	I^- in				
			LiI	NaI	KI	RbI	CsI
a_0(Å)	4.8	3.6	6.2	6.4	7.0	7.1	7.6

31.15. Discuss the types of bonds that are formed when a substance crystallizes. Include the following materials in your discussion. Ice, magnesium, NaCl, diamond, copper, benzene, graphite, silicon carbide, CCl_4, zinc oxide, zinc telluride. What other factors, aside from bond type, are important in determining the crystalline structure of a particular substance?

31.16. An oxide of copper crystallizes in a cubic unit cell with oxide atoms at 0, 0, 0 and $\frac{1}{2}, \frac{1}{2}, \frac{1}{2}$. Copper atoms are located at $\frac{1}{4}, \frac{1}{4}, \frac{1}{4}$; $\frac{1}{4}, \frac{3}{4}, \frac{3}{4}$; $\frac{3}{4}, \frac{1}{4}, \frac{3}{4}$; and $\frac{3}{4}, \frac{3}{4}, \frac{1}{4}$. Draw the unit cell showing the positions of all atoms in the cell. How many copper atoms are there in the unit cell? How many oxide atoms? What is the simplest formula of this oxide? (n = 4 Cu atoms.)

31.17. How must the oxygens of the ClO_4^- be arranged in Figure 31.18? Sketch in a possible orientation.

31.18. Draw a representation of the ν_1 mode (symmetrical stretch) for $NO_3^-{}_{(aq)}$. Would this frequency be infrared active? Sketch a mode for $NO_3^-{}_{(aq)}$ which surely would be infrared active.

31.19. Draw the symmetry axes in each of the following diagrams (all geometrical shapes shown are cubic) and identify the crystal class of each object. All spheres are centered at corners, except in the second from left, where it is on the edge of the cube. In which of these structures could a nitrate ion, a flat equilateral triangle, be inserted at the center of the cube without lowering the symmetry? Show its orientation.

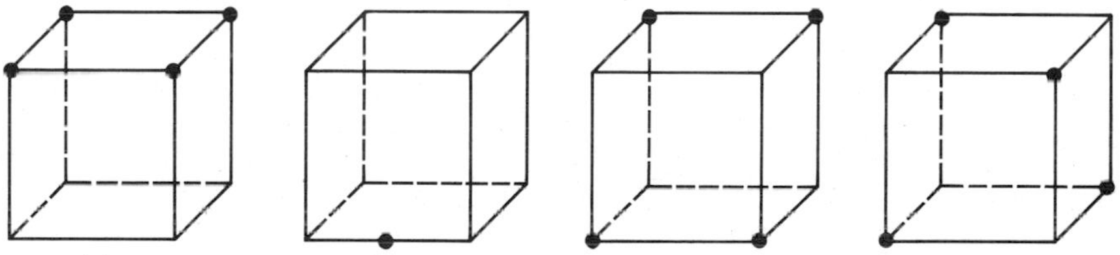

(a) (b) (c) (d)

31.20. Quartz (SiO_2) has a structure which can be thought of as a hexagonal closest-packed array of O^{2-} (1.45 Å) in which every fourth tetrahedral hole is occupied by a Si^{4+} (0.41 Å). What is the probable structure of the common mineral potassium feldspar (orthoclase), which has the composition $KAlSi_3O_8$? (K^+, 1.33 Å; Al^{3+}, 0.45 Å.) Does your answer help to explain why feldspar actually has a *somewhat* modified crystal structure (monoclinic instead of hexagonal, as for quartz)?

31.21. Some recent diffraction work in Claremont was directed toward the analysis of some tropenium mercuric iodide complexes. It was desired to operate the X-ray tube at a potential which would generate hard radiation insufficient in energy to cause fluorescence of iodine atoms. Calculate by some suitable approximations the absorption edge for iodine, and also the Kα wavelength. What would be a satisfactory potential for the X-ray tube? ($V \cong$ 30,000 volts.)

III

31.22. Could $SO_4^=$ ions be located in a mirror plane, on a 2-fold axis, on a 6-fold axis, on a 4-fold axis, at a center of inversion, on a general point? Sketch a possible orientation for each feasible arrangement.

31.23. A cubic elementary crystal irradiated with X-rays of 1.54 Å wavelength gave its first nine reflections at the following angles and with the listed intensities (*w*, weak; *s*, strong; *m*, medium; *v*, very.) Calculate the Miller indices corresponding to each line. Calculate the unit cell dimensions. Identify the crystal system. Explain the intensity relation between lines 4 and 5 in terms of the crystal structure.

Line	1	2	3	4	5	6	7	8	9
Angle (°)	13.70	15.89	22.75	26.91	28.25	33.15	37.00	37.60	41.95
Intensity	*w*	*vs*	*s*	*vw*	*m*	*w*	*w*	*m*	*m*

31.24. (*a*) The molecules of phosphorus pentachloride are trigonal bipyramids with three chlorines equatorially located about the phosphorus and two in the polar positions. Draw a projection of the molecule.

(*b*) Assume that crystalline phosphorus pentachloride is cubic with a phosphorus atom at each corner of the cube and one at the center. Could the units within the cell be molecules of phosphorus pentachloride? Why?

(*c*) The actual units within the cell are an equal number of tetrahedral PCl_4^+ and octahedral PCl_6^- ions. The former may be considered to be at the cube center and the latter at the cube corners. How must each ion be oriented in space, assuming that they are not freely rotating, or is there no required orientation? Draw a single cubic unit cell showing clearly the orientation of one corner group and one centered group.

(*d*) How do you account, in terms of bonding theory, for the experimentally observed shapes of the two ions?

31.25. A crystal is examined with an optical goniometer and the face development suggests orthorhombic symmetry. The following faces, among others, are indexed: (110), $(1\bar{1}0)$, $(\bar{1}10)$, (100), $(\bar{1}00)$. The normals to the faces (110) and $(1\bar{1}0)$ make an angle of 105°. What is the axial ratio a/b? If the morphologist made a mistake and should have indexed the above faces as (210) and $(2\bar{1}0)$, what would the ratio be? Draw a cross-sectional view of the crystal, showing all of the faces listed above, and indicate the axes and all angles between crystal faces. ($a/b \cong \frac{4}{3}$.)

See page 1093 for a list of references and readings in the recent chemical literature related to the material in this chapter.

CHAPTER 32

Solid State Reactions, Surface Chemistry

The variations which accompany changing symmetry and changing availability of nucleation centers make the study of surface reactions, especially on crystals, a fascinating research area full of rewarding insights.

It would be easy to defend the statement that all chemistry is surface chemistry. Substances can react only when they come together, and the place where they come together is, by definition, a surface. For example, molecular interactions occur at the surfaces of the molecules. In this chapter we shall briefly discuss the reactions between molecules and then turn to reactions that occur at the interface between two phases. Typical reactions are solution of one phase in another, corrosion, heterogeneous catalysis, and electrode processes.

SURFACE MOLECULES

Figure 32.1 makes it clear that a molecule in a surface should have a very different reactivity (escaping tendency, thermodynamic activity, chemical potential) than a molecule in the bulk material. It should also be clear that, under most circumstances, different surface molecules will have different escaping tendencies because of irregularities in the surface. The same effect is found with the atoms in molecules, of course; recall the difference in reactivity at primary, secondary, and tertiary carbon atoms (Chapter 24). Figure 32.1 also makes clear one of the great difficulties of studying surface chemistry—the difficulty of obtaining a uniform and reproducible surface, especially on crystals.

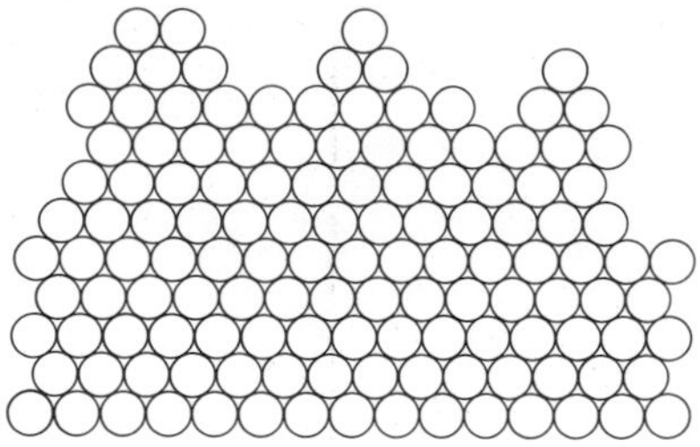

Figure 32.1 Possible molecular arrangements on crystal surfaces ranging from a "perfect" face (bottom), to a considerably disordered face (top). Clearly the more "exposed" molecules will have a higher reactivity, and those within the bulk of the crystal will have a much lower reactivity.

SURFACE TENSION

The difference of chemical potential between the surface molecules and those within a drop of liquid is readily observed in the tendency of unrestrained liquids to assume a spherical form. One of the characteristics of a sphere is that it is the geometrical shape having the smallest ratio of surface area to volume. Thus a smaller percentage of the total molecules present are on the surface of a spherical drop than would be true of any other shape. This indicates that the chemical potential of the surface molecules not only differs from those in the bulk liquid, but that the chemical potential of the surface molecules is higher than those in the bulk liquid. Molecules "prefer" bulk packing.

A substance in field-free space is a closed system at constant temperature and pressure. The Gibbs free energy of such a system will be a minimum at equilibrium, as we have already shown (p. 665). Any deformation of a spherical drop requires work; the free energy of the system must be increased. The amount of work necessary to increase the surface of a substance by one square centimeter is called the surface tension, γ, of the substance. Thus

$$dG = \gamma \, dA = \text{work to increase surface area}$$

Surface tension, γ, can be measured either in dynes/cm or ergs/cm^2; thus it can be thought of either as force per unit edge of surface or as work (or energy) per unit area.

If a drop of liquid rests on a surface which it does not wet, the drop flattens because of the gravitational field. However, the surface tension keeps the drop from flattening indefinitely, since flattening means that the surface area is increasing. Thus the extent of flattening might be used to measure the surface tension. This apparently simple measurement can be made in some cases, but the measurement is complicated by the facts that the weight and size of the drop are important variables and that an additional surface must now be considered—that between the liquid and the supporting solid. Molecules at the interface between the liquid and solid will have a chemical potential different from those at the liquid-gas interface. The amount of work necessary to increase this interface by one square centimeter is called the interfacial tension. Low interfacial tensions lead to spreading, or wetting, in liquid-solid systems. High interfacial tensions lead to drop formation.

Exercise 32.1

The surface tension of the fluid in a can of aerosol spray is 10.70 dynes/cm (or ergs/cm^2). Calculate the work required to "atomize" 10 ml of the bulk liquid to drops of spray 10^{-4} mm in diameter. *Answer:* work $= \int \gamma \, dA = \gamma(A_2 - A_1)$, assuming γ is independent of A. A_2 = (number of drops) · (area per drop) = [10 ml/ $(4\pi r^3/3)$ ml][$4\pi r^2$] = $(10 \cdot 3)/(r)$, where $r = 10^{-4}$ mm $= 10^{-5}$ cm. Thus $A_2 = 3 \cdot 10^6$ cm^2. A_1 will be negligible compared to this. Thus work = 10.70 ergs cm$^{-2} \cdot 3 \cdot 10^6$ cm^2 $= 3 \cdot 10^7$ ergs = 0.7 cal, a small but not negligible amount. Note that the value for water would be 7 times greater. Note also the cooling effect caused by this increase in area must be considered in designing the sprayer. Is the effect significant?

MEASUREMENT OF SURFACE TENSION

Figure 32.2 shows what is perhaps the most direct method of measuring surface tension. A drop of liquid is placed between a wire U and a movable wire straightedge. The wire straightedge is then pulled away from the bottom of the U, and the work required to produce the two-sided area, $dA = 2l\,dx$, is measured. The surface tension is calculated by the formula

$$\frac{dG}{dA} = \frac{\text{work}}{\text{change in area}} = \frac{f\,dx}{2l\,dx} = \frac{f}{2l} = \gamma \tag{32.1}$$

A much simpler way, and therefore a much more frequently used method, is to measure the difference in height of a liquid inside and outside a capillary of radius r_c mounted with one end below the surface of bulk liquid, as in Figure 32.3.

The liquid is mechanically sucked up into the capillary and then released, forming a new liquid-gas interface as it falls. The work of forming this surface is

$$dG_{\text{surf}} = \gamma(2\pi r_c)\,dh$$

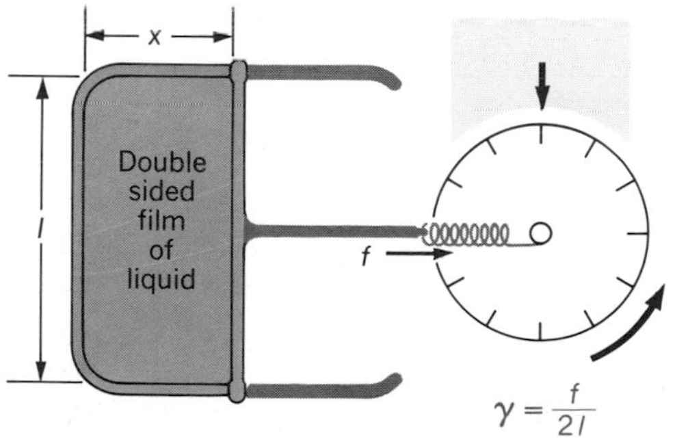

Figure 32.2 "Two-dimensional piston" for measuring surface tension.

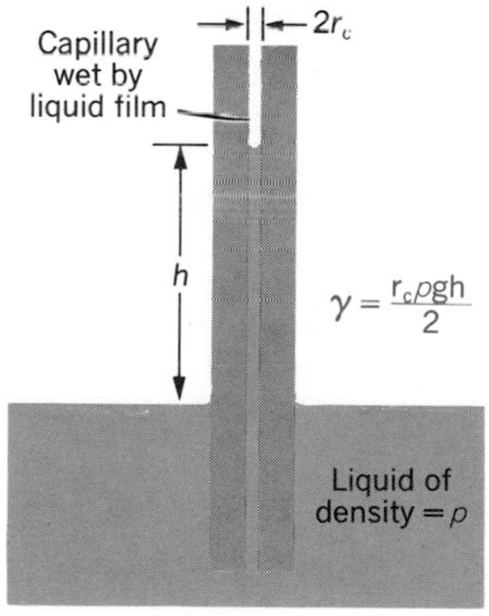

Figure 32.3 Differences in height, h, between liquid inside capillary of radius r_c and outside bulk liquid are due to surface tension.

where h is measured from the bulk surface outside the capillary. The work comes from gravitational effects tending to lower the liquid level:

$$dG_{\text{grav}} = f\,dh = (\pi r_c^2 \rho g h)\,dh$$

At equilibrium the two free-energy changes are equal and

$$\gamma(2\pi r_c)\,dh = (\pi r_c^2 \rho g h)\,dh$$

$$\gamma = \frac{g h r_c \rho}{2} \tag{32.2}$$

Note by comparing Figures 32.2 and 32.3 that the capillary is exactly analogous to a two-dimensional piston that is curved into a cylinder and has only one side.

We have implicitly assumed that the force on the capillary film is directly downward, that the liquid wets the capillary, and that the density, ρ_0, of the column of gas of height h above the bulk liquid equals zero. A more complete derivation gives

$$\gamma = \frac{g h r_c(\rho - \rho_0)}{2\cos\theta} \tag{32.3}$$

where θ is the angle the lower surface of the meniscus makes with the perpendicular wall of the capillary.

Experimental results for water in a glass capillary of 0.123 cm radius show that the meniscus is 1.21 cm above the level of the bulk water at 20°C, and $\theta = 0$. This gives

$$\gamma = \frac{980\text{ cm sec}^{-2} \cdot 1.21\text{ cm} \cdot 0.123\text{ cm} \cdot 0.998\text{ g cm}^{-3}}{2} = 72.8\text{ dynes cm}^{-1}$$

as the surface tension of the water against air, assuming that the contact angle is 0° and that ρ_{air} is negligible compared to ρ_{H_2O}.

Some typical values of surface tension are given in Table 32.1. Note that the surface tension always drops as T increases; at the critical temperature, $\gamma = 0$. This is consistent with the idea that, as the total energy of the molecules increases

Table 32.1 Surface tensions (dynes/cm or ergs/cm²) of some liquids *(upper)*, and as a function of *T* *(lower)*.

Substance	T (°C) 0	10	20	25	40	60	80	100	Against
Water	75.6		72.65		69.56	66.18	62.6	58.9	Air
$(C_2H_5)_2O$			17.0					8.0	Air
C_2H_5OH			22.3			19.0			Air
C_6H_6		30.2	28.9			23.7			Air
Mercury				48.4					$Hg_{(g)}$

	Substance (against) NaCl(air)	AgCl(air)	NaF(air)	Na(Ar)	$Ag(H_2)$	Ni(Ni)
γ[T(°C)]	94[1080]	125[452]	200[1010]	206[110]	900[1000]	1700[1470]

with temperature, the potential energy difference between bulk, surface, and gaseous molecules gets less and less.

It is interesting to note that, though there is a rough parallelism between volatility and surface tension, it is by no means exact. Volatility measures the relative tendency to enter the gas phase as opposed to the liquid phase. Surface tension measures the tendency to enter the surface as opposed to the bulk liquid.

We note that the surface tension varies from about 10 to 2000 ergs/cm^2. What does this mean in terms of energy required to move a mole of molecules into the surface? The small molecules we most commonly deal with have areas in the neighborhood of 10 Å^2 = 10^{-14} cm^2, and there are thus about 10^{14} molecules per square centimeter of surface. With a value of 10 ergs cm^{-2} (a rough value for γ for such molecules) we obtain 10^{-13} ergs per molecule, or about 1 kcal per mole. (See Appendix I for conversion factors.) Heats of vaporization are usually a few kilocalories per mole, and consequently the work or energy necessary to create a new surface averages about 10 to 50% of the energy necessary to free the molecule completely from the condensed phase. Such a figure should strike you as reasonable in terms of the proposed interpretation of surface work.

Exercise 32.2

Calculate the ratio of surface energy to energy of evaporation for cubical molecules in cubic packing. *Answer:* Cubical molecules in the bulk will be surrounded by six other molecules, in the surface by five others, in the gas by no others. If the interatomic energy per unit of surface remains constant (and neglecting differential entropy effects), the surface energy will be $\frac{1}{6}$ or 17% of the vaporization energy. This compares favorably with the values cited above.

SURFACE TENSION OF SMALL PARTICLES

For a long time it has been experimentally observed that small droplets of liquid have a higher vapor pressure than do large droplets and that small particles of solids have a higher solubility than do large particles. Thus a fine precipitate which runs through most filters may be made filterable by boiling. The tiny particles dissolve and reprecipitate out on the larger ones, and this process is hastened at the higher temperature. It was Kelvin, of Kelvin temperature fame, who first presented a mathematical formulation of the problem.

If a spherical particle of radius r grows to $r + dr$, the surface increases by $dA = d(4\pi r^2) = 8\pi r\, dr$. Thus

$$dG_{\text{surf}} = \gamma\, dA = \gamma(8\pi r\, dr) \tag{32.4}$$

The number of moles of added material is

$$dn = \frac{\rho}{M}\, dV = \frac{\rho}{M}\, d\,\frac{4\pi r^3}{3}$$

$$= \frac{(4\pi r^2\, dr)\rho}{M}$$

or

$$dr = \frac{M\, dn}{4\pi r^2 \rho}$$

Substituting into (32.4) gives

$$\frac{dG_{\text{surf}}}{dn} = \frac{2M\gamma}{r\rho} \tag{32.5}$$

Since the free energy of the surface changes, as in Equation (32.5), the free energy of the gas must also change if equilibrium is to be maintained. We have an appropriate relation (assuming ideal gas) in Equation (27.17). If P = pressure of a droplet of radius r, and P_0 = pressure of a flat surface of liquid ($r = \infty$),

$$dG_{\text{gas}} = (\Delta\overline{G}\, dn)_{\text{gas}} = \left(RT \ln \frac{P}{P_0}\right) dn$$

The two changes in free energy must be equal for equilibrium to be maintained; thus

$$dG_{\text{surf}} = dG_{\text{gas}}$$

$$\frac{2M\gamma\, dn}{r\rho} = \left(RT \ln \frac{P}{P_0}\right) dn$$

or,

$$\ln \frac{P}{P_0} = \frac{2M\gamma}{RTr\rho} \tag{32.6}$$

This equation assumes that both γ and ρ are independent of r. A similar relation between r and the logarithm of the solubility holds for crystals in equilibrium with a saturated solution.

Results of calculations using Equation (32.6) are given in Table 32.2 and schematically plotted in Figure 32.4. Note that the equation holds both for positive curvature of the liquid surface (liquid drops surrounded by gas phase) and negative curvature (gas bubbles surrounded by liquid) when the signs are appropriately adjusted. Thus the properties of bubbles are also useful in determining surface tensions. At total pressures slightly lower than the equilibrium vapor pressure at any T, large bubbles tend to grow but small bubbles tend to collapse—making nucleation of small bubbles unlikely.

Table 32.2 Gaseous pressure of water in equilibrium with water surfaces of various radii. $T = 25°C$, $P_0 = 23.756$ mm.

Water	Radius (cm)			
	10^{-4}	10^{-5}	10^{-6}	10^{-7}
Drops				
P/P_0	1.001	1.011	1.111	2.88
Approximate number of molecules in drops	10^{11}	10^{8}	10^{5}	10^{2}
Approximate percent of molecules in surface	0.1	1	10	80
Bubbles				
P/P_0	0.999	0.989	0.901	0.348

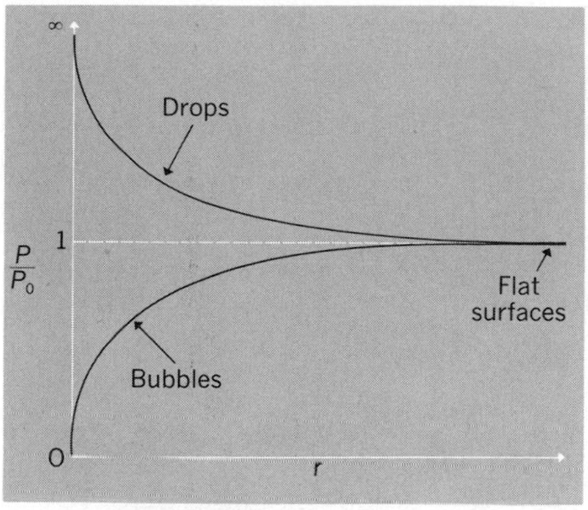

Figure 32.4 Schematic variation of (P/P_0) with r at constant T for liquid drops and gaseous bubbles. Note that small drops have high values for their vapor pressure, and small bubbles have low vapor pressure at the same value of T. Thus it is improbable that gases will condense to liquids or that liquids will boil if the initial phase is very pure.

NUCLEATION OF PHASE CHANGES

Figure 32.4 indicates why gases tend to supersaturate. It also indicates why liquids tend to superheat. In both of these phase changes, it is difficult to form the initial small nucleus of molecules on which further growth of the new phase may occur. Cloud seeding to increase rain is a large-scale practical example of a method of enhancing nucleation. It may interest you to know that there is as yet no acceptable theory for either boiling of liquids or condensation of gases, since nucleation phenomena are not yet understood.

Nucleation can be a very real problem in highly purified materials, but most materials contain small particles of contaminants that can serve as nuclei. This is routinely assured in the laboratory by adding "boiling chips" to encourage smooth nucleation and boiling in liquids (see Figure 32.5). Figure 32.6 shows a beautiful example of nucleation in a solution to crystal transition.

A dramatic example of undercooling and lack of nucleation was found a few years ago in fish caught at the bottom of the Hebron Fjord in Labrador. Their body temperature was $-1.7°C$, yet the freezing point of their blood was $-0.7°C$. They can exist in the deep water since there is no ice there to nucleate. When they are brought to the surface and touched with a piece of ice, freezing propagates from the point of contact and they die.

Figure 32.5 Boiling chips act as nuclei for bubble formation. Good boiling chips are not wet by the surrounding liquid (have high interfacial tensions) and are rough (providing many sites at which small bubbles nucleate).

Figure 32.6 Nucleation in the silicone polymer

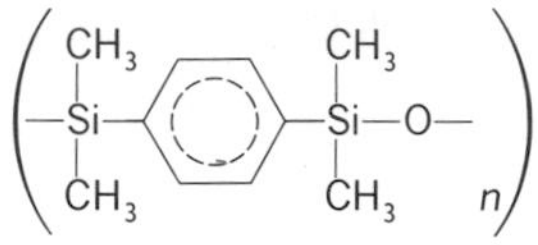

initiated at two separate times; hence the two different sized clumps of crystals. See also the dust jacket of this book. [Courtesy of Fraser P. Price, Research and Development Center, General Electric Co., Schenectady, N.Y.]

THE NATURE OF SURFACES

The evidence is now overwhelming that the surfaces of calm liquids are readily reproducible and almost perfectly smooth at the molecular level. The "bumps" caused by the continual vaporization and condensation of molecules are quickly smoothed. Dramatic evidence for this smoothness may be obtained from surface-film experiments similar to those shown in Figure 32.7 and Table 32.3.

Figure 32.8 presents even more direct evidence in the form of an electron photomicrograph of a metal-shadowed aqueous surface. Stearic acid is not readily soluble in water, but its —COOH group is, so the acid molecules stand in a monolayer on the water surface with the —COOH group immersed in the water. The stearic acid is not only spread smoothly in monolayer form, but the sections of the monolayer are circular, thus minimizing their own edge surface. The water surface is not only flat; it offers an almost frictionless plane on which the stearic acid molecules can skid about to form the almost perfect discs. Do you see why discs, rather than squares or some other shape, form?

The surfaces of crystals and other rigid media are normally much rougher than those of liquids and may easily be made very rough indeed. This may be confirmed by electron photomicrographs. Very flat crystal surfaces may be prepared if great care is taken in cleaving the crystal and if the surface is then cautiously etched with an appropriate solvent. But by the very structure of crystals, no crystalline sphere can have a truly smooth surface. Furthermore, the rigidity of crystals, resulting from the high symmetry and the strong forces often acting, ensures that the rate of thermal smoothing of crystalline surfaces will be much

Moles stearic acid = $3.72 \cdot 10^{-7}$
Diameter of "clear" circle = 25 cm
Length of stearic acid molecule = 24 Å
Area per molecule

$$= \frac{\pi \cdot 25^2\ \text{cm}^2 \cdot 10^{-16}\ \text{Å}^2\ \text{cm}^{-2}}{4 \cdot 3.72 \cdot 10^{-7}\ \text{moles} \cdot 6.02 \cdot 10^{23}\ \text{molecules moles}^{-1}} = 22\ \text{Å}$$

Figure 32.7 A surface film experiment. Talcum powder is first dusted on a clean water surface. A drop of benzene containing a known number of moles of a long-chain organic acid is then gently placed on the surface. The benzene quickly evaporates and the talcum powder recedes from the added drop, leaving an apparently clear circular area. Calculations using the known number of added acid molecules and their known length (from X-ray crystal data) give figures for the average area occupied by each molecule. These figures (about 20 Å²) correspond to the cross sections found in crystals and indicate that the surface is smooth and covered with a monomolecular layer of acid molecules standing almost perpendicular to the surface (see Table 32.3).

lower than that for fluid liquids. As a first approximation we can assume that no smoothing at all occurs unless the temperature approaches that of the melting point. As the melting point is approached, however, the mobility of surface atoms becomes appreciable. Crystal imperfections tend to disappear, the most stable faces (lowest surface tension) grow at the expense of the less stable faces (see Figure 32.9), and neighboring crystals may even grow together or "sinter" to form a single crystal. Some common surface imperfections are shown in Figure 32.10. Changes tend to propagate from such imperfections.

Exercise 32.3

Rationalize the observation that bulk metals are shiny and of different colors whereas metallic powders are all black. *Answer:* Shininess is due to reflected light, but no

Table 32.3 Cross-sectional areas obtained from surface film experiments.

Substance	Formula	Area (Å²)[a]
Palmitic acid	$C_{15}H_{31}COOH$	21
Stearic acid	$C_{17}H_{35}COOH$	22
Cerotic acid	$C_{25}H_{51}COOH$	25
Cetyl alcohol	$C_{16}H_{33}OH$	21
Myricyl alcohol	$C_{30}H_{61}OH$	27

SOURCE: Ketelle and Boyd, *J. Am. Chem. Soc.*, **69,** 2808 (1947).
[a] The slight increase in area with increasing chain length may be due to additional thermal motion in the longer chains or to an increasing tendency to incline at an angle to the surface rather than remain perpendicular to it. Why do the molecules tend to stand perpendicular to the water surface?

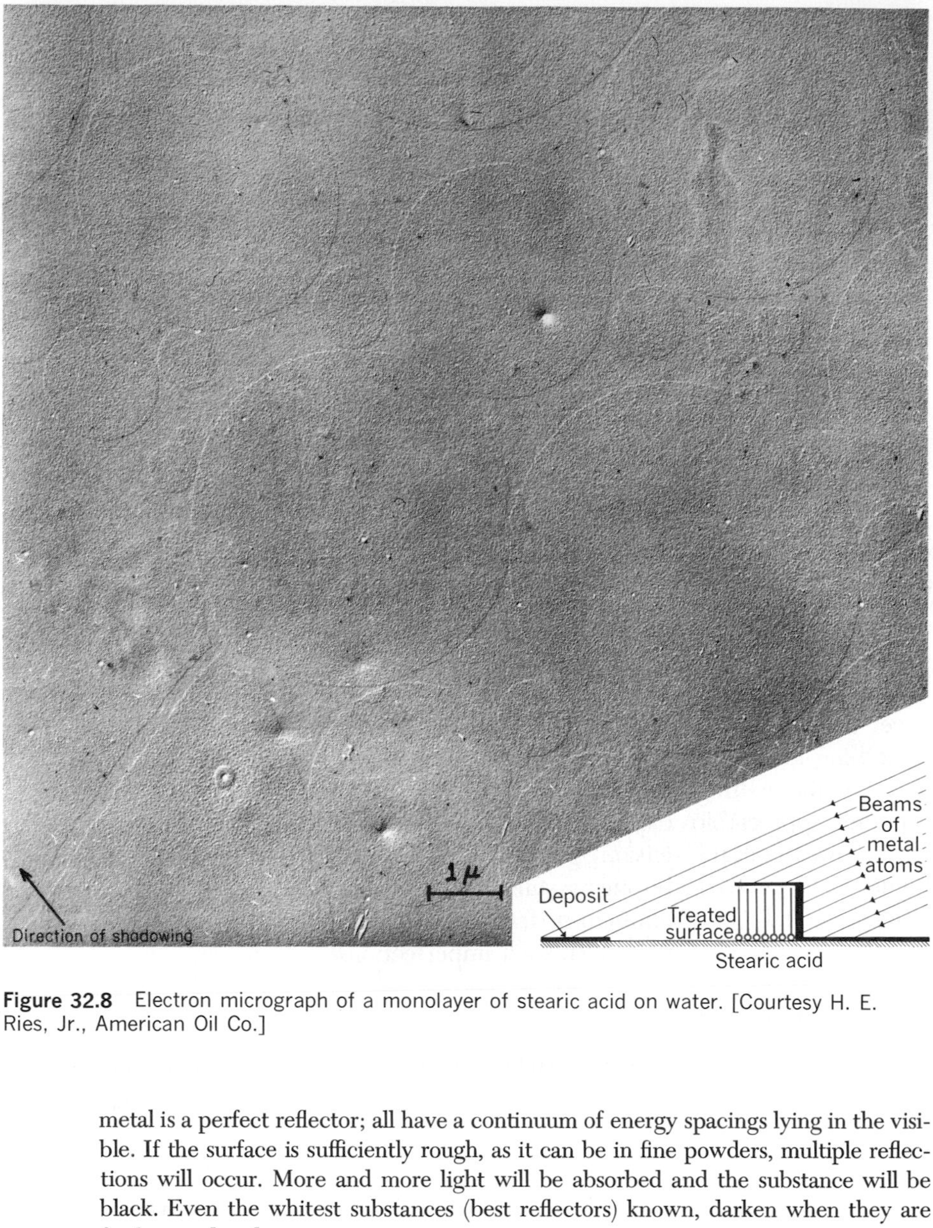

Figure 32.8 Electron micrograph of a monolayer of stearic acid on water. [Courtesy H. E. Ries, Jr., American Oil Co.]

metal is a perfect reflector; all have a continuum of energy spacings lying in the visible. If the surface is sufficiently rough, as it can be in fine powders, multiple reflections will occur. More and more light will be absorbed and the substance will be black. Even the whitest substances (best reflectors) known, darken when they are finely powdered.

SURFACE-ACTIVE AGENTS: DETERGENTS

A common problem with surfaces is that of removing unwanted material from them and leaving them clean. The material may be dirt on your skin, grease on your clothes, oil on a machine part, or oxide on a metal. The fact that the surface is covered indicates a relatively low interfacial tension between the contaminant and the surface—the two stick to each other. They may be separated by mechani-

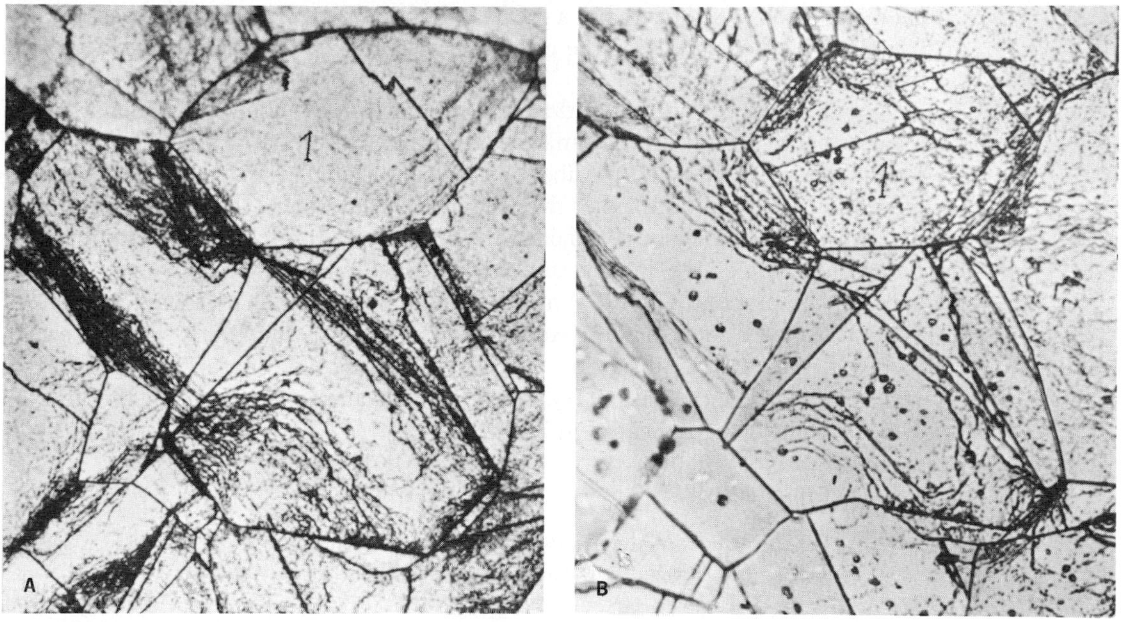

Figure 32.9 Photograph (×595) of a polycrystalline sample of brass (65% Cu, 35% Zn). (**A**) Before annealing. (**B**) After annealing for two hours at 500°C, polishing to dissolve 5 μ, annealing at 600°C for 45 minutes, and repolishing to dissolve 6 μ. Note the general smoothing of the surfaces and the growth of some crystal faces at the expense of others. Note also that some interfaces are quite stable. [P. Jacquet, *Compt. Rend.*, **237**, 1248 (1963), *Acta Met.*, **2**, 752, 770 (1954).]

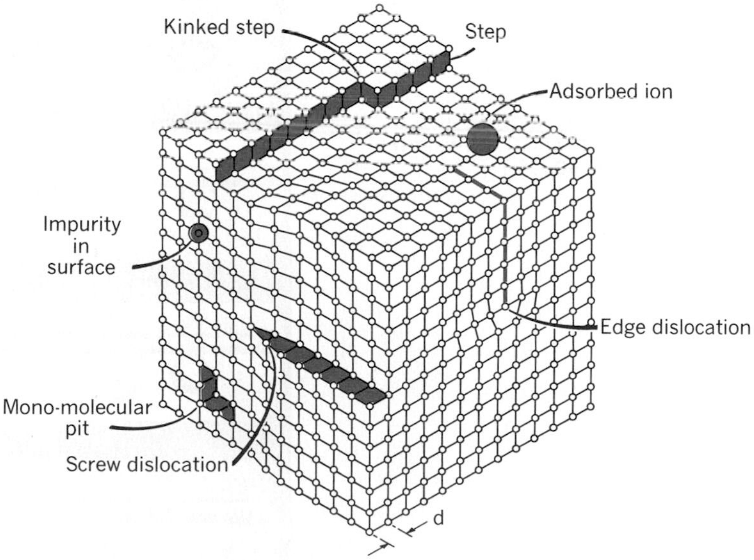

Figure 32.10 Surface imperfections on a crystal.

cal means such as scouring, but a great deal of energy will be dissipated as friction. Chemical methods, utilizing the concepts of surface energy and surface work, are often more efficient.

Figure 32.11 provides dramatic photographic evidence of the working of a surface-active agent in the removal of oil. Originally the oil coats the fiber surface. A detergent that wets the fiber better than the oil does is added (the detergent-fiber interfacial tension is lower than the oil-fiber interfacial tension). The oil starts to form drops and eventually falls off the fiber. It is probably also true that the detergent changes the interfacial tension of the oil with respect to air, further assisting the process. The usual mechanism of this action is explained in terms of "double-ended" detergent molecules. One end has polar bonds like those of a carboxyl, —COOH, or a sulfate, $—OSO_3H$; the other end has nonpolar bonds, as in a hydrocarbon radical, $C_nH_{2n+1}^-$. The mechanism of action on the fiber-oil system might be as indicated in Figure 32.12.

Exercise 32.4

Sodium lauryl sulfate, $C_{12}H_{25}OSO_3Na$, is a much better detergent than is sodium sulfate, $NaOSO_3Na$. Rationalize this observation. *Answer:* Na_2SO_4, in contact with

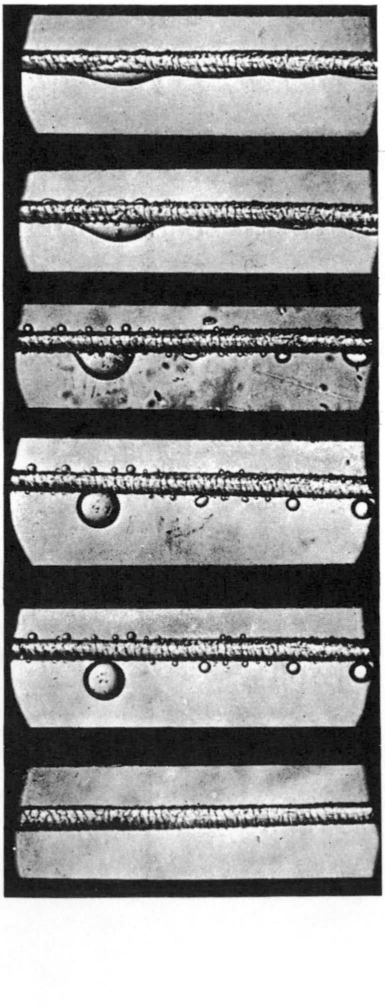

Figure 32.11 Detergent action in removing oil from fibers. [R. C. Palmer, *J. Soc. Chem. Ind.*, **60**, 59.]

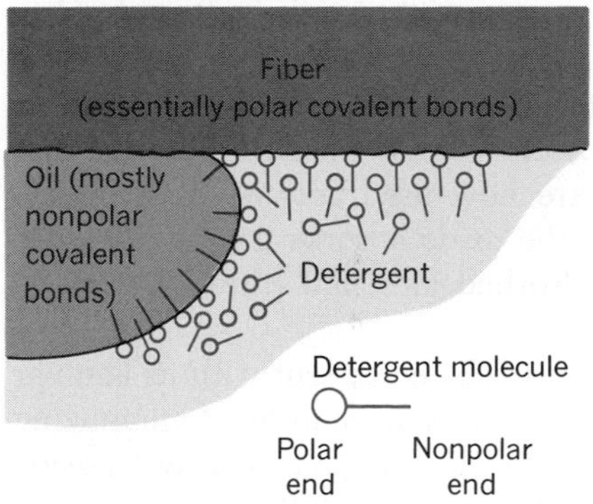

Figure 32.12 Possible mechanism of detergent action. In the competition for interfacial contact and the tendency to minimize total surface forces, the strong forces between polar detergent and polar fiber plus those between nonpolar detergent and nonpolar oil overwhelm the weaker forces between polar fiber and nonpolar oil. The fiber-oil surface diminishes and the fiber and oil both become covered with a detergent-air interface.

water, will give $Na^+_{(aq)}$ and $SO_4{}^{=}{}_{(aq)}$, both of relatively large charge density and strongly aquated. The lauryl compound will give $Na^+_{(aq)}$ and $C_{12}H_{25}OSO_3{}^-$. The lauryl cation consists of a long, essentially electrically neutral hydrocarbon chain which is readily soluble in oils (and other nonpolar media) while the $—OSO_3{}^-$ end remains in the water. The resulting bridge between the two phases leads to detergent action.

LUBRICANTS

One of the great problems in an industrial society is maintaining motion of solid materials in contact with one another; gears, axles, wheels, pulleys, runners, valves, and pistons are typical examples. It was early noted that two identical surfaces tended to stick more firmly, or slide less freely, than two different surfaces. Brass surfaces tend to "seize" on other brass surfaces, as does steel on steel or wood on wood. Your knowledge of crystal structure should allow you to interpret this. After all, if the atoms in two surfaces have the same symmetry and bonding forces, they will match and exert strong attractive forces on one another—they will "seize," as does brass on brass. But because a brass surface is not so likely to match a steel surface at the atomic level, attractive forces will be less and the coefficient of friction less.

It was discovered by the ancients that liquids lubricate solid-solid movement. Prehistoric people did phenomenal jobs of moving very massive objects weighing tens of tons many miles (as at Stonehenge, Easter Island, Egypt, ancient Greece, and many other places). Such accomplishments would have been impossible without some use of liquid lubricants, water at least, to provide flow and cooling at the interfaces.

Modern lubricants are designed for particular surfaces and for specialized working conditions of pressure, temperature, and surrounding materials. Many simple lubricants for metals are calcium salts of fatty acids, such as calcium stearate. Apparently these greases form salts with the metal surface to be lubricated, providing a set of hydrocarbon surfaces that prevent the metal surfaces from coming into contact; they slide readily over one another because of their weak van der Waals forces. Modern technology spans an ever-increasing range of temperatures and pressures, requiring continued search into the fundamental nature of surface reactions to provide the necessary lubricants for new conditions.

Aluminum is a cheap metal with low density and high conductivity but has been excluded from many uses because it was difficult to lubricate. The problem has now been minimized by the discovery that the metal strongly adsorbs ethylene, C_2H_4, and that aluminum oxide strongly adsorbs esters. Lubricants containing vinyl stearate, $CH_3(CH_2)_{16}COOCH{=}CH_2$, are now used and work very well. Exposed metal adsorbs the $CH{=}CH_2$ group, the oxide adsorbs the COO group. Both surfaces become covered with tightly adsorbed lubricant [the $CH_3(CH_2)_{16}$ group] and seizing is minimized.

Graphite is a good lubricant under light loads, consistent with its laminar crystal structure. But recall the discussion (p. 386) of its mechanism of minimizing friction with itself. In a similar fashion, many metals may glide primarily on oxide coatings (see p. 418). Others, including some otherwise difficult to machine, can form crystalline lamellar iodides containing planes of iodide atoms. Lubrication of these metals with liquids containing iodine forms a tough surface coating of the lamellar iodide which prevents seizing.

Exercise 32.5

What properties should a ski wax have? *Answer:* The wax must bond to the ski and have a coefficient of friction that provides maximum speed but retains control of direction. The more the wax bonds to ice, the more snow adheres to the ski. The less the wax bonds to ice, the less the skier can control his progress. If the bonds are of the van der Waals type, they will be weak; if hydrogen bonds, they will be stronger; if ionic forces exist, the bonding will be still stronger. The bonding between the wax and the ski will almost certainly contain hydrogen bonds because of the carbohydrate nature of wood and the necessity that the wax stick to the ski.

CORROSION

One of the greatest technical problems facing man and his society is that of corrosion. Billions of dollars of damage are done every year and other billions are spent to minimize the destruction it causes. The simplest preventative technique, since this is clearly a surface problem, is to cover a surface with paint, grease, plating, paper, or even a tarpaulin. Clearly these are all temporizing measures that replace one surface with another, counting on the second surface to be more resistant to corrosion or at least cheaper to replace.

The forms of corrosion include all possible interactions. Some examples are the pounding of waves on beaches, piers, and ships (combination of frictional wear and solution in water), the action of air and water on iron alloys (chemical oxidation), the flaking and powdering of paint (combination of effects of sunlight, air, and water), the pitting of glass (friction of small particles plus dissolving action of water), and the erosion of rocket nozzles (high temperatures and very reactive surroundings).

It is probable that water and oxygen are the two most corrosive substances in terms of actual damage caused annually. (However, review the discussion starting on page 418.) This is quite reasonable in terms of the ubiquitous occurrence of these two substances (all exposed surfaces are continually bombarded by H_2O and O_2), as well as their wealth of possible reactions. The next most damaging substances are probably salt and carbon dioxide, for very similar reasons. Why do surfaces interact so strongly with these substances that they corrode? We shall discuss first one of the most widespread types of corrosion—rusting—and then consider the nature of surface reactions in greater detail.

Exercise 32.6

Car bodies rust away much faster in Chicago than in Phoenix. Suggest a reason. *Answer:* Phoenix is much drier, both in humidity and in rainfall, and water is necessary for rusting. Furthermore, many northern cities sprinkle salt (NaCl or $CaCl_2$) on their streets in order to melt ice. The resulting ionic solutions corrode iron by electrolytic action.

RUSTING

Iron is a bright shiny metal almost as lustrous as silver, but we seldom see it in this form, although iron objects that are carefully polished and then stored in a dry place will remain shiny indefinitely. But if they are marked by fingerprints or exposed to air and water, they quickly become covered with rust at those spots. There is no stoichiometric formula for rust (as discussed on p. 418), but it can be identified as $Fe_2O_3 \cdot nH_2O$. It then becomes clear why oxygen and water are necessary for rusting, but not why this substance forms instead of Fe_2O_3 or Fe_3O_4, both very stable compounds. (As a matter of fact it is Fe_3O_4 that forms if iron is heated in air, thus accounting for the black iron pipe which comes directly out of hot-pipe mills. We shall not here investigate the thermodynamics of iron oxidation, but an examination of Figure 29.7 is informative.)

Since the exact nature of rust is not known, it is not surprising that the exact nature of rusting is not known either, in spite of much research. But the following experimental facts are well established. (1) The reaction is accelerated by the presence of inert electrolytes in the water—inert in the sense that they do not enter into net reactions. (2) The reaction is also accelerated by certain anions, including Cl^-. (3) The reaction is slowed down by the presence of any of a large number of anions, including phosphate, $PO_4^{\equiv}$, and $CrO_4^{=}$. (4) The reaction is catalyzed by acids and slowed down by bases. (5) Stressed iron corrodes more rapidly than do single crystals. (6) Iron away from air-water interfaces—under rivet heads, for example—corrodes faster than iron near an air-water interface.

The net reaction

$$2Fe_{(c)} + \tfrac{3}{2}O_{2(g)} + nH_2O_{(l)} = Fe_2O_3 \cdot nH_2O_{(c)}$$

is far too complicated to constitute a mechanistic step, but it does show that both oxidation of the iron to Fe^{+3} and hydrolysis must occur in the process. The simplest first approach to a mechanism might be to assume that redox half-reactions were involved, followed by precipitation and rust formation.

Reduction: $O_{2(g)} + 2H_2O_{(l)} + 4e^- = 4OH^-_{(aq)}$

Oxidation: $\begin{cases} Fe_{(c)} = Fe^{++}_{(aq)} + 2e^- \\ Fe^{++}_{(aq)} = Fe^{+++}_{(aq)} + e^- \end{cases}$

Precipitation: $Fe^{+++}_{(aq)} + 3OH^-_{(aq)} = Fe(OH)_{3(s)}$

Rust formation: $2Fe(OH)_{3(s)} + (n - 3)H_2O = Fe_2O_3 \cdot nH_2O_{(s)}$

These steps are not to be considered a mechanism, only possible net processes. Another possible set of processes differs in that $Fe(OH)_2$ forms, then is oxidized.

Reduction:	$O_{2(g)} + 2H_2O_{(l)} + 4e^- = 4OH^-_{(aq)}$
Oxidation:	$Fe_{(c)} = Fe^{++}_{(aq)} + 2e^-$
Precipitation:	$Fe^{++}_{(aq)} + 2OH^-_{(aq)} + 2OH^-_{(aq)} = Fe(OH)_{2(s)}$
Further oxidation:	$Fe(OH)_{2(s)} + \frac{1}{4}O_{2(g)} + \frac{1}{2}H_2O_{(l)} = Fe(OH)_{3(s)}$
Rust formation:	$2Fe(OH)_{3(s)} + (n - 3)H_2O_{(l)} = Fe_2O_3 \cdot nH_2O_{(s)}$

Other possible processes are known but those above allow at least partial interpretations of all the experimental data mentioned.

1. The reaction is accelerated by inert electrolytes—the half-reactions involving oxidation of iron and reduction of oxygen can occur at widely separated points, setting up an electric cell (see pp. 474–479). The presence of an electrolyte allows greater ionic currents to flow in the solution, and hence speeds the corrosion.

2. Acceleration by Cl^- and similar ions is due to complex ion formation with the Fe^{++} and/or Fe^{+++} (Lewis acid-base reaction; see p. 430), lowering the chemical potential of the iron ions and making the free-energy change for the oxidation more negative.

3. The cations which slow the corrosion—$PO_4^{\equiv}$, $CrO_4^{=}$, OH^-—form insoluble compounds or tightly bonded surface compounds with iron, and so protect the surface from further oxidation. These ions act like a monomolecular paint. Iron is almost free from corrosion in strongly basic solutions, for example, partly because OH^- ions coat the iron surface and protect it.

4. Catalysis by acids may be due to the oxidizing nature of acids ($H^+_{(aq)} + e^- = \frac{1}{2}H_{2(g)}$) plus the fact that they tend to keep the protective hydroxide coatings from forming.

5. Stressed iron surfaces contain iron atoms that are more reactive (have a higher chemical potential), since they have a higher surface energy (possibly are more exposed to attack).

6. Iron away from the air-water interface cannot become covered with a protective hydroxide coating, since the hydroxide ions form where the oxygen is, at the air-water interface. Thus the iron oxidizes and the resulting ions leave the corroding surface before finding hydroxide to precipitate them.

Note that the suggested processes depend very much on electrochemical principles and on the rates at which various substances reach the corroding surface. The processes by which substances move through solutions are called diffusional processes, and reactions whose rates depend on diffusion processes are said to be diffusion-controlled. Under many circumstances surface reactions are diffusion-controlled. The slow step is bringing the potential reactants together. The actual interchange of electrons or atoms, or the growth of a precipitate, is often rapid compared to the rates of diffusion.

The usual methods of protecting iron and other metal surfaces are also consistent with the processes discussed. The methods are to cover the surface (paint, grease, galvanize with zinc, tin plate, sherardize [phosphate treatment]);

maintain a high electron potential in the iron (connect the metal to a zinc, magnesium, or aluminum ingot, each of which will oxidize more readily than the iron, while reducing back to metallic iron any ferrous ions that form); exclude oxygen (gasoline and petroleum storage tanks); exclude chloride and similar ions; or keep the total ionic content of the solution as low as possible.

Exercise 32.7

Write net equations illustrating how chunks of magnesium fastened to the hull of a ship minimize corrosion. *Answer:* Ship hulls are mainly iron, which may oxidize according to the half-reaction $Fe_{(c)} = Fe^{++}{}_{(aq)} + 2e^-$, $\mathcal{E}^0 = 0.440$ volts. Magnesium metal oxidizes as in $Mg_{(c)} = Mg^{++}{}_{(aq)} + 2e^-$, $\mathcal{E}^0 = 2.375$ volts. When the iron and magnesium are in electrical contact, electrons can readily flow from the magnesium to the iron. The higher oxidation potential of the Mg thus tends to keep the iron supplied with electrons and so reduces its tendency to corrode (be oxidized). The magnesium, of course, corrodes quite rapidly but can be replaced and does not contribute to the strength of the hull.

CRYSTAL FACES AND SURFACE REACTIONS

Figure 32.13,A shows a remarkable example of differential surface reactions, using a spherical single crystal—copper in 10 mm of oxygen for 10 minutes at 250°C. The cubic symmetry of the crystal is apparent (note the four three fold axes) as is also the fact that the rate of reaction varies greatly from crystal face to crystal face. Figure 32.13,B shows data determined in a similar manner over a longer period of time for a single copper crystal at 178°C. The initial rates vary remarkably with

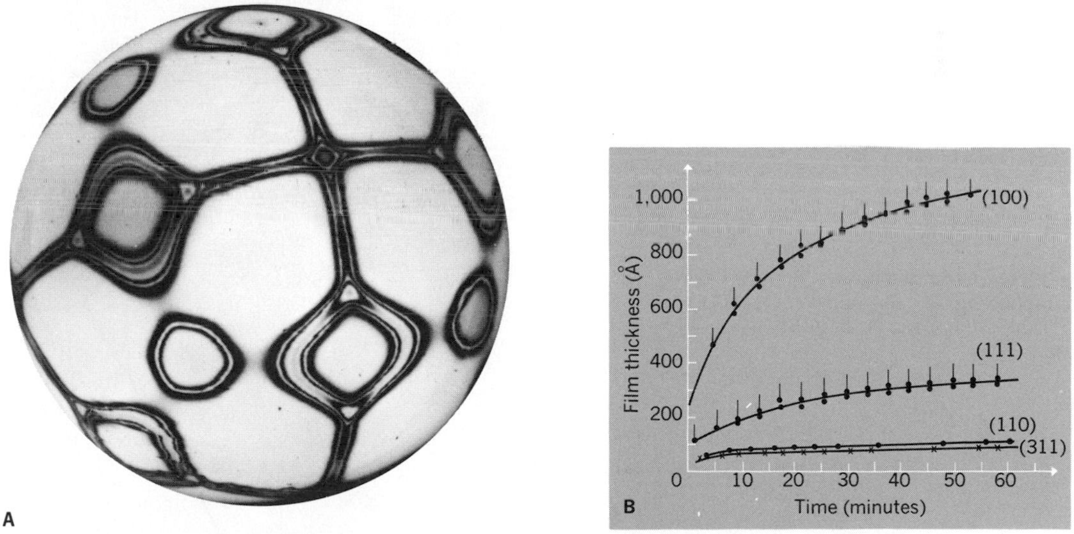

A

Figure 32.13 (**A**) Interference color pattern on a single copper crystal oxidized in an oxygen pressure of 10 torr for about 10 minutes at 250° C. (**B**) Oxidation of four faces of a single copper crystal at 178° C. Thickness versus time. [A. T. Gwathmey and K. R. Lawless, "Influence of Orientation on Oxidation," in *The Surface Chemistry of Metals and Semiconductors,* Wiley, 1960.]

crystal symmetry, but, as might be anticipated, all seem to approach zero rate as the film thickness increases.

CRYSTAL GROWTH

Figure 32.14 shows a shadowed electron photomicrograph of a small crystal of a paraffin hydrocarbon. The crystal growth steps are clear. It is also clear that there is really a single spiral step whose inner end terminates at a crystal imperfection where crystal growth initiates. Additional molecules add to the crystal by fitting into the kinks generated by the spirals as they originate at the imperfection and grow away from it. It is now clear that a great many crystals, probably all, grow from such imperfections. Note that this resolves the problem of a rapidly increasing tendency to escape as particle size grows smaller, as presented in Figure 32.4 and summarized in the Kelvin equation. Spontaneous nucleation of a perfect crystal in a pure phase seldom, if ever, occurs. Growth always nucleates on an impurity or possibly an imperfect aggregate of molecules, and continues from there. The imperfections from which spiral growth occurs are known as screw dislocations (illustrated in Figure 32.10). Many surface properties are interpretable in terms of screw dislocations.

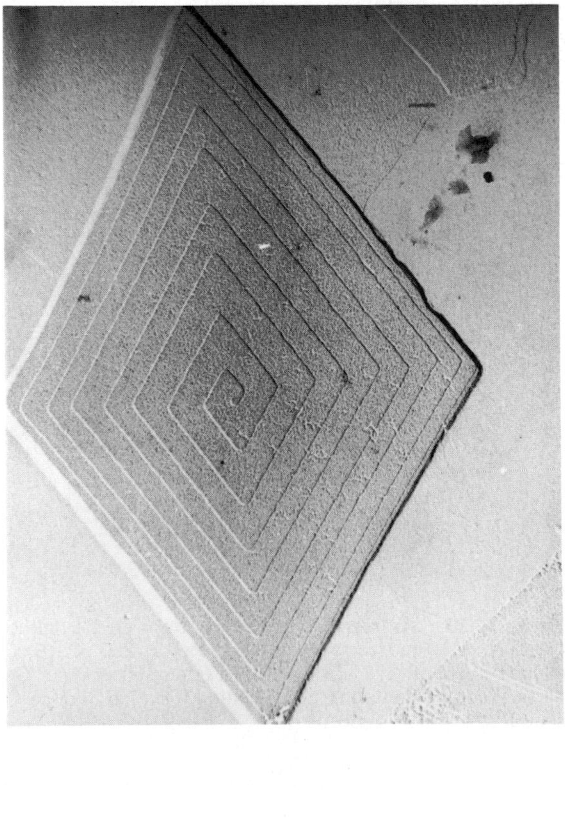

Figure 32.14 Growth spiral on paraffin $C_{36}H_{74}$, photographed by Kay and Appelbe (×1500). [F. C. Frank, *Adv. Phys.*, **1**, 91 (1952).]

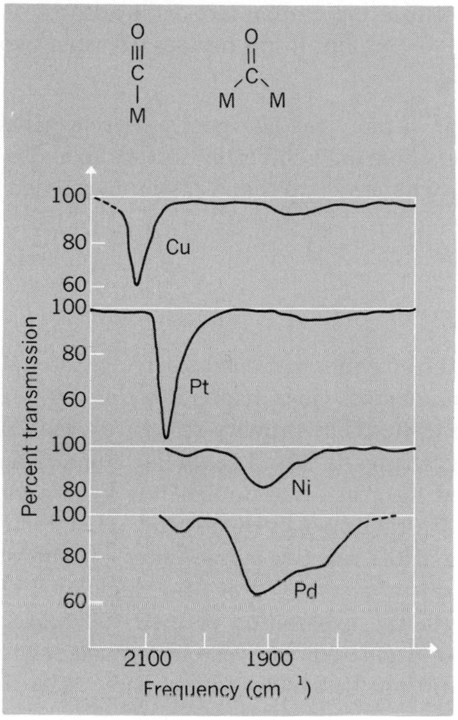

Figure 32.15 Spectra of carbon monoxide adsorbed on thin films of metals on silica. [R. P. Eischens, "Chemisorption and Catalysis," in *The Surface Chemistry of Metals and Semiconductors*, Wiley, 1960.]

HETEROGENEOUS CATALYSIS

We have mentioned many syntheses which proceed rapidly only in the presence of a solid-phase catalyst. Examples are ammonia (p. 266), synthesis gas (p. 267), and sulfur dioxide (p. 436).

The design of such catalysts is still primarily a matter of trial and error, but the number of trials (and the number of errors) is being rapidly decreased as more and more research is done on surface reactions.

It has been agreed for a long time that the catalyst surface adsorbs at least some of the reactant molecules and makes them more rapidly reactive, possibly by orienting them favorably for further reaction (enzymes almost certainly do this) and possibly by weakening some of the bonds, which then break more readily, resulting in a lower activation energy for the rate-determining step. Other effects are also discussed, but we will concentrate on these two possibilities.

That bond strengths are changed upon adsorption can now be directly demonstrated in many cases by taking the infrared spectra of the adsorbed molecules. Figure 32.15 shows the infrared absorption spectrum of carbon monoxide adsorbed on four different metals. The fact that there is any absorption of infrared radiation at all indicates that the bonds have changed appreciably, since gaseous CO is almost nonpolar and absorbs infrared only weakly at 2143 cm^{-1}. Organic ketones, on the other hand, absorb in the range of 1900 to 1600 cm^{-1}. Thus, if CO is adsorbed on copper, its bond frequency is only slightly changed, but the frequency on palladium, Pd, is almost that of the carbonyl group in ketones. The spectra in Figure 32.15 are interpreted to mean that carbon monoxide adsorbs on a single atom of copper or platinum as $\mathrm{M{-}C{\equiv}O}$, but forms bridges between two atoms of nickel or palladium as $\mathrm{M{-}\overset{\overset{O}{\|}}{C}{-}M}$, a more readily reactive species. It is therefore not surprising that nickel and palladium are good catalysts for the hydrogenation of carbon monoxide to methane, whereas copper and platinum are poor catalysts.

ENZYMES

A great many scientists are now exploring the enzymes that catalyze living systems. All known enzymes are long chains of α amino acids (see Chapter 40) coiled into a compact form and exposing certain reactive sites. The primary structure—that is, the sequence of amino acids in the long chain—is now known for some. The secondary structure—the general nature of the coil—is approximately known for several enzymes and should soon be well established by X-ray and other techniques. The tertiary structure—the nature of the reactive surface sites—is almost completely unknown. The search for these surface structures, the elucidation of their detailed mechanism of operation, and the exploration of their full role in living systems constitute one of the most exciting fields currently available to chemical research, a field that probably will not be exhausted for many years to come, if ever.

Exercise 32.8

What are the signs of ΔS, ΔG, and ΔH for adsorption of a gas on a crystal? *Answer:* ΔG must be negative for any spontaneous process; ΔS must be negative, since a gas molecule is condensing; therefore ΔH must be negative. The process of adsorption of gases on surfaces is always exothermic. Hence, from Le Châtelier's principle, this kind of equilibrium adsorption always decreases as T increases.

Exercise 32.9

If equilibrium adsorption always decreases as T increases, how is it that rates of heterogeneously catalyzed gas-phase reactions often increase as T increases? *Answer:* The activation energy for adsorption may be high, giving a low rate of adsorption at low T. Another possibility is that adsorption of one of the reactants is so complete at low T that there is no surface left to adsorb further reactant and so no reaction occurs. Note, however, that all heterogeneous catalysis will decrease in effectiveness at very high values of T because of fall-off in adsorbed species.

ELECTRIC DOUBLE LAYERS

An interesting surface reaction, which depends on equilibrium rather than rate, is found in the exchange equilibria between surfaces and solutions. All substances tend to release a few ions into any surrounding medium, especially if the surrounding medium is polar, like water, and if the crystal is held together largely by ionic bonds. Equilibrium is, of course, always achieved most rapidly if a large interface is present between the two phases. Thus smooth glass dissolves very slowly indeed in water. Its appreciable solubility is, however, shown by the pink color that rapidly appears when powdered glass is added to neutral, aqueous phenolphthalein. One of the reasons the bulk glass does not dissolve rapidly is its three-dimensional structure in which sodium ions are embedded (see p. 643). When the sodium ions dissolve, the residual surface network is left negatively charged. This charge tends to hold the sodium ions in the vicinity and is an example of the formation of an electric double layer between a crystalline phase and a solution. Similar double layers always form when crystals are placed in contact with electrolytic solutions. The electric effects are especially strong if ions of one charge are more tightly held to the crystal surface than ions of the opposite charge. Figure 32.16 outlines one model of a double layer.

Many of the properties of crystalline particles suspended in fluids are strongly affected by these double layers. For example, addition of alum [$KAl(SO_4)_2 \cdot 12H_2O$] to muddy water leads to settling of the mud, because mud is normally composed of negatively charged particles (mud is a silicate) and these have their negative charge neutralized by adsorbing the high-charge density aluminum ions [$Al^{+++}{}_{(aq)}$] from the alum. The resulting electrically neutral particles stick together and settle out.

Electric double layers are common in biochemical systems, especially at cell walls. The clotting of blood is probably accompanied by loss of the electric charge which normally prevents clotting. Nerve impulses appear to be carried by a collapse and then a regeneration of a double layer parallel to the neuron axis, and muscle action seems also to involve variation in electric double layers.

Exercise 32.10

When concentrated aqeous $FeCl_3$ solution is added to hot water, a deep red-brown suspension is obtained. What is a probable composition of the solid formed (write a possible net equation) and what is the electrical charge on the solid side of the resulting double layers? *Answer:* $FeCl_{3(aq)} + 3H_2O = Fe(OH)_{3(c)} + 3H^+{}_{(aq)} + 3Cl^-{}_{(aq)}$ may well occur due to the increase in entropy on forming $H^+{}_{(aq)}$ and $Cl^-{}_{(aq)}$ plus the probable negative value of ΔH that is due to formation of $Fe(OH)_3$ with its strong

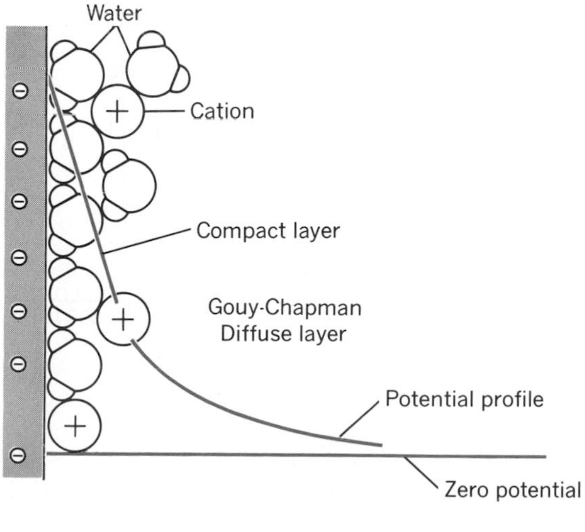

Figure 32.16 Potential profile in the double-layer according to Stern's model.

Fe—OH and hydrogen-bonding systems. Note that the $Fe(OH)_3$ will actually be aquated to $Fe(OH)_3 \cdot nH_2O$. The chances are great that the solid will have a positive charge, since it would be much more likely that Fe^{+++} would stick to it tightly than that OH^- or Cl^- would, consistent with the higher charge density of the Fe^{+++} ions.

ION EXCHANGE RESINS

Many naturally occurring silicates have the property of selectively adsorbing certain ions. Usually the adsorption becomes stronger and stronger as the positive charge density of the adsorbed ion increases. Many home water softeners work on this principle. Hardness in water is caused primarily by $Ca^{++}{}_{(aq)}$ and $Mg^{++}{}_{(aq)}$. If hard water is passed over a natural silicate called "zeolite," which has its surface covered with sodium ions, the dipositive ions replace the singly positive ions on the surface and are thus rendered innocuous, and the sodium ions enter the water phase.

Synthetic resins, some of which can adsorb positive ions and some adsorb negative ions, are now available. When water is passed through two such resins sequentially, the following reactions occur (R^- represents a negative resin and Q^+ a positive resin):

$$RH_{(c)} + M^+{}_{(aq)} = RM_{(c)} + H^+{}_{(aq)}$$
$$QOH_{(c)} + Y^-{}_{(aq)} = QY_{(c)} + OH^-{}_{(aq)}$$
$$H^+{}_{(aq)} + OH^-{}_{(aq)} = H_2O$$

Deionized water of very low conductivity may be produced in this way.

Modern resins can be made so selective that they can even be used to separate ions as similar in charge density as the rare earth ions or the lanthanide ions (see Figure 32.17). The ions are all initially adsorbed on the resin, much as

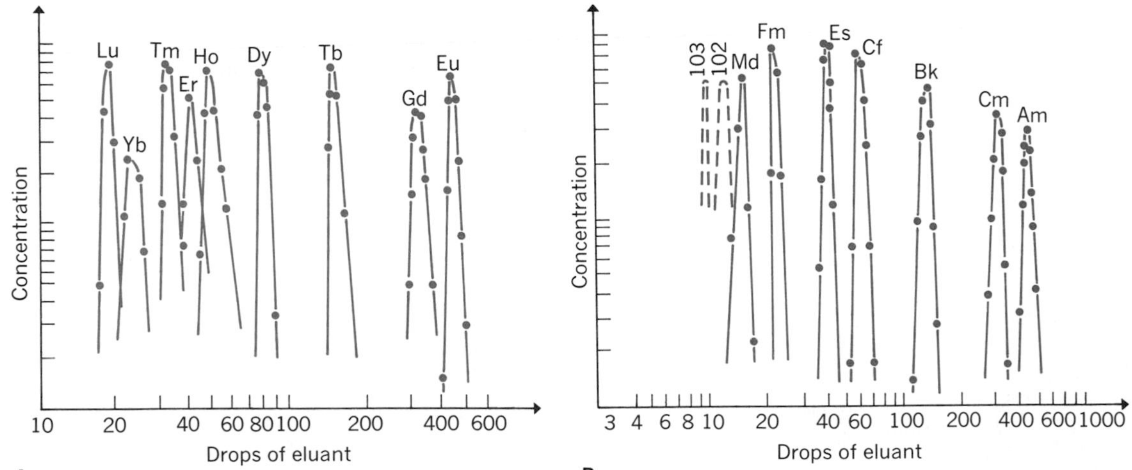

Figure 32.17 Elution of tripositive lanthanide and actinide ions from Dowex-50 ion-exchange resin with ammonium alpha-hydroxy-isobutyrate. The predicted positions for elements 102 and 103 are indicated by dotted lines. [G. T. Seaborg, *Man-Made Transuranium Elements,* Prentice-Hall, 1963.]

they are from hard water. A complexing agent, called an eluant, is then passed over the resin. The least tightly adsorbed ions, or the ones most readily complexed by the eluant, flow away in the first drops of eluant, to be followed by the more tightly adsorbed ions as the limited supply of eluant (here, the α-hydroxyisobutyrate ion) picks them off the surface in sequences of ion size. For example, first,

$$R^{-3}Lu^{+3}{}_{(aq)} + 3NH_4{}^+{}_{(aq)} + 4C_3H_7CHOHCO_2{}^-{}_{(aq)} = R^{-3}(NH_4{}^+)_3 + Lu(C_3H_7CHOHCO_2)_4{}^-{}_{(aq)}$$

followed in order by Yb, Tm, Er, and so on.

Exercise 32.11

Rationalize the observation (Figure 32.17) that the ions of smallest ionic radius—Lu, Yb, or Md, Fm—are released preferentially by the resin to the eluant. *Answer:* It is believed that all these M^{+++} ions hydrate strongly and that the ions of smaller ionic radius actually hydrate to a larger extent and so have a larger effective ionic size but a smaller effective charge density than do the ions of larger ionic radius. These more thoroughly hydrated ions are then held somewhat less tightly on the resin and are swept out in the first part of the eluant. Note the importance of the nature of the double layer in these cases.

ELECTRODE REACTION

Any two electrical conductors placed in a solution that can conduct electricity will generate electric double layers and an electric potential, as can be readily tested with a good voltmeter (see Figure 32.18). Even if the two conductors, such as copper strips, are cut from the same bar and the solution around each electrode is identical, a voltage will be noted, though it may drop to zero quickly. Zero voltage means, of course, that the free energy of the system is at a minimum, since $\Delta G = -n\mathfrak{F}\mathfrak{E}$.

Assuming that the two electrodes are of the same material and that a single electrolytic solution is used, the voltage is a measure of the difference in the surface energies, or crystal imperfections, in the two samples. When the surface energies become identical, the voltage will drop to zero. Even with the external voltage at zero it is still quite likely that surface reactions will continue to occur within each

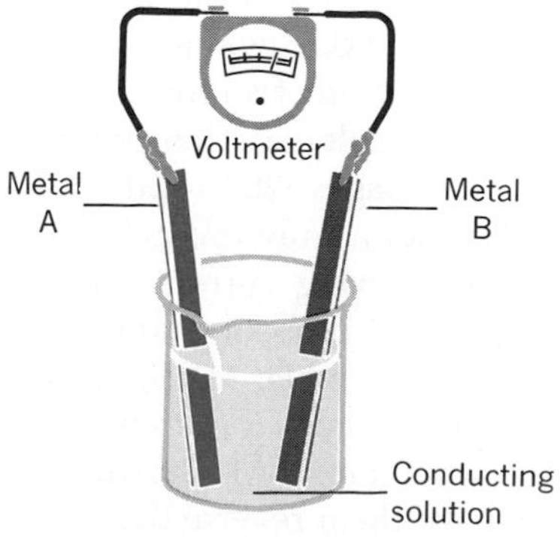

Figure 32.18 Any two pieces of metal placed in an electrically conducting solution will generate a voltage.

electrode, since it is most unlikely that the total surface of the electrode has the same type of atomic coverage. The more highly reactive atoms will tend to go into solution, leaving electrons on the electrode. These electrons will travel to parts of the electrode of lower surface energy and there convert ions from the solution into metal. The net effect is to transfer metal from the regions of high surface energy to regions of low surface energy, just as in surface smoothing of droplets.

We may minimize the effect of these surface irregularities for many metals by coating the surface with mercury. Mercury forms a liquid alloy, or amalgam, with many metals. Since liquid surfaces are readily reproducible, the amalgamated electrode may be used for work of high precision.

In many cases amalgamation is not possible. It is then necessary to prepare the electrode surfaces with great care. It is also usual to allow the electrodes to remain together in an appropriate electrolytic solution until the surface inhomogeneities have a chance to minimize, and thus have a negligible effect on the voltage measurements. In some cases these residual inhomogeneities may cause voltages of the order of hundredths of a volt, but ordinarily the differences can be decreased to less than a microvolt by the proper techniques.

Exercise 32.12

Plumbing lines composed of part iron and part copper piping rust out much more rapidly than all-copper or all-iron lines. Suggest an interpretation. *Answer:* The electrode potentials of iron and copper are quite different, the iron being the more readily oxidized. Thus the iron portions become the anode, the copper portions the cathode. Two effects enhance the corrosion: (1) oxidation is concentrated on the places where there is iron; (2) there is little chance for protective coatings to form on the iron, since reduction of oxygen to form OH^- is occurring far away from the iron.

REVERSIBLE AND IRREVERSIBLE ELECTRODES

Every driver of a car knows that leaving the lights on when the motor is not running "runs down the battery"; the lights may stay on undimmed for several hours and then rather suddenly flicker and go out. A check will show that the battery now has a voltage of zero, and must be renewed by "charging" it. The voltage returns to the value of two volts per cell expected in an operational car. Figure 32.19 represents cell voltage versus time for such a cycle. When the curves of the observed $\mathcal{E}$ versus moles of chemicals consumed follow the Nernst equation, we say that the cell is operating reversibly. Under these conditions the direction of all the changes in the cell can be reversed by an infinitesimal change in the voltage. (Compare the previous discussions of thermodynamic reversibility on pages 222 and 661–662.) Close study of the car battery will show that it is not a truly reversible cell in the thermodynamic sense. Turning on the lights or drawing current for any other purpose reduces the voltage measurably. (You have probably noted the marked dimming that occurs if you try to start the engine while the lights are turned on.) A reversible cell would not change voltage appreciably if current were drawn from it. But all actual cells do drop in voltage when current is drawn, and all actual cells require a somewhat higher voltage to make them reverse than they

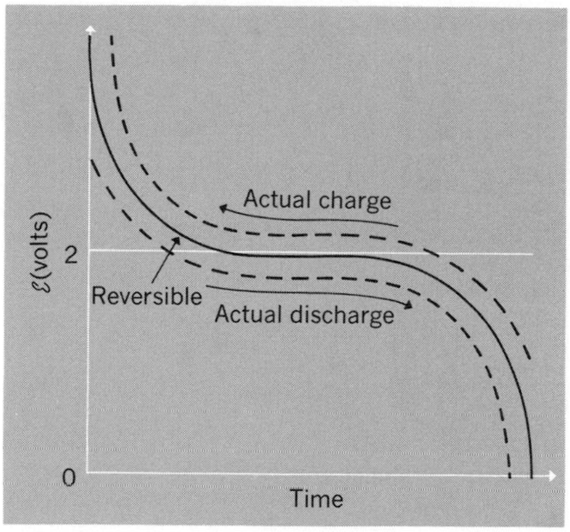

Figure 32.19 Discharge-charge cycle for a reversible and an actual cell.

will generate when operating spontaneously. Thus, all actual cells are irreversible in the sense that more energy must be expended in reversing them than they deliver spontaneously. The question arises—why?

Let us consider the changes that occur in a cell during charge and discharge and their effect on the voltage of the cell. We shall concentrate on the changes near the electrode surface, but shall need to consider briefly other changes as well.

Exercise 32.13

Automobile batteries sometimes freeze if an attempt is made to start a car with them in very cold weather. Account for this observation. *Answer:* The discharge process clearly has $\Delta G = -$. Electrical work or heat equal to $-\Delta H$ is accomplished outside the battery. $\Delta G = \Delta H - T\,\Delta S$, so heat equal to $-T\,\Delta S$ is generated inside the battery. Remember the discussion in Figure 29.1. Consider the net equation $Pb_{(c)} + PbO_{2(c)} + 2H^+_{(aq)} + 2HSO_4{}^-_{(aq)} = 2PbSO_{4(l)} + 2H_2O_{(l)}$. One would guess a small value of ΔS since moles of solid remain constant; $H^+ + HSO_4{}^-$ combine, but waters of hydration are freed. Since the battery freezes, the system must require energy from outside; thus $T\,\Delta S$ must be positive, which means that ΔS must be positive, but not large positive, consistent with our estimate. The approximate figures are $\Delta H = -86$ kcal, $\Delta S = 10$ eu, $\Delta G = -89$ kcal. It is the positive value of ΔS (and $T\,\Delta S$) which leads to freezing.

NET REACTIONS IN AN ELECTRIC CELL

We have already diagrammed some electric cells in Figures 20.1 and 20.2, so you are familiar with the general construction and necessary ingredients. Figure 32.20 is a similar diagrammatic figure of the cell most commonly used in car batteries—the lead storage cell. It consists of a container, an electrolyte, a porous barrier down the middle of the cell which permits ions and solvent to penetrate but minimizes gross mixing, two electrodes, and provision for electron flow through an external circuit.

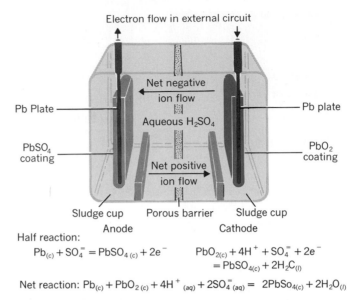

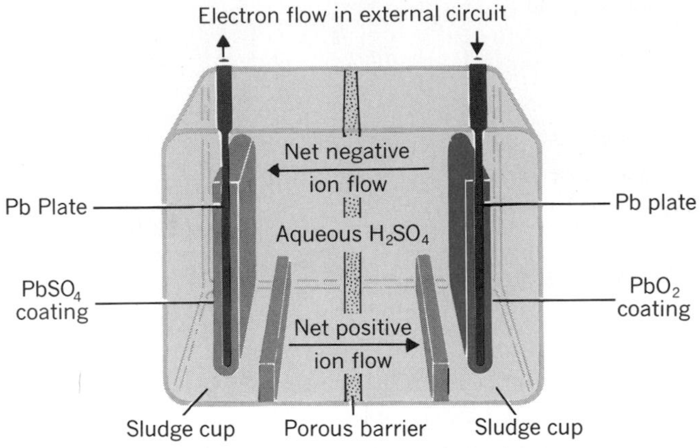

Anode | Cathode

Half reaction:

$Pb_{(c)} + SO_4^{=} = PbSO_{4\,(c)} + 2e^-$ $\qquad$ $PbO_{2(c)} + 4H^+ + SO_4^{=} + 2e^- = PbSO_{4(c)} + 2H_2C_{(l)}$

Net reaction: $Pb_{(c)} + PbO_{2\,(c)} + 4H^+{}_{(aq)} + 2SO_4^{=}{}_{(aq)} = 2PbSo_{4(c)} + 2H_2O_{(l)}$

Figure 32.20 Schematic representation of a lead storage battery and its operation during discharge. All reactions reverse during charge.

The net reactions at anode, cathode, and for the total cell are shown in Figure 32.20. Every cell involves an oxidation half-reaction and a reduction half-reaction. The oxidation half-reaction always occurs at the electrode called the anode and the reduction half-reaction at the cathode. In fact, these are the fundamental definitions of anode and cathode in electrochemistry.

Note also that there is a net decrease in negative charge in the electrical double layer around the anode during discharge. Similarly there is a net decrease in positive charge in the double layer around the cathode. This is true in all cells, as you should be able to prove from the fate of the electrons at the anode and cathode respectively. As these electrical double layers change, two related effects will occur. Consider their effect at the anode. (1) The potential of the double layer with respect to the solution will become more positive, tending to draw in negative ions and to repel positive ions, and so to counterbalance the decrease in negative charge caused by the electrode reactions. (2) The ion diffusion currents, which are merely the random thermal movements of the ions when the cell is at equilibrium, are upset in the sense that fewer negative ions will be diffusing away from the anode, since their concentration has been reduced by the electrode reaction. This will cause a net diffusion of negative ions toward the anode. Both these changes are, of course, consistent with Le Châtelier's principle.

Both effects cause a net movement of negative ions toward the anode. For this reason (motion toward the anode) negative ions are called anions. Likewise, both effects cause a net movement of positive ions (cations) toward the cathode. Please note that we are not intimating that there is an orderly procession of negative ions toward the anode and an orderly procession of positive ions toward the cathode. Rather, there is superimposed on the random thermal motions of the ions a small average drift of positive ions in one direction and of negative ions in the other. The total net electrical current passing any plane in the solution is the sum of the net positive-ion current and the net negative-ion current crossing that plane, and must equal the electron current in the external circuit.

Thus there are at least three effects in an electric cell: oxidation at the anode, reduction at the cathode, and net ionic migration in the electrolyte. The electron current flows from the anode to the cathode in the external circuit.

Exercise 32.14

Measurements on a lead storage battery discharging at a rate of 1 ampere show that $8.5 \cdot 10^{-6}$ moles of hydrogen ion penetrate the porous barrier per second. Calculate the rate of disappearance of lead and the rate at which sulfate ions are going through the barrier. *Answer:* 1 ampere = 1 coulomb sec^{-1} = (1/96,500) Faraday sec^{-1} = (moles $e^{-} \cdot sec^{-1}$) = 208/(2 · 96,500)g Pb · sec^{-1} = 0.00109 g Pb · sec^{-1}. 1/96,500 Faraday $sec^{-1} = 1.05 \cdot 10^{-5}$ moles of electrons per second, $1.05 \cdot 10^{-5} - 8.5 \cdot 10^{-6} = 2.0 \cdot 10^{-6}$ charges carried by $SO_4^{=}$ per second = $1 \cdot 10^{-6}$ moles of $SO_4^{=}$ penetrate the barrier per second. Note that about 80% of the current in solution is carried by hydrogen ions, about 20% by sulfate ions.

MECHANISTIC STEPS IN ELECTRIC CELLS— IONIC TRANSFER

Even though it is not a surface reaction, let us first briefly discuss the net motion of the electrolyte. Most ions are solvated in solution. As they move, they carry the solvated molecules with them. This migration of solvent, together with that of the ions, can actually be observed if the barrier separating the electrodes is kept permeable to ions but is strong enough to withstand some hydrostatic pressure.

The ions will lose their solvated molecules when the ions are discharged at the electrodes. This interprets the experimental observation that electrolysis of aqueous copper(II) sulfate in a U-tube results in net transport of water [and of copper(II)] into the cathode end of the U—the water level rises there, falling in the anode end. Some water is carried by the sulfate toward the anode (as can be shown by tracer experiments), but the copper carries more water and hence gives net transport of water toward the cathode.

Hydrogen ions in water solution are a special case. Their rate of apparent migration is ten times as great as that of most other ions. Hydroxide ions also move more rapidly through water than similar negative ions. Both effects are interpreted in terms of a Grotthuss chain reaction.

It is known from tracer experiments that the movement of the hydrogen ions is not as rapid as the change in the acidity (by a factor of almost ten). By this we mean that changes in acidity are observable at ten times the distance that isotopic hydrogen is known to move in the same time. The Grotthuss chain mechanism suggests that proton transfer through solution occurs by attachment of a proton to the anode side of a water molecule. The resulting $H_3O^+{}_{(aq)}$ then releases another proton on its cathode side, but without the water molecule rotating. A second water molecule accepts this released proton, releasing a third proton, and so on through the solution. Thus the rate of proton transfer, or buildup of acidity, greatly outstrips the actual movement of individual protons.

Hydroxide ions behave similarly but the effect is not as marked, since, unlike protons, hydroxide ions are not symmetrical. It is quite likely that a principal mechanism of hydroxide transfer is a reverse Grotthuss chain. The oxygen atoms do not move much. The apparent movement of hydroxide ions toward the anode is actually due to a transfer of protons in the reverse direction. It should be clear that other ionizing solvents (such as liquid ammonia) will show similar effects.

Exercise 32.15

Experiments show that sodium ions migrate more rapidly than do lithium ions in an electric cell. Rationalize this fact. *Answer:* The ionic radii are $Li^+ = 0.60$ Å, $Na^+ = 0.95$ Å. One might guess that the smaller Li^+ ions would be more mobile. But remember hydration. The hydration energy of Li^+ is much greater than that of Na^+. Thus, it is (1) harder for Li^+ to break free from one location and move to another in water, and (2) the hydrated Li^+ ion has a larger effective size (due to its greater degree of hydration) than does a less hydrated sodium ion, slowing down the rate of diffusion of the more highly hydrated ion.

ELECTRODE MECHANISMS

As the ions approach the double layer at the electrode surface (partly because of potential differences, partly because of random thermal motion), the nature of the surface will have more and more effect on the mechanism of reaction. However, if the surface has been carefully equilibrated (see p. 811), each area will be much like every other area. This must be true on a reversible electrode, since, if it is to reverse its reactions with a differential change in potential, its own potential must be the same everywhere on the surface.

Copper electrodes are quite readily reversible against Cu(II) aqueous solutions. But other studies show that Cu^{++} is strongly hydrated by four water molecules, $Cu(H_2O)_4^{++}$. A possible mechanism here is

$$\underset{\text{bulk water}}{Cu(H_2O)_4{}^{++}{}_{(aq)}} \overset{1}{\rightleftharpoons} \underset{\text{double layer}}{Cu(H_2O)_4{}^{++}{}_{(aq)}} \underset{-e^- + H_2O}{\overset{\substack{2 \\ +e^- - H_2O}}{\rightleftharpoons}} \underset{\text{double layer}}{Cu(H_2O)_2{}^{+}} \underset{-e^- + H_2O}{\overset{\substack{3 \\ +e^- - H_2O}}{\rightleftharpoons}} Cu_{(surf)} \overset{4}{\rightleftharpoons} Cu_{(c)}$$

Again water must diffuse away from the double layer.

A much-studied reaction is the H_2—$H^+_{(aq)}$ half-reaction on metal electrodes. The most readily available reversible system uses a very rough platinum electrode (Pt black) made by reducing aqueous $PtCl_6^=$ onto a piece of ordinary, shiny platinum. A possible mechanism for the H_2—$H^+_{(aq)}$ half-reaction on this surface is

$$\underset{\substack{\text{bulk} \\ \text{solution}}}{H^+_{(aq)}} \overset{1}{\rightleftharpoons} \underset{\substack{\text{double} \\ \text{layer}}}{H^+_{(aq)}} \underset{-e^- + H_2O}{\overset{\substack{2 \\ +e^- - H_2O}}{\rightleftharpoons}} \underset{\substack{\text{surface} \\ \text{of Pt}}}{H} \overset{3}{\rightleftharpoons} \underset{\substack{\text{surface} \\ \text{of Pt}}}{H_2} \overset{4}{\rightleftharpoons} \underset{\text{bubble}}{H_{2(g)}}$$

Another mechanism assumes a layer of water adsorbed on the electrode as the reducing surface.

Note that in every case suggested at least three interfaces must be bridged by the reaction: (1) the solution-double layer interface, (2) the double layer itself, (3) the surface-bulk interface of the reduced phase.

The mechanisms we have suggested are all oversimplified, but the problems they present are understandable in terms of the ideas previously discussed. A truly reversible system must consist of individual mechanistic steps, each of which is rapidly reversible under all conditions. Yet it is clear that, at least at high current densities, the first step in each of the above mechanisms will become diffusion-controlled, and other steps may also. It should also be clear that the hydrogen electrode may be quite sensitive in its behavior to the nature of the surface, since the reaction $2H = H_2$ has to occur. The rapidity of this reaction should be a function of the mobility of hydrogen atoms on the surface. Apparently on platinum black there is high mobility.

Since all electrode reactions must perforce have rather complicated mechanisms, there can be no truly reversible electrodes. For this reason, electrode equilibria are ordinarily studied at very low current densities, using potentiometers to measure the potentials. In the limit of zero current density (usual units are amperes per square centimeter), all electrodes become reversible. In practice, reversibility is often impossible to achieve.

Although there are a few applications in which a steady voltage at zero current is all that is needed, most electric cells must deliver power if they are to be usable. Thus, one of the fundamental problems today is to produce cells sufficiently close to reversibility that they can reliably deliver power at a practical level.

FUEL CELLS

We discussed in Chapter 26 the problem of efficient use of energy and showed that a machine utilizing heat has a maximum (reversible) efficiency of

$$e = \frac{w}{q_1} = 1 - \frac{q_2}{q_1} = 1 - \frac{T_2}{T_1}$$

Thus, if the available range of temperatures is small, most of the heat must be discharged to the cold reservoir and only a little can be used in accomplishing work. Electric cells do not operate with this handicap. The full free energy is available for useful work (neglecting $P\,dV$); see page 727. Let us compare the two possibilities.

Consider the reaction

$$C_{(c)} + O_{2(g)} = CO_{2(g)}$$
$$P\,dV = 0$$

and therefore

$$\Delta G = -w_{\max}$$

At $T = 298°$K (from Table 27.1), $\Delta G^0_{298} = -94.265$ kcal, $\Delta H^0_{298} = -94.054$ kcal mole^{-1}. For all practical purposes $\Delta G^0_{298} = \Delta H^0_{298} = -94$ kcal/mole $= w_{\max} = q_{1(\text{rev})}$. If we burn the coal at its maximum flame temperature in air of about 1300°K, using condenser water at 300°K, we get

$$e = \frac{w}{q_1} = 1.00 - \frac{300}{1300} = 0.77$$

or

$$w = 0.77 \cdot 94 = 72 \text{ kcal mole}^{-1}$$

Thus we have "lost" almost a quarter of our energy in the room-temperature condenser, rather than being able to use it as work. The loss in a real boiler is much greater. The practically realizable efficiency is often 25% or less. Furthermore, we have had to build a high-temperature, high-pressure plant, with all its accompanying problems. Small wonder that a great deal of effort is expended in seeking a fuel cell that will generate electric power directly from coal. There appear to be two fundamental problems: (1) coal is not a good conductor of electricity and so does not make a good electrode; (2) surface problems create irreversible systems both at the coal and the oxygen electrode. The first problem is minimized by graphitizing the coal. The second problem has not as yet been solved satisfactorily, though hundreds of man-years have been spent trying. It is very likely that it will be solved in the next twenty years, but no one is yet sure how. However, after years spent mostly on cut-and-try approaches, it now seems that a fundamental attack on the problems of comprehending the molecular behavior at the surface may pay off.

Other fuel cells are already going into operation, especially cells using hydrogen and oxygen. But even these can stand great improvement, and it is still true that no complete understanding of either the hydrogen or the oxygen electrode is available. A fuel cell using natural gas and air would be intermediate in usefulness between coal and hydrogen (after all most hydrogen is made from natural gas). Progress is being made but a considerable number of problems remain for investigation, solution, and reward.

You may remember that one of the main problems with space missiles has been lack of reliability in the fuel cells. A little more attention here to the molecular problems at the interfaces would probably be useful.

Exercise 32.16

Mixed feed fuel cells containing liquid CH_3OH and O_2 in a basic aqueous solution are being explored. Write possible electrode half-reactions and discuss the required electrode properties. *Answer:* Anode: $CH_3OH_{(aq)} + 6OH^-{}_{(aq)} = CO_{2(g)} + 5H_2O + 6e^-$; cathode: $\frac{3}{2}O_{2(aq)} + 6e^- + 3H_2O = 6OH^-{}_{(aq)}$. Each electrode must catalyze only one of the half-reactions and the rate of the uncatalyzed direct reaction must be low. Such cells have many advantages, for example: single fuel, fuel reservoir, pumping system, and no porous barrier.

SUMMARY

All chemical reactions are surface reactions in the sense that interactions can occur only when two surfaces touch. In both molecules and bulk phases, surface atoms tend to have higher chemical potentials and to be more reactive. The difference in reactivity between surface and bulk atoms can be measured in terms of the surface tension or the interfacial tension. Liquid surfaces tend to be mobile and thus to be readily reproducible, so that most surface tension data is for interfaces involving a liquid.

Crystals have a symmetry imposed by the crystal structure. This, plus the general rigidity of crystals, makes it difficult to get reproducible, uniform crystal faces for the study of surface reactions. Many of the most interesting, and most of the applied reactions of chemistry (heterogeneous catalysis, solution and precipitation, electrode reactions) involve surface chemistry, so that an enormous amount of research is currently going on in this area.

Surface effects are generally interpretable in terms of surface free energy, surface structure, electrical charge distribution, and diffusion.

The great psychological lesson of history for chemists is the realization that every important step forward in structural theory has violated accepted physical principles.
—H. A. Bent, University of Minnesota.

PROBLEMS

32.1. Steam condenses on ordinary copper surfaces as a film which interferes with heat exchange—in boilers, for example. Coating the copper surface with organic sulfides leads to drop-by-drop condensation of the water. Why a film in the one case and drops in the other? Draw a cross section of each surface, showing molecular interactions which give these effects.

32.2. Addition of a drop of water to a glass "full to the brim and rounded" causes no change, but addition of a drop of detergent causes the water to run over the brim. Suggest a mechanism.

32.3. Brass, an alloy of copper and zinc, often turns red and becomes brittle when used in plumbing. Suggest an interpretation at the molecular level, using net equations to describe a possible mechanism. Be as quantitative as possible.

32.4. Silverware tarnished with Ag_2S may be brightened by dropping it into an aluminum pan of boiling water. Addition of sodium bicarbonate to the water speeds the polishing action. Write net equations and outline a possible mechanism.

32.5. Silica powder can be used to adsorb diethyl ether and alcohols from an air stream. Suggest the nature of the surface interaction.

32.6. Which do you think would be the better adsorbent for benzene vapors (assuming each surface had the same available area): activated charcoal or silica gel?

32.7. Overcharging a lead storage battery shortens battery life. Suggest a possible mechanism for this.

32.8. A simple laboratory test of cleanliness of glassware is whether water forms a film or forms drops on the glassware as it drains. Comment on the interpretation of this phenomenon at the molecular level.

32.9. If oxygen is adsorbed on carbon, then removed by pumping, a rather large yield of CO is obtained. What does this indicate about the nature of the adsorbed layer?

32.10. Under what circumstances is a catalyst desirable for a chemical reaction?

32.11. One of the most effective means of cleaning greasy surfaces is to wash them with a basic solution. A solution of tri-sodium phosphate, Na_3PO_4, is more effective than one of borax, $Na_2B_4O_7$. How can you interpret the difference in the two solutions in terms of the equilibria involved? Name one other common household cleaner whose effectiveness depends on the presence of hydroxide ions. Write the equation for the net reaction in each of the three equilibria.

32.12. Interpret each of the following experimental facts using the ideas we have discussed.

(*a*) The raisins in raisin toast burn the fingers more than the toast does, even though both are at the same temperature.
(*b*) A pile of logs in a fireplace burns well, but each log goes out when they are separated from one another.
(*c*) Addition of solid ammonium chloride to water rapidly gives an aqueous solution much colder than the ingredients. Explain the rapidity, the cooling, and the fact that the reaction occurs at all.

32.13. Skiis coated with Teflon, $(CF_2)_n$, are very much "faster" than ordinary waxed skiis. Account for this.

32.14. Assume a shadowing angle of 10° and calculate the size of the steps in Figure 32.14. How many molecules per step? (Step $\cong$ 70 Å.)

32.15. Mixing solutions of barium hydroxide and sulfuric acid gives a milky suspension, which coagulates to a white precipitate upon heating. Discuss possible mechanisms for each step in the above process.

32.16. Why does water, when heated, tend to "bump" less in glass vessels than do solutions of sodium hydroxide? Would you expect soap solutions to "bump" more or less than does water? ("Bumping" describes the violent, intermittent formation of bubbles in superheated systems.)

II

32.17. Estimate the length of the stearic acid molecules in Figure 32.8, if the shadowing angle was 10°. Estimate the uncertainty in your estimate. Compare with a reasonable value for the molecular length. (Step $\cong$ 30 Å.)

32.18. According to Germer and MacRae, using slow electron diffraction [*Proc. Nat. Acad. Sci. U.S.*, **48**, 997 (1962)] the surface layers on metals generally have the same lattice as do bulk atoms, but covalent materials such as silicon and germanium have different surface lattices. Rationalize this.

32.19. High-surface-area materials often show hysteresis effects requiring lower pressures to desorb gas which adsorbed only at higher pressures. Rationalize this effect in terms of the nature of a very rough surface.

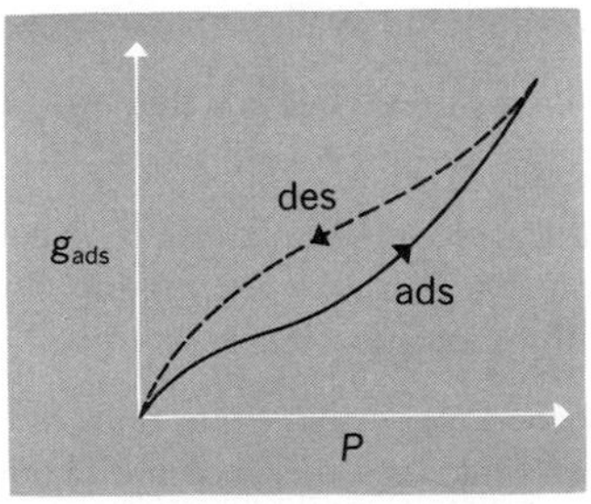

III

32.20. According to Schwab and Leuter [*J. Catalysis*, **1**, 192 (1961)], formaldoxime, $H_2C{=}NOH$, decomposes catalytically to hydrogen cyanide and water on basic catalysts having large cations, but to ammonia and carbon monoxide on more acidic catalysts. Suggest mechanisms for these two reactions. (Schwab and Leuter suggest formamide, $HCONH_2$, as an intermediate in the acid-catalyzed mechanism.)

32.21. Measurements of heats of adsorption of gases on solids show that most values lie between 0.1 and 10 kcal $mole^{-1}$ or between 20 and 100 kcal $mole^{-1}$. Rationalize these two sets and the reason for the gap between them.

32.22. The differential heat of adsorption of n-hexane on graphite as a function of surface coverage θ is shown. Rationalize the main features of the curve.

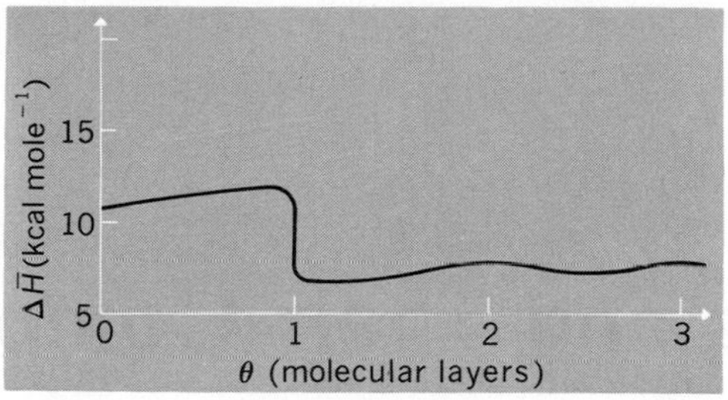

See page 1093 for a list of references and readings in the recent chemical literature related to the material in this chapter.

CHAPTER 33

Metals and Their Compounds

Metals may be considered as slightly expanded structures of positive ions surrounded by a sea of delocalized valence electrons occupying crystalline molecular orbitals.

Metals are so commonly used that almost everyone can identify them on sight by their lustrous appearance. Most people also realize that metals are excellent conductors of both electricity and heat, and that most metals can be deformed without breaking (they are malleable and ductile). Not so common is the knowledge that although many metals are chemical elements, most contain more than one element (some of which may be nonmetallic elements), and many are compounds of well-defined formulas. We shall concentrate mainly on metals containing only metallic elements, but shall also deal briefly with substances such as fool's gold, FeS_2, which are metallic but contain nonmetallic elements as well.

METALLIC ELEMENTS

We have already discussed in Chapter 5 many of the properties of the elements, including their metallic nature, and in Chapters 16 and 17 we introduced some ideas on bonds in metals. Table 33.1 is a periodic table, which lists the electrical conductivity, the coordination numbers, and the crystal type of each element. Note that most elements are metallic, all the nonmetals are at the top, the most common coordination number is 12, and the most common crystal structures are the face-centered cubic (*fcc*) or the hexagonal close-packed (*hcp*). There are about 30 known examples of each among the elements.

The packing achieved by spheres when they get as close together as pos-

Table 33.1 **Structures and electrical conductivities (1/milliohm · cm) of the elements. *CN* given in parentheses. □ = *fcc* (12), △ = *hcp* (12), ○ = *bcc* (8), + = special, X = molecular crystals. Concentric symbols indicate changing structure–highest temperature form is outside. Note tendency toward *bcc* as temperature increases. Nonmetals are to the left of, and above, the colored lines.**

He □	Ne □	Ar □	Kr □	Xe □	Rn □	
H △(H_2)	F X(1)	Cl X(1)	Br X(1)	I X(1) $7.7 \cdot 10^{-13}$	At X(1)	
	O X(1)	S X(2) $5 \cdot 10^{-21}$	Se X(2) 170	Te X(2) 5	Po +(6)	
	N X(1)	P X(3) $1 \cdot 10^{-14}$	As X(3) 30.1	Sb +(3) 25.6	Bi +(3) 9.36	
	C +(4) 0.727(graph) $<10^{-10}$(diam)	Si +(4) $5 \cdot 10^{-9}$	Ge +(4) $2.17 \cdot 10^{-5}$	Sn +(4) 91	Pb □ 48.4	
	B + $5.6 \cdot 10^{-10}$	Al □ 378	Ga +(1) 57.5	In +(4) 120	Tl ○ with △ inside 54.5	
			Zn △ 169	Cd △ 147	Hg +(6) 10	
			Cu □ 598	Ag □ 629	Au □ 426	
			Ni □ 146	Pd □ 92.5	Pt □ 94	
			Co □ or △ 160	Rh □ 222	Ir □ 190	
			Fe ○ with □ inside 103	Ru △ 132	Os △ 105	
			Mn ○ with □ and + inside 5.4	Tc △	Re △ 51.8	
			Cr ○ 77.5	Mo ○ 192	W ○ 177	
			V ○ 40	Cb ○ 80	Ta ○ 80.4	
			Ti ○ with △ inside 24	Zr ○ with △ inside 25	Hf ○ with △ inside 28.5	
			Sc △ or □ 16.4	Y △ 18	Lanthanides, mostly △, about 10–100	Actinides, mostly + or ○ about 10–100
	Be △ 250	Mg △ 225	Ca ○ with △ inside 256	Sr ○ with △ inside 43	Ba ○	Ra
H △(H_2)	Li △ with ○ inside 117	Na ○ 238	K ○ 163	Rb ○ 80	Cs ○ 50	

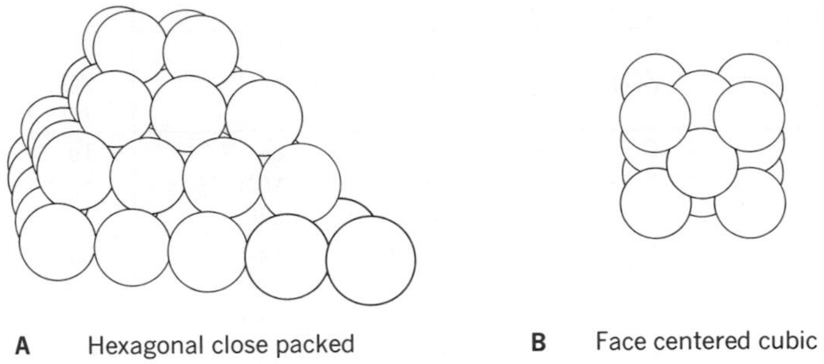

Figure 33.1 The two types of close-packed structures. $CN = 12$. (**A**) *hcp*. (**B**) *fcc*.

sible is $CN = 12$, which is thus the packing to be expected if a general, nondirectional, attractive force field is acting between spheres. If we extend this idea (of spherical atoms having equally strong bonds in any direction) to the metallic elements, we find it not only fits with the most common packing but also accounts for the high malleability: if the force field is nondirectional, the atoms can slide or glide past one another with minimum activation energy. Such gliding will most easily occur parallel to the atomic planes. Since *fcc* contains 12 different glide planes and *hcp*, (with much lower symmetry) has only 3, we expect *fcc* crystals to be more malleable. This is borne out by experiment. Figure 33.1 illustrates the *fcc* and *hcp* structures, and Figure 33.2 shows some of the glide planes.

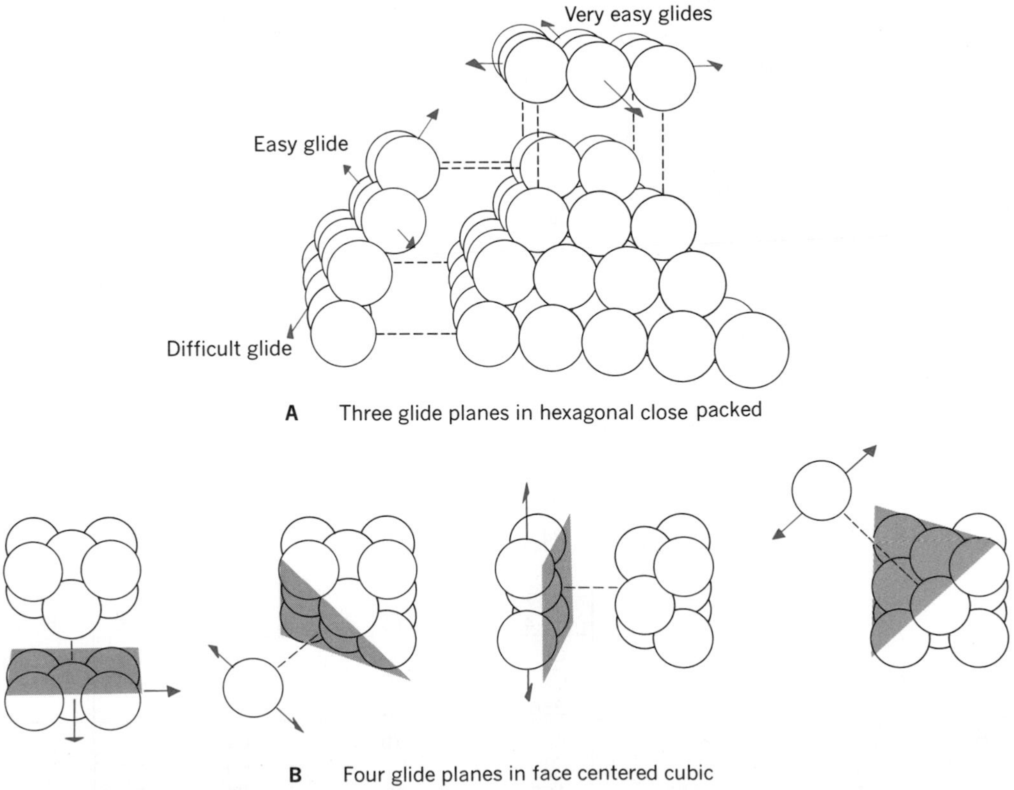

Figure 33.2 Some glide planes. (**A**) In *hcp* structures. (**B**) In *fcc* structures.

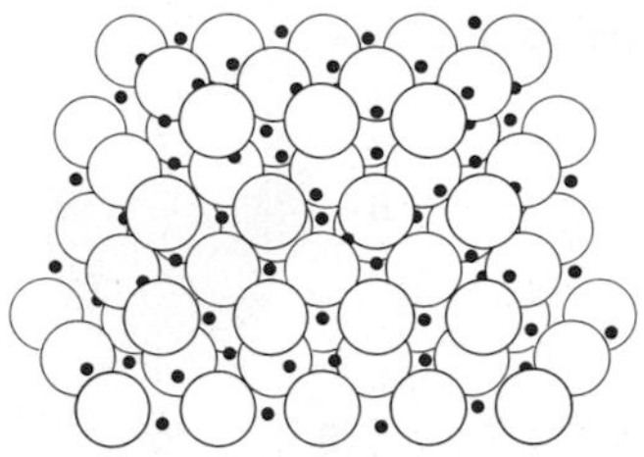

Figure 33.3 Electron sea model of metals.

The electrical conductivity of the metals may also be considered within this model if we assume that the slightly expanded structures of Figure 33.3 represent positive ions surrounded by a sea of delocalized valence electrons occupying crystalline molecular orbitals. Not only can the positive ions glide through the electron sea under minimal mechanical stress, but the electrons can glide past the positive ions under minimal electrical stress. Furthermore, heat (kinetic energy) will be transmitted rapidly through the crystal by the delocalized electrons, accounting for the high thermal conductivity.

Exercise 33.1

Rationalize the fact that transitions from *hcp* and *fcc* to *bcc* become common at high temperatures. *Answer:* $CN = 12$ for *hcp* and *fcc*, but $CN = 8$ for *bcc*. As T rises, internuclear distances tend to increase. Apparently at low T, 12 short bonds are stronger than 8 short bonds, but at higher T, 8 short bonds are stronger than 12 longer ones. Thus the volume and entropy can increase by going from $CN = 12$ to $CN = 8$ while still retaining short strong bonds. Since metallic bonds are relatively nondirectional, there is little loss in bonding ability when the CN changes. The smaller CN also helps "accommodate" the higher entropy found at higher temperatures.

CLOSE-PACKED STRUCTURES

More metals exhibit $CN = 12$ than any other packing, so we shall concentrate on this type of structure in interpreting metallic properties and reactions. Figure 33.4 shows the relationship between the two possible $CN = 12$ structures, *fcc* and *hcp*. Both can be viewed as made up of stacked atomic layers, each layer having $CN = 6$ in the layer. The two structures *hcp* and *fcc* differ in whether the repeating pattern is *AB AB AB* (*hcp*) or *ABC ABC ABC* (*fcc*, also called cubic closest packing, *ccp*). Figure 33.5 shows that the *ABA* pattern is converted to the *ABC* pattern by rotating the third layer 60° in its plane.

A *hcp* (ABAB layers) **B** *fcc* (ABCA layers)

Figure 33.4 Relationship of *hcp* to *fcc* structures.

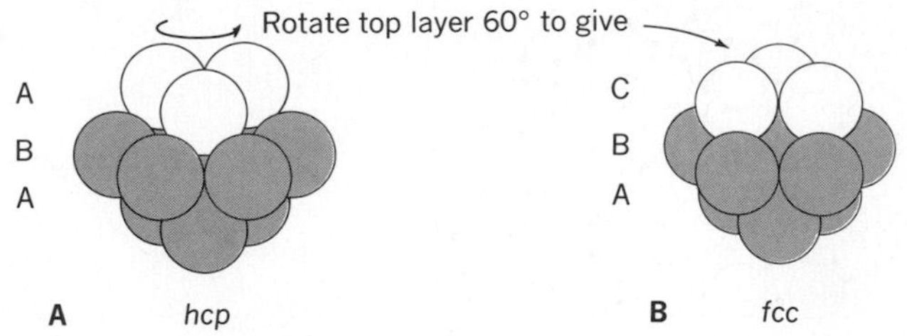

Figure 33.5 Interconversion of *hcp* and *fcc*.

The relationships, and our future arguments, are clarified if we start with a single close-packed layer of spheres and add further layers to it. Figure 33.6 shows that each sphere in the close-packed layer is surrounded by six others in its own plane and by six trigonal cusps above the plane. (There are also, of course, six more trigonal cusps around the sphere below the plane.) With the addition of a second close-packed layer, three of the upper trigonal cusps serve as sockets for added atoms (and three of the upper cusps remain empty). Addition of a third layer, as in Figures 33.4 and 33.5, gives two possibilities: *ABA* (*hcp*) or *ABC* (*fcc*), for the three-layer sequence, depending on whether the third layer fits in the set of trigonal cusps above the atoms in the first layer (*hcp*) or in the other set of cusps above the "holes" in the first layer (*fcc*).

Exercise 33.2

Suggest an interpretation at the molecular level for the complete mutual solubility of crystalline silver and crystalline gold. *Answer:* Both crystalline silver and gold are *fcc* ($CN = 12$). The metallic radius of silver is 1.442 Å and that of gold is 1.445 Å. Thus the atoms, which have similar electron structures, may interchange at random in the crystal without appreciably altering the crystal structure. Hence the two show complete mutual solubility.

HOLES IN CLOSE-PACKED STRUCTURES

Even the close-packed structures discussed so far contain voids, if we assume that the atoms are spherical. In *fcc* and *hcp* 26% of the volume is "empty"; in *bcc* it is 32%. Let us look at the holes (remembering the discussion in Chapter 16). A sphere in a close-packed lattice will be surrounded by 24 trigonal holes, 8 tetrahedral holes, and 6 octahedral holes. Each trigonal hole is surrounded by 3 spheres, each tetrahedral hole by 4 spheres, and each octahedral hole by 6 spheres. Thus in a close-packed crystal containing n spherical atoms there will be $8n$ trigonal holes,

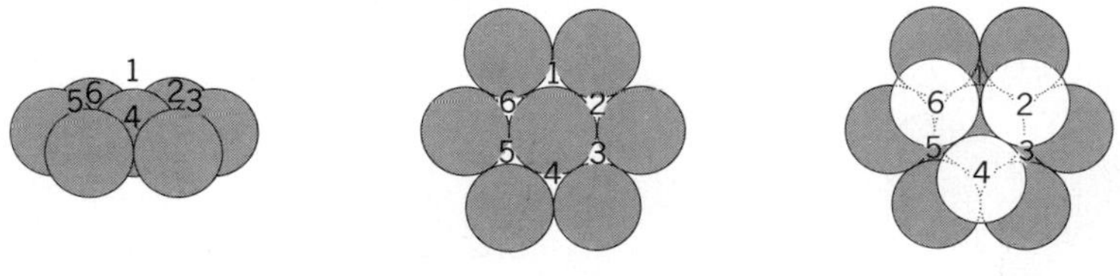

Figure 33.6 Close-packed layers and trigonal cusps.

A Slant view of close packed layer

B Top view of close packed layer

C Cusps 2,4,6 occupied by a second close packed layer. Cusps 1,3,5 unoccupied

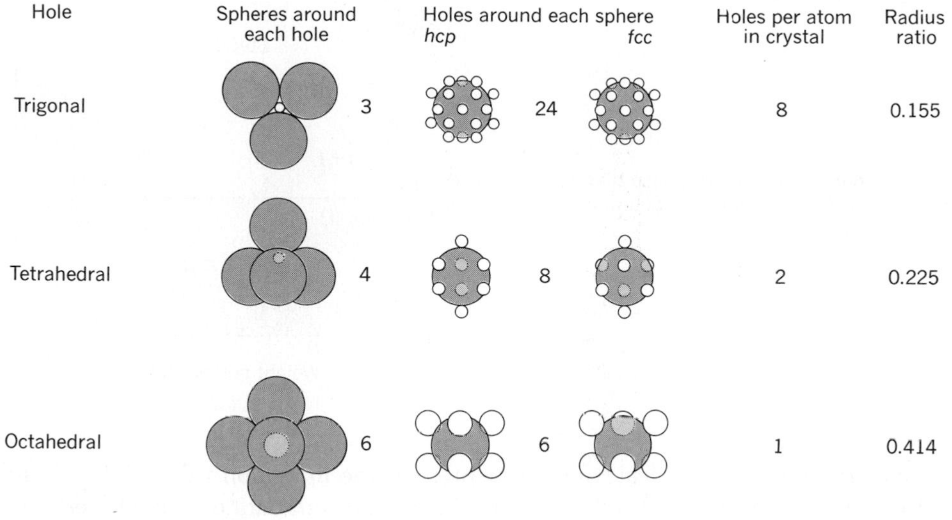

Hole
Spheres around each hole
Holes around each sphere
hcp
fcc
Holes per atom in crystal
Radius ratio
Trigonal
3
24
8
0.155
Tetrahedral
4
8
2
0.225
Octahedral
6
6
1
0.414

Figure 33.7 Holes in close-packed structures.

$2n$ tetrahedral holes, and n octahedral holes. [These last numbers follow from the fact that the ratio of numbers of different kinds of sites in a crystal must be the same as the ratio of the *CN*'s at those sites. These ratios for the crystal of n atoms are (24 trigonal holes per sphere)/(3 spheres per trigonal hole) = 8; (8 tetrahedral holes per sphere)/(4 spheres per tetrahedral hole) = 2; (6 octahedral holes per sphere)/(6 spheres per octahedral hole) = 1.] Figure 33.7 summarizes and illustrates the above. There can also be substitutional holes formed by removing an atom from its crystal site. We shall find that these various holes are an important factor in determining the structure of metallic compounds and alloys, just as we found them to be in Chapter 16 for ionic compounds. Imperfect crystals, (that is, all real crystals) will contain additional voids, as shown in Figure 32.10.

BINARY METALLIC SYSTEMS

We have already discussed the criteria for equilibrium between several components and several phases in Chapter 6. The general relationship, if the only variables are composition, pressure, and temperature, is the

PHASE RULE:
$$F = C - P + 2 \tag{33.1}$$

where C represents the number of components, P the number of phases, 2 the independent variables pressure and temperature, and F the number of degrees of freedom (independent variables) which may be arbitrarily changed without destroying any equilibrium phase. We have already used some phase diagrams (pressure-temperature diagrams) to illustrate the ranges in which various phases can exist (see Figures 5.14 and 6.6). Most equilibria involving binary metal systems are studied at 1 atm pressure, so Equation (33.1) reduces from $F = C - P + 2$ to

$$F = 2 - P + 1 = 3 - P \tag{33.2}$$

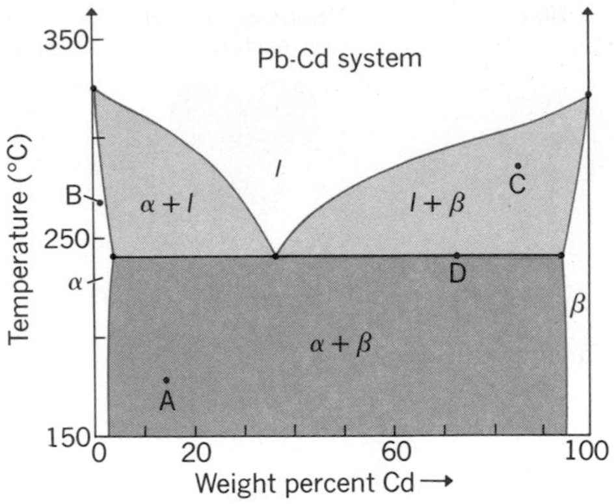

Figure 33.8 A portion of the lead-cadmium phase diagram at one atmosphere pressure. A simple eutectic diagram.

Since there must be at least one phase present, the minimum value of P is 1 and the maximum value of F is 2. Thus, all the equilibrium data can be plotted on a two-dimensional figure, using composition, N, and temperature, T, as abscissa and ordinate. Figure 33.8 shows the Pb-Cd system. It indicates the equilibrium phase, or phases, for every possible temperature and composition in the range covered. The clear areas each represent a single phase, either liquid or crystal (α or β). The lines bonding these phases give the composition and temperature values at which each phase will begin to change into another phase. The shaded regions indicate N–T values at which more than one phase will be present at equilibrium in the system (α-l, l-β, α-β). These equilibrium phases (α, β, l) are those at the ends of the isothermal drawn through any point in one of the gray areas. For example, at the over-all composition and temperature represented by point A, we would actually find two phases, α and β, in equilibrium. At point B, since it is in a clear, single-phase area, only one phase, α, would be present. At point C we would find two phases, l and β, in equilibrium. The system consisting of the lowest freezing liquid and the two solid phases α and β is called the eutectic system. The temperature (240°C) is the eutectic temperature, and the composition (35% Cd) the eutectic composition.

In the figure clear areas represent single phases and shaded areas represent regions in which two phases are in equilibrium. This leaves the heavy, horizontal line (isothermal) to be interpreted. It represents the temperature, 240°C, at which three phases, α, l, β, coexist. For example, point D represents a system consisting of α crystals, liquid, and β crystals, three separate phases. In this system the three-phase line is the eutectic isotherm.

Exercise 33.3

What would you see in a test tube containing substances corresponding to point C in Figure 33.8? *Answer:* Crystalline β (almost pure Cd $\cong$ 98% Cd) would be sitting in a liquid containing about 60% Cd and 40% lead. Point C is at about 87% Cd. Thus, the relative amounts of the two layers will be (98 − 87) g liquid/(87 − 60) g crystal $\cong$ (1/2.5) g liquid per g of crystal. Both layers will look shiny and silvery metallic. The cadmium should be floating, since its density is probably less than that of the lead-containing solution.

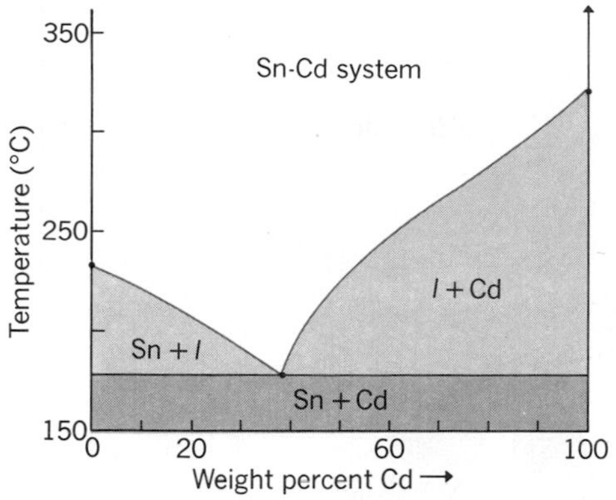

Figure 33.9 The tin-cadmium phase diagram. The two crystalline metals have very small solubility in one another. A simple eutectic system.

In terms of Equation (33.2) the clear areas represent $P = 1$, $F = 2$; the boundaries of the shaded areas represent $P = 2$, $F = 1$. The horizontal line represents $P = 3$, $F = 0$; it is an isothermal connecting three compositions that represent the three equilibrium phases.

Thus we see that the Pb-Cd system can exist as the following phases: liquid solution of cadmium and lead, solid solution α, and solid solution β. Since the composition range of the α phase extends from pure lead to 4 mole percent cadmium at 240°C, we conclude that cadmium must be soluble in crystalline lead without changing the crystal structure—they exist as a solid solution. Each element must, according to Figure 33.8, be somewhat soluble in the crystals of the other. But the two solid solutions apparently have different crystal structures, since they do not dissolve in one another but coexist in equilibrium over a wide range of temperatures (up to 240°C) before either melts.

For many binary systems the two substances are almost insoluble in one another, and the phase diagram looks like Figure 33.9. The crystal solubility ranges (range of solid solution) are so small as to be undetectable by most methods, but it is now known that all substances are somewhat soluble in one another, so that a solubility zone, even if small, does exist. We also know that many of the most interesting and useful, and sometimes annoying, properties of metals are due to traces of dissolved material.

Figure 33.10 is the phase diagram for the Cu-Zn system. Note that there are now many possible crystalline phases and thus many kinds of brass—since brasses are made by melting Cu and Zn together. All these phases, and indeed almost all phases made from metallic elements, are themselves metallic. They are given the general name alloys, but we will try to characterize them more specifically.

Exercise 33.4

Which is more soluble in β brass—Cu or Zn? *Answer:* At all values of T the composition range of β brass extends further toward the copper-rich side than toward the zinc-rich side. Thus copper is more soluble in CuZn than is zinc. The composition corresponding to CuZn is, of course, 50 mole % of each element.

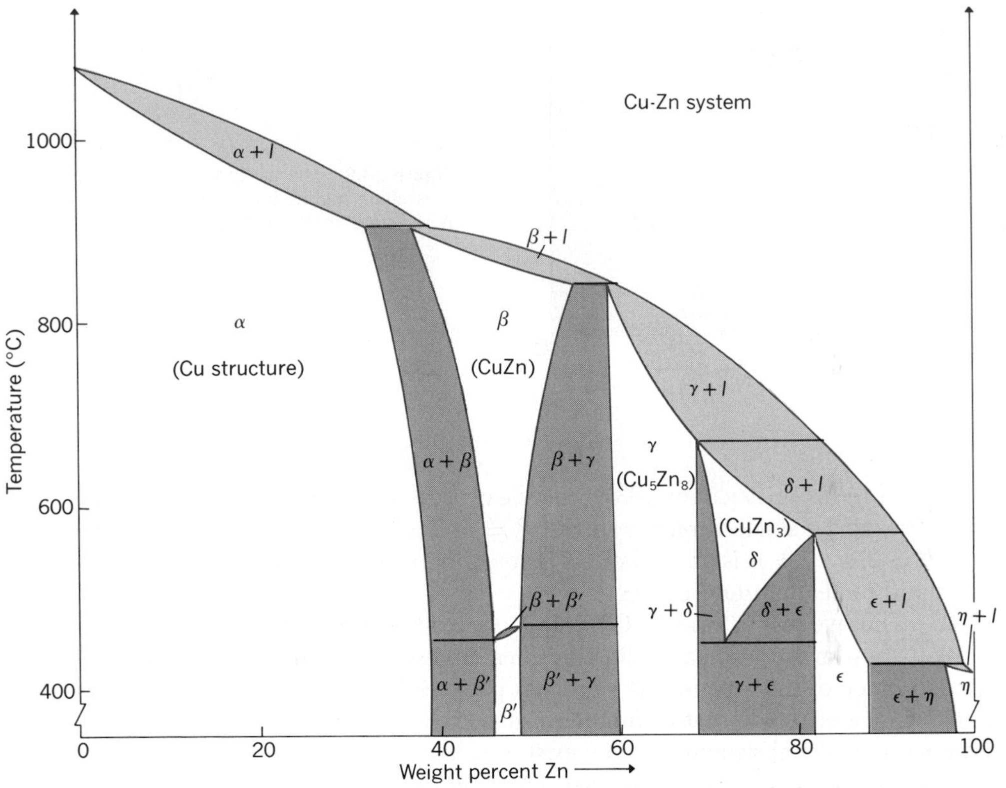

Figure 33.10 The copper-zinc (brass) phase diagram. A complex system.

SUBSTITUTIONAL ALLOYS

Sometimes one metal dissolves another by replacing one of its own atoms with an atom of the second element to give a substitutional solid solution. Such interchange can occur if the two atoms are the same size ($\pm$15%), and have similar orbital patterns. (Symmetry is important in forming bonds as well as in forming crystals.) Thus silver and gold form a complete range of solid solutions, as shown in Figure 33.11. They not only have similar metallic radii (Ag = 1.442; Au = 1.445) and similar atomic orbital structures (Ag = $1s^2$; $2s^2$, $2p^6$; $3s^2$, $3p^6$, $3d^{10}$; $4s^2$, $4p^6$, $4d^{10}$; $5s^1$; Au = $1s^2$; $2s^2$, $2p^6$; $3s^2$, $3p^6$, $3d^{10}$; $4s^2$, $4p^6$, $4d^{10}$, $4f^{14}$; $5s^2$, $5p^6$, $5d^{10}$; $6s^1$); they also have the same crystal structures—*fcc*. Thus all silver-gold alloys are substitutional solid solutions, a fact confirmed by X-ray crystallography.

Copper and zinc also form substitutional solid solutions, as shown in Figure 33.10.

Exercise 33.5

Use Figure 4.9 and Table 33.1 to predict several pairs of elements which might be mutually completely soluble in the crystalline phase. *Answer:* Criteria are that the two elements have the same crystal structure when pure and have both similar atomic radii and electron structures. Possible pairs: Cu-Ni, Pd-Pt, Mo-W, Zr-Hf, Rb-Cs.

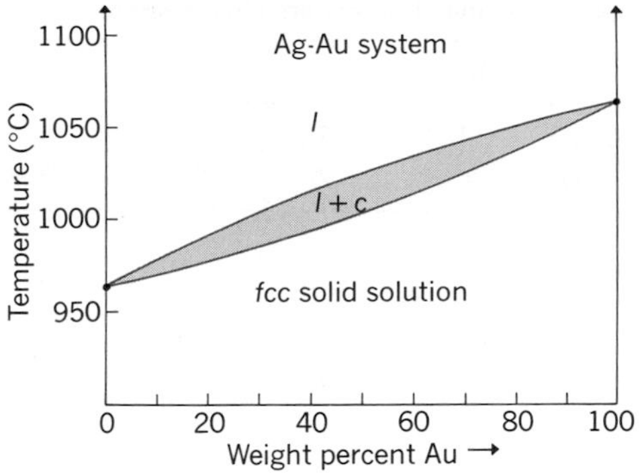

Figure 33.11 The silver-gold phase diagram. A single solid solution.

INTERMETALLIC COMPOUNDS

Copper and zinc also form some compounds. All of these—CuZn (β), Cu_5Zn_8 (γ), $CuZn_3$ (δ), and so on—exist over a considerable composition range and are not nearly as stoichiometric as the compounds more customarily found in the chemistry lab. But note that β' (CuZn) exists over a relatively smaller range. The nonstoichiometric compounds are often substitutional alloys of one or both of the components in the lattice of the ideal stoichiometric compound.

This is a good place to point out that truly stoichiometric compounds are extremely rare—and exist almost by accident. This follows from the universal mutual solubility of substances (no matter how small it may be), from the unlikeliness of ever obtaining (when numbers as large as one mole are involved) exactly the stoichiometric ratio of 1–1 or 1–2, etc., and, in the limit, from the problem of isotopic variation. However, many chemicals are extremely close to stoichiometric ratios even if prepared with minimal care. But it is becoming more and more clear that properties can be sensitive to fairly minute amounts of impurity, and for this reason nonstoichiometric systems are becoming of greater and greater interest.

INTERSTITIAL ALLOYS

In addition to stoichiometric intermetallic compounds and substitutional alloys we find a very large class of alloys in which one set of atoms is located in interstices, or holes, in the host metal. Many of the hydrides, borides, nitrides, and carbides of the metals are also interstitial, as might be expected from the small size of these atomic kernels compared to those of the metallic elements (see Table 14.3). Typically the radius ratio is about 0.5, suggesting that octahedral holes ($R = 0.414$) would be the most common sites for B, N, and C atoms in metals. Hydrogen, being smaller, might more commonly be found in tetrahedral holes. Table 33.2 gives some experimental results; see also Figure 16.3.

Interstitial substances, unlike substitutional alloys and many metallic compounds, are brittle. The interstitials may be lustrous and good conductors but they are seldom malleable. These properties are, of course, consistent with our model of metals. The atoms still sit in a sea of electrons occupying delocalized orbitals, but now the glide planes have disappeared, since the interstitial atoms act as "pegs"

Table 33.2 **Structures of some interstitial substances. The metal atoms are close-packed.**

	Substance						
	WC TiC	Mo_2N W_2N	Mn_4N Fe_4N	TiH_2 CrH_2	TiH ZrH	Pd_2H	Zr_4H
Fraction of octahedral holes occupied	1	$\frac{1}{2}$	$\frac{1}{4}$	—	—	—	—
Fraction of tetrahedral holes occupied	—	—	—	1	$\frac{1}{2}$	$\frac{1}{4}$	$\frac{1}{8}$

locking the planes together. For the same reason the electrical conductivity drops, but not as much as the malleability. The interstitials tend to "plug" the electron conductivity channels—though not as effectively as they lock in the larger atoms—thus minimizing glide. Such phenomena as "caustic embrittlement" of iron electrodes used commercially in electrolyzing aqueous sodium hydroxide arise from the penetration of hydrogen atoms (formed by reduction of water) into the iron cathode.

Surface hardening or "case hardening," as in armor plate, is accomplished by baking the alloy in a cyanide or carbide bath or exposing it to hot nitrogen gas. In each case carbon and/or nitrogen atoms diffuse into interstitial positions and harden the metallic surface. Do you see why it is desirable that only the surface be hardened in an armor plate? Why not make the whole body of the metal hard?

Exercise 33.6

Use Figure 35.12 and Figure 5.15 to suggest a site for the carbon atoms in the β solid solution of carbon and iron. *Answer:* The crystal structure of β phase is *bcc*. The largest available hole is in the center of the face of each cubic unit cell. The carbons are almost certainly in the distorted octahedral holes corresponding to these face-centered positions. The δ phase is probably similar. Note that neither β nor δ dissolves much carbon, suggesting that the holes are not very "suitable" for carbon atoms.

METALS, METALLOIDS, AND NONMETALS

Having looked into the structure of metallic substances, let us return to bonding theory for a closer interpretation of the properties of the metals. One striking property is the occurrence of high coodination numbers. In nonmetals and their compounds, coordination is usually 4 or less and very rarely exceeds 6. In metals, 8 and 12 are the common values. Metals can clearly form more bonds per atom than can nonmetals. At the orbital occupancy level we find that metals have many too few electrons to fill the available atomic orbitals, but nonmetallic atoms usually have their available atomic orbitals more than half full in the gaseous state, as shown in Table 33.3. See Table 4.2 for a full set of examples. Thus metals are elements that have too few electrons to fill the available orbitals using small coordination numbers; nonmetals are elements that have enough electrons to fill the available atomic orbitals easily (often leaving nonbonding electrons on the atoms);

Table 33.3 Differentiation of metals and nonmetals in terms of the ratio of valence electrons to low-lying atomic orbitals.

	Metals			Metalloid	Nonmetals		
	Na	Cr	Zn	Si	P	S	Kr
Number of valence electrons	1	6	2	4	5	6	0
Number of low-lying atomic orbitals	4(sp^3)	9(sp^3d^5)	4(sp^3)	4(sp^3)	4(sp^3)	4(sp^3)	0

metalloids are elements that have just enough electrons to fill the orbitals, normal $CN = 4$, but few, if any, nonbonding electrons are "left over." In these terms (of filling the available orbitals) metals are electron-deficient. One result of having more orbitals than electrons is a delocalization of the electron cloud, accounting for the properties associated with metals. Nonmetals, on the other hand, have localized electron clouds, since all the low-lying orbitals are full and the Pauli exclusion principle "prevents" electron delocalization.

We now can see why metallic character normally increases as we go down most of the families in the periodic table. Cesium is more metallic than sodium, lead is more metallic than silicon, and iodine is more metallic than fluorine because, in every case, additional low-lying orbitals are present in the element of higher atomic number, and its ionization energy is less.

DEFECT COMPOUNDS

There is a large group of compounds of metals and nonmetals—for example, pyrites (FeS_2), tungsten bronzes ($NaWO_3$), cuprous oxide (Cu_2O)—which have high metallic luster and relatively good electrical conductivity, though somewhat lower than most metals. The delocalization of electrons in these substances, which are not very close to being stoichiometric in composition, arises from deficiencies of anions or cations, and the resulting freeing, or delocalization, of some of the electrons.

Thus the tungsten bronzes are deficient in oxygen. Typical compositions are $Ca_{0.10}WO_3$ and $NaWO_{<3}$ (instead of the expected $Ca_{0.010}WO_{3.10}$ and $NaWO_{3.5}$). Such compositions can be interpreted to mean that the bronzes contain tungsten having an oxidation state between 5 and 6, but the bronzes can also (and better) be considered to be formed by the reaction

$$O^{=}{}_{(c)} = \tfrac{1}{2}O_{2(g)} + 2e^{-}{}_{(c)}$$

in which an oxygen atom leaves the crystal and the electrons remain to give the luster and conductivity found in the resulting slightly reduced substances. Fe_2O_3, CdO, and ZnO form similar oxygen-deficient lattices. The lattice is that expected for the stoichiometric formula, but there are holes in the lattice where anions are missing, plus free electrons to keep the overall lattice charge equal to zero. The free electrons conduct negative current and hence these substances are called *n*-type (negative) semiconductors. "Semi" since their conductivity is less than that of most metals.

Cation-deficient structures also exist, such as $Fe_{0.95}O$, $Fe_{\ 1}S_2$, $Fe_{0.86}S$, and $Cu_{1.96}S$ (rather than the expected FeO, FeS_2, FeS, and Cu_2S). In these substances there are vacant cation sites which act as positive holes in the lattice. For example, $Fe_{0.95}S$ consists of close-packed sulfur nuclei with 95% of the octahedral holes occupied by iron nuclei. The whole structure is electrically neutral. Thus 5% of the octahedral sites are empty and can be thought of as holes with two units of positive charge. Alternately, all of the sulfurs and 90/95ths of the irons may be considered as $S^{=}$ and Fe^{++} entities respectively. The other irons then act like Fe^{+++}, each containing one less electron than an Fe^{++}. Thus the Fe^{+++} act as positive holes in the lattice. Electrons migrating from Fe^{++} to the Fe^{+++}, or from Fe^{++} to the positive octahedral holes, give an effective positive current in the reverse direction. The Fe^{+++}, or the positive holes, appear to be moving in the direction opposite to that of the electrons. These substances are therefore said to be *p*-type (or positive) semiconductors. They also may have metallic luster, as do *n*-type semiconductors.

METALS AS CATALYSTS

We have already discussed catalysts in a general way in Chapter 32. Now we can use our additional knowledge of metals to investigate their catalytic behavior more thoroughly. Metals are particularly good catalysts for reactions involving hydrogen.

Hydrogenations: $N_{2(g)} + 3H_{2(g)} = 2NH_{3(g)}$ (33.3)

$C_2H_{4(g)} + H_{2(g)} = C_2H_{6(g)}$ (33.4)

Dehydrogenation: $C_2H_{6(g)} = C_2H_{4(g)} + H_{2(g)}$ (33.5)

Hydrogenolysis: $\rangle\!\!-C-X_{(g)} + H_{2(g)} = \rangle\!\!-C-H_{(g)} + HX_{(g)}$ (33.6)

The fact that reaction (33.5) is the reverse of (33.4) should remind you that all catalysts catalyze both the forward and reverse reactions equally and do not change the equilibrium state.

Metals are also used in some oxidations—remember the platinum-catalyzed conversion of SO_2 to SO_3—but most oxidations are catalyzed by metallic oxides.

We shall concentrate on hydrogenation reactions, some of which have been previously mentioned. The fact that metals catalyze hydrogen reactions is consistent with the existence of many hydrides (Figure 12.1) and the preceding discussion of interstitial compounds. But it should be clear that heterogeneous hydrogenations must occur at the surface of the metal and not in the bulk metal, so that it is surface interactions between metals and hydrogen that we must examine in interpreting the experimental results.

ADSORPTION ON METALS

All metals except gold show the same sequence of adsorption power. Oxygen is most strongly adsorbed, and nitrogen least strongly, in the following sequence:

$$O_2 > C_2H_2 > C_2H_4 > CO > H_2 > CO_2 > N_2$$

Table 33.4 relates this sequence to metallic properties.

Since heterogeneous catalysis requires adsorption, Table 33.4 allows the rapid elimination of many possibilities in the search for a catalyst. Note the trends

Table 33.4 Adsorption power of some gas-metal systems (+ = adsorption; − = adsorption negligible).

Adsorbent metal (in periodic table form)	Adsorbate gas: O_2 >	C_2H_2 >	C_2H_4 >	CO >	H_2 >	CO_2 >	N_2
Ti V Cr Fe Zr Nb Mo Hf Ta W	+	+	+	+	+	+	+
Co Ni	+	+	+	+	+	+	+
Rh Pd Ir Pt	+	+	+	+	+	−	−
Al Mn Cu Au[a]	+	+	+	+	−	−	−
K	+	+	−	−	−	−	−
Si Mg Zn Ge As Ag Cd In Sn Sb Pb Bi	+	−	−	−	−	−	−

[a] Au does not adsorb oxygen, but is otherwise similar to Cu, Al, and Mn.

in catalytic power of the metals as related to the periodic table, as well as related to the bonding situation in the adsorbate.

Exercise 33.7

What property do all the strongly adsorbing metals have in common? *Answer:* All the strongly adsorbing metals are near the middle of the periodic table. They have intermediate values of I.E. and atomic size, and they all have empty *d* orbitals. These conditions allow adsorption of a large variety of adsorbates, since a variety of orbitals with varying symmetry are available for bonding.

CATALYTIC HYDROGENATION ON METALS

Using hydrogen and nickel as an example, adsorption could occur as molecules of H_2 or as atoms of H, and the sites could be either individual nickel atoms or pairs or groups of atoms, as in Figure 33.12, where a few possibilities are shown. Evidence is accumulating that the most usual arrangement is hydrogen atoms in the cusps. See Table 33.2 for the preference of H atoms for tetrahedral sites. The energetics of the adsorption process are shown schematically in Figure 33.13.

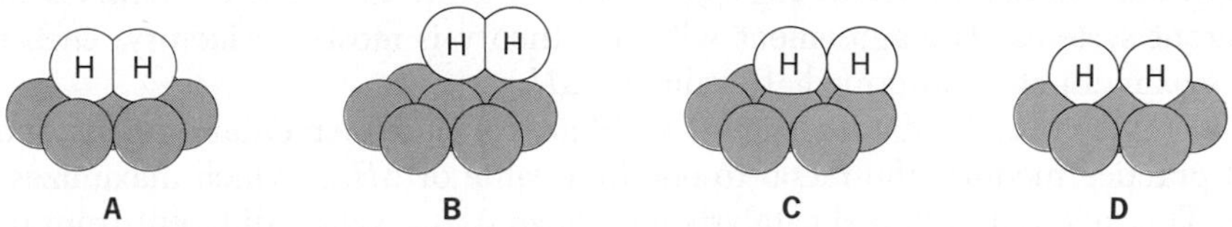

Figure 33.12 Possible adsorption site occupancies for hydrogen on nickel.

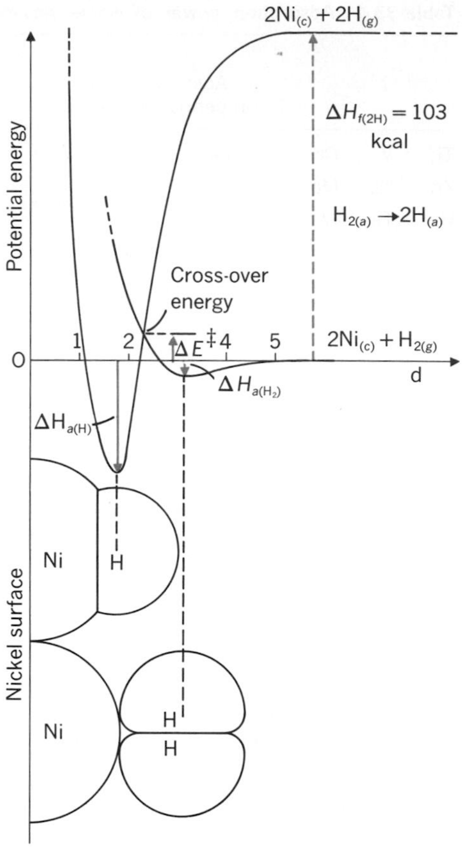

Figure 33.13 Energetics of hydrogen adsorption on nickel.

From our discussion in Chapter 32 it should be clear that the heat of adsorption, ΔH_{ads}, will strongly affect the catalytic reaction. If ΔH_{ads} (which is always negative) is very large, the adsorbed atoms will be tightly held; the ΔG_{des} for their desorption or removal will tend to be positive in spite of the positive entropy change on removal. Reaction will be both slow (high activation energy) and have an unfavorable adsorption equilibrium (unfavorable ΔG_{des}). On the other hand, if ΔH_{ads} is very small, few atoms will be adsorbed, since ΔS favors the gas phase, and ΔG_{ads} will tend to be positive. The low rate of reaction, limited by the small surface coverage, will more than cancel out any favorable ΔG for the over-all catalytic step, and there will be little catalytic effect. We thus expect a maximum catalytic effect at some intermediate value of ΔH_{ads}, where the surface coverage is high enough to give a satisfactory rate and ΔH_{ads} is low enough to allow the desorption reaction to occur. Figure 33.14 gives some experimental data for three different systems. The agreement with our theory is most satisfactory; each rate is a maximum at an intermediate value of ΔH_{ads}.

Note that the data in Figure 33.14 are for pure elementary metals. Industrial practice modifies the metal to obtain a value of ΔH_{ads} which maximizes the rate. Thus alloys and doped catalysts may have ΔH_{ads} values different from those of the pure elements and may be even better catalysts.

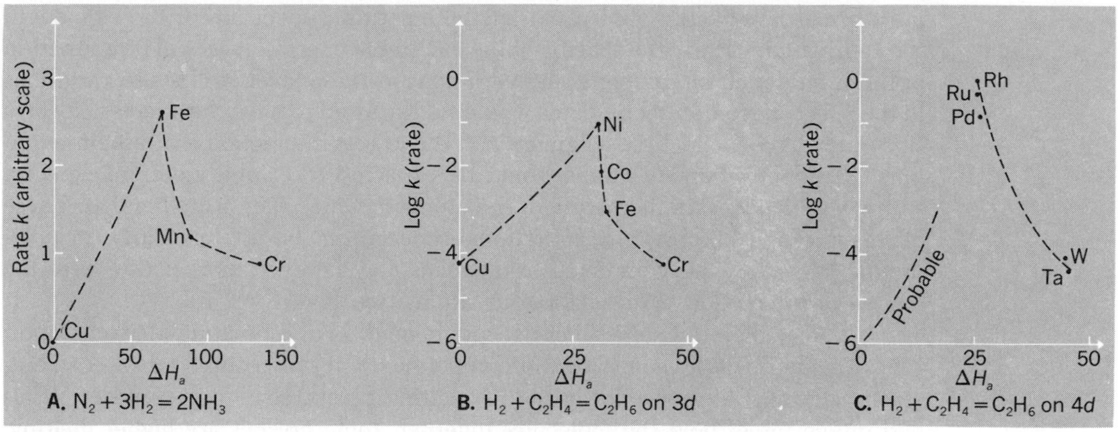

Figure 33.14 The rates of three catalyzed reactions as a function of the heat of adsorption of hydrogen or nitrogen on the metal catalyst. (**A**) Nitrogen is adsorbed in the rate-determining step. (**B** and **C**) The absorption of H_2 is rate-determining.

COMPOUNDS OF METALS AND NONMETALS

The metallic elements and most of the intermetallic compounds are characterized by highly delocalized electrons in crystal orbitals. In many cases the electrons are still delocalized in the liquid state, though not in the gaseous state. As elements form compounds with other elements that differ more and more from them in relative electronegativity, the compounds become more and more ionic and the electrons become more and more localized. The metallic element usually forms positive ions in these compounds if its oxidation state is low, and the charge on the positive ion often equals the oxidation state of the element. Thus all the elements of Group I show an oxidation state of $+1$ in their compounds with nonmetals and they exist as ions of $+1$ charge in the crystalline and liquid state of the compounds. In the same way the Group II elements show only a $+2$ oxidation state and exist in all their thermodynamically stable compounds at room temperature as positive ions of $+2$ charge.

The situation is not so clear with the elements of Group III. True, scandium, yttrium, and lanthanum and the lanthanides all form a $+3$ oxidation state, which always is considered as made of $+3$ charged species, as is also true of the $+3$ state of actinium and the actinides. But the lanthanides and actinides show thermodynamically stable states other than $+3$, and aluminum and boron compounds show evidence of a high degree of covalent character and delocalized bonding.

Similar complications arise, to an increasing degree, as the relative electronegativities of the metallic elements increase further toward those of the nonmetals. The number of stable oxidation states increases, as does the likelihood of finding compounds that appear largely covalent in bonding. In general, the covalency increases as the oxidation state of the metallic element becomes more positive. For example, chromium is quite ionic in the $+2$ state, is either ionic or covalent in the $+3$ state, and is largely covalent in the $+6$ state.

The degree of ionic character may be estimated in several ways but the most direct is probably observation of the electronic spectrum of the element in the compound. Clearly the spacing of the electronic energy levels will be a function of the interatomic interactions, and variations in these levels will cause variations in the spectra. Noninteracting ions would be expected to have the simplest spectra since they have the highest symmetry and the lowest interactions with their neighbors. Covalently bonded atoms would be expected to exhibit electronic spectra strongly dependent on the nature of the atoms to which they were bonded. These effects are, indeed, observed. Vibrational spectra may be used similarly for polyatomic ions since the vibrational frequencies may be even more sensitive to the degree of interaction with neighboring atoms (see Figure 33.15).

A simpler, but sometimes deceptive, method of estimating ionic character relies on the melting points of the compounds. Crystals composed of covalent, electrically neutral molecules have low melting points, since only van der Waals and dipole forces hold the molecules together. Ionic crystals are higher melting, since coulombic forces are stronger than dipole or van der Waals forces. The evidence is accumulating, however, that the converse of the above may not be true. Some low-melting substances are ionic, since some ionic substances form electrically neutral aggregates in the crystal because of the stoichiometry of the substance and the coordination numbers achieved. Thus the sharp transition in melting point

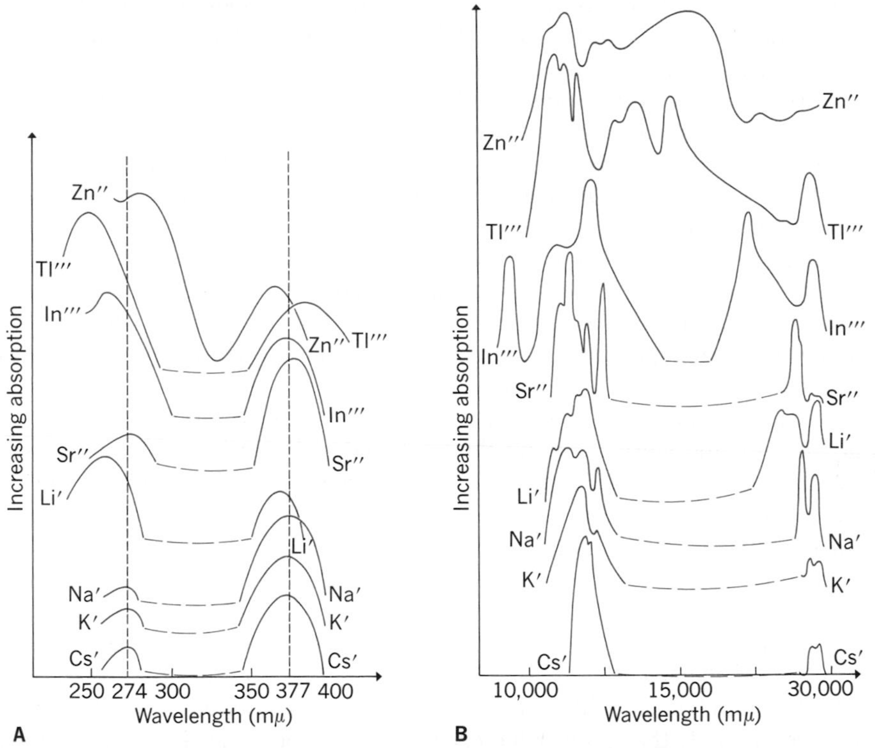

Figure 33.15 Parts of the (**A**) electronic, and (**B**) vibrational spectra of chromate ion in several crystals. Note the similarity within each type of spectra for the Group I chromates, suggesting they are almost equally ionic, and the increased deviation from this simple spectrum as the charge density and *d*-orbital availability of the metallic element increase from bottom to top of the figure.

Table 33.5 Correlation of melting point (°K) and ionic-covalent character of the bonding.

Primarily ionic		Primarily covalent				
LiCl (883)	$BeCl_2$ (678)	BCl_3 (167)	CCl_4 (250)	NCl_3 (<230)	OCl_2 (213)	Cl_2 (170)
NaCl (1081)	$MgCl_2$ (987)	Al_2Cl_6 (465)	$SiCl_4$ (205)	PCl_3 (181)	SCl_2 (195)	BrCl (207)

from $MgCl_2$ to $AlCl_3$ shown in Table 33.5 is better interpreted, perhaps, in terms of neutral Al_2Cl_6 aggregates with $CN = 4$ presenting a uniform Cl surface to similar surrounding molecules, whereas the $MgCl_2$ cannot achieve any such neutral, symmetrical aggregates due to the radius ratio, stoichiometry, and resulting CN in the $MgCl_2$ crystal. The other low-melting substances in Table 33.5 are usually treated as primarily covalent; the high-melting substances primarily ionic.

Metallic fluorides and oxides are usually highly ionic, as are almost all Group I and Group II compounds, plus many chlorides and perchlorates. Note that all these species have rather low charge densities and lack unfilled orbitals. We shall discuss the detailed chemistry of these metallic compounds later.

SUMMARY

Metals are substances containing highly delocalized electrons. The delocalization results from the much greater number of low-lying orbitals than of available valence electrons. The high electrical and thermal conductivity and the luster of metals depend on the high electron mobility in the delocalized orbitals. The high malleability depends on the existence of glide planes and the minimal directional nature of metallic bonds.

Alloys form through substitution of various similar atoms in the host lattice, through interstitial introduction of secondary atoms, or through compound formation with a resulting new lattice. Alloys are normally lower in conductivity, luster, and malleability than the most metallic of their constituents, since the electrons tend to be more localized and there are fewer glide planes in the alloy.

Catalytic effects on metallic surfaces correlate well with this picture of metallic structure and the resulting variation of ΔH_{ads} from system to system.

The existence of stable covalent compounds with metal-metal bonds raises the possibility of studying bonds that vary systematically from purely metallic to purely covalent, just as we already study bonds that combine ionic and covalent properties in varying degrees.

In research and invention work you fail hundreds and even thousands of times and if you succeed once you are in.—
C. Kettering, in G. Thomson, The Inspiration of Science, Oxford University Press, New York, 1961.

I seem to have spent much more of my life not solving [crystal] structures than solving them.—*Dorothy C. Hodgkin,* Science, **150,** 979 (1965).

PROBLEMS

33.1. Zirconium and hafnium are almost identical in chemical behavior. Interpret this fact.

33.2. Yttrium is commonly found associated with the lanthanide elements in their ores. Interpret this fact. Scandium is more apt to be found separately. Why?

33.3. Only polonium, of all the elements, has a simple cubic structure. Suggest a reason for the scarcity of this structure.

33.4. If a metal can exist in either a close-packed or *bcc* structure, which would you expect to be the high-temperature form?

33.5. A common brass is known as 60–40. What phases are apt to be present? Why is this a common brass—that is, what desirable properties will it probably have?

33.6. Two metallic surfaces are made very flat and clean in a vacuum, then clamped together for a long time at a temperature just below their melting points. What would you expect to happen if the two metals were: (*a*) Both copper? (*b*) Both chromium? (*c*) Copper and zinc? (*d*) Silver and copper? (*e*) Lead and iron? Be as specific as possible.

33.7. Suggest a method of research for finding an improved catalyst for the hydrogenation of ethylene.

33.8. Rationalize the fact that malleability of metals normally increases as T rises, whereas electrical conductivity decreases.

33.9. Tiny amounts of impurities, sometimes in the parts-per-million range, can markedly affect electrical conductivity of metals. Suggest an interpretation.

33.10. Cold working (such as bending, deep drawing, or hammering) of a metal at room temperature usually makes it harder and less malleable. Suggest a molecular mechanism and a means of minimizing the effect.

33.11. Addition of ferric oxide catalyzes the decomposition of hydrogen peroxide into water and oxygen. Can you suggest a possible mechanism for the interaction? What should be the relative effectiveness of finely ground rather than coarse ferric oxide?

33.12. Tempering (heating, holding at a set temperature, then cooling rapidly) can produce very hard steels, but actually softens most brasses. Why the difference? Compare Figures 33.10 and 35.12.

33.13. The introduction of minute amounts of metallic sodium into a sodium chloride lattice gives a blue crystal. Suggest an interpretation.

33.14. What properties would you expect for the following compounds? (*a*) AlP, (*b*) $Na_{11}Hg$, (*c*) TiC, (*d*) FeH_2, (*e*) ZrB, (*f*) Cu_5Sn, (*g*) $FeZn_7$, (*h*) $TiO_{0.69}$.

II

33.15. Predict probable metallic radii and crystal structures for elements 103, 104, 105, and 106.

33.16. Identify the structure of the η phase in the Cu-Zn system.

33.17. The thermal conductivities (watts inch^{-1} °K^{-1}) of annealed (highly crystalline) and drawn (distorted crystalline) silver is given as a function of T. Interpret the trends in terms of atomic-crystalline behavior.

T (°K)	20	30	80	300
Annealed	132	47	10.4	10.2
Drawn	5.8	7.0	7.6	10.0

33.18. Raney nickel, a much-used hydrogenation catalyst, is prepared by treating a Ni-Al alloy of 50-50 percent by weight with water at 70–80°C and storing the product under water until it is needed. Suggest (*a*) the equation for the net reaction with water, (*b*) the reason the resulting catalyst is so much more catalytic than ground-up nickel, (*c*) why the catalyst is stored under water, rather than dry.

III

33.19. Ytterbium undergoes a transition from *fcc* to *bcc* at 40,000 atm and 25°C [H. T. Hall, J. D. Burnett, L. Merrill, *Science*, **139**, 111 (1963)]. (*a*) Calculate the expected change in volume in going from *fcc* to *bcc* if there is no change in atomic radius. Is this consistent with the experimental facts? (*b*) There is an actual volume decrease of 3.2 percent. Estimate the *bcc* atomic radius if the *fcc* radius is known to be 1.82 Å at this high pressure. (*c*) Look up the electron structure of Yb and account for this unusual behavior.

33.20. The flow of electrons in a thermistor and the effect of temperature on the characteristics of a thermistor are analogous (1) to viscous flow in liquids, or (2) to the vaporization of a liquid. (*a*) Briefly discuss each of these analogies in terms of the mechanism of the processes being compared. (*b*) A student obtained the following laboratory data for the resistance of his thermistor as a function of temperature. Calculate the activation energy for electron flow in this thermistor in kcal/mole.

R (ohms)	9442	3956	330
T (°C)	0	22	99

(*c*) What is the temperature when the thermistor has a resistance of 3000 ohms? (*d*) What fraction of the electrons, which can become conducting with the activation energy calculated in *b* above, are conducting at 22°C? ($\Delta E_{\text{act}} \cong 7$ kcal mole^{-1}.)

33.21. Vanadium (at. wt. 51.0) crystallizes in a body-centered cubic structure with $a =$ 3.04 Å. Boron (at. wt. 10.8) can be dissolved in vanadium to the extent of 4 atom percent. Assuming that the lattice parameter is essentially unchanged, calculate the density of the saturated solution (*a*) if interstitial, and (*b*) if substitutional. Could reasonably accurate measurements of density distinguish between the two structures? ($\rho_{\text{sub}} \cong 0.97\ \rho_{\text{V}}$.)

33.22. The work function of a metal surface is defined as the potential (or potential difference) in volts that an electron must overcome before it can escape from the surface of the metal to infinity with no resultant kinetic energy. Light of wavelength 3000 Å is incident upon an aluminum sheet and causes photoelectrons to be emitted from the surface. One such electron escapes to a great distance and collides with a proton, ending up in the third excited state of the hydrogen atom. What was the wavelength of the photon emitted in the process if the work function for aluminum is 3.0 volts? ($\lambda \cong 6000$ Å.)

See page 1094 for a list of references and readings in the recent chemical literature related to the material in this chapter.

CHAPTER 34

Fluids

Crystals exist when a repetitive unit cell is the most probable molecular arrangement. At higher temperatures and/or lower pressures, entropy effects lead to less structured, or fluid, phases.

We have now dealt at considerable length with atomic structure, molecular structure, and crystal structure. In each of these systems strong restoring forces give spatial entities which retain their shape and symmetry over long periods of time. Thus we have nodal patterns in electron structures, bond lengths and angles in molecules, and lattices in crystals. In this chapter we will consider systems, called fluids, in which the restoring forces are much smaller and in which symmetry is more evanescent.

GASES, LIQUIDS, AND CRYSTALS

The distinction most commonly made between crystals, liquids, and gases is that crystals have a shape determined by the crystal phase, liquids have a shape determined by the bottom of the container, and gases have a shape determined by the total volume of the container. We say that gases flow in all directions until they fill their container, liquids flow "downward" under the influence of gravity until they fill the bottom of their container, and crystals do not flow—they retain their shape. Unfortunately this definition is not very operational. All liquids, for instance, flow more and more slowly as they are cooled, and all crystals can be made to flow if the applied stress is great enough. In fact there are many crystals which flow more rapidly than do many liquids, even though the stress and temperature may be the same for both systems. For example, at room temperature it is far easier to extrude metallic sodium or aluminum (both crystalline) into formed shapes than it is to deform glass (a fluid).

A much more satisfactory and operational distinction can be based on the degree of structural symmetry in the phase. Crystals have high symmetry, expressed in a regularly repeating pattern or lattice (Chapter 31). Fluids do not have such a repeating pattern. Fluids are amorphous.

STRUCTURE IN LIQUIDS

Figure 34.1 shows X-ray scattering patterns for liquid mercury, compared with those obtained for crystalline mercury. The pattern from crystalline or dilute gaseous mercury is almost independent of temperature and pressure. Only a slight broadening of the lines occurs as the temperature and/or pressure increases. For any liquid, however, the pattern is a strong function of the temperature, as shown in Figure 34.1.

We saw in Chapter 31 that the X-ray scattering pattern is a function of the

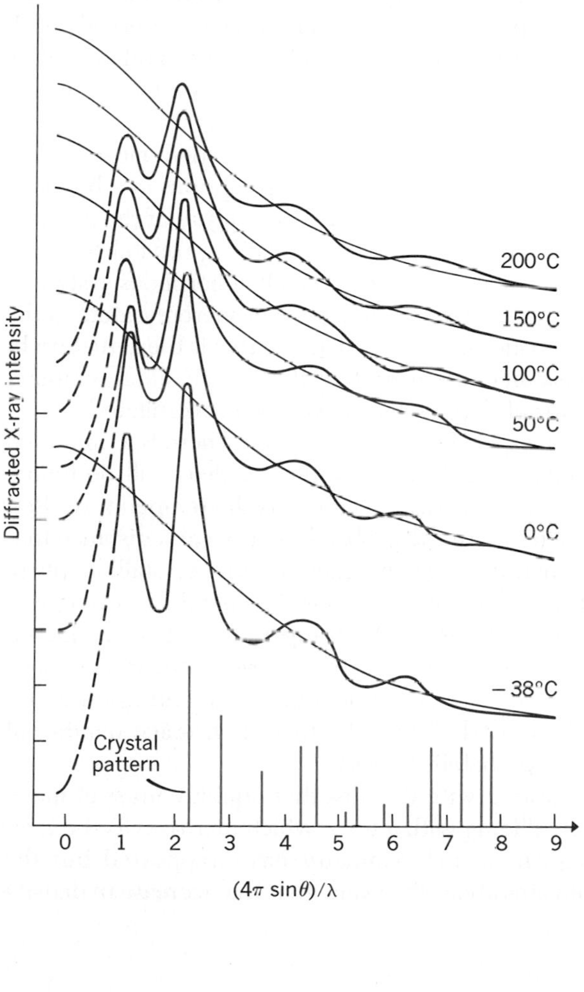

Figure 34.1 Intensity of X-rays diffracted by liquid mercury versus an angular function. Note the diffused nature of the diffraction as contrasted to the sharp lines obtained from crystals. The smooth curves would be obtained if there were no structure. [J. A. Campbell and J. H. Hildebrand, *J. Chem. Phys.*, **2,** 330 (1943).]

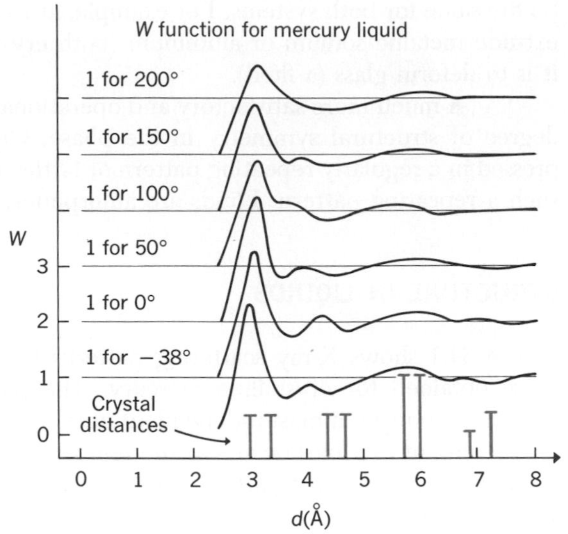

Figure 34.2 Relative probability of finding a mercury nucleus at distance *d* from any one nucleus compared to a continuous uniform distribution as having $W = 1$. The height of the crystal distance markers indicates number of atoms (6, 12, or 3). [J. A. Campbell and J. H. Hildebrand, *J. Chem. Phys.*, **2**, 330 (1943).]

electron distribution in the scattering system. Apparently the electron distribution in liquid mercury varies with temperature. Similar variation is observed in all liquids. On the other hand, the electron distribution in ideal gases and crystals is independent of temperature and pressure, though highly compressed gases (which are never ideal) show variations similar to those found in liquids.

Analysis of X-ray diffraction patterns from liquids is carried out in a manner similar to that followed for crystals, except that no assumptions can be made about a repeating symmetry pattern. The results of such an analysis of the patterns in Figure 34.1 are shown in Figure 34.2 in the form of a relative probability curve. The horizontal line at $W = 1$ is calculated for a completely amorphous system in which the probability of finding the center, or nucleus, of a mercury atom is the same at all distances from any given atom. The undulating curve is the actual probability distribution found in liquid mercury at each of the experimental temperatures. Similar curves are found for all liquids that have been investigated.

The following features are especially noteworthy. (1) There is a minimum distance within which it is negligibly likely that another nucleus will be found. (2) This "distance of closest approach" decreases slightly as the temperature rises. (3) There is a relatively sharp maximum in the probability curve at a distance that closely approximates the internuclear distance found in the crystalline phase (3.00 Å). (4) The position of this first maximum is almost independent of temperature, but the curve broadens and flattens as the temperature rises. (5) Lower maxima, which are quite temperature-sensitive in many cases, occur at greater distances, but the maximum at about 6 Å does not shift much, and again corresponds to a distance found in the crystal. Table 34.1 lists the average number of atoms represented by each of the probability peaks.

All of these data are consistent with the idea that liquids consist of molecules that are in contact and are colliding with a force which increases as the temperature increases, that the regular crystal symmetry has disappeared but the average internuclear distance remains about the same, that the decrease in density typical of crystal-to-liquid transitions is caused by a loss in packing efficiency rather than by the molecules moving further apart, and that order, in the sense of highly probable internuclear distances, is characteristic only of the first few sets of neighboring atoms.

Similar data have been obtained for most of the elements that can be readily liquefied (see the coordination numbers for liquids listed in Figure 5.13), for some simple polyatomic liquids (such as CCl_4, H_2O, SnI_4), and for some salts (such as alkali halides). The results are consistent with the model presented in the last paragraph.

Exercise 34.1

The W curve for liquid sulfur has an area under its first peak equivalent to two atoms and the curve drops to 0 at higher d before rising again to values of $W = 1$ and higher, as for mercury in Figure 34.2. Rationalize the area of the first peak in sulfur and the value $W = 0$ just beyond it. *Answer:* A $CN = 2$ indicates chains or rings of atoms in sulfur. The value of $W = 0$ indicates strong bonds within the chains and rings with little bond breaking, so that the only probable distance for a nearest neighbor is at the covalent bond distance. Remember our past discussions of crystalline and liquid sulfur.

LIQUID CRYSTALS

A most interesting class of systems is typified by para-azoxyanisole,

$$CH_3OC_6H_4NN(O)C_6H_4OCH_3.$$

The crystalline material is yellow and melts at 84°C to give a murky yellow liquid, which at 150°C changes to a clear brown liquid. Each of the liquids is highly fluid. Cooling the system reverses each change. Furthermore, each change occurs at a well-defined temperature. Since, at a fixed pressure, $F = C - P + 1$ and here $C = 1$, a fixed transition temperature indicates that $F = 0$ and $P = 2$.

Thus both the murky yellow liquid and the clear brown liquid must be single pure phases of *para*-azoxyanisole. Many pure substances are known which can exist in more than one liquid phase. Often as many as three identifiable liquid phases are found. A large number of these substances are biologically active molecules, such as cholesterol and other steroids.

X-ray diffraction and other studies of these liquid phases indicate that the low-temperature forms always exhibit more structure than the higher-temperature phases, consistent with the second law. Figure 34.3 indicates the accepted interpretation in terms of a

Table 34.1 Distance (in Ångstroms) and number of atoms per coordination "layer" in liquid mercury.

		Peak I		Peak II		Peak III	Peak IV
T (°C)	r_{min}	Position	No. of atoms	Position	No. of atoms	Position	Position
200	2.24	3.05	5.9	—	—	6.2	—
150	2.29	3.00	5.3	3.95	3.8	6.0	—
100	2.32	3.00	5.5	3.85	5.8	6.0	—
50	2.34	3.00	5.8	3.95	4.7	6.0	7.0
0	2.36	3.00	5.8	4.17	6.0	6.1	6.9
−38	2.40	3.00	6.0	4.08	5.0	6.0	6.7

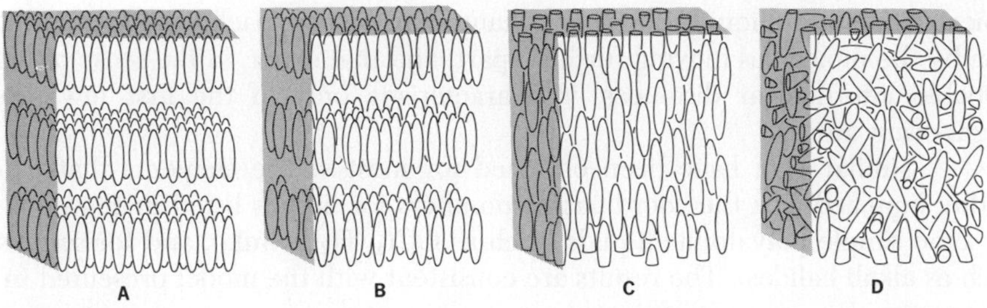

Figure 34.3 Comparison of crystal, liquid-crystal, and liquid structures. **A.** Crystal: three-dimensional order. **B.** Smetic: two-dimensional order; disorder in planes. **C.** Nematic: one-dimensional order; two-dimensional disorder. **D.** Liquid: three-dimensional disorder.

single liquid phase and one or more liquid-crystal phases, in which symmetry in one or two dimensions in the fluid is obtained, owing to the symmetry of the molecules and the strength of their intermolecular forces.

The murkiness of liquid crystals indicates that they contain aggregates whose dimensions exceed the wavelength of visible light, consistent with the picture in Figure 34.3.

It is very likely that the combination of high fluidity and high structure found in liquid crystals is consistent with their probably major role in living systems, where these two properties both have high survival value.

Exercise 34.2

What molecular properties are apt to lead to the formation of liquid crystals? *Answer:* A high degree of asymmetry—long thin molecules, or flat planar ones—will tend to allow little rotation in the liquid state at low T. The intermolecular bonding in the solid must not be strong or melting may not occur until T is so large that rotation will immediately set in when the substance melts.

VISCOSITY

We have already pointed out that differences in viscosity are not a satisfactory means of distinguishing crystals, liquids, and gases, but we will be able to clarify our discussion of fluids if we first investigate viscosity, generally defined as "resistance to flow." Fluidity is the inverse of viscosity.

Qualitatively it is easy to say that dilute gases have low viscosities, most crystals have high viscosities, and most liquids have intermediate viscosities. But everyone knows that viscosity varies with temperature; familiar instances involve glass, sulfur, and tar. Let us investigate viscosity quantitatively, together with its variation with temperature.

Viscosity is defined as the force necessary to impart unit velocity gradient per unit of area (as in Figure 34.4); by

NEWTON'S LAW:

$$\eta = \frac{F}{(dv/dr)A} = \frac{mlt^{-2}}{(lt^{-1}/l)l^2} = ml^{-1}t^{-1} \tag{34.1}$$

We may interpret viscosity at the molecular level in the following ways: (1) the molecules in one level exert intermolecular forces on those in the next level, and these forces must be overcome if relative motion is to occur, or (2) the random

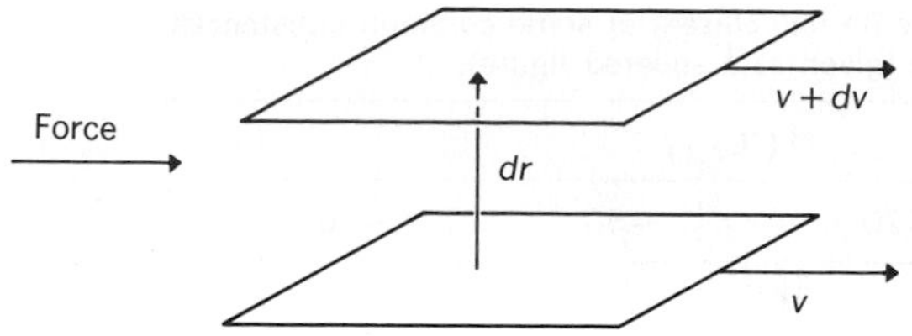

$$\eta = \frac{F}{(dv/dr)A} = \frac{mlt^{-2}}{(lt^{-1}/l)l^2} = ml^{-1}t^{-1}$$

Figure 34.4 Newton's definition of viscosity. The most common unit is the poise (g cm^{-1} sec^{-1}).

kinetic motions of the molecules will lead to their moving from one layer into the next, and this transfers momentum, which tends to slow down the faster moving layer and speed up the slower layer, again giving a force which must be overcome if a velocity gradient is to be maintained.

A viscosity analogy could be two passenger trains traveling close together in the same direction on parallel tracks, but at slightly different speeds. "Viscous drag" will occur if the passengers either reach out and grab hands between the two trains (effect 1), or if they leap back and forth between the two trains (effect 2).

DETERMINATION OF VISCOSITY

Determinations of viscosity are often made with an Ostwald viscometer (Figure 34.5) used as a comparison instrument. The time of flow of a known volume of liquid of known viscosity and density (usually water) is measured accurately. The viscometer is then cleaned and the same volume of the liquid whose viscosity is to be determined is introduced. Its time of flow is determined, and its density measured. The unknown viscosity can then be calculated with the equation:

$$\eta_{\text{unk}} = \frac{\eta_{\text{std}}(\rho\,\Delta t)_{\text{unk}}}{(\rho\,\Delta t)_{\text{std}}} \tag{34.2}$$

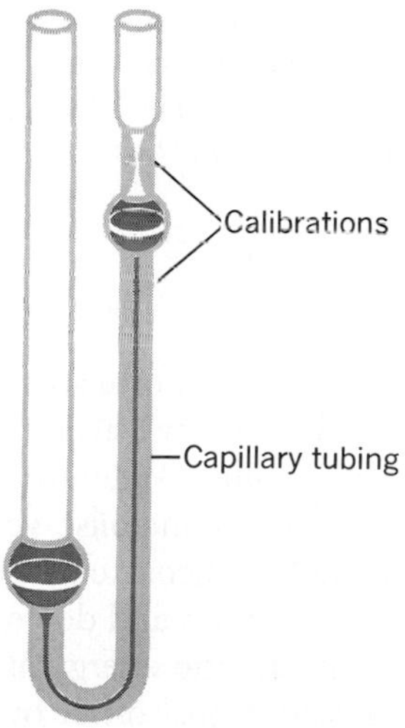

Figure 34.5 One type of Ostwald viscometer. Note that ΔP varies with time of flow but will vary reproducibly for all fluids as long as the viscometer is filled with the same volume of fluid each time.

Table 34.2 Presently accepted viscosities (in millipoises) of some common substances as a function of temperature (given as a supered figure).

Substance	T (°C) ~0	~20	~50	~100	Trend (⟶)
Liquids					
H_2O	17.93^{0}	10.02^{20}	5.48^{50}	2.83^{100}	decrease
C_6H_6	9.12^{0}	6.52^{20}	4.42^{50}	3.29^{80}	decrease
C_2H_5OH	17.73^{0}	12.00^{20}	7.00^{20}	5.04^{70}	decrease
$C_3H_5(OH)_3$	$121{,}100^{0}$	$14{,}900^{20}$	$6{,}290^{30}$	—	decrease
Gases					
H_2	0.0835^{0}	$0.0876^{20.7}$	$0.0976^{53.4}$	$0.109^{129.4}$	increase
Cl_2	$0.130^{12.7}$	0.133^{20}	0.147^{50}	0.168^{100}	increase
N_2	$0.171^{10.9}$	$0.178^{27.4}$	$0.189^{53.5}$	$0.219^{127.2}$	increase
He	0.186^{0}	0.194^{20}	—	0.228^{100}	increase
O_2	0.189^{0}	$0.202^{19.1}$	$0.216^{53.5}$	$0.257^{127.7}$	increase
Ar	0.210^{0}	0.222^{20}	—	0.269^{100}	increase

At any fixed temperature, $\eta_{\text{unk}} = K_T\,(\rho\,\Delta t)_{\text{unk}}$, where K_T is known as the viscometer constant at temperature, T.

In Table 34.2, which gives viscosity data for a few liquids and gases at least three notable trends are shown: (1) the liquids are about 100 times as viscous as the gases, (2) the liquids decrease in viscosity as T increases, and (3) the gases increase in viscosity as T increases. Most other liquids and gases behave similarly. Experiment shows that both liquid and gaseous viscosities are almost independent of density.

Exercise 34.3

A viscometer has been carefully calibrated with water. Would the viscometer be readily useful in determining the viscosity of glycerine? *Answer:* The time of flow of water should be at least one minute, if it is to be measured with any accuracy. The same viscometer would give, at 20°C with glycerine, a time of flow of about 1000 minutes or 16 hours—hardly a convenient figure. The viscosities of very viscous materials are customarily measured with other instruments, such as spheres falling through the liquid, which can give absolute viscosities directly.

VISCOSITY AND TEMPERATURE

A decrease in viscosity as temperature increases is what we think of as normal behavior. When viscosity increases with temperature, as in liquid sulfur, we suspect unusual structural effects, such as the chain formation found in sulfur. When the viscosity of a liquid is almost independent of temperature, as for silicone oils, we again look for a structural interpretation. In this case we find that the silicone chains tend to coil at low temperatures (because of the alternating polarity up and down the chain) and to uncoil at higher temperatures (because of the kinetic energy of the chain segments). The normally expected decrease in viscosity is just offset by the increase due to chain tangling, similar to that found in sulfur. This constancy of viscosity throughout a large temperature range makes silicone oils useful, even though costly, in engines which must start rapidly regardless of ambient temperatures.

The variation of viscosity with temperature for many liquids is found to follow the

DE GUZMAN RELATIONSHIP:

$$\frac{1}{\eta} = Ae^{-\Delta E^{\ddagger}/RT} \tag{34.3}$$

as shown in Figure 34.6. Note that this is the same type of relationship we found before for equilibrium constants [Figure 29.2 and Equation (29.21)] and for rate constants [Figure 22.2 and Equation (23.9)]. This has led to the interpretation of viscous flow in terms of a rate-determining step with activation energy, $\Delta E^{\ddagger}$. Eyring further interprets this rate-determining step as the breaking of enough intermolecular bonds to allow diffusion of a molecule into an adjacent hole. Note that this theory emphasizes the role of intermolecular forces in determining viscosity, our first model for viscous behavior. Normally the hole is too small to contain the full diffusing molecule, and this fractional size he calculates by dividing the activation energy for viscous flow by the energy of vaporization of the substance—that is, by the energy necessary to free a mole of molecules completely from the liquid state.

The increase of gaseous viscosity with temperature is consistent with our second model of the cause of viscosity (p. 868). As temperatures increase, the velocities and momenta of the molecules increase. At the higher temperature, each molecule transfers, on the average, more momentum every time it passes from one flowing layer to the next, and also makes the transfer more often. Thus the rate of momentum transfer, which is proportional to the viscosity, increases. The same effect holds in liquids, of course, but note that the rate of change in viscosity in gases that is due to this effect is far less than the rate of change in liquids. (See the data in Table 34.2.) Thus the activation energy effect predominates in liquids, but is, in turn, negligible in gases, where there are already plenty of "holes." Clearly

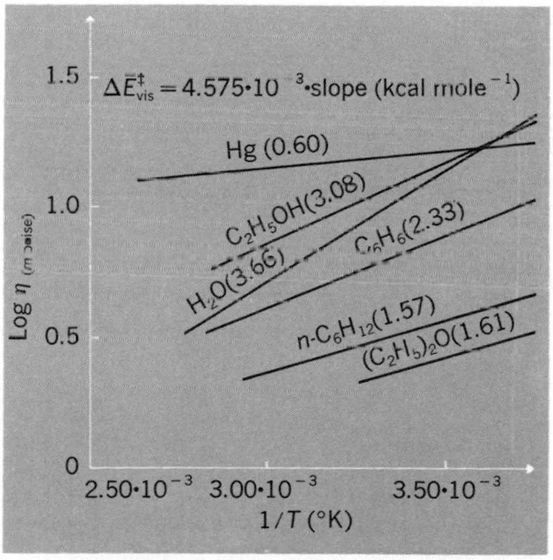

Figure 34.6 De Guzman plot: $1/T$ versus $\log \eta$. $\Delta \bar{E}_{vis}{}^{\ddagger}$ in parentheses.

there will be a range of densities where the two effects will almost balance. Therefore there should be a range of conditions for any substance in which its viscosity would be almost independent of changes in temperature. Experimental data shows such a region, but it is often above the critical temperature.

Exercise 34.4

Account for the high value of $\Delta \bar{E}^{\ddagger}_{vis}$ for H_2O in Figure 34.6. *Answer:* H_2O has the largest intermolecular forces of the substances listed because of its strong H bonds.

DISTINCTIONS BETWEEN CRYSTALS, LIQUIDS, AND GASES

We thus see that many of the flow properties of both gases and liquids are interpretable in terms of the same model if we merely adjust our arguments to be consistent with the changing ratio of molecular volume to total volume. Gases have a low ratio, liquids a high ratio. At intermediate ratios gases and liquids behave similarly. If we re-examine the phase diagrams for a single-component system (first presented in Figure 6.6), we find an even more remarkable fact, illustrated in Figure 34.7. It is possible to proceed from the gaseous state to the liquid state, or vice versa, without ever undergoing a phase change. In the general sense, gases and liquids constitute a single phase, the fluid phase.

We shall continue to find it useful to refer to gases and liquids as two distinct phases, but it should be remembered that there is no set of criteria which can distinguish a gas from a liquid, unless both are present, as along line *OT* in Figure 34.7. The denser fluid is called liquid, the less dense is called gas.

The operational distinctions we use for crystals, liquids, and gases often

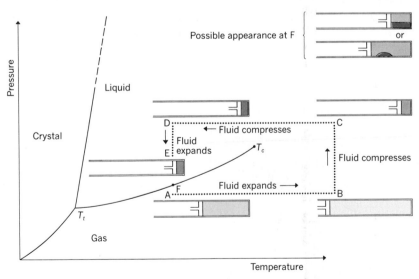

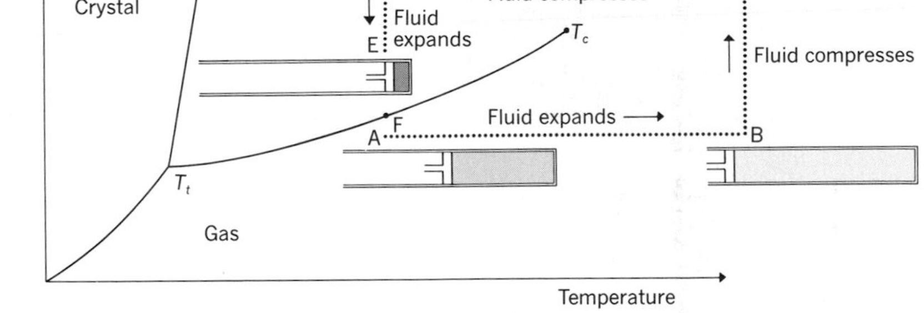

Figure 34.7 Change of appearance of system in moving from A → B → C → D → E, or vice versa, correlated with the phase diagram. Note that only a single phase is ever present. Only along line OT, as at F, are two phases, *l* and *g*, observable.

have to do with their relative fluidity and expansibility, but we have pointed out some of the inadequacies of these criteria. A better set would be the presence or absence of repeating unit cells to distinguish crystals from fluids, and the presence or absence of surface tension to distinguish crystals and liquids from gases. Liquids and crystals exist and are identifiable when the surface tension (intermolecular forces as opposed to kinetic forces) of the phase is high enough to define a fixed volume for the phase (either crystalline or liquid). Crystals exist when the temperature is low enough and the pressure high enough to make the repetitive unit cell the most probable molecular arrangement. At higher temperatures and/or lower pressures, entropy effects lead to nonstructured, or fluid, phases. (But remember that there are liquid crystals which do show two- and one-dimensional patterns.) It is well to remember that surface tension is measurable only when a surface exists, so we again see that liquids and gases are distinguishable only when both are present.

You should expect, and would find, that surface tension decreases as temperature rises, going to zero at the critical point (point T in Figure 34.7). The difference in enthalpy between liquid and gas—that is, the heat of vaporization of the liquid—also goes to zero. In fact, all properties that could serve to distinguish gases and liquids become identical at the critical temperature.

Exercise 34.5

Draw an approximate curve for $\Delta\bar{S}_{\text{vap}}$ versus T and comment on its shape. *Answer:* At 0°K, $\Delta\bar{S}_{\text{vap}} \longrightarrow \infty$, since $\bar{S}_{\text{crystal}} = 0$ and $\bar{S}_{\text{gas}} \longrightarrow \infty$ at zero pressure. At all T's, $\Delta\bar{S}_{\text{vap}} = \Delta\bar{H}_{\text{vap}}/T$. This means that $\Delta\bar{S}$ drops, rapidly at first and then slowly, since $\Delta\bar{H}$ is approximately constant over most of the pressure range, but T is increasing. As $T \longrightarrow T_C$, $\Delta\bar{S}$ again drops rapidly (due to decreasing $\Delta\bar{H}$), becoming zero at $T = T_C$.

EQUILIBRIA BETWEEN PHASES—ONE-COMPONENT SYSTEM

Consider a one-component system with two phases in equilibrium, using the

PHASE RULE: $$F = C - P + 2 = 1 - 2 + 2 = 1$$

Since there is only one degree of freedom, fixing either T or P fixes the other, and the T-P relationship will be a line on the phase diagram $T = \varphi(P)$. Let us calculate the equations of such lines. At equilibrium between phase α and phase β, $a_\alpha = a_\beta$ (activities are equal), and $\bar{G}_\alpha = \bar{G}_\beta$ (molar free energies are equal). If a change in P and/or T occurs and equilibrium is maintained, both molar free energies must change such that

$$dG_\alpha = dG_\beta, \qquad dP_\alpha = dP_\beta, \qquad \text{and} \qquad dT_\alpha = dT_\beta$$

From Table 26.3,

$$d\bar{G} = \bar{V}\,dP - \bar{S}\,dT$$

and thus

$$\bar{V}_\alpha\,dP - \bar{S}_\alpha\,dT = \bar{V}_\beta\,dP - \bar{S}_\beta\,dT$$

or

$$\frac{dP}{dT} = \frac{\bar{S}_\alpha - \bar{S}_\beta}{\bar{V}_\alpha - \bar{V}_\beta} = \frac{\Delta\bar{S}}{\Delta\bar{V}}$$

From Equation (27.6),

$$\Delta\bar{S}_{\text{phase change}} = \frac{\Delta\bar{H}_{\text{phase change}}}{T_{\text{phase change}}}$$

Substituting gives us the

CLAPEYRON EQUATION:

$$\frac{dP}{dT} = \frac{\Delta\bar{H}}{T\,\Delta\bar{V}} = \frac{\bar{H}_\alpha - \bar{H}_\beta}{T(\bar{V}_\alpha - \bar{V}_\beta)} \tag{34.4}$$

The Clapeyron equation holds for any phase change (vaporization, fusion, sublimation, liquid-liquid, crystal-crystal) in a one-component system. The Clapeyron equation is exact and is our desired *P-T* relationship.

The Clapeyron equation can be integrated for certain equilibria, especially if one phase, α, is an ideal gas. Then $\bar{V}_\beta \ll \bar{V}_\alpha = RT/P$, and

$$\frac{dP}{dT} = \frac{\Delta\bar{H}}{T(RT/P)}$$

$$\frac{d\ln P}{d(1/T)} = \frac{-\Delta\bar{H}}{R} \tag{34.5}$$

If we assume that $\Delta\bar{H}$ is independent of P and T (as is almost always true over short ranges), then we get the

CLAUSIUS-CLAPEYRON EQUATION:

$$\ln\frac{P_2}{P_1} = \frac{\Delta\bar{H}}{R}\left(\frac{1}{T_1} - \frac{1}{T_2}\right) = \frac{\Delta\bar{H}(T_2 - T_1)}{RT_1T_2} \tag{34.6}$$

We may also write this as

$$\log P = -\frac{\Delta\bar{H}}{2.303\,RT} + \text{const} = -\frac{a}{T} + b \tag{34.7}$$

Thus a plot of log P versus $1/T$ for an equilibrium between a condensed phase (crystal or liquid) and a gas gives a straight line of slope $(-\Delta\bar{H}/R)$. Figure 34.8 shows typical examples. The straight line indicates that $\Delta\bar{H}$ (indicated on the curves) is essentially constant in the range plotted as assumed in the derivation.

These straight lines are reminiscent of Figures 22.2, 29.2, and 34.6 in which log k, log K, and log η were all plotted versus $1/T$ to give straight lines. Note that all these functions (k, K, and η) are related to rate phenomena. The similarity in dependence on T should not be surprising since all these relationships involve reaction rate constants. In all these cases, use of experimental data at two points allows calculation of data over the whole equilibrium range, if $\Delta\bar{H}$ is constant.

Equation (34.7) also shows that a plot of P versus T for an equilibrium between a gas and a condensed phase is always a curve in which P increases more rapidly than does T, as shown in Figure 34.9 for a few typical substances.

For most equilibria between two condensed phases both $\Delta\bar{H}$ and $T\,\Delta\bar{V}$ prove to be almost independent of P and T. Then the Clapeyron equation becomes

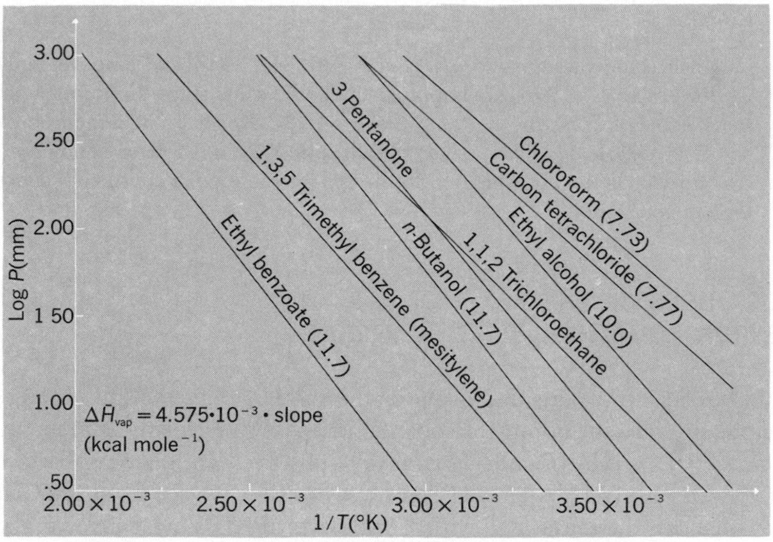

Figure 34.8 Calculation of enthalpy of phase changes involving gases from *P-T* data and the Clausius-Clapeyron equation. $\Delta\bar{H}$ is given in parentheses in units of kcal mole^{-1}. Note the rather small range of values, consistent with Trouton's rule. Deviations of 5–10% from values in Table 34.6 are mainly due to gas imperfections; the values here are high, since they assume ideal gas as a final state.

$$\frac{dP}{dT} = \frac{\Delta\bar{H}}{T\,\Delta\bar{V}} = b, \text{ a constant}$$

or

$$P = \frac{\Delta\bar{H}}{T\,\Delta\bar{V}}\,T + \text{constant} = bT + \text{constant} \qquad (34.8)$$

and the *P-T* curve approximates a straight line, as seen in Figures 6.8, 34.7, 34.10, and 35.1.

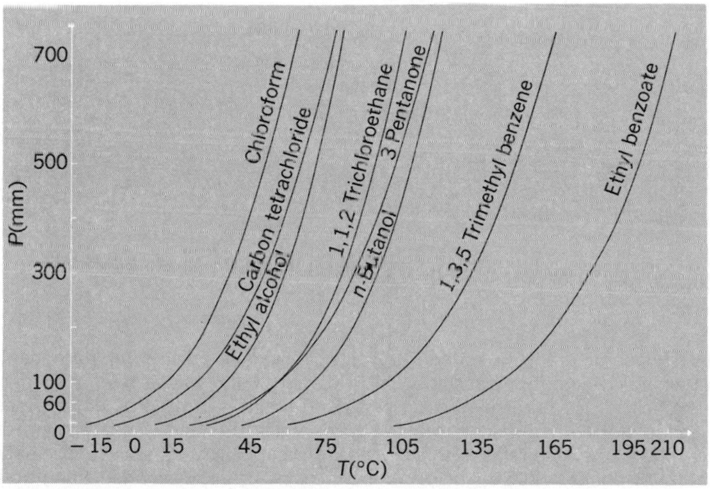

Figure 34.9 *P-T* curves for some typical covalent substances.

Exercise 34.6

Rationalize the variations in $\Delta\overline{H}_{\text{vap}}$ in Figure 34.8. *Answer:* Nonpolar liquids have the lower values of $\Delta\overline{H}_{\text{vap}}$, all approximately the same since the forces acting in all these liquids are nearly the same. Polar liquids, especially hydrogen bonded ones like C_2H_5OH, have higher values of $\Delta\overline{H}_{\text{vap}}$, indicating stronger bonding and more structure in the liquid compared to the gas for these polar substances compared to the nonpolar ones.

FURTHER USES OF THE CLAPEYRON EQUATION—$dP/dT = \Delta\overline{H}/T\,\Delta\overline{V}$

It should be clear from our discussion of thermodynamics that any increase in T of a system, at constant P, must involve an increase in H for the system, and vice versa, since $\Delta H = \int C_P\,dT$ and C_P is always positive. Thus any isobaric heating must involve a positive $\Delta\overline{H}$. Since T is always positive, we see from the Clapeyron equation that any increase of P with T (positive dP/dT) must involve a positive $\Delta\overline{V}$ (increase in $\overline{V}$). Similarly, any decrease in P as T increases (negative dP/dT) must involve a phase change of negative $\Delta\overline{V}$ (decrease in $\overline{V}$). Figure 34.10 illustrates this generalization, using the phase diagram for water. All P-T lines of positive slope involve a phase change, as T rises, of positive $\Delta\overline{H}$ and positive $\Delta\overline{V}$. All P-T lines of negative slope involve a phase change, as T rises, of positive $\Delta\overline{H}$ and negative $\Delta\overline{V}$. Thus the phase diagram not only contains P-T data, it also contains information on $\Delta\overline{H}$ and $\Delta\overline{V}$. From P-T lines of phase equilibria, and density data on the two phases (to give $\Delta\overline{V}$), $\Delta\overline{H}$ can be calculated. (Sometimes even the varia-

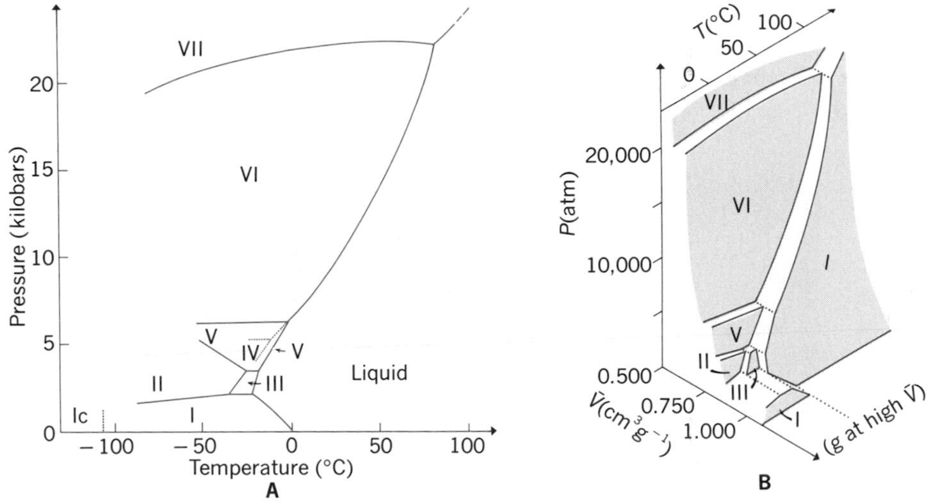

Figure 34.10 Phase diagram for water. The solid phases (ice polymorphs) are identified by the Roman numeral designations assigned by Bridgman, upon whose data the diagram is based. (**A**) The field of ice IV in relation to ice VI and liquid is plotted by dotted lines within the ice V field, and is plotted by analogy to D_2O ice, for which the field was actually measured; ice IV is everywhere unstable relative to ice V. Ice Ic ("cubic ice") is shown schematically below the temperature of about −105°C, below which it forms by vapor condensation and above which it inverts to ice I; it is not known to have a field of actual stability. [B. Kamb, *Science*, **150,** 206 (1965). Copyright 1965 by the American Association for the Advancement of Science.] (**B**) $\overline{V}$ also shown. Dotted lines at triple points.

Table 34.3 Data on crystal-liquid equilibria.

	$\Delta\overline{H}_{\text{fus}}$ (kcal mole^{-1})	$T_{\text{m.p.}}$ (°K)	$\Delta\overline{S}_{\text{fus}}$ (cal mole^{-1} °K^{-1})	$\Delta\overline{V}_{\text{fus}}$ (cm^3 mole^{-1})	K_m (exptl)
H_2	0.028	14	2.0	+	
Ar	0.280	83	3.38	+	
C_2H_5OH	1.10	156	7.05	+	
HF	1.09	190	5.26		
H_2O	1.43	273	5.25	−	1.86
C_6H_6	2.35	278	8.45	+	4.90
CH_3COOH	2.80	290	9.65	+	3.9
$C_{10}H_8$		353		+	6.8
			Metals		
Hg	0.58	234	2.48	+	
Na	0.63	371	1.70	+	
Sb	4.8	904	5.3	−	
Al	2.55	932	2.73	+	
Fe	3.56	1802	1.97	+	
			Ionic crystals		
$NaNO_3$	3.84	579	6.65	+	15.0
KNO_3	2.57	581	4.42	+	
AgCl	3.15	728	4.33	+	
KCl	6.41	1043	6.15	+	
NaCl	7.22	1073	6.72	+	
$BaCl_2$	5.75	1232	4.65	I	

tion of $\Delta\overline{H}$ with T can be determined, and hence the difference in heat capacities of the two phases.) Thus a combination of phase diagrams and thermodynamics gives a great deal of information from a simple, one-component phase diagram.

Exercise 34.7

Which has the higher molar enthalpy at equilibrium, ice II or ice III? the higher molar volume? *Answer:* The isobaric phase change (ice II ⟶ ice III) involves an increase in T; hence an increase in molar enthalpy. The isothermal phase change (ice II ⟶ ice III) involves a decrease in P; hence an increase in volume. Thus ice III has a higher molar enthalpy and a higher molar volume than does ice II at equilibrium.

FUSION

Note that the great majority of crystals melt to give more voluminous liquids, but water and antimony do not (see Table 34.3). This is consistent with the small CN's in ice and crystalline Sb as compared to the more common higher CN's found in liquids. When ice melts, the voluminous crystal structure (determined by intermolecular H-bonds) collapses into a denser water structure in which there are fewer and less directional H-bonds because of the higher temperature of the water. But, for most substances, (dP/dT) is positive for crystal to liquid transitions—ΔH and ΔV are both positive.

Every isothermal fusion has a positive ΔS, consistent with the more disordered nature of liquids. But ΔS_{fus} does not exhibit the approximate constancy found in ΔS_{vap} (remember Trouton's rule).

Exercise 34.8

Rationalize the large differences in $\Delta \bar{S}_{fus}$ of benzene and water at such similar melting points. *Answer:* The larger $\Delta \bar{S}_{fus}$ for C_6H_6 indicates a larger change in available states as a result of melting for C_6H_6 than for H_2O. Liquid water still retains many hydrogen bonds which restrict rotation and translation. Benzene, on the other hand, has much weaker intermolecular bonds, primarily π-π overlap, which is largely ineffective in ordering the molecules in the liquid state at room temperature.

VAPORIZATION

Note that $\Delta \bar{V}_{vap}$ is always positive, consistent with the positive dP/dT found for all vaporization processes, owing to the very large entropies of gases as compared to their equilibrium liquids (see Table 34.4). Note also the number of liquids for which $\Delta \bar{S}_{vap} \cong 21 \pm 1$ eu (see colored values in Table 34.4). Known as Trouton's rule, this relationship allows an estimation of $\Delta \bar{H} = T\,\Delta \bar{S}$ if the boiling point of the liquid is known. An even higher consistency in $\Delta \bar{S}$ is obtained if it is calculated for liquid-gas systems at a constant value of $\Delta \bar{V}$ (Hildebrand's rule); see Problem 27.13. At constant $\Delta \bar{V} \cong \bar{V}_{(g)}$, the entropy of the gases tends to remain constant [if their values of $(mT)^{3/2}$ are similar (see Table 28.2)], whereas the variation in $\bar{S}_{(g)}$ at the boiling point of the liquid, due to widely varying values of $\bar{V}_{(g)}$, limits the usefulness of Trouton's rule, as shown in Table 34.4.

Deviations from Hildebrand's or Trouton's rule usually indicate structural effects either in the liquid or gas (usually the former) which lower the entropy of the structured phase and so alter $\Delta \bar{H}$ $(= T\,\Delta \bar{S})$. Note that the hydrogen-bonded liquids in Table 34.4 have high values of $\Delta \bar{H}$—that is, high values of $\Delta \bar{S}$ that are due to their highly structured liquid phases. Why is *HF* an exception?

SUBLIMATION

The direct conversion of a crystal to a gas is called sublimation. Clearly, from thermodynamics and the nature of state functions,

$$\Delta \bar{H}_{sub} = \Delta \bar{H}_{fus} + \Delta \bar{H}_{vap} \tag{34.9}$$

as long as the temperature is constant. In actual cases, since ΔH values are relatively unaffected by changes in *T*, Equation (34.9) holds for most systems even when $\Delta \bar{H}_{fus}$ at the melting point is combined with $\Delta \bar{H}_{vap}$ at the boiling point to give $\Delta \bar{H}_{sub}$ at temperatures below the melting point. Note, however, that $\Delta \bar{S}$ values are not similarly additive. Why?

Table 34.4 Data on liquid-gas equilibria.

	$\Delta\bar{H}_{vap}$ (kcal mole^{-1})	$T_{b.p.}$ (°K)	$\Delta\bar{S}_{vap}$ (cal mole^{-1} °K^{-1})	$\Delta\bar{V}_{vap}$ (l)	K_b (exptl)
He	0.020	4.25	4.7		
H_2	0.22	20	11.	1.5	
N_2	1.333	77.3	17.2		
HF	1.8	293	6.1	22	
Ar	1.88	88	21.3	7.1	
CH_4	1.955	112	17.5		
C_2H_6	3.517	184	19.2		
Cl_2	4.878	239	20.4		
n-C_4H_{10}	5.352	273	19.6		
NH_3	5.581	240	23.2		
CH_3COOH	5.82	391	14.9		
n-C_6H_{14}	6.896	342	20.2		
$CHCl_3$	7.02	344	20.4		3.63
CCl_4	7.17	350	20.5	29	5.03
C_6H_6	7.35	353	20.8	29	2.53
C_2H_5OH	9.22	352	26.2	29	1.22
H_2O	9.72	373	26.0	30	0.512
$(CH_3)_2CO$	10.08	329	30.6		1.71
PbI_2	24.8	1145	21.6		
		Metals			
Hg	14.0	630	22.2	52	
Na	23.4	1156	20.2	97	
Al	67.9	2600	25	210	
Fe	84.6	3008	28	250	

Exercise 34.9

Estimate the heat of sublimation of ice. *Answer.* From Table 34.3 for H_2O, $\Delta\bar{H}_{fus} = 1.43$ kcal mole^{-1}, $\Delta\bar{H}_{vap} = 9.72$ kcal mole^{-1}. Thus $\Delta\bar{H}_{sub} \cong 1.43 + 9.72 = 11.15 \cong 11$ kcal mole^{-1}. The accepted value at 0°C is 12.2 kcal mole^{-1}, higher than predicted since ΔH_{vap} rises as T falls.

PHASE EQUILIBRIUM BETWEEN A PURE SINGLE COMPONENT PHASE AND A SOLUTION PHASE AS A FUNCTION OF TEMPERATURE

It is relatively common to find a two-component system consisting of a liquid and either a crystal or a gas phase, such that (1) component A and B are mutually soluble only in the liquid phase, not in the crystal phase, (2) component B is nonvolatile (very low vapor pressure) compared to component A. Most systems involving ionic substances (such as salts) and water meet both these criteria. Since electrolytic solutions constitute a field of great chemical interest, let us investigate the behavior of these fluids.

Consider a single-component equilibrium system of two phases, l and α, of which l is liquid. From Equations (29.1) and (29.2) we have

$$\overline{G}_l = \overline{G}_\alpha \qquad \text{or} \qquad \mu_l = \mu_\alpha$$

Now we add a solute which dissolves only in the liquid phase. That is, the solute is insoluble in any possible crystalline phase, and the solute is nonvolatile (insoluble in any gas phase). Addition of the solute will change the activity, molar free energy, and chemical potential of the liquid, l. For equilibrium to be maintained, an identical change in chemical potential must occur in the other equilibrium phase, α. Since the other phase, α, is pure and it cannot change in composition, its chemical potential can change only by changing temperature and/or pressure. Let us consider what changes will then result as the system maintains equilibrium after addition of the solute to the liquid.

Assume that the liquid phase forms an ideal solution with the solute: $a = X$. Then, from Equation (29.4),

$$\mu_l = \mu_l^0 + RT\ln X_A$$

where μ_l^0 is the chemical potential of the pure component, A, in the liquid phase, μ_l is the chemical potential of A in the solution with added solute B, and X_A is the mole fraction of component A in the solution. Since $\mu_\alpha = \mu_l$ and $\mu_i = \overline{G}_i$, we write

$$\mu_\alpha = \mu_l = \mu_l^0 + RT\ln X_A$$

$$\overline{G}_\alpha = \overline{G}_l^0 + RT\ln X_A$$

$$\frac{\overline{G}_\alpha}{T} - \frac{\overline{G}_l^0}{T} = R\ln X_A \tag{34.10}$$

which gives the general condition for equilibrium between the liquid solution, l, and any other pure phase, α.

Either (or both) T or P could vary to maintain equilibrium upon the addition of component B to the liquid. Let us assume that P is kept constant and all the variation is in T. Then we should take the partial derivative of our equilibrium expression, Equation (34.10), at constant total P, with respect to T:

$$\left[\frac{\partial(\overline{G}_\alpha/T)}{\partial T}\right]_P - \left[\frac{\partial(\overline{G}_l^0/T)}{\partial T}\right]_P = R\left[\frac{\partial \ln X_A}{\partial T}\right]_P$$

But from Equation (27.21),

$$\left[\frac{\partial(G/T)}{\partial T}\right]_P = -\frac{H}{T^2}$$

Therefore

$$-\left(\frac{\overline{H}_\alpha}{T^2}\right) - \left(-\frac{\overline{H}_l^0}{T^2}\right) = R\left[\frac{\partial \ln X_A}{\partial T}\right]_P = -\frac{(\overline{H}_\alpha - \overline{H}_l^0)}{T^2}$$

and now

$$(\overline{H}_\alpha - \overline{H}_l^0) = \Delta\overline{H}_A\Big|_l^\alpha = \text{molar enthalpy change of component A from liquid, } l, \text{ to phase } \alpha$$

since $\overline{H}_\alpha$ = molar enthalpy of A in the second phase, and $\overline{H}_l^0$ = molar enthalpy of A in the pure liquid. Thus

$$\left[\frac{\partial \ln X_A}{\partial T}\right]_P = -\frac{\Delta \bar{H}_A\Big|_l^\alpha}{RT^2} \tag{34.11}$$

Remembering P = constant and $X_A = 1$ when $T = T^0$, we can write

$$\int_1^{X_A} d \ln X_A = -\int_{T_A^0}^{T} \frac{\Delta \bar{H}_A \, dT}{RT^2}$$

Now assume that $\Delta\bar{H}$ is independent of T. Then, for an ideal solution, at constant total P, we get another useful form of the

CLAUSIUS-CLAPEYRON EQUATION:

$$\ln X_A = \frac{\Delta \bar{H}_A}{R}\left[\frac{1}{T} - \frac{1}{T_A^0}\right] = -\frac{\Delta \bar{H}_A}{R}\left[\frac{T - T_A^0}{TT_A^0}\right] \tag{34.12}$$

or

$$\log X_A = -\frac{\Delta \bar{H}_A}{4.575\, T} + b$$

Thus, at constant P, the new equilibrium temperature, T, is related to the equilibrium temperature, T_A^0, of the pure component, the molar enthalpy change for the phase change, $\Delta\bar{H}_A$, and the concentration, X_A, of component A in the liquid solution. Again, a plot of log X_A versus $(1/T)$ is a straight line of slope $(-\Delta\bar{H}/R)$.

As X_A decreases (the solution becomes more concentrated in component B), the equilibrium temperature at constant pressure will either rise or fall, depending on the sign of ΔH. Since ΔH_{vap} is always positive, the boiling point will always rise [$(T - T^0)$ becomes more positive as X_A decreases]. Since ΔH of crystallization is always negative, the freezing point of the solution will always fall as X_A decreases. The same arguments hold for $c \longrightarrow g$ (sublimation), and any other phase equilibrium between a pure component (c, l, or g) and an ideal solution (c, l, or g).

Note that the temperature of a liquid in equilibrium with a gas has to rise to maintain the constant pressure assumed in our derivation if X_A decreases. Clearly this means that addition of a nonvolatile solute at constant temperature to give an ideal solution must lead to a fall in the vapor pressure of component A. Thus the p-T curve for the solution will always lie below the p-T curve for the pure liquid, as shown in Figure 34.11.

We may define an ideal solution as one which follows

RAOULT'S LAW:

$$p_A = X_A p_A^0 \tag{34.13}$$

where p_A^0 = vapor pressure of pure A, X_A = mole fraction of A in solution, and p_A = vapor pressure of A over the solution. Substituting Equation (34.13) into (34.12) again gives us the

CLAUSIUS-CLAPEYRON EQUATION:

$$\ln \frac{p_A}{p_A^0} = -\frac{\Delta \bar{H}}{R}\left[\frac{T - T^0}{TT^0}\right] \tag{34.14}$$

identical to Equation (34.6). Thus the p-T curve for an ideal solution of a nonvolatile solute will parallel the p-T curve for the pure component, and log p versus $1/T$ gives a straight line, of slope $(-\Delta\bar{H}/T)$, for both systems, if the assumptions used in the above derivation hold.

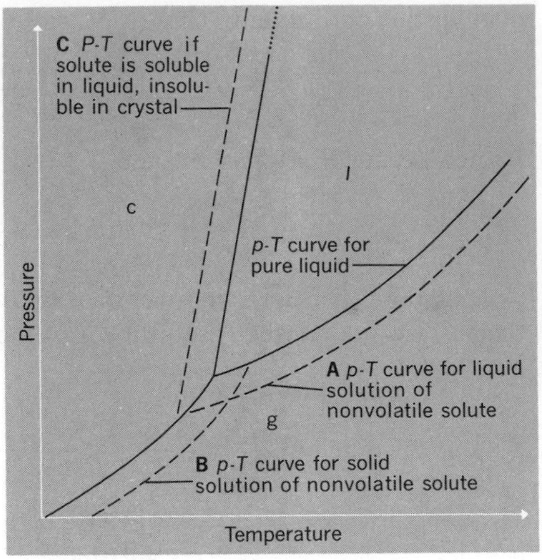

Figure 34.11 Effect of lowering of vapor pressure, at constant temperature. (**A**) By a solute soluble in liquid, insoluble in gas (nonvolatile). (**B**) By a solute soluble in crystal, insoluble in gas (nonvolatile). (**C**) By a solute soluble in liquid, insoluble in crystal. The **A** and **C** effects commonly go together.

Remember the assumptions: (1) the solute is soluble only in the liquid phase, *l*, not in the crystalline or gaseous phases, and (2) the liquid solution is ideal and follows Raoult's law. The first assumption is often closer to the truth than the second assumption.

Note that Equation (34.14) is not really restricted to an ideal *liquid* solution phase of a nonvolatile solute in equilibrium with another phase. It applies to the equilibrium between any single-component phase and another phase—either liquid, crystal, or gas—in which a second component has dissolved and followed Raoult's law $p_A = X_A p_A^0$, where A represents the initial component. Three possible cases are illustrated in Figure 34.11.

Exercise 34.10

Anthracene, $C_{14}H_{10}$, may be considered nonvolatile. What would be the relative vapor pressures of equally concentrated solutions (mole fractions) of anthracene in C_6H_6 and in C_2H_5OH? *Answer:* For each system, $\ln(p_A/p_A^0) = -(\Delta\bar{H}_A/R)(T - T^0)/TT^0$. Comparing the two systems gives $\ln(p_A/p_A^0) - \ln(p_B/p_B^0) = -(\Delta\bar{H}_A/R)(T - T_A^0)TT_A^0 + (\Delta\bar{H}_B^0/R)(T - T_B^0)TT_B$. Let $p_A^0 = 1$ atm $= p_B^0$. Now $T_A^0 = 353°K$, $T_B^0 = 352°K$, so assume that $T_A^0 = T_B^0 = 352°K$. Then $\ln(p_A/p_B) \cong [(\Delta\bar{H}_B - \Delta\bar{H}_A)/R] \cdot [(T - T^0)/TT^0] = [(9.22 - 7.35)/1.99 \cdot 10^{-3}] \cdot [(T - 352)/352T] = 2.68 - 943T^{-1}$, where B = C_2H_5OH. This assumption that $T_A^0 = T_B^0 = 352°K$ will lose validity for small concentrations where ΔT is not large compared to 1°K.

BOILING TEMPERATURES

The *boiling point* of a liquid is the temperature at which its vapor pressure equals 760 torr. The *boiling temperature* is the temperature at which the vapor pressure equals the pressure of the surrounding atmosphere. Equation (34.12) allows a general calculation of the variation of either the boiling point or the boiling temperature, with concentration of added nonvolatile solute, within the assumptions of the preceding section:

$$\ln X_A = -\frac{\Delta \bar{H}_{vap}}{R}\left[\frac{T - T_A^0}{TT_A^0}\right]$$

where T represents the new boiling temperature at pressure P when the mole fraction of the solvent is reduced to X_A from $X = 1$. If the liquid solution is ideal, Equation (34.12) applies, since the gas phase is now a pure single component (solute nonvolatile). An empirical test of ideality in the solution is constancy of $\Delta \bar{H}_A$ calculated from experimental data.

If only a small amount of solute is added, then (*a*) $\ln X_A \cong -X_B$ [since $\ln X_A = \ln(1 - X_B) = -X_B - X_B^2/2 - X_B^3/3 - X_B^4/4 - \cdots$ and the power terms are negligible when X_B is small], and (*b*) $TT_A^0 = (T_A^0)^2$ [since ΔT will be small]. Then

$$X_B = \frac{\Delta \bar{H}}{R}\frac{\Delta T}{(T_A^0)^2}$$

$$\Delta T_b = \frac{X_B R (T_A^0)^2}{\Delta \bar{H}} \qquad (34.15)$$

Thus the change in boiling temperature is proportional to X_B, over a small change in X_B.

It is common to express concentrations in terms of molality, m (m = moles of solute per 1000 g of solvent of molar weight M_A), since molality, unlike molarity, does not change if the temperature of the system changes:

$$X_B = \frac{n_B}{n_A + n_B} = \frac{m}{1000/M_A + m} \xrightarrow{m \to 0} \frac{m}{1000/M_A} (= kM_B)$$

Substituting into (34.15) gives

$$\Delta T_b = \frac{R(T_A^0)^2 M_A m}{1000(\Delta \bar{H}_{vap})_A}$$

which simplifies to the

BOILING POINT RISE EQUATION: $\Delta T_b = K_b m$ (34.16)

where K_b is called the molal boiling point constant, and

$$K_b = \frac{R(T_A^0)^2 M_A}{1000(\Delta \bar{H}_{vap})_A} \qquad (34.17)$$

See Table 34.4.

Exercise 34.11

Calculate K_b for H_2O and compare to the value in Table 34.4. *Answer:* $K_b = R(T_A^0)^2 M_A/1000\,\Delta \bar{H}_{vap}$. $(K_b)_{H_2O} = 1.987 \cdot 373.2^2 \cdot 18.02/(1000 \cdot 9720) = 0.513$°K mole^{-1} *l*. Table 34.4 gives $K_b = 0.512$.

VAPOR PRESSURES

In the same way, since $p_A = X_A p_A^0$ from Raoult's law, and $X_A = 1 - X_B$, we get for the vapor pressure of an ideal solution

$$p_A = (1 - X_B)p_A^0$$

$$p_A^0 - p_A = \Delta p_A = X_B p_A^0 = \frac{m_B p_A^0 M_A}{1000}$$

This gives us the

VAPOR PRESSURE LOWERING EQUATION: $$\Delta p_A = K_{vp} m \qquad (34.18)$$

Variation of vapor pressure with concentration of nonvolatile solute is often measured by the isopiestic method illustrated in Figure 34.12. A single solvent is used to make up two solutions, one of a subtance, C, that is easy to analyze, and the other of a substance, B, of unknown composition, by weighing out the solutes and adding them to known weights of solvent, A. The beakers containing the solutions are then inserted into a copper block whose temperature can be measured, and allowed to come to equilibrium. The volatile solvent, A, will diffuse through the vapor phase from one solution to another until the two solutions come to the same vapor pressure. Net flow will then cease. Analysis of known solution C and referral to standardized charts of p versus m_C at the equilibrium T give the value of p at equilibrium. Weighing the other container gives the grams of the unknown substance, B, per 1000 g of solvent A in solution α at equilibrium. (Remember that the unknown is nonvolatile and all of it placed in the α beaker is still there.) The molar weight of the unknown can then be calculated from the relationship

$$p - p^0 = K_{vp} m = \frac{K_{vp} 1000 g_B}{g_A M_B} \qquad (34.19)$$

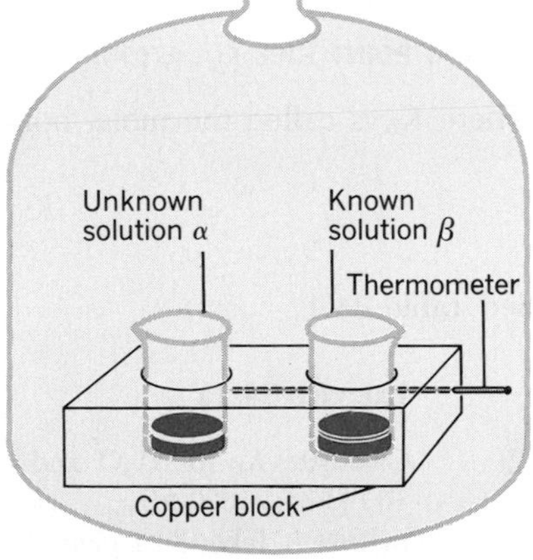

Figure 34.12 Isopiestic equilibrium method of determining molar weights in solution.

MELTING TEMPERATURES

The *melting point* is the temperature at which crystal and liquid are in equilibrium at 760 torr pressure. The *melting temperature* is the temperature at which crystal and liquid are in equilibrium at total applied pressure, *P*. In a fashion exactly analogous to our obtaining Equation (34.15), we may derive an equation for the change in melting point (or freezing point) of a solution fitting our assumptions:

$$\Delta T_m = -R(T^0_A)^2 \frac{M_A m_B}{1000(\Delta \overline{H}_{fus})_A}$$

which gives the

FREEZING POINT LOWERING EQUATION: $$\Delta T_m = -K_m m \qquad (34.20)$$

Note that melting points fall (whereas boiling points rise) when a solute soluble only in the liquid phase is added (see Table 34.4).

We thus see why salt is effective when added to ice in an ice cream freezer or in clearing icy sidewalks or streets, or why automobile antifreezes like ethylene glycol are used. See also the discussion on page 817 of the freezing point of fishes.

Molten salts can dissolve other salts to give close to ideal solutions, since the interionic forces are relatively independent of the nature of the ions and thus relatively constant from one simple ion to another simple ion. Table 34.5 shows the remarkable constancy of K_m for $NaNO_3$ systems. But note that all potassium salts give results that are uniformly low. This is consistent with the 10% solubility of potassium ions in the crystalline $NaNO_3$.

Exercise 34.12

What weight of ethylene glycol, $C_2H_4(OH)_2$, should be added to water to give a solution which would not freeze until −20°C? *Answer:* $\Delta T_m = -K_b m$, $m = 20/1.86 = 11$ moles $C_2H_4(OH)_2$ per 1000 g of $H_2O = 11 \cdot 62 = 680$ g of glycol per 1000 g of

Table 34.5 Freezing point constant, K_m, for molten sodium nitrate: $T_m = 580.0$ °K.

1 foreign ion		2 foreign ions		3 foreign ions	
Salt	$K_m = (°K \cdot m^{-1})$	Salt	$K_m = (°K \cdot m^{-1})$	Salt	$K_m = (°K \cdot m^{-1})$
NaCl	15.0	LiCl	29.8	$CaCl_2$	45.4
Na_2CO_3	14.8	CsCl	31.4	$SrCl_2$	44.8
Na_2SO_4	15.1	KCl	(28.5)	$BaCl_2$	44.5
$NaBrO_3$	15.0	$KBrO_3$	(28.0)	K_2CO_3	(42.7)
Na_2WO_4	15.1	KIO_3	(29.0)	K_2SO_4	(41.3)
Na_2MoO_4	15.0			$K_2Cr_2O_7$	(41.7)
$Pb(NO_3)_2$	15.2				44.9 ± 0.3
$LiNO_3$	15.1				
KNO_3	(13.5)				
	15.0 ± 0.1				

SOURCE: E. R. Van Artsdalen, *J. Phys. Chem.*, **60**, 172 (1956).

water. Note that deviations from ideality would be expected in a solution of such high concentration. Thus the figures are only rough estimates. Use Equation (34.12) to get $X_{H_2O} = 0.813$, a less approximate figure. This means 793 g of glycol per 1000 g H_2O. Note the appreciable difference.

COLLIGATIVE PROPERTIES OF LIQUID SOLUTIONS

Let us summarize the linear equations found in the past three sections.

For boiling point rise:

$$\Delta T_b = K_b m_B, \qquad K_b = \frac{R(T_A^0)^2 M_A}{1000(\Delta \overline{H}_{vap})_A} \tag{34.16}$$

For vapor pressure lowering:

$$\Delta p_A = K_{vp} m_B, \qquad K_{vp} = \frac{p_A^0 M_A}{1000} \tag{34.18}$$

For melting point lowering:

$$\Delta T_m = -K_m m_B, \qquad K_m = \frac{R(T_A^0)^2 M_A}{1000(\Delta \overline{H}_{fus})_A} \tag{34.20}$$

Thus changes in boiling points, vapor pressures, and melting points are all linear in the molality, m, for dilute solutions of substances soluble only in the liquid phase. Such properties, linear in m, are called colligative properties.

If you remember the assumptions, you will see that colligative properties are strictly linear in m only as $m \longrightarrow 0$. Thus you should expect to find that the greatest use of colligative properties is in connection with extrapolation methods.

Perhaps their most common use is in determining molar weights of unknown substances, since

$$m_B = \frac{[\text{grams B/molar wt B}]}{1000 \text{ g solvent}} = \frac{1000 \text{ g}_B}{\text{g}_A M_B}$$

Thus a measurement of ΔT_b, Δp_A, or ΔT_m for a solvent of known properties (known K_b, K_{vp}, and/or K_m), when a known number of grams of B are added to a known weight of solvent, allows the immediate estimation of M_B, the average molar weight of B in the solution. Carrying out the measurements over a range of added weights of B (range of m) allows extrapolation to zero m, and gives a value for the average molar weight of B in the ideal solution of infinite dilution (see Figure 34.13).

The colligative-property effects may be readily summarized in terms of escaping tendency: addition of a second component to any phase lowers the escaping tendency of the initial component. The escaping tendencies of the initial component in all phases in equilibrium with that solution phase must also fall to maintain equilibrium. This can occur, for example, by change of temperature if pressure is kept constant, or by change of pressure if temperature is kept constant,

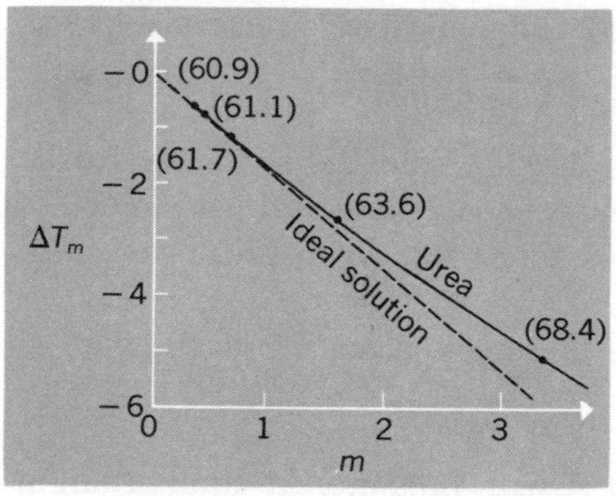

Figure 34.13 Values of M_B (given for each experimental $m - \Delta T$ point) calculated from freezing point lowering of urea solutions in water. $K_m = 1.860 = \lim (\Delta T/m)$. $M_{\text{urea}} = 60.06$.

or both may change simultaneously. Remember that raising the temperature increases the escaping tendency of any phase, as does raising the pressure. Thus the direction of temperature and/or pressure change following addition of a solute soluble in only one phase can be predicted with certainty from the fact that the escaping tendency of the solvent from that phase will decrease.

OSMOTIC PRESSURES

A fourth colligative property is much used, especially in the determination of formula weights of polymeric substances, because of the sensitivity of the method in solutions of very low molality. We may consider a rise in boiling point to result from the inability of the solute to pass from the liquid into the gas phase, and a lowering of melting point to result from the inability of the solute to pass from the liquid into the crystal phase. It is also possible with many systems to construct a membrane barrier such that one or more components cannot pass from one phase to the other. This is accomplished by using semipermeable membranes. These membranes allow certain molecules to pass through, but not all (see Figure 34.14).

When a semipermeable membrane separates a solution from one of its pure components, A, net flow of A occurs into the solution until the pressure drop across the barrier equals the osmotic pressure, π, of the solution. The more concentrated the solution, the higher is π. Increasing T also increases π.

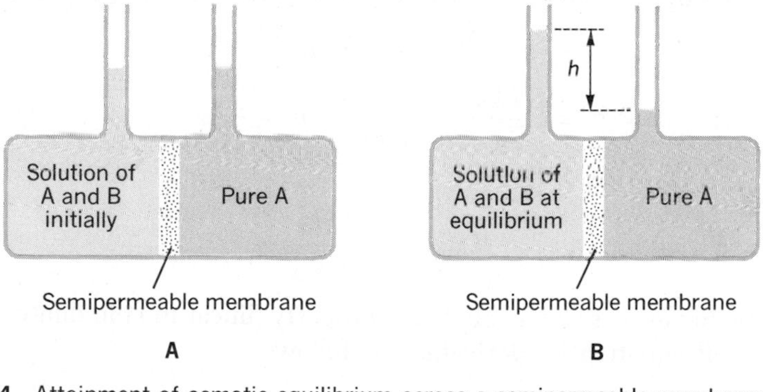

Figure 34.14 Attainment of osmotic equilibrium across a semipermeable membrane. Note net flow of A from pure A to solution until an equilibrium differential pressure (represented by hydrostatic head, h) is attained, giving a constrained (nonisobaric) equilibrium.

Van't Hoff, in 1885, first suggested that the quantitative relationship was

$$\pi = cRT \qquad \text{or} \qquad \pi V = n_B RT \tag{34.21}$$

where c = concentration of solutes in moles liter^{-1}. Note the similarity to the ideal gas laws. In this model, the solute molecules behave like ideal-gas molecules in that they adjust their π/c ratio (analogous to PV/n for an ideal gas) until it equals RT.

From Equations (29.2) and (27.15), a thermodynamic approach gives

$$\mu_A = \overline{G}_A, \qquad d\mu_A = d\overline{G}_A = \overline{V}\, dP$$

as the change in chemical potential of solvent A with pressure. At equilibrium in an osmotic experiment, $\mu_l = \mu^0$ for the solvent, where μ_l refers to the chemical potential of the solvent in the solution and μ^0 to that in the pure solvent. Thus the change in μ_l due to increase in P from P^0 to $(\pi + P^0)$ is

$$d\mu_l = \int_{P^0}^{\pi+P^0} \overline{V}_A\, dP$$

The change in chemical potential of the solvent, A, at constant T, due to addition of the solutes, B, can be obtained from Equation (29.4) as

$$\mu_l = \mu^0 + RT \ln X_A = \mu^0 + RT \ln (1 - X_B)$$

and differentiating gives

$$d\mu = -\frac{RT}{1 - X_B}\, dX_B$$

But $d\mu_l$ due to pressure change must exactly equal $-d\mu_l$ due to concentration change if equilibrium is attained. Thus

$$\int_{P^0}^{\pi+P^0} \overline{V}_A\, dP = \int_0^{X_B} \frac{RT}{1 - X_B}\, dX_B = \int_1^{X_A} - \frac{RT}{X_A\, dX_A}$$

$$= -RT \ln X_A \tag{34.22}$$

If $\overline{V}$ is independent of P (and it usually is at low P),

$$\overline{V}_A \pi = -RT \ln X_A \tag{34.23}$$

When X_B is small [see derivation of Equations (34.21) and (34.22)], this becomes

$$\overline{V}_A \pi = RTX_B \tag{34.24}$$

$$\pi = \frac{RTX_B}{\overline{V}_A} = \frac{RTM_A}{1000\overline{V}_A}\, m = K_{osm} m \tag{34.25}$$

where

$$K_{osm} = \frac{RTM_A}{1000\overline{V}_A}$$

Thus osmotic pressure is also a colligative property (linear in m in dilute solutions). The Van't Hoff equation is "derivable" as follows:

$$\pi = \frac{RTX_B}{\overline{V}_A} = \frac{RT}{\overline{V}_A} \frac{n_B}{n_A + n_B}$$

but, in dilute solutions, $n_B \ll n_A$ and $V = n_A\overline{V}_A$ (V = solution volume); therefore, from Equation (34.21),

$$\pi V = n_B RT$$

Osmotic pressures of 1 F solutions are about 25 atm. Since pressures of a few millimeters may be measured accurately, it is clear that osmotic pressures of 10^{-5} F solutions are measurable. Since the other colligative properties show negligible changes at such low concentrations, osmotic pressure is widely used in determining M for polymers of high molecular weight and limited solubility.

The effects of osmotic pressure are of great importance also in living systems, since most biological membranes—intestines, cell walls—are semipermeable. Too large a concentration gradient across a cell wall will either burst or desiccate the cell. Thus bacteria are killed by desiccation when they land on sugar candy, a fact which may have saved the lives of many of your ancestors before this day of modern packaging.

The human kidney is a particularly effective osmotic device. Blood and urine flow counter to one another on opposite sides of a set of semipermeable membranes which first let most of the small waste materials and ions leave the blood and go into the urine, then actively pump (using biochemical energy) some ions back into the blood. Thus, the waste products are effectively moved from the blood to the urine but the biochemically important ions, such as Na^+ and Cl^-, are conserved and returned to the blood. Water loss through the kidneys is controlled by the antidiuretic hormone, which adjusts the permeability of the kidney osmotic membranes to water. High hormone concentration in the blood tends to increase the permeability of the final membrane, past which the urine leaves the kidney, and makes it easy for water to leave the urine and re-enter the blood, and vice versa when the hormone concentration drops. Thus the kidney-hormone combination controls both the rate of elimination of water and of small waste molecules.

Exercise 34.13

Estimate the average molecular weight of a polymer which gives an osmotic pressure of 10.0 mm of water when 1.372 g of it are dissolved in 100.0 ml of H_2O. *Answer:* Assume $T = 27°C$. From Equation (34.21), $M_B = g_B RT/\pi V = 348{,}000$ g mole^{-1}. Under these conditions X_B is certainly small, so Equation (34.23) need not be tried.

SPECIES IN LIQUIDS

Species in crystals can be studied directly by X-ray diffraction, and in gases by gas density measurements (see Figures 6.13 and 6.14). The colligative properties give a great deal of similar information on the species present in solutions and on the nature of forces in the liquid state. Consider the boiling point data in Figure 34.15.

How do we interpret the fact that the limiting molar weight of NaCl in aqueous solution is 29.2, whereas the formula weight of NaCl is 58.4? After all, the limiting molar weight of sugar is 340, in agreement with the accepted value of 342.30 for $C_{12}H_{22}O_{11}$. The clue to the apparent discrepancy in NaCl is that 29.2 is half of 58.4. We believe we get two moles of particles for each mole of NaCl

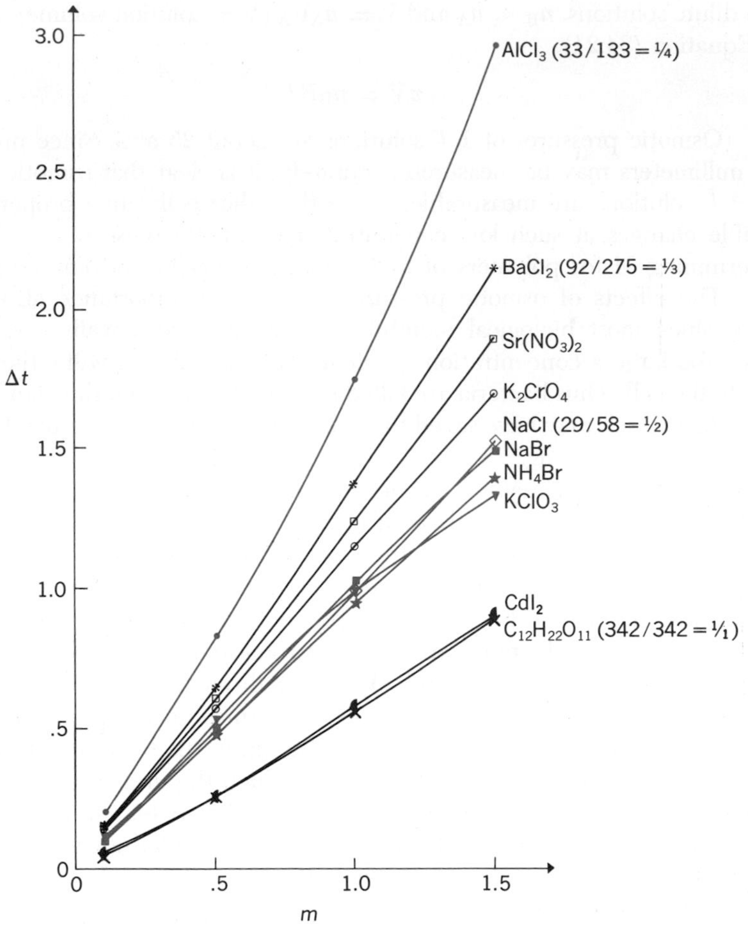

Figure 34.15 Rise of boiling point in H_2O as a function of *m* for some simple substances, and, in parentheses, limiting formula weights as $m \longrightarrow 0$ over actual formula weights.

in solution. In other words, $Na^+{}_{(aq)}$ and $Cl^-{}_{(aq)}$ are the species present in dilute aqueous NaCl. Similar interpretations account for the other values in Figure 34.15. Note that most binary compounds of elements widely separated in the periodic table are ionic, as we have previously decided from other evidence. But note also that CdI_2 exists even in dilute aqueous solution (0.1 *m*), principally as $CdI_{2(aq)}$, not as the ions. (The low electrical conductivity of the solution confirms this diagnosis but indicates that species such as $CdI_4{}^{=}{}_{(aq)}$ and $CdOH^+{}_{(aq)}$ are also present, so that the good agreement of the average apparent formula weight from the colligative properties with the accepted value for CdI_2 is partly fortuitous, owing to the averaging process.)

Sulfuric acid as a colligative solvent gives some very interesting results. According to Gillespie et al. [*J. Chem. Soc.*, **1950,** 2504], a solution of N_2O_4 in pure H_2SO_4 gives a lowering of the freezing point as $m \longrightarrow 0$, corresponding to six moles of particles in solution per mole of N_2O_4 dissolved. They assume the following reaction to interpret the data:

$$N_2O_{4(g)} + 3H_2SO_{4(l)} = NO_2^+ + NO^+ + H_3O^+ + 3HSO_4^-$$

where the ionic species are all solvated by the H_2SO_4. Similar interactions with the solvent are found in other systems, including water. The presence of the presumed species can often be checked by spectroscopic techniques.

SUMMARY

The common classifications of phases as crystal, liquid, or gas are clarified if we recognize that crystals are characterized by a repeating, symmetrical structure, whereas liquids and gases do not have this structural repetitiveness. On the other hand, both crystals and liquids have self-defining surfaces because their surface tensions are appreciable compared to their molecular kinetic energies, whereas the surface tension of gases is too low in comparison with their kinetic energies to maintain a fixed volume. Crystals can always be identified by their structure, but liquids and gases can be distinguished from one another only when both are present and the defining surface can be seen. Above critical temperature, the liquid and gaseous states of any substance become indistinguishable. These are some of the reasons liquids and gases are often classified together as fluids.

The flow, viscosity, surface tension, enthalpy, entropy, and other properties of fluids all support the model of random molecular motion, motion which becomes more restricted as the intermolecular volume decreases.

The Clausius-Clapeyron equation describes the *P-T* equilibrium relationships in a single-component system and may be extended to solutions, especially if the added component is soluble in only one of the phases present at equilibrium.

Studies of colligative properties provide considerable insight into the species present in solutions and hence into the nature of the forces acting in liquid phases.

Science in the making, science as an end to be pursued, is as subjective and psychologically conditioned as any other branch of human endeavor. Albert Einstein

---

PROBLEMS

34.1. What conclusions can you draw from a visual examination of the variation with T of the curves in Figure 34.1?

34.2. Estimate ΔH_{vap} for the liquids in Figure 34.8 for which no values are listed. Rationalize any variations in ΔH_{vap} as a function of molecular structure. ($\Delta H_{vap} \cong$ 10 kcal mole^{-1}.)

34.3. The viscosity of liquid uranium has been measured by D. Ofte (1966) from 1141°C (m.p.) to 1248°C. The respective extreme values are 6.5 and 5.4 centipoises. Calculate $\Delta E^{\ddagger}_{\text{vis}}$. It is interesting to note that this is the most viscous liquid metal known. ($\Delta E^{\ddagger}_{\text{vis}} \cong 7$ kcal mole^{-1}.)

34.4. Use the data of Table 34.5 to calculate ΔH_{fus} for $NaNO_3$. The calorimetric value is 45.3 cal g^{-1}.

34.5. Arrange the following in order of decreasing freezing point: 0.01 *M* HCl, 0.05 *M* sugar, 0.01 *M* HOAc, 0.02 *M* $BaCl_2$, 55.5 *M* H_2O, 0.01 *M* H_2SO_4.

34.6. The melting point of a 0.5 molal solution of cadmium iodide, CdI_2, is listed as −0.93°C. What can you deduce from this result? How do you interpret this result in terms of the relative positions of cadmium and iodine in the periodic table?

34.7. Explain the following in terms of molecular behavior.

(*a*) Salt is added to ice in an ice-cream freezer to freeze ice cream.

(*b*) High pressure aids in the preparation of ammonia from nitrogen and hydrogen, whereas pressure has little effect on the preparation of nitric oxide (NO) from nitrogen and oxygen.

(*c*) Silver chloride is more soluble in a water solution of potassium nitrate than in a sodium chloride solution.

(*d*) Ethyl alcohol is soluble both in water, a highly polar liquid, and in nonpolar carbon tetrachloride.

(*e*) The reaction of iodine with iron produces ferr*ous* iodide, but chlorine and iron yield ferr*ic* chloride.

(*f*) A solution of ammonium chloride is acid to litmus.

34.8. What experimental evidence indicates that the degrees of ionization of water solutions of sodium acetate and sodium hydroxide are comparable but different from that of acetic acid?

34.9. Describe the observations one could predict if the pressure on a sample of ice I were increased from 1 to 23 kilobars at a constant temperature of 270°K.

34.10. Account for the very low value of ΔS_{vap} for HF. Use electron structures.

34.11. Account for the high value of ΔS_{vap} for C_2H_5OH. Use electron structures.

34.12. Estimate a value of ΔH for the process (ice I $\longrightarrow$ ice III). What is the sign of ΔV? ($\Delta H \cong 0$.)

34.13. The United States Dept. of Agriculture states, "Cookery scientists find that it makes little difference whether salt is added before or after cooking meat. Add the seasoning when it is convenient, they say. Salt does draw out juice from meat and for this reason it should not be added until the meat is ready to cook unless the meat is sprinkled with flour after salting." Comment on "draw out juice." Is this true? Why? Why is the flour effective?

34.14. What may be expected to happen (be as quantitative as possible) as a result of these actions?

(*a*) A water solution containing 1 g of a polymer (molar weight 100,000) in 100 g of water is cooled slowly to −5°C. ($T_m \cong -0.005$°C.)

(*b*) One mole of hydrogen chloride gas is bubbled into 100 ml of 1 molar aqueous sodium hydroxide. (About half a mole of water boils away.)

(*c*) Sodium and sulfur are heated together.

(*d*) Water solutions of barium nitrate and sodium sulfate are mixed.

II

34.15. Calculate (*a*) the activation energy and (*b*) the hole size for viscous flow of each of the liquids in Table 34.2. [$(\Delta E^{\ddagger}_{\text{vis}})_{H_2O} \cong 4$ kcal mole^{-1}.]

34.16. Interpret the direction and size of each of the volume changes in the pistons shown in Figure 34.7 in terms of the corresponding changes in P and T.

34.17. Calculate the heat of fusion of ice, knowing the following vapor pressures: ice (−10°C) 1.950 torr; ice (0°C) 4.579 torr; water (10°C) 9.209 torr; water (−10°C) 2.149 torr. ($\Delta H_{\text{fus}} \cong 1$ kcal mole^{-1}.)

34.18. A solution of benzoic acid (1.22 g) in benzene (10.0 g) boils at 81.5°C. Calculate and comment on the average molecular weight of the benzoic acid. ($M \cong 200$.)

34.19. Estimate the boiling temperature of carbon tetrachloride at 730 mm pressure if its boiling point is 77°C. The entropy of vaporization is 21 cal/mole deg.

34.20. The "best" value for the surface area of an *n*-butanol molecule, C_4H_9OH, at surface saturation on water is about 30 Å^2. (*a*) Draw a relatively accurate figure of an *n*-butanol molecule and (*b*) show a probable orientation to the surface consistent with the experimental area. (Bond distances: C—C 1.54, C—H 1.10, C—O 1.4, O—H 0.96; van der Waals radii about 1.3.)

34.21. A solution which contains 1.22 g of benzoic acid (C_6H_5COOH) in 100 g of benzene freezes at 0.25°C below the melting point of pure benzene. The formula weight of C_6H_5COOH is 122. Draw the structural formula for the above solute in benzene solution. ($M \cong 200$.)

34.22. The coefficient of viscosity for CO_2 has the following values at various pressures and temperatures: all viscosities in micropoise. Explain, on a molecular basis.

35°C	40°C	
156	157	1 atm
163	166.5	20 atm
610	483	100 atm

34.23. Ethylene glycol, $C_2H_4(OH)_2$, costs 16 cents per pound. Glycerine, $C_3H_5(OH)_3$, costs 27 cents a pound. Which would you add to the water in the radiator of a car as an antifreeze, assuming that the resulting solutions were ideal in each case? (Relative cost effectiveness ≅ 2/5.)

34.24. The osmotic pressure of a solution containing 0.10 g of protein in 10 ml of water is 10 torr at 25°C. What is the molecular weight of the protein? ($M \cong 2 \cdot 10^4$.)

34.25. The osmotic pressure of blood corresponds to (is isotonic with) a 0.155 *F* NaCl aqueous solution. Calculate the osmotic pressure of blood. ($\pi \cong 8$ atm.)

III

34.26. Calculate the triple point and heat of fusion of white phosphorus, P_4, from the following. Calculate $\Delta\bar{S}_{\text{fus}}$ and interpret the value in terms of Table 34.3 and the structure of phosphorus: p is in atm. Compare Table 30.1.

$$-\log p_{(c)} = \frac{2875}{T} - 5.36$$

$$-\log p_{(l)} = \frac{2740}{T} - 4.95$$

($T \cong 330$°K, $\Delta\bar{S}_{\text{fus}} \cong 2$ eu.)

34.27. The Clapeyron equation is often written, $dP/dT = \Delta H/T\,\Delta V$. The P-T diagram below is for a chemical element. Plot rough graphs of (a) V as a function of T in going from A to E, (b) H as a function of T in going from A to E.

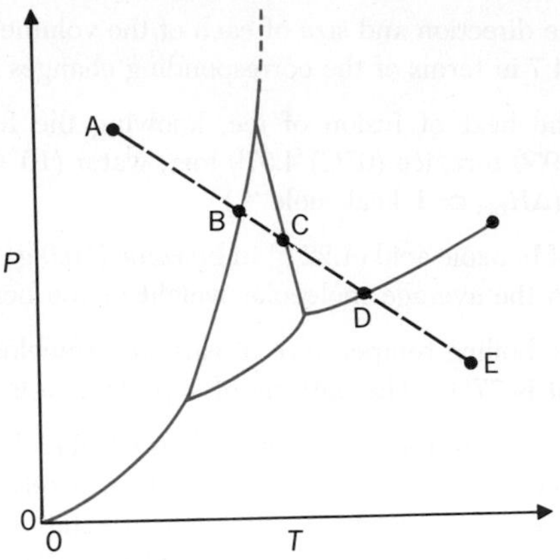

See page 1094 for a list of references and readings in the recent chemical literature related to the material in this chapter.

CHAPTER 35

Solutions and Separation Processes

TAD A. BECKMAN

One condition for equilibrium is that the chemical potential, μ, of each component be the same in every phase accessible to it.

The great majority of readily available materials are solutions or heterogeneous mixtures rather than pure elements or compounds. The clean atmosphere, for example, is a solution of gases, of which only about one-fifth is oxygen. Oceans, lakes, and streams, although principally water, vary widely in composition, depending upon the materials with which the water that feeds into them has been in contact. Few ores or minerals are stoichiometric compounds. In the laboratory very few synthetic experiments lead directly to pure compounds. The products of such experiments are usually solutions or heterogeneous, and the chemist must put almost as much effort into achieving a separation of the desired substances as he originally put into inventing a plan for their synthesis.

Since a fundamental problem of experimental chemistry is the preparation of pure elements and their compounds, the separation of solutions and heterogeneous systems into their components is a matter of great concern. At the same time, although chemical reactions occasionally figure in separation processes, by far the most important processes are based upon the solubilities and volatilities of the mixed systems and their components. Such techniques as distillation, sublimation, and crystallization have been used by technologists and chemists for several thousand years. But it was only rather recently—during the last half of the nineteenth century—that thermodynamics began to lay the basis for a theoretical understanding of these phase separations. In many instances, new understanding of the properties of solutions suggested refinements of technique or new means of effecting separations; in this way both subjects of investigation—the thermodynamics of solutions and the techniques of separation—have advanced rather rapidly during the last century.

THE PHASE RULE AND PHASE DIAGRAMS

The phase rule states that the number of degrees of freedom (F) in an equilibrium system is given in terms of the number of components (C) and the number of distinguishable phases (P) present.

PHASE RULE:
$$F = C - P + 2 \tag{35.1}$$

See Chapter 6 for a full derivation.

The phase rule indicates the number of variables (F) of a system which may be chosen independently before the thermodynamic state of the system is completely determined. We have already discussed equilibria in one-component systems (pure substances) in Chapters 5, 6, and 34.

Exercise 35.1

Calculate the number of degrees of freedom in the following closed systems: (*a*) $CaCO_{3(c)} = CaO_{(c)} + CO_{2(g)}$, (*b*) $H_2O_{(c)} = H_2O_{(l)} + H_2O_{(g)}$. *Answer:* (*a*) $F = 2 - 3 + 2 = 1$. Any two of $CaCO_3$, CaO, and CO_2 can be the components (since the third can be formed from the other two, $S = 3$, $R = 1$, $C = 2$); $CaCO_{3(c)}$, $CaO_{(c)}$, and $CO_{2(g)}$ are three phases. (*b*) $F = 1 - 3 + 2 = 0$, water is the only component; *c*, *l*, and *g* are the three phases.

TWO-COMPONENT SYSTEMS

A binary solution has a maximum dimensionality of three, $F = C - P + 2 = 2 - P + 2 = 4 - P$; $F_{\max} = 3$. The full phase diagram for a binary system is three-dimensional (see Figure 35.1). Clearly such a three-dimensional diagram contains an enormous amount of information, but it is also very difficult to use, especially when printed on a two-dimensional page. For ease of discussion, we shall consider only two-dimensional "slices" from this phase diagram. The independent variables available are pressure, temperature, and composition,* and any pair of these (T, X; T, P; X, P) can be used as axes for a two-dimensional representation (the third variable then being held constant). Of the many possibilities, temperature-composition diagrams are by far the most used. But whatever phase diagram is convenient for the system involved, it is a condensation of much thermodynamic information about the system as well as an important key to possible means of separating the system into its components.

Exercise 35.2

How many dimensions would be required for a complete phase diagram for a three-component system? *Answer:* $F = C - P + 2 = 5 - P = 4$, since P cannot be less than 1. No method is known of constructing physical four-dimensional systems; thus three-component systems are usually plotted at constant pressure, which allows their representation in three-dimensional models in which the variables are T and the concentrations (see Figure 35.14).

---

*Composition is usually expressed as mole fraction or weight fraction, since both run from 0 to 1 and serve as good coordinates. Molarity is almost never used as the composition coordinate. Can you see why?

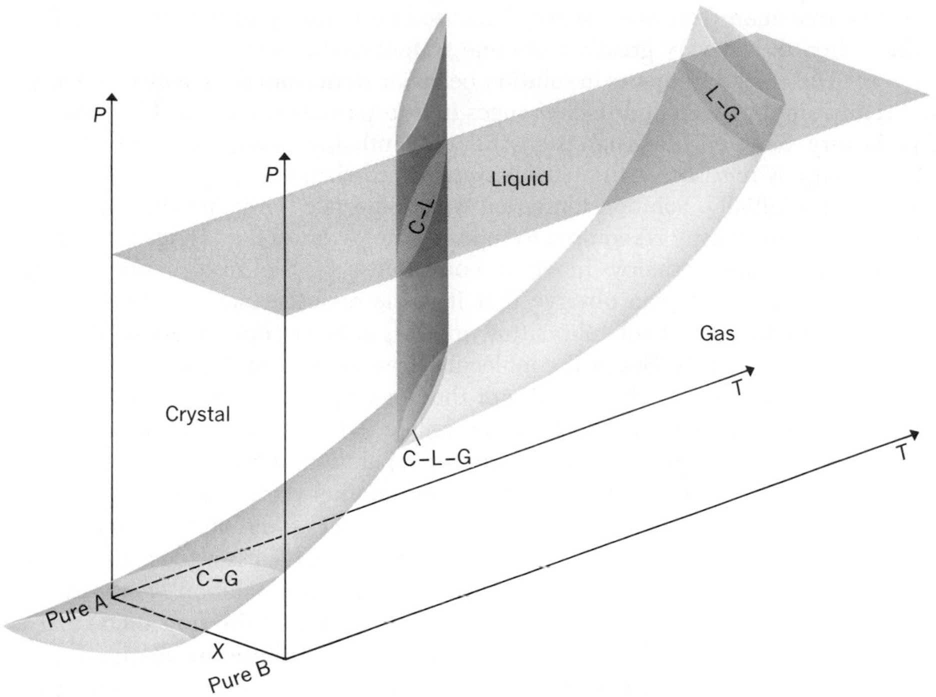

Figure 35.1 Part of the low-temperature, low-pressure portion of a complete three-dimensional phase diagram for two components that are mutually soluble both in the crystalline and liquid phases. Note that there are three separate three-dimensional regions representing *X*, *P*, and *T* conditions in which crystals (low *T*, high *P*), gas (high *T*, low *P*), or liquid can exist. These three regions are separated by three "wing-shaped" volumes whose surfaces define the two-phase regions representing equilibrium between C–G (lower left wing), C–L (vertical center wing), and L–G (right wing). Note that the front *P*–*T* surface gives the phase diagram (solid lines) for pure B, the back *P*–*T* surface that for pure A (dashed), the left *P*–*X* surface is an isothermal section showing C–G equilibrium, and the (horizontal) isobaric section is a *T*–*X* phase diagram showing C–L and L–G equilibria.

MOLECULAR BEHAVIOR AND REAL SOLUTIONS

The process of solution formation can be imagined at the molecular level as follows. Each set of molecules in the pure substances must first be rearranged, so that the molecules will be separated by the interparticle distances appropriate to the final solution concentrations. (For example, in a dilute solution of methanol in water the methanol particles are very far apart, but the water particles are almost as close together as in pure water.) Then the expanded systems must be brought together to give the final density. Energy must be absorbed by the pure substances in order to separate the particles initially; however, energy is evolved when the expanded systems are brought together to form the solution. It should also be noted that the mixing of particles increases the statistical "disorder" of the system, and this quantity is directly related to a positive entropy change, which will give a negative contribution to the thermodynamic free-energy change. In all solution processes there is an inherent tendency toward spontaneity (toward negative free-energy changes) simply because of the mixing of particles. The $T\,\Delta S$ values often do not vary greatly from one system to the next.

The chief differences in solution behavior stem from the balance of energy input and output associated with changes in interparticle distances. The values of ΔH do vary. Solution formation is exothermic (enthalpy change is negative) when more energy is released as the particles are mixed than was required to separate the particles initially. Solution formation is endothermic (enthalpy change is positive) when more energy is required to separate the particles than is released during mixing. Since the enthalpy function contributes to the free-energy change, $\Delta G = \Delta H - T\,\Delta S$, we can observe that it is the endothermic case that is most likely to lead to limited solubility; this, indeed, is borne out by actual thermodynamic measurements. But at the molecular level the reason for an endothermic process must be that the like particles of the pure liquids, on the average, attract one another to a greater degree than the unlike particles of the mixture. Hence more energy must be put into the system for separation of the like particles than is obtained as the unlike particles approach one another during mixing.

Unfortunately the foregoing discussion involves some simplifying assumptions, and the actual problem of explaining solution behavior is often considerably more difficult. As an example, we assumed that the final solution would exhibit a completely random distribution of particles and ignored the possibility that it might have some nonrandom structure. If structure contributes to solution formation, then the entropy contribution will be less positive and, regrettably, less easily analyzed. Nevertheless, the correlation of positive deviations and limited solubility with attractive energies between like particles is a reasonably good first approximation.

In summary, solution formation can occur as long as the chemical potentials of components are appreciably reduced upon entering the solution phase. A theoretical model of this process conceives of the reduction in chemical potential as being derived from randomizing effects of particle mixing and energetic effects of particle attractions. When the attractive energies between like species are larger than the attractive energies between unlike species, the reduction in chemical potential is large only for very dilute solutions and soon becomes so small that further solubility is not energetically favorable, at least at equilibrium. It is possible, then, to predict whether pairs of substances will exhibit high or low mutual solubility; we need only estimate the degrees to which like particles attract one another.

Heats of vaporization are a convenient and often good measure of these attractive energies, though we must keep in mind the contributions of such other factors as molecular sizes and specific particle-particle interactions. In general, limited solubility can be expected when one of the two components has a much higher heat of vaporization than the other. Some examples of solution pairs and their correlation to solubility properties are given in Table 35.1. Heats of vaporization have been presented in kilocalories per *gram* in this table in order to eliminate, to some degree, the influence of differing molecular sizes. Note in particular the series of alcohols, in which solubility diminishes as the heats of vaporization grow further apart. But note also, by comparing ethyl ether and, say, *n*-pentanol that such a simple correlation is imperfect. The ether is more soluble than its heat of vaporization would seem to indicate. It is clear that a further explanation would

Table 35.1 Correlation between enthalpies of vaporization and solubility properties.

Solute	Solvent	Enthalpy of vaporization (kcal/g)		Solubility (g/100 g of solvent at approx. 25°C)
		Solute	Solvent	
methanol	water	0.26	0.54	∞
ethanol	water	0.20	0.54	∞
n-propanol	water	0.16	0.54	∞
n-butanol	water	0.14	0.54	7.9
n-pentanol	water	0.12	0.54	2.7
ethyl ether	water	0.084	0.54	7.5
chloroform	water	0.059	0.54	1.0
carbon tetrachloride	water	0.047	0.54	0.08
carbon tetrachloride	ethyl ether	0.047	0.084	∞
n-butanol	ethyl ether	0.14	0.084	∞

have to begin by citing the longer carbon chains involved in *n*-pentanol and their contributions to the structural properties of the system.

LIQUID-LIQUID EXTRACTION

The occurrence of pairs of liquids having limited mutual solubility provides us with an important means of effecting certain chemical separations. Suppose that we wish to separate two components, such as I_2 and H_2O, which are initially in solution with one another. A separation is possible if we can find a third substance which has low solubility in H_2O but in which I_2 will dissolve readily. CCl_4 is such a substance. When CCl_4 and the aqueous I_2 solution are mixed together and shaken, the limited solubility of H_2O and CCl_4 causes the system to remain in two separate liquid phases but most of the I_2 dissolves in the CCl_4. If we ignore the small solubility of H_2O and CCl_4, the two liquid phases are essentially I_2 in H_2O and I_2 in CCl_4. Thus, I_2 is said to be "distributed" between the two phases. Since I_2 is more soluble in CCl_4 than in H_2O, the equilibrium distribution will have a higher concentration of I_2 in the CCl_4 layer than in the H_2O layer; separation of the two layers physically will, then, effect a partial separation of I_2 from H_2O. Of course, I_2 is not isolated as a pure substance in this way; it is merely separated from another substance, H_2O. Frequently, as in this instance, simpler means of complete isolation can be used on the final system (here I_2 in CCl_4) than on the initial system (here I_2 in H_2O).

A classic example of the usefulness of extraction techniques is the saponification of organic esters. For example, when ethyl benzoate is heated with aqueous sodium hydroxide, a mixture of sodium benzoate, ethyl alcohol, unreacted ester, and other substances is formed. In most cases benzoic acid is the desired product, but must be separated from the variety of substances of varying polarity with which it is mixed. Water and ether (diethyl ether) make a good extraction pair because they are relatively insoluble in one another and because nonpolar or slightly polar materials tend to dissolve best in ether and ionic materials to dissolve best in water. (Do you see why, in terms of ΔH and molecular forces?) The products of the saponification reaction are therefore distributed between water and ether: the sodium benzoate, the other ionic substances and the ethyl alcohol in the water. When the water and the ether have been separated, the water can be acidified to produce electrically neutral benzoic acid, which is almost insoluble in water but very soluble in ether. When pure ether is added to the mixture of water and acid and allowed to separate it yields an ether solution with a high concentration of essentially pure benzoic acid. Evaporation of the ether leaves crystalline benzoic acid. The process of purification can be repeated to any desired purity of benzoic acid, taking full advantage of the fact that sodium benzoate is primarily soluble in water and benzoic acid primarily soluble in ether.

The equilibrium distribution of a component between two liquid solutions is in many cases almost independent of concentration. This can be understood quite easily if we consider the thermodynamics of solutions. In all events, the equilibrium condition is that chemical potentials of components should be the same in the different phases that are in contact. Thus, referring to component A in equilibrium with both α and β solutions,

$$\mu_{\mathrm{A}}\,(\text{soln }\alpha) = \mu_{\mathrm{A}}\,(\text{soln }\beta)$$

Application of Equation (34.10) and activity coefficients, then, indicates that ${}_{\alpha}\gamma_{\mathrm{A}}\,{}_{\alpha}X_{\mathrm{A}} = {}_{\beta}\gamma_{\mathrm{A}}\,{}_{\beta}X_{\mathrm{A}}$ to give the

DISTRIBUTION LAW:
$$\frac{{}_{\alpha}X_{\mathrm{A}}}{{}_{\beta}X_{\mathrm{A}}} = \frac{{}_{\beta}\gamma_{\mathrm{A}}}{{}_{\alpha}\gamma_{\mathrm{A}}} = K_d \qquad (35.2)$$

where K_d is known as the distribution coefficient of component A between α and β. Obviously, K_d would be unity only if A formed ideal solutions in both α and β or had otherwise equivalent behavior in the two. In most cases, if A is quite soluble in α, ${}_{\alpha}\gamma_{\mathrm{A}}$ will be small; if A is only slightly soluble in β, ${}_{\beta}\gamma_{\mathrm{A}}$ will be large (greater than unity). Thus the distribution coefficient, K_d, will be larger than unity. Although it is often quite close to being a constant over large concentration ranges, it should be recalled that the activity coefficients are always functions of composition as well as temperature and pressure; thus the efficiency of an extraction procedure changes as it progresses, usually becoming much less efficient as very dilute solutions are reached. (Why?)

In most laboratory procedures a system is chosen for which the distribution coefficient is favorably large and the degree of purification demanded is not great. In these cases, a few extractions with small amounts of the extracting liquid are sufficient to effect separation. The layers are physically separated with a separatory funnel, a funnel that may be stoppered for shaking, and fitted with a stopcock so that the denser liquid layer can be drawn off. When the distribution coefficient is less favorable or when a more nearly complete separation is required, extraction can still be used but the procedure must be carried through many times in succession. A variety of continuous extractors have been designed for this purpose and they are of particular importance in isolating components of biochemical systems (see Figure 35.2).

Exercise 35.3

K_d of distribution of I_2 between H_2O and CS_2 is 650. Calculate the residual concentration of $I_{2(aq)}$ if 5 ml of 0.1 M $I_{2(aq)}$ is shaken with 1 ml of CS_2. *Answer:*

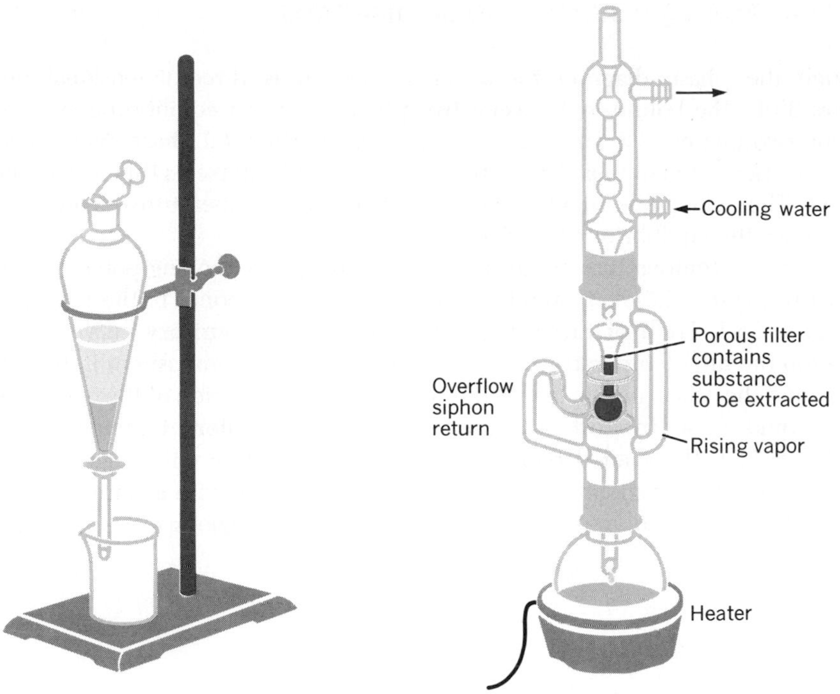

Figure 35.2 (**A**) Separatory funnel for single batch extraction. (**B**) Soxhlet-type continuous extractor.

$K_d = {}_{CS_2}X_{I_2}/{}_{H_2O}X_{I_2} = 650 = {}_{CS_2}M_{I_2}/{}_{H_2O}M_{I_2}$ if M is small (see p. 883). But, from a mass balance, $0.1\ M \cdot 5$ ml $= {}_{CS_2}M_{I_2} \cdot 1$ ml $+ {}_{H_2O}M_{I_2} \cdot 5$ ml. Thus ${}_{CS_2}M_{I_2} = 0.5\ M$, ${}_{H_2O}M_{I_2} = 0.0008\ M$. The extraction has been quite efficient.

RAOULT'S AND HENRY'S LAWS FOR REAL SOLUTIONS

For all solutions in the limit as $X_A \longrightarrow 1$, we find for component A (where p_A^0 = vapor pressure of pure A):

RAOULT'S LAW: $$p_A = p_A^0 X_A \tag{35.3}$$

The behavior of component B under these conditions (as $X_B \longrightarrow 0$), incidentally, must follow:

HENRY'S LAW: $$p_B = k_B X_B \tag{35.4}$$

where k_B is a constant characteristic of the system. Both Raoult's and Henry's laws have been experimentally verified for a large number of very dilute solutions. The simplicity and generality of these two equations makes them very useful.

Exercise 35.4

Calculate the solubility of H_2S in water at 0.1 atm pressure if the solubility at 1 atm pressure is 0.1 M. *Answer:* From Henry's law $p_B = k_B X_B \simeq k_B M_B$ if M_B is small (see p. 883). Thus $(p_B/M_B)_{0.1\text{ atm}} = k_B' = (p_B/M_B)_{1.0\text{ atm}}$, or $0.1\text{ atm}/M_B = 1\text{ atm}/0.1\ M$, $M_B = 0.01\ M$, assuming constant T throughout.

LIQUID-VAPOR EQUILIBRIUM PHASE DIAGRAMS

Though the phase diagram for a binary system is three-dimensional (as in Figure 35.1), the boundary between two phases, as in an equilibrium system involving two phases, is a surface. A section through the total phase diagram, such as the temperature-composition section of Figure 35.1 intersects this surface along a curve. Thus, along this intersection, a choice of either temperature or composition determines the equilibrium completely.

Some temperature-composition phase diagrams (boiling-point diagrams) appear in Figure 35.3, A, B, and C. Figure 35.3, C corresponds to the L-G section of Figure 35.1. Each of these diagrams contains two boundary curves. One of these (on the high-temperature side) is a function of the composition in the vapor phase, and the other (on the low-temperature side) is a function of the composition in the liquid phase. In most cases the two phases have different compositions. As in Figure 33.8, the shaded regions between the boundary curves are more like holes (or imaginary regions) in the graphs; no single phase with a composition and temperature indicated by a point within one of these regions exists. Instead, at

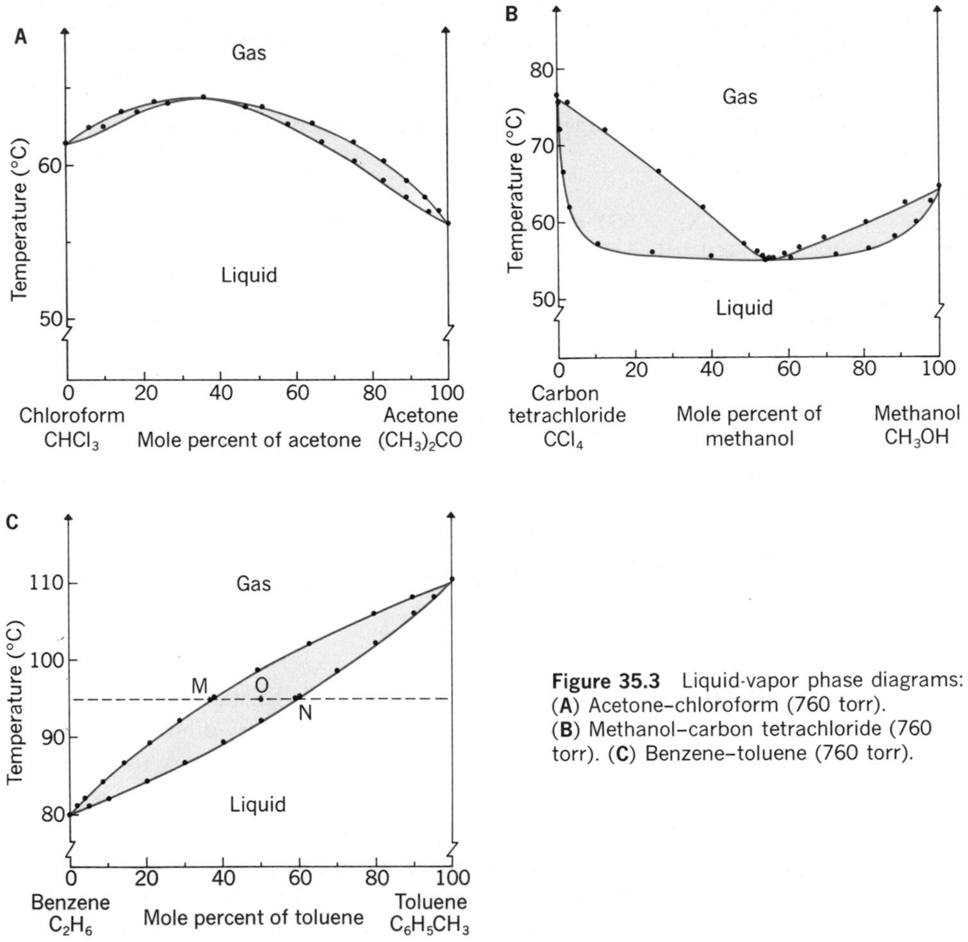

Figure 35.3 Liquid-vapor phase diagrams: (**A**) Acetone–chloroform (760 torr). (**B**) Methanol–carbon tetrachloride (760 torr). (**C**) Benzene–toluene (760 torr).

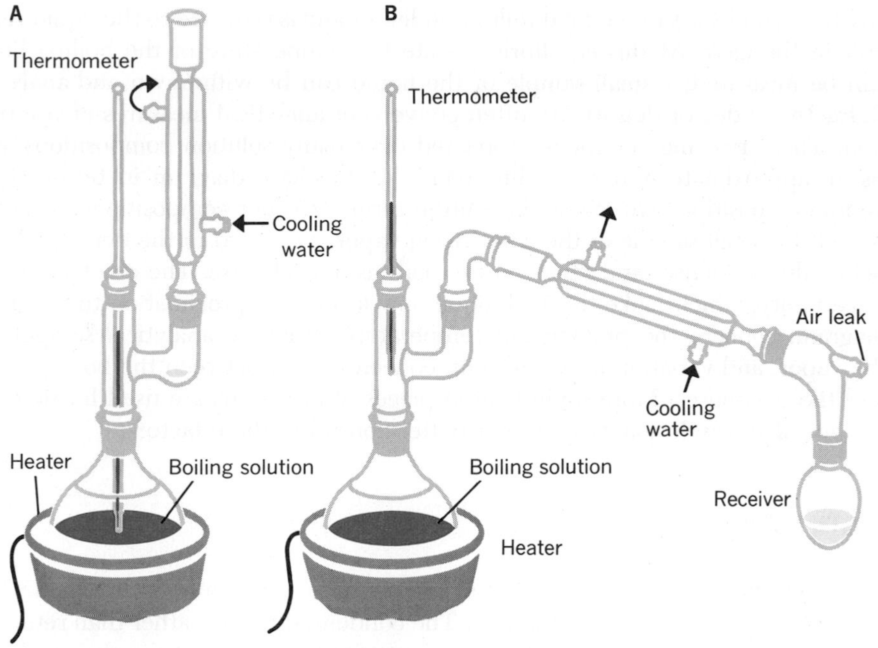

Figure 35.4 Apparatus arranged for (**A**) total reflux, and (**B**) simple distillation.

each isothermal the two boundary curves indicate the compositions of the two different phases that are in equilibrium. A gross composition such as O in Figure 35.3, C corresponds to a vapor phase of composition M and a liquid phase of composition N; the relative amounts of the phases present are given by the line-segment ratios, MO/ON, as before.

In the limit of mutual insolubility of the two pure components as liquids, Figure 35.3, B shows a flat isothermal from pure A to pure B through the minimum boiling point. The conditions of Equation (34.12) are then satisfied (since all gas phases approach ideality) and each of the l-g boundary curves follows the Clausius-Clapeyron equation $\ln X_i = (\Delta\overline{H}_i/R)[1/T_i - 1/T_i^0]$. The minimum boiling temperature and the composition there are given by the intersection of the two curves.

Exercise 35.5

Which of the diagrams in Figure 35.3 would match the liquid-gas diagram for the chloroform-methanol system? *Answer:* $CHCl_3$ and CH_3OH can form hydrogen bonds with one another stronger than those $CHCl_3$ forms with itself. This gives negative deviations and a maximum in the l-g diagram similar to that in Figure 35.3, A.

DETERMINATION OF *T-X* DIAGRAMS

Figure 35.4, A, illustrates an apparatus that can be used to obtain rough data for such boiling-point diagrams. A liquid solution is placed inside the boiling flask and heated gently. When boiling has been established, the heating rate is reduced until a state of equilibrium is reached. The small amount of liquid vaporized at any time condenses in the total reflux condenser and is returned to the liquid reservoir in the flask. At this equilibrium state the temperature of the boiling liquid can be measured; a small sample of the liquid can be withdrawn and analyzed. Refractive index or density are often convenient analytical measures of composition. These two measurements, repeated over many solution compositions, give us an approximate isobaric boiling-point (T, X) phase diagram in terms of the liquid composition. The phase diagram in terms of vapor composition can be obtained if a small sample of the condensing vapor is trapped in the depression just below the condenser and removed for analysis in each case. The chief sources of uncertainty, which make this technique only a rough approximation to the phase diagram, concern the problems of temperature variation, analytical sampling of the vapor, and variation in equilibrium concentrations between the boiling liquid and the condenser. More sophisticated pieces of apparatus are used for determinations of research quality and offer better control of these factors.

DISTILLATION

With only the slight rearrangement of our apparatus, as shown in Figure 35.4, B, we can carry out a simple distillation. The condensed vapor, rather than returning to the liquid reservoir in the flask, passes out of the apparatus down the condenser to some suitable receiver. No over-all state of equilibrium can be established in this system, since there is a net, directional mass transfer. Furthermore, as the liquid is vaporized its composition changes, so that both the boiling temperature and the composition of the condensate vary during the distillation.

Let us imagine the simple distillation of a benzene-toluene solution; the phase diagram for this system has been reproduced in Figure 35.5 for convenience. Suppose that the liquid to be distilled is initially of composition X_1. The very first vapor to be in equilibrium with this boiling liquid has the composition Y_1; this is also the very first condensate to appear at the receiver. On the other hand, it will be noted that the vapor is more concentrated than the liquid in the more volatile (lower-boiling) benzene; when a finite amount of this condensate has been formed, the loss of benzene, in excess of its proportion in the liquid, will have caused the liquid to change composition, becoming more concentrated in the higher-boiling toluene. According to the phase diagram, this new liquid will have a slightly higher

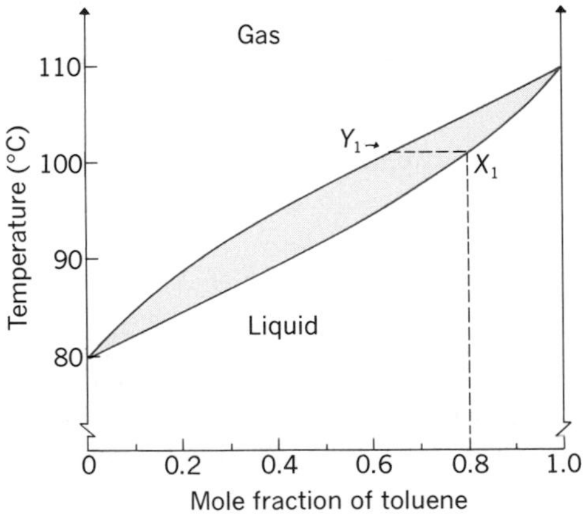

Figure 35.5 Liquid-vapor phase diagram of benzene-toluene (750 torr); simple distillation.

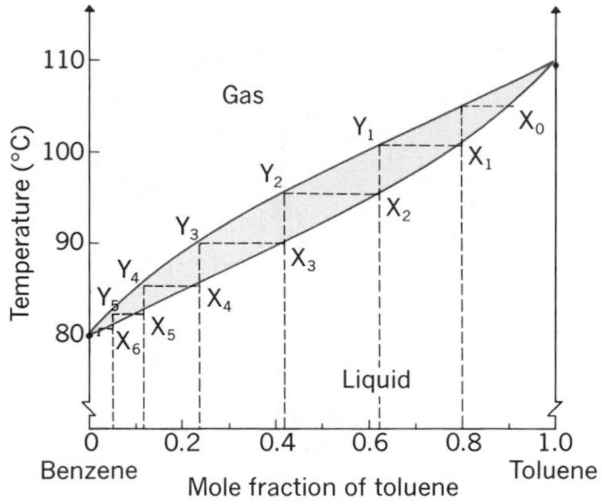

Figure 35.6 Liquid-vapor phase diagram of benzene-toluene (750 torr); fractional distillation.

boiling temperature and its vapor will be slightly higher in toluene concentration. Note, however, that though the vapor continually becomes more concentrated in toluene, it is always more concentrated in benzene than is the corresponding liquid; thus, in a simple distillation the liquid phase composition varies continuously toward pure toluene, the higher-boiling component. At the same time, the boiling temperature rises steadily toward the boiling point of pure toluene. When pure toluene is reached, however, the amount of liquid remaining is only infinitesimal.

No separation of the components is effected in a complete simple distillation. However, receivers can be changed any number of times during the distillation, so that the liquid can be broken up into any number of fractions, having compositions that range from about Y_1 to almost pure toluene.

Suppose, now, that the first fraction of the liquid received were placed in an identical apparatus and distilled a second time. The liquid having composition $Y_1 = X_2$ would produce a vapor of composition Y_2, considerably richer in benzene. This distillation might be divided into fractions by using different receivers, as before; then the process might be repeated, each time using the first fraction to be collected. The next vapor would have composition Y_3, the next Y_4, and so on until practically pure benzene would be obtained, as illustrated in Figure 35.6. This method of successive distillation is capable of effecting a separation of the components. Unfortunately, it would be tedious to perform and the losses in discarded fractions along the way would be staggering.

Exercise 35.6

What would be the composition of the first gas bubble which formed when a 50-50 mole solution of benzene and toluene was distilled? *Answer:* Draw an isothermal through $X = 0.5$ in Figure 35.14. This indicates the bubble would be about 70 mole percent benzene and 30 mole percent toluene.

FRACTIONAL DISTILLATION

Figure 35.7, A shows an apparatus called a fractionating column, which accomplishes the same operations internally and easily.

The separation outlined in the preceding section is achieved because each

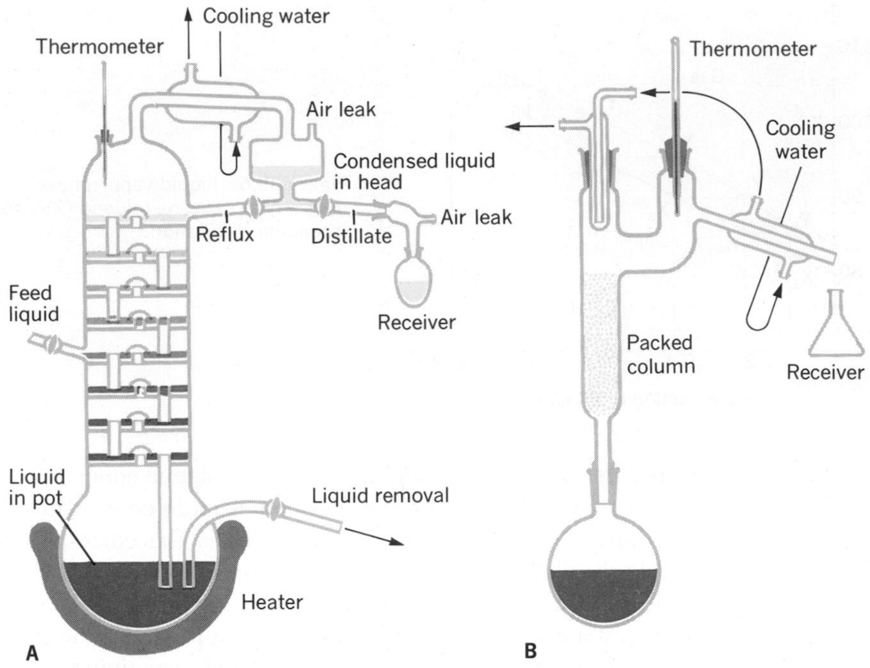

Figure 35.7 Fractionating column. (**A**) Plate column. (**B**) Packed column.

vaporization followed by condensation produces a liquid with a higher concentration of the lower-boiling component. The degree of separation, then, is a function of the number of times that vaporization occurs. A fractionating column works on the principle of condensing and revaporizing the vaporized material many times as it flows through the column. Imagine the fractionating column operating with the system that we have been discussing. Suppose that liquid of composition X_4 in Figure 35.6 is fed onto the fourth plate, as shown in Figure 35.7. Vapor Y_4 will condense on the fifth plate to give liquid of composition X_5. This liquid will revaporize, partly by heat exchange with vapor rising from plate four and partly by heat exchange with the heated walls. The resulting vapor of composition Y_5 rises to the sixth plate, where it is similarly condensed. Following this process up the column, it will be seen that the liquid at the last plate has the composition X_8. Thus the vapor which emerges from the fractionating column and which condenses into the receiver is of composition X_9, approximately pure benzene. It should be noted that the separation at each vaporization is a process of diminishing returns; it would take infinitely many partitions in the fractionating column to produce a perfect separation. Within reasonable bounds, however, a large number of partitions can be built into the column.

Simultaneously, the composition of toluene is rising on the lower plates so that the liquid removed from the pot will have the composition $X_0 = 0.92$ mole fraction toluene, as indicated in Figure 35.6. Thus the pot acts as an additional plate.

The fractionating plate column of Figure 35.7, A is not the only design possible and, indeed, it is not much used for laboratory work even though widely used in industry. Actually, it is not essential that the condensation stages of a fractionating column be so completely separated; a certain amount of fractionation occurs in almost every simple-distillation apparatus because some of the vapor tends to condense on the sides of the flask and tube leading to the condenser, being then revaporized by contact with hot vapor rising in the system. (This same phenomenon creates a critical problem in phase-diagram determinations, since in these we must be certain that the vapor analyzed represents one and only one equilibrium.) A distillation apparatus can be made into a better and better fractionating column as one increases the surface area between the gas and the liquid. This can first be accomplished by inserting a plain glass tube between the condenser head and the neck of the boiling flask. Further improvement can be obtained by packing the tube with various materials that increase its surface area. A tube of approximately one meter, packed with loosely matted glass helices and warmed with electrical heaters to about the boiling temperature of the liquid, often can give a very high degree of separation of the components. Clearly it is easier to pack a column than to build one with plates in it (see Figure 35.7, B).

THEORETICAL PLATES

Since the degrees of separation vary widely from one column to another, it is convenient to invent some quantitative measure of column efficiency. For this purpose we can define the notion of a theoretical plate. Suppose that we have fitted a boiling pot with a fractionating column and a condenser head. After the system has been warmed to a steady state with the topmost condensate being completely returned to the column, the steady-state temperature at the head of the column is noted. A sample of this head condensate and a sample of the pot liquid are then removed and analyzed. We use the appropriate T, X diagram to mark the compositions of the head and pot liquids and determine the number of liquid-vapor equilibrations which would theoretically have to occur in order to produce this vapor. At total reflux the number of equilibrations equals the number of steps (as in Figure 35.6) to get from head to pot composition. This number is the number of theoretical plates. If the liquid had been benzene-toluene of pot composition X_1 and the vapor collected of head composition X_6, inspection of the phase diagram, as in Figure 35.6 would indicate a total of five theoretical plates for the apparatus, or four for the column, since the pot is one theoretical plate.

At less than total reflux it is necessary to measure the reflux ratio, R (the ratio between the volume of fluid returning to the pot and the volume being taken off as product). An operating line of slope $R/(R + 1)$ is then drawn instead of the 45° line on an X-Y diagram and used as the lower boundary in determining the number of theoretical plates in the column.*

Occasionally it is of value to compare efficiencies of different packing materials; in this case the height equivalent to a theoretical plate (HETP) can be calculated by dividing the height of the column by the number of theoretical plates which *it* includes (remembering that one plate occurs at the liquid-vapor surface in the flask). Table 35.2 shows some values of HETP for different packing materials and indicates the separation achieved for benzene-toluene with 20-cm columns. Note the considerable differences in efficiencies of the three packings.

AZEOTROPES—MAXIMUM AND MINIMUM BOILING POINTS

Next let us consider an attempt to fractionate a solution of acetone and chloroform. Suppose that the solution to be separated has a mole fraction of 0.8 in chloroform. Pure acetone is more

*See McCabe and Thiele, *Ind. Eng. Chem.*, **17**, 605 (1925), or a book on the theory of distillation practice.

Table 35.2 **Efficiencies of several fractionating columns.**

Column composition	HETP (cm)	Mole fraction toluene	
		Pot	Head
Glass helices	4–5	0.80	0.09
Metal turnings (stainless steel)	6–7	0.80	0.22
Raschig rings (6-mm glass tubing)	10–12	0.80	0.47

volatile than pure chloroform, so we might expect acetone to appear at the top of a good fractionating column. Paradoxically, we find chloroform instead. Inspection of the phase diagram in Figure 35.3, A gives us the answer. Because of the maximum boiling point in this system, the vapor which is first produced by 0.8 mole fraction chloroform in acetone is more concentrated in chloroform than in acetone. Thus each further vaporization simply increases the chloroform concentration. If the original liquid had been more concentrated in acetone—for example, a mole fraction of 0.4 in chloroform—the opposite situation would have existed, with each vaporization producing higher acetone concentration and with acetone as the component emerging at the condenser head.

The minimum-boiling system of methanol-carbon tetrachloride in Figure 35.3, B presents a similar situation. In this case, however, only one liquid can appear at the top of a fractionating column regardless of the original liquid composition. This liquid, however, is not one of the pure components; instead, it is the minimum-boiling azeotrope, the solution that exists at the minimum temperature in the phase boundary curve. There can be no further fractionation of this solution at constant pressure, since each successive revaporization of it yields a vapor of the same composition. Similar reasoning shows that the solution found at the bottom of a fractionating column with the acetone-chloroform always approaches the maximum-boiling azeotrope.

Complete separation of a solution into its components is possible in fractional distillation only if there are no extrema in the phase boundary curves. When extrema exist, the best that can be expected is a partial separation, obtaining one of the pure components and a solution. In many cases one can vary the pressure or add further components and so accomplish separations of azeotropes.

CRYSTAL-LIQUID EQUILIBRIA

Application of the phase rule to problems of phase equilibria is actually independent of the physical descriptions of the phases involved; the only factor of importance is the number of phases involved. For this reason, there is a solid-liquid and a solid-gas phase diagram that corresponds to every liquid-vapor phase diagram that we have now discussed. Similarly, solid-solid phase diagrams offer nothing new for analysis. It should be noted, however, that we have explored only simple diagrams. Many much more complicated phase diagrams are known (remember Figures 33.8 and 33.10).

When solids are involved, separation procedures tend to be fitted more specifically to the unique aspects of the system; it is fair to say, in general, that the possibilities of effecting separations of the components are more limited. The reasons for such limitations will be clear if we consider the general principles underlying any separation procedure. First, the equilibrium between phases must create a difference in composition; all separation procedures are designed to capitalize on this composition change, and it is more difficult for viscous materials such as solids to come to equilibrium. Second, the new phase must be easy to separate physically from the old phase. Solids again give problems.

The vaporization of either a liquid or a solid creates a gas, which expands away from the original phase; hence this separation occurs rather cleanly. With fluid liquids, a separatory funnel can be used to take advantage of the separation that gravity effects on the liquid layers. But mixtures of solid phases and solid-liquid mixtures present more difficulties. Solids often crystallize together, so that the separate crystalline phases are only microscopically evident; there is no convenient means of picking them apart. Crystals can, of course, be separated from liquids by filtration or centrifugation, but this can involve such technical problems as surface wetting of the crystal by the liquid. In general, the means of fractional refinement of separated samples are even further limited and must be carried through manually; few internal means such as the fractionating column are available.

CRYSTAL-LIQUID PHASE DIAGRAMS

Figure 35.8, A shows the temperature-composition phase diagram for the copper-nickel system in the neighborhood of the crystal-liquid equilibrium. This phase diagram is illustrative of both of our points. First, since copper and nickel dissolve in all proportions in both the solid and the liquid phases, the phase diagram resembles the liquid-vapor diagram for an ideal liquid solution, such as the benzene-toluene of Figure 35.3, C. Second, it indicates the difficulty of producing a separation of copper and nickel. If a solid solution of the two is heated to the point at which liquid appears, a composition difference does arise, but it is necessary to separate the phases manually at the high temperature necessary. Presuming that the liquid phase is less dense and forms at the top, it might be decanted from the mixture. Something like a simple distillation could then be accomplished by decanting the liquid melt continuously into separate receivers. A fractionation process, though, would be considerably more difficult. Each of the liquid melts, after being solidified, would have to be partly remelted separately and repeatedly. Consequently this kind of process can be carried out more readily as a fractional crystallization. That is, all of the solid solution can be melted and then allowed partly to

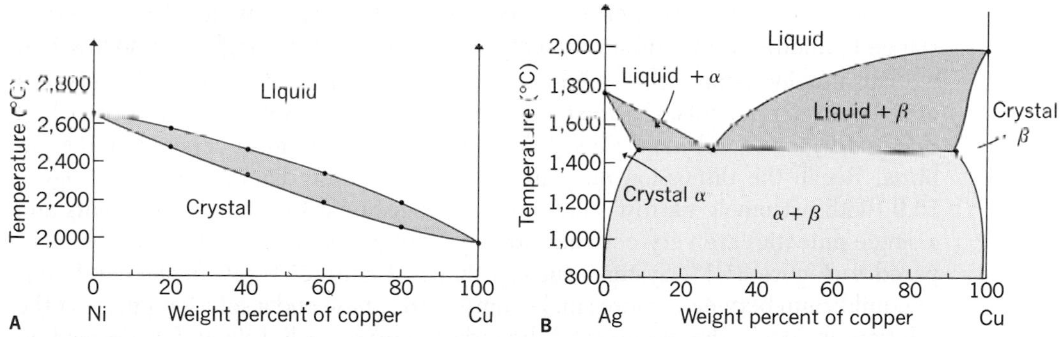

Figure 35.8 Crystal-liquid phase diagrams. (**A**) Copper–nickel. (**B**) Copper–silver.

crystallize. The first crystals to form contain more nickel than copper and may be filtered off. If these crystals are entirely melted and then partly recrystallized, the new crystals will have a yet higher nickel concentration. The principle is identical to that of fractional distillation, but the procedure is clumsy, owing to the difficulty of handling solid-liquid systems.

We discussed in Chapter 33 the reasons many metals dissolve so well in one another even in the solid phase. Let us review them, using copper and nickel as examples. Pure copper and nickel crystals both have the cubic closest-packed structure, and both copper and nickel atoms have about the same (metallic) radius—1.246 Å for nickel and 1.278 Å for copper. The proximity of copper and nickel in the periodic table indicates that the orbital symmetry and forces that lead to metallic binding in each may well be about the same (see p. 387).

The copper-silver system illustrated in Figure 35.8, B presents an interesting contrast. Copper and silver are only partly miscible in the solid phase, even though both have a cubic closest-packed structure in the pure state. To explain their limited solubility it is necessary to note the differences between them. The interatomic forces in silver are considerably smaller than those in copper; one indication of this is that silver is a softer metal. Comparison of heats of sublimation, analogous to the correlation developed in Table 35.1, shows 104 kcal/mole for nickel, 82 kcal/mole for copper, and 68 kcal/mole for silver. Also, and perhaps of greatest importance, the metallic radius of silver is 1.34 Å, considerably larger than the metallic radius of copper (1.17 Å). It is very often the structural, or packing, problem that creates the greatest limitation on solubility of solid phases.

If we warm a 50-50 mixture of solid phases in the copper-silver system until liquid first appears, the liquid will have a specific composition (about 30% by weight copper), which does not change until one of the two solid-solution phases disappears. If a liquid melt containing 50% copper is cooled, the first crystals to separate are solid solutions in which the concentration of copper is very high; as crystallization proceeds, the concentration of copper in the solid solutions decreases. Eventually the temperature of the three-phase equilibrium is reached; here, while the solid solution of high copper concentration continues to precipitate, a new solid solution with a high silver concentration begins to precipitate. Coprecipitation of these solid solutions continues until the melt has been entirely solidified. With a 50-50 mixture separation by fractional crystallization is possible for a copper-rich phase, but a silver-rich solid phase is almost impossible to separate by crystallization.

The structural properties of crystals tend to differ so widely from one substance to another that mutual solubility is most often exceedingly low, so low that we can usually assume that solid-phase mixtures consist of intermingled crystals of the pure components. Complete immiscibility, which is seldom even approached in liquid-vapor equilibria, is thus at least approximated in most crystal-liquid equilibria. Recall the discussion on pages 849–851. Phase diagrams such as Figure 35.9 (with extremely narrow solid-solution ranges near the pure components and a single eutectic) are very common for crystal-liquid systems and should be compared to Figure 35.17. Systems such as that in Figure 35.9 satisfy the conditions of equilibrium between a pure single component phase and a solution phase. If the solution is ideal, the liquid-solid boundary curves will follow [as derived in Equation (34.12)] the

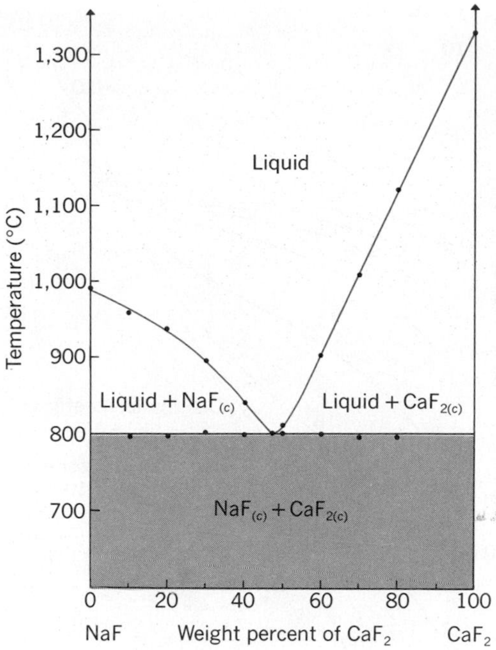

Figure 35.9 Solid-liquid phase diagram for sodium fluoride-calcium fluoride. A simple eutectic system.

CLAUSIUS-CLAPEYRON EQUATION:

$$\ln X_i = -\frac{\Delta \overline{H}_i}{R}\left[\frac{1}{T_i} - \frac{1}{T_i^0}\right] \tag{35.5}$$

These curves may be thought of as the solubility versus temperature curves for each pure component in the solution. From them, if the above assumptions hold, $\Delta \overline{H}$ may be calculated. Vice versa, if $\Delta \overline{H}$ is known, the curves may be calculated. The eutectic temperature and composition may be calculated as the point of intersection of the two curves.

Separation of a pure sample of one component is relatively easy in systems like that of Figure 35.9; since it is the "pure" solid which first precipitates and it can be filtered away directly. Attempts to separate a pure sample of the other component, however, are thwarted just as much as in the preceding example.

The boundary curves for crystal-liquid systems could be calculated by using Equation (34.12), the Clausius-Clapeyron equation for a multicomponent system, if it were a good assumption that the liquid solution is ideal. Unfortunately this is seldom a reasonable assumption except in dilute solutions.

Exercise 35.7

What is present at $X_{Cu} = 80$ and $T = 1600°C$ in a Cu-Ag system? *Answer:* Draw an isothermal at $T = 1600°C$. The point $X_{Cu} = 80$, $T = 1600°C$ lies in a heterogeneous region bounded isothermally by liquid of $X_{Cu} \cong 30$ and solid $\beta \cong 90$. Presumably the solid (being mainly Cu) will float in the liquid (which is mainly Ag, a higher density substance). The relative amount of solid and liquid phases will be solid/liquid = (80 − 30)/(90 − 80) = 5/1 as a weight ratio.

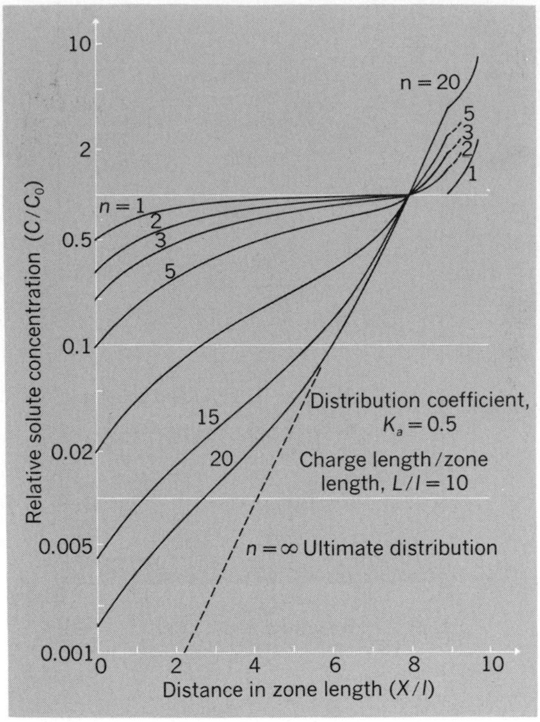

Figure 35.10 Zone melting. Schematic relative solute concentrations as a function of the length of the charge after n passes of the molten zone. [W. G. Pfann, *Zone Melting*, John Wiley & Sons, 1958.]

ZONE MELTING

Although most fractional crystallizations demand considerable manual labor, there is an internal technique comparable to fractional distillation; this is known as zone melting (see p. 639). Suppose that we have a long rod of a given metal that contains low concentrations of other metals; it might be a sample of germanium that has to be purified for use in the manufacture of transistors. It does not particularly matter which of the three phase diagrams just discussed best describes the germanium sample; in all cases, if the sample is partly melted, the first melt produced will have a different concentration of the impurities than did the original sample. In zone melting a narrow heater is passed along the length of the metal rod, heating a narrow zone that changes continuously as the heater moves along the bar. Melting takes place at the zone's leading edge, freezing at the following edge. Thus, if the impurities are more soluble in the melt than in the crystal, the heater moves the impurities along its path. If the impurities are less soluble in the liquid than in the crystal, they tend to move in the direction opposite to that of the melted zone. In either case, at the end of the zone-melting procedure, the "impurity end" of the rod can be cut off, leaving behind a rod of much higher purity. Figure 35.10 shows a typical graph of the impurity concentrations along a metal rod as a function of the number of passes made by the heater.

Since zone melting involves intense local heating, its applicability is limited to thermally stable substances. Air must often be excluded to eliminate the possibility of oxidation, and other possible chemical reactions must be taken into account. The actual process of drawing impurities along the line of heater motion (assuming that impurities concentrate in the liquid) is somewhat more complicated than the preceding description would indicate. A better explanation can be derived if we concentrate attention on the edge from which the heater is being withdrawn, and ask what material will first crystallize from the melt. The answer is that, although the melt itself has a high concentration of impurities, the first materials to crystallize have a low concentration of them (approaching zero as the solids approach mutual insolubility). The impurities, once in the liquid phase, tend to remain in the liquid phase. The degree of purification decreases as the heater moves along, since the melt phase builds up a high concentration of the impurities.

DETERMINATION OF CRYSTAL-LIQUID PHASE DIAGRAMS

Thus far, nothing has been said about the experimental techniques through which phase diagrams of the crystal-liquid type can be determined. In this regard, the careful analysis of "cooling curves" is by far the most important and instructive procedure. We begin with a liquid melt of known composition and observe the thermal and structural behavior of the system as the system loses energy to the surroundings. As solid phases are precipitated they may be collected and analyzed (chemically or by diffraction or spectroscopic techniques); but even the rate of cooling, when carefully observed, provides a great deal of information. Figure 35.11 gives hypothetical cooling curves for the BeF_2-CaF_2 system.

Curves *a* and *f* represent cooling curves for pure BeF_2 and pure CaF_2, respectively. The temperature stops falling abruptly when the pure solids begin to crystallize, goes through a small region of undercooling, then becomes constant, since at a given pressure there are no degrees of freedom remaining for a two-phase single component at constant pressure ($F = C - P + 1 = 1 - 2 + 1 = 0$). As time continues to pass, the temperature does not change ($F = 0$), since complete crystallization requires the loss of considerable amounts of heat. The heat lost here is due to the enthalpy of crystallization, $-\Delta H_{fus}$. When crystallization is complete, the temperature again drops rapidly. The heat lost during cooling when there is no phase change occurring is attributable to heat capacities alone. Thus the steepest parts of the curve correspond to cooling without phase change, $F = 1$.

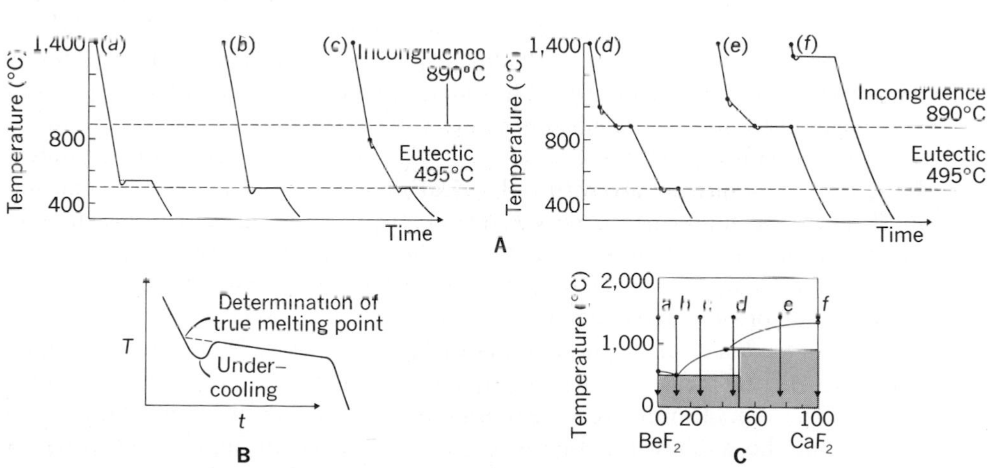

Figure 35.11 (**A**) Hypothetical cooling curves for the calcium fluoride-beryllium fluoride system. (**B**) Detail of method of extrapolation through under-cooling "trough" to obtain true melting point (see also Figure 36.2) (**C**) Corresponding phase diagram.

Curve *b* represents the behavior of a two-component system, $F = 3 - P$ (since pressure is fixed). The constant temperature at 495°C indicates $F = 0$. Therefore, $P = 3$ and there must be three phases in equilibrium during this "hold." Visual examination will show crystals forming from a single liquid phase; thus there must be two separate crystalline phases forming. As soon as all the liquid disappears, $F = 1$ (or more, if one of the crystals also disappears) and the temperature drops again.

In curve *c* the slope changes abruptly at 800°C, but the temperature continues to fall, though more slowly. This change of slope arises from the precipitation of $BeF_2 \cdot CaF_2$, a fact that can be verified by analysis of the crystals that may be filtered from the mixture. The temperature falls less rapidly at this point because of the heat of crystallization, which must be removed; however, it continues to fall in spite of the second phase because this is a two-component system with one degree of freedom ($F = 2 - 2 + 1 = 1$). Another interesting feature of curve *c* is that it eventually comes to another abrupt change in slope—one having constant temperature. Application of the phase rule shows us that a third phase must have appeared at this point ($F = 0 = 2 - P + 1$; $P = 3$); and, since time elapses before the temperature again falls, some process must occur here. Since this $T =$ 495°C, the same as that in curve *b*, we surmise that the same three phases are present. Microscopic analysis does show that a second solid phase appears here, and chemical analysis show that it is pure BeF_2. Further analysis would also show that the liquid remains at a constant composition during the level part of the cooling curve. With the disappearance of liquid in this cooling process, the temperature again falls, now with a steep slope that is determined only by the heat capacities of the two solids, $F = 1$.

Curve *d* is uniquely complicated. As in curve *e*, solid CaF_2 is first to crystallize out of the melt and its crystallization is followed by a constant-temperature, three-phase reaction at 890°C in which melt and CaF_2 combine to form the compound $BeF_2 \cdot CaF_2$. In this case, however, there is an excess of melt and the solid CaF_2 is used up in the second reaction. When the temperature again decreases we know there are only two phases present, solid $BeF_2 \cdot CaF_2$ and liquid. The slope showing the temperature change is not as steep as in curve *e*, where two solids are being cooled; rather the slope is gradual, indicating that crystallization is occurring. Analysis of the crystals formed would indicate that they are solid $BeF_2 \cdot CaF_2$. Eventually the temperature again becomes constant, indicating the occurrence of another three-phase mixture ($F = 0 = 2 - 3 + 1$). At this point pure crystals of BeF_2 begin to coprecipitate with $BeF_2 \cdot CaF_2$ compound. This process continues until all of the liquid has been consumed; then the temperature falls rapidly, indicating that only the heat capacities of the solids are involved.

The small dips normally associated with each decrease in slope arise from undercooling or slow nucleation by a new phase (see p. 817). As the temperature drops, the tendency of the new phase to form increases. When the new phase starts to form, ΔH is released, heating the undercooled solution and causing a small trough. The equilibrium break temperature is obtained by extrapolating back through this dip, as shown in Figure 35.11, B. Otherwise the equilibrium T may be below the true value, due to change in composition of the liquid during the initial crystallization following undercooling.

In summary, the phase rule helps us to analyze cooling curves for a system by predicting the number of phases required to keep the temperature constant. For instance, in binary systems a constant-temperature period occurs whenever three phases are in equilibrium. Careful observation of the temperature-time slope discloses much information about the kinds of processes that may occur in the system. The steepest slopes indicate systems cooling without accompanying phase changes. The onset of crystallization and other phase transitions can almost always be recognized by the resulting gradual slopes, since the enthalpy changes for these processes contribute to the total amount of heat that must be removed in cooling. In a two-component system at constant pressure, constant temperatures indicate that $F = 0$; that is, there are three coexisting phases. Further information, if needed, can be gained by separation and analysis of the phases present. The ideality of the liquid solution (assuming negligibly small solid solution formation) can be checked with the Clausius-Clapeyron equation.

IRON-CARBON EQUILIBRIA

One of the classic examples of phase equilibria is the iron-carbon system, illustrated in part in Figure 35.12. Perhaps the most obvious feature of this diagram is the typical structure of crystal-liquid boundary curves for a system with partial miscibility of crystals, the chief solid solution being austenite, the γ phase. On the other hand, the phase diagram is complicated by a number of crystal-crystal phase transitions that occur at low temperatures and in systems low in carbon. The β phase is a low-temperature form of iron in which very small amounts of carbon may be dissolved. The α iron has the same crystal structure as β, but can be magnetized. When austenite is cooled to a temperature between about 1300 and 1000°K, depending upon its composition, it becomes unstable and first decomposes to the more stable β phase or the compound Fe_3C, cementite. These transitions are two-phase equilibrium processes; hence temperature and composition can vary. The boundary curves for the transitions are diagonal, indicating that the austenite does indeed change its composition as the temperature falls. For example, austenite with 0.5% carbon, when cooled to about 1140°K, begins to decompose to the β phase. On the phase diagram the system enters a two-phase region in which the β phase and austenite coexist. As temperature is reduced in this region, both austenite and the β phase change their compositions, austenite and β both becoming more concentrated in carbon. At

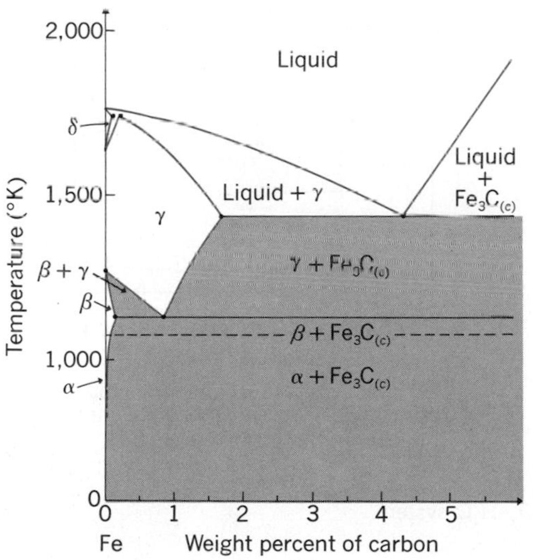

Figure 35.12 Solid-liquid phase diagram for dilute solutions of carbon in iron (see also Figure 5.14).

about 1100°K the temperature ceases to fall, indicating the appearance of a third phase; this third phase is cementite, $Fe_3C_{(c)}$. The temperature decreases again once all of the austenite has been converted to a mixture of β phase and cementite.

The solid solutions of iron-carbon are of particular importance because they are easily worked, being homogeneous phases. Steels can be heated until austenite is formed, worked into the desired shape, and then cooled back to a hard multiphase composition. Cast iron contains a higher percentage of carbon, so the only homogeneous phase available upon heating is the liquid phase. It is consequently more convenient to form these materials by melting and then casting them.

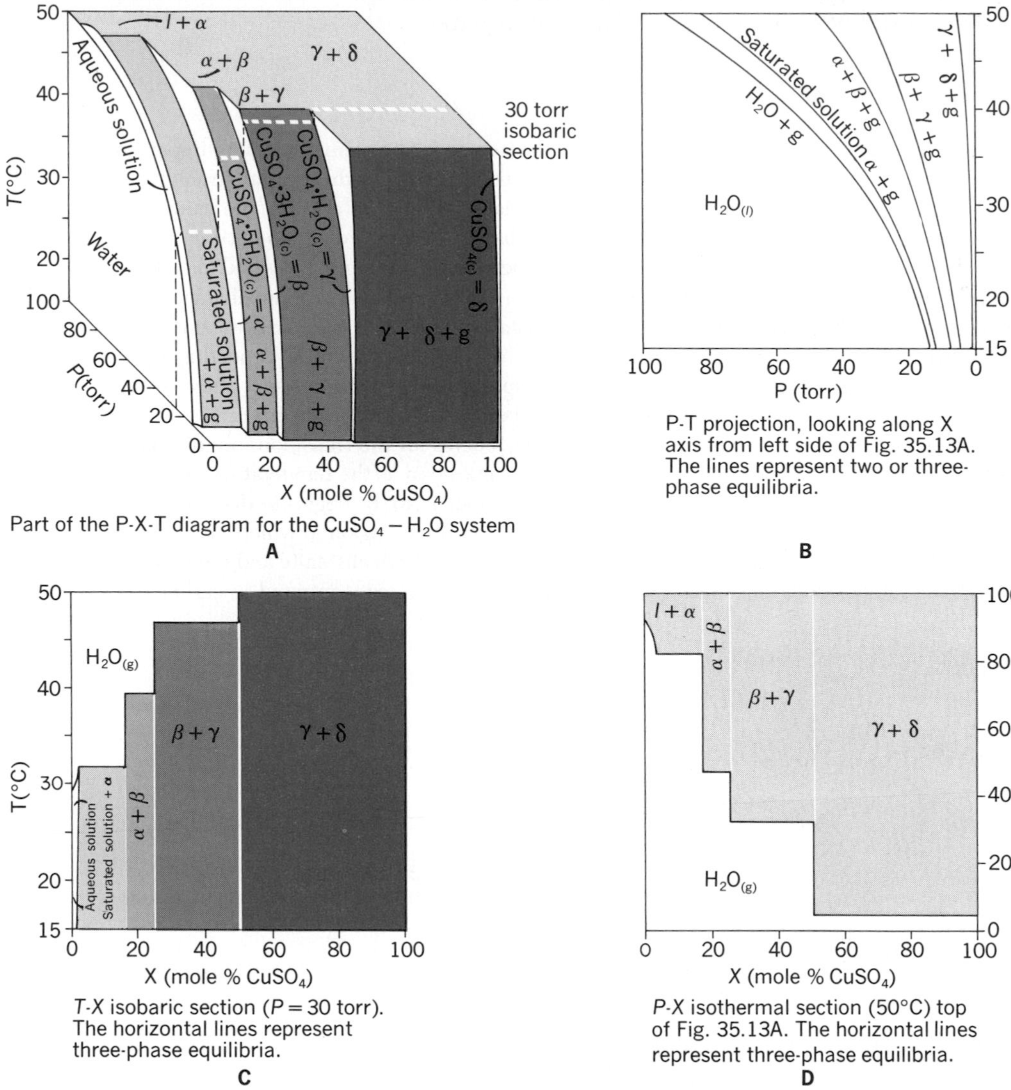

Part of the P-X-T diagram for the $CuSO_4 - H_2O$ system

A

P-T projection, looking along X axis from left side of Fig. 35.13A. The lines represent two or three-phase equilibria.

B

T-X isobaric section (*P* = 30 torr). The horizontal lines represent three-phase equilibria.

C

P-X isothermal section (50°C) top of Fig. 35.13A. The horizontal lines represent three-phase equilibria.

D

Figure 35.13 Phase relationships in the $CuSO_4$-H_2O system.

EQUILIBRIA BETWEEN CRYSTALS AND GASES

A common chemical problem is removal of a volatile substance from a crystal—for example, the dehydration of a crystalline hydrate. Such systems consist of two components, which we may take as water and the anhydrous crystal. Possible phases will be gas, liquid solution, crystalline hydrates, and anhydrous crystal.

$$F = C - P + 2 = 2 - P + 2 = 4 - P$$

If four phases coexist, $F = 0$, three phases give a single degree of freedom, two phases give two degrees of freedom, and one phase gives three degrees of freedom.

Figure 35.13 shows a p-T-X diagram for such a system—$CuSO_4$ and water—and some sections in a projection of the figure. For convenience the hydrates are identified as α, β, γ, and δ as indicated in Figure 35.13, A, which consists of a doubly-curved surface on the left representing all the equilibrium systems consisting of liquid and gas. The double curvature indicates two degrees of freedom, consistent with the presence of two phases—l and g. The balance of the diagram consists of four singly-curved surfaces (indicating one degree of freedom) representing the possible three-phase systems, and bounded by four planes of constant composition representing the three hydrates and the anhydrous crystal.

Figure 35.13, B gives data for the equilibrium vapor pressure as a function of T for the four possible three-phase systems plus the two-phase liquid H_2O-gaseous H_2O system (one component if no $CuSO_4$ is present). Increase in T causes increase in p as expected. Figure 35.13, C is a T, X isobaric section showing the two-phase equilibria in the crystalline phases, equilibrium between crystalline $CuSO_4 \cdot 5H_2O$ and a saturated solution (indicating a slight increase in solubility as T rises), and the two- and the three-phase equilibria involving $H_2O_{(g)}$ and the condensed phases. Note that the Clausius-Clapeyron equation should describe most of these experimental curves.

Figure 35.13, D is the same as the top of Figure 35.13, A and is an isothermal section showing the same equilibria as does 35.13, C.

It is important to note that there is no such quantity as the vapor pressure of a crystalline hydrate. The pressure is determined by which *two* condensed phases are in equilibrium with the gas. It should also be noted that merely heating a hydrate to 110°C (above the boiling point of water) may have little effect on dehydration of the crystals, since the equilibrium state may have a very low p at that T. The best method is to place the sample in a vessel that can be evacuated, then slowly heated. This can keep the vapor pressure of gaseous water so low that the crystal is completely dehydrated. The low temperature also minimizes chances of thermal decomposition or reaction of the crystal. There are, however, substances that hold water so tightly that they cannot be completely dehydrated even at red heat in a vacuum, Fe_2O_3 is an example.

THREE-COMPONENT DIAGRAMS

For three components

$$F = C - P + 2 = 5 - P$$

so four dimensions would be needed for a complete representation and three dimensions for a constant-pressure diagram. The constant-pressure diagram in three dimensions utilizes an interesting property of an equilateral triangle: the sum of the normal distances from any point in an equilateral triangle to the three edges equals the length of one side of the triangle. Thus we may use the three edges as mole fraction coordinates (A-B, B-C, C-A, respectively) and the third, vertical

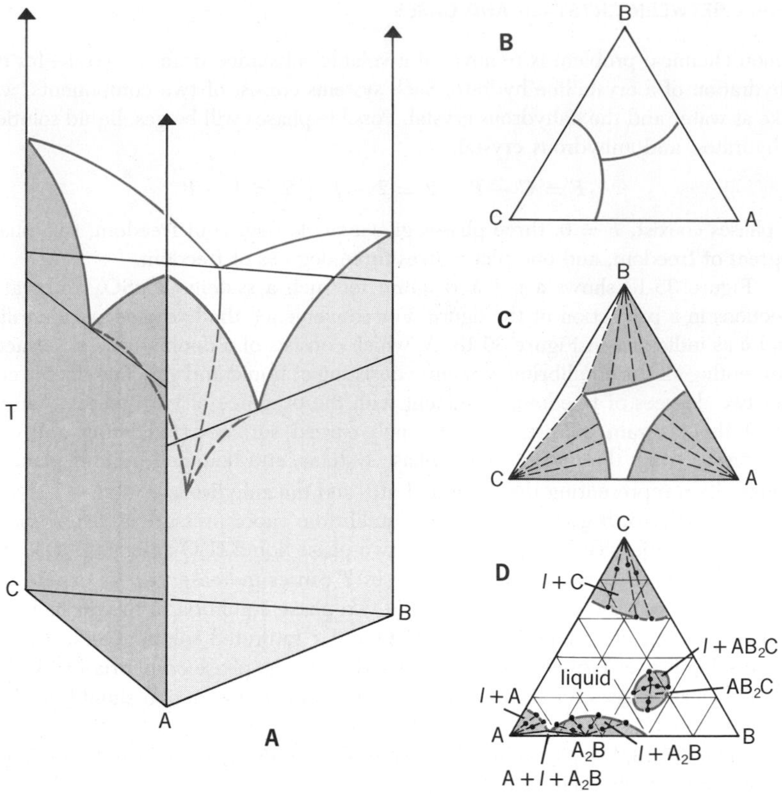

Figure 35.14 Some three component phase diagrams. (**A**) Constant-pressure diagram showing compositions as a function of *T*. (**B**) Projection of **A** along the *T*-axis. (**C**) Constant-temperature section through **A**, showing tie lines. (**D**) Constant-*T* section of a complicated constant-*P* system, showing formation of binary and ternary compounds and some tie lines.

dimension as *T*. Figure 35.14 shows four possible diagrams: (A) a full three-dimensional figure (note that each of the two-component systems is a simple eutectic system represented on a face of the triangular prism), (B) a projection of A along the *T*-axis; (C) an isothermal section through A, and (D) a diagram illustrating binary and ternary compound formation. Isothermal sections are most common, as in C and D. They usually consist of areas representing single phases, lines representing regions of coexistence of two phases, and points representing coexistence of three (or four) phases. The compositions of binary compounds are represented by points along the triangular edges, and of ternary compounds by points within the triangle, as shown in D.

The compositions of binary and ternary compounds are experimentally determined by using tie-lines, also shown in Figure 35.14, D. Suppose one has a liquid in equilibrium with a crystal. Analysis of the liquid is accomplished easily by pipetting some of it out of the system and performing a total analysis. Analysis of the crystal is more difficult, since it is surrounded by liquid from which it can be separated only with difficulty. But if one analyzes a wet mush of crystal and liquid and knows the analysis of the wetting liquid, he knows that a tie-line connecting these two analyses must also go through the composition of the crystal. The intersection of several tie-lines will give the composition of the crystal phase without ever requiring the isolation of dry, pure crystals.

BIOCHEMICAL SEPARATIONS

Biochemical systems involve very large numbers of phase equilibria: the lung-air interface, oxygen uptake by blood, bone formation, liquid-liquid interactions at cell walls, and many others. In a living system few actual equilibria are attained, since such a state would normally mean the death of the individual. But many steady states are achieved and, since thermodynamic efficiency increases markedly in systems operating near their equilibrium state, many biochemical processes proceed almost at equilibrium. The ideas developed in this chapter are widely applied to the study, prediction, and control of such systems, even though the complexities are somewhat greater than those of the two-component systems upon which we have concentrated.

SUMMARY

Our discussion has been limited for the most part to binary systems; however, the same kinds of features appear in phase diagrams with more components, complicated only by the addition of more variables. The phase diagram, as a key to separation processes, gives a complete description of the phase composition of a system as a function of the variables that may be physically controlled—concentrations, temperature, and pressure. Separation of components can be achieved when variation of the temperature or pressure produces phase changes with accompanying composition changes if it is also possible to achieve a physical separation of the phases produced. This, as we have seen, involves some laboratory problems, but a variety of techniques have been invented for performing the needed tasks. The determination of phase diagrams is usually the result of laborious experimentation, but in certain instances thermodynamic analysis is capable of producing boundary-curve equations which, together with small amounts of experimental data, can accurately give the phase diagram.

The Clausius-Clapeyron equation often gives good agreement with experimental data under isobaric conditions—deviations between the two indicating lack of ideality in solution and/or mutual solubility in both equilibrium phases.

No scheme for education, and least of all for scientific education, can be complete without some facility and encouragement for browsing. The dangers of our modern efficient schemes remind one of Matthew Arnold's line "For rigorous teachers seized my youth." Poor youth!—A. N. Whitehead, The Interpretation of Science, *Bobbs-Merrill, Indianapolis, 1961.*

PROBLEMS

35.1. $\Delta\bar{S}_{form}$ for real solutions is always less than or equal to $\Delta\bar{S}_{form}$ for ideal solutions, for the same compositions and temperatures. Give a "statistical" rationalization for this fact.

35.2. Assuming that carbon tetrachloride and chloroform form ideal solutions, calculate the total pressure of a solution at 25°C in which $X_{CCl_4} = 0.4$. Also calculate the composition (in Y_{CCl_4}) of the equilibrium vapor for this solution. (Vapor pressures of pure carbon tetrachloride and pure chloroform at 25°C are 114.5 torr and 119.1 torr, respectively.) ($Y_{CCl_4} \cong 0.4$.)

35.3. Suppose that the distribution coefficient for a substance A between water and ether is $X_A(\text{water})/X_A(\text{ether}) = 0.25$ and that it is reasonably constant. Demonstrate that extraction of A from 100 g of an aqueous solution in which $X_A = 0.2$ with three successive 10-g portions of ether is more effective than extraction with a single 30-g portion. (Fraction extracted $= 1/(1 + a)^i$, $a =$ (moles ether$/k_{dist} \cdot$ moles H_2O), $i =$ number of extractions.)

35.4. Describe exactly the observable effects that occur when carbon tetrachloride is added in small increments to a system which was originally pure methanol. Assume that the system is enclosed in a piston-cylinder apparatus which maintains constant atmospheric pressure and which is thermostated at 60°C. Use Figure 35.3, B. Give a reasonable explanation of these rather unusual phenomena in molecular terms.

35.5. Using Figure 35.5 with the liquid solution shown ($X_{toluene} = 0.80$), describe completely the changes in phases and phase compositions which occur as the temperature is raised from 80 to 120°C. First assume that the system is open; then assume that it is closed. In both cases assume that there is only one surface of equilibrium.

35.6. How do you account for the fact that so many more substances are mutually soluble in the liquid phase than in the crystal phase?

35.7. You have a sample represented by point P in the phase diagram illustrated. (*a*) How would you go about obtaining a sample of component A of high purity starting with P? (*b*) How would you obtain a sample of component B of high purity?

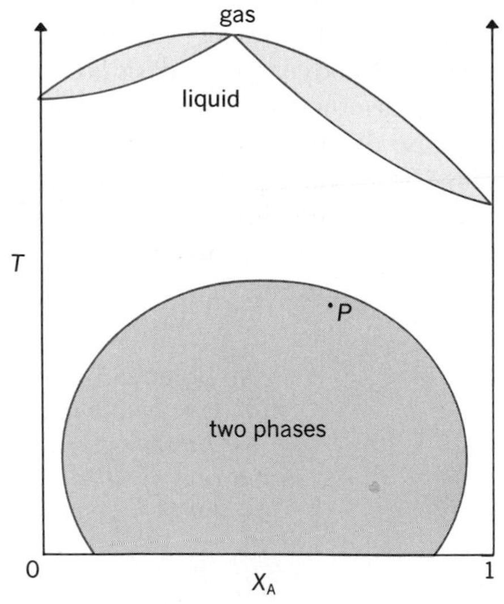

35.8. Consider that 2 ml of a nitric acid solution containing 4 mg of bromine is shaken with 1 ml of carbon tetrachloride. What fraction of the bromine is extracted if the distribution ratio at 25°C is $K_D = [Br_2]_{CCl_4}/[Br_2]_{\text{acid soln}} = 22.7$? (About 90% removed.)

35.9. Where does the heat come from that melts the ice when salt is spread on an icy sidewalk?

35.10. At which end of the charge would the purest component A material be found if a high purity sample of component A were subject to zone refining? Draw a rough picture of a simple zone refiner and show where the "impurity" will concentrate.

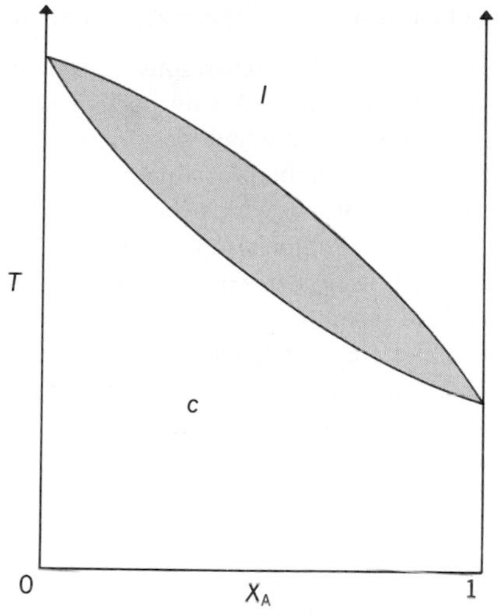

II

35.11. Many thermodynamic calculations of solution properties require data taken under constant-pressure conditions as well as constant-temperature conditions (for example, those calculations based on use of $\Delta G = 0$ as an equilibrium criterion). On the other hand, the vapor pressures of solutions usually vary considerably as a function of composition. Sketch an apparatus in which the experimentalist can hold the pressure of the system constant without disturbing the composition; evaluate the sources of error in this method.

35.12. The concentration of salts in the ocean is equivalent to about 30,000 parts per million of sodium chloride by weight. (*a*) Calculate the vapor pressure of seawater. ($p_{25°C} \cong 23$ mm.) (*b*) Assume sea water is an ideal solution and calculate the minimum work, ΔG, necessary to purify 1 kg of seawater to pure water and pure salt. (*c*) Comment on the validity of the assumption of ideality in *b*. If deviations were to occur, would you think the vapor pressure of water would be higher or lower than ideal?

35.13. (a) Sketch a possible phase diagram from the idealized cooling curves given.

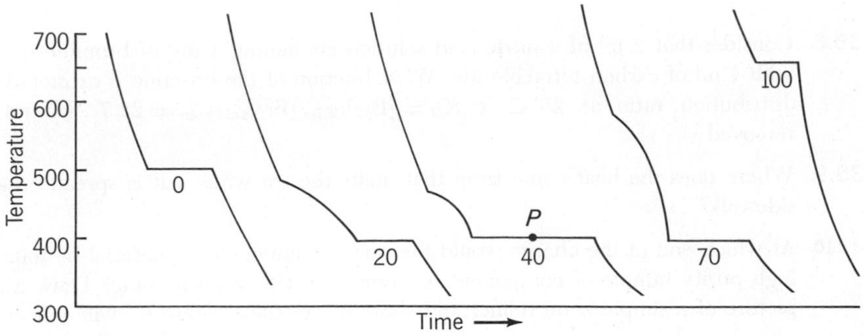

(*b*) What would you see when the system is at the state represented by point *P*?

35.14. Chemists often use gas chromatography to separate and analyze volatile samples containing several substances. A tiny portion of the sample is introduced into a stream of gas, such as argon, which passes through a long, heated tube packed, for example, with silica gel, carbon, or alumina.

(*a*) Explain the principle on which the apparatus operates.

(*b*) Suppose that a microliter sample of natural gas (mainly methane and ethane) was introduced, using carbon in the tube. Describe the mechanism by which they would be separated.

(*c*) Which would emerge first, the ethane or the methane?

(*d*) The composition of the exit gases is determined by passing the gases over a hot wire kept at an elevated temperature by a constant applied voltage and measuring the resistance of the wire. What variation in gaseous property causes the resistance of the wire to change?

(*e*) Would a given partial pressure of methane have a larger or smaller effect on the resistance of the wire than the same partial pressure of ethane?

(*f*) Account for the change in resistance of the wire in terms of simple solid-state theory of the nature of the wire.

(*g*) Which solid, sugar or salt, would you use as packing if you wished to separate dimethyl and diethyl ethers [$(CH_3)_2O$ and $(C_2H_5)_2O$, respectively] from one another?

35.15. Use the data in the accompanying table, selecting one or two systems, to (*a*) draw a possible phase diagram, (*b*) estimate the heat of fusion of each element, (*c*) estimate the ideality of the liquid solution formed.

Melting points of mixtures of metals (°C).

Metals		Weight percentage of metal in second column										
		0%	10%	20%	30%	40%	50%	60%	70%	80%	90%	100%
Pb	Sn	327	295	276	262	240	220	190	185	200	216	232
	Te	327	710	790	880	917	760	600	480	410	425	446
	Ag	327	460	545	590	620	650	705	775	840	905	959
	Na	327	360	420	400	370	330	290	250	200	130	98
	Cu	327	870	920	925	945	950	955	985	1005	1020	1084
	Sb	327	250	275	330	395	440	490	525	560	600	630
Al	Sb	650	750	840	925	945	950	970	1000	1040	1010	630
	Cu	650	630	600	560	540	580	610	755	930	1055	1084
	Au	650	675	740	800	855	915	970	1025	1055	1075	1063
	Ag	650	625	615	600	590	580	575	570	650	750	961
	Zn	650	640	620	600	580	560	530	510	475	425	419

Metals		Weight percentage of metal in second column										
		0%	10%	20%	30%	40%	50%	60%	70%	80%	90%	100%
Al	Fe	650	860	1015	1110	1145	1145	1220	1315	1425	1500	1515
	Sn	650	645	635	625	620	605	590	570	560	540	232
Sb	Bi	630	610	590	575	555	540	520	470	405	330	268
	Ag	630	595	570	545	520	500	505	545	680	850	959
	Sn	630	600	570	525	480	430	395	350	310	255	232
	Zn	630	555	510	540	570	565	540	525	510	470	419
Ni	Sn	1455	1380	1290	1200	1235	1290	1305	1230	1060	800	232
Na	Bi	98	425	520	590	645	690	720	730	715	570	268
	Cd	98	125	185	245	285	325	330	340	360	390	322
Cd	Ag	322	420	520	610	700	760	805	850	895	940	961
	Tl	322	300	285	270	262	258	245	230	210	235	302
	Zn	322	280	270	295	313	327	340	355	370	390	419
Au	Cu	1063	910	890	895	905	925	975	1000	1025	1060	1084
	Ag	1063	1062	1061	1058	1054	1049	1039	1025	1006	982	961
	Pt	1063	1125	1190	1250	1320	1380	1455	1530	1610	1685	1775
K	Na	64	17.5	−10	−3.5	5	11	26	41	58	77	98
	Tl	64	133	165	188	205	215	220	240	280	305	302
Cu	Ni	1084	1180	1240	1290	1320	1355	1380	1410	1430	1440	1455
	Ag	1084	1035	990	945	910	870	830	788	814	875	961
	Sn	1084	1005	890	755	725	680	630	580	530	440	232
	Zn	1084	1040	995	930	900	880	820	780	700	580	419
Ag	Zn	961	850	755	705	690	660	630	610	570	505	419
	Sn	961	870	750	630	550	495	450	420	375	300	232

35.16. An *n*-propanol-water solution with $X_{n\text{-propanol}} = 0.60$ is placed in an infinitely efficient fractionation apparatus. What material would collect at the top of this apparatus and what material would collect in the "pot"? About how many theoretical plates would an actual apparatus have to have in order to approach this ideal separation? How high would such a fractionating column be if it were made with glass helices?

$X_{n\text{-propanol}}$ (liquid)	$Y_{n\text{-propanol}}$ (vapor)	T (°C)
0.00	0.00	100.0
0.02	0.22	92.0
0.06	0.35	89.3
0.20	0.39	88.1
0.43	0.43	87.8
0.60	0.49	88.3
0.80	0.64	90.5
1.00	1.00	97.3

See page 1094 for a list of references and readings in the recent chemical literature related to the material in this chapter.

PART 7

Reaction Chemistry

HOW ARE CHEMICAL REACTIONS USED?

CHAPTER 36

Chemical Identification

ROY A. WHITEKER

A chemical method of analysis must: (1) go to completion within the desired accuracy, (2) have a sufficiently high rate, (3) be reproducibly stoichiometric, and (4) have a detectable completion, or equivalence point.

Anyone who is interested in an experimental problem in material systems must necessarily be involved in some aspect of chemical identification. That is, he needs to know what species are present, and often to know their relative amounts. He might, for example, be an inorganic chemist who has synthesized a new coordination compound containing chromium, chlorine, and pyridine and wants to determine its stoichiometry—the weight or molar relationships between the various species contained in the compound. He might be a chemist studying the kinetics of formation of a new polymer, a physicist investigating the products formed during a nuclear bombardment, an engineer developing a new ablation shield for a space capsule, or a mathematician investigating the statistical behavior of springs. In any kind of chemical identification, some type of analysis must be made. In some instances the analysis is merely qualitative, to find out what chemical species are present; in other instances a quantitative analysis must be made in order to determine the amounts of the various species present. And frequently both kinds of information are needed. These analyses can be made either by means of chemical tests or by the measurement of some appropriate physical property, depending on the kind of information desired and the equipment available. The range of this chapter therefore encompasses all areas of experimental chemistry, and the topics discussed will include those that are fundamental to almost any problem of chemical identification.

You have already been exposed to a great deal of analytical experience in your laboratory work in chemistry. You probably have learned how to use an analytical balance so that weighings can be made to the nearest 0.1 mg (where this is desired), to handle burets and pipets, the indispensable tools of volumetric analysis, to operate a simple spectrometer in order to measure the intensity of light absorption by a solution, to use a *p*H meter to determine the acidity of a solution, to make simple qualitative tests for some of the common inorganic species, and to identify some substances merely by sight. The instruments and techniques available to the experimental chemist include these as well as others that may be much more sophisticated and subtle. In this chapter we shall discuss a wide variety of analytical methods and techniques—though not all, by any means—and in sufficient depth that you will have some idea of the range of their applicability, if not the full details of their application.

PREVIOUS HISTORY OF THE SAMPLE

The most important single piece of information about a sample is its previous history. If you have prepared the sample yourself you will have some idea of just where to begin in its analysis. But, even if you have not, information about where the sample has been obtained, details of its preparation, and so on, can frequently allow you to omit many stages in a qualitative analysis. Generally, if you want to make a quantitative analysis, you already know qualitatively what is in the sample. If you do not, then a preliminary qualitative analysis should be run, as most samples will contain substances that will interfere with the analyses you may wish to run, and will have to be separated from the sample or at least rendered chemically inert before you make your quantitative analysis.

SAMPLING

Before beginning any analysis, one of the most important considerations is to make sure that a representative sample of material has been obtained. It is obvious that the most careful and precise analysis is quite worthless if made on an inhomogeneous sample, but often the unwary analyst loses sight of this fact. If you use all the material for one analysis, you do not have to worry about its homogeneity, but you will not be able to estimate the precision of your analysis. Nor will you have a sampling difficulty if you have already determined that you are working with a pure substance. But if you have a mixture, or are not sure that you have a pure substance, then sampling is exceedingly important. It can be very misleading and financially disastrous to analyze for the gold in a boxcar full of ore if you take only one rock for analysis.

Exercise 36.1

How would you sample a tank car of molasses for sugar content? *Answer:* Remove half a dozen samples with a hollow probe from different levels and different lateral positions in the tank. Dilute them equally with water and measure their optical rotation in a polarimeter. If all agree within the desired experimental uncertainty, the content of the tank car is homogeneous and any sample is a good one. If rotations vary, an average should be adequate unless the individual variations that occur are such that one sample changes the average more than the allowable uncertainty of the result. If the contents are more heterogeneous than the above criterion allows, more detailed statistical methods must be used to determine the optimum number of samples and the most probable average composition.

PRELIMINARY CONSIDERATIONS

After sampling, the next question to consider is "What kind of information is desired about the sample?" Is it enough merely to find out what elements are present? That is, will a qualitative elemental analysis of the sample suffice? Or do you wish to know not only what elements it contains but what specific chemical species are present? In general, it will be more difficult to identify species if chemical procedures are used, since the species initially present may be altered in the course of various stages of the analysis. Many physical methods allow the species to be identified about as readily as the elements.

Assume that you have a pure compound that you want to identify qualitatively, and that the compound is presumably ferrous ammonium sulfate, $Fe(NH_4)_2(SO_4)_2 \cdot 6H_2O$. For an elemental analysis it is sufficient to determine that the compound contains Fe, N, S, H, and O. In fact, you might ordinarily merely verify the presence of Fe, N, and S if you were following a simple chemical procedure. But, on the other hand, you might wish to know that the compound is composed of iron in the oxidation state, +2, nitrogen as NH_4^+ ions, sulfur as $SO_4^=$ ions, and contains some water of hydration. The more informative analysis that would show this for ferrous ammonium sulfate would not involve much more work than the elemental analysis, since NH_4^+ and $SO_4^=$ ions are not decomposed in most qualitative procedures and would be detected as these species. And, having found iron present, you would merely have to test the original sample to determine the iron's oxidation state. Here are some appropriate equations:

$$Fe(NH_4)_2(SO_4)_2 \cdot 6H_2O_{(c)} + H_2O \longrightarrow Fe^{++}{}_{(aq)} + 2NH_4^+{}_{(aq)} + 2SO_4^={}_{(aq)} \quad (36.1)$$

$$Fe^{++}{}_{(aq)} + Fe(CN)_6^{\equiv}{}_{(aq)} + K^+{}_{(aq)} = KFeFe(CN)_{6(c)}, \quad (36.2)$$

deep blue precipitate indicates Fe(II)

$$[Fe^{+++}{}_{(aq)} + Fe(CN)_6^{\equiv}{}_{(aq)} = FeFe(CN)_6,$$

deep brown indicates Fe(III), if present]

$$NH_4^+{}_{(aq)} + OH^-{}_{(aq)} = NH_{3(g)} + H_2O, \quad (36.3)$$

heat and detect basic gas to indicate NH_4^+

$$SO_4^={}_{(aq)} + Ba^{++}{}_{(aq)} = BaSO_{4(c)} \quad (36.4)$$

white precipitate indicates $SO_4^=$

However, it would be very difficult to identify correctly the species in a sample of cupric hydrogen arsenite, $CuHAsO_3$, by a simple chemical procedure, since most available methods alter the species that distinguish this compound from others—for example, $Cu_3(AsO_3)$, $Cu_3(AsO_4)_2 \cdot 4H_2O$, and $Cu_5H_2(AsO_4)_4 \cdot 2H_2O$. Or if the original sample was a mixture of calcium carbonate, $CaCO_3$, and barium sulfite, $BaSO_3$, simple chemical and flame tests would easily demonstrate the presence of Ba^{++} and Ca^{++} (flame tests) and $CO_3^=$ and $SO_3^=$ (acid gives CO_2

and SO_2 gases respectively) in the original sample, but they would not show whether the calcium was combined initially with the carbonate, the sulfite, or both. Elaborate physical measurements, such as those obtained from X-ray and infrared spectra, would be necessary.

Exercise 36.2

Examination of a powdered solid shows lustrous, yellow grains. What do you suggest as a next test? *Answer:* Luster indicates metallic properties. Yellow suggests gold or brass or pyrites, possibly FeS_2. Add concentrated HNO_3. Gold is unaffected, brass and pyrites dissolve. If your sample dissolves, neutralize the solution and test for Cu^{++} by adding aqueous ammonia. A blue solution, $Cu(NH_3)_4^{++}$, indicates copper, which is a component of brass. If this test is negative, test for Fe^{+++}, from pyrites, by adding $Fe(CN)_6^{-4}$: blue color indicates iron. Of course there are many other possibilities.

QUALITATIVE AND QUANTITATIVE ANALYSIS

Normally a simple qualitative determination of a sample (without also knowing at least roughly how much of each constituent is present) is hardly worthwhile. For example, if our sample of ferrous ammonium sulfate contained a minute amount of arsenic as an impurity and the detection procedure used was sensitive enough to detect it, to report that the sample contained Fe, N, S, and As would be extremely misleading. At least an order of magnitude for each constituent—such as large, moderate, small, or trace—should be reported, even in a qualitative analysis.

Frequently, although we know the qualitative composition of a sample without testing or have made a qualitative identification, we want to determine the stoichiometric relationships existing in the compound, or perhaps its degree of purity, by making a quantitative analysis.

Consider again our sample of ferrous ammonium sulfate. We could determine the amount of iron by a volumetric oxidimetric titration with a standard solution of potassium permanganate, as in the equation

$$5Fe^{++}{}_{(aq)} + MnO_4^{-}{}_{(aq)} + 8H^{+}{}_{(aq)} = 5Fe^{+++}{}_{(aq)} + Mn^{++}{}_{(aq)} + 4H_2O$$

We can determine the ammonium ion by an acidimetric titration of the ammonia evolved on treating the sample with base [Equation (36.3)], the sulfate by a gravimetric precipitation of barium sulfate [Equation (36.4)], and the water of hydration by driving off the water by heat and determining the loss in weight of the sample or collecting the evolved water vapor in solid calcium oxide ($CaO_{(c)} + H_2O_{(g)} = Ca(OH)_{2(c)}$) and measuring its gain in weight. To determine the stoichiometry of the compound, quantitative determinations of all the various species in the compound would have to be made, but the accuracy of each determination need only be good enough to show unambiguously that the stoichiometry of the compound is $1Fe^{++}:2NH_4^{+}:2SO_4^{=}:6H_2O$ per mole of the salt. On the other hand, to determine the purity of the sample, only one of the above quantitative determinations is absolutely necessary, but that one must be capable of a high degree of accuracy. Figure 36.1 suggests a possible set of experiments.

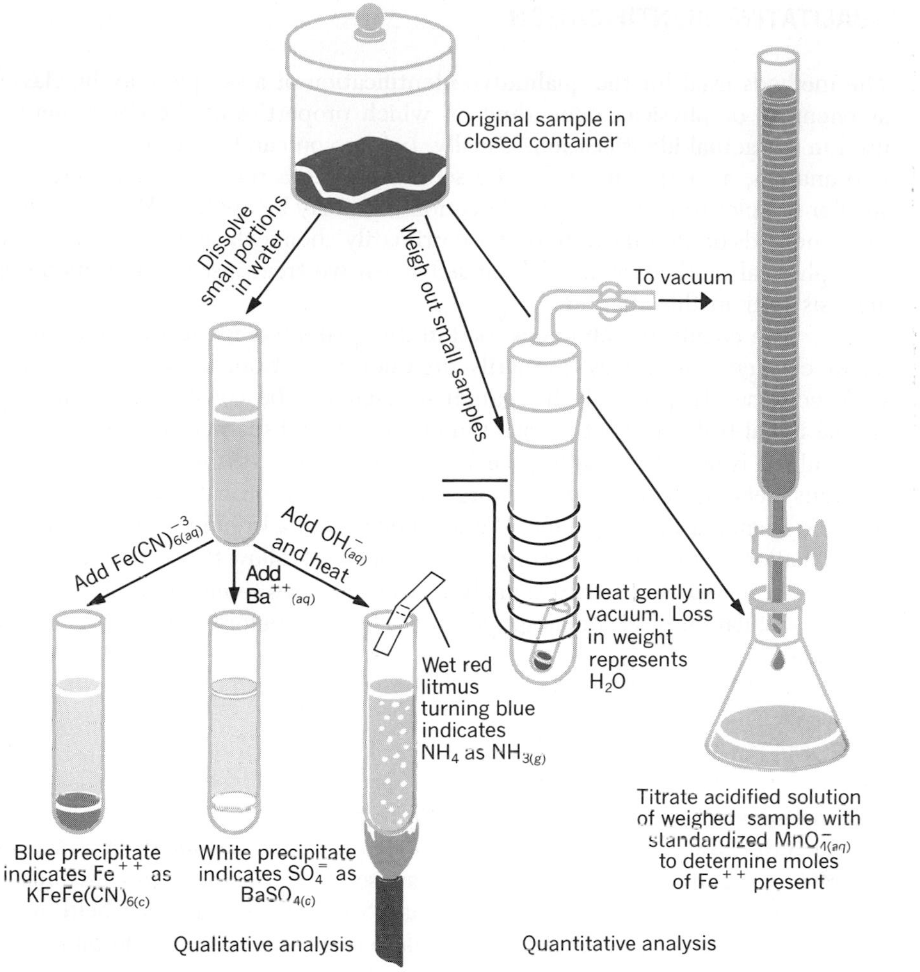

Figure 36.1 Possible analysis of a sample thought to be relatively pure $Fe(NH_4)_2(SO_4)_2 \cdot 6H_2O$.

Exercise 36.3

A sample of ferrous ammonium sulfate weighing 20.46 g requires 34.71 ml of 0.2893 F MnO_4^- in a titration. Calculate the purity of the sample. *Answer:* Assuming that all the iron is present in the "pure" compound, of formula weight 391.01, we get

$$\% \text{ purity} = \frac{\text{grams pure compound} \cdot 100}{20.46 \text{ g sample}}$$

$$= \frac{100}{20.46 \text{ g}} \left[391.0 \text{ g (mole Fe}^{++})^{-1} \frac{5 \text{ mole Fe}^{++}}{1 \text{ mole MnO}_4^-} \cdot 0.2893 \text{ (moles MnO}_4^-)\text{l}^{-1} \cdot \frac{34.71 \text{ ml}}{1000 \text{ ml/l}} \right]$$

$$= 95.62\%.$$

QUALITATIVE IDENTIFICATION

The methods used for the qualitative identification of a sample may be classified as chemical or physical, depending on which properties of the components are used in the actual identification. Usually, before you can begin to make a qualitative analysis, a sample must first be separated into a relatively small number of smaller samples to which various detection tests may be applied. We will first consider methods of identification that are primarily chemical; some of the more common physical methods will be discussed when we treat instrumental methods of analysis later in this chapter.

The chemical techniques used in the qualitative identification of molecular or covalent substances (primarily organic) differ from those used to identify ionic compounds (primarily inorganic) so each will be considered separately. A simple initial test is to heat a small sample on a metal spatula in the open air. If a residual ash is left after heating the spatula to a red heat, the substance probably contains metallic elements and is inorganic. If not, it is probably composed of nonmetallic elements and is organic. We will begin with a brief look at the qualitative identification of an ash-free, or organic, sample, and follow this with a more extensive look at inorganic qualitative analysis. In most cases some separation technique such as distillation or chromatography must be used before full identification can be made.

CHROMATOGRAPHY

Chromatography may be defined as a differential-migration method of separation in which the flow of a solvent or carrier gas causes the components of a mixture to migrate at different rates through a porous sorptive medium. This medium may be a solid adsorbent (such as alumina, charcoal, or starch) a liquid held on some solid support (such as water held on cellulose or silicone grease held on celite), or an ion exchanger. Whether the mechanism of sorption is adsorption on some surface active medium, partition between two liquid phases, or something else, the selective retention of the various components of the mixture by the sorptive medium causes them to move at different rates through the medium.

Various types of chromatographic methods have been developed. Thus we have gas chromatography, in which the mobile phase is a gaseous solution and solution chromatography, in which it is liquid. These two types are further classified by the nature of the sorptive medium. Adsorption chromatography requires a surface-active solid or liquid. Ion-exchange chromatography uses zeolites or organic ion exchangers. Partition chromatography requires a stationary polar or nonpolar liquid on some solid support. Paper chromatography may be either paper-adsorption (if only paper is used) or paper-partition (if a stationary liquid is held on the paper support). Figure 36.2 shows a dramatic example of paper chromatography in the analysis of a hemoglobin.

In many cases chromatography is not merely a separation method but also an analytical method, since some device for detection is part of the chromatographic apparatus used. Chromatography has undoubtedly exerted a greater influence on organic chemistry than any other separation method. As a separation

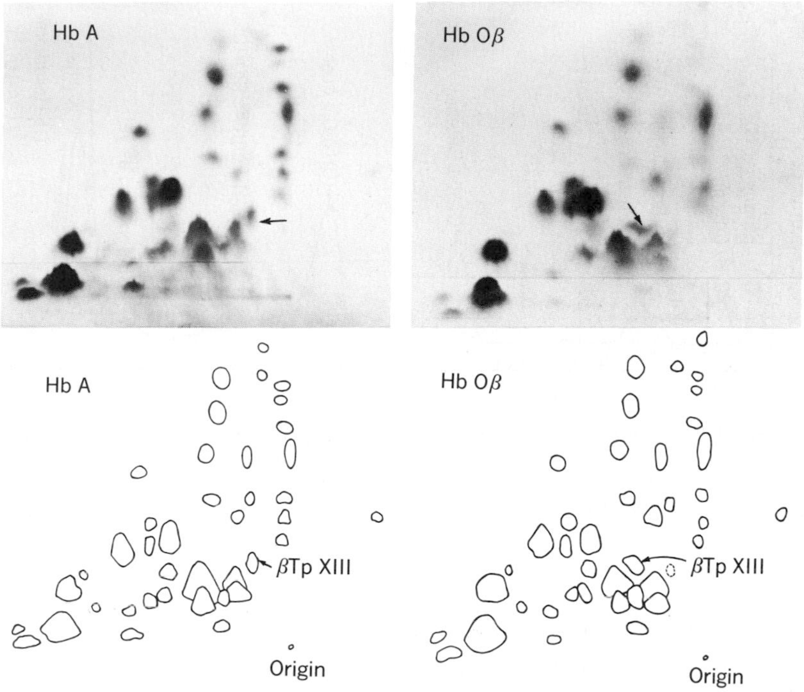

Figure 36.2 Paper chromatograph of decomposed normal hemoglobin, HbA, and abnormal hemoglobin, HbOβ. The sample was first migrated from the origin to the left under the influence of an electric field. The bottom of the paper was then dipped in a 4:1:5 solution of butanol, acetic acid, and water, which further separated the fractions as the solvent flowed up the paper. Note that the positions of all the fractions are the same except the one marked βT_p XIII, indicating that it is more highly charged in the abnormal hemoglobin. This abnormal hemoglobin is found in humans in the Nile delta of Egypt and is inherited. [K. A. Kamel et al, *Science*, **156**, 397 (1967). Copyright 1967 by the American Association for the Advancement of Science.]

technique it has also found wide application in inorganic systems, although not to the extent it has in organic systems.

Gas chromatography is a chromatographic separation method in which the mobile phase is a gas and the stationary phase is either a solid adsorbent or a liquid held on a solid support. In gas-solid chromatography the principal mechanism responsible for the separation of a mixture into its components is adsorption, but in gas-liquid chromatography partition between the carrier gas and the stationary liquid phase is most important. Determining the length of time a given component is retained by a chromatographic column before it passes into a detector is one way of making a qualitative identification; the area under a detection peak is related to the amount of material present, as in Figure 36.3. A more reliable method of qualitative identification is to use the gas chromatograph merely as an instrument for separation and to pass the carrier gas (together with the separated components as they emerge from the detector) into the inlet system of a mass spectrometer, from which the mass spectrum for each component is obtained (Figure 36.9).

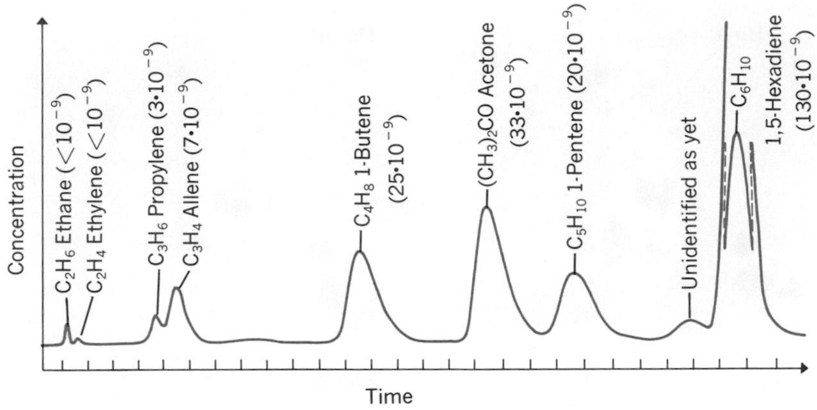

Figure 36.3 Vapor-phase chromatograph of some photolysis products of gaseous 5-hexene-2-one. The position of each peak (retention time) identifies the species. The area of each peak quantitatively indicates the number of moles (given in parentheses). The adsorbent was a styrene-divinyl benzene polymer. [S. Filseth.]

Exercise 36.4

A gaseous solution of benzene and ethane is passed over a chromatographic column filled with activated charcoal. Which substance will emerge first? *Answer:* Charcoal is essentially graphitic in nature with hexagonal rings of carbon held together by a resonating π-bonding system. Benzene has similar bonding, but ethane has a σ-bond system. Thus benzene, being more like charcoal, should stick more tightly and the ethane should emerge first.

IDENTIFICATION

Once a mixture has been separated into its components you can proceed with the identification of each component. If a compound has been studied by others its melting point, boiling point, refractive index, and infrared and NMR spectra can be found in published data, and comparison of your laboratory observations with such data will identify your compound. To identify new compounds, more information is needed. This can be obtained by following a well-planned sequence of operations, which include making some simple preliminary tests, analyzing for elements that are frequently present in organic compounds, and determining the presence or absence of possible functional groups. By carefully comparing the laboratory results with properties of known compounds, the possibilities can often be narrowed down to a very few. The compound actually present can then be unambiguously identified by carrying out the following procedures: obtaining infrared, NMR, or mass spectra and comparing these with standard spectra, making quantitative determinations, such as molecular and equivalent weight, and undertaking quantitative elemental analysis for carbon, hydrogen, and other elements and functional groups.

Preliminary tests ordinarily include observation of the physical state, color, and odor (CAUTION!) of the compound; an ignition test to determine its flammability, the nature of the flame produced, whether the compound is explosive, whether it melts, whether a gas is evolved, and the nature of any residue that remains after ignition; and a determination of the melting-point or boiling-point range.

Elements such as N, S, F, Cl, Br, or I, commonly present in organic compounds, are tested for by first fusing the compound with metallic sodium, thus converting the halogens to their sodium salts (nitrogen to NaCN, sulfur to Na_2S) and also forming NaSCN if both nitrogen and sulfur are present.

Table 36.1 A division of organic (covalent carbon) compounds into solubility classes (S = soluble, I = insoluble). The examples are for substances of low molecular weight (7–9 carbon atoms or less). Higher molecular weights lead to decreasing solubilities, in general, since rate, ΔH, and ΔS all become less favorable to the solution process.

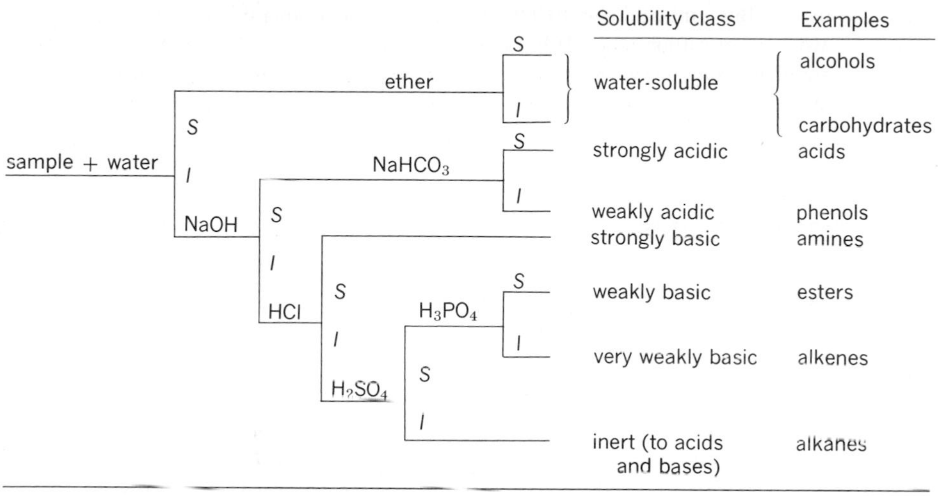

SOLUBILITY

The solubility class of a compound can be determined by following the sequence of solubility tests shown in Table 36.1. From these tests, the kinds of functional groups that are present, as well as an estimate of the number of carbon atoms in the compound, can often be determined. Since the presence of certain functional groups tend to increase the solubility of an organic compound, whereas carbon chains or rings tend to decrease its solubility in polar solvents, it is often possible to make an estimation of the molecular weight of a compound from simple solubility tests. For example, in many homologous* series of compounds containing only one functional group, those members of the series with less than five carbon atoms are usually quite water-soluble but those with more than five are not.

As can be seen in Table 36.1, strong and weak acids are both soluble in NaOH but can be differentiated by their solubility in the weakly basic solvent $NaHCO_3$. Basic substances, on the other hand, are differentiated by their solu-

*Members of a homologous series of hydrocarbons differ from one another by a single $—CH_2—$ group; for example, CH_4, C_2H_6, C_3H_8, and so on.

bility in HCl or in more strongly acidic solvents such as concentrated H_2SO_4 or concentrated H_3PO_4. For example, compounds containing oxygen atoms (with their unshared pairs of electrons) or a double bond, or two or more alkyl groups on an aromatic ring, are usually basic enough to react with concentrated H_2SO_4. Most of the so-called inert compounds are aliphatic or simple aromatic hydrocarbons and their halogen derivatives, which are too weakly basic even to dissolve in concentrated H_2SO_4.

Exercise 36.5

Suggest a structural rationalization for the fact that phenols have lower acidity than RCOOH compounds. *Answer:* Ionization of either gives a hydrated proton and a hydrated negative ion, so there is little to differentiate the two with respect to ΔH or ΔS. But ionization of RCOOH enhances the resonance in the $—CO_2$ system whereas ionization in φOH has less effect and may even diminish the resonance by supplying a higher electron concentration in the ion. Thus RCO_2^- is relatively more stable than φO^-, and RCOOH is the stronger acid, and hence more soluble in bases, as in Table 36.1.

FUNCTIONAL GROUPS

On the basis of the preliminary tests, elemental analysis, and solubility tests, you can significantly narrow the possible types of compounds that may be present. However, it will probably also be necessary to perform a number of tests for specific functional groups (see Chapter 21).

For example, let us assume that you have a liquid that has been shown by elemental analysis to contain no elements other than C, H, and O. On the basis of the analysis alone you might possibly have an acid, ester, ether, aldehyde, ketone, alcohol, or phenol. Solubility tests, however, indicate a modest molecular weight and eliminate the possibility of acids (soluble both in NaOH and $NaHCO_3$) and phenols (soluble in NaOH). Since the compound still might be an ester, ether, aldehyde, ketone, or alcohol, it is necessary to run some classification tests to narrow down the remaining possibilities.

Classification tests are available for functional groups such as amines, halogens, aldehydes, ketones, phenols, unsaturation, nitro compounds, esters, alcohols, aromatic hydrocarbons, and ethers. For example, decolorization of bromine indicates double bonds and oxidizable groups ($C_2H_4 + Br_2 = C_2H_4Br_2$), and metallic sodium releases hydrogen gas from alcohols and other compounds containing acidic hydrogen atoms ($ROH + Na_{(c)} = RONa + \frac{1}{2}H_{2(g)}$).

Several tests are often available for the same functional group and some are more reliable than others. It is generally from the results of these classification tests, together with information obtained from the solubility tests, elemental analysis, and observation of physical properties, that an unknown compound can be tentatively identified, subject to confirmation by a total synthesis and/or spectroscopic and X-ray structural data.

Exercise 36.6

Would a mild reducing agent be a better test for an amine or for an aldehyde? *Answer:* In RNH_2 every atom has a full set of σ bonds and no π bonds. In RCHO there is a double bond (σ–π) between C and O. This can be reduced to a full set of σ bonds if RCH_2OH forms, as in $RCHO + H_2 = RCH_2OH$. Addition of hydrogen is a reduction, so the aldehyde is easier to reduce. Note that the oxidation state of carbon changes from +2 to 0 during the reduction. (Oxidation number of R is −1, H is +1, O is −2.)

INORGANIC (IONIC) QUALITATIVE ANALYSIS

There are no hard-and-fast rules that apply to the qualitative identification of an ionic (inorganic) sample any more than to that of a covalent (organic) sample.* How you proceed is highly dependent on the sample and the information desired. In general it is not feasible to separate a mixture of ionic compounds into its unchanged chemical components prior to analysis, as it is with covalent mixtures. It would, of course, be possible in some instances, but in most separation procedures you could not be sure that there had been no interchange of ionic species, resulting in the isolation of compounds that were not actually present in the original sample. Separation techniques such as fractional crystallization or distillation can sometimes be used to separate simple mixtures into their component compounds, but in general you must be content either with making an elemental analysis of the whole sample or with determining the ionic species originally present. The most commonly used schemes involve separating the elements as ionic species of similar properties.

It would of course be advantageous to be able to take a mixture of several inorganic species and add specific reagents, each of which would react only with one constituent. Some chemists spend their professional lives developing such spot tests. Unfortunately the chemistry of many elements, in particular those in the same column of the periodic table, is so similar that spot tests are not universally valid but are only useful in the absence of these similar elements.†

Table 36.2 outlines some of the methods used to dissolve substances prior to analysis.

Exercise 36.7

Suggest a spot test for detecting Br^- impurity in NaCl. *Answer:* Add some of the NaCl to be tested to a test tube containing a few milliliters of aqueous Cl_2 and a lower layer of CCl_4. Stopper and shake. Appearance of a red-brown color in the CCl_4 layer indicates the presence of Br^- (see p. 301).

* The terms "organic" and "inorganic" originally referred to the sources of compounds in living or nonliving systems. Since this distinction is of limited chemical usefulness compared to distinctions based on properties of the compounds, it is often more profitable to use "covalent" and "ionic" as the adjectives. Remember that many biochemicals are ionic and many inorganic compounds are covalent, but that similar methods are used, for example, to identify and study all covalent compounds regardless of source.

† Standard reference sources are F. Feigl, *Spot Tests in Inorganic Analysis*, 5th ed., American Elsevier, 1962, and F. Feigl, *Spot Tests in Organic Analysis*, 7th ed., American Elsevier, 1966.

Table 36.2 Preparation of the solution.

Solvents used	Type of solvent action	Types of substances dissolved
H_2O	Solvation	See Table 36.3 for general rules of solubility in H_2O
HNO_3, dilute	I. Hydrogen-ion effects 1. Neutralization	Hydroxides, basic oxides, basic salts, salts of weak acids
	2. Oxidation (reduction of H^+)	Easily oxidized metals (Zn, Al)
	II. Oxidation (reduction of NO_3^-	Compounds of good reducing agents (Fe^{II}, Sn^{II} salts)
HNO_3, conc., hot	I, II	Reducing compounds (sulfides, alloys, metals)
HCl, conc.	I, III. Reduction (oxidation of Cl^-)	Powerful oxidizing agents, higher oxides (MnO_2), oxidizing salts ($PbCrO_4$)
	I, IV. Complex-ion formation	Lewis acids forming chloro complexes ($HgCl_4^=$, $SnCl_6^=$)
HCl, conc. + HNO_3, conc. (aqua regia)	I, II, III, IV	Noble metals requiring both oxidation and complexing (Au, Pt)
$HClO_4$, fuming	I, II, V. Volatilization of original anions leaving crystalline perchlorates	Salts of volatile acids (sulfides, halides)
$HClO_4$ + HF	IV	Compounds of elements forming fluoro complexes (primarily silicates)
Na_2CO_3, aqueous solution	VI. Metathesis (exchange of ions) followed by solution of carbonate and hydroxide in acid	Compounds of elements forming insoluble carbonates and hydroxides ($2MX + Na_2CO_3 \longrightarrow M_2CO_3 + 2NaX$)
	VII. Hydroxyl effects 1. Neutralization	Acidic and amphoteric oxides, salts of weak bases
	2. Complexing by OH^-, oxidation by H_2O	Easily oxidized and complexed metals (Al, Zn)
Na_2CO_3, fusion	VI, VIII. High temperature	As with VI, VII, but more rapid and extensive
Na_2CO_3, $NaNO_3$, fusion	II, VI, VIII	Compounds of elements forming acids in their higher oxidation states (Cr, Mn)

INORGANIC QUALITATIVE SCHEMES

Following preliminary tests such as determination of general appearance, solubility, color imparted to a flame, the sample is put into solution and the actual procedures of separation and analysis for the various species begun. Schemes of qualitative analysis differ in many ways—including the method of putting the sample into solution and the separation procedures used—depending on the species they were designed to identify. One of the best known is the classical (Fresenius) hydrogen sulfide scheme of cation analysis, which is designed for the elements (Ag, Hg, Pb), (Bi, Cu, Cd, As, Sb, Sn), (Fe, Mn, Ni, Co, Zn, Al, Cr), (Ba, Sr, Ca, Mg), (Na, K): the elements listed together in parentheses constitute the groups of one separation scheme. As can be inferred from the name of the scheme, many of the separation procedures are based on the varying solubilities of the sulfides. As has already been pointed out (p. 440) the sulfide-ion concentration of a solution can be controlled readily by controlling the *p*H of a solution. Thus by choosing an appropriate *p*H and saturating the solution with hydrogen-sulfide gas, elements whose sulfides have similar solubilities can be precipitated from solution as part of a major group.

A second scheme of qualitative analysis is that of Swift and Schaefer. In this scheme the sample is put into solution by an alkaline fusion and is divided into three major groups of elements on the basis of their basic, amphoteric, or acidic properties. The scheme, which was developed during World War II for the United States Army Chemical Corps, is commonly used as an instructional device to emphasize the principles of typical chemical reactions and the structural and periodic relationships of the elements. The list of the elements to which the scheme is applicable differs somewhat from that given for the classical hydrogen sulfide scheme: it does not include Hg, Bi, Cd, Sb, and Co, but adds Ti, V, Si, P, S, and the halogens.

Exercise 36.8

You are asked to identify the liquid contents of a sealed glass ampule. How do you proceed? *Answer:* The ampule is sealed because it contains a volatile and/or noxious substance. Cautiously and slowly, in a hood, immerse the sample bottle in liquid nitrogen until the liquid freezes. Make a file mark and break off the top of the capsule. Fasten the ampule to a vacuum line and transfer the sample to the vacuum line by warming the sample slowly while surrounding a receiver in the vacuum line with liquid nitrogen. Once the sample is in the line, its melting point, boiling point, vapor pressure, and other properties can be measured without danger to the experimenter or loss of sample.

SOLUBILITY RULES

Table 36.3 shows some of the general solubility rules for common cation and anion species in water. Such rules help students recognize the kinds of substances that are soluble in water, but the table is far from complete and, in any specific case, a student should not to rely on general rules but consult actual solubility tables.

Exercise 36.9

Write an equation for the formation of any precipitate which will occur when 0.1 *F* aqueous solutions of the following are mixed: (*a*) Na_2SO_4, PbI_2; (*b*) KCl, $HClO_4$; (*c*) $Y(NO_3)_3$, Rb_3PO_4; (*d*) Na_2S, $CdSO_4$; (*e*) $Ba(OH)_2$, H_2SO_4. *Answer:* (*a*) $SO_4{}^{=}{}_{(aq)} + Pb^{++}{}_{(aq)} = PbSO_{4(c)}$; (*b*) Possibly $K^{+}{}_{(aq)} + ClO_4{}^{-}{}_{(aq)} = KClO_{4(c)}$ if K_{sp} for $KClO_4$ is exceeded; (*c*) $Y^{+++}{}_{(aq)} + PO_4{}^{\equiv}{}_{(aq)} = YPO_{4(c)}$; (*d*) $S^{=}{}_{(aq)} + Cd^{++}{}_{(aq)} = CdS_{(c)}$; (*e*) $Ba^{++}{}_{(aq)} + SO_4{}^{=}{}_{(aq)} = BaSO_{4(c)}$ [and $H^{+}{}_{(aq)} + OH^{-}{}_{(aq)} = H_2O$]. Note that generally (except in *b*) it is the ions of high charge density that form precipitates.

Table 36.3 General solubility rules in water. (Soluble, $> 0.1\ F$; moderately soluble, $0.1\ F$ to $0.001\ F$; insoluble, $< 0.001\ F$.) Note that ions forming soluble salts tend to have low charge densities. Those tending to form insoluble salts tend to have larger charge densities and one-to-one stoichiometry or, as in the hydroxides, strong hydrogen bonding in the crystal.

General rule	Common exceptions
Soluble (usually ions of low charge density)	
Nitrates, nitrites, chlorates and acetates are soluble	$AgNO_2$, AgOAc, $Hg_2(OAc)_2$ are moderately soluble
Alkali-metal and ammonium-ion salts are soluble	Moderately soluble ones of analytical importance: $NaSb(OH)_6$, $K_2NaCo(NO_2)_6$, $NaMg(UO_2)_3(OAc)_9 \cdot 6H_2O$, $KClO_4$, K_2PtCl_6, $KB(C_6H_5)_4$
Chlorides, bromides, iodides, and thiocyanates are soluble	AgCl, AgBr, AgI, AgSCN, Hg_2Cl_2, Hg_2Br_2, $Hg_2(SCN)_2$, CuCl, CuI, CuSCN, BiOCl, SbOCl are insoluble. Hg_2I_2, CuBr, $PbBr_2$, $PbCl_2$, PbI_2, $Pb(SCN)_2$, HgI_2, $Hg(SCN)_2$ are moderately soluble
Sulfates are soluble	$BaSO_4$, $SrSO_4$, $PbSO_4$ are insoluble. $CaSO_4$, Ag_2SO_4, $Hg_2(SO_4)_2$ are moderately soluble
Insoluble (usually ions of high charge density)	
Carbonates, sulfites, oxalates, phosphates, and arsenates are insoluble	Those of alkali metals and ammonium ion are soluble
Oxides and sulfides are insoluble	Those of alkali metals and ammonium ion are soluble. Sulfides of alkaline earth metals, Cr_2S_3, Al_2S_3, are decomposed by water into insoluble hydroxides
Hydroxides are insoluble	Those of alkali metals and ammonium ions are soluble. Hydroxides of Ba, Sr, Ca are moderately soluble

THE SWIFT AND SCHAEFER SCHEME

In the Swift and Schaefer scheme of qualitative analysis the solution of the sample is effected primarily by a fusion treatment. If the sample is believed to contain a metal, it is first treated with HNO_3 and $NaClO_3$, followed by NaOH and H_2O_2. Any residue from this treatment—or the original sample if elementary metals were known to be absent—is fused with solid NaOH, $NaNO_3$, and Na_2CO_3. Fusion is followed by a treatment of the melt with water, during which the elements that form basic oxides or hydroxides precipitate, and the amphoteric or acidic elements go into solution as anions, frequently complexed with oxide or hydroxide.

The solvent action of the fusion process is due to the high hydroxide ion activity and the effect of high temperatures in making endothermic reactions more nearly complete. The $NaNO_3$ is present to ensure the elements are oxidized to their higher oxidation states. For example, any sulfur-containing compounds are converted to sulfates by this treatment ($SO_3^{=} + 2NO_3^- = SO_4^{=} + 2NO_2 + O^{=}$); if any existed as sulfides or sulfites after fusion, they would be lost by volatilization during acidification of the solution in a later step. The Na_2CO_3 is added to ensure complete precipitation of calcium and barium as the carbonates because the hydroxides of these elements are too soluble.

Table 36.4 shows the Swift and Schaefer scheme.* From Table 36.4 you can see that the acidic and basic properties of the elements in a reaction with hydroxide ion form the basis

*Details can be found in E. H. Swift and W. Schaefer, *Qualitative Elemental Analysis*, San Francisco, W. H. Freeman and Company, 1962.

Table 36.4 Swift and Schaefer qualitative analysis scheme. Elements included are Ag, Al, As, Ba, Br, Ca, Cl, Cr, Cu, F, Fe, I, Mg, Mn, Ni, P, Pb, S, Si, Sn, Ti, V, Zn.

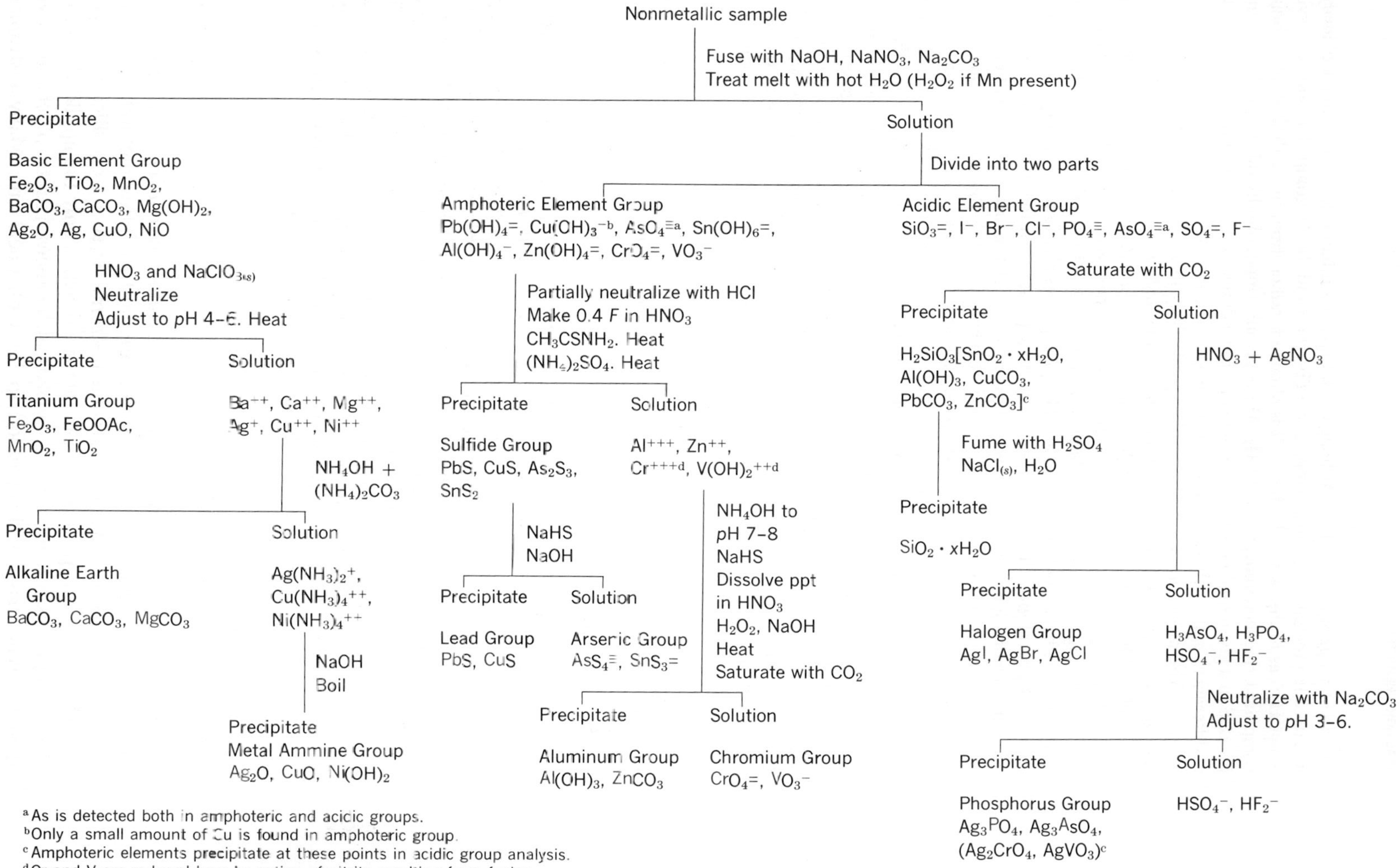

[a] As is detected both in amphoteric and acidic groups.
[b] Only a small amount of Cu is found in amphoteric group.
[c] Amphoteric elements precipitate at these points in acidic group analysis.
[d] Cr and V are reduced here by action of nitrite resulting from fusion.

for the major group separations. Although sulfide plays a minor rule in this scheme of analysis, it is used in precipitating and separating the Pb group and the As group. The source of sulfide is not H_2S, as in the classical scheme; it is obtained, rather, from the hydrolysis of an organic compound, thioacetamide, CH_3CSNH_2. Although one cannot blindly substitute thioacetamide for H_2S in a given qualitative analysis scheme, procedures have been worked out to take care of differences in the behavior of these two precipitating agents.

The properties of thioacetamide—particularly its moderate rate of hydrolysis at the temperatures employed in the separation procedures and the fact that its hydrolysis products are produced homogeneously throughout the solution—overcome some of the unpleasantness of sulfide precipitations involving H_2S. In particular, the loss of H_2S to the atmosphere is not as great, cutting down both on the obnoxious odor as well as its health hazard (hydrogen sulfide is almost as lethal as hydrogen cyanide). The precipitates also form larger crystals because of their slow rate of growth, making them easier to separate from the solution and to wash free of contaminating ions. The mechanism of precipitation of the metal sulfides either with H_2S or with thioacetamide is not well understood. It is known that the hydrolysis of thioacetamide depends on the acidity as well as on the particular elements present and is therefore extremely complex. Although a large amount of work has been done recently in this area, a great deal more remains to be done if we are to understand fully the precipitation of metal sulfides.

Other separation procedures used in the Swift and Schaefer scheme include the formation of ammonia complexes in the separation of the metal-ammine group from the alkaline-earth group [$Ni^{++}{}_{(aq)} + 4NH_{3(aq)} = Ni(NH_3)_4{}^{++}{}_{(aq)}$], the use of the greater acidic character of higher oxidation states (higher positive charge density) as in the separation of the Cr group (Cr^{+6}, V^{+5}) from the Al group (Al^{+3}, Zn^{++}), the precipitation of the halogen group with silver nitrate in an acid solution, and the separation of sulfate and fluoride from the phosphorus group by precipitating the silver salts of certain weak acids (Ag_3PO_4, Ag_3AsO_4) from a neutral solution. Na^+, $NO_3{}^-$, and $CO_3{}^=$ are tested for in portions of the original sample since they are added as reagents in the initial fusion. K^+ and $NH_4{}^+$ are also easier to test for initially because of the generally high solubility of their compounds.

Exercise 36.10

A colored aqueous solution which could contain Cu^{++}, Fe^{+++}, Ca^{++}, Ag^+, and Al^{+++} gives a brown precipitate when treated with HNO_3 and $KClO_3$ and then adjusted to *p*H 5 and boiled. Treatment of the resulting solution with NH_3 and $(NH_4)_2CO_3$ gives a white precipitate and a blue solution. Which of the five ions must be present, and which must be absent or cannot be detected by these reactions? *Answer:* The original color indicates Cu^{++} and/or Fe^{+++}. The brown precipitate must be hydrous Fe_2O_3, indicating $Fe^{+++}{}_{(aq)}$. The blue solutions indicate $Cu^{++}{}_{(aq)}$ [and $Cu(NH_3)_4{}^{++}$]. The white precipitate must be $CaCO_3$. There is no evidence for Ag^+ or for Al^{+++}, whose white precipitate would be concealed by the Fe_2O_3. The Al^{+++} would behave much like Fe^{+++}, as you should guess from the similar charge density and charge.

QUANTITATIVE ANALYSIS

Quantitative methods of analysis are often classified for convenience into chemical methods and instrumental methods. Because most analytical methods require both the use of chemicals (reagents) and some instruments, such a classification is hardly a rigid one. For our purposes, if the method requires only the application of relatively simple instruments such as analytical balances, burets, pipets, and ovens, then we will consider the method to be a chemical one. Many instrumental methods are based on either optical or electrical properties of the analyte (the substance being analyzed) or solutions of it, and are therefore usually divided into optical, electrical, and miscellaneous methods. Many quantitative methods require that a qualitative analysis of the sample be made first; the quantitative data then give the composition in percentages of the different species present.

CHEMICAL METHODS OF QUANTITATIVE ANALYSIS

Chemical quantitative analytical methods may be classified into those in which the determination of a weight is the final measurement and those in which the determination of a volume is the final measurement. The former are called gravimetric methods; the latter, volumetric or titrimetric methods.

SELECTION OF CHEMICAL METHODS

For a given reaction to be applicable as a chemical method of analysis, it must satisfy stringent requirements.

1. The reaction must go to completion to within the desired accuracy of the method. This means that the equilibrium constant for the reaction must be large. Data such as solubility products, dissociation constants, and electrode potentials are used to predict the equilibrium state for a given system.
2. The rate of reaction must be high enough to ensure that the reaction will be complete within a reasonable length of time; otherwise the analysis may become prohibitively tedious when the concentration of reactants becomes small. Even though stoichiometry and the equilibrium state of a proposed reaction are favorable, the rate of the reaction must be checked experimentally. Frequently, even if the rate appears unfavorable, all is not lost; a catalyst can often be found. Remember, however, that no catalyst can overcome an unfavorable equilibrium state; it can only affect the rate of attainment of the equilibrium state.
3. The reaction must be reproducibly stoichiometric. In gravimetry this means that the formula of the product must be well defined. In titrimetry it means that the reaction can be described by an equation giving the relationship between the moles of titrant added and the moles of analyte in the sample. Thus the titrant and analyte may react only with one another and only in the ratio described by the chemical equation; they cannot react with oxygen from the air, or with any other constituent of the solution, or with each other in any way other than that given by the stoichiometric equation.
4. The reaction must have a detectable completion point for precipitation in gravimetry, or in titrimetry—that is, where the ratio of the moles of titrant added to the moles of analyte taken is that prescribed by the chemical equation.

GRAVIMETRY

In general, the operations of a gravimetric analysis include first converting the analyte in a known amount of a sample into a species that can be separated from the remainder of the sample, performing the separation (including the removal of any contaminating species), and then drying the separated material or igniting it to form a compound of a definite known composition, in which form it can be weighed.

As an example, uranium in the +4 oxidation state can be precipitated from an acid solution by the addition of oxalic acid. After the uranium oxalate precipitate has been filtered out of the solution and washed to remove any contaminants, it can be ignited to form U_3O_8 in a furnace at 900°C:

$$U^{+4}{}_{(aq)} + 2C_2O_4{}^{=}{}_{(aq)} = U(C_2O_4)_{2(c)}$$

$$3U(C_2O_4)_{2(c)} + 4O_{2(g)} \overset{\text{heat}}{=} U_3O_{8(c)} + 12CO_{2(g)}$$

From the weight of U_3O_8 obtained and the weight of the original sample taken, the quantity of uranium(IV) in the original sample can be determined. Another common type of gravimetry is electrodeposition. In this method the analyte is electrolytically reduced (a few are oxidized) and deposited on a previously weighed electrode, usually made of platinum. After the deposition is complete the electrode is removed from the solution, washed and dried, and the weight of the deposit is determined (see p. 36).

Exercise 36.11

A 0.3042-g sample of ore gave 0.2741 g of U_3O_8 upon careful extraction, precipitation, and ignition. Calculate the percent of uranium in the ore. *Answer:*

$$\%\ \text{U in ore} = \frac{100 \cdot 0.2741\ \text{g}\ U_3O_8 \cdot 714.0\ \text{g U/(mole}\ U_3O_8)}{0.5042\ \text{g ore} \cdot 842.0\ \text{g}\ U_3O_8\text{/(mole}\ U_3O_8)} = 47.75\%$$

TITRIMETRY

In a volumetric method, the final measurement is the determination of the volume of a standard solution that reacts either directly or indirectly with a known amount of the analyte. Thus the amount of uranium(IV) in a solution can be determined volumetrically by adding a solution of potassium permanganate of known concentration from a buret—an operation known as a titration—until a pink color due to a slight excess of $MnO_4{}^-$ persists in the solution, as in

$$2H_2O + 2MnO_4{}^-{}_{(aq)} + 5U^{+4}{}_{(aq)} = 5UO_2{}^{++}{}_{(aq)} + 2Mn^{++}{}_{(aq)} + 4H^+{}_{(aq)}$$

The $KMnO_4$ solution is called a standard solution and its concentration must be known to at least the same degree of accuracy that is desired in the result.

To prepare a standard solution of $KMnO_4$ it might seem reasonable to go to the reagent shelf for a bottle of the best-available, reagent-grade $KMnO_4$, weigh out accurately an appropriate amount of the solid, dissolve it in water, and dilute the solution to a known volume in a volumetric flask. Unfortunately, such a procedure does not give the desired result for $KMnO_4$, and in general will not work if you want to know the concentration of a standard solution to the nearest 0.1 or 0.2%. Even the best commercially available $KMnO_4$ is contaminated with a surface layer of MnO_2, and the distilled water will almost certainly be contaminated by dust, dissolved reducing gases, organic compounds, or other reducing substances that will react with $KMnO_4$ to produce MnO_2 on standing. Thus any $KMnO_4$ solution prepared in this way will be less concentrated than would be calculated from the amount of the solid used. What is even more troublesome is that the concentration of the $KMnO_4$ solution will decrease on standing, since the MnO_2 formed serves as a catalyst for the further decomposition of the solution. The best technique, therefore, is to prepare a $KMnO_4$ solution of the approximate concentration desired, heat it to boiling for a time to oxidize any reducing substances present, filter it to remove the MnO_2 formed, and then standardize the solution against some primary standard.

To qualify as a primary standard a compound must satisfy several very stringent requirements. It must first of all be capable of purification to a compound of definitely known composition. It must be stable to atmospheric constituents, in particular toward reaction with oxygen, H_2O, and CO_2. It must not be hygroscopic or efflorescent; if it is, drying and weighing become difficult. It should give a reasonably large equivalent weight so that weighing errors will be small relative to other errors involved in the standardization. For the $KMnO_4$ solution, either sodium oxalate, $Na_2C_2O_4$, or arsenious oxide, As_4O_6, can be used as primary standards. Both of these solids are readily available with a purity of 99.95 to 100.05% and are ready for use after drying for an hour at about 110°C to remove adsorbed surface moisture. The net half-reactions are

$$5e^- + MnO_4^-{}_{(aq)} + 8H^+{}_{(aq)} = Mn^{++}{}_{(aq)} + 4H_2O$$
$$Na_2C_2O_{4(c)} = 2CO_{2(g)} + 2Na^+{}_{(aq)} + 2e^-$$
$$10H_2O + As_4O_{6(c)} = 4H_3AsO_{4(aq)} + 8H^+ + 8e^-$$

Although many gravimetric methods are inherently more accurate than volumetric methods, volumetric methods are generally preferred. This is because volumetric methods are usually less tedious and time-consuming than gravimetric methods, especially after the requisite standard solutions have been prepared. Volumetric methods capable of an accuracy of $\pm 0.1\%$ are available for most analyses.

Exercise 36.12

The uranium(IV) obtained from 0.5-g samples of ore containing about 50% uranium is routinely titrated at a smelter. What concentration of $KMnO_4$ should be used to give titers of about 25 ml? *Answer:*

moles liter^{-1} (F) $KMnO_4$

$$= \frac{(0.5 \text{ g ore} \cdot 0.50 \text{ g U/g ore}) \cdot (2[\text{moles } MnO_4^-]/5[\text{moles U(IV)}])}{238 \text{ g U/[mole U]} \cdot 0.025 \text{ liter}}$$

$= 0.017\ F\ KMnO_4$

EQUIVALENCE POINTS AND END POINTS

It is in the area of detecting the equivalence point of a titration that the greatest amount of work on volumetric methods has taken place. There are only a limited number of chemical reactions that will satisfy the conditions of equilibrium, rate, and stoichiometry, but there are many different kinds of techniques that can be used to detect the equivalence point of a titration. Regardless of the technique used, it must give some observable indication that the stoichiometric reaction has been completed; the point at which this indication occurs is called the end point of the titration.

Naturally we wish to make our end point coincide as closely as possible with the equivalence point. Sometimes the titrant itself has such a distinctive and intense color that even a slight excess can be detected. $KMnO_4$ is an excellent example of a titrant that can be used as its own indicator. More frequently, however, a reagent that will react in some way with an excess of titrant to give some detectable change must be added to the solution as an end-point indicator: for example, bromthymol blue for acid-base reactions, starch for iodine reactions, chromate for silver reactions. Even though there is rarely exact coincidence of the end point and the equivalence point (after all, some titrant is required to react with the indicator), the difference between the two in terms of the volume of titrant is often less than can be read on a buret because of the large concentration changes that occur in the region of the equivalence point.

In addition to chemical methods a great number of instrumental methods are also available for indicating the end point of a titration. In these techniques an instrument is used to monitor changes in properties of the solution during the titration. Some of these techniques will be discussed in subsequent sections.

Exercise 36.13

What indicator should be used in the aqueous titration of 0.2 *F* acetic acid with 0.2 *F* sodium hydroxide? *Answer:* Final solution, at equivalence point, will contain 0.1 *F* NaOAc, which hydrolyzes: $OAc^- + H_2O = HOAc + OH^-$, $K_{hyd} = [HOAc][OH^-]/[OAc^-] = [OH^-]^2/[OAc^-] = K_w/K_a$. $[OH^-] = (K_w[OAc^-]/K_a)^{1/2} = K_w/[H^+]$, $[H^+] = (K_aK_w/[OAc^-])^{1/2} = (10^{-14} \cdot 1.8 \cdot 10^{-5}/10^{-1})^{1/2} = 1.3 \cdot 10^{-9}$ *F*, $pH = 8.87$. Use phenolphthalein indicator, as indicated in Table 18.12.

THE PERMANGANATE-ARSENIOUS ACID REACTION

Let us now return to the standardization of a solution of $KMnO_4$ against arsenious oxide. In this example of a volumetric method we shall see how each of the four requirements listed on page 943 is satisfied.

1. *Equilibrium.* After the arsenious oxide has been dissolved in NaOH and the solution acidified, $KMnO_4$ is added as a titrant to oxidize the aqueous arsenious acid:

$$As_4O_{6(c)} + 4OH^-_{(aq)} + 2H_2O = 4H_2AsO_3{}^-_{(aq)}$$
$$H_2AsO_3{}^-_{(aq)} + H^+_{(aq)} = H_3AsO_{3(aq)}$$

The equation for this titration reaction may be written as follows:

$$5H_3AsO_{3(aq)} + 2MnO_4{}^-_{(aq)} + 6H^+_{(aq)} = 5H_3AsO_{4(aq)} + 2Mn^{++}_{(aq)} + 3H_2O \tag{36.5}$$

To see if the equilibrium for this reaction is favorable we will calculate the equilibrium constant for the reaction; we shall also see how the concentration of MnO_4^- changes in the region of the equivalence point. The data needed for these calculations are the standard reduction potentials for each of the half-cell reactions (see Table 20.2):

$$\tfrac{1}{5}MnO_4^- + \tfrac{8}{5}H^+ + e^- = \tfrac{1}{5}Mn^{++} + \tfrac{4}{5}H_2O, \qquad \mathcal{E}^0 = 1.491,\ pK = -25.2 \tag{36.6}$$

$$\tfrac{1}{2}H_3AsO_4 + H^+ + e^- = \tfrac{1}{2}H_3AsO_3 + \tfrac{1}{2}H_2O, \qquad \mathcal{E}^0 = 0.559,\ pK = -9.4 \tag{36.7}$$

The equilibrium constant for our titration reaction is therefore 10 times the difference between the pK values, since each of the half-cell reactions given above must be multiplied by 10 to give the net titration reaction:

$$pK = 10[-25.2 - (-9.4)] = -158$$

$$K = \frac{[H_3AsO_4]^5[Mn^{++}]^2}{[H_3AsO_3]^5[MnO_4^-]^2[H^+]^6} = 1 \cdot 10^{158}$$

Thus K is a large number and we can be reasonably sure that the equilibrium of our titration will be favorable. To see the changes in the concentration of MnO_4^- in the region of the equivalence point, let us assume that the volume of solution at the equivalence point is 100 ml; the concentration of $H^+ = 1.0\ M$; 0.500 millimole of As_4O_6 is taken for the titration; and the concentration of the $KMnO_4$ titrant is 0.0200 F.

We will first calculate the potential of a platinum electrode in equilibrium with the solution, and compare it with the potential of a normal hydrogen electrode 0.1% before the equivalence point. Here 99.9% of the arsenic(III) has been oxidized to arsenic(V) and therefore the ratio H_3AsO_3/H_3AsO_4 will equal 0.1/99.9. From the Nernst equation (29.15):

$$\mathcal{E} = +0.559 - \frac{0.0592}{2}\log\frac{[H_3AsO_3]}{[H_3AsO_4][H^+]^2} = +0.559 - \frac{0.0592}{2}\log\frac{1}{(10^3)(1.0)^2}$$

$$\mathcal{E} = +0.559 + \frac{0.059}{2}(3) = +0.559 + 0.089 = +0.648 \text{ volt}$$

Since all half-cell reactions in the same solution will have the same potential at equilibrium ($\Delta G = O$), we can use this potential to calculate the concentration of MnO_4^- at 0.1% before the equivalence point:

$$+0.648 = +1.491 - \frac{0.0592}{5}\log\frac{[Mn^{++}]}{[MnO_4^-][H^+]^8}$$

$$\log\frac{[Mn^{++}]}{[MnO_4^-][H^+]^8} = \frac{5(1.491 - 0.648)}{0.0592} = \frac{5(0.843)}{0.0592} = 71.2$$

Thus

$$[MnO_4^-] = 6 \cdot 10^{-72}[Mn^{++}]$$

We can calculate the concentration of Mn^{++} by referring to our original assumptions. As there are 8 equivalents per mole of As_4O_6 and 5 equivalents per mole of

$KMnO_4$, we find that

$$\frac{8 \text{ eq mole}^{-1} \cdot 0.500 \text{ millimole}}{5 \text{ eq mole}^{-1} \cdot 0.0200 \text{ mole liter}^{-1}} = 40.0 \text{ ml}$$

of the permanganate solution will be required to reach the equivalence point. Therefore the concentrations of Mn^{++} (almost all the manganese present) and of MnO_4^- at 0.1% before the equivalence point, can be obtained:

$$[Mn^{++}] = \frac{(40.0)(0.0200)}{100} = 8.00 \cdot 10^{-3}\ M$$

$$[MnO_4^-] = 4.8 \cdot 10^{-74}\ M$$

By following a similar approach we can calculate the solution potential and the permanganate concentration 0.1% beyond the equivalence point. Here the MnO_4^-/Mn^{++} ratio is 10^{-3} and the potential is easily calculated from the permanganate-manganese half-cell. From such a calculation the solution potential is found to be +1.455 volt and the concentration of $MnO_4^- = 8.0 \cdot 10^{-6}\ M$.

The results of these calculations show that there is an enormous change in potential and in the permanganate concentration (factor of 10^{+68})—from 0.04 ml (0.1%) before the equivalence point to 0.04 ml beyond the equivalence point in this titration. Thus we have shown that the equilibrium for this reaction is highly favorable. Furthermore, our calculations should suggest to us several possibilities for end-point methods. Figures 36.4 and 36.5 show the titration curves for this system in terms of potential, or log MnO_4^- versus fraction of H_3AsO_3 titrated.

2. *Rate.* Our next consideration is the rate of the reaction. As the stoichiometric reaction [Equation (36.5)] shows, acid is consumed in the titration. Let us first see what happens when we try to perform this titration in sulfuric acid at room temperature. Experiment shows that the first permanganate added is rapidly decolorized, but that after a few milliliters have been added the solution becomes yellowish, then greenish orange, and finally dark brown. These colors disappear only slowly, even when the solution is heated. It is apparent that there are some complicated reactions occurring, many of which appear to be slow, and this observation might prompt us to reject the reaction of arsenious acid with permanganate

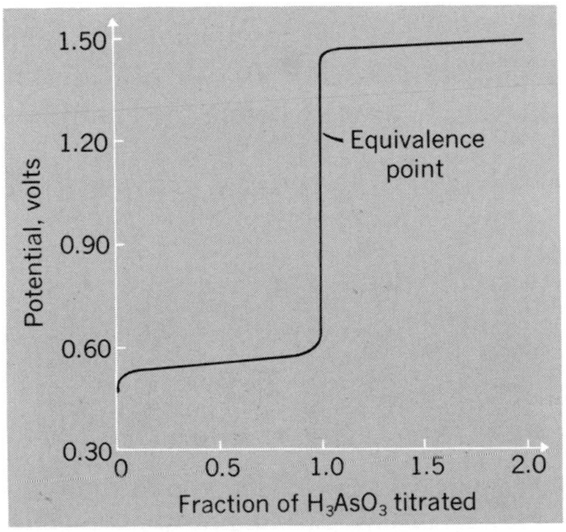

Figure 36.4 Changes in potential during titration of H_3AsO_3 with MnO_4^-. Note the rapid change near the equivalence point.

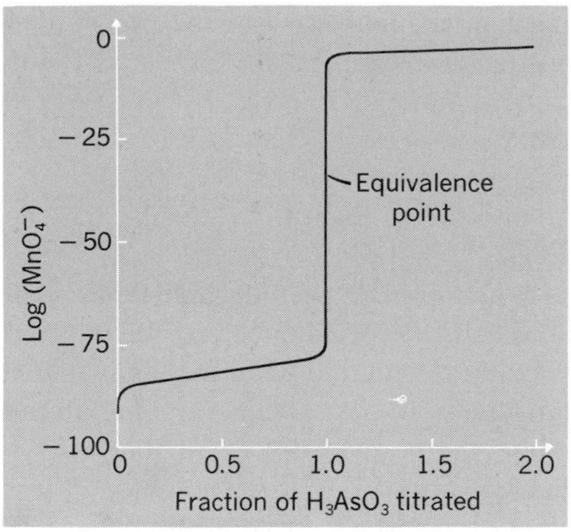

Figure 36.5 Changes in MnO_4^- during titration of H_3AsO_3 with MnO_4^-. Note the rapid change near the equivalence point.

as the basis of a good volumetric method. If we change the medium from cold sulfuric acid to hot hydrochloric acid we find that we still get transient brownish colors, but they are not too troublesome if we add the titrant slowly enough. Unfortunately, however, the pink color of the excess MnO_4^- fades rather rapidly in this hot solution because of oxidation of chloride by the permanganate.

The observations clearly suggest that some catalyst is needed, and it has been found that a trace of iodine in any of its oxidation states will cause an increase in the rate of the desired reaction. Indeed, it has been found that if iodine monochloride, ICl, is added to a room-temperature HCl solution of H_3AsO_3 and MnO_4^-, no correction needs to be made for the amount of catalyst added. The ICl behaves as shown in the following equations; it is used up in the oxidation of arsenious acid and is regenerated by the reduction of permanganate, resulting in the net reaction of Equation (36.5):

$$2ICl_{(aq)} + H_3AsO_{3(aq)} + H_2O = I_{2(aq)} + H_3AsO_{4(aq)} + 2H^+{}_{(aq)} + 2Cl^-{}_{(aq)}$$

$$5I_{2(aq)} + 2MnO_4^-{}_{(aq)} + 10Cl^-{}_{(aq)} + 16H^+{}_{(aq)} = 10ICl_{(aq)} + 2Mn^{++}{}_{(aq)} + 8H_2O$$

From this example it should be clear that to serve as a catalyst both the oxidized and reduced forms of a catalytic pair (here, ICl and I_2) must react rapidly with the reductant and oxidant, respectively, of the titration reaction and that the standard potential for the catalytic pair must lie between the standard potentials for the two half-cells involved in the titration reaction. In the present case the potential for the half-cell reaction, $2ICl + 2e^- = I_2 + 2Cl^-$, is equal to $+1.06$ volt in 1 F HCl, just about equidistant between the half-cell potentials of the participants in the net titration reaction.

3. *Stoichiometry*. There are many reactions that could conceivably occur in a system made up of arsenious acid, potassium permanganate, and hydrochloric acid that might invalidate our titration results. Three possible competing reactions together with their equilibrium constants are given here:

$$2MnO_4^-{}_{(aq)} + 3Mn^{++}{}_{(aq)} + 2H_2O = 5MnO_{2(s)} + 4H^+{}_{(aq)} \qquad K = 3 \cdot 10^{42}$$

$$2MnO_4^-{}_{(aq)} + 10Cl^-{}_{(aq)} + 16H^+{}_{(aq)} = 2Mn^{++}{}_{(aq)} + 5Cl_{2(g)} + 8H_2O \qquad K = 2 \cdot 10^{22}$$

$$H_3AsO_{3(aq)} + \tfrac{1}{2}O_{2(g)} = H_3AsO_{4(aq)} \qquad K = 5 \cdot 10^{22}$$

From the moderately large equilibrium constants shown we can see that any of these reactions is a possible cause of nonstoichiometric results for our titration reaction. Fortunately, the rates of these three reactions are quite low even in the presence of ICl, so that we can get stoichiometric results. The rate of oxidation of chloride by permanganate is, however, high enough that we may be troubled by fading color of the excess MnO_4^- at the end point. Even this difficulty may be overcome, as we shall see in the next section.

4. *End-Point Method.* As has been mentioned, permanganate has such an intense color that it can act as its own indicator. Experiments have shown that a concentration of $6 \cdot 10^{-6}$ *M* MnO_4^- is readily detectable near the equivalence point in titrating arsenious acid with permanganate. In our calculation for a sample titration we have shown that at 0.1% beyond the equivalence point the MnO_4^- concentration is $8 \cdot 10^{-6}$. Thus we see that we would introduce an error of less than 0.1% into our results by using the color of excess MnO_4^- to indicate the equivalence point. It is possible, however, to find a potential indicator that will make the end point agree even more closely with the equivalence point; but what is even more important here is that the end point can now be taken when the concentration of MnO_4^- is too low to oxidize the chloride in the solution. Such an indicator is the ferrous *ortho*-phenanthroline complex, which undergoes the following changes.

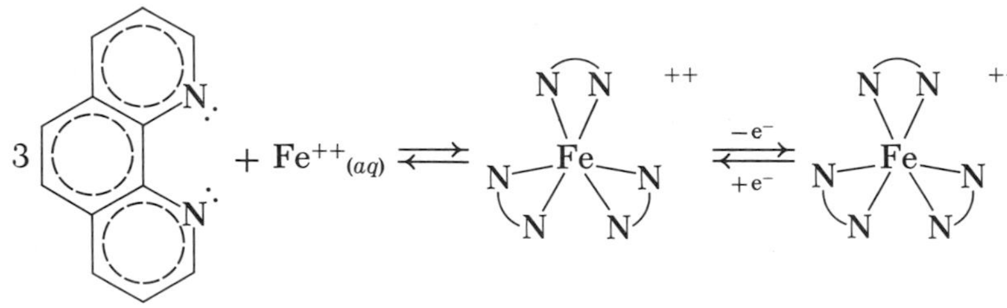

o-phenanthroline intense red faint blue

This substance is red in the reduced form and very pale blue in the oxidized form; it undergoes this transition at +1.12 volt. At this potential we can show that MnO_4^- is $3 \cdot 10^{-34}$ *M* and H_3AsO_3 is $2 \cdot 10^{-21}$ *M*. Clearly the oxidation of H_3AsO_3 is complete but there is no appreciable excess of MnO_4^- present.

By the addition of ICl as a catalyst and ferrous *ortho*-phenanthroline complex as a potential indicator we have succeeded in converting a system that had a favorable equilibrium constant but an unfavorable rate into a rapid and accurate volumetric method of analysis.

Considerations such as those we have just discussed have to be taken into account for any chemical reaction that is being considered as the basis of a volumetric method. It should be quite obvious by now that we cannot devise a new titration procedure on the basis of theoretical considerations alone. Any proposed procedure must be checked experimentally, particularly with regard to rate and stoichiometry. Similarly, we cannot modify any step in a standard analytical method without carefully considering the reasons for such a step and then experimentally testing our proposed modification.

Exercise 36.14

Calculate $\mathcal{E}$ and the concentrations of H_3AsO_3, H_3AsO_4, Mn^{++}, and MnO_4^- at the equivalence point in 1 *M* H^+ when 0.1 *M* solutions are used in the titration. *Answer:* From Equation (36.5) the concentration ratio of H_3AsO_4 to Mn^{++} at equivalence will be 5 to 2, as will that of H_3AsO_3 to MnO_4^-. Furthermore, essentially all the arsenic and manganese will be present as H_3AsO_4 and Mn^{++}, as seen from the equilibrium constant

$$K = 1 \cdot 10^{158} = \frac{[H_3AsO_4]^5[Mn^{++}]^2}{[H_3AsO_3]^5[MnO_4^-]^2[H^+]^6}$$

Thus the equilibrium concentrations are $[H^+]=1\ M$, $[MN^{++}]=\frac{2}{7}\cdot 0.1\ M$, $[MnO_4^-]= xM$, $[H_3AsO_3] = (5x/2)\ M$, $[H_3AsO_4] = \frac{5}{7} \cdot 0.1\ M$.

$$K = 1 \cdot 10^{158} = \frac{[0.5/7]^5[0.2/7]^2}{[5x/2]^5[x]^2[1]^6}$$

$x = 8 \cdot 10^{-25}\ M = [MnO_4^-]_{eq}$, $[H_3AsO_3]_{eq} = 2 \cdot 10^{-24}\ M$, which are very small values. $\mathcal{E} = 0$ at equilibrium for any system, so the two half-cell potentials will be equal. Thus,

$$\mathcal{E}_{As} = 0.559 - \frac{0.0592}{2} \log \frac{2 \cdot 10^{-24}}{7 \cdot 10^{-2} \cdot 1^2} = 1.23 \text{ volts} = \mathcal{E}_{Mn}$$

INSTRUMENTAL METHODS OF ANALYSIS

Instrumental methods are often classified in the same categories—qualitative or quantitative, gravimetric or volumetric—as chemical methods. In addition, instrumental procedures are often categorized as destructive or nondestructive and direct or titration methods.

In a nondestructive procedure the method of analysis does not change the molecular species or the equilibrium existing in the sample. Chemical methods are always destructive, since the original equilibrium state is shfted by precipitation, complexation, oxidation-reduction, or acid-base reactons. Many instrumental methods, on the other hand, are nondestructive.

In a direct method we make a single measurement of some property of the system and from this determine the concentration of one constituent of the sample. Such a method may be destructive or nondestructive, depending on whether the desired measurement can be made on the original sample without modifying it. The measurement of the *p*H of a solution by means of a glass electrode and a *p*H meter is a nondestructive, direct method of analysis. The determination of the *p*H of a sample by measuring the absorption of light by a solution to which an indicator has been added is a destructive, direct method, even though conditions should be such that the addition of the indicator will not shift the equilibrium appreciably. The titration of an acid with a base, in which the end point is determined from the changes in the *p*H of the solution as measured with a *p*H meter, is of course an example of a destructive, titration method.

There are far too many instrumental methods of analysis for us to treat them all in this chapter—even to give a working understanding of those we do consider. The interested reader can find any number of good, elementary treatments of the most important methods of instrumental analysis.*

Exercise 36.15

Suggest one nondestructive instrumental and one chemical (destructive) method for determining each of the following: (*a*) $[H^+]$ in 0.1 F aqueous weak acid, (*b*) % Cu in brass, (*c*) pressure of a gas. *Answer:* Instrumental: (*a*) pH meter, electrical conductivity; (*b*) X-ray fluorescence, electrical conductivity, reflectivity; (*c*) manometer or other pressure gage. Chemical: (*a*) acid-base indicator, catalytic effect on rate of reaction; (*b*) add NH_3 and measure depth of color of sample dissolved in HNO_3, react dissolved copper with I^-, titrate excess I^- with $S_2O_3^=$; (*c*) dissolve known volume of gas at known T and measure number of moles chemically to calculate P from gas laws.

ELECTRODEPOSITION

Elaborate and expensive equipment is not usually necessary for an electrogravimetric method, as indicated in Figure 36.6, and the method possesses some important advantages over a chemical gravimetric method. The material being determined is deposited directly onto a weighed electrode, as in

$$Cu^{++}{}_{(aq)} + 2e^- = Cu_{(c)}$$

The processes of separating the precipitate from the solution and washing it are much simpler than in a chemical method. An electrolytic separation is frequently much cleaner, essentially without the contamination of the precipitate by soluble species that occurs in chemical precipitation methods. In addition, the procedure can be made to be extremely selective. Careful control of electrode potentials allows quantitative separation of species whose reduction potentials differ by only a few tenths of a volt. Thus, species that are chemically very similar, such as Zn^{++} and Cd^{++}, can often be separated easily by electrolytic techniques;

*H. H. Willard, L. L. Merritt, and J. A. Dean, *Instrumental Methods of Analysis*, 4th ed., Van Nostrand, 1965, is particularly useful.

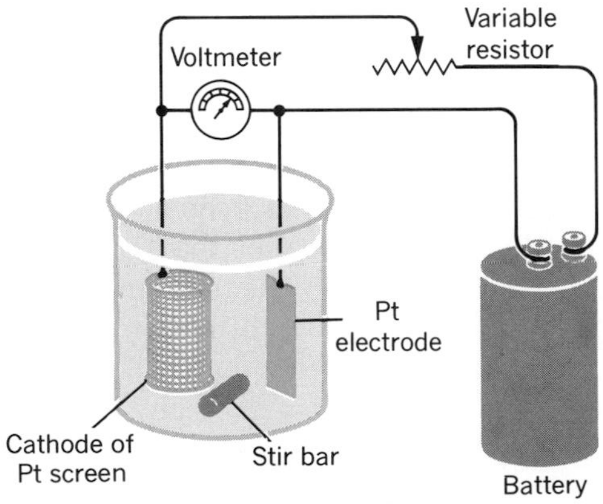

Figure 36.6 Diagram of apparatus for electrolytic deposition (for example, of copper from $Cu_{(aq)}^{++}$) onto a platinum screen which is weighed before and after deposition.

$$Zn^{++}{}_{(aq)} + 2e^- = Zn_{(c)}, \qquad \mathcal{E}^0 = -0.7628$$
$$Cd^{++}{}_{(aq)} + 2e^- = Cd_{(c)}, \qquad \mathcal{E}^0 = -0.403$$

Exercise 36.16

Calculate the ratio $[Cd^{++}]/[Zn^{++}]$ present when $Zn_{(c)}$ just begins to deposit during electrolysis of a solution initially 0.1 F in each ion. *Answer:* Cd will deposit first and $[Cd^{++}]$ will decrease until $\mathcal{E}_{Cd^{++}} = \mathcal{E}_{0.1\ M\ Zn^{++}}$, at which $\mathcal{E}$ value $Zn_{(c)}$ will begin to form. This is the same potential at which $Cd_{(c)} + Zn^{++}{}_{(aq)}$ (0.1 M) $= Zn_{(c)} + Cd^{++}{}_{(aq)}$ (x M) will have $\mathcal{E} = 0$, $\Delta G = 0$, and be at equilibrium.

$$\mathcal{E}^0 = \frac{0.0592}{2} \log \frac{[Cd^{++}]}{[Zn^{++}]} = 0.0296 \log \frac{[Cd^{++}]}{0.1}$$

$\mathcal{E}^0 = 0.7628 + 0.403 = -0.360$ volts; $[Cd^{++}] = 7.1 \cdot 10^{-14}$ M; $[Cd^{++}]/[Zn^{++}] = 7.1 \cdot 10^{-13}$, a very good separation.

CONDUCTIMETRY

Some major electroanalytical methods depend on measurement of electrical current. In a conductimetric method we can determine the resistance, $R = E/I =$ volts/amperes = ohms, or, for electrolytic solutions, a quantity related to the reciprocal of the resistance, the equivalent conductance, as in the

CONDUCTANCE LAW: $$\Lambda = \frac{1000d}{AC} \cdot \frac{1}{R} = \frac{1000d}{AC} \cdot \frac{I}{E}$$

The equivalent conductance measures the alternating electrical current, I, per volt, E, carried by a solution containing $C/1000$ equivalents per milliliter placed between two electrodes of area A, separated by the distance d. The value of the equivalent conductance approaches a limit, Λ^0, as the concentration of ions decreases toward zero. This limit is called the equivalent conductance at infinite dilution. Since experiments show it to depend only on the ions present, each ion can be assigned a value of Λ^0, called l^0, as shown in Table 36.5. In general,

$$\Lambda = \Sigma l \tag{36.8}$$

The total equivalent conductance is the sum of the ionic equivalent conductances, l.

From a measurement of the conductivity of an electrolyte such as a weak acid, we can determine the extent of ionization and the ionization constant of the acid. The fraction ionized, α, is given by $\alpha = \Lambda/\Lambda^0$, the ratio of the observed equivalent conductance to the equivalent conductance of the completely ionized acid found in dilute solutions. Thus the experimental Λ for 0.03162 F HOAc is 9.260. Using Equation (36.8), Λ_0 for HOAc is (from Table 36.5) $349.82 + 40.9 = 390.7$. Therefore

$$\alpha = \frac{9.260}{390.7} = 0.02370, \text{ decimal fraction ionized}$$

$$K = \frac{(H^+)(OAc^-)}{(HOAc)} = \frac{\alpha C \cdot \alpha C}{(1 - \alpha)C} = \frac{\alpha^2 C}{1 - \alpha}$$
$$= \frac{(0.02370)^2 \cdot 0.03162}{0.9763} = 1.819 \cdot 10^{-5}$$

Table 36.5 **Equivalent ionic conductances, l^0, at 25°C, obtained by extrapolating conductivity data to infinitely dilute solutions. Note that most values lie between 50 and 80, with H^+ and OH^- notable exceptions.**

Kohlrausch law: $\Lambda^0_{soln} = \Sigma l^0$

Ion	H^+	Tl^+	NH_4^+	Ag^+	K^+	Na^+	Li^+	$1/2Ba^{++}$	$1/2Sr^{++}$	$1/2Ca^{++}$	$1/2Mg^{++}$
l^0	349.82	74.7	73.4	61.92	73.52	50.11	38.69	63.64	59.46	59.50	53.06

Ion	OH^-	I^-	Br^-	Cl^-	ClO_4^-	OAc^-	$1/2SO_4^=$	$1/3Fe(CN)_6^{-3}$	$1/4Fe(CN)_6^{-4}$
l^0	198	76.8	78.4	76.34	68.0	40.9	79.8	101.0	110.5

This value checks with that given earlier in Table 18.13.

We can determine the total acid concentration in a solution of HOAc of unknown concentration by titrating with a standard solution of NaOH and measuring the conductance of the solution as a function of the amount of added base. In a conductimetric titration it is not necessary to know the cell geometry as long as it remains fixed throughout a series of measurements. Such a titration can be used for any system in which there is a marked change in the number and/or character (to be exact, the equivalent conductance) of the ions during the course of the titration. It is a particularly useful method for acid-base titrations because the equivalent conductances of H^+ and OH^- ions are so much greater than those of any other species (see Table 36.5); it is also effective for precipitimetric and complexometric titrations. The method is not generally applicable to redox systems because they commonly require such high concentrations of ions such as H^+ or OH^- that the total conductance of the solution changes only slightly during the course of the titration. A relative error of about 1% is ordinarily obtainable in a conductimetric titration.

Figure 36.7 shows a schematic representation of the curves for conductimetric titration with both NaOH and NH_3 for a strong acid such as HCl; a moderately weak acid with a *pK* of about 3, such as chloroacetic acid; a weak acid with a *pK* of about 5, such as HOAc; and a very weak acid with a *pK* of about 9, such as boric acid. The end points are obtained by extrapolation from the straight-line portions of the curves; points some distance from the end point are therefore more important in determining the end point than are points in the immediate vicinity. Many other important observations about conductimetric titrations can be made by referring to these curves.

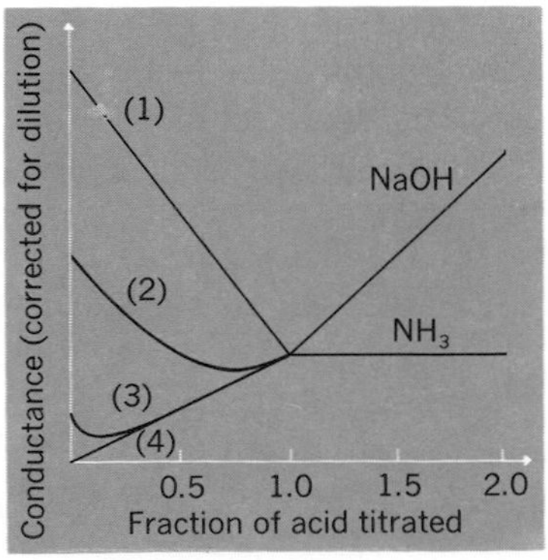

Figure 36.7 Schematic conductometric titration curves for acids of various dissociation constants with NaOH and NH_3. (1) HCl, (2) chloroacetic acid, $CH_2ClCOOH$, (3) acetic acid, CH_3COOH, (4) boric acid, H_3BO_3. Note that four conductivity measurements are enough to determine the equivalence point for strong and for very weak acids, since the equivalence point is then the intersection of two straight lines.

The end point for the titration of HCl with NaOH lies at the lowest point of the curve, since at this point the original HCl has been replaced by NaCl and the equivalent conductance of Na^+ is much less than that of H^+;

$$H^+_{(aq)} + Cl^-_{(aq)} + Na^+_{(aq)} + OH^-_{(aq)} = H_2O + Na^+_{(aq)} + Cl^-_{(aq)}$$

Addition of excess NaOH causes the conductance of the solution to increase again, although not as markedly as it does in the presence of an excess of HCl. This is to be expected; the equivalent conductance of OH^-, though larger than that of most ions, is still less than that of H^+.

In a titration with NH_3, addition of excess NH_3 beyond the equivalence point does not cause much of an increase in the total conductance of the solution because NH_3 is a weak base and the NH^+_4 ions present as a result of the neutralization reaction repress the hydrolysis of the excess NH_3:

$$H^+_{(aq)} + Cl^-_{(aq)} + NH_{3(aq)} = NH_4{}^+_{(aq)} + Cl^-_{(aq)}$$
$$NH_{3(aq)} + H_2O = NH_4{}^+_{(aq)} + OH^-_{(aq)}$$

As the strength of the acid being titrated decreases, we observe a marked change in the shape of the initial region of the titration curve. As can be expected, this is due to the extent to which the acid is dissociated. For boric acid, which has such a small dissociation constant that the acid in the original solution is essentially all undissociated, the conductance is seen to increase linearly from zero to the end point as the ionized salt, sodium borate, is formed in the neutralization reaction. With chloroacetic and acetic acids two competing effects are operating, which give rise to a minimum in the conductance curve. First, there is some dissociation of the acid in the original solution, producing H^+ ions of a high equivalent conductance:

$$HOAc_{(aq)} = H^+_{(aq)} + OAc^-_{(aq)}$$

As NaOH is added, a solution of the sodium salt of the acid is produced,

$$HOAc_{(aq)} + Na^+_{(aq)} + OH^-_{(aq)} = H_2O + Na^+_{(aq)} + OAc^-_{(aq)}$$

causing an increase in conductance, while at the same time the additional amount of anion now present represses dissociation of the acid:

$$OAc^-_{(aq)} + H^+_{(aq)} = HOAc_{(aq)}$$

At first the decrease in the concentration of H^+ ions is a more important factor than the amount of salt formed, and the conductance decreases. Eventually the conductance due to the ions of the salt is more important and the total conductance again increases.

It is perhaps startling to find that a better end point is obtained for the titration of a weak acid than for a somewhat stronger acid, since the opposite would be true in potentiometric titration. Another advantage that a conductimetric titration has over a potentiometric titration, at least in aqueous solution, is that though potentiometry can be used for weak acids only with pK values less than 6, conductivity is useful for much weaker acids (larger pK values).

Exercise 36.17

Conductimetric titration of 21.86 ml of an aqueous HNO_3 solution with 0.1352 *F* KOH gave the following data: ml KOH added 0, 11.26, 20.45, 38.92; corresponding relative conductance (corrected for dilution) 1.0000, 0.6079, 0.3635, 0.6050. What is the concentration of the nitric acid? *Answer:* Plotting milliliters versus relative conductivity gives two straight lines (strong acid-strong base) intersecting at 18.92 ml. Thus $F\ HNO_3 = 0.1352\ F\ OH^- \cdot 18.92\ \text{ml}\ OH^-/21.86\ \text{ml}\ H^+ = 0.1169\ F$.

COULOMETRY

Coulometry is an electroanalytical method based on the measurement of the quantity of electricity, measured in coulombs, which has passed through a solution and caused some net chemical reaction to occur. From the number of coulombs involved and the value of the Faraday, $\mathcal{F} = 96{,}487$ coulombs per equivalent (1 coulomb = 1 ampere second), we obtain

FARADAY'S LAW:

$$\text{number of equivalents reacting} = \text{number of moles of electrons flowing} = \frac{It}{\mathcal{F}} \tag{36.9}$$

Coulometry can be carried out at constant potential or at constant current. In coulometry at constant potential, the potential of the working electrode is maintained at a potential that will allow only a single reaction to occur. The current will then decrease exponentially with time as reacting species are removed, and the reaction is considered complete when the current has fallen to some small fraction of its initial value. The number of coulombs involved in the reaction is determined by means of a coulometer, which measures the number of coulombs passed through the solution. This method is similar to electrodeposition at constant potential except that in coulometry the material being determined need not be obtained as an electrode deposit so long as the number of coulombs passed through the solution is measured.

Coulometry at constant current is the more widely used method. No coulometer is required, since the number of coulombs can be determined merely by multiplying the value of the constant current (obtained from the potential across a standard resistor, measured with a potentiometer, $I = E/R$) by the time the current was used. This method is applicable to species that can react directly at an electrode or indirectly through some electrolytically generated intermediate species so long as all the current is used to produce some stoichiometric net redox reaction. In a coulometric titration method the electron has replaced the standard solution of a conventional volumetric method. Thus the time-consuming operation of preparing standard solutions can be eliminated, and reactions involving relatively unstable titrants can be used. In addition, the method is particularly useful in the milligram to microgram range; it has excellent precision and accuracy and lends itself well to automation.

Exercise 36.18

A copper coulometer is connected in series with an electrode at which 100.16 ml of aqueous Fe^{++} is being oxidized to Fe^{+++}. A total of 0.1857 g of copper are precipitated before the total current at constant potential falls to a negligibly small value. What is the initial concentration of the $Fe^{++}{}_{(aq)}$? *Answer:*

$$[Fe^{++}] = \frac{\text{no. of equiv. oxidized}}{\text{liter}}$$

$$= \frac{0.1857 \text{ g Cu} \cdot 2 \text{ eq Cu/(mole Cu)}}{63.55 \text{ g Cu(mole Cu)}^{-1} \cdot 0.1002 \text{ liter}} = 0.05832\ M$$

OPTICAL METHODS OF ANALYSIS

Many optical methods—in particular, infrared, NMR, and X-ray methods—have already been treated extensively in previous chapters, and the reader should therefore be more familiar with these methods than he was with the various electrical methods discussed in the preceding sections. In general, optical methods of analysis are based on the absorption, scattering, or emission of electromagnetic radiation in various frequency regions by atoms, molecules, or nuclei. Thus we may classify optical methods into absorption, scattering, or emission methods.

Optical methods may be either qualitative or quantitative, but they are probably more widely used for qualitative applications. The absorption spectrum of a sample, particularly in the infrared region, serves as a "fingerprint" from which a qualitative identification of the sample can be made.

If a quantitative analysis is desired, we can always make an empirical plot of intensity of absorption or emission versus concentration for samples of known concentration and then compare an unknown sample with this plot. In certain favorable cases, however, we can make use of a simple relationship called Beer's law [Equation 22.2]. Beer's law may be written in the form $A = \epsilon cl$, where A is the measured absorbance $= -\log (I/I_0) = -\log T$ (T = transmittance), or in the form $I = I_0 e^{-\epsilon' cl}$ ($\epsilon' = 2.303\epsilon$). Beer's law can of course be used for quantitative identification in any region of the electromagnetic spectrum, although it is most frequently applied to electronic transitions occurring in the visible and ultraviolet regions. In general, quantitative measurements of concentration are subject to relative errors of about 1 to 2%, and the useful range of concentration depends on the magnitude of the molar absorptivity, ϵ, for a particular absorbing species.

The necessary components for any instrument designed for absorption measurements are shown schematically in Figure 36.8. Light from an appropriate source is collimated and focused on a sample contained in a sample holder. Any light not absorbed by the sample is then dispersed and focused on an appropriate detector. Depending on the particular instrument and on the desired application, the actual components used and their spatial relationships will be different.

Exercise 36.19

The molar absorptivity, ϵ, of Br_2 is given as 160 l mole^{-1} cm^{-1} at 400 mμ. Calculate the concentration of a sample that absorbs 75% of the light incident on a cell 1 cm thick. *Answer:* If 75% is absorbed, 25% is transmitted, so $I/I_0 = 0.25$. $\epsilon cl = -\log(I/I_0)$, $c = -(\log 0.25)/\epsilon l = 0.602/160 \cdot 1 = 3.76 \cdot 10^{-3}\ M$.

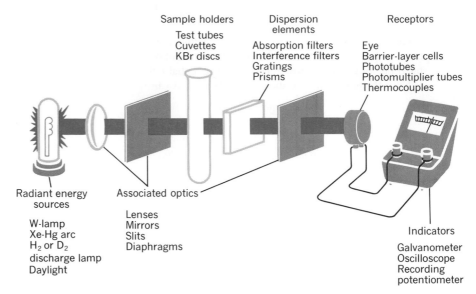

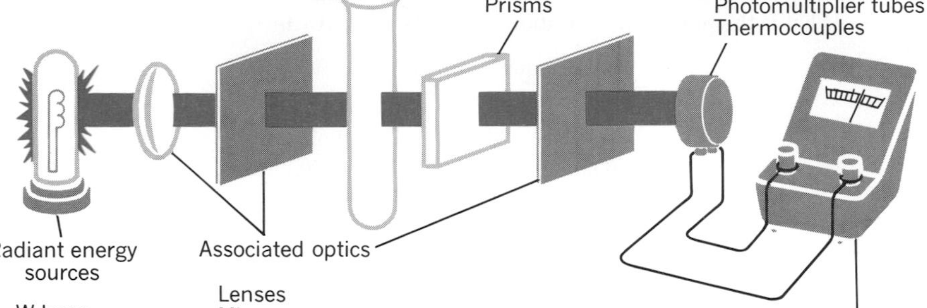

Figure 36.8 Components of instruments designed for absorption measurements.

MISCELLANEOUS METHODS

Several important instrumental techniques are not designated as either electrical or optical methods of analysis. Among these are radiochemical methods, thermoanalytical methods, and mass spectrometry. We again refer the interested reader to textbooks on instrumental methods of analysis.

The principles of mass spectrometry have already been considered in Chapter 2 of this book and the reader may review this material. When a molecule is bombarded with electrons whose energies are greater than the ionization energy, usually of the order of 15 ev, ionization and fragmentation will occur. If the bombardment is done in a mass spectrometer, the result is a unique mass spectrum for the compound, consisting of peaks for the parent ion and for the various ion fragments produced. The position of the peaks in the spectrum will give the masses of the ions and the height of the peaks will be related to their relative abundances. As the analysis of a mass spectrum will usually yield not only an empirical formula for a compound but also its structural formula, mass spectrometry is a fingerprint method for volatile compounds, similar in this respect to infrared spectroscopy and NMR spectrometry. Frequently it is even possible quantitatively to identify different molecules in a complex mixture, as indicated in Figure 36.9. Quantitative identification of mixtures can be made if mass spectra are available for each pure component of the mixture at a known pressure. Electronic computers are usually required for the identification of many-component mixtures, since n-simultaneous equations are required in the analysis of an n-component mixture. This technique has been used to analyze hydrocarbon mixtures containing up to as many as 30 components and to detect quantities of material as low as 0.001 mole percent.

It is detection techniques such as these that make it possible for us to use some of the modern, highly potent insecticides and herbicides. Without such extremely sensitive detection devices, the use of the potent materials would be for-

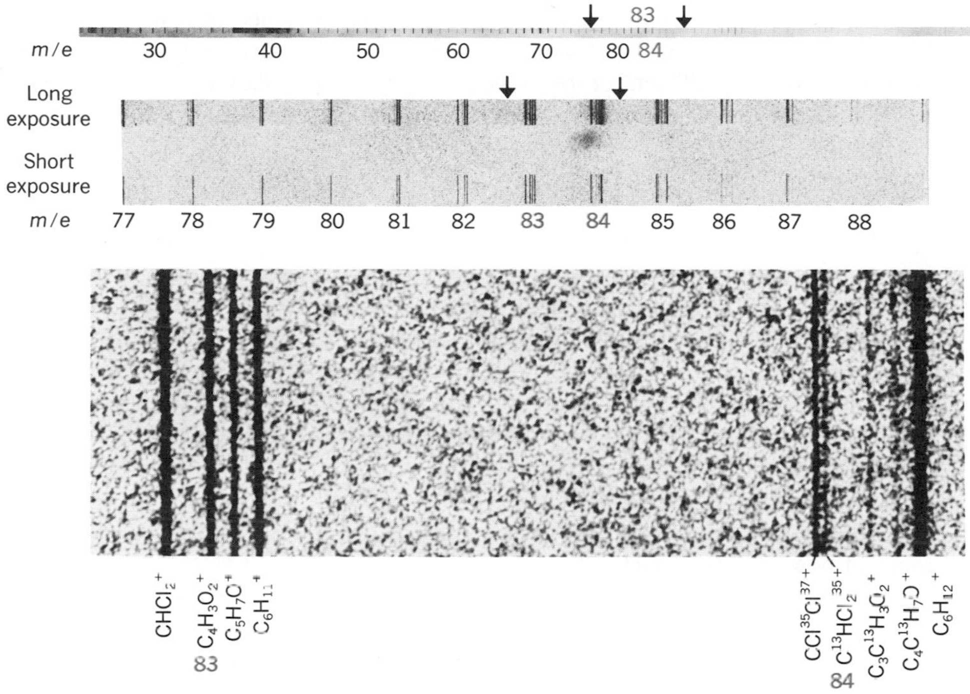

Figure 36.9 The high-resolution mass spectrum of tetramethylcyclobutan-1,3-dione (molecular weight, 140) containing chloroform as an internal mass standard. (*Top*) Magnification of the photographic-plate spectrum for the region from *m/e* 24 to *m/e* 141. (*Middle*) Enlargement of a long and short exposure for the region *m/e* 77 to *m/e* 89. (*Bottom*) Magnification of the region from *m/e* 83 to *m/e* 84. The presence of oxygenated ions had not been suspected in this research. [F. W. McLafferty, *Science*, **151**, 641 (1966). Copyright 1966 by the American Association for the Advancement of Science.]

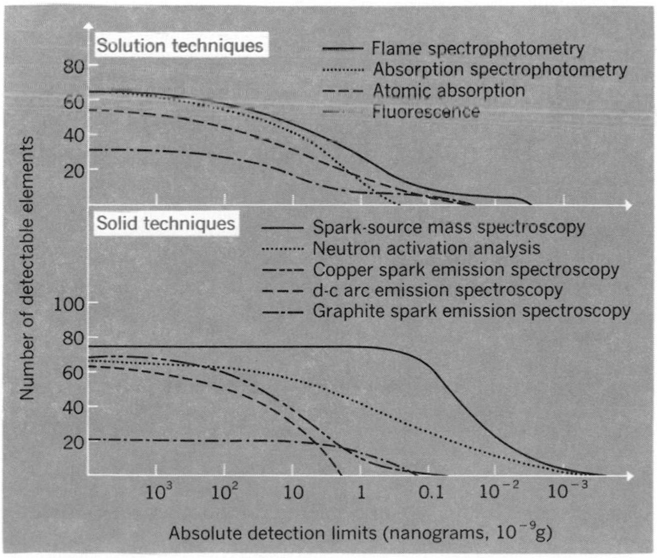

Figure 36.10 Relative sensitivities of some instrumental analytical methods. [*Scientific Research,* **1,** 21 (1966).]

bidden, since there would be no way to detect the presence of residual toxic or lethal doses in food. And without the insecticides and herbicides it would be impossible to raise sufficient crops to feed our present population.

Figure 36.10 shows the relative applicability of some of the methods discussed.

SUMMARY

A wide selection of analytical techniques and methods are currently available. Regardless of how they may be classified—as chemical or instrumental, as qualitative or quantitative, as gravimetric or volumetric, as optical or electrical, or as being applicable to organic or inorganic species—all analytical methods are based on physical and/or chemical properties of the system to be identified. With the development of new instrumentation and new techniques of analysis the chemist has the means to undertake ever more complex problems. And conversely, as he attempts to solve ever more difficult problems, he generates a need for the development of new analytical methods.

Analysis is central to any problem in science, and it is probable that use of inadequate and inaccurate chemical identification by researchers has vitiated more research results than any other single cause. *Moral:* Learn to take and to evaluate analytical data.

Grind up cabbages or grind up kings, the chemicals found are the very same things.—Anonymous

---

PROBLEMS

36.1. Calculate the percentage purity of a sample of ferrous ammonium sulfate, $Fe(NH_4)_2(SO_4)_2 \cdot 6H_2O$, from the following data: 0.3304 g of primary standard sodium oxalate, $Na_2C_2O_4$, in 1 *F* H_2SO_4 required 46.21 ml of a $KMnO_4$ solution to reach an equivalence point; 1.3653 g of the ferrous ammonium sulfate sample required 32.50 ml of the same $KMnO_4$ solution to reach an equivalence point. (Purity $\cong$ 100%.)

36.2. Clearly explain the difference between an equivalence point and an end point.

36.3. The standard reduction potential for the U(VI)/U(IV) couple is +0.334 volts:

$$UO_2^{++} + 4H^+ + 2e^- = U^{+4} + 2H_2O, \qquad \mathcal{E}^0 = +0.334 \text{ volts}$$

Calculate the equilibrium constant for the reaction between MnO_4^- and U^{+4} in an acid solution. ($pK \cong -200$)

36.4. Assume that you are titrating 50.00 ml of a 0.1000 *F* solution of $U(SO_4)_2$ with 0.02000 *F* $KMnO_4$ and the $[H^+]$ stays 1.0 *M*. Calculate the concentrations of Mn^{++}, MnO_4^-,

U^{+4}, and UO_2^{++} in the solution 0.1% before the equivalence point. ($[MnO_4^-] \cong 10^{-92}$)

36.5. Use the same assumptions as in Problem 36.4, and calculate the same four concentrations 0.1% beyond the equivalence point. ($[U^{+4}] \cong 10^{-40}$ *M*.)

36.6. An AC spark is a source of much higher energy than is an AC arc. Predict which of these two excitation methods would produce emission spectra due predominantly to neutral atoms? Which to ions? Explain qualitatively how the emission spectrum of Na^+ would differ from that of Na.

II

36.7. An electric cell consisting of a hydrogen electrode (pH = 8.0) and a Ag – Ag^+(0.01 *F*) electrode has $\mathcal{E} = 1.0$ volts. The cell is allowed to operate. Bromthymol blue around the hydrogen electrode changes from blue to yellow and $\mathcal{E}$ becomes 0.82 volts. What is the pH around the hydrogen electrode now? Enough 1 *M* $Na_2S_{(aq)}$ is now added to the silver compartment to give $[S^=] = 10^{-3}$ *M*. The cell voltage changes to -0.50 volts. Calculate K_{sp} for silver sulfide. (Publ. $K_{sp} \cong 10^{-50}$.)

36.8. For *one* of the following outline an experimental method for obtaining the information. (*a*) The charge on the copper ion. (*b*) The molecular formula for chlorine gas. (See Table 18.13.)

36.9. Indicate single chemical reagents which will distinguish between the materials in the following pairs. Describe the observations you would make including chemical equations for all reactions. (*a*) CuO, MnO_2; (*b*) $CaCl_2$, $CaBr_2$; (*c*) $NH_{3(aq)}$, $KOH_{(aq)}$.

36.10. The wavelengths of maximum absorbance for methyl red in the acidic and basic forms, respectively, are 528 mμ and 400 mμ. A $1.03 \cdot 10^{-3}$ *F* solution of methyl red in 0.1 *F* HCl has an absorbance of 0.065 at 400 mμ and 1.467 at 528 mμ. A $1.36 \cdot 10^{-3}$ *F* solution of methyl red in 0.1 *F* $NaHCO_3$ (pH ~ 9) has absorbances of 0.940 and 0.000 at these same two wavelengths. A small amount of the indicator is dissolved in an acetic acid-sodium acetate buffer solution. The pH of the resulting solution is 4.79 and it has absorbances of 0.313 and 1.163 at 400 mμ and 528 mμ. The same cuvette was used for all absorbance measurements. Calculate the dissociation constant of methyl red from these data. (See Table 18.13.)

36.11. A current of 10 amperes is passed through a solution of sodium chloride for 965 sec, using platinum electrodes. At the anode, both chlorine and oxygen are produced according to the equations:

$$2Cl^- = Cl_{2(g)} + 2e^-$$
$$2H_2O = O_{2(g)} + 4H^+ + 4e^-$$

(*a*) The mixture of the two gases evolved from the cell contains 0.04 moles of $Cl_{2(g)}$. How many moles of oxygen are in the mixture of Cl_2 and O_2?
(*b*) If you measured the density of the gas mixture and calculated the molecular weight, what value would you find for the molecular weight? ($M \cong 70$.)

36.12. Complete the following paragraph by filling in the blanks. Show all mathematical work.

The electrolysis of a solution of sodium bromide and ammonium chloride at low voltage produces (*a*) ________, (*b*) ________, and hydrogen. Two Faradays of current would release (*c*) ____ g of hydrogen. This weight of hydrogen would occupy (*d*) ____ liters at standard conditions and contain (*e*) ____ molecules of hydrogen.

36.13. Write the equation for the electrolysis reaction which uses a solution of sodium chloride as the raw material and produces chlorine. Assuming that each electrolytic cell used generates 0.01 ton of chlorine per 24 hours of service, what current, in amperes, must be passing through the cell? ($I \cong 300$ amp.)

36.14. All parts of this problem deal with unknowns. On the basis of the information given in each part, select the substances that must be present or absent among those listed. Also list those for which no definitive evidence is given.

(*a*) An unknown solution has been made by dissolving one or more of the following solids in water: mercurous nitrate, silver nitrate, zinc chloride, ammonium nitrate, potassium hydroxide. The solution is alkaline and on addition of dilute nitric acid gives a white precipitate insoluble in excess acid.

(*b*) An unknown solid mixture is made from one or more of the following: calcium oxide, silver nitrate, ferric oxide, zinc sulfide, cupric oxide. Treatment with water gives a dark precipitate and a colorless solution. Treatment with dilute hydrochloric acid gives a white precipitate and a colorless solution.

(*c*) A clear solution is made by dissolving one or more of the following solids in water: ammonium nitrate, potassium hydroxide, calcium nitrate, ferric nitrate, mercurous nitrate, zinc nitrate, silver nitrate. A sample of the solution gave a yellow color with indigo carmine. The solution when treated with 6 *F* hydrochloric acid gave a white precipitate, insoluble in excess of acid.

(*d*) An unknown mixture may contain one or more of the following solids: calcium carbonate, zinc sulfide, mercuric sulfide, ferric chloride. The mixture leaves a residue when treated with water, but dissolves without residue in dilute hydrochloric acid. A colorless precipitate forms when this solution is made alkaline with ammonia water.

(*e*) An unknown white solid is soluble in water, in hydrochloric acid, and in sulfuric acid. The water solution is acidic and colorless and gives no precipitate when treated with silver nitrate. What single compound of the ions H^+, Na^+, K^+, Ag^+, Cu^{++}, Ca^{++}, Zn^{++}, OH^-, Cl^-, NO_3^-, $CO_3^=$, $SO_4^=$, $S^=$, could be the white solid?

(*f*) An unknown solid is made up of one or more of the following: calcium carbonate, barium chloride, sodium sulfate, silver nitrate, zinc sulfate, sodium hydroxide, ammonium chloride. The solid is completely soluble in water; the solution is odorless and gives a red color with phenolphthalein. When 1 *F* hydrochloric acid solution is added, a precipitate is produced which dissolves in excess of the acid.

(*g*) An unknown solution may contain two or more of the following species: Al^{+++}, Cr^{+++}, Fe^{+++}, NH_4^+, Ag^+, Hg^{++}, H^+, OH^-, $SO_4^=$, Cl^-, NO_3^-, $CO_3^=$. When 2 *F* sodium hydroxide is slowly added in excess, a green precipitate is seen to appear and then to dissolve completely. When 0.1 *F* hydrochloric acid is added to a fresh portion of the original unknown solution, a white precipitate is formed. After filtration this precipitate proves to be soluble in ammonia water.

III

36.15. The specific conductance of pure water is $5.54 \cdot 10^{-8}$ ohm^{-1} cm^{-1} at 25°C. The equivalent conductances of the hydrogen and hydroxyl ions may be taken as 349.8 and 198.6 ohms^{-1} cm^2 respectively. Calculate the ion product for water.

36.16. In an experiment in freshman chemistry the students determined the solubility of cadmium iodate, $Cd(IO_3)_2$ in various solutions by an indirect volumetric determination of iodate. Typical results were as follows.

Solubility (F)	*Solution*
$4.03 \cdot 10^{-4}$	H_2O
$6.3 \cdot 10^{-5}$	0.1 *F* $Cd(NO_3)_2$
$1.21 \cdot 10^{-3}$	0.1 *F* HNO_3

Explain the above results—as, for example, to one of the freshman students.

36.17. You have synthesized a new compound which you believe to be either

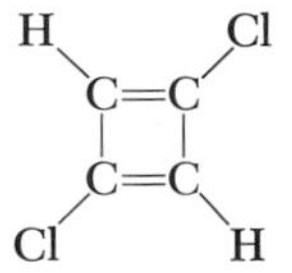

or

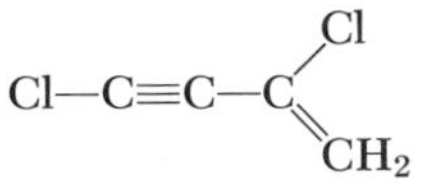

Outline two independent methods of deciding which one you have prepared, methods which leave the total amount of sample unchanged in composition.

36.18. To prepare solutions for qualitative analyses, individual samples of (*a*) HgS, (*b*) silica, SiO_2, (*c*) AgI, (*d*) ignited Cr_2O_3, (*e*) $Cd(OAc)_2$, (*f*) MnO_2, (*g*) Au, and (*h*) $Ca_3(PO_4)_2$ were successively treated with the following reagents: (1) water, (2) 6 *F* HNO_3, (3) 16 *F* HNO_3, (4) 12 *F* HCl, (5) aqua regia, 3 parts 12 *F* HCl, 1 part 16 *F* HNO_3, (6) $HClO_4$, fuming, (7) HF and $HClO_4$, fuming, and (8) Na_2CO_3 and $NaNO_3$, fusion. Predict which reagent will first cause each sample to dissolve and write a chemical equation to illustrate the solvent action occurring.

See page 1094 for a list of references and readings in the recent chemical literature related to the material in this chapter.

CHAPTER 37

Chemical Synthesis

MITSURU KUBOTA

Few, if any, substances are currently discovered by hit or miss alchemical mixing of ingredients. Syntheses are planned using available starting materials, thermodynamic, kinetic, and structural ideas, and are designed to solve specific problems. But the results may be a true surprise.

Chemists spend a large fraction of their time synthesizing, or attempting to synthesize, new chemical systems. They produce about half a millon new chemical compounds each year and an even larger number of new mixtures—solutions, alloys, plastics, and others. Most modern synthetic problems concern the design and experimental testing of methods of preparing a particular desired substance. The substance may be already known in nature, but be desired in larger or cheaper quantities. It may be a newly discovered natural compound, the aim of the synthesis being to verify its structure, or it may be an unknown compound that is believed to have desirable properties.

The usual steps in any synthesis are: (1) to define the formula, structure, and properties of the desired substance so that it may later be identified; (2) consider the type of separation processes which will allow it to be purified; (3) outline as many paths as possible by which it might be synthesized; (4) select the most promising synthesis, using thermodynamics, kinetics, and feasibility of starting material as criteria; and (5) attempt the synthesis, purification, and identification of the desired product in the laboratory. The experiments give additional information which is then used to design more effective synthetic steps.

It should be clear that no exact thermodynamic, kinetic, or property data can be available for an unknown compound; even the data for many known systems are either unavailable, sketchy, or inaccurate. For these reasons synthetic chemists must be skilled in the prediction of unknown properties from a broad basic knowledge of the properties of known systems.

COSMOLOGICAL SYNTHESES

We have already discussed our general ideas of how naturally occurring materials have been synthesized. Let us review them here for the insights they may give to syntheses in the laboratory. Historically, of course, the natural syntheses are usually deduced from laboratory experiments.

The most widely accepted view of cosmological synthesis postulates an initial, rather small, undifferentiated blob of very hot ($> 10^8\,°K$) matter composed of what might most simply be considered as neutrons. (Where these came from is a contested question, as is much of cosmology.) In the course of a short space of time, perhaps an hour, this system generated the chemical elements in roughly the ratio they are now found in the universe, and then exploded, sending the atoms in all directions. Condensation then occurred to give systems such as galaxies, stars, and planets. The stars continue to carry out nuclear reactions such as those outlined in Table 2.5.

Approximately ten billion years ago the earth formed as a separate entity, and began to lay down the geological record now available to us. At some early stage the temperature was high enough to allow sedimentation by gravity. Then cooling led to formation of a primordial atmosphere, as described on page 133. By this time the world had become essentially a closed system of constant temperature and pressure, and most subsequent processes can be dealt with using such thermodynamic equations as

$$\Delta G = \Delta H - T\,\Delta S = RT \ln Q - RT \ln K$$

and such kinetic equations as

$$\frac{d[X]}{dt} = \left\{A \exp\left(-\frac{\Delta H_{\text{act}}}{RT}\right)\right\} \varphi_i[i]^n = \left\{e\left(\frac{kT}{h}\right)\exp\left(\frac{\Delta S^{\ddagger}}{R}\right)\exp\left(-\frac{\Delta H^{\ddagger}}{RT}\right)\right\}\varphi_i[i]^n$$

where there are i species whose concentrations affect the rate.

Furthermore, nuclear reactions had dropped to nearly their present low rate on earth and the common chemical species had formulas we would recognize as stable today. The composition of the atmosphere and crust of the world were, however, appreciably different from those at present.

The earth's crust has undergone continual change in composition through volcanic action, phase separation in the solidifying lava, attack by the atmosphere with resulting weathering, sedimentation, separation of weathered products by density, burial of early materials under later volcanic flows or sedimentary deposits, remelting and reconstitution of the buried material at the high pressures and temperatures that exist beneath the earth's crust—and then repetition of the cycle.

For about three billion years living organisms have had an active part in crustal and atmospheric chemistry. There is evidence, for example, that many ore bodies may have been concentrated by biological action, and it is practically certain that the present atmosphere owes its existence and composition primarily to biological action. For example, there is insufficient oxygen in the atmosphere to transform all the carbon on the earth's surface to CO_2, the one thermodynamically stable substance in the carbon-oxygen system at moderate temperatures. Thus the elementary oxygen must have been generated by an endothermic process, presumably biological. This hypothesis is consistent with all the available biohistory as well.

BIOSYNTHESIS IN NATURE

Many meteors contain carbonaceous material. Gaseous solutions similar to the primordial atmosphere postulated on page 133 have been subjected in the laboratory to electric discharge (simulating primordial lightning) and high-energy radio frequencies. The products yielded are similar to those predicted by equilibrium thermodynamics and also to those found in meteors.

Detailed investigation of reaction mechanisms gives data such as those of Sanchez, Ferris, and Orgel.* They generated a spark across a tungsten electrode gap of 5 mm in a flask containing 20 ml of methane and 88 ml of nitrogen at atmospheric pressure. Periodic analysis by gas chromatography revealed the presence of methane, acetylene, diacetylene, cyanoacetylene, hydrogen cyanide, benzene, and various hydrocarbons. Subsequently, a mixture of 0.1 *M* cyanoacetylene, 5.0 *M* ammonia, and 1 *M* hydrogen cyanide heated at 100°C for 24 hours was shown to give a yield of 10–15% asparagine. Figure 37.1 outlines a possible path.

How the amino acids, presumably synthesized as Sanchez et al suggest, aggregate into proteins, and how they combine with carbohydrates and phosphates to give genetic material is not yet fully understood, although recent laboratory syntheses of protein and of genetic material indicate that the questions may soon be answered.

Two other important problems appear to require much more research: (1) how the in vitro synthesis of a cell from noncellular material takes place, and (2) how cells differentiate during growth of an organism. It is widely believed that when these processes are understood it will be possible to generate living systems in a laboratory, from simple molecules, without introducing already living systems other than the researchers into the synthesis. Certainly this is one of the most exciting and active research areas in science—but it is also one of the most complicated, requiring an extensive knowledge of the fundamentals of all branches of science and their interrelationships. Perhaps a discussion of somewhat simpler systems that presumably involve the same ideas will help us understand how great the problems are.

---

* *Science,* **154,** 784 (1966).

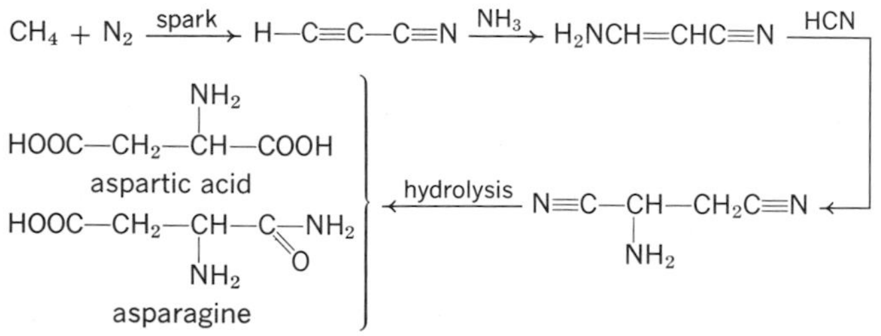

Figure 37.1 Possible primordial synthetic route to give amino acids, the precursors of proteins.

RAW MATERIALS

Just as syntheses in the earth's primordial atmosphere were limited by the molecular species present, so every synthesis must still start from available raw materials. For millions of years the most widely available raw materials have been air, silicates, sunlight, water, and living systems. By utilizing only these man can—and for well over 95% of his existence did—live a reasonably comfortable life. Air, water, light, and living systems provide sustenance, wood supplies an external source of heat, and silicates plus a little wood provide shelter. However, for some tens of thousands of years man has been enlarging the number of synthesized materials which he finds useful or interesting, until he now has available several million pure substances plus a large and rapidly increasing number of combinations.

Every living system synthesizes within itself a large number of substances essential for its growth, but many humans now live in an environment where almost nothing is a naturally occurring raw material. The water, air, and food that they ingest, the flowers in their gardens, the clothes they wear, their means of locomotion, have all been modified from a natural state. It is small wonder that major ecological crises are predicted for the near future.

The main raw materials are still those we have just mentioned, but man has slowly added others—sea salt (NaCl), a few metals, limestone, coal, sulfur, natural gas, petroleum—obtainable as relatively pure substances in nature, although living systems and the wood, coal, and petroleum that these systems produce are very complicated mixtures. This small list almost covers the total supply of readily accessible natural raw materials. Almost everything else, except rarities like gemstones, must be synthesized or at least purified. Table 37.1 lists the most common raw materials and some of their synthetic products. Let us consider a few synthetic modifications of pure materials.

THE CHANGING NATURE OF THE SEARCH FOR SYNTHETIC METHODS

Man has been using synthetic substances such as glass, soap, iron, and brass for a very long time, but the discovery of the synthetic methods by which they are produced were almost certainly accidental, based on chance and almost random trial and error. Some of our most common, important and relatively recent syntheses are the results of accidents; that is, they were found by a person looking for something different. Cement, aspirin, coal tar dyes, and penicillin were all accidental discoveries.

Even the investigation of a comparatively simple industrial problem may lead to discoveries of fundamental importance. For example, a major obstacle in the production of sodium carbonate by the Solvay process prior to 1890 was the rapid corrosion of nickel valves on the tanks in which ammonium chloride was vaporized. Ludwig Mond showed that the corrosion was due to small amounts of carbon monoxide in the carbon dioxide used to sweep ammonia out of the tanks. A study of the reaction between carbon monoxide and nickel led to the discovery and synthesis of nickel tetracarbonyl, $Ni(CO)_4$. This synthesis, which established

Table 37.1 The principal raw materials of the world. United States figures are 10–40% of these. Remember that water and air (N_2 and O_2) are other major raw materials.

Raw material	World production (tons/yr)	Typical products (tons/yr)[a]
Silicates	$6 \cdot 10^9$	cement $4 \cdot 10^8$, asbestos $3 \cdot 10^6$, mica $2 \cdot 10^5$
Coal and petroleum	$5 \cdot 10^9$	gasoline $2 \cdot 10^8$, cheapest reducing agent (C)
Iron ore	$6 \cdot 10^8$	steel $5 \cdot 10^8$
Mg^{++} (ocean)	10^8	magnesium 10^5
NaCl	10^8	chlorine products, Cl_2, HCl
Limestone	10^8	steel making $5 \cdot 10^7$, cheapest base CaO $5 \cdot 10^7$
Phosphate rock [$Ca_3(PO_4)_2$]	$6 \cdot 10^7$	fertilizer
Gypsum [$CaSO_4$]	$5 \cdot 10^7$	construction
Bauxite [Al_2O_3]	$3 \cdot 10^7$	aluminum $7 \cdot 10^6$
N_2	$2 \cdot 10^7$	fertilizer
S	10^7	H_2SO_4 $3 \cdot 10^7$ (cheapest acid)
K salts	10^7	fertilizer
U ore	$6 \cdot 10^6$	nuclear fuel, U_3O_8 $3 \cdot 10^4$
Cu ore	$5 \cdot 10^6$	copper $5 \cdot 10^6$
Zn ore	$5 \cdot 10^6$	zinc $5 \cdot 10^6$
Pb ore	$3 \cdot 10^6$	lead $3 \cdot 10^6$
Ilmenite [TiO_2]	$3 \cdot 10^6$	white pigment $5 \cdot 10^3$
Fluorite [CaF_2]	$3 \cdot 10^6$	processing steel and uranium, fluorocarbon refrigerants 10^5

[a] Note that the most common categories of products are (1) energy producers (fossil fuels, uranium), (2) construction materials (silicates, iron, magnesium, gypsum, metals), (3) fertilizers (phosphate, nitrogen, potassium); all these are indispensable to mankind at his present population level.

a pattern for the reaction of carbon monoxide with a metal, led within a year to the first preparation of iron pentacarbonyl, $Fe(CO)_5$. More than two hundred compounds in which carbon monoxide is bonded to a metal are now known, and many of our best insights into chemical bonding and synthesis have come through the study of these compounds.

Exercise 37.1

Suggest electron structures to account for the stability of $Ni(CO)_4$ and $Fe(CO)_5$ from the Mond synthesis. *Answer:* Carbon monoxide has the electron structure $:C\equiv O:$ so it can donate two electrons per molecule to a single atom of Fe or Ni. Ni has 28 electrons, 8 short of Kr with 36. Fe has 26 electrons, 10 short of Kr with 36. Thus Ni has a set of four empty orbitals and forms $Ni(CO)_4$, while Fe has five empty orbitals and forms $Fe(CO)_5$. Note that Cr, with 24 electrons, might be expected to form $Cr(CO)_6$. It does. Similarly, Mn (25 electrons) forms $Mn(CO)_5^-$. Do you see why?

On the other hand, more and more discoveries are now being based on thermodynamic, kinetic, and structural predictions. Polyethylene, nylon, birth control pills, and high-tensile-strength concrete have resulted from detailed analysis of specific problems, and comprehension of behavior at the atomic-molecular level.

At present, synthetic chemistry is based almost equally on trial and error and on predicted discoveries, but the trend is overwhelmingly toward the latter. Truly remarkable accidental discoveries will always be made, but the evidence is strong that the quickest way to solve most problems is to understand a system at its most elementary level, and then to perform a synthesis which is based on this knowledge. We shall, in the rest of this chapter, examine some synthetic problems of current laboratory interest as a means of exploring this approach in some of its currently incomplete stages.

Exercise 37.2

It has been said that Fleming would not have discovered penicillin if his lab had not been next to the Horse Guard stables in London. Is this possible? *Answer:* Penicillin was discovered when a mold accidentally contaminated a culture in Fleming's laboratory and prevented growth of the culture. It is very likely the mold blew from the manure in the stables through the open window of the lab. The key human contribution was Fleming's awareness of, and inquisitiveness into, the lack of growth in his culture.

SOME GENERAL PRINCIPLES OF SYNTHESIS

Before beginning a detailed study of some rather simple synthetic problems, let us summarize some thermodynamic, kinetic, and structural principles.

Thermodynamically (under the common conditions of constant T and P in a closed system) it is desirable to find exothermic processes that increase the entropy of the closed system, thus giving a negative value to

$$\Delta H - T\Delta S = \Delta G = RT \ln \frac{\prod_i (\text{prod})_i^{n_i}}{\prod_j (\text{react})_j^{n_j}} - RT \ln K$$

$$\Delta G = RT \ln Q - RT \ln K$$

Reactions are exothermic ($\Delta H = -$) if stronger bonds form than break. Examples are formation of insoluble precipitates, formation of weakly dissociated substances through acid-base reactions, formation of strongly bonded species such as N_2, CO_2, H_2O. Favorable entropy changes ($\Delta S = +$) are associated with decomposition reactions, such as formation of volatile products or increase in number of moles of gases. Entropy effects become increasingly important as T rises.

If the system is open and one or more of the products of a reaction can escape from the system, the reaction is bound essentially to reach completion even though it might come quickly to equilibrium in a closed system. Dehydration is a common example. Both laundry and wet chemicals dry rapidly in a flowing stream of warm dry air, but would not in a closed system. Similarly, limestone, $CaCO_{3(c)}$, may be quantitatively converted to $CaO_{(c)}$ by heating in the open air and so allowing the gaseous CO_2 to escape from the system.

It is well to remember that all syntheses are really carried out in a system presumed to be isolated—the universe. Thus the thermodynamically controlling factor is always the entropy change of the universe; the entropy of the universe increases. This increase consists of the dispersion of energy and of matter from more concentrated to less concentrated states. The ultimate goal of a well-designed synthesis is to minimize these dispersal processes and so to approach $\Delta S_{univ} = 0$ as a limit. The most thermodynamically efficient synthesis is always the one which most closely approaches thermodynamic reversibility. However, as reversibility is approached the rate drops to zero, and all real syntheses are thus a compromise between the thermodynamic desirability of reversibility and the kinetic demands of appreciable yield. If energy is expensive, the thermodynamic demands get more weight: If ample sources of cheap energy are available the kinetic demands get more emphasis.

Rapid rates are likely in reactions between simple molecules in intimate contact at high temperature and at high concentrations. Thus, solid-phase reactions (except explosions) tend to be slow and diffusion-controlled. Reaction rates in gaseous and liquid phases vary enormously, depending on the complexity of the mechanism and the availability of activation energy. In general, ionic reactions are rapid in liquid phases because of low activation energies and simple orientation requirements. Reactions between covalent molecules are usually slower.

If we had thermodynamic data for all pure substances and their solutions, and had values of $\Delta E^{\ddagger}$ and $\Delta S^{\ddagger}$ for all possible reactions, syntheses could be designed on paper with considerable certainty that they would succeed. Actually, though thermodynamic and rate data are accumulating rapidly, it is, of course, impossible to measure values until a compound has been synthesized. Thus initial syntheses must be guided by analogies with existing compounds and their syntheses, and intuitive extrapolations based on the presumed properties of the desired product. All good synthetic chemists are adept at making these educated guesses. In the rest of this chapter we shall investigate (1) some syntheses for which thermodynamic and kinetic data are available, (2) some molecular properties that are useful in correlating reactivities, (3) types of reaction and their theoretical interpretation in the absence of numerical data, (4) some structural principles affecting syntheses, and (5) syntheses in nonaqueous environments.

Exercise 37.3

Suggest a synthesis of HNO_3 from $NaNO_3$. *Answer:* $NaNO_3$ is an ionic substance, HNO_3 a covalent one. Covalent substances are usually more volatile than ionic ones. Add a strong nonvolatile acid to crystalline $NaNO_3$ and distill out HNO_3 (favorable ΔS and high rate at high T). Either H_2SO_4 or H_3PO_4 (with much more H— bonding than has HNO_3) are sufficiently strong and nonvolatile to serve.

THE SULFURIC ACID SYNTHESIS

One of the most common chemical needs is a strong nonvolatile acid. None exists in nature in appreciable quantities, but sulfuric acid, H_2SO_4, has been known for several hundred years to have these properties. How can it be made?

Examination of Table 37.1 suggests that H_2O, S, and O_2 (from the air) would be suitably plentiful raw materials for the synthesis of H_2SO_4. Such a direct synthesis, if reactions go almost to completion, produces no contaminants and may make purification unnecessary. All the thermodynamic data for the direct synthesis at 298°K are available.

	ΔH^0	ΔS^0	ΔG^0	
$S_{(c)} + \frac{3}{2}O_{2(g)} + H_2O_{(l)} = H_2SO_{4(l)}$,	−148	−94	−120	(37.1)

Experiment shows that putting water and sulfur together in the presence of air does indeed produce H_2SO_4, but the rate is very slow. Heating the ingredients in a closed system produces H_2SO_4 more rapidly, but contact rates between the solid (or liquid) sulfur and the other ingredients are still slow: there are also undesirable side reactions.

Suppose we consider mixing the reactants in pairs. Both water and oxygen and water and sulfur are thermodynamically stable with respect to reaction under most conditions, but sulfur burns rapidly and readily in air (O_2) to give SO_2 (+4 sulfur). The further reaction to SO_3 (+6 sulfur) does not occur rapidly, but, once formed, SO_3 does react with H_2O. Let us again look at the data at 298°K.

	ΔH^0	ΔS^0	ΔG^0	Rate 360°K	Rate 1000°K
$S_{(c)} + O_{2(g)} = SO_{2(g)}$,	−71	1.7	−72	slow	rapid
$SO_{2(g)} + \frac{1}{2}O_{2(g)} = SO_{3(g)}$,	−23	−23	−16	slow	slow
$SO_{3(g)} + H_2O_{(l)} = H_2SO_{4(l)}$,	−54	−73	−32	rapid	—

(37.2)

All three reactions have favorable thermodynamics and they add to give the desired net equation (37.1). The problem is the slow rate of oxidation of SO_2 by O_2 at attainable temperatures. Research shows that vanadium oxides and metallic platinum both catalyze the process at red heat. Thus the three-step synthesis outlined becomes feasible.

Each of the three steps is operated as an open, continuously flowing system to insure as complete reaction as possible. The gaseous SO_2 (from step one) and excess O_2 leave the burning sulfur and flow to the catalyst site for step two, from which the gaseous SO_3 flows into an aqueous absorption system for step three. Liquid water enters one end of this absorption system and concentrated sulfuric acid flows out the other. The system is essentially at steady state.

The large negative values of ΔH [Equations (37.2)] indicate the synthesis will be less and less effective as T increases, $[\partial \ln K/\partial(1/T)]_P = -\Delta H^0/R$. Note also that the ΔG^0 terms are so negative and we are so close to the standard state that we need not calculate ΔG for the actual conditions; we can be sure each will be a large negative value. Had any calculated value of ΔG^0 lain in the range ± 10 kcal, or had actual conditions deviated greatly from standard, a more careful calculation would have been required.

The sulfuric acid synthesis illustrates several general problems: (1) finding a satisfactory raw material, (2) converting the raw material into the desired product by thermodynamically feasible steps—removing and adding energy as required, (3) adjusting the rates of reactions so that the desired product predominates over all others. A principal problem is that naturally occurring raw materials tend to be both thermodynamically and kinetically stable, consistent with their occurrence in nature.

Exercise 37.4

Calculate a suitable set of conditions for the synthesis of hydrogen from methane in the following two gas-phase processes: (*a*) $CH_4 + H_2O = CO + 3H_2$; (*b*) $CO + H_2O = CO_2 + H_2$. *Answer:* Rate—the molecules are simple and the reaction occurs in the gas phase but the bonds to be broken are all strong (C—H = 99 kcal, H—O = 110 kcal) so ΔE_{act} will be high. You need to operate at high T to get fast reaction. Probably you also need a catalyst. The reaction involves H and O exchange, so try an oxide catalyst. (Metal would be fine for hydrogen exchange but would form oxide in this system.) From Table 27.1, for reaction (*a*): $\Delta H^0_{298} = +49$ kcal, $\Delta G^0_{298} = +34$ kcal; for (*b*): $\Delta H^0_{298} = -10$, $\Delta G^0_{298} = -7$ kcal. Thus the equilibrium for *b* is favorable ($\Delta G^0 = -$) at 298°K and gets less favorable ($\Delta H^0 = -$) as T rises. Reaction *b* should be carried out at as low a T as possible consistent with a reasonable rate. Reaction *a* has an unfavorable equilibrium at 298° ($\Delta G^0 = +$) but the equilibrium becomes more favorable as T rises ($\Delta H^0 = +$). Try 1000°K. From Table 28.5, $\Delta G^0_{1000} = -6$ kcal. Thus reaction *a* can be carried out at high T, especially if a specific catalyst for it is found.

PATTERNS OF REACTIVITIES

In the absence of thermodynamic and kinetic data—for instance in the synthesis of a new compound—we study similar compounds and use their properties to design possible syntheses for the new compound. Once the compound is prepared, measurement of its properties allows improvements in the synthesis. Let us look at a few examples.

It has been noted (p. 240) that synthesis of the compound $XePtF_6$ was guided by recognition of the pattern of reactivity suggested by the almost identical ionization energies and sizes of xenon and oxygen. Similar arguments, based on known halogen compounds, predicted the synthesis of XeF_2, XeF_4, and XeF_6. Some of the known fluorides from groups V, VI, and VII are listed below in isoelectronic groups. The inclusion of the xenon fluorides is logical. Not only do the xenon fluorides fit the pattern but all the halide structures (see Figures 11.3 and 15.4) are correctly predicted on the basis of this analogy. We use the Gillespie E to represent an unshared pair of valence electrons.

Ten valence electrons on a central element (all are variations of a trigonal bipyramid):	PF_5	SF_4E	BrF_3E_2	XeF_2E_3
Twelve valence electrons on a central element (all are variations of an octahedron):	PF_6^-	SF_6	BrF_5E	XeF_4E_2
Fourteen valence electrons on a central element (all are variations of a pentagonal bipyramid):	SeF_6E^{2-}	TeF_7^-	IF_7	XeF_6E

Consideration of the data in Table 37.2 may be instructive in determining how each of the three xenon fluorides may be obtained in high purity by varying the reaction conditions. According to the data, formation of the xenon fluorides is favored at low temperatures, but no products are observed below 120°C in the

Table 37.2 **Equilibrium constants for the xenon-fluorine system. Values in italic type were measured; all others were calculated.**

Reaction	Temperature (°K)					
	298.15	523.15	573.15	623.15	673.15	774.15
$Xe + F_2 = XeF_2$	$1.23 \cdot 10^{13}$	$8.79 \cdot 10^{4}$	$1.02 \cdot 10^{4}$	$1.67 \cdot 10^{3}$	$3.89 \cdot 10^{2}$	29.8
$XeF_2 + F_2 = XeF_4$	$1.37 \cdot 10^{11}$	*$1.73 \cdot 10^{3}$*	*$1.55 \cdot 10^{2}$*	*27.2*	*4.86*	*0.50*
$XeF_4 + F_2 = XeF_6$	$8.6 \cdot 10^{5}$	*0.944*	*0.211*	*0.0558*	*0.0182*	0.003

SOURCE: Data from *Chem. Rev.*, **65**, 199 (1966).

thermal reaction. Since enough energy to loosen the fluoride bond (38 kcal mole^{-1}) is required, thermal reactions are conducted at temperatures greater than 300°C ($RT = 18$ kcal mole^{-1}). Energy sources such as electrical discharge, irradiation with high-pressure mercury arcs, or gamma rays from Co^{60} have been used to effect reaction at lower temperatures. The synthesis of XeF_2 depends on its rapid removal from the reaction zone containing a minimum of excess F_2 to prevent further reaction to produce XeF_4. Xenon and fluorine in a 1:5 ratio heated at 400°C in a nickel container give essentially quantitative yields of XeF_4. The hexafluoride is obtained in 95% yield by heating a 1:20 ratio of xenon-fluorine mixture at 50 atm and 210–250°C. Conversion is almost quantitative at 700°C and 200 atm. One of the surprising properties of these compounds is the thermal stability of the Xe—F bonds: the first attempts to synthesize the compounds were made at low T because of the presumed weakness of the Xe—F bond to thermal disruption.

Exercise 37.5

Suggest an interpretation of the following: (*a*) IF_7 and TeF_7^- can be synthesized with *CN* 7, (*b*) $SeF_6^{=}$ can also form with $CN = 7$ counting the unshared pair of electrons, but SeF_7^- is not known, whereas (*c*) the highest *CN* shown by S is in SF_6. *Answer:* All these atoms (S, Se, Te) have sufficient orbitals to hold 14 valence electrons but the orbitals are more closely spaced energetically in Se and Te, and thus more accessible. Furthermore, Se, Te, and I are appreciably larger atoms than S, allowing a higher *CN* without crowding. Size variation probably also accounts for $SeF_6^{=}$ rather than SeF_7^-, assuming that a fluorine atom is effectively larger than a pair of unshared electrons.

In many cases the predictions based on pattern of reactivity proves incorrect—occasionally to the delight of the researcher.

A classic example of departure from a pattern that led to a new concept is the discovery of ferrocene (see p. 384). Kealy and Pauson in 1951 attempted to synthesize dihydrofulvalene, using $FeCl_3$ as a catalyst, by a route analogous to the known procedure for preparing biphenyl. Instead of the dihydrofulvalene expected, they obtained an orange-colored product, $C_{10}H_{10}Fe$, which melted without decomposition at 173°C, dissolved in nonpolar solvents, and was inert to sodium hydroxide, hydrochloric acid, and boiling water. They assigned structure $Fe(C_5H_5)_2$, in which the iron atom is bonded to all ten carbon atoms. A new type of metal-carbon bonding system was thus discovered and now serves as a structural pattern for synthesis of numerous similarly bonded complexes.

ISOELECTRONIC COMPONENTS

Table 17.4 and its accompanying discussion illustrated the application of isoelectronic concepts to bonding. The ideas are similarly useful in synthesis. A common synthetic problem is the introduction of an OH group into a molecule, as in making alcohols from hydrocarbons, phenol from benzene, hydroxides from salts. Many such syntheses are known to give highly useful products. But they may also be extended to predict more compounds and routes to their synthesis.

The —OH group is isoelectronic with F^-, $—NH_2$, $—CH_3$ and effectively isoelectronic, in terms of valence electrons, with many others such as Cl^-, —S—H, $—PH_2$. In the same way, H_2O is isoelectronic with NH_3. Thus, knowing of the existence of H_2CO_3 and CO_2, one would predict the existence of the other compounds in Figure 37.2 and their likely synthesis. All are indeed known and their properties are interpretable in terms of the difference in electronegativity of O and N, and the additional proton on each N group.

The fact that $PO(OH)_3$, usually written H_3PO_4, can be synthesized by dissolving PCl_5 in liquid H_2O suggests that similar reactions would occur between PCl_5 and the isoelectronic HF and NH_3. They do:

$$\left.\begin{array}{lll}
PCl_{5(l)} + 5HF_{(l)} \longrightarrow 5HCl_{(HF)} + PF_{5(HF)} & & \\
PCl_{5(l)} + 5H_2O_{(l)} \longrightarrow 5HCl_{(aq)} + P(OH)_{5(aq)} & \xrightarrow{-H_2O} & PO(OH)_{3(aq)} \\
PCl_{5(l)} + 10H_3N_{(l)} \longrightarrow 5NH_4Cl_{(NH_3)} + P(NH_2)_{5(NH_3)} & \xrightarrow{-H_3N} & PN(NH_2)_{2(NH_3)}
\end{array}\right\} \text{all liquid solutions}$$

Note that PF_5 is stable to decomposition whereas $P(OH)_5$ and $P(NH_2)_5$ are not, consistent with the high free energy of formation of H_2O and NH_3 and the lack of similar possible products from PF_5. PF_5 might lose F_2 to give PF_3, but the small fluorine atoms do not cause much crowding in PF_5 and F_2 is not a tightly bonded molecule, so ΔG is unfavorable for the elimination of F_2 from the PF_5. It is far easier for PCl_5 to decompose into PCl_3 and Cl_2, as you should be able to show; $AsCl_5$ has never been isolated.

Table 37.3 gives further examples of syntheses based on isoelectronic systems. In this case the systems all share a linear arrangement of B, C, N, and/or O atoms, 16 valence electrons, and enough hydrogen atoms to complete the isoelectronic structure.

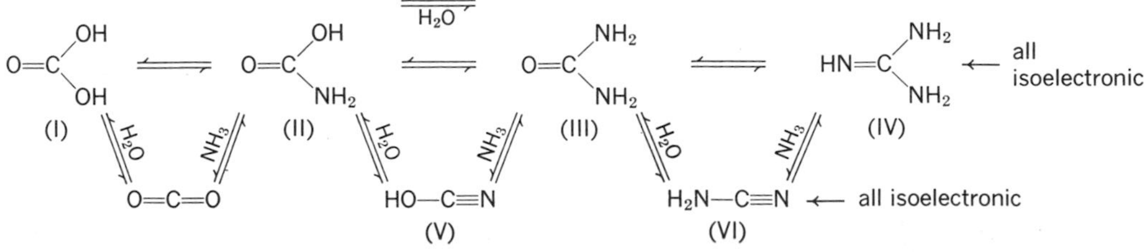

Figure 37.2 The aquo-ammono carbonic acids. (I) carbonic acid; (II) carbamic acid; (III) urea; (IV) guanidine; (V) cyanic acid; (VI) cyanamide. All are related by the addition or elimination of H_2O and NH_3.

Table 37.3 Some reactions of isoelectric species.

$$O{=}C{=}N^- \xrightarrow{\text{Na in NH}_{3(l)}} CN^- + OH^- + NH_2{}^-$$

$$O{=}N{=}N \xrightarrow{\text{Na in NH}_{3(l)}} N_2 + OH^- + NH_2{}^-$$

$$HN{=}N{=}N \xrightarrow{h\nu} N_2 + HN: \xrightarrow{H{-}NH_2} H_2N{-}NH_2$$

$$HN{=}C{=}O \xrightarrow{h\nu} CO + HN: \xrightarrow{:NH} HN{=}NH$$

$$H_2C{=}N{=}N \xrightarrow{h\nu} N_2 + H_2C: \xrightarrow{H{-}CH_3} H_3C{-}CH_3$$

$$H_2C{=}C{=}O \xrightarrow{h\nu} CO + H_2C: \xrightarrow{:CH_2} H_2C{=}CH_2$$

$$O{=}C{=}O \xrightarrow{H_2O} HO{-}C\!\!\begin{array}{c}OH\\\\O\end{array} \xrightarrow{H_2O} H_3O^+ + HO{-}C\!\!\begin{array}{c}O^-\\\\O\end{array}$$

$$HN{=}C{=}O \xrightarrow{H_2O} H_2N{-}C\!\!\begin{array}{c}OH\\\\O\end{array} \xrightarrow{H_2O} H_3O^+ + H_2N{-}C\!\!\begin{array}{c}O^-\\\\O\end{array}$$

$$H_2C{=}C{=}O \xrightarrow{H_2O} H_3C{-}C\!\!\begin{array}{c}OH\\\\O\end{array} \xrightarrow{H_2O} H_3O^+ + H_3C{-}C\!\!\begin{array}{c}O^-\\\\O\end{array}$$

$$H_3B{-}C{=}O \xrightarrow{H_2O} H_3B{-}C\!\!\begin{array}{c}OH\\\\OH\end{array} \xrightarrow{H_2O} H_3O^+ + H_3B{-}C\!\!\begin{array}{c}OH\\\\O\end{array}$$

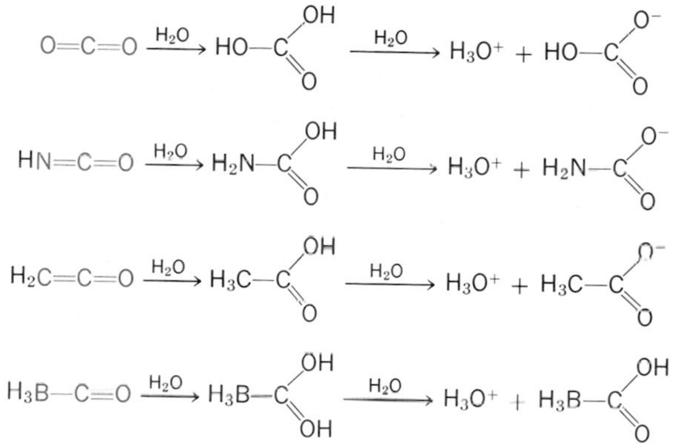

Exercise 37.6

Refer to the discussion of benzene and borazine on page 649 and predict the chances of synthesizing "beroxine,"

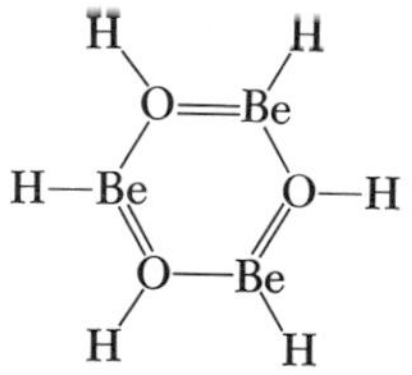

Answer: "Beroxine" is isoelectronic with benzene and borazine. It is also isoelectronic with Be + H_2O and with BeO + H_2, two rather stable sets of compounds of higher entropy, and (probably) lower energy, than "beroxine." Furthermore, the Be—O bond, because of the large difference in electronegativity, would be highly polar, lowering the delocalization of the ring electrons and minimizing resonance stabilization. It is very unlikely that this compound would be thermodynamically stable with respect to Be and H_2O, and even less likely that it would be with respect to BeO and H_2; nor is it likely to have appreciable activation energy for the decomposition. $Li_3F_3H_6$ would be even less stable. Both are probably unstable both thermodynamically and kinetically.

SATURATED CLOSED SHELL COMPOUNDS (sp^3 AND d^5sp^3)

We have frequently referred to and used the idea of the extra stability associated with sp^3 inert-gas electron structures. These ideas are most commonly applied to first row elements and elements in Groups IVA (especially carbon), VA, VIA, and VIIA; but they also apply to the *d* elements (IVB–IIB) and synthesis of their compounds.

Because details of more organic reactions (more than two million compounds) than of inorganic reactions (a few hundred thousand compounds) are currently known, a useful guide in inorganic synthesis is to draw analogies from organic systems. Indeed, many outstanding inorganic chemists did their early research in organic syntheses. The principles are the same. Reactive intermediates in organic reactions tend to give saturated species with closed-shell configurations (sp^3): reactive inorganic compounds likewise give saturated species with closed-shell configurations (for example, d^5sp^3). Recognition of the analogous course of reaction of unsaturated inorganic species and organic species can be based on a comparison of coordination numbers and nonbonding electrons, as illustrated in Table 37.4.

But again surprises occur. Let us examine the pattern in closer detail—specifically, with respect to the addition reaction

$$L_2Cl(CO)Ir + XY \longrightarrow L_2Cl(CO)Ir\begin{matrix}X\\ \\ Y\end{matrix}$$

where, for example, X = Y = I; or X = Cl, Y = CF_3CO; and L = $:P(C_6H_5)_3$ = triphenyl phosphine. The iridium atom is at the center of a coordination system of 4 or 6 ligands respectively in these compounds. When this reaction was tried with X = N_3, Y = RCO, an unexpected reaction was observed by Collman and Kang.* Instead of the expected product, octahedral $L_2Cl(CO)N_3Ir(RCO)$, a novel compound $L_2ClIr—N_2$ (*CN* = 4), in which iridium is bonded to molecular nitrogen, was obtained. They unexpectedly discovered a compound that might provide clues to the fixation of atmospheric nitrogen (discussed on page 266). Similar compounds, such as L_2ClIrN_2 (a yellow solid stable at room temperature), L_3CoN_2H, $Ru(NH_3)_5N_2^{++}$, and $Os(NH_3)_5N_2^{++}$ are known.

Sometimes the *CN* and the number of valence electrons remain constant and redox appears to occur. When this is true, the formal zero oxidation state of the metallic atoms in the reactants with d^8 configuration is

Oxidation states: 0 0 0   0   0 +2 0 −1   0

$$L_2Os(CO)_3 + Br_2 = L_2Os(CO)_2Br_2 + CO \qquad (37.3)$$

Oxidation states: 0 0 0   +1 −1   0 +2 0 −1 −1   0

$$L_2Ru(CO)_3 + HBr = L_2Ru(CO)_2HBr + CO \qquad (37.4)$$

converted to +2 in the products with electronic configuration d^6. The process is often considered as an oxidative addition reaction. [Note the −1 oxidation state for H in Equation (37.4); there is an Ru—H bond.]

An extension of this pattern of reactivity is the assumption that unsaturated complexes with d^{10} configuration should undergo similar oxidative addition reaction. Reaction

J. Am. Chem. Soc., **88**, 3459 (1966).

Table 37.4 Species of related configuration and reactivities in sp^3 and d^5sp^3 chemistry.

Reactant	Organic *sp* species (React to give full electron shells, sp^3, $CN = 4$): Change in *CN*	Change in nonbonding electrons	Characteristic reactions	Inorganic *dsp* species (React to give full electron shells, d^5sp^3, $CN = 6$): Change in *CN*	Change in nonbonding electrons	Characteristic reactions (plus inert gas species isoelectronic with reactant metal atom)
Saturated molecule	$4 \rightarrow 4$	$0 \rightarrow 0$	Substitution (acid-base) $R_3C{-}Br + Cl^- = R_3CCl + Br^-$	$6 \rightarrow 6$	$6 \rightarrow 6$	$RhCl_6^{3-} \xrightarrow{H_2O} RhCl_5OH_2^{2-} + Cl^-$ $[Xe] \longrightarrow [Xe]$[a]
Free radical	$3 \rightarrow 4$	$1 \rightarrow 0$	Dimerization $2R_3C\cdot = (R_3C)_2$ Abstraction $R_3C\cdot + HR = R_3CH + R\cdot$ Addition $2R_3C + H_2C{=}CH_2 = R_3CCH_2CH_2CR_3$	$5 \rightarrow 6$	$7 \rightarrow 6$	$\cdot Co(CN)_5^{3-} \xrightarrow{Co(CN)_5^{3-}} Co_2(CN)_{10}^{6-}$ $\cdot Co(CN)_5^{3-} \xrightarrow{CH_3I} Co(CN)_5I^{3-} + CH_3\cdot$ $\cdot Co(CN)_5^{3-} \xrightarrow{HC\equiv CH} (NC)_5Co(H)C{=}C(H)Co(CN)_5^{6-}$ $[Kr{:}]^+ \longrightarrow [Kr]$
Biradical	$2 \rightarrow 4$	$2 \rightarrow 0$	Addition $R_2C{:} + H_2C{=}CH_2 = H_2C{-}CH_2$ (bridged by CR_2, cyclopropane) (carbene) Insertion $R_2C\cdot + H_3C{-}CH_3{=}CH_3CH_2CR_2H$	$4 \rightarrow 6$	$8 \rightarrow 6$	[b]$Ir(CO)IL_2 \xrightarrow{C_2H_4} Ir(CO)IL_2C_2H_4$ [b]$Ir(CO)IL_2 \xrightarrow{HCl} Ir(CO)IL_2HCl$ $[\cdot Rn \cdot]^{++} \longrightarrow [Rn]$
Lewis acid	$3 \rightarrow 4$	$0 \rightarrow 0$	Addition of Nucleophile $R_3C^+ + Cl^- = R_3CCl$ (carbonium ion)	$5 \rightarrow 6$	$6 \rightarrow 6$	[c]$Co(CN)_5^{2-} \xrightarrow{I^-} Co(CN)_5I^{3-}$ $[Kr]^{++} \longrightarrow [Kr]$
Lewis base	$3 \rightarrow 4$	$2 \rightarrow 0$	Addition of Electrophile $R_3C + H^+ = R_3CH$ (carbanion)	$5 \rightarrow 6$	$8 \rightarrow 6$	$Mn(CO)_5^- \xrightarrow{H^+} Mn(CO)_5H$ $[{:}Kr] \longrightarrow [Kr]$

SOURCE: Adapted from J. Halpern, *Chem. Eng. News*, Oct. 31, 1966, p. 70.

[a] Each inorganic reaction is interpreted in terms of the electronic changes in the corresponding noble gas set of energy levels, which always ends up full of electrons. Note that in each pair of corresponding examples the changes in CN are the same, and the changes in numbers of nonbonding electrons are the same. Carbon compounds tend to go to CN = 4 with sp^3 hybridization; metals with d electrons (transition metals) tend to go to CN = 6, with 6 nonbonding valence electrons and 12 bonding electrons (the total of 18 gives the inert gas structure, d^5sp^3).

[b] L = triphenyl phosphine, $:P(C_6H_5)_3$.

[c] Intermediate in S_N1 substitution reactions of $Co(CN)_5OH_2^{2-}$ (see p. 632).

(37.5) illustrates some reactions of platinum(0); note that the *CN* changes from 3 to 4, and the number of nonbonded electrons from 10 to 8:

Oxidation states: 0 0 0 0 +2 −1

$$L_3Pt + XY \longrightarrow L + L_2Pt\begin{matrix} \diagup X \\ \diagdown Y \end{matrix} \qquad (37.5)$$

where X = Y = I; X = RCO, Y = Cl; and X = C_6H_{11}, Y = Cl are typical examples. Further changes toward the more common states, *CN* = 6 (nonbonded electrons = 6), could be expected.

Exercise 37.7

Suggest a possible synthetic product obtainable from $Fe(CO)_5$. *Answer:* From Exercise 37.1 we remember that $Fe(CO)_5$ has the Kr d^5sp^3 structure, but only five pairs of electrons are required to bond the CO groups. Thus, there are further electrons to act as Lewis bases and a sixth coordination position is open. Bubbling $Fe(CO)_5$ into an acid solution should give $Fe(CO)_5H^+$. Or, $[:C{\equiv}N:]^-$ ions are isoelectronic with $:C{\equiv}O:$. Bubbling $Fe(CO)_5$ into a solution of CN^- (say KCN in liquid NH_3 to avoid H_2O and its strong acid-base and redox interactions with iron) might give $Fe(CO_4)CN^-$, $Fe(CO)_3(CN)_2^=$, and so on. [$Fe(CN)_6^{\equiv}$ should form if an oxidizing agent is present.] Apparently the cyanide reaction has not been attempted yet.

Exercise 37.8

What atoms are most apt to exhibit octahedral complexes? *Answer:* Octahedral complexes require *CN* = 6, and, if covalent, 6 bonding orbitals. Thus the central atom must not be small and must have at least 6 orbitals available for bonding. First-row elements are out, both because of their small size and because they have only sp^3 orbitals. Alkali and alkaline earth metals are unlikely becuse their *d* orbitals again are at rather high energies. Transition metals and the nonmetals of the third to seventh rows of the periodic table seem likely candidates. The most common orbital pattern is probably d^2sp^3. Acceptance of up to 12 electrons is more likely for positively charged atoms than for neutral ones, so that the octahedral complexes are likely to be between central atoms (or, more likely, between positive ions) acting as acids and accepting shares of electron pairs from 6 surrounding bases. The most stable complexes will therefore probably contain a central element with a high positive (hence highly acidic) oxidation state,

REACTION TYPES

Synthetic problems and their solutions are often best understood in terms of reaction types. Table 37.5 gives one type of classification in which A and B can be monatomic or polyatomic, electrically neutral or charged.

It is probable that most if not all actual chemical reactions, or mechanistic steps (as opposed to net reactions), can be considered within the 8-reaction framework of Table 37.5. All those in Table 37.4 can, for example.

Since stable free radicals are rare (O_2 and NO are the most common ones), we shall not discuss, except briefly, syntheses that depend on the generation of free radicals. Most of the problems were dealt with in Chapters 22 and 23.

Table 37.5 Some types of reaction.

	Type	Applicable theory
Addition and decomposition:	A + B = A B	
1,2.	$:\ddot{A} + :\ddot{B}: \underset{2}{\overset{1}{\rightleftharpoons}} :\ddot{A}-\ddot{B}:$	Lewis acid-base
3,4.	$A\cdot + \cdot B \underset{4}{\overset{3}{\rightleftharpoons}} A-B$	free radical
(Decompositions 2 and 4 are the reverse of additions 1 and 3)		
Substitution:	A + B C = A B + C	
5.	$:\ddot{A} + :\ddot{B}-\ddot{C}: \rightleftharpoons :\ddot{A}-\ddot{B}: + \ddot{C}:$	Lewis acid-base
6.	$A\cdot + B-C \rightleftharpoons A-B + C\cdot$	free radical
7.	$A-B + C-D \rightleftharpoons A-C + B-D$	general acid-base
Electron transfer:		
8.	$A + B \rightleftharpoons A^{+n} + B^{-n}$	redox

A common question, after it is decided to synthesize a desired compound and some possible starting materials have been chosen, is whether acid-base theory (Chapters 12 and 18) or redox theory (Chapter 20), or both, should be used in designing the synthetic steps. In the sulfuric acid and nitric acid syntheses both acid base and redox reactions were used, but, since good numerical data were available, little recourse was had to either theoretical treatment. In most of the examples that follow, however, numerical data will be minimal and theoretical treatments will be required. We shall discuss some electron-transfer processes first.

Exercise 37.9

Which of the following syntheses require redox and which do not: (*a*) $H_2S \longrightarrow S$, (*b*) $SO_2 \longrightarrow Na_2SO_3$, (*c*) $Na_2SO_3 \longrightarrow Na_2SO_4$, (*d*) $Na_2SO_4 \longrightarrow Na_2S_2O_3 \cdot 5H_2O$, (*e*) $Ba(OH)_2 \longrightarrow BaH_2$, (*f*) $C_2H_5OH \longrightarrow CH_3CHO$, (*g*) $O_2 \longrightarrow O_3$, (*h*) $CO_2, H_2O \longrightarrow C_{12}H_{22}O_{11}$? *Answer:* Reduction. (*d*) $+6 \longrightarrow +2$ S, (*e*) $+1 \longrightarrow -1$ H, (*h*) $+4 \longrightarrow 0$ C. Oxidation. (*a*) $-2 \longrightarrow 0$ S, (*c*) $+4 \longrightarrow +6$ S, (*f*) $-2 \longrightarrow -1$ C. Neither. (*b*) $+4 \longrightarrow +4$ S, (*g*) $0 \longrightarrow 0$ O.

SYNTHESIS OF RADIOACTIVE SPECIES

Radioactive tracer techniques are so powerful and widely used that the preparation of well-characterized radioactive species is a common problem. Normal technique is to bombard a known sample and then to extract the radioactive element in the form of the desired species. But exchange reactions are also used.

Suppose it is desired to make radioactive manganate ions, $Mn^*O_4^=$ (the asterisk indicates a radioactive atom). $MnO_4^=$ ions [containing Mn(VI)] are usually made by reducing MnO_4^- [containing Mn(VII)] in a highly basic solution, a process requiring considerable time, effort, and care in handling the solutions, difficulties that would be enhanced if the solution contained radioactive material. The MnO_4^-

is readily prepared by oxidizing Mn or almost any of its compounds, and once prepared, the manganate is reasonably stable.

An easy alternative approach is suggested by the fact that MnO_4^- and $MnO_4^=$ differ by one electron, and consequently might conceivably exchange an electron if they collided in such a way that the orbitals matched. The chance of a match is good, since their symmetries (tetrahedral) are identical and their bond distances very similar. The chance of a collision is good because of the relatively low charge densities.

Mixing a solution of nonradioactive $MnO_4^=$ with radioactive $Mn^*O_4^-$ does result in rapid electron exchange, and the desired species, $Mn^*O_4^=$, is thus readily prepared. The intermediate is called an "outer-sphere activated complex," since the two manganese atoms do not share any ligands during the collision.

In the same way $Fe(CN)_6^{-4}$ and $Fe(CN)_6^{-3}$, as well as $W(CN)_8^{-4}$ and $W(CN)_8^{-3}$, exchange electrons rapidly. The electron interchange between $Co(NH_3)_6^{2+}$ and $CO(NH_3)_6^{3+}$ is slow. The symmetries are identical but the bond distances [shorter in the Co(III) complex] are too different. This is a limitation to electron transfer similar to the Franck-Condon principle for photons discussed in Figure 23.5.

Exercise 37.10

A 10-ml solution of 0.1 M MnO_4^- containing 10^6 counts per second of radioactive Mn is mixed with 10 ml of 0.01 M solution of nonradioactive $MnO_4^=$. Calculate the equilibrium distribution of radioactive manganese between the two oxidation states. *Answer:* Equilibrium will occur rapidly through outer-sphere activated complexes and the radioactive Mn will become distributed in exactly the same ratio as the nonradioactive form. Since the ratio of MnO_4^- to $MnO_4^=$ will remain 10 to 1 (0.05 M to 0.005 M), the radioactive distribution will also be 10 MnO_4^- to 1 $MnO_4^=$ at equilibrium.

GENERAL REDOX SYNTHESES

Whenever there is a change in oxidation state between the starting material and the desired product, redox is indicated. Redox may also be involved in intermediate steps even if not in the over-all conversion. The properties sought in the added reagent are: (1) a value of $\mathcal{E}$ sufficient to accomplish the redox with a minimum amount of side reactions, (2) smooth reaction under the conditions, especially of state, temperature, and acidity, and (3) minimum contamination of the product.

Elementary redox agents are often used because they introduce only one kind of atom. Thus

$$Fe_{(c)} + 2Fe^{+++}{}_{(aq)} = 3Fe^{++}{}_{(aq)} \qquad \text{(so no contamination)}$$

or

$$FeCl_{2(c)} + \tfrac{1}{2}Cl_{2(g)} = FeCl_{3(c)} \qquad \text{(again no contamination)}$$

Electrode reactions are even better in many instances (see Chapter 36), since no chemicals at all are added to the system:

$$Fe^{++}{}_{(aq)} + 2e^- = Fe_{(c)}$$

or

$$2Cr^{+++}{}_{(aq)} + 7H_2O = Cr_2O_7{}^{=}{}_{(aq)} + 14H^+{}_{(aq)} + 6e^-$$

Table 20.2 provides a list of $\mathcal{E}^0$ values from which suitable redox agents may be selected, and from which their $\mathcal{E}$ values may be calculated as a function of pH for any given synthesis involving redox. More extensive tables are, of course, available in standard references. We shall return to these problems in the discussion of pH-$\mathcal{E}^0$ diagrams in Chapter 38.

Exercise 37.11

Suggest a method of synthesizing a sample of highly radioactive aqueous $Fe(CN)_6{}^{-4}$, starting from irradiated $Fe_{(c)}$. *Answer:* Work in shielded surroundings, by remote control if possible. It is necessary to oxidize the Fe from 0 to +2 and to complex it with 6 CN^-, ending with an aqueous solution. Since O_2 is an easily handled oxidizing agent and CN^- is a powerful complexing agent, try dissolving the radioactive metal in molten KCN (slightly more than the stoichiometric amount) in the presence of a slight excess of O_2 bubbled into the melt. Dissolve the product, which should be $K_4Fe(CN)_6$, in water. First try the method using nonradioactive iron to determine feasible conditions of temperature, time, amounts, and concentrations. Some $Fe(CN)_6{}^{=}$ will almost certainly form. Reduce it to $Fe(CN)_6{}^{4-}$ ($\mathcal{E}^0 = -0.69$ volts) with a mild, noncontaminating, easily removed reducing agent. Would H_2O_2 work? Acid or basic solution?

Exercise 37.12

Suggest syntheses for the following: (*a*) Cl_2 from NaCl, (*b*) $BaCrO_4$ from Cr_2O_3, (*c*) H_2S from FeS. *Answer:* (*a*) Cl must be oxidized from −1 to 0. $\mathcal{E}^0 = 1.3583$ is so high that electrolysis is used on molten NaCl, $Na^+{}_{(l)} + Cl^-{}_{(l)} = Na_{(l)} + \frac{1}{2}Cl_{2(g)}$. (*b*) Cr must be oxidized from +3 to +6. Dissolve Cr_2O_3 in base, $Cr_2O_{3(c)} + 7H_2O + 2\ OH^-{}_{(aq)} = 2Cr(OH)_4(H_2O)_2{}^-{}_{(aq)}$, add H_2O_2 to get oxidation, $2OH^- + 2Cr(H_2O)_2(OH)_4{}^- + 3H_2O_2 = 2CrO_4{}^{=}{}_{(aq)} + 12H_2O$. Add aqueous $BaCl_2$, $Ba^{++}{}_{(aq)} + CrO_4{}^{=}{}_{(aq)} = BaCrO_{4(c)}$. Filter and dry. (*c*) No redox required. S remains −2, so add a strong acid, H^+, to compete with the weaker acid, Fe^{++}, for the strong base, $S^=$. Add aqueous HCl, $FeS_{(c)} + 2H^+{}_{(aq)} = Fe^{++}{}_{(aq)} + H_2S_{(g)}$.

SUBSTITUTION (ACID-BASE) REACTIONS

In the absence of redox, most reactions may be predicted in terms of acid-base theory. In any competitive system the strongest acid will tend to combine with the strongest base, and so on until the weakest acid is left coupled with the weakest base. Thus, mixing aqueous sodium hydroxide (Na^+ and OH^-) and aqueous HCl (H^+ and Cl^-) gives primarily H_2O and aqueous NaCl ($Na^+ + Cl^-$). Evaporation of the aqueous NaCl gives H_2O and crystalline NaCl:

$$Na^+{}_{(aq)} + OH^-{}_{(aq)} + H^+{}_{(aq)} + Cl^-{}_{(aq)} = H_2O_{(g)} + NaCl_{(c)}$$

The strongest base in this system is OH^-, the strongest acid is H^+, the weakest acid is Na^+, and the weakest base is Cl^-. Likewise, benzoic acid forms when aqueous sodium benzoate is mixed with aqueous HCl, since the benzoate is a stronger base than Cl^-.

Similarly, mixing aqueous silver nitrate and sodium chloride gives

$$Ag^+_{(aq)} + NO_3{}^-_{(aq)} + Na^+_{(aq)} + Cl^-_{(aq)} = AgCl_{(c)} + Na^+_{(aq)} + NO_3{}^-_{(aq)}$$

indicating either that $NO_3{}^-_{(aq)}$ is a weaker base than $Cl^-_{(aq)}$ or that $Ag^+_{(aq)}$ is a stronger acid than $Na^+_{(aq)}$: both statements are consistent with other evidence for these ions. Similarly, it is easier to decompose $CaCO_3$ than Na_2CO_3 by heating because Na_2O is a stronger base than CaO.

Here we use Lewis acid-base theory, according to which bases have an unshared pair of electrons and, preferably, high negative charge density, (compare OH^-, Cl^-, and $NO_3{}^-$, and acids have an empty orbital and, preferably, high positive charge density (compare H^+, Ag^+, and Na^+).

Table 18.13 lists some common anions in order of increasing base strength in their competition for protons, $H^+_{(aq)}$.

Exercise 37.13

Suggest syntheses for (*a*) $CsClO_4$ from Cs_2CO_3, (*b*) YPO_4 from YCl_3, (*c*) C_6H_5Cl from C_6H_6. *Answer:* (*a*) $CsCO_{3(c)} + 2H^+_{(aq)} + 2ClO_4{}^-_{(aq)} = 2CsClO_{4(c)} + H_2O_{(g)} + CO_{2(g)}$. Boil off H_2O, leaving pure crystalline $CsClO_4$. (*b*) $YCl_{3(c)} + H_3PO_{4(l)} = YPO_{4(c)} + 3HCl_{(g)}$. Drive off volatile HCl by heating, leaving pure $YPO_{4(c)}$. (*c*) $C_6H_{6(g)} + Cl_{2(g)} = C_6H_5Cl_{(g)} + HCl_{(g)}$. Gas-phase chlorination in presence of excess C_6H_6 (to minimize multiple substitution). *a* and *b* are simple acid-base reactions, *c* is combined redox and free radical (Cl · intermediate).

KINETIC LABILITY AND ACID-BASE REACTIONS

Now consider some effects of rate and mechanism. Most metal ions, even when complexed, react extremely rapidly with Lewis bases; a few complexed metal ions react slowly. Metal complexes are designated as kinetically labile if they react completely at room temperature within the time required to mix 0.1 *M* solutions, and as kinetically inert if their reaction at room temperature is slow enough to be measured by conventional techniques. It is important not to confuse kinetic stability—described by the terms inert and labile—with thermodynamic stability. The inert ion $Co(NH_3)_6{}^{3+}$, which is thermodynamically unstable in acid solution, will not react appreciably with a solvent for several days. The labile ion $Ni(CN)_4{}^{2-}$, which is thermodynamically very stable, exchanges its cyanide ions (as measured with isotopically labeled cyanide ions) at a rate too fast to be measured by ordinary methods.

Representative of the kinetically inert octahedral complexes are $Cr(OH_2)_6{}^{3+}$, $Mn(CN)_6{}^{3-}$, $Fe(CN)_6{}^{3-}$, and $Co(NH_3)_6{}^{3+}$. According to the valence bond model, the hybridization of the metal is d^2sp^3, and inertness of these complexes is attributed to the lack of empty 3*d* orbitals. There are no empty *d* orbitals to which an attacking basic ligand can be attached, thus making an S_N2 reaction unlikely, and there are six strong bonds, making an ionization mechanism, S_N1, unlikely. These reaction types, S_N1 and S_N2, were initially discussed in Chapter 24.

The S_N2 reactions become more common as empty electronic energy levels are more closely spaced. Carbon tetrachloride is quite stable to water, and drastic conditions are required for substitution of the chlorine on the carbon. However, silicon tetrachloride, which has the same tetrahedral structure as carbon tetrachloride, reacts violently with water to give silicic acid, $Si(OH)_4$ (see p. 641). The availability of obitals of low energy for forming a fifth bond on silicon may account for the difference in reactivities. The next higher orbital on carbon, 3*s*, is of too high energy. The reaction with $SiCl_4$ thus proceeds by successive steps in each of which water is added and hydrogen chloride is eliminated:

$$H_2O + SiCl_4 \longrightarrow \begin{matrix} H \\ & \diagdown \\ & & O{-}SiCl_4 \\ & \diagup \\ H \end{matrix} \longrightarrow HO{-}SiCl_3 + HCl$$

Sometimes substitution involves an initial elimination reaction, an ionization mechanism S_N1 (see p. 632). Thus rates of substitution on the central element decrease in the order $AlF_6^{3-} > SiF_6^{2-} > PF_6^{-} > SF_6$. This trend, which accompanies increasing nuclear charge and decreasing size of the central element (increasing positive charge density), is related to increasing strength of the bonds between the central element and the fluorine in the series. A mechanism for substitution of fluorine that is consistent with the above observation is the initial elimination of a fluoride ion, S_N1, followed by addition of an incoming group.

The examples above illustrate two types of mechanisms for substitution reactions. If addition of a base (entering group) to a central element precedes elimination of another base (leaving group), the process is called a displacement or associative mechanism and is often designated S_N2. If elimination of a leaving group precedes addition of an incoming base, the process is called a dissociative mechanism and is designated S_N1. The symbolic representation of these two extreme mechanisms include X, the leaving group; Y, the incoming group; M, the metal ion; and A, the nonparticipating groups that complete the coordination sphere.

Associative mechanism (S_N2):

$$A_5MX + Y \xrightarrow[\text{slow}]{1} A_5M\begin{matrix} \diagup X \\ \diagdown Y \end{matrix}$$

$$A_5M\begin{matrix} \diagup X \\ \diagdown Y \end{matrix} \xrightarrow[\text{fast}]{2} A_5MY + X$$

$$\text{Rate} = k_1(A_5MX)(Y), \text{ second order}$$

Dissociative mechanism (S_N1):

$$A_5MX \xrightarrow[\text{slow}]{1} A_5M + X$$

$$A_5M + Y \xrightarrow[\text{fast}]{2} A_5MY$$

$$\text{Rate} = k_1(A_5MX), \text{ first order}$$

It might appear that the mechanism of a substitution reaction could be readily established by experimental measurement of the rate law. In practice, as we shall see, the difficulty of assessing the role of the solvent and the participation of ion aggregates often make the task so formidable that current interpretations of kinetic data of substitution on metal ions are frequently controversial. Again we see a close parallel between the discussion of reactions of carbon compounds in Chapter 24 and the compounds discussed here.

STEREOCHEMICAL CONSEQUENCES

From rates and mechanisms it is a simple step to move to consideration of the detailed stereochemistry of the reactions. We shall use $Co(en)_2ACl^{n+}$ as our model compound where the cobalt is +3. [The symbol "en" stands for ethylenediamine ($H_2\ddot{N}C_2H_4\ddot{N}H_2$), represented as N∿N below.] The ligand A could, for example, be such a substituent as OH^-, NO_2^-, N_3^-, CN^-, Br^-, Cl^-, NH_3, or NCS^-. Our model reaction is the aquation of the model *cis* or *trans* compound:

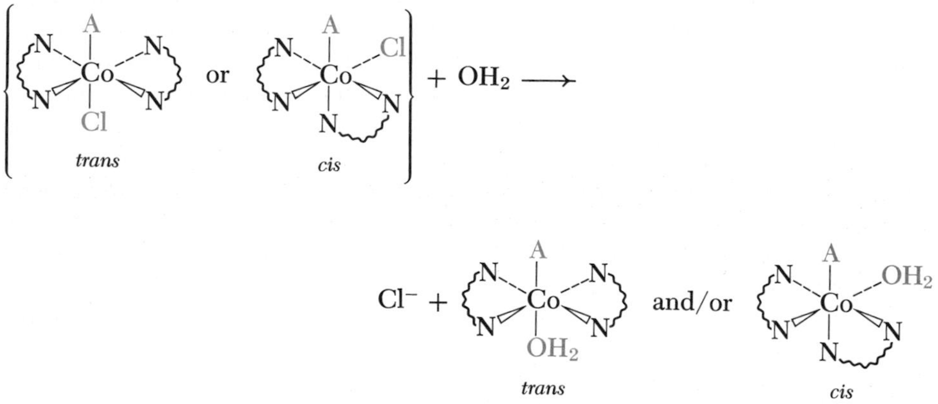

If release of chloride ion occurs by a dissociative (S_N1) mechanism, the five-coordinate intermediate might assume a square pyramidal geometry with A on the apex or on the base, or a trigonal bipyramidal geometry with A on an equatorial position, as indicated in Figure 37.3. We shall assume that the intermediate, with a geometry in which A is on an axial position of a trigonal bipyramid,

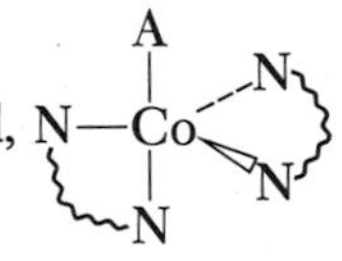

is of negligible importance, since ethylenediamine would then have to bond at positions separated by 120° instead of the usual 90°. It is unlikely that the N∿N bridge could "stretch" that far.

Experiments show that the aquation of *cis* complexes, as indicated in column 5 of Table 37.6, leads to products in which *cis* geometry is completely retained, providing good evidence in support of the square pyramidal intermediate. Retention of configuration in aquation of the *trans*-NO_2^- and *trans*-NH_3 complexes also provides support for the square pyramidal intermediate. The formation of *cis* products from the other *trans* reactants must result from attack of water on the 1,2 or 1,3 equatorial edges of a bipyramidal intermediate. Attack by water on the 2,3 edge would give a *trans* product; on the 1,2 edge, a *cis* product.

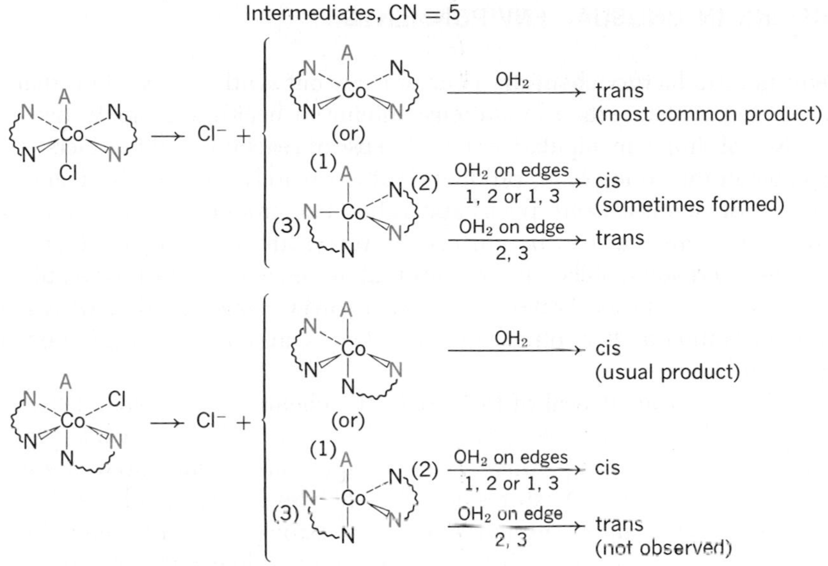

Figure 37.3 Stereochemistry associated with S_N1 mechanisms in octahedral substitutions.

Exercise 37.14

Small, equimolar amounts of *trans*-$Co(en)_2ClNO_2^+$ and $Co(en)_2ClN_3^+$ were simultaneously placed in an aqueous system. What products would you expect and in what relative amounts? *Answer:* The $Co(en)_2ClNO_2^+$ forms 100% *trans*-$Co(en)_2ClH_2O^{++}$. The $Co(en)_2ClN_3^+$ forms 80% *trans*-$Co(en)_2ClH_2O^{++}$ and 20% *cis*-$Co(en)_2ClH_2O^{++}$. Thus the final ratio (assuming complete reaction) is 9 *trans* to 1 *cis*-$Co(en)_2ClH_2O^{++}$. Note that the early ratios will be higher in *trans*, since the NO_2 compound has a rate almost five times as great as the N_3 compound. Thus the first product will be almost pure *trans*.

Table 37.6 Rates of aquation, and retention of configuration for *cis* and *trans*-$Co(en)_2ClA^{n+}$.

	Trans A		*Cis* A	
	k	% *trans* in product	*k*	% *trans* in product
OH^-	9600	25	72,000	0
NO_2^-	6000	100	720	0
N_3^-	1320	80	1440	0
CN^-	492			
Br^-	270		840	0
Cl^-	209	65	1464	0
NH_3	194(63°)	100	8.5(35°)	0
NCS^-	0.30	40	68.4	0
H_2O			90	0

REACTIONS IN UNUSUAL ENVIRONMENTS

Students in introductory chemistry courses carry out synthetic reactions that have been selected under certain limitations: minimum health and safety hazards, a prerequisite of simple manipulative skills, the use of reactants and products that are fairly stable in the atmosphere, products that are readily characterized, and economy of cost of chemicals and special apparatus. The products obtained are preferably either crystals that can be purified by recrystallization, liquids that can be purified by fractional distillation, or gases that are essentially pure when liberated from a condensed phase. Water is the usual solvent, but you should remember that there are thousands of other possible solvents, and an almost infinite variety of other conditions.

There is a great deal of interest in the chemistry of molten salts, which can, for example, serve as media for fuel cells. Molten salts as solvents provide a vast range of operating temperatures, from temperatures slightly above room temperature to about 1500°C. Mixtures of molten halides are frequently used because of their high thermal stabilities and inertness to strong reducing agents. Furthermore, ionic solutes form essentially ideal solutions over a long range of compositions in molten salts. (Do you see why? Consider the forces acting in pure salts and in solution.) Two examples from among the many reactions that proceed only in molten salts are briefly described.

Silica (SiO_2) is unreactive to hydrogen below 1000°C. In a sodium chloride/aluminum chloride melt containing aluminum, conversion of up to 76% silica to silane (SiH_4) can be accomplished at 200°C under a pressure of 200 atm of hydrogen. Introduction of a mixture of silicon tetrachloride and methyl chloride into a sodium chloride/aluminum chloride melt containing aluminum leads to quantitative formation of tetramethylsilane, TMS (used in NMR spectroscopy):

$$3SiCl_4 + 12CH_3Cl + 8Al \xrightarrow[200^\circ C]{AlCl_3/NaCl} \underset{\text{TMS}}{3(CH_3)_4Si} + 8AlCl_3$$

Other compounds that can be made by this procedure include $(CH_3)_4Sn$, $(CH_3)_3B$, $(CH_3)_3Sb$, and $(CH_3)_2Hg$. The primary advantage of the molten salt as the solvent for this reaction is that the reactivity of the aluminum cannot be reduced by the formation of an insoluble coating, as it would be in aqueous solution (see p. 418). Other metals can be used in place of aluminum. The reaction is an economical method of preparing compounds with carbon-metal bonds, since aluminum or other metals used can be recovered by electrolysis of the melt.

Exercise 37.15

Mention some large-scale commercial syntheses which are carried out in nonaqueous liquid media. *Answer:* Most of the really large-scale industrial syntheses are nonaqueous: Fe, Al, Cu, Na, Cl_2, all involve nonaqueous melts, most hydrocarbon syntheses are gaseous, and many polymers are formed in nonaqueous liquids.

SUMMARY

Not only must all known materials not found in nature be synthesized; it is often cheaper to find a synthetic preparation than it is to reclaim the substance from its natural state. Thus considerable research effort is expended to discover more efficient and economic routes for synthesis of well-known materials. Chemicals available in nature only in small amounts and new compounds not occurring in nature will challenge synthetic chemists for generations to come.

Thermodynamic and kinetic factors, often illumined by structural considerations, generally dictate the best reaction route, reagents, and conditions for preparation of a compound. The costs of raw materials and processing play a dominant role in determining which synthetic reactions are chosen in a commercial plant. Convenience and speed of synthesis, plus purity of product, predominate in the choice of synthetic routes in the research laboratory.

Synthesis of a compound by a series of well-understood, carefully documented steps is usually considered the final proof of its structure, and it is one of the more definitive methods of checking theoretical ideas concerning the thermodynamic, kinetic, and structural changes involved.

Ultimately all synthetic processes must start with substances in their natural state; air, water, petroleum products, NaCl, S, and metallic ores are most commonly used. These raw materials are then combined with appropriate addition or removal of energy to produce the wealth of materials with which man surrounds himself, as well as the even greater variety actively being explored in research laboratories.

The emphasis in our treatment has been on simple, well-defined, reasonably well-understood systems. It is here we are most likely to find the basic guidelines that will lead to the production of new synthetic methods, new synthetic products, and, perhaps most importantly, the synthesis of new ideas.

The number and variety of chemicals that affect man has increased at an alarming rate and created a public health problem of major proportions. We are confronted with a profusion of chemicals in the form of industrial and municipal wastes, air and water pollutants, herbicides, pesticides, cosmetics, food additives, as well as drugs administered over extended periods of time, and yet we do not know what these substances do to biological systems. In effect, we are thrust into global experiments for which we are not prepared.— B. Brodie, G. Cosmides, and D. Rall, Science, **148,** 1547 (1965).

PROBLEMS

37.1. Disilane, Si_2H_6, may be prepared by passing silane, SiH_4, through an electrical discharge. Disilane decomposes in the discharge zone. Disilane and silane react explosively with air. Design and briefly describe a system that may be used to prepare the maximum yield of disilane from a given amount of silane. Discuss all the usual variables.

37.2. Interpret the observation that anhydrous chromium(III) chloride dissolves slowly in ordinary water, but dissolves rapidly in water containing a catalytic amount of chomium(II). Why is the thermodynamically stable product, $Cr(OH_2)_6{}^{3+}$, not formed as a primary product in the catalyzed dissolution of chromium(III) chloride?

37.3. Substitution reactions on platinum(II), such as

$$Pt(NH_3)_4{}^{2+} + Cl^- = Pt(NH_3)_3Cl^+ + NH_3$$

have rate laws of the type

$$\text{Rate} = -d[Pt(NH_3)_4{}^{+2}]/dt = (k_1 + k_2[Cl^-])[Pt(NH_3)_4{}^{+2}]$$

Devise an experimental scheme for determining k_1 and k_2. Indicate what kind of experimental datá is to be obtained and how these data should be treated.

37.4. Succinonitrile, NC—C_2H_4—CN, reacts with manganese pentacarbonyl chloride to yield the molecular compound $Mn(CO)_3Cl(NC—C_2H_4—CN)$. Suggest a structure for this compound.

37.5. (*a*) Interpret the fact that reactions involving transfer of two electrons simultaneously by an "outer-sphere activated complex" mechanism are extremely slow. (*b*) Suggest a mechanism for the reduction of ClO_3^- to ClO^- by SO_2.

37.6. Which of the following compounds would be most stable thermally and, presumably, easiest to synthesize: $HRe(CO)_5$, $Re(CO)_6$?

37.7. How do you account for the occurrences of diamonds in volcanic residues? Why are they not found in all such residues? Why are diamonds found in the Great Lakes region of the United States, where there are no suitable volcanic residues?

37.8. Insoluble sulfates, such as $BaSO_4$, are often converted to soluble salts by fusing with sodium carbonate, extracting the cooled product first with water, then with aqueous hydrochloric acid. Write net equations for each step and interpret each reaction in terms of acid-base theory.

II

37.9. Irrespective of the nature of the ligand, stability constants of complexes of divalent ions of the first-row transition elements increase in the order Mn, Fe, Co, Ni, Cu. Suggest an explanation for this observation.

37.10. The temperatures necessary for rapid direct reactions of group IV and V elements with methyl chloride (CH_3Cl) in the presence of a copper catalyst are given below, along with some properties of the bonds formed and heats of sublimation of the elements. Discuss how the temperatures required for rapid reaction are related to these properties.

Products	Reaction temperature	M—Cl bond energy	M—C bond energy	Heats of sublimation of central element
$(CH_3)_2SiCl_2$	300°C	91 kcal	72 kcal	105 kcal
$(CH_3)_2GeCl_2$	320	81	51	89
$(CH_3)_2SnCl_2$	315	76	54	72
$(CH_3)_2AsCl$, $(CH_3)AsCl_2$	350	70	55	60
$(CH_3)_2SbCl$, $(CH_3)SbCl_2$	372	74	51	61

37.11. Suggest a possible synthesis for each of the following. Write equations for each step with likely conditions of T and P. Water and air are possible further raw materials in each case.

(*a*) Boric acid, H_3BO_3 (an eyewash), from borax, $Na_2B_4O_7 \cdot 10H_2O$, a boron ore.
(*b*) $Na_2CO_3 \cdot 10H_2O$, washing soda, from $NaHCO_3$, baking soda.
(*c*) $Na_2S_2O_3 \cdot 5H_2O$, photographer's hypo, from NaOH and sulfur.
(*d*) CH_3COOH, acetic acid (vinegar) from C_2H_5OH, ethanol.
(*e*) $NaNH_2$, sodamide, from sodium and ammonia.
(*f*) Anhydrous BaI_2 from $BaI_2 \cdot nH_2O$ plus any other reactants you need.
(*g*) Cs_3PO_4 from CsCl plus any other reactants you need.
(*h*) *Trans*-$Co(en)_2ClH_2O^{++}$ from any reactants you need.
(*i*) $Fe(CO)_5$ from any reactants you need.
(*j*) Very pure iron, using $Fe(CO)_5$ as an intermediate.

See page 1094 for a list of references and readings in the recent chemical literature related to the material in this chapter.

CHAPTER 38

Chemistry and the Periodic Table

The most important single device for correlating chemical information is the periodic table.

We have continually emphasized the correlations between properties of the elements and their compounds that are inherent in the arrangement of the periodic table. The family relationships of elements in the same column of the table served as the basis for our discussions of the noble gases, the halogens, the chalcogens, the nitrogen family, and for carbon and silicon. Row relationships were emphasized in the discussions of electronic structure, relative electronegativity, and chemical bonding, and numerous graphical presentations have been used to show variations in some property as a function of atomic number. Ionization energy, covalent, ionic and van der Waals radii, and thermodynamic properties such as entropy and heats of formation and reaction are but a few of the properties discussed as a function of Z.

In this chapter we shall concentrate on additional chemical reactions of the elements and their compounds and explore the usefulness of the periodic table in correlating them. Figure 38.1 indicates by shading the elements we have discussed so far and thus defines our remaining task as confined primarily to the metallic elements.

ELECTRON STRUCTURES

One of the most fundamental and regular variations with Z occurs in the electronic structures of the monatomic gaseous elements (see Chapters 3 and 4). Elements which are filling *s* and *p* levels are often called representative elements. Those

The Periodic System of the Elements

Reactive metals: s orbitals (IA–IIA) · Transition metals: d orbitals (IIIB–IIB) · Mostly nonmetals: p orbitals (except H, He) (IIIA–0)

Periods	IA	IIA	IIIB	IVB	VB	VIB	VIIB	VIII	VIII	VIII	IB	IIB	IIIA	IVA	VA	VIA	VIIA	0
1	1 H 1.008																1 H 1.008	2 He 4.003
2	3 Li 6.939	4 Be 9.012											5 B 10.81	6 C 12.01	7 N 14.01	8 O 16.00	9 F 18.99	10 Ne 20.18
3	11 Na 22.99	12 Mg 24.31											13 Al 26.98	14 Si 28.09	15 P 30.97	16 S 32.06	17 Cl 35.45	18 Ar 39.95
4	19 K 39.10	20 Ca 40.08	21 Sc 44.96	22 Ti 47.90	23 V 50.94	24 Cr 52.00	25 Mn 54.94	26 Fe 55.85	27 Co 58.93	28 Ni 58.71	29 Cu 63.55	30 Zn 65.37	31 Ga 69.72	32 Ge 72.59	33 As 74.92	34 Se 78.96	35 Br 79.90	36 Kr 83.80
5	37 Rb 85.47	38 Sr 87.62	39 Y 88.91	40 Zr 91.22	41 Nb 92.91	42 Mo 95.94	43 Tc (99)	44 Ru 101.1	45 Rh 102.9	46 Pd 106.4	47 Ag 107.9	48 Cd 112.4	49 In 114.8	50 Sn 118.7	51 Sb 121.8	52 Te 127.6	53 I 126.9	54 Xe 131.3
6	55 Cs 132.9	56 Ba 137.3	57 La 138.9	72 Hf 178.5	73 Ta 180.9	74 W 183.9	75 Re 186.2	76 Os 190.2	77 Ir 192.2	78 Pt 195.1	79 Au 197.0	80 Hg 200.6	81 Tl 204.4	82 Pb 207.2	83 Bi 209.0	84 Po (210)	85 At (210)	86 Rn (222)
7	87 Fr (223)	88 Ra (226)	89 Ac (227)	104 Kh (260)														

Inner transition metals (f orbitals)

Lanthanum series	58 Ce 140.1	59 Pr 140.9	60 Nd 144.2	61 Pm (145)	62 Sm 150.4	63 Eu 152.0	64 Gd 157.3	65 Tb 158.9	66 Dy 162.5	67 Ho 164.9	68 Er 167.3	69 Tm 168.9	70 Yb 173.0	71 Lu 175.0
Actinium series	90 Th 232.0	91 Pa (231)	92 U 238.0	93 Np (237)	94 Pu (242)	95 Am (243)	96 Cm (247)	97 Bk (247)	98 Cf (249)	99 Es (254)	100 Fm (253)	101 Md (256)	102 No (256)	103 Lw (257)

Mass numbers of the most stable or most abundant isotopes are shown in parentheses

Atomic weights are given to four significant figures. See also page 8.

Figure 38.1 A form of the periodic table.

filling *d* levels are called transition elements, and those filling *f* levels, lanthanide (4*f*) and actinide (5*f*) elements. Trends in the representative elements tend to be simpler than those in the *d* and *f* elements, but each group shows a great many regularities. These regularities in electronic structures are reflected in similarly regular variations in the ionization energies of the gaseous atoms and their electron affinities, as indicated in Figure 38.2 and Table 38.1. Because only a few values of electron affinities are known, the table is fragmentary, but the listing of ionization energies is almost complete.

Ionization energies increase, in general, as one traverses any row in the periodic table from left to right (increasing Z) but decrease with Z in every column. Both of these general effects would be expected in terms of two variables: (1) as electrons enter any series of closely spaced quantum states one after another with each increase in Z, the effective nuclear charge increases and the ionization energy increases (this accounts for the general increases in I.E. in the rows); (2) as higher quantum levels must be entered, the electrons in them tend to be better shielded from the nucleus and the I.E. tends to drop (this accounts for the general decrease in the columns). A third effect—the mutual repulsion between two electrons of opposite spin in the same quantum level—accounts for most of the smaller minima in the curve of I.E. versus Z.

Electron affinities are affected by the same factors and will be large if the added electron is strongly attracted to the nucleus and small if the nucleus becomes better shielded as the interelectron repulsions increase. The maximum in electron affinity at Cl in the halogens may be interpreted in the same fashion as the higher

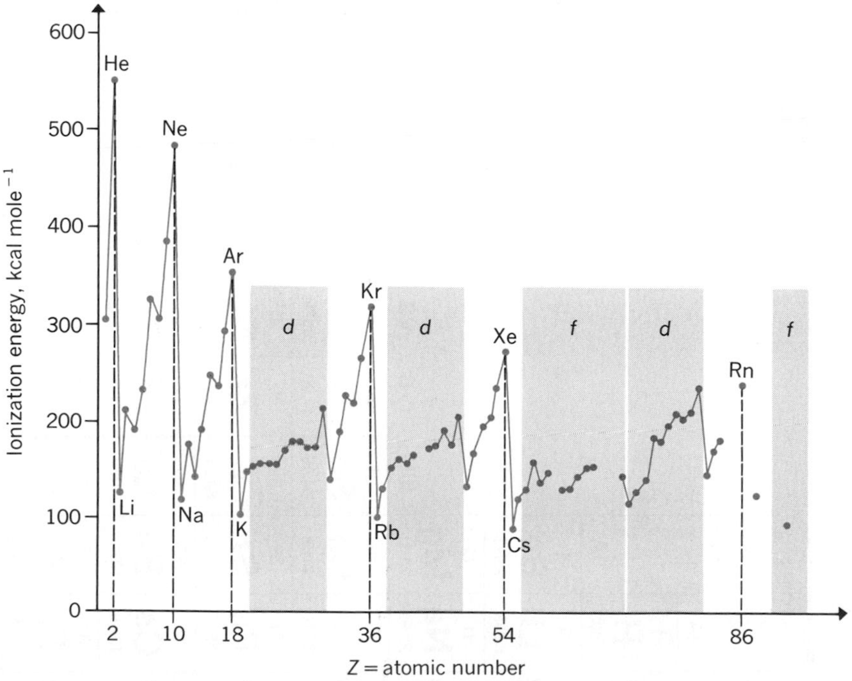

Figure 38.2 First ionization energies of the monatomic gaseous elements. Note the general trends in rows and families of the periodic table and the positions of the maxima and minima. The *d* and *f* regions are shaded.

Table 38.1 **Electron affinities of some representative monatomic gaseous elements. [$-\Delta H$ for ($M_{(g)} + e^-_{(g)} = M^-_{(g)}$) in kcal mole^{-1}.]**

H 17.23							H 17.23
Li 14	Be −14	B 7	C 29	N ~0	O 33.8		F 82.1
Na 19	Mg −7	Al 12	Si 32	P 17	S 47.7		Cl 86.6
K 21							Br 82.6
							I 71.0

than "normal" ionization energy of sodium (Li = 124, Na = 118, K = 99, Cs = 91 kcal mole^{-1}). The elements in this row of the periodic table have less well shielded nuclei than those in the lower rows, where more of the p and d orbitals are occupied.

Exercise 38.1

Account for the drop in I.E. from N to O. *Answer:* N has three $2p$ electrons (one per orbital). O has four $3p$ electrons; hence two must be in the same orbital. Their mutual repulsion lowers the I.E.

ATOMIC RADII

The effective size of an atom is a further indication of the tightness with which the electrons are held to the neighboring nuclei. One result is that the plot of inter nuclear distances in the crystalline elements versus Z is nearly the inverse of the I.E. versus Z curve. Elements with low I.E. have large internuclear distances, or atomic radii, in their crystals—and vice versa—as shown in Figure 38.3.

Ionic radii in crystals confirm the effect of increasing effective nuclear charge on electron distribution (see Figure 38.4).

Exercise 38.2

Estimate a crystal radius for Ne. *Answer:* Ne is isoelectronic with Na^+ and F^- and its nuclear charge is the average of theirs. Since radius versus Z is almost linear, we calculate $[0.95(Na^+) + 1.36(F^-)]/2 = 1.16$ Å for Ne. The accepted value is 1.12 Å.

OXIDATION STATES

One of the more valuable devices with which to categorize and correlate chemical behavior is the oxidation number. Figure 38.5 indicates the more common oxidation states of the elements as a function of Z. Note the periodic variation in oxidation number, consistent with the periodicity of electron structures.

Faced with this wealth of oxidation states, we may logically ask why the elements have the states they do. For about half of the elements there is only one common oxidation state other than zero. All the Group I, Group II, and Group III elements, for instance, have a single positive oxidation state, which is always equal to their column number. This question of stable oxidation state is explored in

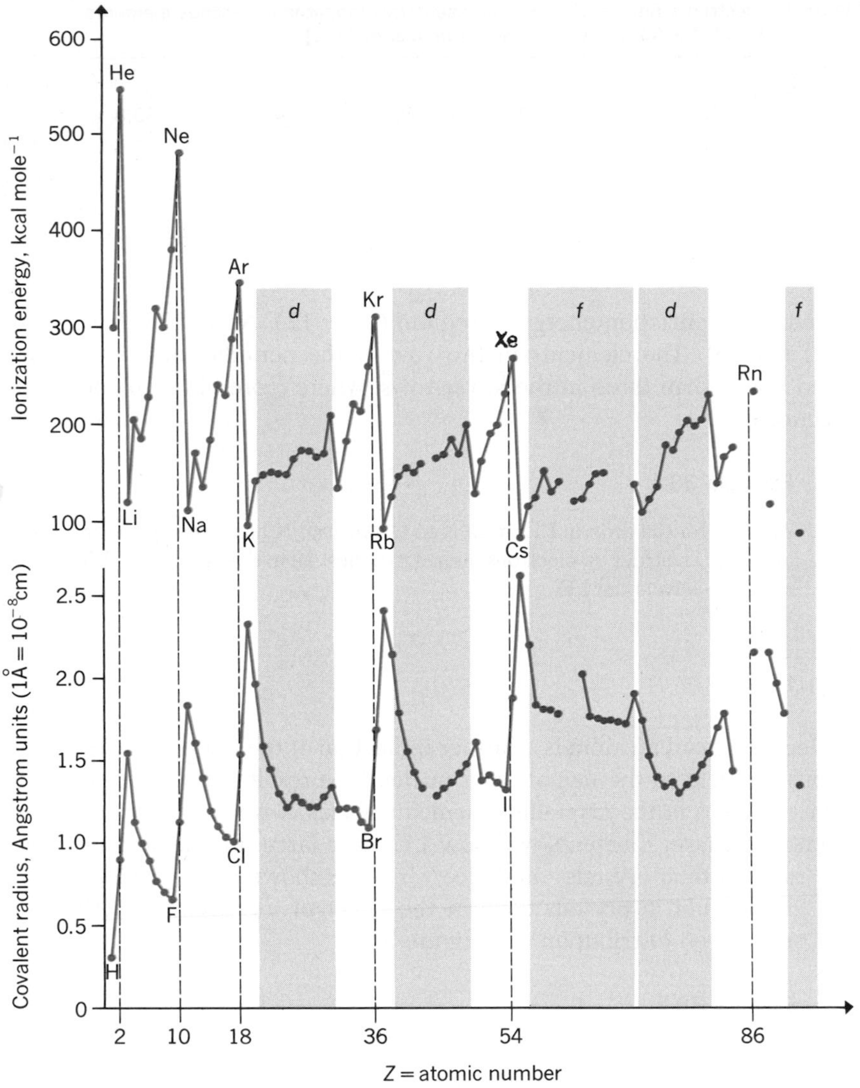

Figure 38.3 Comparison of I.E. and crystalline internuclear distances as a function of *Z*. Note the "mirror" **or** inverse relationship. The *d* and *f* regions are shaded.

Table 38.2, which is based on Born-Haber cycles for three possible calcium chlorides: only $CaCl_2$ has a negative value for ΔH_{form}.

It should be clear that the two dominating factors are the ionization energy, I.E., and the lattice energy, U_{tot}. Both increase as the positive charge on the cation increases, and it is their different rates of increase that mainly determine the magnitude of the heat of formation of the crystal. Since the entropy of formation of the compound is typically small and the variation in this entropy even smaller, it is the enthalpy of formation that is the principal determinant of ΔG_{form} and the extent to which compounds will form. The most stable compounds with respect to decomposition into the elements will be those for which the sum

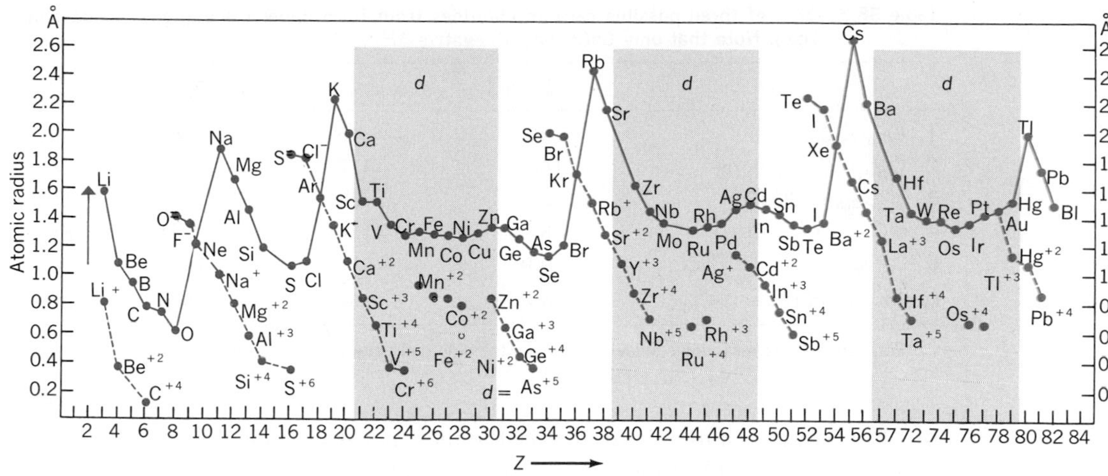

Figure 38.4 Effective atomic radii in the elements (half the observed internuclear distances) and in some positive and negative oxidation states as a function of Z. Note that radius in negative states is larger, in positive states is smaller than that of the parent element. Note the general trends in rows and columns.

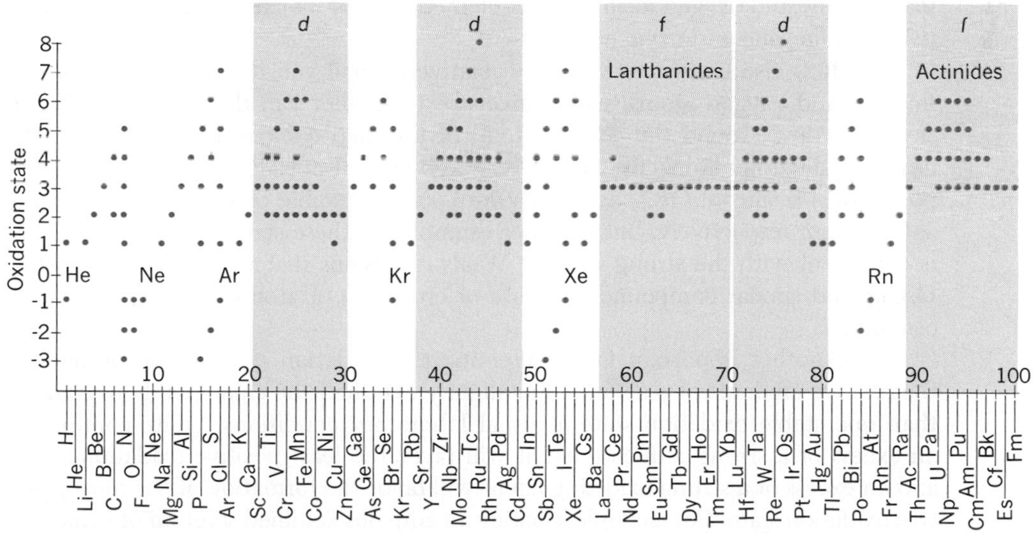

Figure 38.5 Common oxidation states (other than zero) versus Z. The d and f regions are shaded. Note the relative simplicity of the oxidation state variations as Z varies for the representative elements. The maximum positive oxidation state is +8, the minimum negative state is −3. For any given element the maximum state does not exceed its group number, and its minimum state does not exceed 8 minus the group number. The representative elements exhibiting more than one state tend to have them differ by two from one another.

Table 38.2 ΔH_f^0 of three possible calcium chlorides from Born-Haber calculations (all data in kcal). Note that only $CaCl_2$ has a negative ΔH_f^0.

	$n = 1$, CaCl	$n = 2$, $CaCl_2$	$n = 3$, $CaCl_3$	
1. $Ca_{(s)} = Ca_{(g)}$	46	46	46	ΔH_{vap}
2. $Ca_{(g)} = Ca^{+n}{}_{(g)} + ne^-$	142	417	1497	I.E.
3. $n(\frac{1}{2}Cl_{2(g)} = Cl_{(g)})$	29	58	87	ΔH_{diss}
4. $n(Cl_{(g)} + e^- = Cl^-{}_{(g)})$	−87	−174	−251	EA
5. $Ca^{+n}{}_{(g)} + nCl^-{}_{(g)} = CaCl_{n(c)}$	−90[a]	−537	−1000[a]	U_{tot}
6. $Ca_{(c)} + \frac{1}{2}nCl_{2(g)} = CaCl_{n(c)}$	40	−190	~400	ΔH^0

[a] Estimated, using reasonable Madelung constants, ionic radii, and repulsive terms.

of I.E. and U_{tot} is a minimum, that is, the most negative value. Since U_{tot} tends to increase in a smooth fashion as the oxidation number changes,

$$U_{tot} = \frac{N_0 M q_1 q_2 e^2}{d}\left(1 - \frac{1}{n}\right)$$

whereas I.E.'s are strong stepwise functions, the maximum possible oxidation state is usually limited by a very large step in I.E.

We have developed this argument for ionic compounds, but the same rationale is applicable to covalent compounds, except that the lattice energy is replaced by the heat of formation of the covalent bond from the gaseous ions. In other words, strong attractive energies in the product favor its formation. For example, the highest oxidation state of any element is typically obtained in its fluorides and oxides, and often only in these compounds. This is consistent with the strong bonds that fluorine and oxygen form to other elements, all of which are more electropositive than fluorine and oxygen.

It is also consistent with the relatively small van der Waals radii of the fluorine and oxygen atoms, which give rise to smaller van der Waals repulsions (less crowding around the central atom) in the final compound than would, for example, the other halogens. Thus SiF_6 is known, but not $SiCl_6$ or any other compound of +6 silicon. OsO_4 and OsF_6 are known as stable compounds of +8 and +6 osmium respectively, but no other examples of these states are as stable. This is consistent with the strong van der Waals repulsions that would occur in OsF_8, $OsCl_6$, and similar compounds because of crowding of atoms around the central osmium.

Another important factor affecting the oxidation state in the product is the relative amounts of reactants. For slightly over half the elements there is more than one stable oxidation state at usual laboratory conditions. Quite commonly an excess of a strong reducing agent will favor the least positive oxidation state, and an excess of a strong oxidizing agent will favor the formation of the most positive oxidation state. For example, shaking an aqueous acidified solution of vanadate (+5 vanadium, $VO_4^{\equiv}$) ions with amalgamated zinc produces either the +4, +3, or +2 state, depending on the amount of reducing agent (the zinc) in the system.

The final oxidation state can also be varied by varying the strength of the oxidizing or reducing agent used. Vanadate, for example, could be reduced quantitatively to +4 or to +3 or to +2 vanadium by selecting a reducing agent strong enough to accomplish the desired reduction, but not a further one.

Exercise 38.3

Why is +4 the maximum observed oxidation state for carbon? *Answer:* The fourth I.E. of C is 1490 kcal, the fifth is 9050 kcal. It is most unlikely that any chemical attractions could offset this enormous energy requirement.

ACID-BASE REACTIONS

If we apply the Lewis definition of an acid as a substance capable of accepting a pair of electrons, we might expect that atoms which have lost a large number of electrons will form stronger acids than atoms of the same element which have lost fewer electrons. This correlates well with the observation that, for proton acids containing X—O—H bonds (oxo acids), an increase in positive oxidation state in the central element leads to more and more acidic properties in the resulting compounds. An even better correlation is found if we use the formal charge of the central element. The formal charge is determined by writing the valence bond electron structure, then assigning half of all the bonding electrons shared by the central atom to it and calculating the resulting charge. We may, in general, write the oxo acid formulas as H_nXO_m or $(HO)_nXO_{m-n}$. Each HO—X bond contributes nothing to the formal charge since the bond contains one X and one O electron. But each X—O bond contributes +1 to the formal charge since both electrons come from the X. Thus the formal charge usually equals $m - n$. Table 38.3 gives

Table 38.3 **Correlation of acid strength with formal charge. Note also that $pK_3 - pK_2 \cong pK_2 - pK_1 \cong$ 4 to 5.**

Formal charge	Acid	pK_1	pK_2	pK_3	Range of pK_1
0	H_3BO_3	9.22			7–9; very weak acids
	H_3AsO_3	9.22			
	H_6TeO_6	8.80			
	HOBr	8.68			
	H_4GeO_4	8.59	13		
	HOCl	7.50			
1	H_2CO_3	3.58	10.32		1–4; weak acids
	H_3AsO_4	3.5	7.2	12.5	
	HNO_2	3.3			
	H_5IO_6	3.29	6.7	~15	
	H_2SeO_3	2.57	6.60		
	H_3PO_4	2.12	7.2	12	
	$OPH_2(OH)$	2			
	$HClO_2$	1.94			
	H_2SO_3	1.90	7.25		
	$OPH(OH)_2$	1.8	6.15		
2	H_2SeO_4	negative	2.05		~−2(?); strong acids
	H_2SO_4	negative	1.92		
	HNO_3	negative			
3	$HMnO_4$	large negative			very strong acids
	$HClO_4$	large negative			

data for some elements by correlating formal charge with acid equilibrium constants. See also Table 18.13.

In accounting for the strengths of the oxo acids it seems reasonable to attribute the principal effects to enthalpy rather than entropy. The net reaction can generally be written

$$(HO)_nXO_{m(aq)} = H^+{}_{(aq)} + (HO)_{n-1}XO_{m+1}{}^-{}_{(aq)}$$

There will probably be a net decrease in entropy because of the strong hydration of the proton, more than offsetting the gain in entropy from its release. The entropy of the acid and its negative ion will probably be similar, though the negative ion should be somewhat more hydrated, further tending to decrease the entropy. But these effects should be rather constant from one acid to the next, since the interactions with the water will be so similar. The enthalpy effects should vary with the charge density of the central atom, which we have found can be correlated with formal charge.

Direct estimates of charge density are now becoming available from studies of the interaction energies of nuclei and surrounding electrons. The Mossbauer effect is used to study the change in nuclear energy levels when the electron structure of an atom is altered and X-ray-excited electron emission is used to study the effect on electron binding when electron structures are varied. Fadley et al.,* using electron emission, and Hatemeister et al.,** using Mossbauer effects, estimate the following charges on iodine atoms, for example, in the following crystalline materials: $KI_{(c)} = -1$, $KIO_{3(c)} = +0.9 \pm 0.1$, $KIO_4 = +1.3 \pm 0.1$. Clearly the absolute values can be much smaller than the oxidation states of the iodine, but the absolute charge does vary in the predicted manner. Since size decreases as positive charge increases, charge density increases even more rapidly than either size or charge alone.

BINARY ACIDS

Members of the other main group of proton acids contain only two elements—they are binary acids. Ionization of a proton occurs by bond breaking with the central atom, rather than by breaking an O—H bond as with the oxo acids. Table 38.4 indicates that the principal effect is again an enthalpy, rather than entropy, variation from one acid to another, but the entropy effects are not negligible.

Comparison of the bottom lines of Table 38.4 indicates that the principal effect differentiating the halogen binary acids is enthalpy—the HF bond is considerably harder to break than the bonds in the other acids. (Compare the data in step 2 of the corresponding gas-phase reaction.) This is true despite the fact that we find, as we might expect, that the hydration energy of fluoride ion (120 kcal mole^{-1}) is higher than that of the other halide ions (about 80 kcal mole^{-1}), owing to the higher charge density of the fluoride. The entropy changes have a smaller but appreciable differentiating effect, again making hydrogen fluoride a weaker acid than the others. In binary acids the formal charge is zero in the neutral acid molecules, and the ratios of oxidation numbers to covalent radii (a measure of charge density) correlate well with variation in acid strength from element to element (see Table 38.5).

---

* *Science*, **157**, 1571 (1967).
** *Phys. Rev.*, **135B**, 1089 (1964).

Table 38.4 Thermodynamics and acidity of the binary halogen acids. All values in kcal mole^{-1} except pK (dimensionless) and ΔS (eu).

Process	Term	HF	HCl	HBr	HI
1. $HX_{(aq)} = HX_{(g)}$	ΔG^0	5.7	-1	-1	-1
2. $HX_{(g)} = H_{(g)} + X_{(g)}$	ΔG^0	127.8	96.5	81.0	65.0
3. $H_{(g)} = H^+_{(g)} + e$	ΔG^0	315.3	315.3	315.3	315.3
4. $X_{(g)} + e^- = X^-_{(g)}$	ΔG^0	-83.0	-87.6	-82.5	-75.3
5. $H^+_{(g)} + X^-_{(g)} = H^+_{(aq)} + X^-_{(aq)}$	ΔG^0	-361.5	-332.8	-325.7	-317.7
6. $HX_{(aq)} = H^+_{(aq)} + X^-_{(aq)}$	ΔG^0	4.3	-10	-13	-14
	pK	3.2	-7.4	-9.5	-10
	ΔS^0	-21	-13	-9	-3
	$T\,\Delta S^0$	-6.3	-4.9	-3	-1
	ΔH^0	-2	-15	-16	-15

Evidence from the variation of K and pK with size of the ion and with its effective charge indicates that acid strength can be treated satisfactorily in terms of electrostatics. We have pointed out only general trends, but in the few cases for which it has been possible to carry out detailed calculations the results are in such good agreement with experiment that there is little doubt of the general validity of the rationale presented.

Exercise 38.4

Estimate pK_1 and pK_2 for the acid $HClO_3$. *Answer:* $HClO_3$ will have the structure O_2ClOH. The formal charge on the iodine will be $+2$ since there are two Cl—O bonds, and pK_1 will therefore be negative (a strong acid). There will be no pK_2 because the acid contains only one hydrogen. Experimental evidence shows these predictions to be correct.

Table 38.5 Correlation of pK_1 (values in parentheses), oxidation number, and size for some binary acids.

Oxidation number -3	Oxidation number -2	Oxidation number -1
NH_3 ($\sim$30)	H_2O (15.74)	HF (3.14)
	H_2S (7.24)	HCl (-7.4)
	H_2Se (3.7)	HBr (-9.5)
	H_2Te (2.6)	HI (-10)

↓ larger size, stronger acids

→ stronger acids

oxidation number less negative, stronger acids

OXIDES, HYDROXIDES, AND WATER

We have already discussed (Chapter 12) some of the typical reactions of oxides and hydroxides with water. Now let us look at oxides and their reactions in terms of periodic trends. The most commonly found interactions are listed in Table 38.6. These coded types are included in Table 38.7, which lists many of the more common oxides (or hydroxides): the principal trends shown in the table are the following.

Trend	*Interpretation*
1. For any element the acidic strength increases with increase in positive oxidation number or formal charge.	Increasing positive oxidation number or formal charge increases the covalency of X—O bonds and the ionic nature of O—H bonds.
2. At constant oxidation number, oxides become more acidic from left to right in each row in the periodic table.	Increasing nuclear charge accompanies increasing electronegativity; hence the increasing covalency of M—O bonds and the increasing ionic nature of O—H bonds.
3. At constant oxidation number oxides become less acidic from top to bottom of each column in the periodic table.	Increasing distance of valence electrons from the X nucleus enhances the ionic nature of X—O bonds and the covalent nature of O—H bonds.

Table 38.6 Some typical acid-base reactions of oxides and hydroxides with water.

Type	Code	Typical equation	Principal oxide product
Strong acid	*A* (increasing basicity ↓)	$SO_{3(g)} + H_2O = SO_4{}^{=}{}_{(aq)} + 2H^+{}_{(aq)}$	oxy anions
Weak acid	*a*	$CO_{2(g)} + H_2O = HCO_3{}^-{}_{(aq)} + H^+{}_{(aq)}$	hydroxy cations and anions (weak acid through weak base)
Amphoteric acidic	*ab*	$GeO_{2(c)} + 2H_2O + 2OH^- = Ge(OH)_6{}^{=}$	
Amphoteric neutral	*am*	$Zn(OH)_{2(c)} \xrightarrow{H^+} Zn_{(aq)}{}^{++} + H_2O$; $Zn(OH)_{2(c)} \xrightarrow{OH^-_{(aq)}} Zn(OH)_{4(aq)}{}^-$	
Amphoteric basic	*ba*	$Cu(OH)_{2(c)} + H^+{}_{(aq)} = CuOH^+{}_{(aq)} + H_2O$	
Weak base	*b*	$Fe(OH)_{2(c)} = FeOH^+{}_{(aq)} + OH^-{}_{(aq)}$	
Strong base	*B*	$Li_2O_{(c)} + H_2O = 2Li^+{}_{(aq)} + 2OH^-{}_{(aq)}$	hydroxide ion
Inert	*i*	$N_2O_{(g)} + H_2O =$ no appreciable reaction	
Forms -yl ion	*yl*	$ZrO(OH)_{2(c)} + 2H^+{}_{(aq)} = ZrO^{++}{}_{(aq)} + 2H_2O$	oxy cations
Forms poly ion	*po*	$2CrO_{3(c)} + H_2O = O_3CrOCrO_3{}^{=}{}_{(aq)} + 2H^+{}_{(aq)}$	oxy bridges

Table 38.7 **Acid-base properties of some oxides (and hydroxides). The oxides under each element are listed downward in order of decreasing positive oxidation state. Note corresponding decrease in acidity. Note also acid-base trends in rows and columns. Some oxides are so slowly or slightly soluble that it is difficult to observe their acid-base properties.**

He	Ne	Ar	Kr	Xe	Rn	
H_2O, *am* H_2O_2, *a*	F_2O, *i* (oxidizes H_2O)	Cl_2O_7, *A* $HClO_3$, *A* $HClO_2$, *a* $HClO$, *a*	$HBrO_3$, *A* $HBrO$, *a*	H_5IO_6, *A* HIO_3, *A* HIO, *ab*	At	
	O	SO_3, *A, po* SO_2, *a*	SeO_3, *A* SeO_2, *a*	H_6TeO_6, *a* TeO_2, *am*	Po	
	N_2O_5, *A* N_2O_3, *a* H_2NO_2, *a, i*	P_4O_{10}, *A* H_2PHO_3, *A* HPH_2O_2, *A*	As_2O_5, *a* H_3AsO_3, *ab*	H_7SbO_6, *a* H_3SbO_3, *ab, yl*	Bi_2O_5, *a* $Bi(OH)_3$, *a, yl*	
	CO_2, *a* $HCOOH$, *A*	SiO_2, *a, po*	GeO_2, *ab* GeO, *a* (?)	$H_2Sn(OH)_6$, *ab* $Sn(OH)_2$, *am*	PbO_2, *ab, i* $Pb(OH)_2$, *am*	
	B_2O_3, *a* $H_2B_4O_7$, *a*	Al_2O_3, *am*	Ga_2O_3, *ba*	In_2O_3, *b*	Tl_2O_3, *b* Tl_2O, *B*	
			ZnO, *am*	CdO, *b*	HgO, *b* Hg_2O, *b*	
			CuO, *ba* Cu_2O, *b*	Ag_2O, *b*	Au_2O_3, *am* Au_2O, *B*	
			NiO_2, *am* NiO, *b*	PdO_2, *am* PdO, *b*	$H_2Pt(OH)_6$, *ab* PtO, *b*	
			$Co(OH)_3$, *b* CoO, *b*	RhO_3, *a* RhO_2, *am* Rh_2O_3, *b* RhO, *b*	IrO_3, *a* IrO_2, *am* Ir_2O_3, *b*	
			Fe_2O_3, *ba* $Fe(OH)_2$, *b*	RuO_2, *ba* Ru_2O_3, *b* $Ru(OH)_2$, *b*	OsO_4, *a* OsO_2, *ba* Os_2O_3, *b*	
			Mn_2O_7, *A* MnO_2, *am* $Mn(OH)_3$, *b* $Mn(OH)_2$, *b*	Tc_2O_7, *A*	Re_2O_7, *A* ReO_3, *ba*	
			CrO_3, *A, po* Cr_2O_3, *am* $Cr(OH)_2$, *b*	MoO_3, *a, po* MoO_2OH, *ab, yl* $Mo(OH)_3$, *b*	WO_3, *a, po*	UO_3, *ab, yl* UO_2, *b, i* $U(OH)_3$, *b*
			V_2O_5, *ab, po* VO_2, *am, yl* $V(OH)_3$, *b* $V(OH)_2$, *b*	Nb_2O_5, *ab, po* $H_4Nb_6O_{17}$	Ta_2O_5, *ab, i*	Pa_2O_5, *b, i*
			TiO_2, *ab* $Ti(OH)_3$, *b, yl*	ZrO_2, *ba, yl*	HfO_2, *b, yl*	ThO_2, *b*
			Sc_2O_3, *b*	Y_2O_3, *b*	Rare earths M_2O_3, *b* $Eu(OH)_2$, *B*	
	BeO, *am*	MgO, *b*	CaO, *B*	SrO, *B*	BaO, *B*	RaO, *B*
H_2O, *am*	Li_2O, *B*	Na_2O, *B*	K_2O, *B*	Rb_2O, *B*	Cs_2O, *B*	

A = strong acid
a = weak acid
ab = amphoteric acid
am = amphoteric neutral
ba = amphoteric basic
b = weak base
B = strong base
i = inert
yl = forms -yl ion
po = forms poly acids

Three special acid-base phenomena are included in Table 38.6: inertness, formation of -yl ions, and formation of poly ions. Inertness may be thermodynamic (N_2O is more likely thermodynamically than HNO or $H_2N_2O_2$), and/or kinetic (there is a very high potential barrier to the conversion of N_2O to HNO or $H_2N_2O_2$). High oxidation states lead to strong hydrolysis and formation of positive and negative ions containing X—O bonds. The resulting species, such as $ZrO^{++}{}_{(aq)}$, is a -yl ion, called zirconyl. In the same way U(VI) gives $UO_2{}^{++}{}_{(aq)}$, uranyl ion. For many elements, especially nonmetallic ones, the hydrolysis proceeds far enough to give anions, or oxy-ions. Some of the most commonly met ions are of this kind—$CO_3^{=}$, NO_3^-, $PO_4^{\equiv}$, $SO_4^{=}$, ClO_4^-, $CrO_4^{=}$, for example. Note that all the -yl and oxy-ions have central atoms of high positive oxidation number.

Exercise 38.5

If sodium hydroxide is stored in a glass bottle with a glass stopper the stopper will "freeze" to the bottle; it does not affect plastic bottles and stoppers. Account for the difference. *Answer:* Glass is largely silicate. It may be considered as $SiO_2 + Na_2O$. The SiO_2 is acidic, the Na_2O basic in water. In glass the relative amounts are such that the glass is almost neutral. Thus acid will dissolve out some of the Na_2O and base will dissolve out some of the SiO_2. It is the SiO_2 framework which gives glass its three-dimensional structure and strength. Thus base partly dissolves the framework and then reprecipitates the silica elsewhere, causing welding of stopper and bottle, or "freezing." The equilibrium reaction may be approximated by $SiO_{2(c)} + 2OH^-{}_{(aq)} + 2H_2O \rightleftharpoons Si(OH)_6{}^{=}{}_{(aq)}$. Plastic is inert (neither acidic nor basic) so is not attacked by $OH^-{}_{(aq)}$.

*p*H-$\mathcal{E}$ DIAGRAMS

The relationships between acidity and redox have already been discussed in Chapter 26, The Nitrogen Family. For the redox half-reaction

$$NO_3{}^-{}_{(aq)} + 6H^+{}_{(aq)} + 5e^- = \tfrac{1}{2}N_{2(g)} + 3H_2O, \qquad \mathcal{E}^0 = 1.25 \text{ volts}$$

we developed the following relationship between $\mathcal{E}$ and *p*H. From the Nernst equation,

$$\mathcal{E} = \mathcal{E}^0 - \frac{RT}{n\mathcal{F}} \ln Q = \mathcal{E}^0 - \frac{RT}{n\mathcal{F}} \ln \frac{P_{N_2}{}^{1/2}}{[NO_3{}^-][H^+]^6}$$

At the standard state of 25°C and unit activity for $N_{2(g)}$ and $NO_3{}^-{}_{(aq)}$ this becomes

$$\mathcal{E} = 1.25 - \frac{0.0592}{5} \log \frac{1}{1 \cdot [H^+]^6}$$
$$= 1.25 - 0.0592(6/5)pH$$

In general, if all species except $H^+{}_{(aq)}$ are in the standard state of unit activity, we get

$$\mathcal{E} = \mathcal{E}^0 - 0.0592(m/n)pH \qquad (38.1)$$

where m is the number of H^+ used up in the net equation, and n is the number of electrons in the net equation. Equations such as (38.1) give straight lines of slope

0.0592(m/n) when $\mathcal{E}$ is plotted versus pH. These straight lines represent the equilibrium states for the redox system under consideration as the pH varies. Inclusion of the acid ionization equilibrium constants on the same diagram gives a set of lines separating the areas in which each species containing the element of interest can exist at a higher activity than any other species containing that element. Such a region is said to be the region of dominance of that species.

Such pH-$\mathcal{E}$ diagrams summarize the aqueous solution chemistry of an element and indicate which species are thermodynamically stable to redox and to acid-base reaction as a function of pH and $\mathcal{E}$.

The pH-$\mathcal{E}$ diagrams are limited in practice to a pH range of about 0–14 by the properties of water and by the great deviations from unit activity coefficients outside this range. They are also limited in the $\mathcal{E}$ coordinate by the two reactions

$$\tfrac{1}{2}H_2O_{(l)} = \tfrac{1}{4}O_{2(g)} + H^+{}_{(aq)} + e^-, \qquad \mathcal{E} = 1.223 - 0.0592\ p\text{H}$$

$$e^- + H_2O_{(l)} = \tfrac{1}{2}H_{2(g)} + OH^-{}_{(aq)}, \qquad \mathcal{E} = 0.000 - 0.0592\ p\text{H}$$

which correspond to the oxidation and reduction of water and the variation in the corresponding potentials as a function of pH. There is thus only a diamond-shaped area, which we shall bound by the four points indicated in Figure 38.6, that is accessible to common aqueous solution chemistry. Any stable species in water can be represented inside this diamond-shaped pH-$\mathcal{E}$ range.

Because it is possible to exceed the 0–14 pH range in water, our diagrams will actually cover a pH range from −2 to 16. This allows us to note some interesting species that are found in highly acidic or basic media, although the $\mathcal{E}$ values for them are not exact. Similarly, because overvoltage effects commonly allow extension of the $\mathcal{E}$ range, our diagrams run from −1.2 to 1.7 volts: these data also should be used only qualitatively.

pH-$\mathcal{E}$ DIAGRAMS AND THE PERIODIC TABLE

The acid-base and redox trends discussed so far may be summarized by arranging the diamond-shaped areas of the pH-$\mathcal{E}$ diagrams as a periodic table (Figure 38.7).

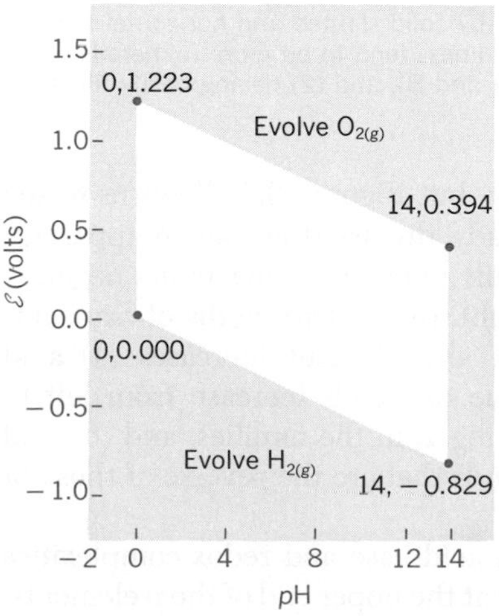

Figure 38.6 Range of pH-ℰ values accessible in aqueous solution.

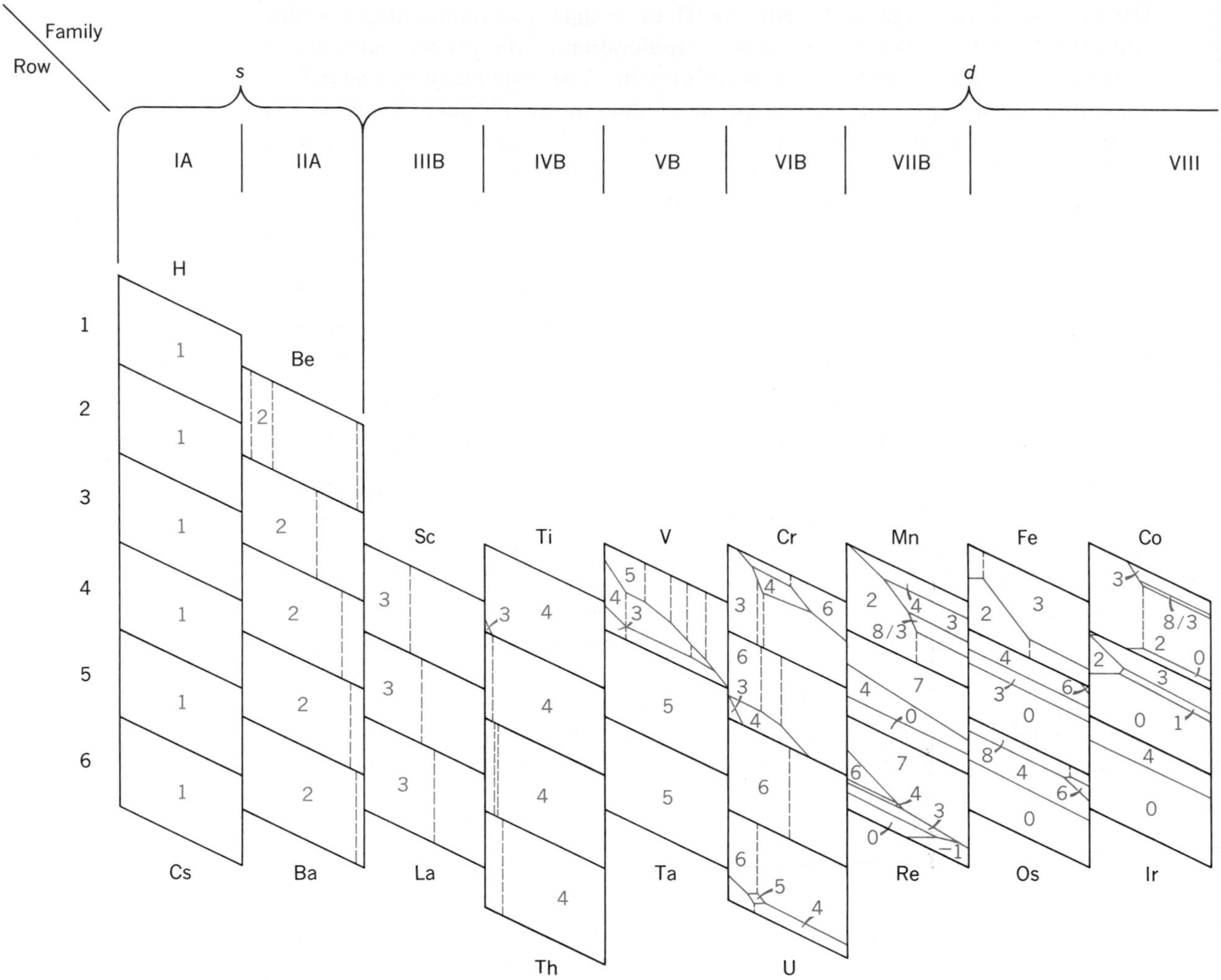

Figure 38.7 The periodic table and some pH-$\mathcal{E}$ diagrams for aqueous systems. [Many by R. A. Whiteker.] Note that both the redox equilibria (indicated by solid slanted and horizontal lines) and the acid-base equilibria (indicated by vertical dotted lines) tend to be more numerous for elements (1) belonging to families V, VI, and VII (both A and B), and (2) having partly filled *d*

We shall use larger scale pH-$\mathcal{E}$ diagrams shortly, but Figure 38.7 allows us to see variations as a function of Z. The trends already discussed are again apparent: (1) maximum positive oxidation state equals family number, (2) maximum negative oxidation state equals family number minus eight, (3) acid strengths of oxy-acids increase as the positive oxidation number of any element increases (4) acid strengths (at constant oxidation number) of the oxy-acids increase from left to right in the rows and (5) decrease with increasing Z in the families, and (6) acid strengths of the binary hydrogen acids have trends that are the reverse of those of the oxy-acids.

In addition it becomes clear that both acid-base and redox complexities have maxima in the middle of the *d* elements and at the upper end of the *p* elements.

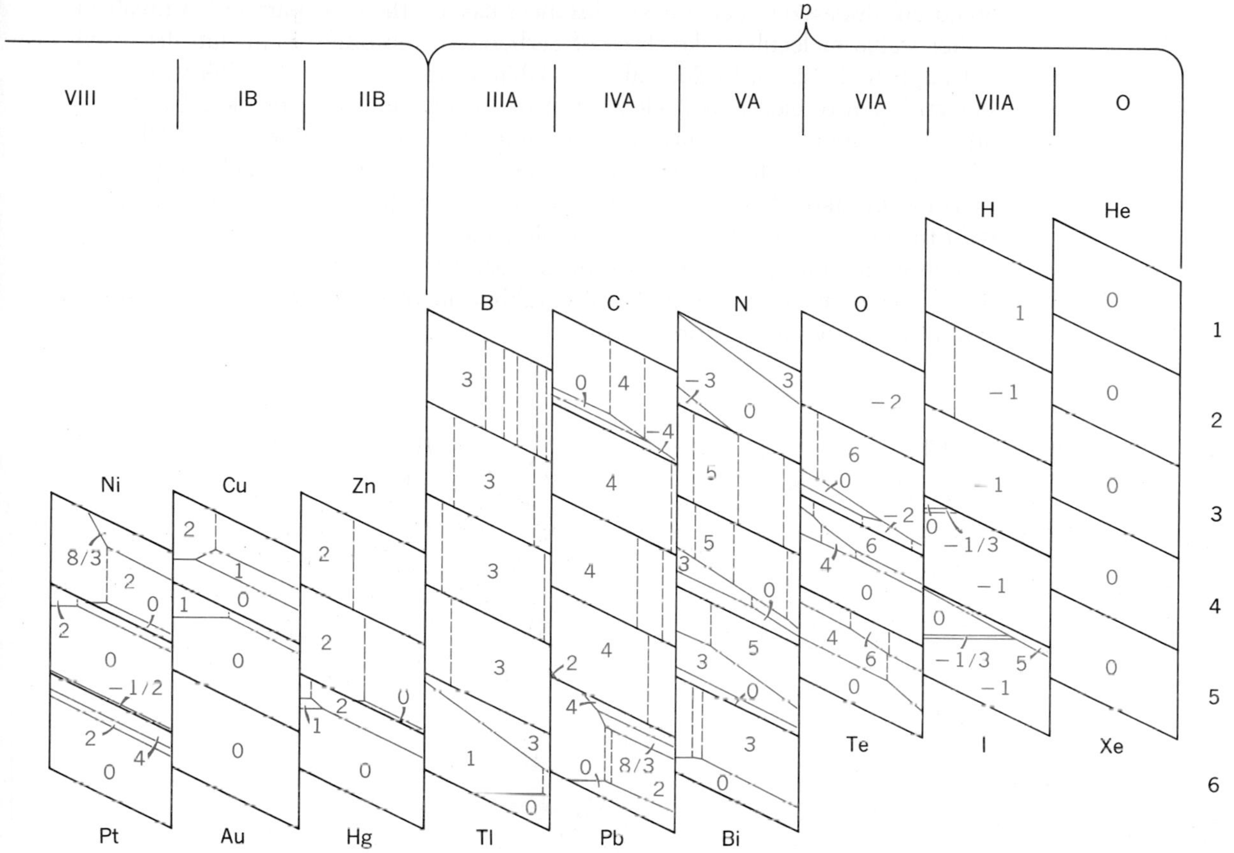

orbitals. This is consistent with the orbital availability in the elements. The following trends are also apparent: (3) acid strength of hydroxy compounds decreases as atomic size increases (see Be and Sc families); (4) the **higher** oxidation states become more stable as pH increases (see V, Cr, Mn, Fe).

This should remind you that redox and acid-base are rather arbitrarily selected ways of viewing chemical behavior and are both related to electron structures and their variations with nuclear charge and number of electrons present.

Exercise 38.6

Why is it so difficult to oxidize an element above its group number? *Answer:* The group represents the number of valence electrons, that is, the number of electrons of relatively low I.E. (see Table 3.1). Removing one additional electron requires much more energy than is recovered in the coordination of the resulting atom by its surroundings.

COMPLEX FORMATION

So far our discussion of chemical substances has, for the most part, either involved rather stable molecules (like those of carbon and the other nonmetals discussed in Chapters 11, 12, 13, 18, 25, and 30) or labile species in which the lability involved loss and gain of electrons (redox) or of hydrogens and oxygens (acid-base). But other labile acid-base systems also exist. Some of these were discussed in Chapter 37 in connection with some synthetic problems. These species, which are thermodynamically stable but which participate in measurable acid-base type equilibria with fragments that are themselves stable molecules, are called complexes. Some complexes are ionic, some are electrically neutral.

Here are a few examples of equilibria involving complexes presented as acid-base (donor-acceptor) reactions.

Acceptor *Donor* *Complex*

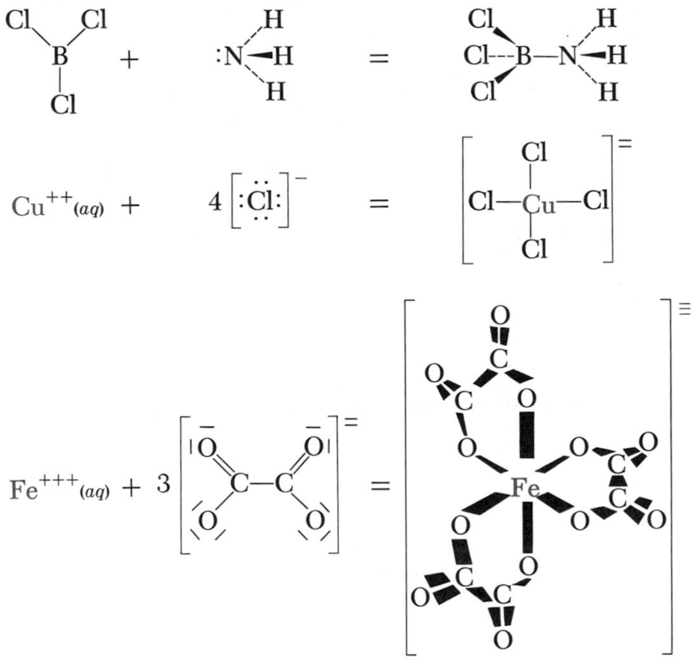

(oxygens are octahedral around the iron)

We see that complexes may be viewed as forming when a Lewis acid (with empty electron orbitals) reacts with a Lewis base (with unshared pairs of electrons). The formula of the resulting complex may often be interpreted in terms of the number of available empty orbitals and the number of available electron pairs. The boron in BCl_3 has one empty orbital, the nitrogen in ammonia one unshared pair, and so a 1–1 complex, Cl_3BNH_3, forms. The copper(II) ion has a d^9 structure and thus has one *s*, three *p*, and half a *d* orbital empty. The chloride ions have four unshared electron pairs but because the pairs are presumably tetrahedrally oriented in sp^3 hybridization only one pair "points" in any given direction, and the product is a 1–4 complex(1–$4\frac{1}{2}$ cannot form since electrons come in pairs).

The iron(III) ion has a d^5 structure: one *s*, three *p*, and two and a half *d* orbitals are available (or six completely empty orbitals). Oxalate ions have ten unshared pairs but their orientation about the planar O_2C—CO_2 ion prevents the use of more than two pairs at a time by a single iron atom. The O—C—C—O bond angles do allow the donation of two pairs per oxalate. Hence we are not surprised that a 6–2 (actually 3–1) complex forms. Note that because of its bent structure

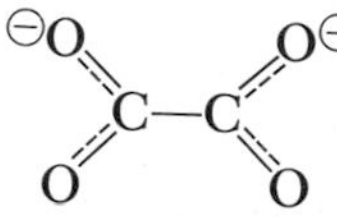

coordinates two of its electron pairs simultaneously to a single iron ion. Such ligands are said to be bidentate (double-toothed). Some ligands are monodentate, some bidentate, and so on up to hexadentate. EDTA, ethylene diamine tetra-acetate, is hexadentate, for example (see Figure 38.8).

Exercise 38.7

Predict probable formulas for the complexes formed by the following: (*a*) Zn^{++} and CN^-, (*b*) Ag^+ and $S_2O_3^=$. *Answer:* (*a*) Zn^{++} is a d^{10} acceptor (sp^3 available), with the :C≡N:$^-$ donating one pair; formula $Zn(CN)_4^=$. (*b*) Ag^+ is a d^{10} acceptor (sp^3 orbitals), with the

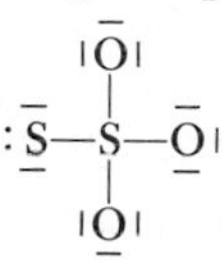

donating one pair; formula $Ag(S_2O_3)_4^{-7}$. But it is unlikely that four large, doubly negative thiosulfates can crowd around one small silver (especially with only +1 charge to hold them), thus $Ag(S_2O_3)_2^=$ with its much smaller net charge and smaller crowding is more probable. Note that two H—Ö—H might fill the other orbitals.

Exercise 38.8

Would you expect $O^=$ or Cl^- to form tighter complexes with an acceptor? *Answer:* The radius of an $O^=$ is less than that of a Cl^- (1.40 Å versus 1.81 Å) and the charge on an $O^=$ is twice than on a Cl^-. Thus the charge density of $O^=$ is much greater and it should form much tighter ionic type bonds. It probably also will be a better donor because of internal electron repulsion. *EA* of $Cl_{(g)}$ = 86.6, *EA* of $O^-_{(g)}$ = −210 kcal $mole^{-1}$.

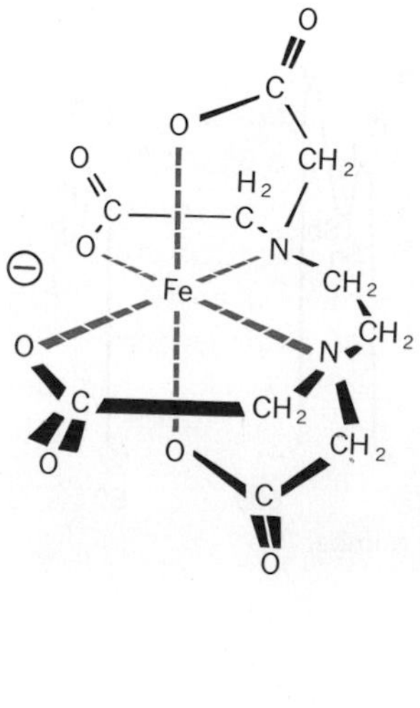

Figure 38.8 The complex of EDTA (ethylene diamine tetra-acetate ion) and Fe (III), $Fe[C_2H_4N_2(CH_2CO_2)_4]^-$.

Exercise 38.9

Plutonium(IV) forms about as many complexes as any other species. Suggest a structure and a reason for their great stability. *Answer:* Pt (Z = 78) gives a d^6 Pt(IV) species isoelectronic with Fe^{+2} or Co^{+3}. Thus we expect it to be similar to Co^{+3} and to form strong octahedral complexes for the reasons given above.

SOLUBILITY

One of the most common chemical processes is the dissolving of one substance in another. At constant T and P in a closed system, solubility can be predicted by the equation

$$\Delta G = \Delta H - T\,\Delta S$$

Solution will occur if ΔH and ΔS have signs and magnitudes such that ΔG will be negative at the temperature of interest. For a saturated solution, $\Delta H = T\,\Delta S$.

When two pure substances are very similar in structure (intermolecular forces and molecular sizes) ΔH tends toward zero and solubility is unlimited (ΔG large negative) since ΔS will always be positive when such systems intermix (only spacial entropy need be considered). Figure 38.9 shows this effect for the solubility of metals in liquid sodium as a function of Z. All the alkali elements except lithium are soluble without limit in liquid sodium at temperatures above their melting points. The extent of solubility of the other metals is related to their distance from Groups IA and IB in the periodic table and reflects the increasing importance of the ΔH term as the difference between metals increases. Similar effects are found for hydrocarbons dissolving in one another and for other related series of compounds.

For ideal solutions in which $\Delta H_{\text{soln}} = 0$, the solubility of either component in the other may be calculated from Equation (34.18), $\ln X_A = -(\Delta\bar{H}_A/R)\,[1/T - 1/T_A{}^0]$. The composition of the mutually saturated solution (the eutectic) may be calculated by solving the A and B equations for T, the temperature of saturation, and setting the two results equal to give:

$$\frac{R}{\Delta\bar{H}_A}\ln X_A - \frac{1}{T_A{}^0} = \frac{R}{\Delta\bar{H}_B}\ln(1 - X_A) - \frac{1}{T_B{}^0}$$

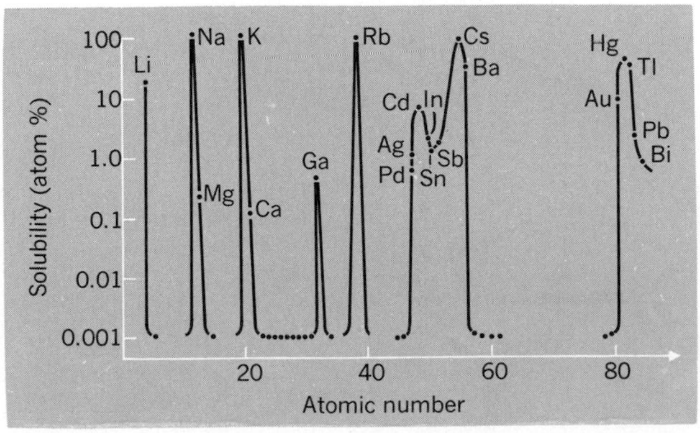

Figure 38.9 Solubilities of metals in liquid sodium at 200°C. Note logarithmic solubility ordinate.

where X_A is the mole fraction of A in the eutectic and T^0 and $\Delta\bar{H}$ are the melting points and heats of fusion of pure A and B respectively.

The most common solvent is, of course, water. When it is the solvent, the interactions of solvent and solute can become so complicated that it is impossible to correlate the known solubilities (see Table 36.3) simply with the periodic table. Normally the structure of the water is partly destroyed by the solution process, tending to make ΔS positive. At the same time the solute molecules may reorient the water molecules, tending to make ΔS negative. If the solute is a solid, the spatial ΔS for its solution will be positive. If the solute is a gas, the spatial ΔS for its solution will be negative; if a liquid, spatial ΔS should approach zero. If the attractions between solute and water are stronger than the average of the attractions between water molecules and the attractions between solute molecules, ΔH will be negative (enhancing solubility) and vice versa.

The presence of so many effects makes quantitative correlation impossible until chemists accumulate more data on these interactions, but examination of Table 36.3 does allow the following generalizations for ionic crystals and water.

Observation	*Example*	*Interpretation*
1. Large ions with small charge (low-charge density) give high solubility.	CH_3COO^-, NO_3^-, NO_2^-, ClO_3^-, ClO_4^-, halides, alkali metals (M^+), NH_4^+, and $SO_4^=$	Small interionic attractions in crystal give $\Delta H \cong 0$. $T\,\Delta S$ is negative.
2. 1–1 electrolytes of high charge (high charge density) have low solubility.	$CaCO_3$, CuS, $LaPO_4$, MgO	Large interionic attractions in crystal give $\Delta H = +$, overcoming ΔS term.
3. Special bonding in crystal gives low solubility.	Hydroxides.	Hydrogen bonding in crystal tends to give $\Delta H = +$. Also, introduction of OH^- ion into H_2O orders the H_2O, giving $\Delta S = -$.

Thus the periodic table reflects the general tendency of crystals having approximately equal numbers of ions of small size and high charge to be insoluble, and the tendency of crystals containing grossly unequal numbers of ions—at least one of large size and small charge—to be soluble.

Exercise 38.10

Rationalize the solubility trends of the alkaline-earth hydroxides. The solubilities in g/100 g H_2O are $Be(OH)_2$, $1.3 \cdot 10^{-15}$; $Mg(OH)_2$, $9 \cdot 10^{-4}\ {}^{18°}$; $Ca(OH)_2$, $0.185^{0°}$; $Sr(OH)_2$, $0.41^{0°}$; $Ba(OH)_2$, $5.6^{15°}$. *Answer:* Note that converting these figures to M will not change the monotonic trend from Be^{++} to Ba^{++}. Assuming that ΔH is more important than ΔS, the terms to consider here are U_{tot} and ΔH_{hyd} of M^{++} (all other terms are common to all the substances). ΔH_{hyd} decreases from Be^{++} (-807 kcal mole^{-1}) to Ba^{++} (-524 kcal mole^{-1}), which would tend to make $Be(OH)_2$ the most soluble. Clearly U_{tot} must change even more rapidly, making $Be(OH)_{2(c)}$ much more stable than $Ba(OH)_2$. This is presumably due to the intense coulombic effects around the small Be^{++} and the strong H-bonding between the close-packed OH^- in $Be(OH)_{2(c)}$ compared to the increasingly smaller corresponding energies in the other alkaline-earth hydroxides.

SYSTEMATIC CHEMISTRY OF THE NONMETALS

You have already studied some of the detailed chemistry of all the nonmetallic elements in Chapters 11 (noble gases), 12 (hydrogen), 13 (halogens), 18 (chalcogens), 21 (carbon), 25 (boron and silicon), and 30 (nitrogen family) as well as in numerous sections of other chapters. To review succinctly, nonmetallic elements are characterized by relatively high values of I.E., relatively small atomic radii, relatively low ΔH_{vap}, the presence of empty *p* orbitals in the monatomic gas (except for the noble gases), and a tendency to form covalent bonds with other nonmetals and ionic bonds with metals. Under usual laboratory conditions most of these elements exist as relatively small molecules, and their rates of reaction are often slow at room temperature because of the high activation energies required to break the strong covalent bonds found in such molecules. Their reactions with other elements, however, are commonly exothermic and proceed almost to completion, since polar bonds tend to be stronger than nonpolar bonds. Entropy effects are more difficult to generalize, but can usually be estimated for the reaction under consideration.

Figure 38.10 reproduces the *p*H-$\mathcal{E}$ diagrams for the elements studied so far as a further means of reviewing their aqueous-solution chemistry. Remember that these diagrams list only the thermodynamically stable species. For example, ClO_3^- is not shown on the chlorine diagram since it is thermodynamically unstable with respect to Cl^- (or Cl_2) and ClO_4^-, even though it is kinetically stabilized and can be kept indefinitely in aqueous solutions, especially at neutrality. Study of the figure should refresh your mind on the trends in acid-base and redox behavior found in the families it includes. Remember that *p*H-$\mathcal{E}$ diagrams are equilibrium diagrams and do not include species that are kinetically but not thermodynamically stable.

TYPICAL METALS

The metals are usually divided into the typical metals [Groups IA, IIA, IIIA, IVA] and the transition metals [groups IIIB, IVB, VB, VIB, VIIB, VIIIB (all three columns), IB, and IIB]. The chemistry of the transition elements is often strongly affected by the presence of unfilled *d* orbitals though the groups IB [Cu(I), Ag(I)] and IIB [Zn(II), Cd(II), Hg(I and II)] have all their *d* orbitals filled in their ground states. Thus, this classification shares with all other classifications a lack of precise definition. We shall discuss the transition metals separately, following this discussion of the typical metals. Figure 38.11 gives $\mathcal{E}$-*p*H diagrams for most of these elements. Note the generally simple aqueous-solution chemistry. Only Tl, Ge, Sn, and Pb have more than one stable oxidized state in contact with water.

There are general trends in the families; the elements tend to become poorer reducing agents and their corresponding oxidation states to become less acidic as Z increases. In the rows the elements again become weaker reducing agents as Z increases, but the acid strengths of comparable compounds tend to increase as Z increases. You should be able to correlate these trends with the terms in the corresponding Born-Haber cycles.

It must be remembered that the diagrams in Figure 38.11 are limited to systems made only of H_2O, H^+, OH^-, and the element under consideration. Similar figures constructed for systems containing 1 *M* Cl^-, Br^-, CN^-, or any other complexing group, would show the *p*H-$\mathcal{E}$ equilibrium range of the various stable complexes. Much of the most interesting chemistry of the elements is related to these complexes and to nonaqueous systems, but neither will be discussed specifically here. You should be able to deduce the general principles by very slight modification of the ideas presented.

GROUP IA

We have already used the alkali metals (Li, Na, K, Rb, Cs, Fr) as frequent examples. Their chemistry is probably as simple and as easily correlated with the periodic table as that of any family. Only the elementary and the +1 oxidation states are known. Figure 38.11 shows that only the $M^+_{(aq)}$ species are stable in water; the metals all reduce H_2O at all *p*H's to hydrogen gas.

All the elements in this group are silvery and highly metallic. Their compounds are almost all ionic and soluble in water. Lithium, as should be expected, has the greatest tendency to form covalent bonds; as in butyl lithium, C_4H_9Li, for example. The ions may be precipitated from aqueous solution with special reagents of low solubility (see Table 36.3) or by evaporation of water from any solution of their salts. The elements are most commonly identified by flame tests and most commonly prepared by electrolysis of their fused salts to which other salts, such as carbonates, have been added to lower the melting point and minimize corrosion and volatility. Table 38.8 lists some properties: note the generally monotonic trends.

Table 38.8 Some properties of the alkali metals, Group IA.

Property	Li	Na	K	Rb	Cs	Trend (⟶)
Electron structure	2, 1	2, 8, 1	2, 8, 8, 1	2, 8, 18, 8, 1	2, 8, 18, 18, 8, 1	
I.E. (kcal mole^{-1}) I	124	118	100	95	91	−
II	1750	1090	735	634	579	−
Metal radius (Å)	1.519	1.858	2.272	2.48	2.655	+
Ionic radius (Å)	0.60	0.95	1.33	1.48	1.69	+
Melting point (°K)	453.6	371	336.7	311.9	301.7	−
Boiling point (°K)	1604	1162	1030	952	963	min
ΔH_{fus} (kcal mole^{-1})	0.715	0.622	0.558	0.560	0.510	
ΔH_{vap} (kcal mole^{-1})	37	26	21	20	19	−
X—X bond energy (kcal mole^{-1})	25.8	17.5	11.9	11.3	10.4	−
ΔH_{hyd} M^+ (kcal mole^{-1})	−119	−93	−73	−67	−59	−
S^0_{298} (cal mole^{-1} °K^{-1})	6.70	12.2	15.2	16.6	19.8	+
$\mathcal{E}^0(M \longrightarrow M^+)$	3.045	2.714	2.925	2.925	2.923	

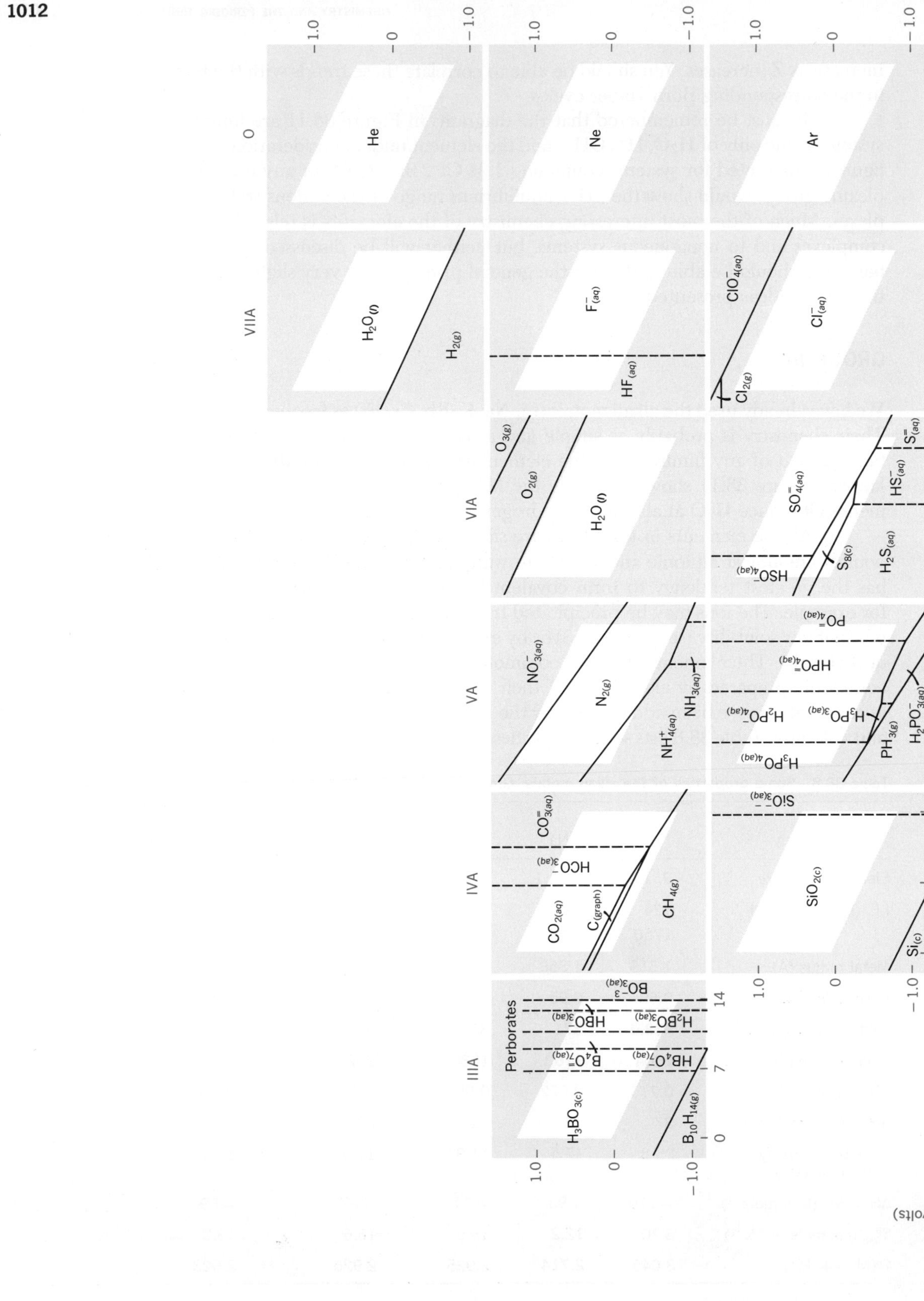

IIIA
IVA
VA
VIA
VIIA
0
$H_3BO_{3(c)}$
Perborates
$B_4O_7^{=}{}_{(aq)}$
$HB_4O_7^{-}{}_{(aq)}$
$HBO_3^{-}{}_{(aq)}$
$H_2BO_3^{-}{}_{(aq)}$
$BO_3^{-}{}_{(aq)}$
$B_{10}H_{14(g)}$
$CO_{2(aq)}$
$HCO_3^{-}{}_{(aq)}$
$CO_3^{=}{}_{(aq)}$
$C_{(graph)}$
$CH_{4(g)}$
$NO_3^{-}{}_{(aq)}$
$N_{2(g)}$
$NH_4^{+}{}_{(aq)}$
$NH_{3(aq)}$
$O_{3(g)}$
$O_{2(g)}$
$H_2O_{(l)}$
$H_{2(g)}$
$F^{-}_{(aq)}$
$HF_{(aq)}$
He
Ne
Ar
$SiO_{2(c)}$
$SiO_3^{=}{}_{(aq)}$
$Si_{(c)}$
$H_3PO_{4(aq)}$
$H_2PO_4^{-}{}_{(aq)}$
$HPO_4^{=}{}_{(aq)}$
$PO_4^{\equiv}{}_{(aq)}$
$H_3PO_{3(aq)}$
$H_2PO_3^{-}{}_{(aq)}$
$PH_{3(g)}$
$HSO_4^{-}{}_{(aq)}$
$SO_4^{=}{}_{(aq)}$
$S_{8(c)}$
$H_2S_{(aq)}$
$HS^{-}_{(aq)}$
$S^{=}_{(aq)}$
$ClO_4^{-}{}_{(aq)}$
$Cl^{-}_{(aq)}$
$Cl_{2(g)}$
1.0
0
−1.0
7
14
(volts)

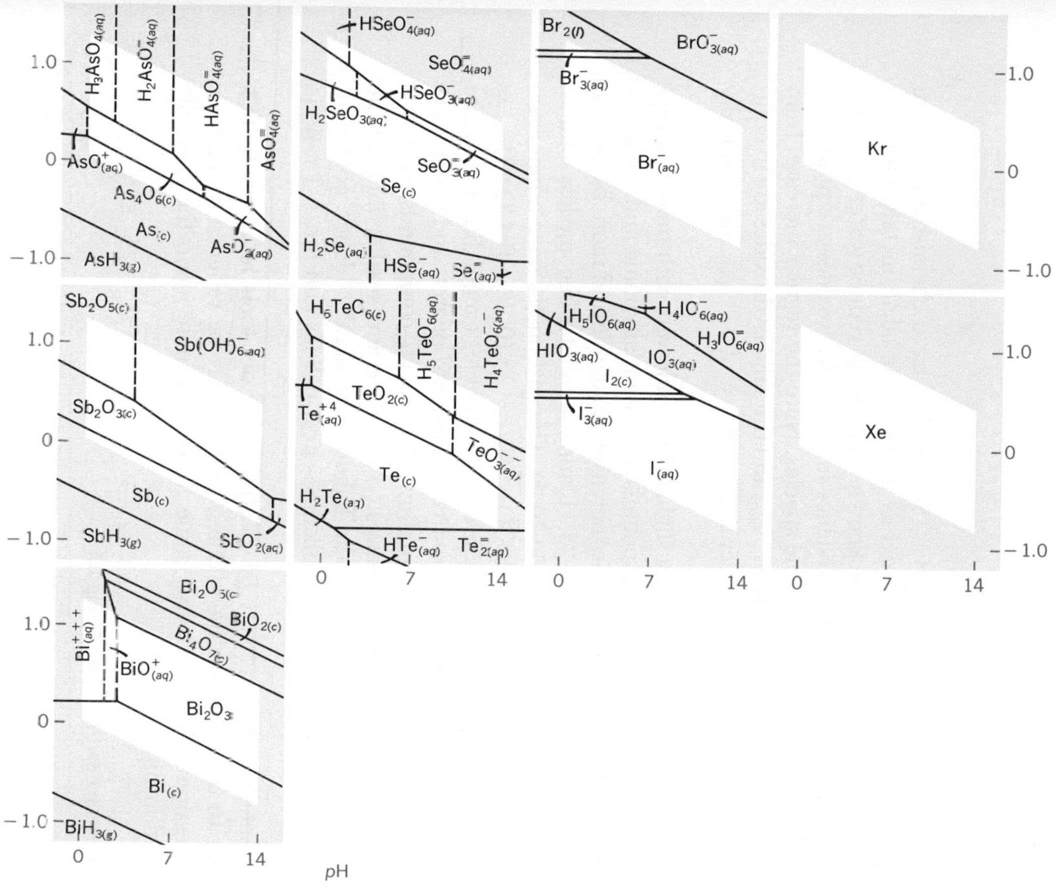

Figure 38.10 pH-$\mathcal{E}$ diagrams, mostly nonmetals.

GROUP IIA

The alkaline-earth elements (Be, Mg, Ca, Sr, Ba, Ra) have chemistries that are almost as simple and easily characterized as those of the alkali metals. Only the metallic and the +2 oxidation states are known. The metals reduce water to hydrogen gas (see Figure 38.11). At high *p*H values insoluble hydroxides are produced; at low *p*H the $M^{++}{}_{(aq)}$ ions are the stable species. Note the regular increase, from Be^{++} to Ba^{++}, of the *p*H at which 1 *M* $M^{++}{}_{(aq)}$ and the solid hydroxides are in equilibrium. This is consistent with the decreasing acidity of $M^{++}{}_{(aq)}$ monotonically from Be^{++} to Ba^{++}.

The metals are silvery and only slightly less endowed with metallic properties than the alkali metals. Their compounds are essentially ionic and many are soluble in water. The hydroxides become increasingly soluble and more basic from $Be(OH)_2$ to $Ba(OH)_2$ as shown in Figure 38.11, and the sulfates become less soluble; $BeSO_4$ (very soluble), $BaSO_4$ ($K_{sp} = 1.5 \cdot 10^{-9}$). The carbonates have a minimum solubility; $MgCO_3$ ($K_{sp} = 8 \cdot 10^{-9}$), $SrCO_3$ ($K_{sp} = 7 \cdot 10^{-10}$), $BaCO_3$ ($K_{sp} = 1.6 \cdot 10^{-9}$). All the nitrates and halides are quite soluble, except barium nitrate ($K_{sp} = 4.5 \cdot 10^{-3}$). The solubilities of the hydroxides, carbonates, and sulfates are generally lower than those of corresponding alkali-metal compounds, which is consistent with the higher charge densities (+2 charge and smaller ions) of the alkaline-earth ions. The solubilities of the halides is generally higher, consistent with the 1–2 cation-anion ratio in the alkaline-earth halides and the 1–1 ratio in the alkali halides.

The metallic elements may be electrolyzed from their halide melts in a manner similar to that used for the alkalies, or they may be reduced by metallic sodium or potassium. Table 38.9 lists some properties: note again the generally monotonic relationships.

Table 38.9 Some properties of the alkaline earth metals, Group IIA.

Property		Be	Mg	Ca	Sr	Ba	Trend (→)
Electron structure		2, 2	2, 8, 2	2, 8, 8, 2	2, 8, 18, 8, 2	2, 8, 18, 18, 8, 2	
I.E. (kcal mole^{-1})	I	293	214	188	172	164	−
	II	714	562	464	428	396	−
	III	4264	2411	1646			−
Metal radius (Å)		1.11	1.60	1.97	2.15	2.17	+
Ionic radius (Å)		.31	.65	.99	1.13	1.35	+
Melting point (°K)		1556	923	1123	1043	977	
Boiling point (°K)		3243	1393	1760	1657	1911	
ΔH_{fus} (kcal mole^{-1})		2.3	2.2	2.2	2.2	6(?)	
ΔH_{vap} (kcal mole^{-1})		70	31.5	40	33.8	35.7	
X—X bond energy (kcal mole^{-1})		16(?)	7.2				
ΔH_{hyd} M^{++} (kcal mole^{-1})		−587	−452	−373	−338	−304	−
S^0_{298} (cal mole^{-1} °K^{-1})		2.28	7.77	9.95	13.0	16	+
$\mathcal{E}^0$ ($M \longrightarrow M^{++}$)		1.85	2.37	2.87	2.89	2.90	+

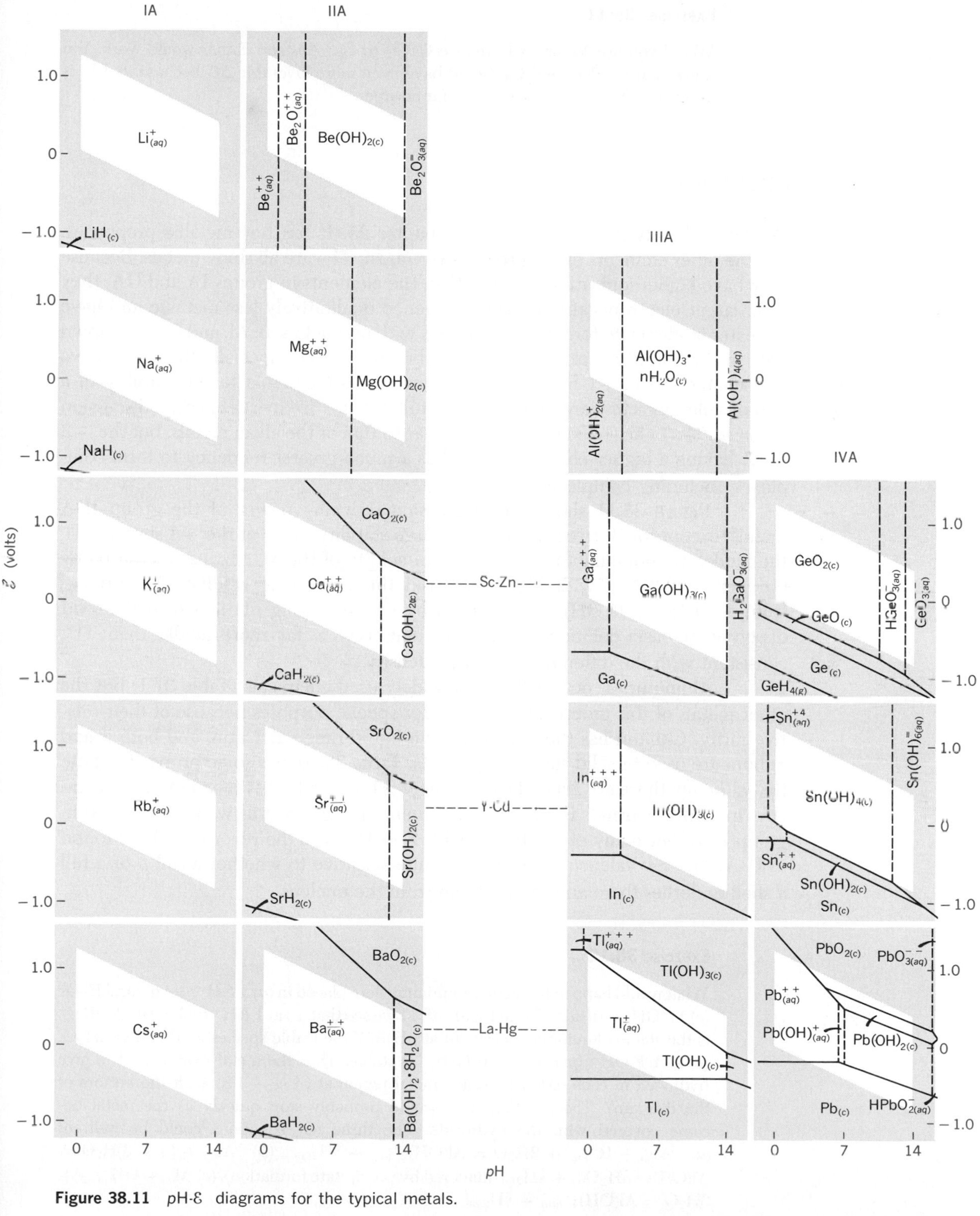

Figure 38.11 pH-$\mathcal{E}$ diagrams for the typical metals.

Exercise 38.11

Would you use Na or Cs to reduce $CaCl_2$ to Ca? *Answer:* Either would work. You know that Na does and Cs should have even more favorable ΔG because its I.E. is lower. But Na is used because it is far cheaper.

GROUP IIIA

We have already discussed boron in Chapter 25. It has few metallic properties, but the other elements in the group—Al, Ga, In, Tl—are all shiny metals. Because they have higher ionization energies than the elements in groups IA and IIA, they have larger electronegativities and are hence qualitatively less metallic and have a greater tendency to form covalent bonds with nonmetals. B, Al, and Ga are known only in the 0 and +3 oxidization states, but In and Tl, especially the latter, have well-characterized +1 oxidation states that are attributable to the stability of a pair of *s* electrons that are underlain by a full *d* shell. (See inert *s* electron discussion on page 746.) The +1 state is quite similar to that of the alkali metals, but the +3 state, having a higher charge density, has a much greater tendency to form complexes, including complexes with water.

Figure 38.11 shows the decreasing reducing power of the group IIIA metals (except for B) from Al to Tl, the large stability range of the +1 state for Tl, the moderate (nonmonotonic) variation in acidity of the $M^{+++}{}_{(aq)}$ as measured by the pH equilibrium with $M(OH)_{3(c)}$, and the decreasing acidity of $M(OH)_{3(c)}$ from $Al(OH)_3$ to $Tl(OH)_3$ as measured by the increasing pH at which the solid dissolves in basic solutions. Note also that Tl^{+3} is far more acidic than Tl^+, consistent with the difference in charge density.

Aluminum is one of the most widely used chemicals (Table 37.1) but the other metals of this group are used only for special purposes because of their relative rarity. Gallium has the longest known liquid range at 1 atm, and both it and indium are used in solid-state components. Table 38.10 lists some properties: note that although there are general trends, there is less regularity than in groups IA and IIA. In terms of trends in properties, aluminum might just as well be included in group IIIB, but many of the trends with Z in IIIB are the reverse of those found in IIIA. The s^2p valence electrons are quite sensitive to whether a full p or a full d shell underlies them and shields them from the nucleus.

Exercise 38.12

What would happen if metallic aluminum were placed in (*a*) 1 *F* H^+? (*b*) neutral H_2O? (*c*) 1 *F* OH^-? *Answer:* From Figure 38.11 we see that (*a*) at 1 *F* H^+ (pH = 0) $Al(OH)_2{}^+$ is the stable aluminum species (*b*) at pH = 7 the stable species is $Al(OH)_3 \cdot nH_2O$, (*c*) at 1 *F* OH^- (pH = 14) $Al(OH)_4{}^-$ is stable. Thus the metal would react to give hydrogen in each case (the stable metal region at $\mathcal{E}^0 < -1.2$, is off the bottom of the diagram). The reaction in *b* would probably stop quickly as the metal became covered with the hydroxide. The three net equations could be written: (*a*) $Al_{(c)} + H^+{}_{(aq)} + 2H_2O = Al(OH)_2{}^+{}_{(aq)} + \frac{3}{2}H_{2(g)}$. (*b*) $Al_{(c)} + (n + 3)H_2O = Al(OH)_3 \cdot nH_2O_{(c)} + \frac{3}{2}H_{2(g)}$ (hindered by precipitate formation). (*c*) $Al_{(c)} + OH^-{}_{(aq)} + 3H_2O = Al(OH)_4{}^-{}_{(aq)} + \frac{3}{2}H_{2(g)}$.

Table 38.10 Some properties of the Group IIIA elements.

Property		B	Al	Ga	In	Tl	Trend (⟶)
Electron structure		2, 3	2, 8, 3	2, 8, 18, 3	2, 8, 18, 18, 3	2, 8, 18, 32, 18, 3	
I.E. (kcal $mole^{-1}$)	I	287	212	206	193	186	–
	II	867	647	680	630	658	
	III	1741	1302	1389	1278	1347	
	IV	7723	4069	2868	2616	2514	–
Metal radius (Å)		.88	1.43	1.22	1.62	1.71	
Ionic radius, M^{+3} (Å)			.50	.62	.81	.95	+
Melting point (°K)		2313	933	309.940	430	576.8	min
Boiling point (°K)			2600	1210	1200	1730	min
ΔH_{fus} (kcal $mole^{-1}$)			2.6	1.336	0.78	1.03	min
ΔH_{vap} (kcal $mole^{-1}$)			67.9	63.8	55.7	40	–
ΔH_{hyd} M^{+3} (kcal $mole^{-1}$)			−1103	−1109	−971	−989	min
S^0_{298} (cal $mole^{-1}$ $°K^{-1}$)		1.56	6.769	10.2	12.5	15.4	+
$\mathcal{E}^0$ [M ⟶ M(III)]		0.87	1.66	0.53	0.342	0.72	

GROUP IVA

Carbon (in the form of diamond) and its congener silicon have already been discussed. Neither shows much in the way of metallic properties, but graphitic carbon has many metallic properties, which indicate that there are close resemblances between the π electron systems in the graphite planes and the delocalized electrons found in metals. Metallic properties become increasingly noticeable down the column from C to Sn, and Pb is quite similar to Sn except for the greater stability range of its +2 oxidation state (owing to the inert $6s^2$ electrons). All elements in this group are known in both the −4, elementary, +2, and +4 oxidation states, but the −4 and +4 states become increasingly less stable as Z increases, −4 oxidizing to 0 and +4 reducing to +2. The +4 to +2 transition provides further evidence for the stability of the $6s^2$ and $5s^2$ electron pairs when underlain by a full set of d orbitals. The +4 state hydrolyzes strongly in water and forms halide and other complexes with a *CN* of 4 or 6. Figure 38.11 also indicates that the acidic properties of these elements are generally weak, and that the acidity of corresponding oxidation states decreases from C to Pb.

The sulfides and oxides are all insoluble in water but the oxides tend to be amphoteric, dissolving in either acid or basic solutions. Tin and lead are easily reduced from their ores and have been known since antiquity. Their uses are based mainly on the general inertness of the metals, which is due to an adherent oxide coating and, with lead, to the high density. Lead compounds were at one time one of the greatest sources of paint pigments but have been largely replaced by less toxic ones: TiO_2, for example, is now often used in place of white lead, whose approximate formula is $Pb_2(OH)_2CO_3$. Table 38.11 lists some properties of this group of elements.

Table 38.11 Some properties of the Group IVA elements.

Property		$C_{(diam)}$	Si	Ge	$Sn_{(white)}$	Pb	Trend (⟶)
Electron structure		2, 4	2, 8, 4	2, 8, 18, 4	2, 8, 18, 18, 4	2, 8, 18, 32, 18, 4	
I.E. ($kcal\ mole^{-1}$)	I	430	275	265	243	219	−
	II	992	650	633	581	567	−
	III	2096	1422	1422	1290	1308	min
	IV	3583	2462	2476	2231	2284	min
	V	12623	6307	4631	4094	3894	−
Metal radius (Å)		. . .	. . .	. . .	1.4	1.75	
Ionic radius, M^{++} (Å)		. . .	. . .	. . .	.9	1.1	
Melting point (°K)		4100	1683	1233	505.1	600.6	min
Boiling point (°K)			2950	3103	2600	2023	max
ΔH_{fus} ($kcal\ mole^{-1}$)			11	8.3	1.69	1.22	−
ΔH_{vap} ($kcal\ mole^{-1}$)						43.0	
ΔH_{hyd} M^{++} ($kcal\ mole^{-1}$)						−346	
S^0_{298} ($cal\ mole^{-1}\ °K^{-1}$)		0.5829	4.47	10.14	12.3	15.51	+
$\mathcal{E}^0$ [M ⟶ M(II)]		. . .	. . .	. . .	0.136	0.126	

Exercise 38.13

One of the crystal structures of tin is similar to that of diamond, but the crystalline tin is soft and a good conductor of electricity. Why? *Answer:* The electron levels in diamond are made up of $2s$, $2p$ orbitals. The next lowest lying are $3s$, which are so much higher in energy that electrons are localized and bonds are strongly directional. Tin has $5s$ and $5p$ orbitals but its $4d$ orbitals have almost as much energy. The net result is much broader crystal energy bands, greater delocalization of the electrons, higher conductivity, and less strongly oriented bonding orbitals.

TRANSITION METALS

Figure 38.12 presents pH-$\mathcal{E}$ diagrams for the d elements, which are often called transition elements. Note the redox and acid-base trends in the rows and in the families. Many of these elements show complex redox and acid-base relationships but the general variations with oxidation number and Z should be interpretable in terms of your experience thus far. The general inertness of Rh, Pd, Os, Ir, Pt, Ag, and Au should be apparent.

Recall that all compounds containing oxygen (oxides or hydroxides) become more powerful oxidizing agents as the pH falls, whereas simple monatomic ions have redox potentials independent of pH. This allows the experimental determination of the formulas of many complex ions in solution—those ions for which the variation of a reversible potential can be studied as a function of pH. Recall that the slope of such a curve for a hydroxide or oxide species is 0.059 (number of H^+)/(number of e^-) for the half-reaction involved. Similar deductions are possible for other complexing groups.

The elements in the *d* set most commonly studied are those in the Sc to Zn row. We shall also concentrate on them. Many of their properties have already been listed, and we shall not repeat them here. See Tables 4.2, electron structure; 5.7, melting point and boiling point; 14.3, metallic radii; 33.1, crystal structures and electrical conductivities; Figures 5.3, occurrence; 5.13, crystal structures; 5.19, molar volumes; 14.4, relative electronegativity; 29.5, entropies; 29.6 and 29.7, entropies and free energies of formation of oxides; 38.2, ionization energies; 38.5, oxidation states.

THE SCANDIUM FAMILY AND THE LANTHANIDES

The scandium family could just as well be considered as congeners of aluminum as *d* elements. The metal orbitals are such that the s^2d electrons are not greatly dissimilar in behavior to the s^2p electrons in Al. In both Al^{+++} and the M^{+++} ions of the scandium group the kernel has an inert-gas structure, the bonding in most substances both Al and the scandium group form is mainly ionic, and the *d* orbitals of the scandium family do not appear to have much effect on the properties of the substances. Note, for example, the regular gradation from Al^{+++} to La^{+++} in the *p*H at which the aqueous (III) ion is in equilibrium with the precipitated $M(OH)_3$. The trends, both in acid-base behavior and redox behavior, are very similar to those found in the alkaline-earth family. The occurrence of the lanthanide 3*f* elements from $Z = 57$ to 71, and the resulting increase of 32 in *Z* between the Zr and Hf rows of transition elements (rathes than 18 as between the Ti and Zr rows) makes the elements of the Hf row smaller in radius and less ready to lose electrons than might be expected. This effect, called the lanthanide contraction, strongly affects the properties of the Hf row.

Exercise 38.14

Discuss what you would observe as 1 *M* OH^- is added to 1 *M* Y^{+++}, initially of $pH = 0$. *Answer:* $Y^{+++}{}_{(aq)}$ has an inert gas structure and thus would be colorless, as is OH^-. As the two colorless solutions are mixed, the *p*H will rise. At $pH = 6.4$, white $Y(OH)_{3(c)}$ will begin to precipitate, as shown in Figure 38.17, and precipitation will be essentially complete at $pH = 8$. Since $pK_{sp} = 22.09$, the $[Y^{+++}] = 10^{-4}$ *M* when $[OH^-] = 10^{-6}$ *M*. Further additions of the 1 *M* OH^- will cause no observable change in the system (except that the volume of liquid increases, of course).

THE TITANIUM FAMILY (IVB)

The easy oxidation of Ti, Zr, and Hf to states higher than +2 ensures more complex redox and acid-base behavior than in groups IA, IIA, IIIA. This is reflected in Figure 38.12. The acidity increases as the positive oxidation state rises, and TiO_2, ZrO_2, and HfO_2 are inert to any but the most acidic substances. In fact, ZrO_2 and HfO_2 are so inert that they cover the whole *p*H-$\mathcal{E}$ stability range in water. The lattice energies of these two oxides are very high, and they are consequently inert to strong bases, are hard substances, and are difficult to melt. They are excellent refractory materials and may be used for furnace linings and crucibles designed to stand many unusually corrosive conditions at high temperatures. MgO and Al_2O_3

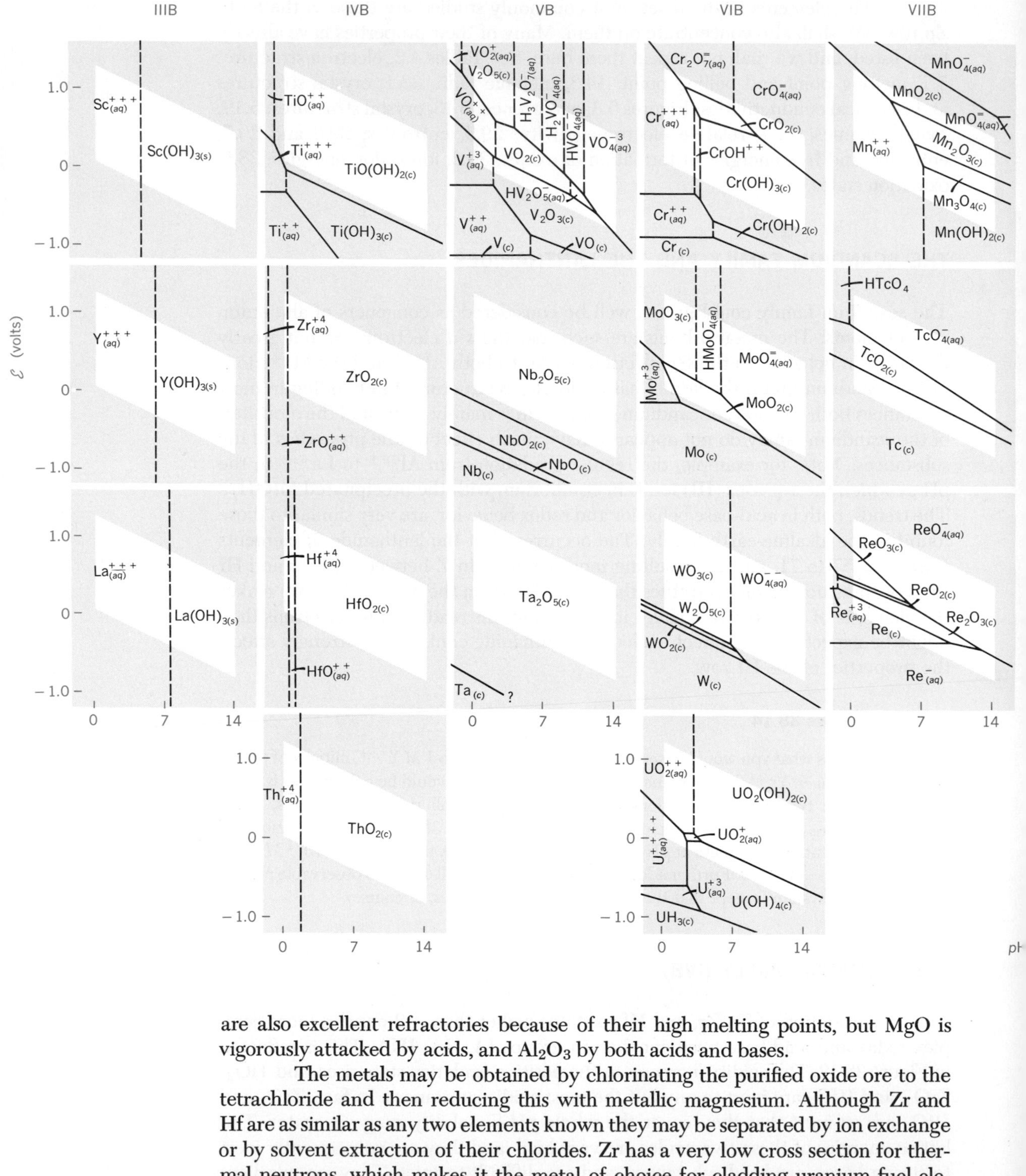

are also excellent refractories because of their high melting points, but MgO is vigorously attacked by acids, and Al_2O_3 by both acids and bases.

The metals may be obtained by chlorinating the purified oxide ore to the tetrachloride and then reducing this with metallic magnesium. Although Zr and Hf are as similar as any two elements known they may be separated by ion exchange or by solvent extraction of their chlorides. Zr has a very low cross section for thermal neutrons, which makes it the metal of choice for cladding uranium fuel elements in nuclear reactors. Its other appreciable use (5% of the 1000 tons per year produced) is in flash bulbs.

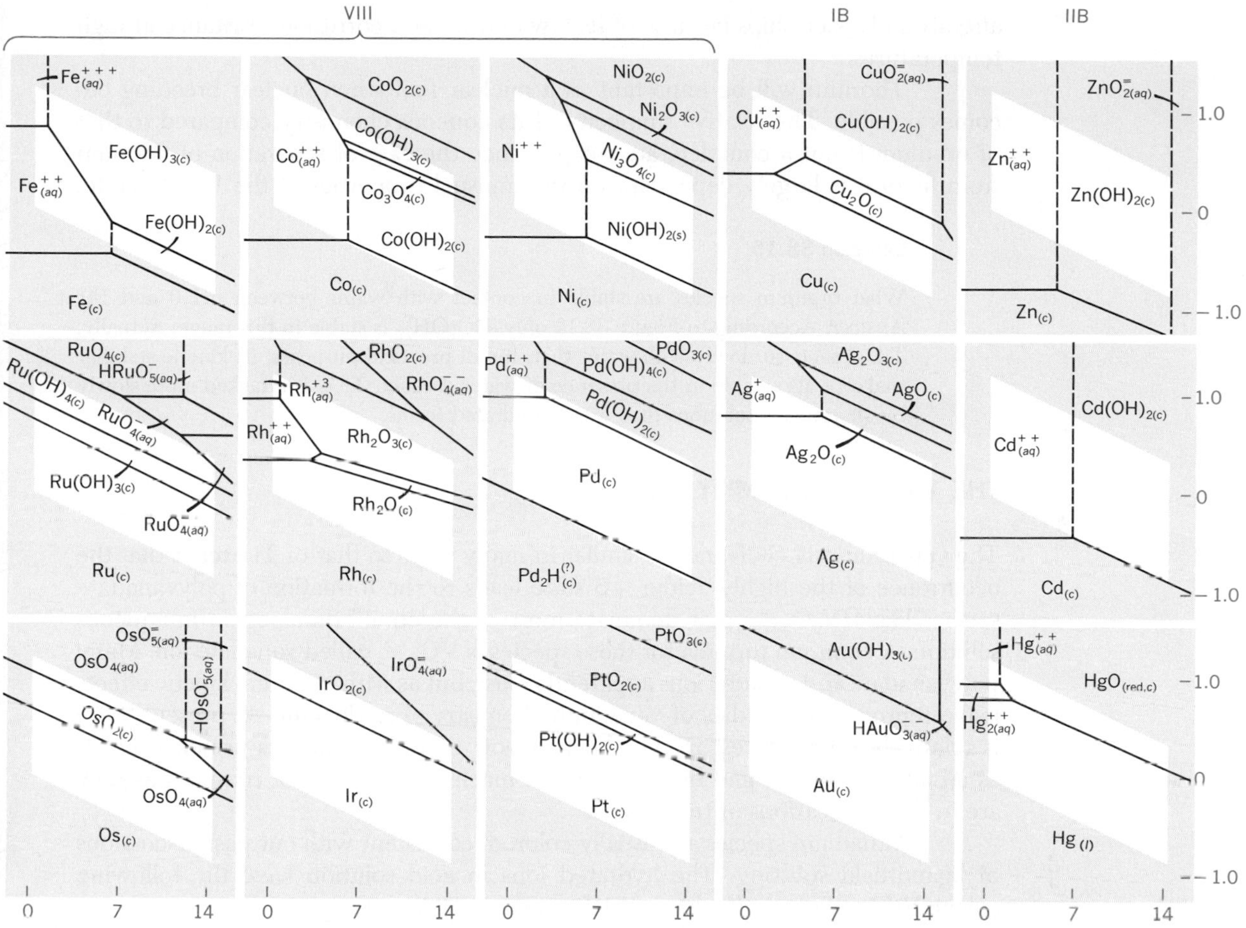

Figure 38.12 pH-ℰ diagrams for the transition (*d*) elements.

The general chemistry of titanium has been determined, but kinetic effects make reproducibility of results very difficult and it is one of the most promising of all elements for further work. Its ores are plentiful (see Table 37.1) and the metal has a superb combination of low density and high resistance to oxidation (owing to an adherent coat of highly inert TiO_2). At present, however, both reduction of the metal from its oxide ore and forming it into desired shapes are expensive operations. Someday, presumably, a simple method of reduction will be discovered and an easily workable alloy developed, thus allowing full exploitation of titanium. But even at the 1969 price of \$3 a pound, it is the metal of choice for high-speed aircraft and space ships because of its low density and corrosion resistance at high temperatures.

Thorium will be important as a nuclear fuel when nuclear breeding becomes possible. The relative simplicity of its aqueous chemistry compared to that of uranium is not a complete advantage, since the ease of separation of uranium from its ores is largely dependent on the unusual properties of the UO_2^{++} state.

Exercise 38.15

What titanium species are stable in contact with water between *p*H 0 and 14? *Answer:* According to Figure 38.12 only $TiO(OH)_2$ is stable in this range. Actually, TiO_2 reacts so slowly with water that, for all practical purposes, its kinetic stability makes it also stable in the presence of water. In fact, TiO_2 is attacked more slowly by all aqueous solutions than are its hydrated forms.

THE VANADIUM FAMILY (VB)

The vanadium *p*H-$\mathcal{E}$ diagram is similar in many ways to that of Ti except that the occurrence of the highly acidic +5 state leads to the formation of polyvanadate species like $HV_6O_{17}^{-3}$ that dominate most of the equilibrium region in aqueous solution. A common formula for these species is VO_4^{-3}, called vanadate ion. Many polyvanadate and vanadyl ions apparently exist, but as with titanium, kinetic effects make reproducible studies of vanadium chemistry very difficult. At present there is relatively little interest in the chemistry of vanadium since its principal use is as an alloying metal, and high purity and machinability are not required as they are in the applications of titanium.

Vanadium species are usually colored, consistent with our past discussions of ligand-field splitting. The hydrated ions in acid solution have the following colors: V(V) yellow, V(IV) blue, V(III) green, V(II) violet.

Niobium and tantalum are used mainly in special alloys. Their aqueous solutions are, like those of vanadium, complicated by the existence of many poly ions which come to equilibrium only slowly.

Exercise 38.16

What would you expect to observe if a vanadate solution of *p*H 3.4 were shaken with metallic zinc? *Answer:* Metallic Zn has a reduction potential of about 0.7 volts at *p*H 3.4, sufficient to reduce the VO_4^{-3} to V^{++} (but not to V). Thus the color of the solution would change from yellow (VO_4^{-3}) to blue (VO^{++}), to green (V^{+++}), to violet (V^{++}) as the successive steps in the process occur. You should also expect to see intermediate colors (probably green between the yellow of pure VO_4^{-3} and the blue of pure VO^{++}) when appreciable amounts of more than one V species are present.

THE CHROMIUM FAMILY (VIB)

We shall not discuss the chemistry of Mo, W, and U (remember that uranium is also included in the actinides) except to remind you of the vital role a knowledge of uranium chemistry now plays in making possible the construction of nuclear power plants—just in time to replace conventional power plants as the earth's fossil fuels become exhausted—and that the modern electric light would be impossible except for the combination of properties found in tungsten. It is much easier to prepare pure elements of this family than pure elements of the more metallic families. Cr may be obtained from Cr_2O_3 with either C or Al; Mo and W are commonly reduced from their oxides with hydrogen. Uranium can be reduced in similar ways or can be electrolyzed from UF_4 dissolved in a mixture of molten $CaCl_2$ and NaCl.

The chemistry of all the elements of this family is complicated by the number of species that can exist in aqueous solution. There are for example, probably more known chromium-containing species than species of any other metallic element. Most of these contain Cr(III). As shown in Figure 38.12, Cr^{++} reduces water to hydrogen and Cr(VI) exists mainly in the equilibria

$$\underset{\text{yellow}}{2CrO_4{}^{=}{}_{(aq)}} + 2H^+{}_{(aq)} = \underset{\text{orange}}{2HCrO_4{}^-{}_{(aq)}} = \underset{\text{orange}}{Cr_2O_7{}^{=}{}_{(aq)}} + H_2O$$

The Cr(VI) species form strong acids and are rapid and powerful oxidizing agents, especially, of course, in highly acid solutions where $Cr_2O_7{}^{=}$ ions and higher polychromate ions predominate. They are often used as oxidizing agents in chemical analysis. The species are not colored intensely enough to serve as their own end-point indicators (as is $MnO_4{}^-{}_{(aq)}$), so the end point is determined potentiometrically or by an additional redox chemical indicator in the system. Chromates have properties similar to those of the corresponding sulfates except for their color, which is due to ligand field splitting of the d levels in $CrO_4{}^{=}$.

We have already referred frequently to chromium and its +3 oxidation state. Cr(III) is almost always octahedrally coordinated; for example, $Cr(H_2O)_6{}^{+++}$ is the purple ion common in its dilute aqueous solutions. Precipitation of hydrous $Cr(OH)_{3(c)}$ is accounted for in terms of loss of H^+ from the coordinated waters. Upon standing in strong HCl solutions $Cr(H_2O)_6{}^{+++}$ is converted to green $CrCl(H_2O)_5{}^{++}$, $CrCl_2(H_2O)_4{}^+$, and $CrCl_3(H_2O)_3$. These complexes are kinetically inert and hold the Cl so tightly that addition of aqueous $AgNO_3$ does not precipitate the chloride. Study of the octahedral Cr(III) complexes has given a great many insights into the factors affecting structure, rate, mechanisms, and energetics of reactions, and an appreciable percentage of the ideas we have discussed in this book have been developed with the help of this species.

The compound CrO_2 is best thought of as a compound of basic Cr(III) and acidic Cr(VI) as in $(CrO)_2CrO_4$, chromyl chromate, rather than as containing +4 chromium. CrO_2 is thermodynamically stable, but is not readily formed from aqueous solutions because of kinetic effects [probably associated with the tendency of Cr(III) to form octahedral complexes rather than CrO^+ ions].

THE MANGANESE FAMILY (VIIB)

Technetium has no stable isotopes and rhenium is a rare element, but manganese and its compounds are common chemicals. The metal is used in many steels and forms highly ferromagnetic alloys when mixed with aluminum, antimony, and a little copper. (Note that none of these elements is ferromagnetic in its stable form at room temperature.) The dioxide is a powerful oxidation catalyst and is used as the oxidizing agent in dry cells. The net reaction may be written

$$Zn_{(c)} + 4NH_4{}^+{}_{(aq)} + MnO_{2(c)} = Zn(NH_3)_4{}^{++}{}_{(aq)} + Mn^{++}{}_{(aq)} + 2H_2O$$

The most common laboratory compound of manganese is potassium permanganate—one of the most widely used powerful oxidizing agents.

Figure 38.12 shows that MnO_4^- should oxidize water at all pH's. But the reaction is slow and $MnO_4^-{}_{(aq)}$ is a kinetically stable species in the absence of other reducing agents. With most reducing agents other than water, reaction is rapid, however, especially in the presence of a small amount of $Mn^{++}{}_{(aq)}$. In highly basic solutions green $MnO_4^={}_{(aq)}$ forms; in weakly basic and weakly acidic solutions brown $MnO_2 \cdot nH_2O_{(c)}$ forms; and in strong acid pink $Mn^{++}{}_{(aq)}$ is the final product. It is the $MnO_4^-{}_{(aq)} \longrightarrow Mn^{++}{}_{(aq)}$ change in acid which is most used. We discussed this reaction at some length on pages 946–951.

The mechanism of the $MnO_4^-{}_{(aq)} \longrightarrow Mn^{++}{}_{(aq)}$ is still not completely understood even though it was one of the earliest reactions studied (in 1865). But the loss of four oxygens and the change in oxidation state from +7 to +2 clearly must require three or more consecutive steps, all of which must be rapid.

GROUP VIII

Iron, cobalt, and nickel are common elements, especially iron and nickel. The principal difference most people note is that iron is cheap but corrodes, whereas nickel is expensive but stays shiny. The difference, as Figure 38.12 shows, does not lie primarily in the metallic state but in the nature of the oxide: nickel is oxidized to the +2 oxide, which adheres tightly to nickel; iron is oxidized to +3, which flakes off. Fe_3O_4 does adhere tightly to iron, but it is black, not transparent in thin layers as is the nickel oxide. We discussed the preparation of iron on pages 137–141, and its rusting on pages 825–827. Rusting is certainly one of the chemical reactions that is most damaging to civilization as we know it; the cost of replacing materials damaged by rust is several billion dollars a year.

Ru, Rh, Pd, Os, Ir, Pt are noble metals. All form adherent oxide coats but all except Ru would be reasonably inert toward water in any case, though not toward oxygen. The pure metals are rather soft, but harden when alloyed with one another, primarily because the differences in sizes of the molecules interfere with the formation of slip planes in the alloys.

The elements of this group form an enormous number of complex ions and coordination compounds. Platinum is probably a close runner-up to chromium in terms of its contribution to chemistry through study of its complexes. Many of the complexes cited in Chapter 37 were formed of elements from group VIII.

The appellation group VIII deserves some comment. As with other groups it indicates the maximum observed oxidation state, as in OsO_4, RuO_4. But it is difficult to see why this is the maximum in terms of electron structures or I.E.'s. The maximum may well be set by the maximum *CN* of powerful complexers like F^-, CN^-, or $O^=$ around these relatively small atoms. There probably just isn't room for $CN > 8$ even though electron structures might seem to permit higher oxidation states. As a matter of fact, this maximum oxidation state is seldom found; the +2 and +3 states are much more stable and hence more common. Thus Fe, Co, Ni typically lose their two *s* electrons to form $M^{++}_{(aq)}$. Fe^{+++} is also formed readily, presumably because the electron repulsion in the d^6 Fe^{++} is greater than that in the d^5 Fe^{+++}. This repulsion, plus the additional coulombic forces in Fe^{+++} complexes, more than equals the work required to ionize an additional electron. Ni and Co do not have such an easy option available, and thus tend to stabilize at M(II). Strong complexers will form M(III), especially with cobalt.

Exercise 38.17

Oxalic acid is useful in removing rust stains. Write a possible net chemical equation. *Answer:* Oxalate is a bidentate complexer and Fe^{+++} tends to form octahedral complexes:

$$Fe_2O_3 \cdot nH_2O_{(c)} + 6H_2C_2O_{4(aq)} = 2Fe(C_2O_4)_3{}^{-3}{}_{(aq)} + (3 + n)H_2O + 6H^+{}_{(aq)}$$

THE COPPER GROUP (IB)

We have used copper and silver frequently for examples of various things. Gold forms many complexes but it is its inertness as a metal which accounts for most of its uses. The family has many interesting chemical properties, and is set off from all other families in two especially apparent ways: (1) two of the metals are colored—a rare property—and (2) the most common oxidation states in aqueous systems are +2, +1, and +3, respectively, for Cu, Ag, and Au. Earlier in this chapter we discussed the oxidation states of copper. Unfortunately similar thermodynamic data are not available for silver and gold nor are there enough data to carry out Born-Haber cycles for the three elements. Thus it is impossible to assess, at this time, what balance of terms leads to the observed behaviors.

The colors of Cu and Au clearly indicate crystal energy levels with a spacing corresponding to the wavelength of visible light; such spacing is not present in silver, which is an almost perfect reflector. The theories that correlate these effects are too complex to be studied here.

The acid-base behavior does follow predictions, as the *p*H's at which precipitation occurs show in Figure 38.12: Ag^+-AgOH, $pH = 8.0$; Cu^{++}-$Cu(OH)_2$, $pH = 4.6$; Au^{+++}-$Au(OH)_3$, $pH = -0.3$.

It is worth noting that the ease of oxidation of the metals increases greatly in families IA, and IIA as Z increases, that in family IB the reverse is true, and that family VIIA acts like IA. Thus we see that at the ends of the rows in the periodic table the elements become easier to oxidize as Z increases, but that in the middle they become harder to oxidize. Close study of Figure 38.7 shows that some of this effect is attributable to the lanthanide contraction and the greater resulting rise in I.E. in the Hf–Hg row than in the Zr–Cd row. But a large part must result from *d* electrons having less shielding effect on the valence *s* electrons than *p* electrons do: this poor shielding is also a main cause of the lanthanide contraction.

THE ZINC GROUP

Zinc, cadmium, and mercury have many industrial uses. Zinc and cadmium are two of the plating metals most widely used to protect iron where a high luster is not required in the plate. The protection is partly due to an adherent oxide-carbonate coating on the zinc or cadmium, partly to the close adherence of the metals to iron, and partly to the reducing nature of Zn and Cd compared to Fe. Even if the plating is abraded and part of the iron is exposed, there is little corrosion of the iron, since the Zn or Cd are more easily oxidized and thus tend to minimize the reaction of the iron with the oxidizing agent.

Mercury has a low melting point, a convenient liquid range, and an approximately constant coefficient of thermal expansion—hence its use in thermometers. Some mercuric compounds are used in explosive caps and detonators. Mercury tends to form relatively weak covalent bonds with N and O—bonds that have low activation energies to breaking and are often exothermic with respect to other bonding possibilities. Mercury isocyanate is a common detonator:

	ΔH^0	ΔS^0	ΔG^0
$Hg(ONC)_2 = Hg_{(g)} + 2CO_{(g)} + N_{2(g)}$,	-110 kcal mole^{-1}	$\sim$40 eu	~ -130 kcal mole^{-1}

Two of the most common mercury compounds are Hg_2Cl_2 (calomel), an internal medicine, and $HgCl_2$ (corrosive sublimate), a deadly poison: the systematic names are mercurous chloride [or dimercury (I) dichloride] and mercuric chloride [or mercury(II) dichloride]. Mercury in all forms is poisonous to humans, but Hg_2Cl_2 is very slightly soluble in body fluids (and is not oxidized by intestinal juices), whereas $HgCl_2$ is soluble—especially in the HCl found in the stomach, with which it forms $HgCl_4^{=}$. The small concentration of Hg_2^{++} from the Hg_2Cl_2 can be beneficial, but the large concentration of $HgCl_4^{=}$, or $HgCl_2$, can be lethal. *Moral:* Always read the label at least twice and think!

Exercise 38.18

Draw an electron structure for Hg_2^{++}. *Answer:* Hg^+ ions would each have a single 6*s* electron. Hg_2^{++} apparently pairs up these electrons (the ions are diamagnetic) so that the two atoms share two electrons in their bonding 6*s* orbital $[Hg\text{-}Hg]^{++}$.

SUMMARY

The periodic table is the most powerful correlative device available to chemists because it is based on electron structures and nuclear charges, which are the determinants of interatomic interactions. Knowledge of the variation of electron structure, I.E., and atomic and ionic sizes allows the classification of a great deal of information on structure, energetics, and dynamics of chemical systems. Devices such as *p*H-$\mathcal{E}$ diagrams and thermodynamic and kinetic data can summarize properties in numerical terms. These, too, may be correlated with the periodic table.

Since a very great deal of chemistry can be interpreted in terms of redox and acid-base behavior, *p*H-$\mathcal{E}$ diagrams and a knowledge of the concepts used to interpret complex formation can supply quick guidance to the solution of chemical problems, which can then be checked with detailed calculations.

Oxidation of the elements becomes easier as Z increases for elements at the ends of the rows in the periodic table, but more difficult for those in the middle families (remember the inertness of Pt compared to Ni, and the greater ease of oxidation of I_2 compared to F_2). This is most simply explained by the greater effectiveness of *p* electrons than of *d* electrons in shielding *s* electrons from nuclear attraction.

The acidic properties of any element increase with increasing oxidation state, and those of the elements in each row increase with Z as long as the oxidation state is constant. This trend is most noticeable in acid-base behavior involving H^+, OH^-, and H_2O. If other complexing groups are added the trends are the same but at least three bases are present (OH^-, H_2O, and the complexer) and the competitive situation is much less simple.

Order and simplification are the first steps toward the mastery of a subject—the actual enemy is the unknown.— Thomas Mann

---

PROBLEMS

38.1. Explain the following, using equations where possible.
(*a*) Chlorine will bleach dyes only if water is present.
(*b*) Sulfur is very fluid when heated just to the melting point, but becomes very viscous if heated to a higher temperature.
(*c*) Copper hydroxide is insoluble in water, but soluble in ammonia water.
(*d*) Sodium carbonate, a salt, can be used to neutralize an acid such as hydrochloric.

38.2. How do you account for the fact that all surface deposits of alkali metal halides are found in desert regions?

38.3. Considering only the alkali metals (Group I in the periodic table), list the one which has the mentioned property in each case in the following list. Give reasons for your answers. M represents a general symbol for any one of these elements as used below. (Do not consider element 87.)
(*a*) Which will be the best reducing agent?
(*b*) Which is the cheapest to prepare?
(*c*) Which will form the strongest base of the formula MOH?
(*d*) Which will react most violently with water?

38.4. Rationalize the high corrosion resistance of objects made from metallic zirconium to concentrated sulfuric and hydrochloric acids in the light of Figure 38.12. Why not build the vessels of the much cheaper oxides?

38.5. Thallium forms two stable chlorides: $TlCl$ and $TlCl_3$. One is soluble in water, the other is not. Which is which and why?

38.6. $BaSO_{4(c)}$ is often fed patients so their digestive tract may be X-rayed. Occasionally the person in charge makes a mistake, feeds $BaCO_{3(c)}$, and the patient dies. How do you account for the different physiological effects in terms of the properties of these two substances?

38.7. Rationalize the observation that, at all temperatures, the equilibrium pressure of $CO_{2(g)}$ is greater over $CaCO_{3(c)}$ than over $Na_2CO_{3(c)}$. Where would K_2CO_3 fit in this sequence?

38.8. Pure liquid H_3PO_4 has a relatively high electrical conductivity which is decreased by the addition of ionic substances. [Munson, 1967.] Suggest a mechanism for the conductivity and for the mode of action of the added ions.

II

38.9. For each of the following pairs indicate a single reagent that would distinguish between the two substances in the pairs and write the equations for the reactions that occur.
(*a*) Na_2S and Na_2O. (*b*) HOH and HBr. (*c*) CO_2 and CH_4.

38.10. If the following pairs are mixed in water solution, indicate whether or not there is a reaction, write the equations for the reactions that occur, and indicate which reactions are oxidation-reduction reactions, naming the oxidizing agent and reducing agent. (*a*) Sodium hydroxide and hydrogen iodide. (*b*) Hydrogen sulfide and sulfur dioxide. (*c*) Sodium and chlorine. (*d*) Sulfur trioxide and water.

38.11. Indicate whether or not an appreciable reaction occurs if the following compounds are mixed in water solution. If there is reaction, write the net equation. If the reaction involves oxidation and reduction, indicate the oxidizing and reducing agent.
(*a*) Iodine and potassium iodide.
(*b*) Manganese dioxide and hydrochloric acid.
(*c*) Nitric acid and potassium hydroxide.
(*d*) Silver fluoride and ammonia water.
(*e*) Ferric chloride and sodium iodide.
(*f*) Iron and bromine.

38.12. Write a balanced equation for the net reaction in each of the following. If no reaction occurs, write "none."
(*a*) Hydrogen is passed over hot Fe_3O_4.
(*b*) Hydrochloric acid is added to a solution of silver nitrate.
(*c*) A pearl is dropped into a bottle of vinegar.
(*d*) Sodium chlorate is melted in a dry container.
(*e*) Hydrogen sulfide is bubbled into 6 *F* nitric acid.
(*f*) Chlorine is generated commercially. List all necessary reagents.

38.13. Account for the color trend: ZnS, white; CdS, yellow; HgS, black.

38.14. What would you expect to observe if a good reducing agent were slowly added to $MnO_4{}^-{}_{(aq)}$ solution of *p*H 14? How about at *p*H 0? Be as quantitative as possible.

38.15. What would you expect to observe if 2 *M* $OH^-{}_{(aq)}$ were slowly added to a 1 *M* solution of $Cr^{+++}{}_{(aq)}$ initially at *p*H 0.

38.16. Discuss the probable relative rates of reaction of the alkaline earth metals with water.

III

38.17. Interpret the monotonic change of $\mathcal{E}^0$ with Z for the alkaline earth metals in contrast to the nonmonotonic changes for the alkali metals.

38.18. After a flood in your basement you find that four identical bottles have lost their labels. You know these bottles contain sodium fluoride (a roach poison), sodium carbonate, alundum (Al_2O_3), and flour. There is no visible difference since all four bottles contain finely ground white powder. How would you distinguish the four using only the materials available in any home kitchen?

38.19. Estimate the feasibility of synthesizing crystalline ScCl or $ScCl_2$.

See page 1095 for a list of references and readings in the recent chemical literature related to the material in this chapter.

CHAPTER 39

Polymers

KENNETH M. HARMON

If a given reaction will join two functional groups together, and if there are at least two functional groups per molecule, then the possibility of polymerization exists.

The chemistry that is discussed in textbooks, lectured about in chemistry courses, and investigated in research laboratories, is in large part the chemistry of small molecules; generally speaking, substances of low molecular weight are easier to prepare, examine, and discuss than are substances with large or complex molecules. Macromolecular materials, however, are of vital importance to us: a great many of the substances that go to make up living things are of very high molecular weight, and there is a vast array of familiar things—that we eat, wear, drive, watch, listen to, build with, paint with, fish with, or ski on—that are made up in whole or in part from macromolecules. A significant part of academic research, a large part of industrial research, and most of biochemical research is devoted to the investigation of both natural and man-made materials of high molecular weight.

We have already noted a wide variety of macromolecular substances, including diamond and graphite (p. 385), a variety of nonmetallic oxides (p. 420), amorphous sulfur (p. 150), silica (p. 642), silicate anions (p. 644), silicones (p. 646), and boron nitride (p. 650). Several of these are simply extended arrays of atoms, but others could be said to be polymeric; that is, they are made up of discrete, repeating units that are, themselves, recognizable chemical entities. In this chapter we begin with a general discussion of polymers, note briefly some natural examples, and then examine in some detail a variety of man-made polymeric materials.

POLYMERS: TERMS

Polymers are substances that are formed by joining together small, identifiable molecular species (*meros* is Greek for parts), usually in a regular, repeating pattern (*poly* is Greek for many). The species linked together to form the polymer are called monomers. A polymer formed by linking together one type of monomer is a homopolymer; one formed by linking two or more monomer types is a copolymer. When two, three, or four monomer units (whether identical or different) are linked together, the polymers so formed are usually termed dimers, trimers, and tetramers, respectively. Polymers that are formed from a very large number of monomer units are called high polymers, and in practice the word polymer usually means a high polymer. A polymer does not have a fixed molecular weight, since the number of monomers that join to form its macromolecules is affected by the conditions under which polymerization takes place. A sample of any polymer contains molecules of many different weights: the molecular weight of polyisobutylene may vary from 40,000 to 4,000,000, depending on the degree of polymerization. Figure 39.1 shows some polymer terms.

It is obvious from examination of the formula of most polymers what the repeating unit is; in polyethylene glycol, for example, the unit is $—CH_2CH_2—O—$. But an easy determination is not always possible; there is no way to determine by examination of polyethylene from just what monomer it was made. The polymer might be formed by joining methylene units ($—CH_2—$) generated in the decomposition of diazomethane, CH_2N_2, or it might be prepared from $—CH_2CH_2CH_2—$ units obtained by opening the ring of cyclopropane. The name polyethylene is used for this polymer because it is, in fact, prepared from ethylene gas. We should note, also, that even when the repeating unit can be clearly identified it is not always obvious what monomer was used to make the polymer. The material we have shown as polyethylene glycol in Figure 39.1 is more commonly known as polyethylene oxide, since it is usually prepared commercially from the monomer ethylene oxide, $\overset{O}{H_2C—CH_2}$. One last point of confusion: a substance may have a formula identical with that of a polymer, but not be one; thus a very long straight chain alkene (p. 512) isolated from crude oil would be essentially identical with polyethylene of low molecular weight, but would be considered a discrete chemical entity. Such large molecules are called macromolecules. Polymers are macromolecules, but macromolecules need not be polymers. Similarly, cyclohexane could be considered a trimer of ethylene but never is, since it is neither made from nor reverts to ethylene. Nor is cyclohexane considered a macromolecule; the term is usually reserved for substances containing at least 100 atoms.

In practice, then, when we call a substance a polymer we are talking about a species that is either biologically or chemically built up from smaller units; the

$HO—CH_2CH_2—OH$	Ethylene glycol (monomer)
$HO—CH_2CH_2—O—CH_2CH_2—OH$	Diethylene glycol (dimer)
$HO—CH_2CH_2—O—CH_2CH_2—O—CH_2CH_2—OH$	Triethylene glycol (trimer)
$(—O—CH_2CH_2—O—CH_2CH_2—O—CH_2CH_2—)_x$	Polyethylene glycol (polymer)
$CH_2{=}CH_2$	Ethylene or ethene (monomer)
$(—CH_2CH_2CH_2CH_2CH_2CH_2CH_2CH_2CH_2CH_2—)_x$	Polyethylene (polymer)

Figure 39.1 Polymer terms.

name will often (but by no means always) indicate the actual substance from which the polymer was prepared.

Polymers are generally assigned to one of two major classes, according to the mode of their formation. Examination of the structure of diethylene glycol relative to the monomer (Figure 39.1) will show that the elements of one molecule of water are lost when two molecules of ethylene glycol dimerize. As the extent of polymerization increases, we find that one water molecule is lost for each monomer unit added to the polymer. Polymers that form with a concurrent loss of small molecules (H_2O, CO_2, NH_3, etc.) as the links are joined are called condensation polymers. In a condensation polymer the repeating unit is always of a lower molecular weight than the monomer. In polyethylene, however, all of the atoms in the ethylene molecule are in the polymer chain; the links have been formed by converting the internal carbon-carbon double bond in the ethylene molecule to intermolecular carbon-carbon single bonds. Polymers that are formed by such self-addition of either unsaturated molecules (molecules containing multiple bonds, such as ethylene) or cyclic molecules (molecules such as ethylene oxide) are called addition polymers. In an addition polymer the atom count of the repeating unit is always the same as that of the monomer.

We should note two additional terms before leaving Figure 39.1. One is degree of polymerization, n, which is the number of moles of monomer per mole of polymer. For triethylene glycol, $n = 3$; for polyethylene glycol as shown, $n = 3x$; and for polyethylene, $n = 5x$. The second term is end group; there must, after all, be something on the end of the long polymer chains. The end groups of polyethylene glycol will usually be hydroxyl groups, and the most common end groups on polyethylene are methyl groups or $—CH{=}CH_2$ groups.

Exercise 39.1

Which of the following would probably form condensation and which addition polymers? *(a)* $CH_2{=}CHCH_3$, *(b)* $\triangle$, *(c)* $(CH_2OH)_2$, *(d)* S_2, *(e)* $(CH_2)_3(COOH)_2$, *(f)* $CH_3—CH\overset{O}{\frown}CH_2$ (epoxide ring: CH—O—CH₂ bridged). *Answer:* Condensation: *(c)* loss of H_2O, *(e)* loss of H_2O. All the rest involve addition either through a double bond or a cyclic structure that opens to a linear one.

PHYSICAL STATE OF POLYMERS

The physical state of a polymer, like that of any other molecular substance, is primarily a function of the interactions between the individual molecules. Since most polymers contain a long chain or backbone of repeating structure within their makeup, a reasonable model is a dish of cooked noodles. The noodles may be short, long, coiled, straight, or lumpy, and they may be stuck together in various ways, each of which will result in changes in the way they feel and act.

If we prepare two dishes, one in which the noodles have been chopped short and one in which they are very long, we will find that the chopped portion will pour, stir, or deform much more easily than the other—the long strands will have difficulty slipping around and past each other and the whole mass will tend to move as a ball. The same effect is found in polymers; many polymers of low molecular weight (short chain length) are liquids, and most of those of high molecular weight are viscous or rigid, or even crystalline. With many simple polymers a gradual increase in molecular weight will give a range of materials ranging from mobile liquids through viscous fluids, or from semisolid greases to tough solids; remember liquid sulfur (p. 153). If the dish of long noodles is held at an angle for a while, the strands may slowly slip around each other and the mass will creep downhill; this is an example of plastic flow. The same thing is observed when stress is applied to polymers composed of simple unbranched chains: slowly applied pressure causes plastic flow. Or, if we suddenly push against the noodles, they jam together and move as a mass; if there are enough of them, they don't move at all. The same effect is observed with many polymers of intermediate chain length; the most familiar example is the silicone material sold under the name of Silly Putty. This material resists a strong blow or shatters if the blow is hard enough, but if pressed slowly, it flows like a very heavy liquid.

Many polymeric materials show no more order than a dish of noodles, and such materials are said to be *amorphous* polymers (see Figure 39.2). They normally undergo plastic flow. The ease of plastic flow is increased by heating, for the energy added to the molecules allows them to slip around each other more easily by increasing molecular motion, separating the molecules, and overcoming the van der Waals forces (p. 347) that hold the chains together. Such polymers gradually soften on heating and harden again when cooled; they are said to be *thermoplastic*.

If the forces between chains are fairly large and the chains are either unsubstituted or very regularly substituted, a polymer may form a crystalline solid. Few polymers are completely crystalline, but many consist of crystalline regions, called crystallites, surrounded by amorphous regions. Such substances are fairly rigid up to the melting point of the crystallites, and are thermoplastic above that point.

If the chains of a polymer are joined together by actual covalent chemical bonds (called cross-links), plastic flow is greatly retarded; if the number of cross-links is high enough, the material will be a rigid solid and will not show plastic flow

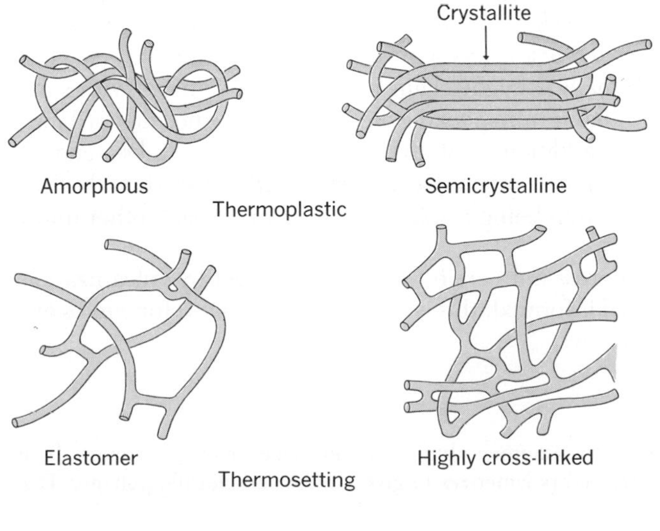

Figure 39.2 Schematic representation of chains in some polymer types.

until the temperature is high enough to rupture chemical bonds. Such materials are called thermosetting polymers.

Exercise 39.2

Rationalize the fact that sulfur becomes very hard if ethylene is bubbled into the hot liquid. *Answer:* Sulfur has either a ring or an unsaturated chain structure. $CH_2{=}CH_2$ is also unsaturated. The two can form an addition copolymer whose chains consist of alternating sulfur and C_2H_4 segments.

NATURAL RUBBER

Natural rubber is a hydrocarbon isolated from the sap of the rubber tree, *Hevea brasiliensis;* it has the empirical formula C_5H_8 and a molecular weight ranging from 50,000 to 3,000,000. Natural rubber has been shown to be an addition polymer of isoprene, a five-carbon diene (Figure 39.3).

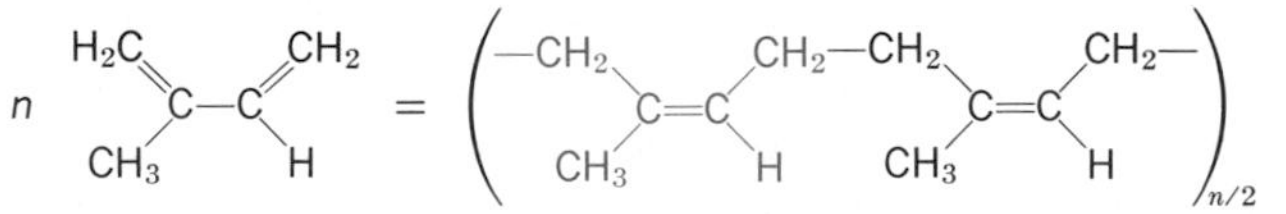

Figure 39.3 Polymerization of isoprene to natural rubber, all-*cis*-polyisoprene.

Besides having a long polymer chain, or backbone, as do polyethylene glycol and polyethylene, the rubber molecule has methyl side groups. In natural rubber the methyl group and the hydrogen attached to the carbons bearing the double bond are always *cis* (p. 512) to each other; rubber is thus an isotactic polymer (see Figure 39.6).

When the rubber hydrocarbon is first isolated from the sap it is thermoplastic, becoming sticky when warm and hard when cold, and it undergoes plastic flow. It is converted to its common, usable elastic form by a process known as vulcanization; this involves heating a mixture of the raw hydrocarbon and sulfur to introduce cross-links between the chains.

If a small amount of cross-linking is introduced, the rubber becomes an elastomer, which is a general name for substances that can be stretched or deformed but that return to their original size and shape when the stress is removed (see Figure 39.2). Elastomers are usually straight-chain amorphous polymers with small side groups that prevent the chains from packing well; this lowers the van der Waals attractions between chains. In addition, elastomers have a few cross-links—enough to cause the chains to return to their original arrangement after distortion, but not enough to prevent the chains from being displaced in relation to each other under stress.

If a large number of cross-links are introduced in rubber by vulcanization, a rigid, thermosetting material is formed; this is the hard rubber used for combs and the cases of lead storage batteries.

Exercise 39.3

Butadiene is similar to isoprene but has no side methyl group. It is $CH_2{=}CH{-}CH{=}CH_2$ and polymerizes to give a rather nonflexible polymer. Diagram the structure of the polymer and rationalize its rigidity. *Answer:* If it polymerizes like isoprene, the structure will be $(\text{—CH}_2\text{—CH=CH—CH}_2\text{—})_n$. The lack of methyl groups allows close packing of the long molecules and the presence of the double bonds restricts free rotation. Thus it is more rigid than rubber (which has the methyl group) or polyethylene (which has no double bonds).

CELLULOSE

Cellulose is a natural polymer that forms the structural material of plant cells. It is of great importance to mankind, whether used directly in the form of wood (which derives its strength from cellulose), cotton (which is almost pure cellulose), or grass (which is converted to meat by domestic animals), or in such modified forms as paper or rayon.

Cellulose is a condensation polymer of the sugar glucose, as shown in Figure 39.4. Glucose plays an important role in animal metabolism; most of our foodstuffs are converted in the body to glucose, and the glucose itself is consumed in the energy-releasing reactions within the cells. Most animals cannot depolymerize cellulose to glucose, but certain microorganisms can (also the snail). Animals such as termites or the grazing mammals that live largely on cellulose are able to do so because their stomachs contain colonies of microorganisms that can break down cellulose to glucose. A great deal of research has gone into the development of chemical methods of preparing glucose for human consumption from cellulose (wood) but food shortages have not yet reached the point where it is economically reasonable to do so on a large scale.

Some of the first plastics, or synthetic polymers, to be produced commercially were modified celluloses, and many are still in use. Rayon fibers for textiles are prepared by dissolving cellulose in carbon disulfide, CS_2, and base; in this process the chains are partly broken down. The mixture is then acidified and the precipitated polymer is spun into thread. Cellulose nitrate and cellulose acetate are prepared by forming ester links (p. 519) between the hydroxyl groups on the cellulose chains and nitric and acetic acids, respectively. The nitrate is used for

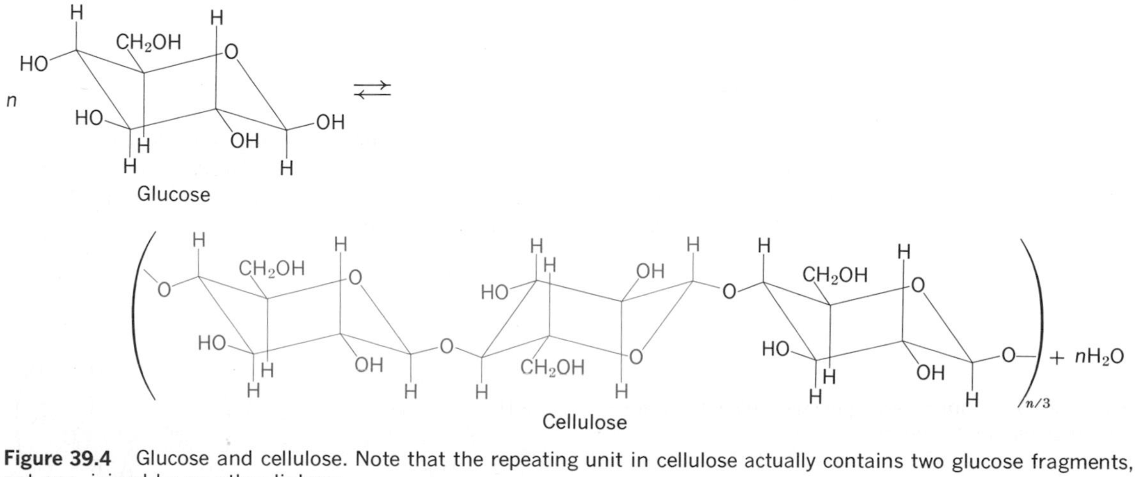

Figure 39.4 Glucose and cellulose. Note that the repeating unit in cellulose actually contains two glucose fragments, not one, joined by an ether linkage.

explosives, and the acetate for photographic film. Cellophane is prepared by dissolving cellulose, as in the preparation of rayon, and then reprecipitating it in a film. The chain strength is due to ether linkages, but the interchain links are mainly hydrogen bonds. The rigidity of cellulose derivatives can be modified by varying the extent of interchain hydrogen bonding. For example, cellulose fibers soften in water.

Exercise 39.4

What do humans lack that makes cellulose merely roughage for their digestive tract? *Answer:* You may say that they lack the suitable microorganisms, but the digestion of cellulose probably involves cleavage of the ether linkage to give glucose, which most animals can digest. They can also digest starches which, like cellulose, are six-membered carbohydrate rings held together by ether linkages. The lack must be the specific enzyme that acts on the ether linkage between two glucose fragments. This enzyme, which distinguishes herbivores from carnivores, is probably a single chemical compound.

PROTEINS

Proteins are biological molecules of extreme importance in all living organisms (see Chapter 40). They are condensation polymers of a type of monomer known as α-amino acids (Figure 39.5); and are held together by amide bonds (p. 523) known as "peptide links," $-\overset{\displaystyle O}{\overset{\|}{C}}-\overset{\displaystyle H}{\overset{|}{N}}-$. Proteins are polypeptides of very high molecular weight. The interchain forces are, as in cellulose, principally hydrogen-bonding. Since there are fewer possible hydrogen bonds per monomer unit, proteins are more flexible than carbohydrates. (Compare the rigidities of plants and animals.)

Proteins, unlike rubber or cellulose, are copolymers, and are much more complicated than the other natural polymers we have studied. There are about twenty different common α-amino acids (that is, with different R— groups), and thus the number of ways in which these can combine is immense. (See Exercise 21.11.)

Exercise 39.5

Assume that amino acids can form peptide linkages in any sequence. How many linear isomers are there containing 10 amino acid units? *Answer:* The number of isomers is 20^n, where n is the number of monomer units in the chain; $20^{10} = 2^{10} \cdot 10^{10} \cong 10^3 \cdot 10^{10}$ or 10^{13} isomers, a large number.

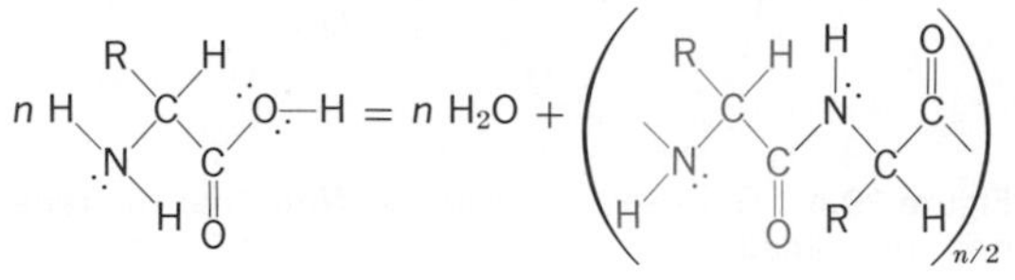

Figure 39.5 α-amino acid polymerization to peptide. One peptide link is shown.

SYNTHETIC POLYMERS

Man has used natural polymeric materials—wood (cellulose), silk, wool, leather (all proteins), and rubber gum—for thousands of years; however, it is only in the past few hundred years that he has made any significant chemical modification in natural polymers, and only in the past fifty years has he produced new, synthetic polymers. It has been a busy fifty years, however, and the number of synthetic polymeric substances in use now far exceeds the number of natural ones. Hardly any phase of our daily lives is unaffected by a synthetic polymeric substance; we truly live in a plastic age.

Most of the synthetic polymers in use today are organic substances; that is, they are primarily compounds of carbon. We have already discussed (Chapter 21) the ability of carbon to bond repeatedly to itself (to catenate), and to form strong covalent bonds to a variety of elements; both of these attributes are important in polymer formation. In addition, carbon compounds from which organic monomers are produced are readily obtained in large quantities from petroleum; the annual United States production of phenol, styrene, and ethylene (as polyethylene) are around 1,000,000,000; 2,000,000,000; and 2,500,000,000 pounds, respectively.

We shall expect to find the same kinds of synthetic reactions—substitution or addition (Lewis acid-base), electron transfer (redox), and free radical—used here as in our discussion in Chapter 37.

Exercise 39.6

Estimate the maximum length of web fiber a spider could spin. *Answer:* Assume that (*a*) nothing is eaten, so that the web must come from stored fluid, (*b*) the diameter of a fiber is 10^{-2} mm, and (*c*) the body sac full of fluid is 1 mm³. Then $(\pi d^2/4) \cdot l = V = 1\ \text{mm}^3$ and $l = 4/\pi(10^{-2}\ \text{mm})^2 \cong 10^4\ \text{mm} = 10$ meters. This seems a little too long. Probably the fiber is thicker and/or the sac is smaller. Common spiders seem to spin 2 to 5 meters of web per session.

VINYL POLYMERS

Vinyl polymers are prepared by polymerization of ethylene or substituted ethylenes. The name is derived from the vinyl group, $CH_2{=}CH{-}$, which is present in many of the monomers. Table 39.1 lists a few familiar examples from the vast array of vinyl polymers known.

The mechanism of the polymerization reaction normally results in the type of "head to tail" products shown by the reaction in Table 39.1. However, the arrangement of the substituent groups around the tetrahedral carbons in the backbone varies according to the actual method of polymerization employed. Consider the styrene molecules shown in Figure 39.6. If we imagine the carbon chain to be fixed in space as a zigzag line (which is the arrangement it takes in crystalline polymers), we see that there are three possibilities for the arrangement of the side groups: they may be attached randomly (such polymers are termed atactic), they may all be attached identically (isotactic), or they may be attached in a regularly

Table 39.1 Vinyl polymers of the type $n \; \overset{A}{\underset{B}{}}\!\!>C{=}C<\!\!\overset{E}{\underset{D}{}} = \left(-\underset{B}{\overset{A}{C}}-\underset{D}{\overset{E}{C}}-\underset{B}{\overset{A}{C}}-\underset{D}{\overset{E}{C}}-\underset{B}{\overset{A}{C}}-\underset{D}{\overset{E}{C}}- \right)_{n/3}$

Monomer[a]	A—	B—	D—	E—	Trade name	Common uses
Ethylene Ethene	H—	H—	H—	H—	polyethylene	films, coatings, containers
Vinyl chloride Chloroethene	H—	H—	H—	Cl—	Geon, Tygon	lab tubing, dielectric
Vinylidene chloride 1,1-dichloroethene	H—	H—	Cl—	Cl—	Saran	film, wrapping, tubing
Chlorotrifluoroethylene Chlorotrifluoroethene	F—	F—	F—	Cl—	Kel-F	oils, greases, dielectric
Tetrafluoroethylene Tetrafluoroethene	F—	F—	F—	F—	Teflon	lab ware, seals, bearings
Propylene Propene	H—	H—	H—	CH_3—	Nalgene, polypropylene	lab ware, household objects
Methyl vinyl ether Methyl ethenyl ether	H—	H—	H—	CH_3O—	poly (vinyl methyl ether)	adhesives
Styrene Ethenylbenzene	H—	H—	H—	(C_6H_5—)	polystyrene	insulating foams, molded objects
Vinyl acetate Ethenyl acetate	H—	H—	H—	CH_3CO_2—	polyvinyl acetate	adhesives
Methyl methacrylate Methyl 2-methylpropenoate	H—	H—	CH_3—	CH_3O_2C—	Lucite, Plexiglas	glass substitute, moldings
Acrylonitrile Propenonitrile	H—	H—	H—	NC—	Orlon	wool substitute

[a] The first word is the common name, the second the IUC name.

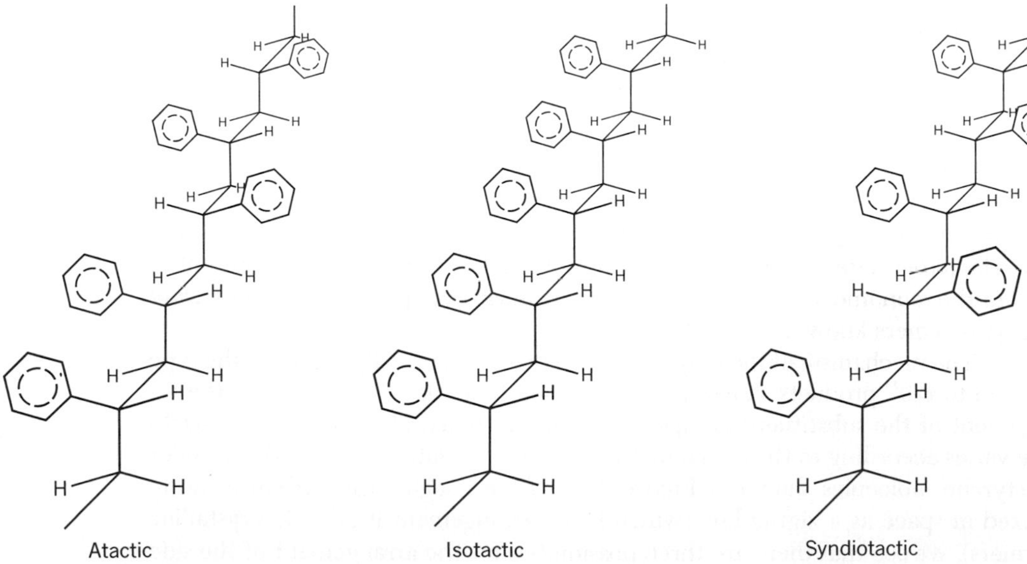

Figure 39.6 Possible spatial arrangements in styrene chains. [From J. D. Roberts and M. C. Caserio, *Basic Principles of Organic Chemistry,* Benjamin, New York, 1965.]

alternating pattern (syndiotactic). We are just beginning to understand the factors that control the type of product produced by a given reaction.

Exercise 39.7

Saran sticks more to itself than does polyethylene. Rationalize this fact. *Answer:* Polyethylene should be nonpolar since it contains only C—H bonds on its periphery. Saran contains both C—H and C—Cl bonds, so the molecular segments will be polar. Polar intermolecular forces are stronger (stickier) than van der Waals forces.

POLYMERS FROM CYCLIC MONOMERS

Certain important polymers are obtained by opening the rings of cyclic compounds and joining together the fragments so formed; several examples are shown in Figure 39.7. (Refer to Figure 21.2 for the symbolism used.)

MECHANISM OF ADDITION POLYMERIZATION

The mechanism (that is, the detailed, step-by-step process by which molecules react) of addition polymerization has been the subject of extensive research. The interested student should refer to a good textbook of organic chemistry, or to a standard reference such as Paul J. Flory, *Principles of Polymer Chemistry* (Cornell University Press, Ithaca, 1953) or *The Chemistry of Cationic Polymerization* (P. H. Plesch, ed., Macmillan, New York, 1963).

Addition polymerization reactions normally have a negative free energy, as the negative enthalpy derived from replacing *n* carbon-carbon double bonds (147 kcal mole^{-1} each) with 2*n* carbon-carbon single bonds (83 kcal mole^{-1} each) is more

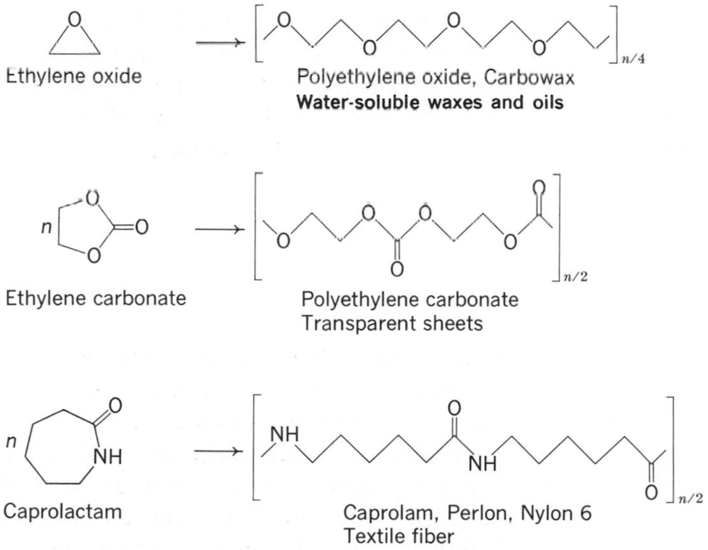

Figure 39.7 Polymers from self-addition of cyclic monomers.

than sufficient at low temperatures to counteract adverse entropy effects (small $T\,\Delta S$). Commercial monomers do not spontaneously polymerize in the absence of an initiator that lowers the activation barrier to reaction; if they did, it would be impossible to store or transport them, and the reactions would be next to impossible to control. Addition polymerization reactions can be divided into two main types: those carried out with chain initiators (usually free radical mechanisms), and those carried out with coordination catalysts (usually acid-base mechanisms).

Since addition polymerization involves the formation of a new bond between former monomer units, it is essential that an empty orbital be provided to form the bond. The role of most initiators is to open up such an orbital by attracting electrons to themselves. Thus initiators are usually either free radicals (having a half-empty orbital) or acids (having a completely empty orbital).

Exercise 39.8

Rationalize the fact that polymerization at high-temperatures is much more likely to produce atactic polymers than at low temperatures. *Answer:* There will normally be one form of addition, that having the lowest activation energy and lowest entropy (presumably the syndiotactic form); at low temperatures it should be produced almost exclusively. But the atactic form has a higher entropy (and probably higher activation energy) and thus is favored at higher T (larger $T\,\Delta S$).

ORGANIC CONDENSATION POLYMERS

For the most part the reactions by which condensation polymers are formed are the standard reactions that organic chemists employ to join two molecules together; there are almost as many possibilities as there are types of functional groups. It would obviously be impossible to discuss in detail such an array of reactions here, and we will limit ourselves to looking at a few representative materials.

The main concept in condensation polymerization is that of *difunctionality*. If a given reaction will join two functional groups together, and there are two functional groups per molecule, then the possibility of polymerization exists. Most of the common monomers of condensation polymers are difunctional; if cross-linking is desired, monomers with three or more functional groups are incorporated in the reaction mixture.

POLYESTERS

The reaction of esterification can be thought of as loss of a molecule of water in the reaction of a carboxylic acid with an alcohol. In practice the reaction is achieved by a variety of special methods, which the interested student will find outlined in an organic chemistry text. Esterification of terephthalic acid with ethylene glycol gives a linear polymer with superior properties for spinning into yarn. When used as a textile it is sold as Dacron (Figure 39.8); in the form of transparent sheets it is known as Mylar. Reaction of phthalic acid with glycerol gives a cross-linked resin, Glyptal (Figure 39.9), one of the alkyd resins used widely in paints.

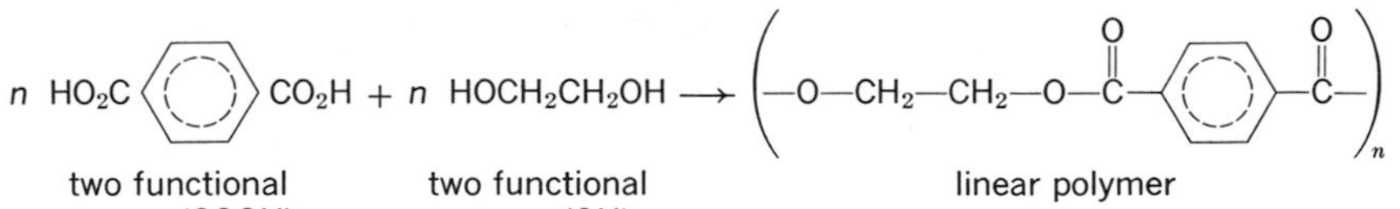

two functional groups (COOH) — two functional groups (OH) — linear polymer

Figure 39.8 Formation of Dacron.

Exercise 39.9

Glyptal comes in cans as a viscous fluid but sets in air to a hard resin. Rationalize its setting in air but not in the can. *Answer:* The polymerization involves loss of H_2O. A can is a closed system and the H_2O does not escape, as it will in the open system outside. Note that this means ΔG is not very negative; if it were, pure water would form in the can. There may also be a catalyst for forming ester linkages in the resin that is activated by contact with air. But note that no species from the air are directly involved in the polymerization steps.

POLYAMIDES

The polyamides or nylons are among the most widely used synthetic polymers. (For example, I often find myself fishing in a nylon jacket and boot socks, peering through nylon framed glasses at a nylon fish line, and thumbing a reel with nylon bearings with a thumb whose once-severed tendons are held together by nylon sutures.) The most common nylon is nylon 66, which is prepared by amide formation between adipic acid, $HO_2C(CH_2)_4CO_2H$, and hexamethylenediamine, $H_2H(CH_2)_6NH_2$. These two materials are synthesized from petroleum products or prepared from waste oat hulls or bran. The starting materials contained in the oat hulls are five-carbon sugars known as pentoses, $C_5H_{10}O_5$ (see Figure 39.10).

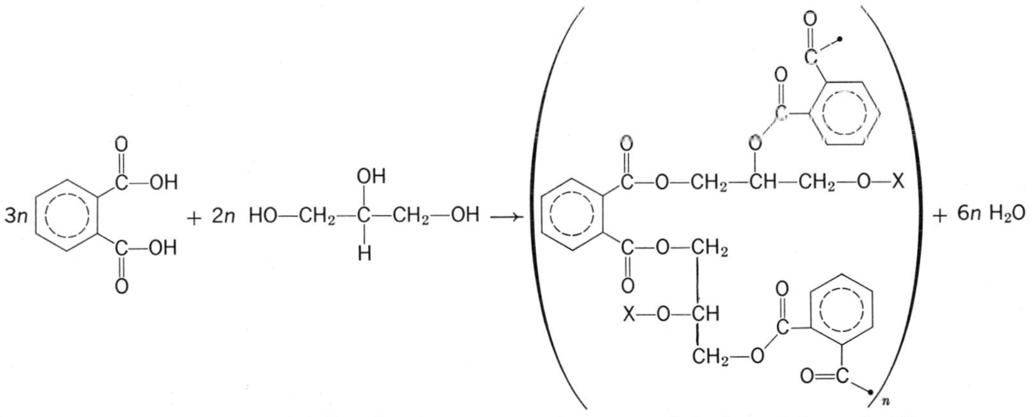

two functional groups (COOH) — three functional groups (OH) — polymer cross-linked at points marked X; •— = continuation of chain

Figure 39.9 Glyptal formation with cross-linking.

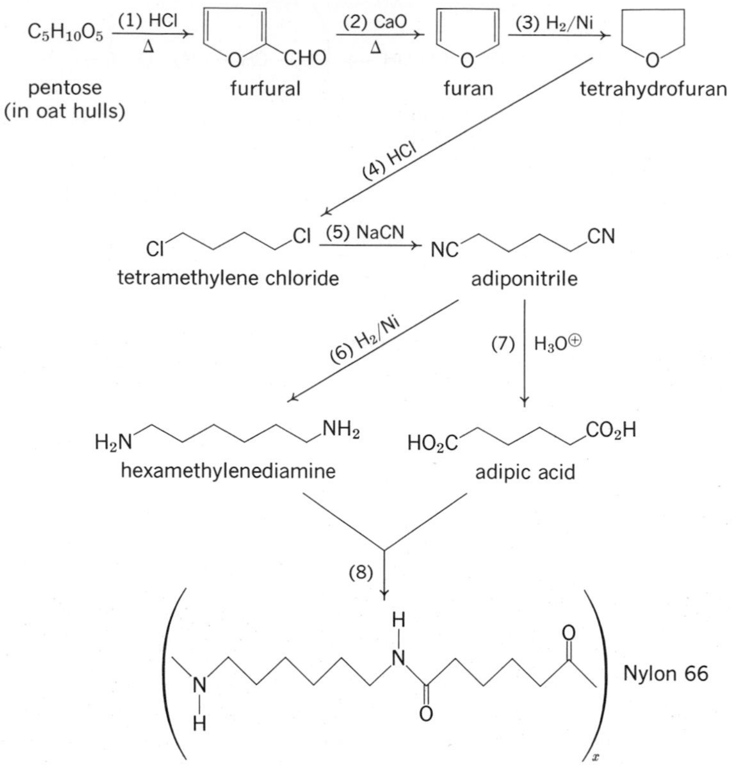

Figure 39.10 Synthesis of nylon from oats.

Exercise 39.10

What other products are produced in the nylon synthesis of Figure 39.10? *Answer:* By steps: (1) $3H_2O$, (2) CO, (4) H_2O, (5) 2NaCl, (7) $2NH_4^+$, (8) $2H_2O$ per double monomer unit.

INORGANIC POLYMERS

All of the synthetic polymers that we have examined are molecules based on a carbon skeleton. These, and a vast number of additional polymers, have found use in a very wide variety of applications, yet there are still many jobs to be done that no presently known polymer can do. One of the major needs is for polymers with extremely high thermal stability, resistance to radiation damage, and certain specific electrical properties, for use in high-speed aircraft, spacecraft, satellites, and extraterrestrial stations. Organic condensation polymers are generally held together with an oxygen or nitrogen linkage, which is susceptible to chemical attack; even the addition polymers with a backbone of only carbon atoms are susceptible to radiation damage and are seldom usable above 250°C.

To find new, high-temperature polymers, chemists have turned to inorganic systems; that is, chains containing few, if any, carbon atoms. The most extensively developed type of polymers with an inorganic backbone are the silicones (Chapter 25). These have a repeating silicon-oxygen skeleton similar to that found in silica, but since their side chains are organic they are not true inorganic polymers. They have, however, found extensive use as structural materials, waterproofing agents, and heat-transfer fluids, and can be prepared in a variety of forms, including light oils, greases, rigid solids, and elastomers, by controlling the nature of the side chains and the degree of cross-linking.

One group of inorganic polymers being investigated extensively is the phosphonitrile polymers. These are addition polymers that consist of monomers

such as $N\equiv P\begin{smallmatrix}R\\\\R\end{smallmatrix}$, in which R— is an alkyl or aryl group, or of the hypothetical

monomer $N\equiv P\begin{smallmatrix}Cl\\\\Cl\end{smallmatrix}$, which is not actually isolated in polymer formation. Polymers

derived from $N\equiv P\begin{smallmatrix}Cl\\\\Cl\end{smallmatrix}$ are completely inorganic and have great thermal stability

(Figure 39.11), which is increased if a small amount of some Lewis acid is added to the reaction mixture; the copolymer in which zinc chloride is present is stable to over 600°C.

A number of the inorganic polymers under investigation are compounds of boron. Boron-nitrogen bonds such as those found in boron-nitride and borazon (Chapter 25) are extremely stable and should provide an excellent polymer backbone. Several active research programs in major industries are directed toward preparing polymers whose backbones are derived from polyhedral boron hydride anions or from carboranes. These species are among the most stable molecules known; many are unaffected by roasting at red heat, about 900°C.

Many macrocrystalline materials can be classified as inorganic polymers: all metals can be considered as three-dimensional addition polymers, as can cement. Figure 39.12 compares the production figures of some natural, metallic, and organic polymers. Note that although the production of the organic polymers is increasing rapidly, they still constitute a small fraction of the total.

Exercise 39.11

Coating the lip of a glass pouring vessel with silicone grease gives a surface that is not wet by water (so making it easier to do dripless pouring) but is very difficult to re-

$$NH_4^+Cl^- + PCl_5 \longrightarrow \left[N\equiv P\begin{smallmatrix}Cl\\\\Cl\end{smallmatrix}\right] + 4HCl$$

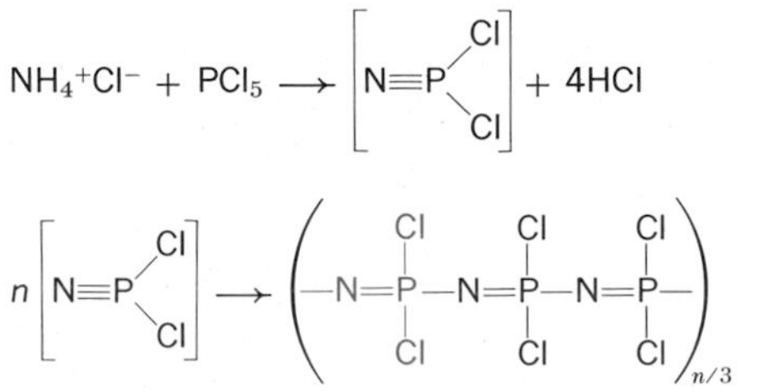

Figure 39.11 Phosphonitrile-type polymer.

$$n\left[N\equiv P\begin{smallmatrix}Cl\\\\Cl\end{smallmatrix}\right] \longrightarrow \left(-N=\underset{\underset{Cl}{|}}{\overset{\overset{Cl}{|}}{P}}-N=\underset{\underset{Cl}{|}}{\overset{\overset{Cl}{|}}{P}}-N=\underset{\underset{Cl}{|}}{\overset{\overset{Cl}{|}}{P}}-\right)_{n/3}$$

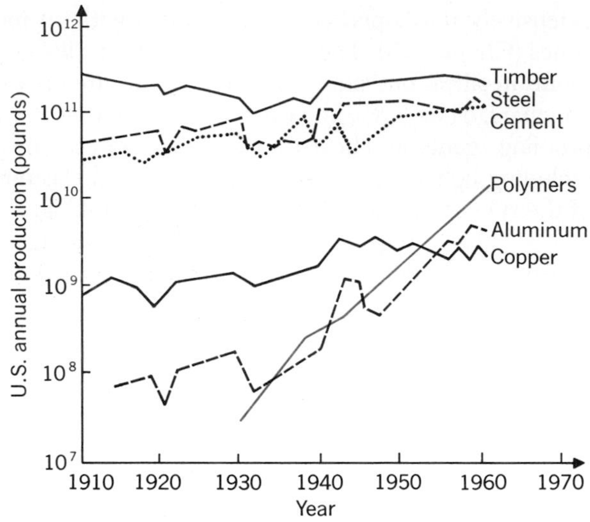

Figure 39.12 Production of some typical polymeric materials. [From "The Competition of Materials," W. O. Alexander. Copyright © 1967 by Scientific American, Inc. All rights reserved.]

move from the glass. Rationalize. *Answer:* Silicone grease consists of Si—O—Si—O zigzag chains with two CH_3 or C_2H_5 groups on each silicon. The exposed oxygens are highly electronegative and just "fit" on a glass surface (also Si—O—Si—O—, etc.), hence the tight adherence. This exposes the hydrocarbon residues, which become the new surface that water does not wet, since to do so would involve breaking many hydrogen bonds and replacing them with van der Waals bonds. ΔH would be $+$, ΔS negligible, making ΔG $+$.

SUMMARY

Man first learned to use naturally occurring materials, then to modify natural materials, and finally to prepare new substances to meet his manifold needs. One of the most important classes of synthetic substances is polymers—materials of macromolecular weight, prepared by condensation or self-addition of small, repeating molecular units known as monomers. The nature of the monomer and of the bulk polymer can be altered almost without limit in order to produce a wide variety of materials. Research into the preparation of new polymers and the detailed mechanism of polymerization is probably the largest single field of industrial chemical research.

In science the credit goes to the man who convinces the world, not to the man to whom the idea first occurs.
—Sir William Osler

PROBLEMS

39.1. If a thick rubber band is suddenly stretched and immediately touched to the forehead, it will be found to be hot; if it is then allowed to regain its original size suddenly, it will get quite cool. Try this, and then give a clear thermodynamic explanation.

39.2. In what mole ratio are phenol, styrene, and ethylene consumed in U.S. polymer production (p. 1037)?

39.3. If a spider must synthesize peptide bonds as he spins his proteinaceous web, how many bonds must be synthesized per second?

39.4. Linear polyethylene is known to crystallize as a folded chain, much like a set of highly collapsed switchbacks on a mountain road. J. D. Hoffman et al. [*Ind. Eng. Chem.*, 58, 41 (1966)], find the surface tension along the edge of a fold to be about 80 ergs cm^{-2}, and that along the ends to be about 10 ergs cm^{-2}. Estimate the relative probability that further crystallization will occur along an edge rather than an end of such a crystallite. (Relative probability $\cong 10^3/1$.)

II

39.5. Reconsider Problem 25.10. How would you modify reactant ratios and substituent size to prepare a crystalline silicone polymer, a silicone elastomer, and a rigid silicone structural material?

39.6. Draw a portion of the structure of an addition polymer of methyl methacrylate; of a condensation polymer of pentaerythritol with terephthalic acid (what mole ratios should be used?).

39.7. Acrylonitrile is readily polymerized by basic initiators such as amide ion, H—$\underline{\overline{N}}$—H$^{\ominus}$, but *iso*-butylene or vinyl chloride are almost completely inert to base initiators. How can you account for this?

39.8. Molecular weights of polymeric materials are often determined by osmotic pressure effects. Why is this method preferred over cryoscopic or vapor-pressure measurements?

III

39.9. In 1958 R. O. Colclough and F. S. Dainton [*Trans. Faraday Soc.*, 54, 886 (1958)] carried out a classic study of the polymerization of styrene initiated by stannic chloride; this work is a fine example of careful and precise experimentation with a very difficult system. The following three questions are based on this work.

(*a*) Stannic chloride does not react with styrene in the absence of a cocatalyst, and the over-all rate of polymerization is found to be proportional to (among other things) the concentration of stannic chloride and the concentration of cocatalyst, both to the first power. With equal concentrations of all species in nitrobenzene solvent, the rate of polymerization with *t*-butyl chloride cocatalyst is much faster than with *iso*-propyl chloride, and this in turn gives a faster rate than does 1,2-dichloroethane. Why is first-power dependence on catalyst and cocatalyst observed, and why do the different cocatalysts have different effects?

(*b*) The reaction was carried out in solvents of different dielectric constant, including nitrobenzene ($\epsilon = 36$), 1,2-dichloroethane ($\epsilon = 10$), and carbon tetrachloride ($\epsilon = 2$). For the over-all rate of polymerization with $M =$ styrene (monomer) and RX = alkyl halide cocatalyst (*t*-butyl chloride), the following rate laws are observed.

Carbon tetrachloride
No reaction.

1,2-Dichloroethane
Rate = $k[SnCl_4][RX][M]^2$.
The rate is corrected for the cocatalytic activity of solvent.

Nitrobenzene
Rate = $k[SnCl_4][RX][M]$.

Account for these differences in mechanistic terms.

(*c*) Account for the fact that, although the over-all rate of polymerization depends on the concentrations of catalyst, cocatalyst, and monomer, the molecular weight of the product increases only as a function of the first power of monomer concentration.

See page 1095 for a list of references and readings in the recent chemical literature related to the material in this chapter.

CHAPTER **40**

Biochemistry

NEAL W. CORNELL

From a biological point of view, the original synthesis of proteins was one of the most significant events to happen on earth.

Most living systems contain walled-in volumes called cells within which much of the synthetic or energy-producing chemistry of the living system occurs. Biochemical reactions occur both inside and outside the cells, and involve many types of molecules. Some are simple species, such as protons or water; Some are very complicated species, such as the globins or DNA, with molecular weights up to 10^8. The most abundant biochemicals are proteins, fats, and carbohydrates, but there is a very large number of other types such as vitamins, bile acids, coenzymes, porphyrins, and so on. We shall concentrate here on proteins, exploring in some depth a well-defined area rather than skimming the surface of the whole field. In doing so we shall find that biochemical reactions are interpretable in terms of the same kinetic, thermodynamic, and structural ideas we have already used.

The characteristics of any living cell derive more from the proteins that the cell contains than from any other constituent. Indeed, most of a cell's structural and functional properties are apparently regulated by the types and amounts of various proteins within the cell. It is appropriate, then that a very major area of biochemistry involves the chemistry of proteins—their structure, biosynthesis, and mechanism of function.

AMINO ACIDS

All proteins are polymers made-up of 20 different kinds of amino acids. At present approximately 75 naturally occurring compounds are known to have the general structure of amino acids, but in the production of proteins cells use only the set of 20. Some proteins lack one or more of the 20 amino acids, but no protein contains amino acids not included among them. It may be helpful at this point to study Figure 40.1, the structure of a hypothetical polymer containing 24 amino acid molecules, with each of the 20 kinds appearing at least once. The number of amino acid molecules in natural proteins varies from 51 in insulin (mol. wt. = 5800) to tens of thousands, as in glutamic dehydrogenase (mol. wt. = $1 \cdot 10^6$). These and other proteins derive their individual properties from (1) the ratio and unique sequence of constituent amino acids and (2) the interactions between those amino acids.

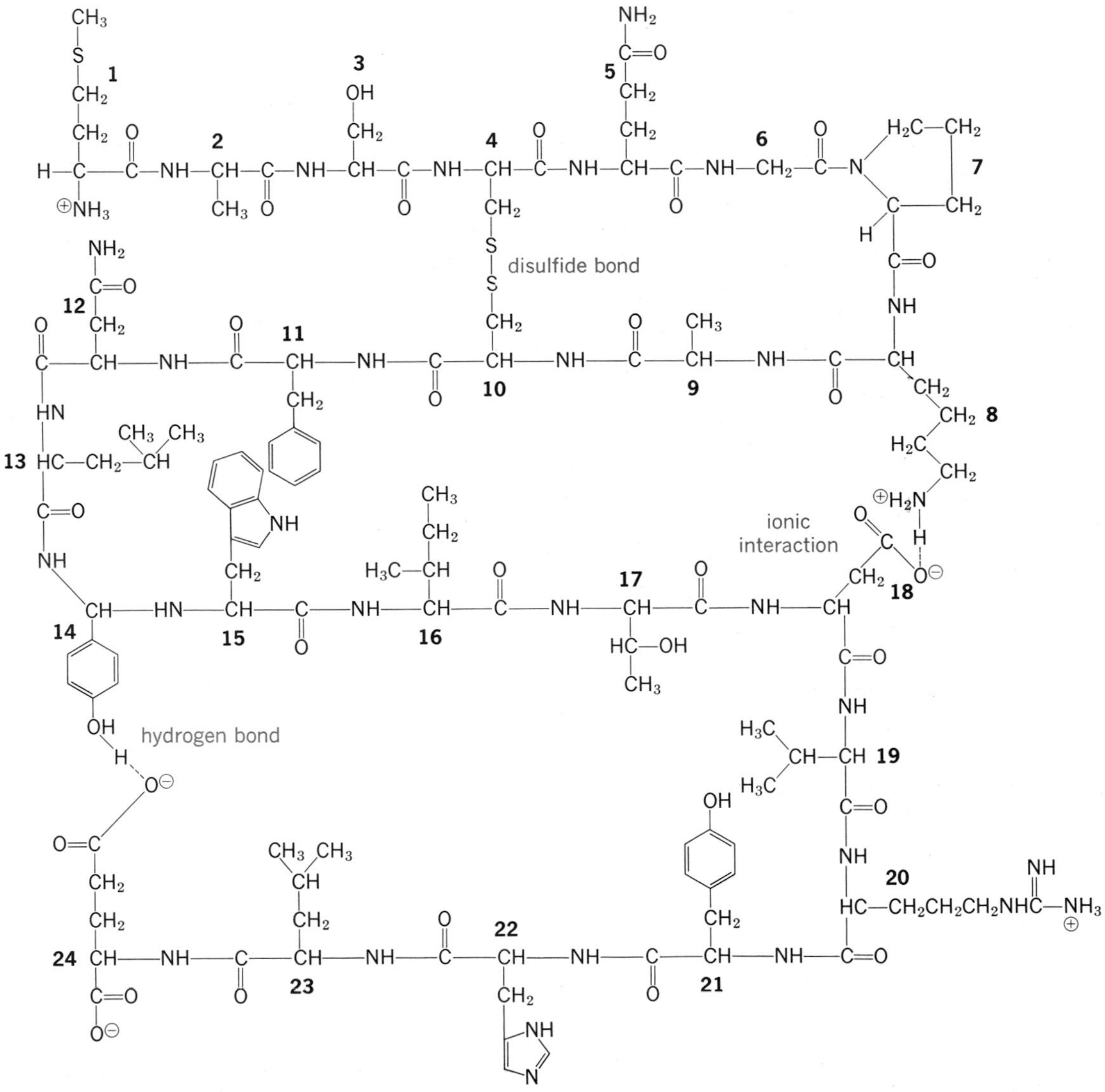

Figure 40.1 Possible amino acid sequence and interactions in protein.

All protein amino acids except proline have an amino group and a carboxyl group attached to the same carbon atom. Their common designation as α-amino acids refers to the location of the amino group on the first or α-carbon, counting from the carboxyl group. Such α-amino acids can be represented as follows:

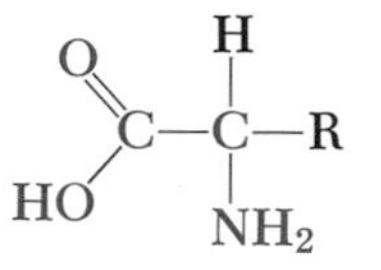

The R group is different for each amino acid and imparts specific chemical properties to each. As shown in Table 40.1, seven classes of amino acids can be differentiated according to the nature of various R groups: aliphatic, nonpolar; aromatic, nonpolar; alcoholic; sulfur-containing; basic; acidic; amide. Proline has its nitrogen in a pyrrolidine ring.

Among the other properties of α-amino acids two should be mentioned. First the *pK*'s (approximately *p*H 2 for carboxyl groups and *p*H 9 for amino groups) are such that, within a *p*H range which includes intracellular values—approximately *p*H 7—amino acids exist as dipolar, or zwitterionic, compounds:

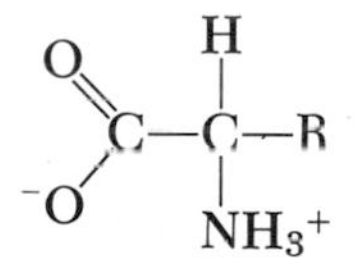

This structural designation is more meaningful than the previous one and suggests chemical reasons for the following properties of amino acids:

1. They have high melting points, commonly around 300°C. Amino acids usually decompose when or before they melt, indicating that in crystals the intermolecular electrostatic attractions approximate the strengh of the intramolecular covalent bonds.
2. They have large dipole moments.
3. They are much more soluble in water than in organic solvents, even when R—is a hydrophobic group.

Asymmetry is another property of amino acids. With the exception of glycine, in which R is hydrogen, all amino acids are asymmetric about the α-carbon atom and are optically active. Consider the following structures:

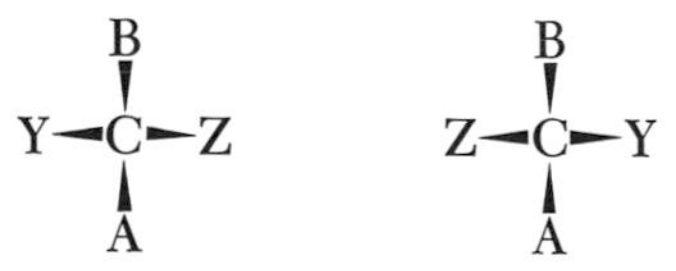

A, B, Y, and Z are four different groups attached tetrahedrally to α-carbon to form isomers that are said to be asymmetric because they cannot be superimposed—they are mirror images. Such isomers, called enantiomers, are identical in

Table 40.1 **The twenty essential amino acids and their positions in Figure 40.1. Nine of the ten marked with an asterisk cannot be synthesized by man and thus must be present in his food: arginine can be synthesized by man but at too low a rate to meet requirements.**

Amino acid (and abbreviation) arranged according to properties of R		R in formula 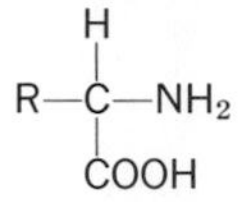	Positions in peptide structure (Figure 40.1)	Number of codons (see Table 40.3)
Aliphatic, nonpolar				
Glycine	(Gly)	H—	6	4
Alanine	(Ala)	CH_3—	2, 9	4
Valine*	(Val)	$(CH_3)_2CH$—	19	4
Leucine*	(Leu)	$(CH_3)_2CHCH_2$—	13, 23	6
Isoleucine*	(Ile)	$(C_2H_5)(CH_3)CH$—	16	3
Proline	(Pro)	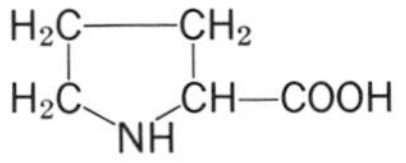 (total structure)	7	4
Aromatic, nonpolar				
Phenylalanine*	(Phe)	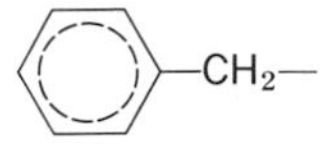	11	2
Tryptophan*	(Try)	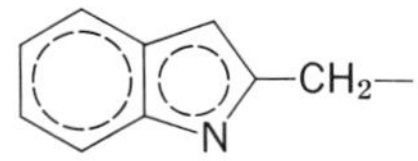	15	1
Alcoholic				
Serine	(Ser)	$HOCH_2$—	3	6
Threonine*	(Thr)	$CH_3CH(OH)$—	17	4
Tyrosine	(Tyr)	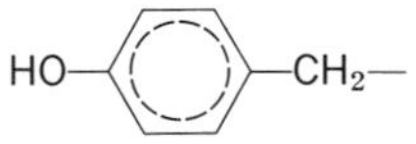	14, 21	2
Sulfur-containing				
Cysteine	(CySH)	$HSCH_2$—	4, 10	3
Methionine*	(Met)	$H_3CSCH_2CH_2$—	1	1
Basic				
Lysine*	(Lys)	$H_2NCH_2CH_2CH_2$—	8	2
Histidine*	(His)	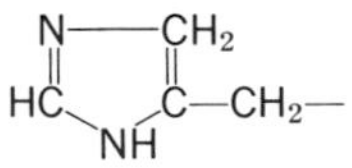	22	2
Arginine*	(Arg)	$HN{=}C(NH_2)NHCH_2CH_2CH_2$—	20	6
Acidic				
Aspartic acid	(Asp)	$HOOCCH_2$—	18	2
Glutamic acid	(Glu)	$HOOCH_2CH_2$—	24	2
Amide				
Asparagine	(Asn)	H_2NCOCH_2—	12	2
Glutamine	(Gln)	$H_2NCOCH_2CH_2$—	5	2

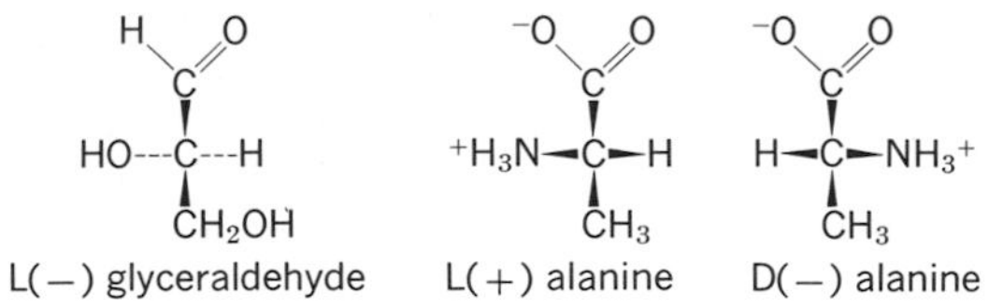

Figure 40.2 L and D stereoisomer conventions. Protein amino acids are exclusively L.

most chemical properties but differ in the direction in which they rotate the plane of polarized light. Some amino acids rotate polarized light clockwise, or to the right; that is, they are dextrorotatory (designated by a plus sign). Some are levorotatory (designated by a minus sign), rotating light to the left. The two different arrangements of groups attached to an α carbon are designated by comparison with the enantiomers of glyceraldehyde for which the absolute configurations are known (see Figure 40.2).

Without exception, proteins consist entirely of amino acids of the L type. In contrast, most naturally occurring sugars have the D configuration. It has been hypothesized that the presence of only one enantiomer in each of these two ubiquitous classes of biological compounds reflects the conditions or processes operating during the origin and early evolution of living systems.

Exercise 40.1

Is $CH_2NH_2CH_2COOH$ an α-amino acid? *Answer:* Since the NH_2 group is on the first removed carbon, not the carbon adjacent to the COOH group, this is a β-amino acid.

THE PEPTIDE BOND

The linkage between individual amino acids in proteins is called a peptide bond. These bonds may be formed with the elimination of the elements of water from two amino acids, as in Figure 40.3.

The product of the condensation reaction is a dipeptide. If the dipeptide reacts similarly with a third amino acid, the resulting product is a tripeptide. A compound with a structure such as that in Figure 40.1 is called a polypeptide. There is no universally accepted criterion for designating one substance a polypeptide and another a protein, but the most common practice is to begin with insulin (51 amino acids, mol. wt. = 5800) and label it and all larger polypeptides as proteins.

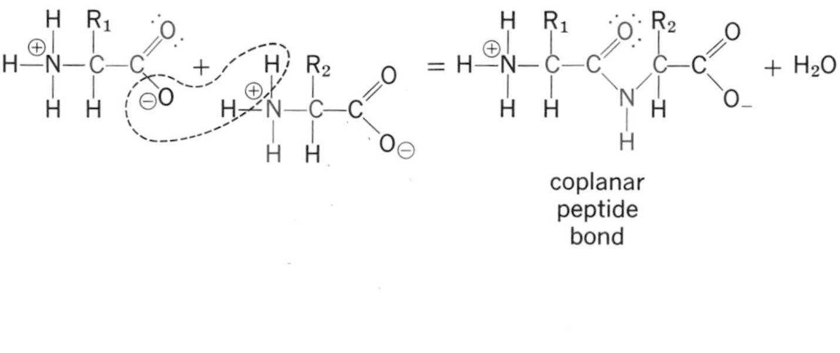

Figure 40.3 Peptide bond formation.

Exercise 40.2

The H and O of a peptide bond are always *trans*. Rationalize this fact. *Answer:* If the H and O were *cis*, they would not give as good interpeptide chain H-bonding, since it would then be difficult for the O—H—N bonds to be linear, as they must be for maximum strength.

PROTEIN STRUCTURE

Discussion of protein structure is facilitated by distinguishing four different structural levels: primary, secondary, tertiary, and quaternary. Primary structure refers to the linear sequence of amino acids in a polypeptide chain, as in Figure 40.1. Secondary structure is the designation for the way the polypeptide chains are arranged in space. This structure is determined by the translational and rotational events occurring along the peptide chain and by the hydrogen bonding between components of the peptide linkage: the entire polypeptide structure assumes a three-dimensional conformation. Tertiary structure is the term for this over-all conformation and the chemical events specifying it. Quaternary structure is that due to the association of the two or more peptide chains that the continuing study of protein biochemistry indicates constitute most biologically functioning proteins.

PRIMARY PROTEIN STRUCTURE

The determination of primary protein structure is today a matter of routine in biochemical laboratories, but to make it so required ten years of great effort by Sanger, who developed both the strategy and most of the pertinent techniques. Sanger's aim, realized in 1955, was the elucidation of insulin's amino acid sequence, and for his singular contributions to protein chemistry he received the Nobel Prize for Chemistry* in 1958.

The sequence of amino acids is determined in a very precise matter by an organism's genetic information. The phenomenon of genetic mutation manifests itself biochemically in the alteration of one or several amino acids in a given protein, or, less often, in the loss of ability to produce it. The biological implications are illustrated by sickle-cell anemia, a human disease characterized by physiological inadequacy and early death, which results from a single mutation in the genes directing hemoglobin synthesis. Diseased individuals produce hemoglobin in which only one amino acid out of several hundred is different from that in normal hemoglobin, but the longevity of the individual is appreciably reduced.

Exercise 40.3

Suggest a structural reason for the relationship of primary to tertiary structure. *Answer:* Presumably bonds between various sections of the primary chain establish the tertiary configuration. Variation in the primary structure would vary the likelihood of forming these crosslinks.

---

* His Nobel lecture [*Science*, **129** 1340 (1959)] contains an account of the work on insulin and a more complete description of techniques than is possible here.

AMINO ACID ANALYSIS

The amino acid composition of proteins is now routinely determined by ion-exchange chromatography. Ion-exchange resins are insoluble materials prepared by attaching an ionizable group to a cross-linked polymer, a common one in protein research being polystyrene sulfonate, illustrated below:

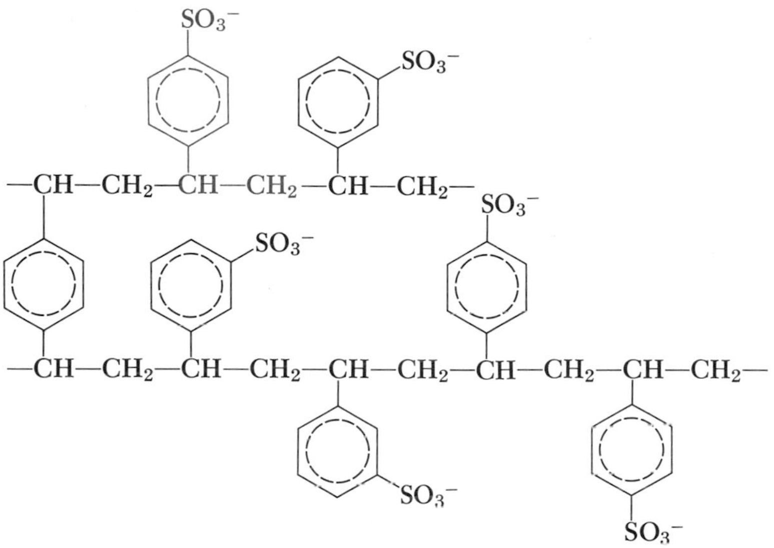

Polystyrene sulfonate is a cation-exchange resin. By selection of the ionizable group attached to the resin it is possible to control somewhat the strength of the resin-particle interaction and definitely to control the charge of the particle interacting with the resin.

The procedure used in protein chemistry illustrates the general principles of ion-exchange chromatography, which are also applicable to studies with other materials, such as nucleic acids. First, the protein is hydrolyzed in 6 *F* HCl for 12 or more hours at 110°. This breaks the polymer into amino acids, which are then placed on a resin previously formed into a column, perhaps 150 by 1 cm in size, and equilibrated with a buffer containing a cation that interacts with the sulfonate group more weakly than the cationic amino group of the amino acids. The latter displace the buffer cations and become bound to the resin. Next, a buffer containing cations which will displace the amino acids is passed through the column and, by varying the buffer concentration, individual amino acids are eluted in an order that is predictable and known from earlier studies. As an amino acid is eluted from the resin, it is reacted with ninhydrin to give a colored complex that can be measured quantitatively in a colorimeter. (See Figures 32.17 and 36.2.)

ANALYSIS FOR AMINO ACID SEQUENCE

Sequential steps in determining primary structure are here described for a small peptide, since the procedure is similar to that for proteins, but simpler. The first requirement is to establish which amino acids occur at the chain ends. Notice in

Figure 40.1 that the amino acid at one end has a free α-amino group, and that at the other end has a free α-carboxyl group. These are referred to as N-terminal and C-terminal residues, respectively. One of the procedures developed by Sanger in his work with insulin was the use of 1-fluoro-2,4-dinitrobenzene to form the stable dinitrophenyl derivative of the N-terminal residue, which after acid hydrolysis can be separated from free amino acids, thus permitting its identification. The identity of the C-terminal residue can be learned by careful treatment with an enzyme, carboxypeptidase, which specifically catalyzes the hydrolysis of the C-terminal peptide bond, freeing that single amino acid from the rest of the chain. Other procedures are available for determining N- and C-terminal residues, but the two mentioned are those used most frequently.

Assume that we have the following octapeptide: Ala-(Glu, Val, Thr, Phe, Leu, Hist)-Ser with Ala and Ser known to be the N- and C-terminal residues; the identity of the other residues has been established, but not their sequence. Some method must now be employed to cleave the peptide chain selectively. For example, the enzyme chymotrypsin would selectively catalyze hydrolysis of a peptide bond involving the carboxyl group of Phe. Suppose this resulted in a pentapeptide: (Glu, Val, Thr, Lys)-Ser. We would then know that the tripeptide sequence was Ala-Arg-Phe. Following determination of the new N-terminal residue of the pentapeptide, the latter could then be cleaved, as by partial acid hydrolysis, into smaller peptides, and these in turn subjected to terminal-group analysis, to give an unambiguous sequence for the entire octapeptide.

Exercise 40.4

Hydrolysis of a protein with carboxypeptidase produces valine in the solution. Interpret this result. *Answer:* Valine must be at the carboxyl terminal end of the protein,

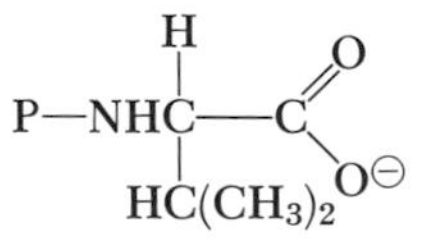

PEPTIDE SYNTHESIS

Much valuable information will probably be gained about protein structure-function relationships when biochemists discover how to synthesize proteins that differ in precise and predictable ways from their natural analogues, and the medical treatment of disorders such as diabetes, which result from deficiencies in protein or polypeptide hormones, should be facilitated.

The traditional approach to the ordered synthesis of peptides involves reaction in solution of two amino acids with the reacting amino and carboxyl groups activated and the nonreacting groups blocked or protected.

Such a procedure was actually used in the chemical synthesis of insulin, a feat that required two years and 221 individual steps. At best, an *in vitro* yield of 80% can be expected in each such step, making the yield after 25 reactions approximately 5% of the starting material; this illustrates the severe limitations of the procedure.

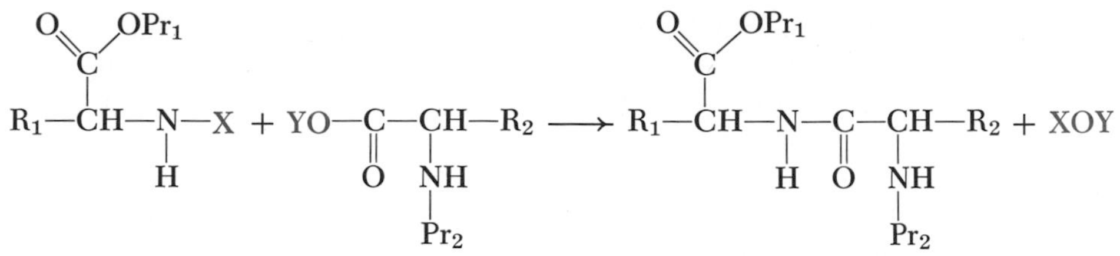

X,Y = activating groups   Pr = protecting group

A much more satisfactory method was first announced by Merrifield in 1963 and it has been improved since then. Taking advantage of chemical experience showing that ordered reactions are more successfully conducted on surfaces that are large relative to the volume of the reactants, Merrifield devised a solid-phase method in which the starting amino acid is attached to an insoluble polymeric material before condensation with a second activated, soluble amino acid. The resulting peptide remains attached to the material, which can easily be separated from the reaction mixture. Morever, in this system the condensation reaction can be driven to completion with essentially 100% yield. The method uses a solid copolymer resin of 98% styrene and 2% divinylbenzene in the form of small beads. In 1967 Merrifield reported that the complete synthesis of insulin had been accomplished in just one month, using the solid-phase method. The procedure has been adapted to automatic controls, which promises to make it even more efficient.

SECONDARY PROTEIN STRUCTURE

Secondary structure is determined by two things: (1) the folding and bending of the polypeptide chain, and (2) the hydrogen bonds associated with the folded structure. The general rules governing secondary structure were deduced by Pauling and Corey from extensive studies on crystalline amides of low molecular weight. Those rules are summarized here.

1. The atoms of the peptide bond, CONH, all lie in the same plane, with bond lengths and angles identical with those found in crystals of simple amides.

   There are actually 6 coplanar atoms:

   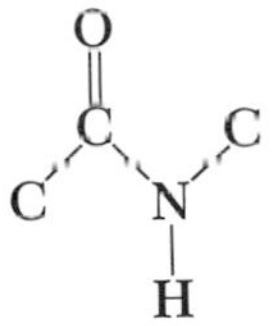

2. Hydrogen-bonded H atoms lie on a line joining the oxygen and nitrogen atoms that participate in the formation of the hydrogen bond: N—H · · · O.
3. Every carbonyl oxygen and amide nitrogen is involved in hydrogen bonding.
4. In translation along and rotation about a central axis, the operation in going from one residue to the next is the same for every step.

Pauling and his co-workers proposed two types of structures that meet all the above criteria. The first is a helical structure that involves the formation of intrapeptide-chain hydrogen bonds: of several alternative helices, the α helix (Figure 40.4), is energetically favored. At the time of Pauling's proposals, the early 1950's, the α helix was thought to be characteristic of some fibrous proteins, and strong evidence in support of this view was presented. It was also thought to be present in some globular (approximately spherical) proteins, but no means existed either to prove or to disprove the theory directly, although data from optical rotatory dispersion, infrared spectroscopy, and deuterium exchange studies were interpreted as indicating the existence of helical structures. Early in the 1960's the interpretation was verified when Kendrew climaxed a decade of effort with the publication of the complete structure of myoglobin, an oxygen-transporting protein. Like all other known helical proteins, it contains right-hand helices.

The structure of myoglobin was solved by X-ray diffraction, which made it possible to assign approximate positions to every one of the 2600 atoms in the molecule. When this was done, 77% of the myoglobin chain was found to exist in an α-helical structure with the bond angles and dimensions given in Figure 40.5. Myo-

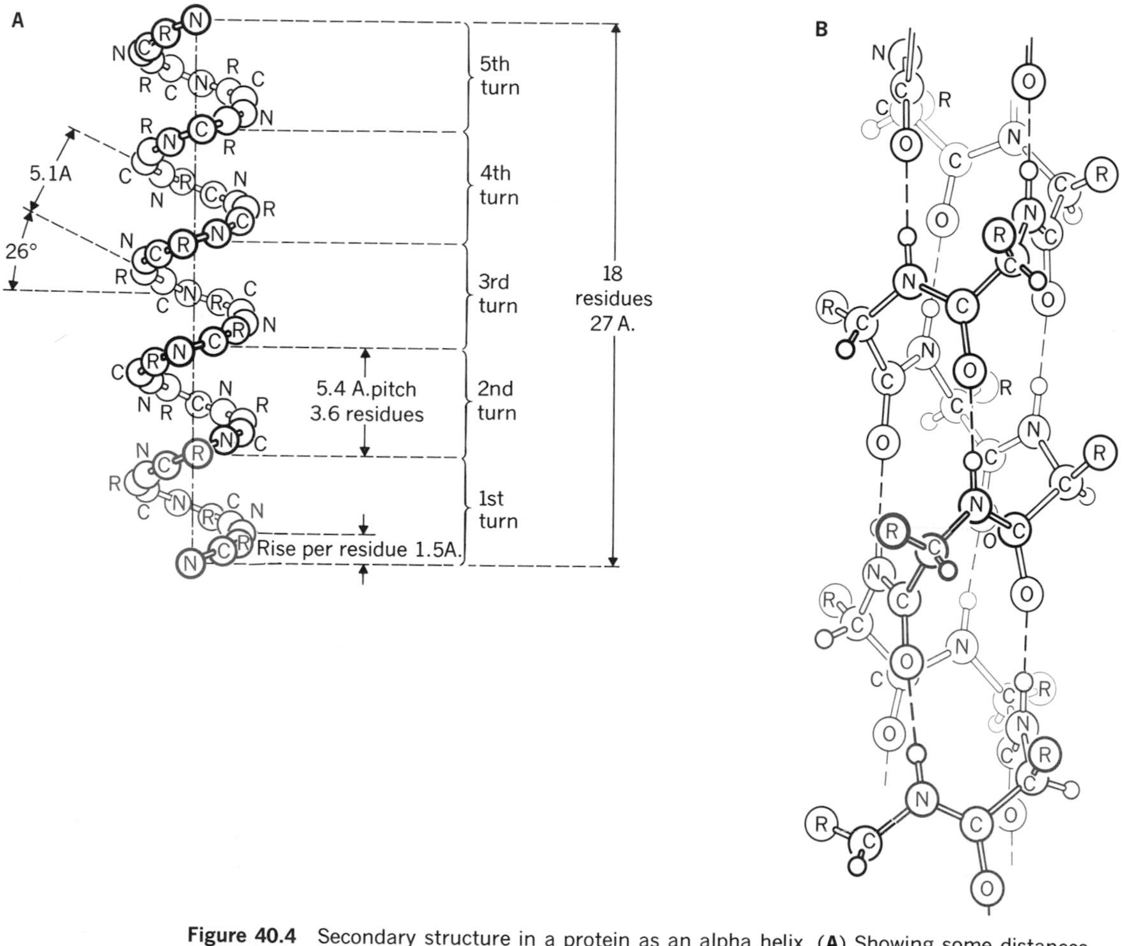

Figure 40.4 Secondary structure in a protein as an alpha helix. (**A**) Showing some distances. (**B**) Showing H bonding. [L. Pauling, *College Chemistry* 3d ed., W. H. Freeman and Company. © 1964.]

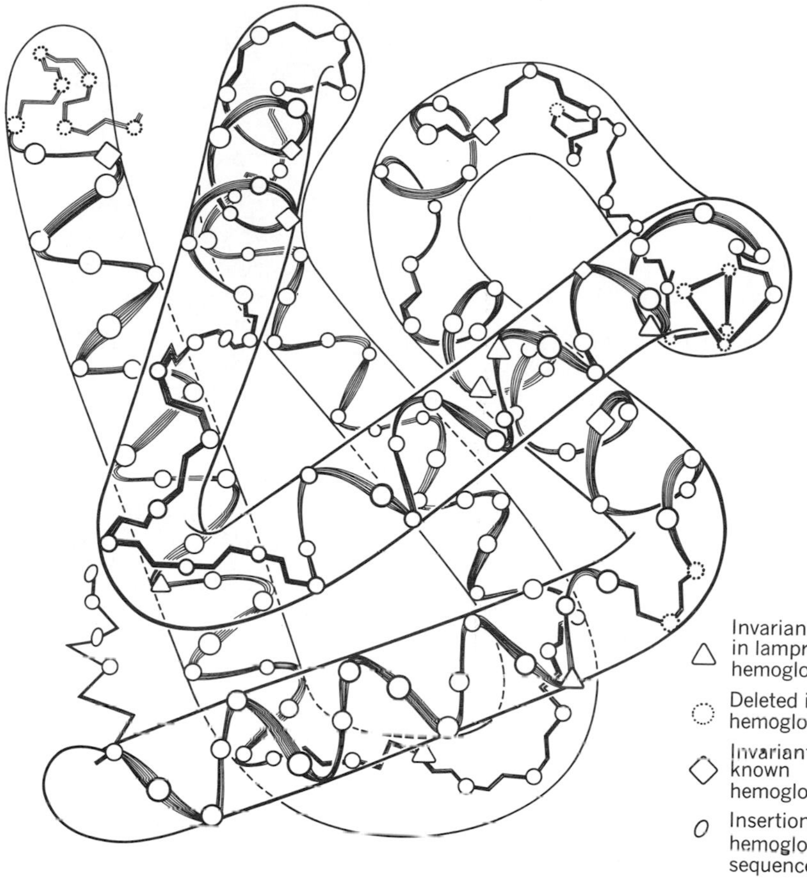

Figure 40.5 Tertiary structure in a protein as found in myoglobin. [E. V. Eck and M. O. Dayhoff, *Protein Sequence and Structure* 1966, National Biomedical Research Foundation.]

globin is now known to have a higher degree of helical structure than any other natural globular proteins, which vary in their helical content from 0 to 70%. Nonhelical regions may have a secondary structure arising from intrachain interactions (see p. 1048) or they may have no fixed secondary structure. Regions of the latter type are designated as random-coil structures.

The second structure meeting the criteria proposed by Pauling and Corey is the pleated-sheet structure illustrated in Figure 40.6, which is found in some fibrous proteins, such as silk fibroin. In the pleated-sheet structure, criterion 3 is satisfied by the formation of interchain hydrogen bonds.

Exercise 40.5

Could left-hand α helices form? *Answer:* Two mirror-image molecules (stereoisomers) are equally stable; thus left-hand helices can form. Since they have not been observed, kinetic effects must be involved in the synthesis of proteins, which are solely right-hand: or perhaps the L configuration of the amino acids stabilizes the right-hand helix. Note that left-hand helices of L acids are not mirror images of right-hand helices of L acids.

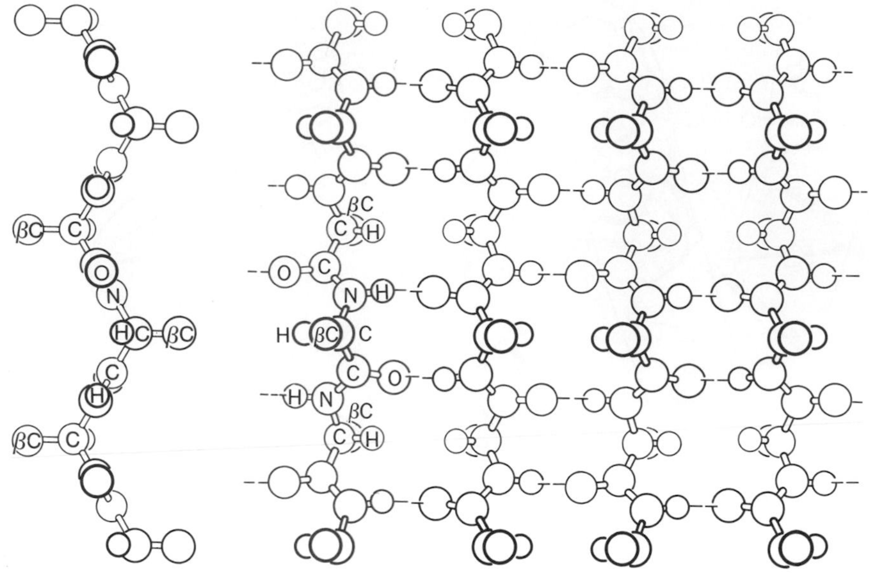

Figure 40.6 Pleated sheet structure of proteins as found in silk fibroin. [L. Pauling, *College Chemistry* 3d ed., W. H. Freeman and Company. © 1964.]

TERTIARY PROTEIN STRUCTURE

Fairly early in the study of proteins it was observed that the viscosity of protein solutions could be greatly increased by chemical treatment without affecting the molecular weight of the proteins. The explanation is that the natural polypeptide chain must be extensively coiled and folded to produce the globular form. An example of the type of folding that occurs is given in Figure 40.5, a diagrammatic representation of the tertiary structure of myoglobin, which has extensive helical regions interrupted by regions with a nonhelical, irregular secondary structure: it is in these regions that folding and bending occur. As predicted and then confirmed by X-ray studies, proline, because of its ring structure, forms peptide bonds having angles that preclude helical structure. This effect is schematically illustrated in Figure 40.1, in which proline has been placed at the upper right corner.

What stabilizes structures such as that of myoglobin or the looping polypeptide in Figure 40.1, which resembles a line-drawing of ribonuclease, a natural nonhelical protein? It might be supposed, in analogy with the α-helix or pleated-sheet secondary structures, that hydrogen bonding would hold proteins, in a fixed configuration. Measurements of the work required to unfold them, however, indicate a much greater degree of stability than could arise from hydrogen bonding alone, which means that other interactions must contribute to this configurational stability. Those interactions are illustrated in Figure 40.1. Numbers in parentheses in the next paragraph refer to amino acid residues noted in that figure.

The hydrogen bonds that usually result from interaction of the phenolic hydroxyl of tyrosine (14) and a carboxyl of glutamic (24) or aspartic acids can contribute to the stabilization of tertiary structure. Ionic interactions—for example, that between the β-carboxyl of aspartic acid (18) and the ϵ-amino of lysine (8)—are also possible contributors to structural stability. Disulfide bonds can be formed between the side chains or R groups of two cysteine (4, 10) residues, and, as might be expected, protein structures fixed by such bonds are very stable. The recent suggestion that the "inside" of a protein structure may resemble an oil droplet is based on a realization that hydrophobic interactions may be a significant factor in the determination of tertiary structure. The nonpolar R groups of such amino acids as phenylalanine (11), leucine (13), tryptophan (15) isoleucine (16) and valine (19) are not compatible with the highly polar character of water, and X-ray diffraction has confirmed the hypothesis that the groups tend to tuck inside polypeptide chains and exclude water from their immediate neighborhood. The consequent stabilization is entropic in origin and although it cannot be evaluated with any precision for proteins, it can be approximated by measuring the thermodynamic parameters in the transfer of hydrocarbons from nonpolar solvents to water. For example,

$$C_2H_{6\,(\mathrm{benzene})} \longrightarrow C_2H_{6\,(H_2O)}$$

measured at 298°K proceeds with a ΔS of -20 entropy units and a ΔH of -2.2 kcal mole^{-1} to give a calculated ΔG of $+3.8$ kcal mole^{-1}.

What has been learned about the stability of the tertiary structure of proteins leads to the belief that a very small amount of energy is required to fold the polypeptide chain. The belief receives support from experiments with such proteins as aldolase and ribonuclease. The latter is a globular, compact protein consisting of 124 amino acids and 4 disulfide bonds. The —S—S— bonds can be broken with reducing agents and the oxidized chain treated with reagents that induce unfolding. On removal of these agents 105 different structures could result from the random formation of four —S—S— bonds from eight cysteine residues. Yet not 105 but only one structure is found when this is done, and that one structure is the native biological configuration of the protein. Considerations such as these underlie efforts now being made in the United States, Italy, and India, to predict tertiary structure from a known primary structure by the use of computers, thereby obviating the laborious and time-consuming method of X-ray diffraction.

Exercise 40.6

Show that there are 105 ways in which eight cysteine residues can combine in four sets of two each. *Answer:* If there are no limitations, there would be $7! = 5040$ ways, but this counts each one twice, leaving 2520, which must be reduced by $1/4! = 1/24$, since there are four sets. Thus there are 105 ways.

QUATERNARY PROTEIN STRUCTURE

It has been proposed, on the basis of experimental results, that most biologically active proteins with molecular weights greater than 50,000 are composed of more than one polypeptide chain held together in functional units by undefined interactions. Such units are said to possess quaternary structure, with each chain, of course, having primary, secondary, and tertiary structure. The two chains of insulin are held together by —S—S— bonds.

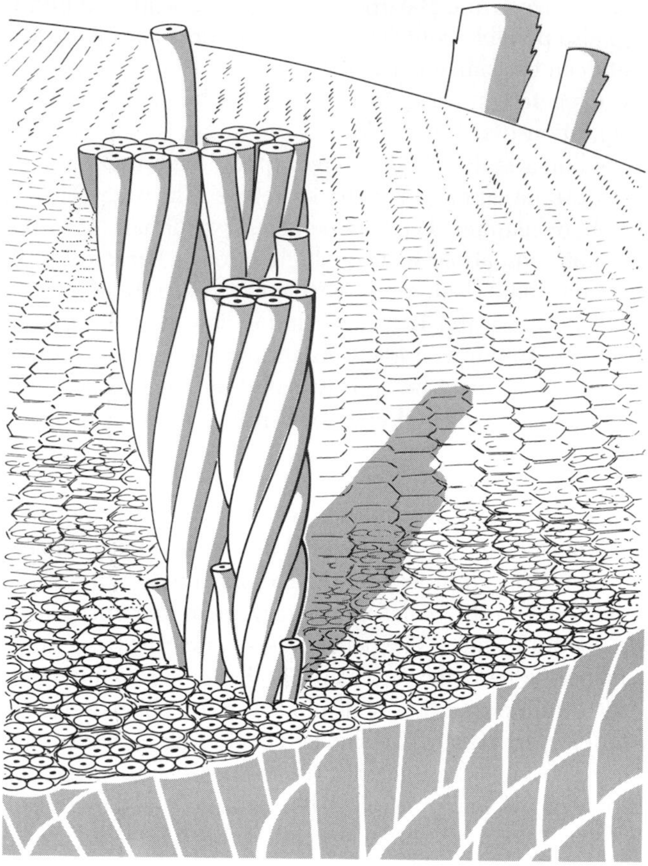

Figure 40.7 Quaternary structure in protein as found in hair.

The enzyme aldolase, molecular weight 150,000, dissociates when treated with acid (*p*H 2.9 or lower) into three chains of molecular weight 50,000 that are identical in primary structure. On readjusting the solution to neutral *p*H the three chains associate again, returning to the native quaternary structure. Many other examples of the association of identical polypeptide chains are known. The extreme situation of this kind is the protein coat of the tobacco mosaic virus in which some 2000 identical units with an aggregate weight of $3 \cdot 10^7$ are associated. Other proteins contain more than one type of chain. For instance, hemoglobin, the oxygen-transporting protein of blood, is composed of four chains, two each of two different types.

Quaternary structure in fibrous proteins such as hair, nails, and horns may take the form of strands and cables, as shown in Figure 40.7. The waving of hair involves the coiling and uncoiling of the strands: hair may be stretched to almost twice its natural length by breaking the H bonds holding the α helices together. Partly stretched hair may then be set in place and new H bonds formed, giving the hair a new texture and form.

PROTEIN FUNCTION

Proteins perform many types of biological functions. For instance, some, which may be called structural proteins, are essential elements of hair, wool, silk, feathers, connective tissue, and muscles. Nucleoproteins, those found complexed with nucleic acids, participate in the chemical expression of genetic information and in the control of genetic function. Others, such as myoglobin, hemoglobin, and the cytochromes, which are classed as respiratory proteins, function in the biological transport and utilization of oxygen. Antibodies are often said to be the biological manifestation of "fighting fire with fire," since this intriguing group of proteins has as its function the protection of the organism against invasion by foreign proteins. Finally, enzymes, the catalysts for biochemical reactions, are also proteins. It is clear that from a biological point of view the original synthesis of proteins was one of the most significant events ever to happen on earth.

Exercise 40.7

Why are proteins more likely structural units for muscle than carbohydrates? *Answer:* Carbohydrates can form more H-bonds per carbon atom in the chain, and thus tend to be more rigid than proteins. Compare plant products such as wood with animal products such as meat.

ENZYMES

The sum of the thousands of reactions that occur in a living cell is referred to as metabolism. Most metabolic reactions are catalyzed by enzymes; and, since enzymes generally catalyze only one reaction, there are approximately as many enzymes as there are biological reactions. Chemically, the phenomenon of enzymatic catalysis is more remarkable (and, to some biochemists, more interesting) than the reactions themselves. The first reason for this is the amazing efficiency of enzymes. Consider, for example, the hydrolysis shown in Figure 40.8.

This reaction can be catalyzed either by acid or alkali or by the enzyme α-chymotrypsin. At 25°C and in neutral solution the enzymatic reaction proceeds at a rate 10^6 times as great as the acid- or base-catalyzed reactions. Rate differences of this order are seldom found when the same reaction is aided by different catalysts (unless one of the catalysts is an enzyme); these very large rate differences are, in a chemical sense, a unique feature of living systems. Most enzymes work at a rate of about 10^3 catalyzed changes per second per enzyme molecule, but catalase has

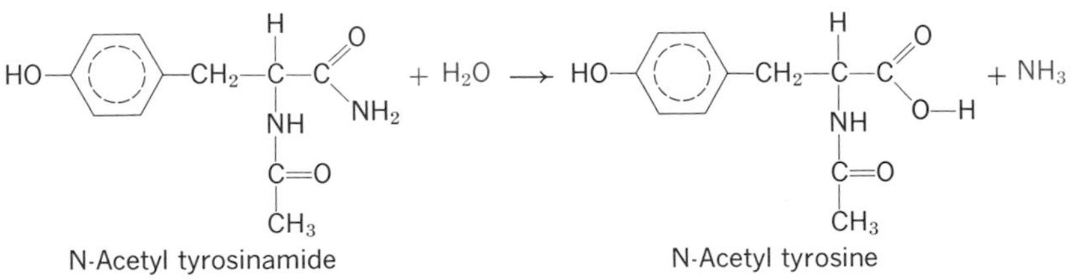

Figure 40.8 Hydrolysis of an amide.

a rate of 10^7 per second per molecule. Note that this average "turnover-number" means about one thousand moles of catalyzed reaction per mole of enzyme per second, an enormous rate.

A second remarkable property of enzymes is the highly selective nature of their action. The specificity of enzymes is illustrated by the observation that only one enantiomer of a D,L pair will serve as substrate for a given amino-acid-oxidizing enzyme. That is to say, the enzyme L-amino oxidase will catalyze the reaction

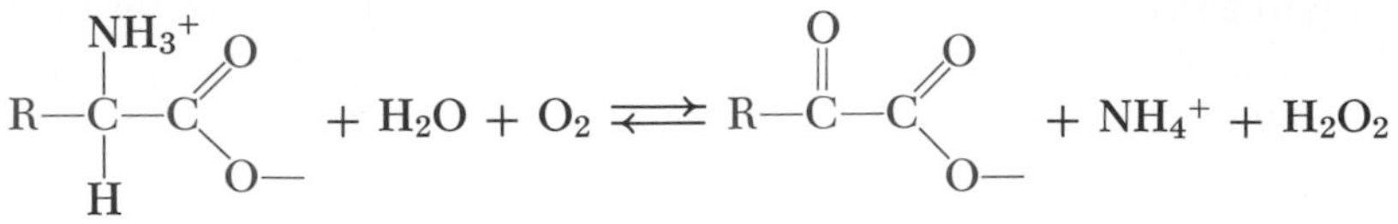

for only the L-amino acid, even when the D-isomer is present in the reaction mixture, and the reverse reaction, amination of the α-keto acid, yields only the L-isomer. Such sterospecific addition contrasts with inorganic catalysis, which generally gives racemic mixtures—that is, equimolar quantities of the D- and L-isomers.

Although the structures of a few enzymes are now known (for example, lysozyme), most enzymes have merely been identified by function; a growing number have been prepared as pure crystals of unknown structure.

Exercise 40.8

How is it possible to know the full primary structure of an enzyme and still not understand its catalytic effect? *Answer:* The catalytic effect almost certainly depends on the configuration at an active site. Since the configuration may be changed by the adsorbate, it is very difficult to determine the structural details at the tertiary and quaternary level.

MECHANISMS OF ENZYME ACTION

The catalytically active site of an enzyme consists of functional groups on the side chains of amino-acid residues. These functional groups may be on adjacent or on widely separated amino-acid residues brought into the necessary spatial relationship as a consequence of tertiary structure. Thus enzyme activity is a function of the active-site geometry that also accounts for substrate specificity. However, recent experiments by Koshland suggest that the active site of a free enzyme has a somewhat flexible geometry arising from the flexibility of protein tertiary structure and that it is substrate binding that induces a precise orientation of functional groups.

The older "lock and key" notion viewed the active site as a fixed, rigid configuration—in contrast to Koshland's "induced fit" hypothesis. The latter implies enzyme-substrate reciprocity; that is, substrate binding brings about the catalytically active configuration that is latent in the enzyme structure (some substrates are known to bind to other, nonenzymatic proteins, with no consequent reaction), but only if the substrate itself possesses a requisite stereochemistry.

The chemical events concomitant with enzymatic catalysis are, in most

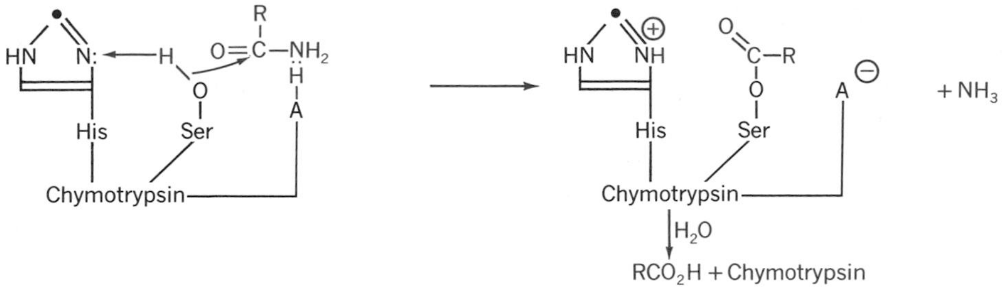

Figure 40.9 Hydrolysis of an amide catalyzed by α-chymotrypsin.

cases, obscure, and even those that are known are known imprecisely. Most adequately described is the mechanism of α-chymotrypsin activity. Figure 40.9 illustrates the chemistry of this enzyme action, although of course the details of the mechanism depend on the specific reaction considered. Two amino-acid residues are shown participating in amide hydrolysis catalyzed by chymotrypsin: histidine and serine. The imidazole ring of a histidine acts as a general base, removing a proton from a serine hydroxyl while the latter attacks the amide carbonyl. Probably the departing amine is protonated by a general acid group on the enzyme. The new ester carbonyl is attacked by water, and the serine oxygen, which leaves with the newly formed carboxylic acid, is protonated by the imidazolium ion.

THERMODYNAMICS OF ENZYME ACTION

In terms of transition-state theory the reaction rate is determined by $\Delta G^{\ddagger}$, the free-energy difference between the transition state and the initial state, and catalyzed reactions proceed at higher rates relative to their uncatalyzed counterparts because of smaller $\Delta G^{\ddagger}$ in the former. Since $\Delta G^{\ddagger} = \Delta H^{\ddagger} - T\,\Delta S^{\ddagger}$, a catalyst, in order to decrease $\Delta G^{\ddagger}$, must either decrease the value that $\Delta H^{\ddagger}$ has in the uncatalyzed reaction, or increase the value of $\Delta S^{\ddagger}$.

$\Delta S^{\ddagger}$ is almost always highly positive in enzymatic reactions because, after binding, the reactant molecules are held rigidly on the enzyme surface before the transition state is reached. This effect is illustrated by the analysis of the hydrolysis that is catalyzed by pepsin (a proteolytic enzyme). The acid-catalyzed and pepsin-catalyzed hydrolyses of carbobenzoxy-glutamyl-tyrosine proceed with $\Delta H^{\ddagger}$ of 20 and 23 kcal respectively. Starting with free enzyme and free substrate, however, $\Delta S^{\ddagger}$ is 16 entropy units for pepsin compared with -16 to -27 entropy units for acid.

Exercise 40.9

Calculate $\Delta G^{\ddagger}$ for both acid- and pepsin-catalyzed hydrolysis of carbobenzoxy-glutamyl-tyrosine. *Answer:* For acid: $\Delta G^{\ddagger} = 20 - 300(-20) = 26$ kcal mole^{-1}; for pepsin: $\Delta G^{\ddagger} = 23 - 300(16) = 18$ kcal mole^{-1}. Thus $k_{\text{pepsin}}/k_{\text{acid}} \cong e^{(26-18)/0.9} = e^{9} = 10^{9/2.3} \cong 10^{4}$ in favor of the pepsin.

BIOCHEMICAL GENETICS

Proteins such as enzymes are highly organized, highly reproducible molecules. It is now believed that the information required to synthesize them in living organisms is transmitted in the genes. Chemical analysis of DNA (deoxyribonucleic acid), structural data on nucleotides (Figure 40.10), the data of Chargaff (Table 40.2), and the X-ray diffraction studies of Wilkins led Watson and Crick to the discovery of the now-famous helix schematically represented in Figure 40.11.

The manner in which DNA exerts a determinative influence on a cell's structure and function can be stated simply: the inherited base sequence in DNA determines the structures of proteins that the cell can synthesize. The causal link between genes and proteins was established in the 1940's by Beadle and Tatum, who formulated the "one-gene–one-enzyme" theory as a consequence of experiments showing that loss of the ability to produce an enzyme resulted from mutation of a single gene. Similarly, synthesis of nonenzymatic proteins is also under genetic control, as is demonstrated by sickle-cell anemia, a severe, inherited disease involving an alteration in the oxygen-transporting protein, hemoglobin. It is now realized that a more accurate statement of the relationship is "one-gene–one-polypeptide-chain," since many proteins contain two or more different polypeptide chains, each of which is synthesized in an independent, genetically determined manner.

ROLE OF RNA

Is it possible to be more precise about the genetic determination of protein structure? In 1967 experimental evidence became available to substantiate the postulate of colinearity, which had been formulated a decade before; it asserts that the primary structure—the linear sequence of amino acids—is determined by the linear sequence of bases in DNA. With one addition, the postulate of colinearity becomes what is facetiously called the "Central Dogma": DNA directs the synthesis of RNA (ribonucleic acid) which directs the synthesis of protein. That is, DNA does not function directly in protein synthesis but, rather, has its information

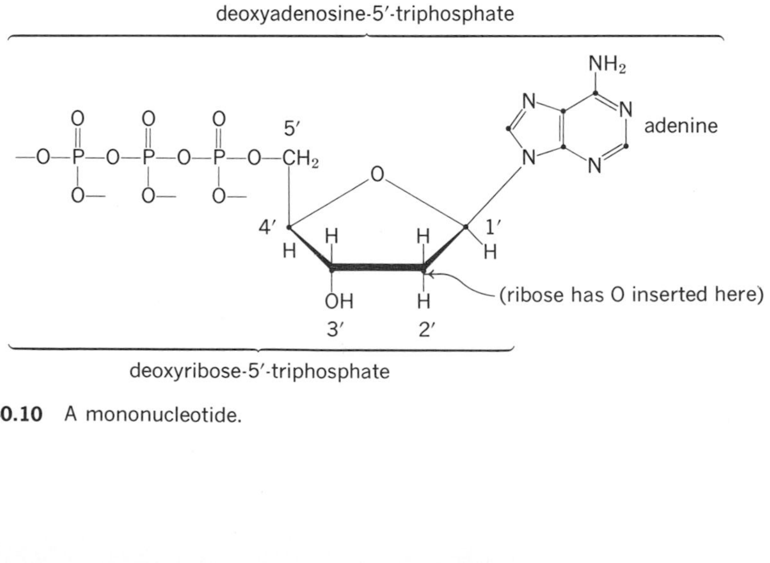

Figure 40.10 A mononucleotide.

Table 40.2 Base composition of DNA.

Organism	Base (%)			
	A	T	G	C
Sarcina lutea	13.4	12.4	37.1	37.1
Esherichia coli	24.7	23.6	26.0	25.7
Wheat	27.3	27.1	22.7	22.8
Chicken	28.8	29.2	20.5	21.5
Cow	28.0	28.0	22.0	21.0
Sheep	29.3	28.3	21.4	21.0
Man	30.9	29.4	19.9	19.8

SOURCE: Data of Chargoff.

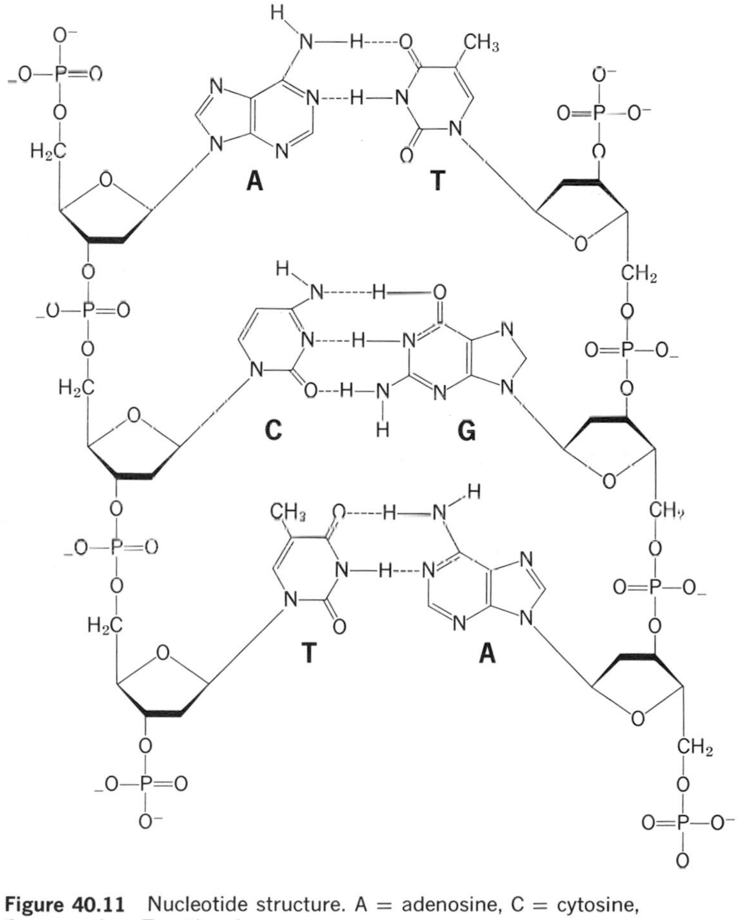

Figure 40.11 Nucleotide structure. A = adenosine, C = cytosine, G = guanine, T = thymine.

transcribed to RNA, and this transcribed version of the genetic information is translated into a polypeptide.

The apparatus and the three recognized types of RNA that function in protein synthesis are shown in Figure 40.12. The largest type of RNA is found in ribosomes, the cellular regions that serve as assembly sites for polypeptides. Ribosomes, which contain 40 to 60% ribosomal RNA (rRNA) have a sedimentation constant of from 30S to 80S,* depending on whether the two dissociable subunits they comprise are found separately or in association. Each subunit contains a char-

---

* The symbol S stands for one Svedberg, which corresponds roughly to a particle weight of 10^4 daltons for globular proteins; see p. 15.

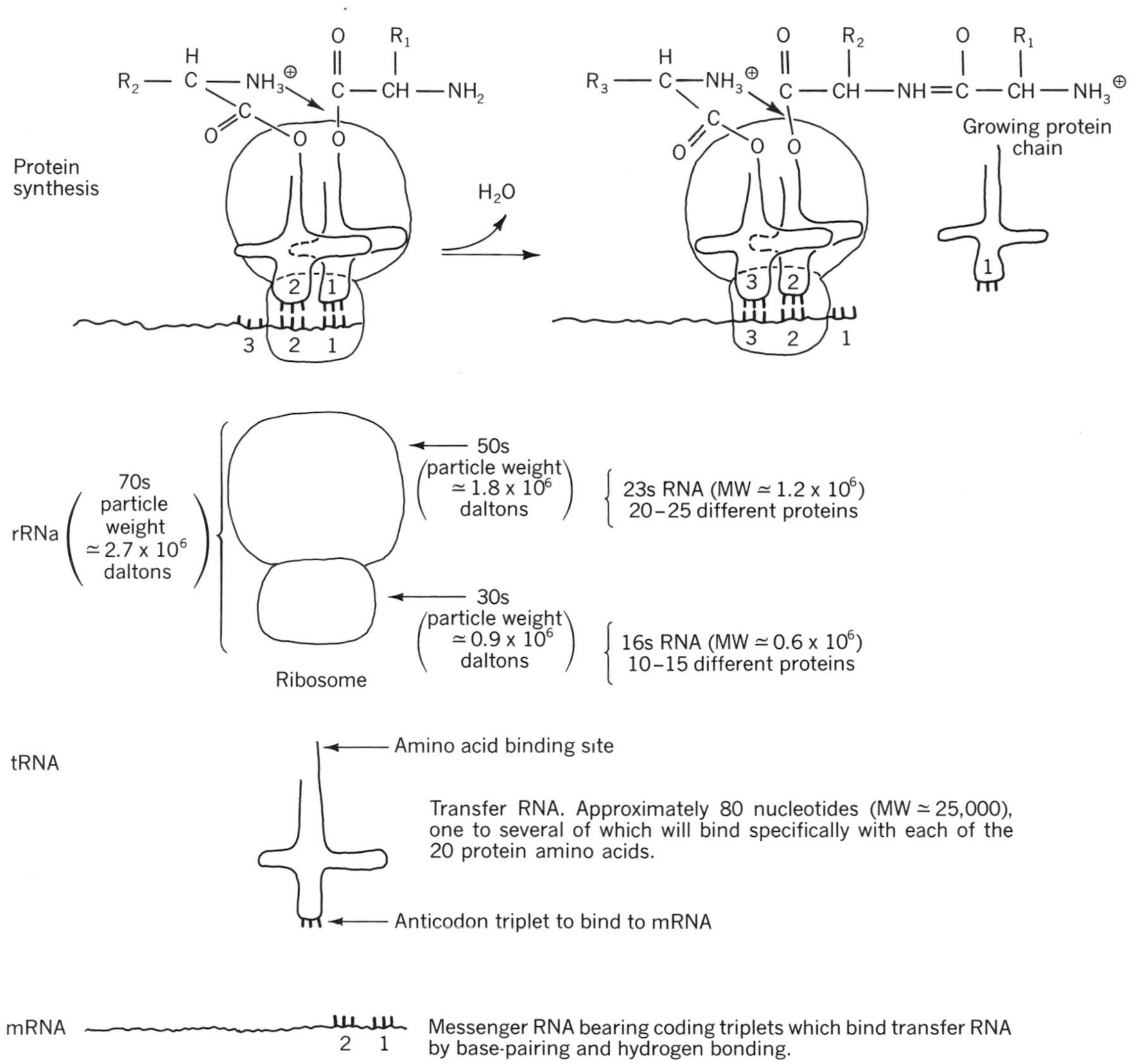

Figure 40.12 Three types of RNA and their role in protein synthesis. Sequence is from bottom to top.

acteristic type of RNA, ranging from 16 S to 30 S, and a number of different proteins with unknown functions. The ribosomes, however, become functional only when programmed by another type of RNA, known as messenger RNA (mRNA), which is decisive in determining the sequence of amino-acid incorporation into protein. There are, of course, as many messengers as there are proteins in a given cell, suggesting that mRNA is composed of molecules ranging in size from about 6S to approximately 15S. The third type—transfer, or soluble, RNA (tRNA)—has the smallest molecules of the three types of RNA, and its function in protein synthesis is to bring amino acids to the messenger-ribosome complex in a reactive form.

Almost nothing more is known at present about the role of rRNA in protein synthesis, but presumably it holds the tRNA molecules in an appropriate configuration, as indicated in Figure 40.12. On the other hand, biochemists have learned much about mRNA, most of it since 1961 when Nirenberg discovered that the use of synthetic polyribonucleotides facilitated its study. It has been found that three sequential nucleotides in mRNA specify the insertion of a single amino acid. Thus, information is said to be coded in triplets of nucleotides, called codons, which agrees with predictions made in the 1950's. Taking the four types of nucleotides in RNA one at a time gives only 4 possibilities, two at a time gives 16 possibilities, but three at a time gives 64 possible combinations. Proteins contain 20 different amino acids, so a simple doublet code would have too little information and can be discounted, but a triplet code would have more than three times the minimum number of required sequences. In the late 1950's it was hypothesized that only 20 triplets would be meaningful and the other 44 nonsense—that is, would specify no amino acid, although they might serve some other function. Now, however, it is known that all but two of the possible triplets do code for amino acids, which means, of course, that some amino acids have more than one triplet specifying their incorporation into a polypeptide chain. The relationships between various triplets and amino acids is conveniently represented in a manner proposed by Crick (see Table 40.3).

Two triplets, UAA and UAG, apparently function as chain-terminate signals; that is, when one of these two appears in the mRNA nucleotide sequence, no amino acid is specified and there is no further addition to the polypeptide synthesized in accord with the triplets preceding the terminators. It is, then, the base sequence of mRNA that instrumentally serves to determine the order of amino-acid incorporation. For the latter to occur, mRNA must associate with the 30S ribosomal subunit (which must also be associated with the 50S subunit), and then amino acids must arrive attached to tRNA through an anhydride linkage between the amino acid α-carboxyl and the OH at one end of the tRNA. Formation of that linkage is catalyzed by "amino acid activating" enzymes, each of which is selective for one amino acid and one tRNA. Thus, for example, a particular activating enzyme catalyzes linkage of tyrosine to Tyr–tRNA, which possesses an "anti-codon" triplet complementary to a codon for Tyr. There are also multiple tRNA's for some, if not all, amino acids; five have been identified that will accept tyrosine and no other amino acid. The conformation of active tRNA is represented by the cloverleaf shape shown in Figure 40.12 and results from the juxtaposition of portions of the polynucleotide chain that have complementary base sequences permitting intrachain hydrogen bonding.

Table 40.3 Triplet RNA coding for protein synthesis. The numbers of triplets for each amino acid are indicated in parentheses. The two triplets indicated by asterisks appear to code "stops" or chain termination.

First base	Second base: U	C	A	G	Third base
Uracil	Phe (2)	Ser (6)	Tyr (2)	CySH (3)	U
	Phe	Ser	Tyr	CySH	C
	Leu (6)	Ser	*	CySH	A
	Leu	Ser	*	Try (1)	G
Cytosine	Leu	Pro (4)	His (2)	Arg (6)	U
	Leu	Pro	His	Arg	C
	Leu	Pro	Gln (2)	Arg	A
	Leu	Pro	Gln	Arg	G
Adenine	Ile (3)	Thr (4)	Asn (2)	Ser	U
	Ile	Thr	Asn	Ser	C
	Ile	Thr	Lys (2)	Arg	A
	Met (1)	Thr	Lys	Arg	G
Guanine	Val (4)	Ala (4)	Asp (2)	Gly (4)	U
	Val	Ala	Asp	Gly	C
	Val	Ala	Glu (2)	Gly	A
	Val	Ala	Glu	Gly	G

The source of RNA—that is, where the synthesis of RNA occurs has not yet been identified, but all evidence indicates that ribosomal, messenger, and transfer RNA are synthesized with the involvement of DNA. RNA polymerase, another enzyme, uses DNA as a template, utilizes the four ribonucleotide triphosphates (ATP, GTP, CTP, and UTP) as substrates, and leads to synthesis of polyribonucleotides having base sequences complementary to the DNA template. Thus the genetic information is transmitted in the form of polydeoxyribonucleotides, is transcribed into polyribonucleotides, and is subsequently translated into polypeptides.

The energy for all this DNA, RNA, and protein synthesis comes mainly from carbohydrate oxidation.

GLUCOSE OXIDATION

Glucose is one of the most common sources of energy for biological systems. When glucose is oxidized in living organisms, the ultimate end products are CO_2 and H_2O, as they are in glucose combustion in a calorimeter:

$$C_6H_{12}O_6 + 6O_2 \longrightarrow 6CO_2 + 6H_2O, \qquad \Delta G^0 = -686 \text{ kcal/mole}$$

In the calorimeter, of course, the energy is released very rapidly and is dissipated as heat. Were this to happen in living systems, the cells would be destroyed. To derive energy from oxidation without self-destruction, glucose metabolism proceeds step by step, with electrons being removed in pairs and transferred to acceptor molecules, which are thus reduced. The reoxidation of the latter compounds is the immediate prerequisite of ATP biosynthesis.

METABOLISM AND BIOLOGICAL ENERGY TRANSDUCTION

Living organisms obtain the energy for chemical, mechanical, and biosynthetic work by the oxidation of foodstuffs. This statement applies equally to photosynthetic and nonphotosynthetic organisms, which differ from each other in that the former can, by processes that require CO_2, H_2O, and light, produce the carbohydrates that will be oxidized to yield energy. Nonphotosynthetic organisms, in contrast, require an external supply of carbohydrates. Energy production is obviously a basic requirement for life; yet, although much research has been done, a precise description of the relevant biological processes remains a challenging problem in biochemistry.

Two sequences that illustrate some general principles of carbohydrate metabolism are shown in Figures 40.13 and 40.14. The first sequence is that of glycolysis or anaerobic metabolism; the second is known alternatively as the citric acid cycle, the tricarboxylic acid cycle, or the Krebs cycle (after Hans Krebs, whose ingenious experiments established the existence of the cycle). Only carbohydrates are shown, since proteins and fats contribute to the energy pool only after being converted to one of several intermediates of the carbohydrate sequences.

The principle most clearly illustrated in these figures is that metabolism consists of sequential reactions, with the product of one step serving as the substrate or reactant for the next. Moreover, compounds generated in one sequence may often serve to initiate other sequences. For example, the compound glucose 6 phosphate may be used in the multireaction synthesis of glycogen (a polymer of glucose, the form in which this sugar is stored in animals), as the initial substrate of the pentose shunt (a multireaction cycle not shown, the source of ribose and deoxyribose) or, as shown in Figure 40.14, it may be converted to fructose-6-phosphate in a continuation of glycolysis.

Because of such interconnections, the events in one metabolic sequence may influence the metabolism of seemingly unrelated substances; for example, a perturbation in glucose metabolism may strongly affect the synthesis and degradation of proteins. Considerations such as this underlie the amazing capacity of living organisms to adapt to transient alterations in their environment and to maintain the constancy of their characteristics. Thus the regular diet of most human beings consists mostly of carbohydrates, but when food is unobtainable their bodies consume their structural proteins. But although protein can serve as an energy source in the absence of carbohydrate and fat, fats and carbohydrates cannot be used by humans to synthesize proteins. The effects of starvation can be offset only if protein is available in the recovery diet.

Since the enzymes of a given sequence are usually found in close association, the concentrations necessary for the formation of metabolites are not distributed uniformly throughout the cells, and a metabolite generally exists principally in the vicinity of the enzyme catalyzing its formation. This explains why some

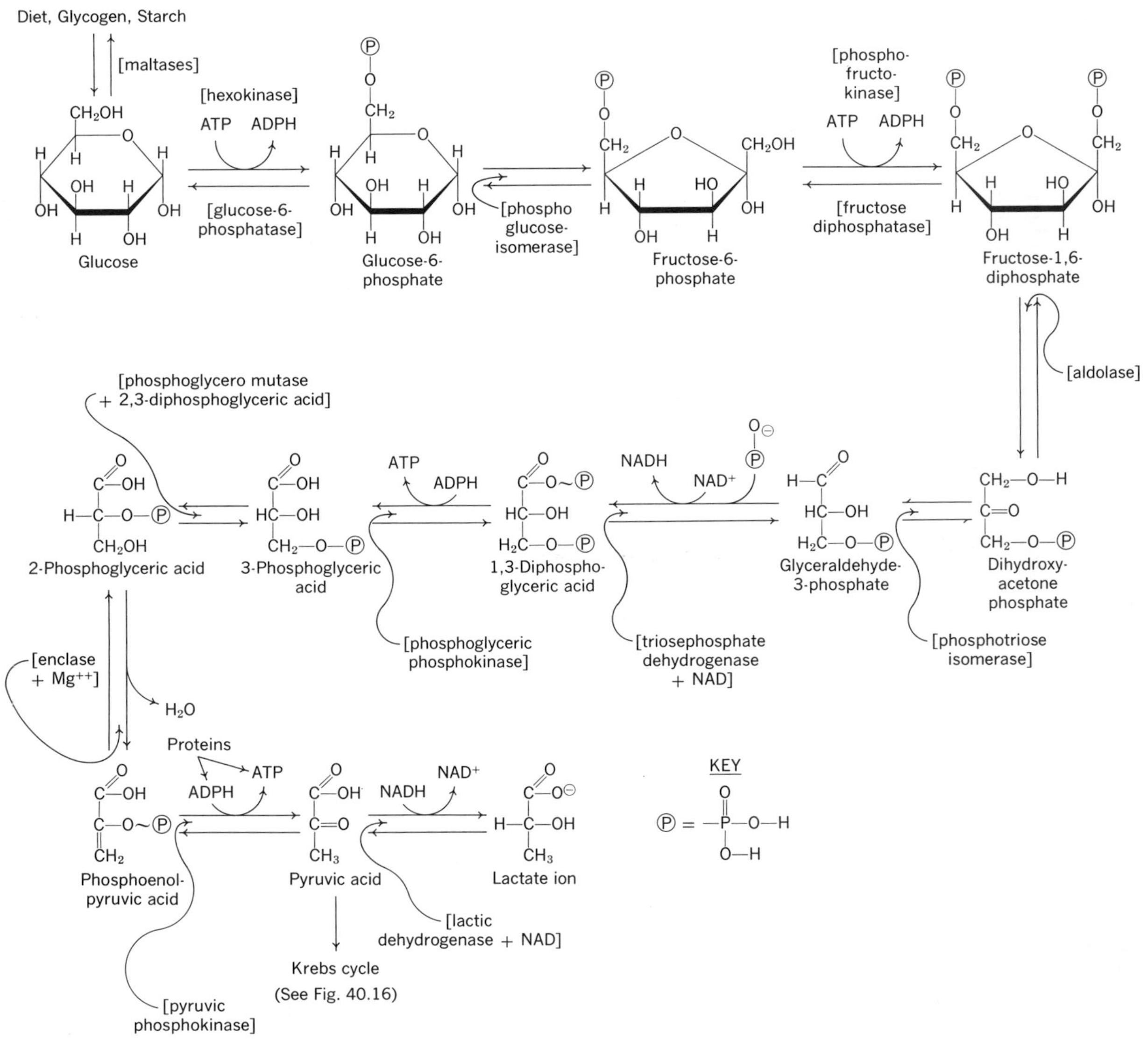

Figure 40.13 Anaerobic glucose metabolism (glycolysis) to form ATP. Some of the required enzymes and coenzymes are given in square brackets.

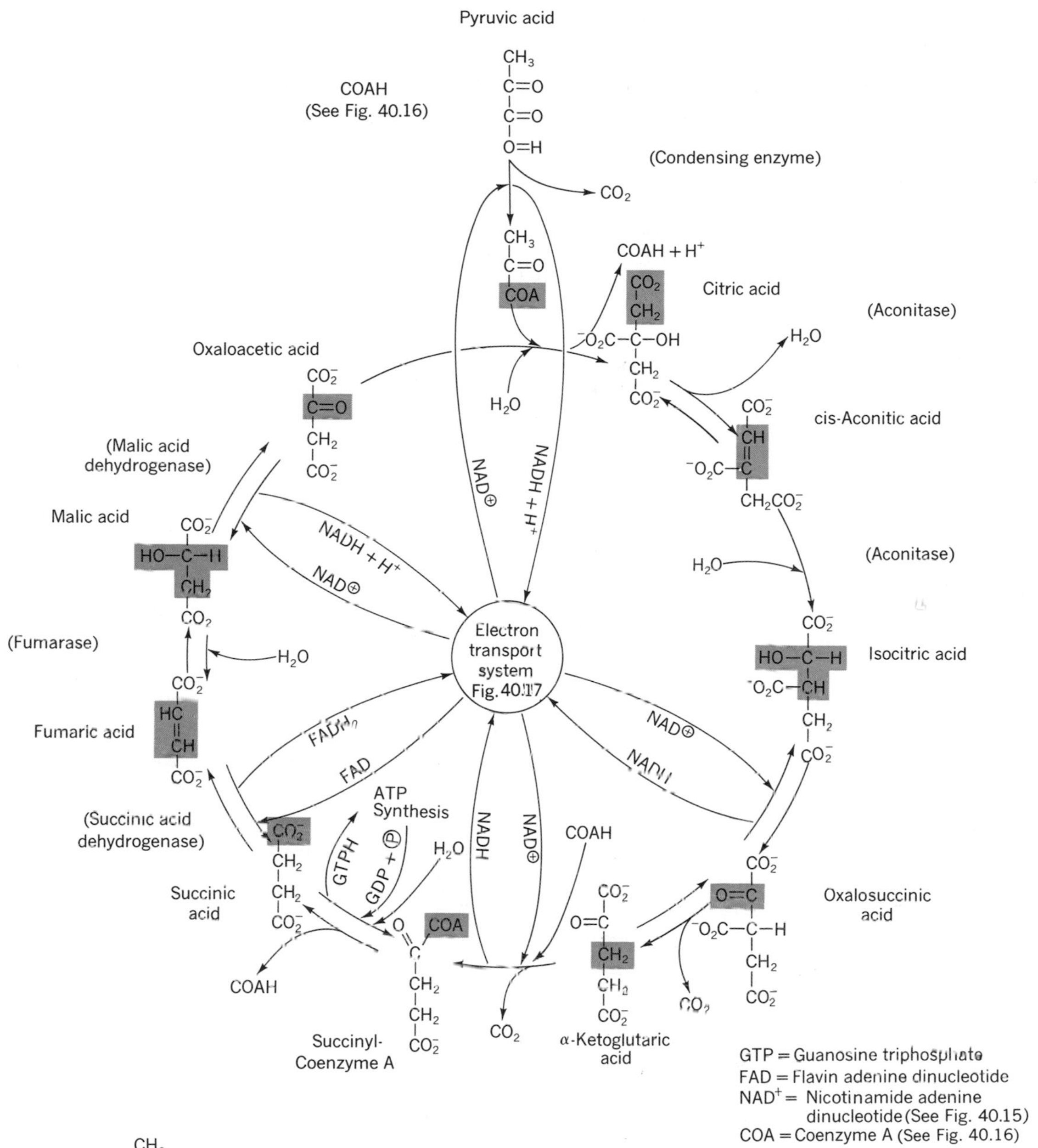

Net reaction:

$$\begin{array}{c}CH_3\\|\\C{=}O\\|\\C{=}O\\|\\OH\end{array} + 3H_2O + \underbrace{4NAD^+ + FAD}_{\text{From electron transport}} + \underbrace{GDP + Ⓟ^-}_{\text{From ATP Synthesis}} = 3CO_2 + \underbrace{4NADH + FADH_2 + 3H^+}_{\text{To electron transport}} + \underbrace{GTPH}_{\text{To ATP Synthesis}}$$

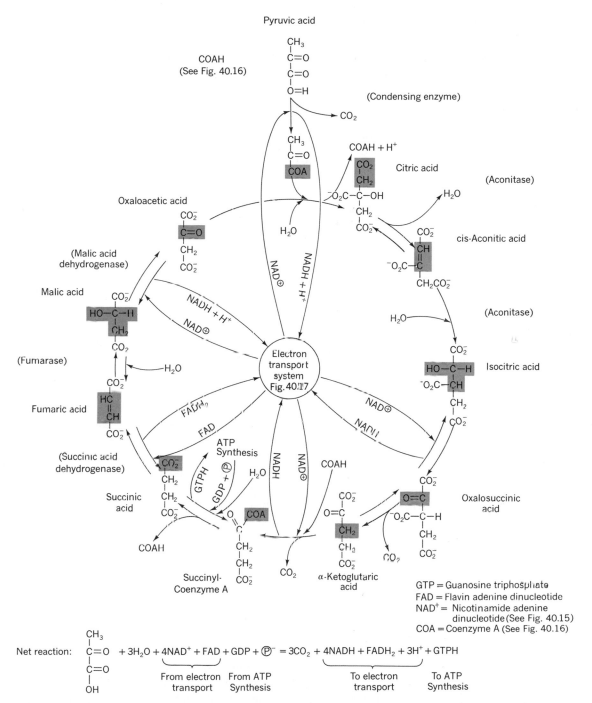

Figure 40.14 Citric acid, or Krebs, anaerobic metabolic cycle. The acids are generally **represented as their ions for simplicity. Some of the enzymes required are listed in parentheses. (See Figure 40.17 and accompanying discussion for NAD and FAD.)**

metabolic reactions proceed in the direction determined to be energetically unfavorable when studied in vitro as isolated reactions. One such case is that involving the conversion of fructose-1,6-diphosphate to glyceraldehyde-3-phosphate and dihydroxyacetone-phosphate. In the test tube, this reaction, catalyzed by the enzyme aldolase, has an equilibrium constant of 10^{-5}, which would constitute a considerable impediment to glycolysis if equilibrium conditions prevailed in the cell. But they don't. Rather, glycolysis proceeds with a net conversion of glucose to pyruvic and/or lactic acid because the products of the aldolase reaction in vivo quickly undergo further reaction.

Exercise 40.10

Can a human survive on a meat-free diet? *Answer:* Most "meat-free diets" actually include fish, milk, and eggs, all of which contain a good deal of animal protein. But there are enough plant proteins usable by humans, especially in nuts, and seeds (legumes), to make a true vegetarian diet possible. Do you see why seeds and nuts are rich in vegetable protein?

"HIGH ENERGY BONDS"

"High energy bond," is a term that appears frequently in biochemical discussions. It is used to designate chemical groupings which supply energy for biochemical processes that, by themselves, are endergonic. "High energy bond" has about the same status that "alcohol" and "ether" have in organic chemistry; all are imprecise terms—scientific colloquialisms—which persist even though their imprecision is recognized. The designation is most often applied to the anhydride bond between the two terminal phosphate groups of adenosine triphosphate (ATP; the same mononucleotide triphosphate used in the synthesis of RNA). Other compounds have a similar energy-transferring function, but ATP is the only one common to all living organisms. It is the active energy source in many biochemical reactions: muscle movement, nerve transmission, biosynthesis, active membrane transport.

The "high energy bond" label for the terminal bond in ATP is doubly misleading. In the first place, it implies that the bond is very labile—one that breaks readily. On the contrary, the bond is thermodynamically quite stable. Second, the biochemical function of this grouping does not concern bond energy at all; the latter refers to the work required to separate the atoms participating in the bond. Klotz has suggested that "group-transfer potential"—that is, the change in chemical potential, ΔG^0, when a group is transferred to a standard acceptor molecule such as H_2O—is a more accurate term.

For ATP the standard free energy of hydrolysis is -7 kcal mole^{-1}, which is an intermediate value for biological compounds having negative free energies of hydrolysis. Of these, several, but principally ATP, interact in biochemical systems to "drive" reactions that are energetically unfavorable. For example, the phosphorylation of glucose,

$$\text{glucose} + HPO_4^{-2} \rightleftharpoons \text{glucose-6-phosphate} + H_2O$$

is an endergonic reaction ($\Delta G^0 = +4$ kcal mole^{-1}). As stated above, however, the hydrolysis of ATP,

$$ATP + H_2O \rightleftharpoons ADP + HPO_4^{-2}$$

is exergonic ($\Delta G^0 = -7$ kcal mole^{-1}). Coupling these two reactions, as in the first step in glycolysis,

$$\text{glucose} + ATP \rightleftharpoons \text{glucose-6-phosphate} + ADP, \qquad \Delta G^0 = -3 \text{ kcal mole}^{-1}$$

makes the phosphorylation of glucose thermodynamically feasible.

The last reaction, which illustrates a second way in which barriers are overcome in biochemical systems, is much more common than the kinetic example given earlier. Conversely, the end result of the reactions in Figures 40.13 and 40.14, from the standpoint of energetics, is to transfer much of the energy content of glucose (or proteins and lipids) to ATP. The latter can then provide the energy required for biological work.

COENZYMES

Figure 40.14 mentions coenzyme A, and in Figures 40.13, 40.14, and 40.17, are two abbreviations, NAD$^+$ and FAD. These coenzymes (small molecules which in combination with certain enzyme proteins constitute catalytically functional units) accept hydrogens and electrons in oxidation reactions. Their function can be illustrated by a reaction involving NAD$^+$ (nicotinamide-adenine-dinucleotide) as in Figure 40.15. Reactions involving FAD (flavin-adenine-dinucleotide) proceed in a similar manner except that both protons as well as both electrons that are removed from the oxidized substrate are transferred to the flavin moiety.

COENZYME A (COA)

Another common molecule involved in enzymatic reactions is coenzyme A (Figure 40.16). The usual form of the coenzyme is COAH, which has an H instead of the acetyl group of Figure 40.16. Coenzyme A illustrates one of the possible roles of vitamins, which, like the essential amino acids, cannot be synthesized in the body.

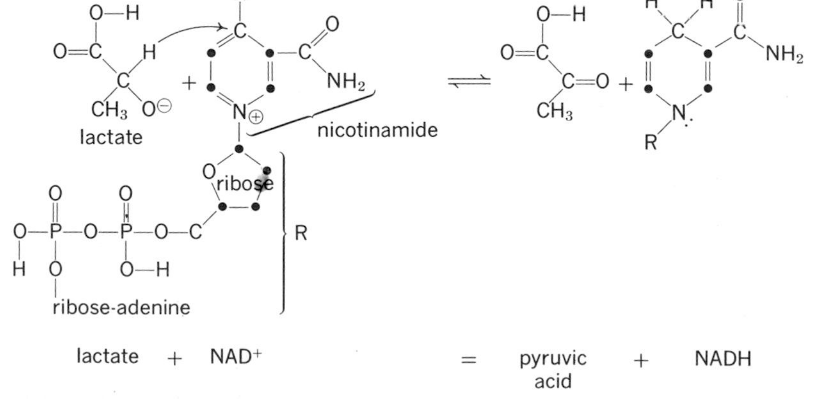

Figure 40.15 Mechanism of NAD$^+$ coenzyme action.

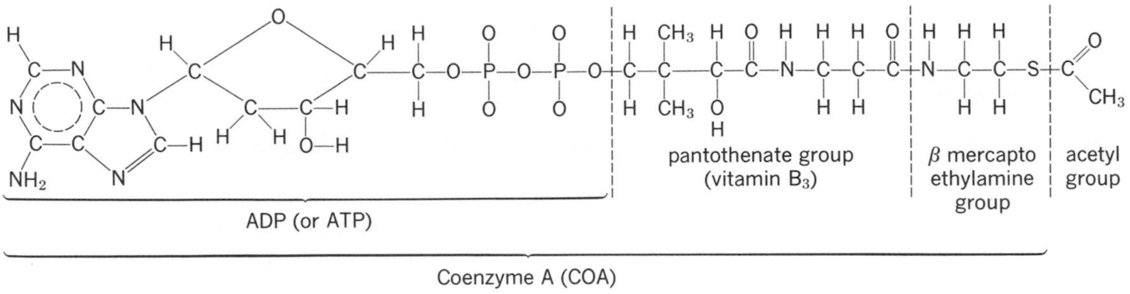

Figure 40.16 Structure of acetyl coenzyme A.

The vitamins often act as coenzymes themselves or are incorporated into coenzymes. The absence of a given vitamin from the diet leads to one or another of the so-called deficiency diseases: scurvy in the absence of vitamin C, rickets in the absence of vitamin D, and so on.

COUPLED REACTIONS

You will notice that reduced coenzymes are generated in the Krebs cycle reactions listed in Figure 40.14. All of these reactions and those of electron transport (see below) take place in the subcellular units known as mitochondria. Glycolysis takes place outside the mitochondria and, if it proceeds only to lactate, no net oxidation (relative to glucose) occurs.

Pyruvic acid, the precursor of lactate, can, however, pass into the mitochondria and become converted to acetyl coenzyme A (instead of lactate), which then condenses with oxaloacetic acid as the first step of the Krebs cycle. In this manner the two sequences are interconnected and the carbon atoms from glucose are given off individually as CO_2. In the process, NADH and $FADH_2$ are generated and, also within the mitochondria, subsequently reoxidized in a multistep sequence

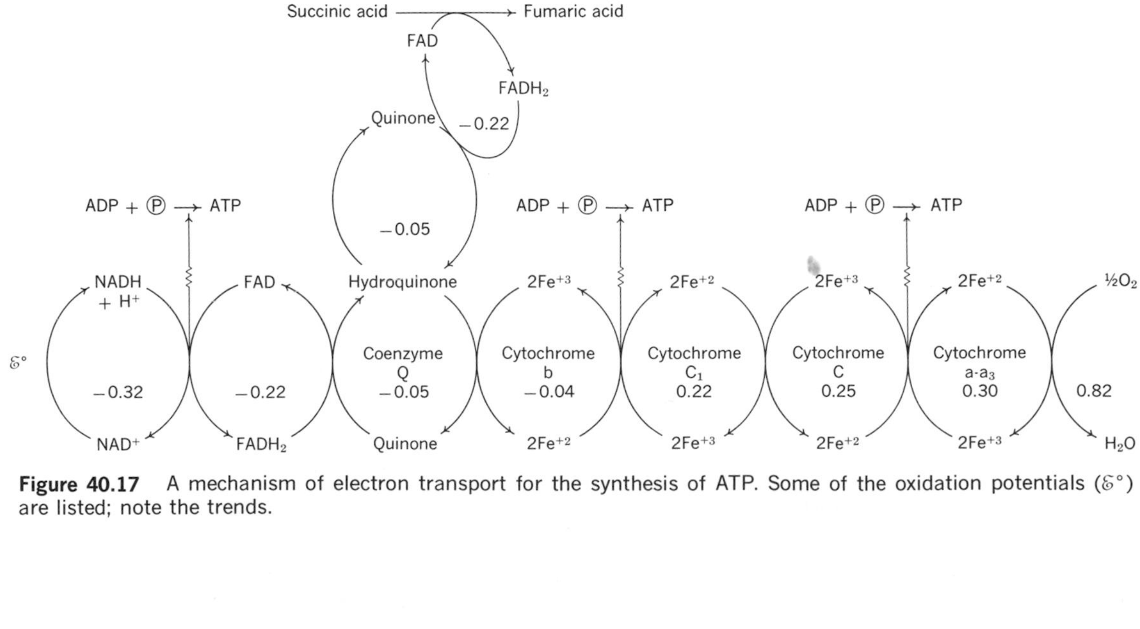

Figure 40.17 A mechanism of electron transport for the synthesis of ATP. Some of the oxidation potentials (ℰ°) are listed; note the trends.

known as electron transport. Figure 40.17 shows this for the succinic acid step in the Krebs cycle of Figure 40.14. Electrons from NADH pass along the transport chain and, in the final step, oxygen becomes reduced to H_2O. Since for the $NADH + H^+/NAD^+$ system, $\mathcal{E}^0 = -0.32$ volts, and for $H_2O/\frac{1}{2}O_2$, $\mathcal{E}^0 = 0.82$, the transfer of 2 electrons down this chain is accompanied by $\Delta G^0 = -52.5$ kcal. About 40% of this energy is "trapped" in 3 moles of ATP and made available biologically. Note that this is much more efficient energy transfer than in the typical heat engine of Chapter 26.

The chemical mechanisms involved remain obscure, but since the mid-1950's it has been assumed that oxidative phosphorylation involves the synthesis of X—Ⓟ, a hypothetical compound in which the transfer potential for the phosphate group is large enough to "drive" the synthesis of ATP. This suggestion has been made in analogy with reactions in glycolysis; for example,

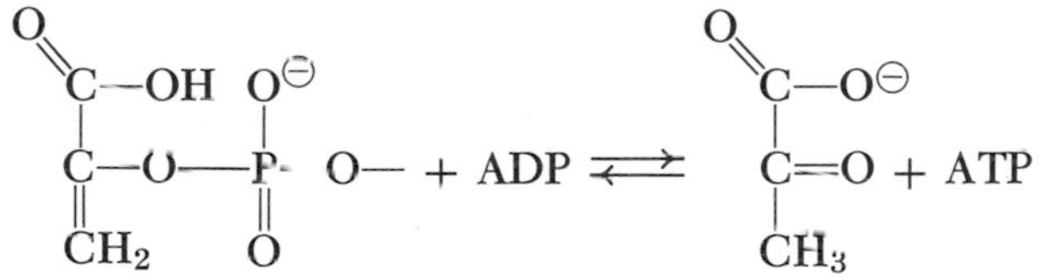

phosphoenolpyruvate + ADP ⇌ pyruvate + ATP, $\Delta G° = -13\ \text{kcal mole}^{-1}$

The above reaction occurs outside the mitochondria (with an efficiency of about 35%) but no phosphorylated compound with the properties of the hypothetical X—Ⓟ has yet been identified in mitochondria.

Exercise 40.11

Assuming the total oxidation of glucose produces ATP at about the same efficiency that is found in the succinic acid step, how many moles of ATP are produced per mole of glucose oxidized. *Answer:* $\Delta G^0 = -686$ for glucose, $\Delta G^0 = -7$ for ATP, average % $\cong$ 40. (Moles ATP)/(moles glucose) $= 0.40 \cdot 686/7 \cong 40$. As you suspect, the actual number is less, since some of the energy is stored in molecules other than ATP. The experimentally observed value is 38 moles of ATP per mole of glucose. Living systems (40% efficiency) thus better steam-electric plants (about 30% thermodynamic efficiency).

SOME UNSOLVED PROBLEMS IN BIOCHEMISTRY

The developments outlined in this chapter have contributed to answering some questions in biochemistry, but they have also raised some new questions and opened the way for studying other, previously intractable problems. A few of the latter will be mentioned here.

PREDICTION OF TERTIARY STRUCTURE

If it could be learned what contribution each amino acid—given the other residues nearby—will make to the three-dimensional configuration, it would be possible to draw the tertiary structure of a protein as soon as the amino acid sequence was known. Sequence determinations are now a matter of routine in biochemical laboratories, but tertiary structures can still be determined only by the laborious and difficult method of X-ray diffraction. Except for the helix-disrupting effect of proline, the contributions of individual amino acids have not yet been identified. There has been some modest success with attempts to predict tertiary structures by computing energy minima for pairwise atomic interactions along the peptide chain, and much more can be expected from these efforts.

ACTIVE SITES ON ENZYMES

The tertiary structure of the enzyme carboxypeptidase has been solved by X-ray diffraction. Then, using the same method, enzyme that had crystallized with a substrate analogue bound at the catalytic site was examined. As predicted by the induced-fit hypothesis, the enzyme conformation was seen to have changed; some amino acid residues had shifted by as much as 14 Å, bringing them closer to the substrate analogue. Through such studies the functional groups involved in enzymic catalysis can be identified unambiguously, and eventually it may be learned why proteins are the most efficient of all known catalysts.

CHEMICAL EVIDENCE ON EVOLUTIONARY SEQUENCES

The codon triplets for individual amino acids are now known; therefore determination of a protein's primary structure permits the deduction of the base sequence for the corresponding gene. Cytochrome C is universal in living organisms and performs the same function in respiration wherever it occurs. Human and monkey cytochrome C structures differ only in one out of a sequence of 104 amino acids (no. 58: Ilu in man, Thr in monkey). Thus, during their separate evolutionary lifetimes, a single mutational event (substituting adenine for guanine—see Table 40.3) has occurred in the gene DNA for cytochrome C. Table 40.4 lists the numbers of mutations that must be postulated in order to relate the cytochrome C gene of a variety of organisms to that of man. The trend is apparent: as biological relatedness decreases, the number of mutations increases. Figure 40.18 summarizes these data in a phylogenetic "tree" in which the length of each branch suggests the time since genetic branching took place.

"TEST TUBE" BIOCHEMICAL SYNTHESES

Solving one problem (as with the solid-phase technique for rapid, automated synthesis of polypeptides) often has enormous practical and scientific consequences, as suggested previously. For example, a variation of the solid-phase technique has already been applied to the synthesis of polydeoxyribonucleotides with a known base sequence. The value of what this implies is difficult to overestimate. Such syntheses will not only aid in working out the basic genetic mechanisms; they also indicate that it may soon be possible to produce synthetic genes that can be used to supplement an organism's natural genetic complement. Although this

Table 40.4 **Number of mutations postulated in a total of 312 gene nucleotides to account for cytochrome C variations between several species.**

Monkey	Dog	Horse	Donkey	Pig	Rabbit	Kangaroo	Duck	Pigeon	Chicken	Penguin	Turtle	Rattlesnake	Tuna	Fly	Moth	*Neurospora*	*Saccharomyces*	*Candida krusei*	
1	13	15	15	13	11	14	15	15	16	16	17	29	29	30	33	64	62	68	Man
	12	15	14	12	11	13	15	14	15	15	16	28	29	29	32	63	61	67	Monkey (*Macacus mulatta*)
		9	8	6	7	8	13	13	13	14	15	26	27	27	30	61	59	65	Dog
			1	5	10	11	15	15	16	16	17	29	29	30	33	64	62	68	Horse
				4	9	10	14	14	15	15	16	28	28	29	32	63	61	67	Donkey
					7	8	13	12	13	13	14	26	27	27	30	61	59	65	Pig
						7	11	11	12	12	13	24	25	25	29	60	57	63	Rabbit
							13	13	14	14	15	27	27	28	31	62	60	66	Kangaroo (*Canopus canguru*)
								3	3	3	8	26	27	27	30	61	59	65	Pekin duck
									4	4	8	26	27	27	30	61	59	65	Pigeon
										2	9	27	27	28	31	62	60	66	Chicken
											9	27	27	28	31	62	60	66	King penguin (*Aptenodytes patagonica*)
												28	29	29	32	63	61	67	Snapping turtle (*Chelydra serpentina*)
													33	34	37	68	66	72	Rattlesnake (*Crotalus adamanteus*)
														35	38	69	67	73	Tuna
															16	59	56	63	Screwworm fly (*Haematobia irritans*)
																62	60	66	Moth (*Samia cynthia*)
																	56	62	*Neurospora crassa*
																		41	*Saccharomyces oviformis*

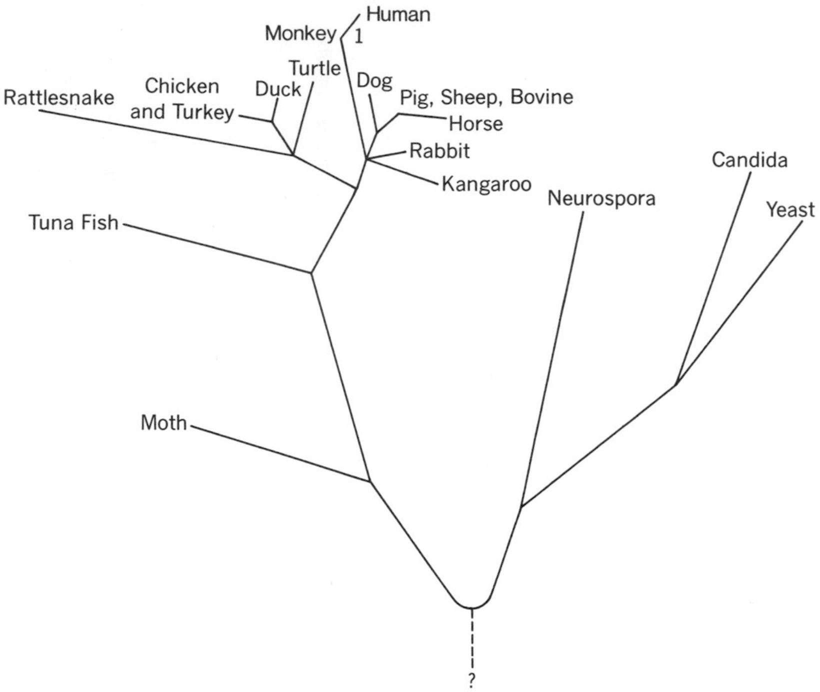

Figure 40.18 Phylogenetic tree based on differences in amino acid sequence in cytochrome C.

sounds like science fiction, the scientific implications and the social consequences of such a synthesis are currently a matter of serious discussion among biochemists.

CONTROL MECHANISMS

Biologically, excessive production of ATP is little better than underproduction, and observations strongly indicate that ATP synthesis is so regulated that production does not grossly exceed utilization. This is a complex phenomenon, but one important aspect of it is the effect of ATP on phosphofructokinase, the enzyme catalyzing the production of fructose-1,6-diphosphate from fructose-6-phosphate (see Figure 40.13). ATP in concentrations greater than normal physiological values strongly inhibits phosphofructokinase activity, but AMP, which is produced when ATP is used in many energy-requiring reactions, strongly stimulates the enzyme. Thus when ATP is low (and AMP is high) in concentration, glycolysis and subsequent regeneration of ATP are accelerated. As the ATP concentration is increased, glycolysis is slowed down and glucose is channeled into other pathways, principally that for glycogen synthesis.

Control phenomena like those associated with phosphofructokinase are designated as feedback controls. The effector molecules (ATP and AMP in the example given) bind at sites on the enzyme which are separate from the catalytic site and induce changes in conformation which either impair or enhance catalytic efficiency. An analysis of specific control sites (for example, on phosphofructokinase) reveals something about the net flow through pathways but it tells us little about the instantaneous flux through individual reactions in the pathway. Stated as a question: how does a change in the rate of phosphofructokinase catalysis affect reactions preceding and following this step in glycolysis, and what are the temporal relationships among these effects? Questions like this are very difficult, if not impossible, to answer experimentally, and consequently some biochemists have turned to computer simulation models in attempts to gain more insight.

CELL DIFFERENTIATION

The preceding discussions should have made it clear that most scientists believe that genetic information is coded in the double DNA helices of the genes, that fertilization involves a joining together of genes from two progenitors and the initiation of the long series of cell divisions which results in the formation of an individual. Ample experimental evidence is available to support the belief that the cells resulting from the earliest divisions are identical and undifferentiated. They can, for example, be dissected from one another and rearranged without altering the individual that is later produced. In every sequence of cell division, however, there appears to be a time at which the cells do begin to differentiate. Rearrangement after that time produces monstrosities with parts misplaced. What leads to cell differentiation? How can it be that the cells remain identical through a certain number of divisions and then begin to differentiate? How does the process of differentiation lead to all the varied parts of an individual—indeed, to such varied single cells as those found in muscle, nerves, skin, eyes, and so on? For example, a human body contains some 10^{12} cells, all descended from a single fertilized cell and ramified into about a thousand types of highly specialized, differentiated, and specifically located cells. Presumably the mechanism of differentiation must be reasonably simple, since it is so highly reproducible.

Gurdon, in 1962, showed that the removal of the nucleus of a frog eggcell and its replacement with the nucleus from an intestinal cell of a mature frog gave a "synthetic" egg which grew into a normal adult frog. Other evidence also indicates that in an individual of any species the nucleus of every cell of every type contains all the genetic information necessary to produce that individual. Presumably this means that cell differentiation leads to certain genes being "turned-on" and/or others "turned-off." For example, all human cells appear to contain the genes required to synthesize insulin, but insulin is synthesized only in the pancreas.

Thus, our differentiation question may be phrased: "What chemical events lead to certain genes in a given cell being active and to others being inactive?" As of 1969—no one knows.

EPILOGUE

You have now viewed a cross section of contemporary knowledge from a chemical point of view. Discussion of approaches and observations have been interwoven with interpretations based on current concepts of energetics, dynamics, and structures in order that you might comprehend bulk properties in terms of molecular behavior. From the individual atoms of the early chapters to the giant molecules and complicated species of the final chapters the emphasis has been on using quantitative-mathematical models whenever possible, but at the same time recognizing the strength of qualitative generalizations that provide insight into the complexity of chemical systems.

Chemistry has made great contributions to human knowledge, wisdom, and progress in the two hundred years since Lavoisier launched the subject on a quantitative basis. But even larger areas remain for you to discover, explore, and reduce to comprehension than are presently understood. Regardless of your role—citizen, engineer, chemist, mathematician, biologist, physicist—you will surely both contribute to and profit from this continued growth.

All this leads to the conclusion that it is likely that we shall find some activity of the brain correlated with every recognizable activity of the mind, and therefore that ultimately we shall possess explanations of those mental activities in physicochemical terms.

I suggest that one of the essential ingredients of such a view should be the primacy of the private, personal, subjective, individual experience over any public account which science can give. This means that persons are to be regarded as values in themselves, and not as reducible to either physicochemical systems or bundles of psychological trends or impulses. The social and political implications of this are important. One of them is that science, though an end in itself to the scientist, is only a means to an end where other people are concerned, that end being the possibility of their greater fulfillment as persons.—W. R. Brain, Science, **148**, 195, 197 (1965).

PROBLEMS

40.1. Enzymes are usually much larger than the substrate molecules whose reactions they catalyze. What does this imply about the mechanism of enzyme catalysis?

40.2. Review Problem 1.25 in terms of Table 40.1 and discuss the advantages of enriching rice with lysine.

40.3. Draw the structures of L and D proline.

40.4. Draw the total configuration of atoms, including secondary structure, around a typical peptide. Estimate each of the bond angles involved.

40.5. Draw a disulfide bond, estimating each of the bond angles involved.

40.6. Suggest a reason most globular proteins do not contain pleated-sheet structures.

40.7. Suggest how muscle function could be correlated with a filamentous protein structure [T. Hill, *Proc. Natl. Acad. Sci. U.S.*, **61**, 889 (1968)].

40.8. Give a structural interpretation of the efficacy of water in causing hair to "stay in place."

40.9. Vitamins are often classed as water-soluble and water-insoluble. To which group would Vitamin B_5, pantothenic acid, probably belong? Write the full structure of the pure acid, assuming the two end linkages in Figure 40.16 to be ester and amide links, respectively.

40.10. It has been suggested that the production of synthetic radioisotopes of all the elements is the greatest contribution to biology since the invention of the microscope. Justify or attack this suggestion even if you cannot compare it to all other contributions.

40.11. Platinum catalysts are used in a plant producing 2000 tons of H_2SO_4 per 24-hour day. If the catalyst had the same turnover number as the average enzyme, how much platinum would be needed? (About 40 grams.)

40.12. Ingestion of large amounts of alcohol by humans causes some enzymes to lose their active structures. Suggest a possible mechanism at the molecular level.

40.13. The heat of denaturation (or uncoiling), ΔH^0, of the protein "soybean trypsin inhibitor" is 57 kcal mole^{-1}. Denaturation proceeds spontaneously at 50°C. Estimate a value of ΔS^0 for the denaturation and interpret the value in terms of molecular behavior, being as quantitative as possible. [M. Kunitz, *J. Gen. Physiol.*, **32**, 257 (1948).]

40.14. Enzymes fall into two classes, based either on mechanism of reaction or turnover number: (1) involving only electron transfer, (2) involving both proton and electron transfer. Which mechanism is probably associated with turnover numbers of 10^3? which with 10^8?

40.15. Draw valine-proline dipeptides (*a*) with N-terminal valine, (*b*) with N-terminal proline. Discuss any differences.

40.16. Estimate the number of mononucleotides in the DNA of a nucleus in animal cells. ($n \cong 10^9$.)

40.17. A pentapeptide is found to contain the top four amino acids of Table 40.1 plus phenylalanine with glycine N-terminal and alanine C-terminal. Treatment with chymotrypsin gives a dipeptide and a tripeptide. What can you say about the structure of the original pentapeptide? What would you do next to complete the analysis of this primary structure?

II

40.18. It is well known that camels can survive for long periods without eating or drinking. During these periods the fat in their humps disappears. Look up the formula of a typical fat and write a possible chemical equation to show the fat's reaction in meeting the camel's needs. Would the camel be better off storing carbohydrate in its hump?

40.19. Hemerythrin, Hr, is an oxygen-carrying molecule in *Golfingia gouldii*. Calculate ΔH^0, ΔS^0, and ΔG^0 at 25° for the reaction $O_{2(g)} + Hr_{(aq)} = HrO_{2(aq)}$ from the following data on equilibrium O_2 pressure versus T. Guess approximate values before you begin. ($\Delta S \cong -50$ eu.)

T (°C)	0	25
P (atm)	$1.096 \cdot 10^{-4}$	$2.64 \cdot 10^{-3}$

40.20. Plant carbohydrates, such as $(C_6H_{12}O_6)_n$, are the normal precursors of animal fats, and animal fatty acids all contain an even number of carbon atoms. Postulate a general mechanism for this conversion in the animal. The fat of each animal tends to be characteristic of that species and to differ from that of other species. Is this result consistent with your general mechanism?

III

40.21. Enzyme reactions are often studied by fastening to the substrate molecules a light-absorbing fragment (chromophore) whose atomic constitution remains unchanged during reaction even though its electron energy levels are affected. The shifts in electrons are revealed by studying the absorbance of the system as a function of time. The accompanying figure shows the change of absorbance of such a chromophore during a reaction catalyzed by trypsin at pH 5.3, 25°C, 470 mμ. Suggest a possible mechanism and comment as quantitatively as possible on the reaction orders and rate constants.

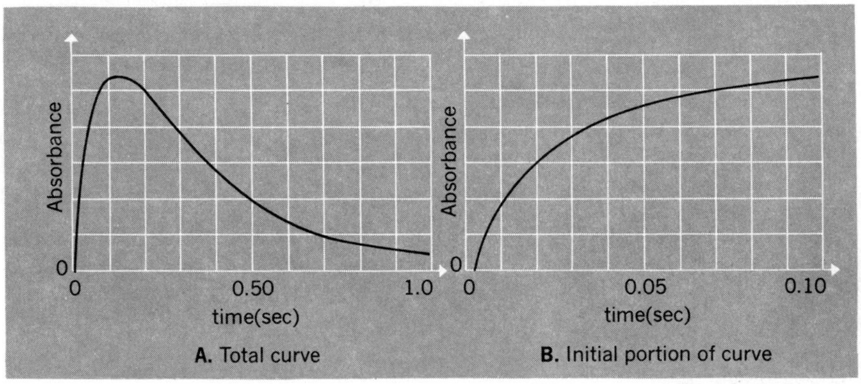

40.22. The enzyme aspartate transcarbanylase from *Escherichia coli* is a tetramer having three mutually perpendicular 2-fold axes. Assume that each monomer is a plate whose cross section looks like

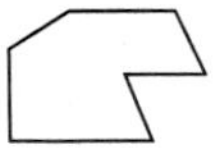

Sketch a possible tetramer.

See page 1095 for a list of references and readings in the recent chemical literature related to the material in this chapter.

Appendixes

APPENDIX I

Universal Constants and Conversion Data

A. UNIVERSAL CONSTANTS YOU SHOULD KNOW FOR WORK IN CHEMISTRY

(3 significant figures are enough to memorize)

Further values may be found in National Bureau of Standards, *Technical News Bulletin*, October 1963, or "The International System of Units," E. A. Mechtly, NASA SP-7012.

N_0	Avogadro number	$6.02252(\pm 0.00028) \cdot 10^{23}$ molecules mole^{-1}
h	Planck constant	$6.6256(\pm 0.0005) \cdot 10^{-27}$ erg sec molecule^{-1}, or g cm^2 sec^{-1} molecule^{-1}
$\mathcal{F}$	Faraday constant	96,487.0 ($\pm$1.6) amp sec (or coulombs) mole^{-1} 23.053 ($\pm$0.004) kcal eq^{-1} volt^{-1}
$k = R/N_0$	Boltzmann constant	$1.38054(\pm 0.00018) \cdot 10^{-16}$ erg $°\text{K}^{-1}$ molecule^{-1}, or g cm^2 sec^{-2} $°\text{K}^{-1}$ molecule^{-1}
R	Gas constant	1.9872 ($\pm$0.0003) cal $°\text{K}^{-1}$ mole^{-1} 0.082053 ($\pm$0.000012) l atm $°\text{K}^{-1}$ mole^{-1} $8.3143(\pm 0.0012) \cdot 10^7$ erg $°\text{K}^{-1}$ mole^{-1}, or g cm^2 sec^{-2} $°\text{K}^{-1}$ mole^{-1}
	Triple point of water	273.16°K
π		3.14159

$\ln_e x = 2.3036 \log_{10} x$

x	1	2	3	7	10
$\log x$	0	.301	.477	.845	1.000

Note that log 4, 5, 6, 8, 9 are readily calculable from log 2 and log 3. Thus knowledge of three logs (2, 3, 7) allows many rapid calculations.

B. UNIVERSAL CONSTANTS OF CONSIDERABLE USE

c	Speed of light	$2.997925(\pm 0.000003) \cdot 10^{10}$ cm sec^{-1}
e	Electron charge	$4.80298(\pm 0.00020) \cdot 10^{-10}$ esu, or $(\text{g cm}^3 \text{ sec}^{-2})^{1/2}$ $1.60210(\pm 0.00007) \cdot 10^{-19}$ coulombs
m_e	Electron rest mass	$9.1091(\pm 0.0004) \cdot 10^{-28}$ g

m_p	Proton rest mass	$1.67252(\pm 0.00008) \cdot 10^{-24}$ g
m_n	Neutron rest mass	$1.67482(\pm 0.00008) \cdot 10^{-24}$ g
g	Gravitational acceleration	980.621 cm sec^{-2}
e	Base of natural logarithms	2.71828

C. CONVERSION FACTORS OF CONSIDERABLE USE

Energy

1 kcal $mole^{-1}$ = 41.2929 liter atm $mole^{-1}$ = $6.94725 \cdot 10^{-14}$ ergs $molecule^{-1}$
= $4.184 \cdot 10^3$ (exactly) joules $mole^{-1}$ = $4.33634 \cdot 10^{-2}$ electron volts $molecule^{-1}$

For oscillators

1 kcal $(mole)^{-1}$ = $1.04855 \cdot 10^{13}$ sec^{-1} (ν) = $3.49759 \cdot 10^2$ $cm^{-1}(\bar{\nu})$

$$E = h\nu = hc\bar{\nu} = hc/\lambda$$

General

1 cal = 4.184 (exactly) joules = $4.184 \cdot 10^7$ (exactly) ergs = 10^{-3} (exactly) kcal
= $4.6553 \cdot 10^{-14}$ grams

1 atm = 760 torr = 760 mm Hg (standard conditions) (exactly) = 14.696 lb in^{-2}
= 1.0132 bar = $1.0132 \cdot 10^6$ dyne cm^{-2} = 1.0332 kg m^{-2}

R ln to $1.9872 \cdot 2.3026$ log = 4.5757 log

RT ln to $1.9872 \cdot 298.15 \cdot 2.3026$ log = 1364.2 log

1 pound avoirdupois = 453.292 g

1 inch = 2.54005 cm

1° F = 5/9°K = 5/9° C (exactly)

1 ft^3 = 7.481 gal = 28.32 liter

Prefixes for use in exponential notation:

10^{12} tera T	10^1 deka da	10^{-9} nano n
10^9 giga G	10^{-1} deci d	10^{-12} pico p
10^6 mega M	10^{-2} centi c	10^{-15} femto f
10^3 kilo k	10^{-3} milli m	10^{-18} atto a
10^2 hecto h	10^{-6} micro μ	

The exponent in exponential notation, if positive, indicates the number of zeros in the multiplier. Thus 10^6 = 1,000,000; 10^3 = 1,000, 10^1 = 10. Negative exponents equal the number of zeros in the divisor. Thus 10^{-6} = 1/1,000,000 = 0.000001, 10^{-3} = 1/1000 = 0.001, 10^{-1} = 1/10 = 0.1. Note that $10^x \cdot 10^{-x} = 10^0 = 1$.

APPENDIX II

Dimensions

Some useful dimensions.

(In this table: m = mass in kilograms, l = length in meters, t = time in seconds, T = temperature in degrees Kelvin, Q = charge in coulombs.)

Symbol		Dimension	MKS unit	CGS unit
E	Energy	ml^2t^{-2}	joule	erg
F	Force	mlt^{-2}	newton	dyne
p	Momentum	mlt^{-1}		
P	Power	ml^2t^{-3}	watt	erg/sec
a	Acceleration	lt^{-2}		
C	Capacitance	$m^{-1}l^{-2}t^2Q^2$	farad	
Q	Charge	$m^{1/2}l^{3/2}t^{-1}$	coulomb	esu
β	Coefficient of thermal expansion	T^{-1}		
σ	Conductivity, electrical	$m^{-1}l^{-3}tQ^2$	mho meter^{-1}	
I	Current, electric	$t^{-1}Q$	ampere	
ρ	Density	ml^{-3}		
μ	Electric dipole moment	lQ	coulomb meter	
E	Electric field strength	$mlt^{-2}Q^{-1}$	volt meter^{-1}	
ϵ	Electric potential	$ml^2t^{-2}Q^{-1}$	volt	
S	Entropy	$ml^2t^{-2}T^{-1}$	joule °K^{-1}	
G	Free energy—Gibbs	ml^2t^{-2}		
C	Heat capacity	$ml^2t^{-2}T^{-1}$	joule °K^{-1}	
H	Enthalpy or heat content	ml^2t^{-2}	joule	
H	Magnetic field intensity	$l^{-1}t^{-1}Q$	amp turn meter^{-1}	
I	Moment of inertia	ml^2		
P	Pressure	$ml^{-1}t^{-2}$		
R	Resistance, electric	$ml^2t^{-1}Q^{-2}$	ohm	
σ	Surface tension	mt^{-2}		
T	Temperature	ml^2t^{-2}		
μ	Viscosity (absolute)	$ml^{-1}t^{-1}$		poise

Some dimensionless groups.

Name		Use
Knudsen	$Kn = l/D = \dfrac{\text{mean free molecular path}}{\text{characteristic linear dimension}} = \dfrac{Ma}{Re}$	gas flow
Mach	$Ma = v_f/v_a = \dfrac{\text{flow speed}}{\text{acoustic velocity}} = \dfrac{lt^{-1}}{lt^{-1}}$	objects moving through gases
Reynolds	$Re = Dv\rho/\mu = \dfrac{(l)(lt^{-1})(ml^{-3})}{(ml^{-1}t^{-1})}$	fluid flow (Chapter 34)
Oscillator	$x = h\nu/kT = \dfrac{(ml^2t^{-1})(t^{-1})}{(ml^2t^{-2}T^{-1})(T)}$	quantum theory of molecular oscillators (Chapter 8)

Of course, the product of two dimensionless groups is itself dimensionless, as in the Knudsen number. See C. E. Gall and R. R. Hodgins, *J. Chem. Ed.*, **42**, 611 (1965) for a general discussion of the relationships between many dimensionless groups.

APPENDIX III

Statements of the Second Law of Thermodynamics

1. "Every system which is left to itself will, on the average, change toward a condition of maximum probability" (G. N. Lewis).
2. "The state of maximum entropy is the most stable state for an isolated system" (Enrico Fermi).
3. "Every system left to itself changes, rapidly or slowly, in such a way as to approach a definite final state of rest. No system, except through the influence of external agencies, will change away from the state of equilibrium" (G. N. Lewis).
4. "There is a general tendency in nature for energy to pass from more available to less available forms" (J. A. V. Butler).
5. "In any irreversible process the total entropy of all bodies concerned is increased" (G. N. Lewis).
6. "The entropy function of a system of bodies tends to increase in all physical and chemical processes occurring in nature, if we include in the systems all such bodies which are affected by the change" (Saha).
7. "It is impossible in any way to diminish the entropy of a system of bodies without thereby leaving behind changes in other bodies" (Max Planck).
8. "When any actual process occurs it is impossible to invent a means of restoring *every* system concerned to its original condition" (G. N. Lewis).
9. "Every physical or chemical process in nature takes place in such a way as to increase the sum of the entropies of all the bodies taking part in the process. In the limit, i.e., for reversible processes, the sum of the entropies remains constant" (Max Planck).
10. "For the equilibrium of any isolated system it is necessary and sufficient that in all possible variations of the state of the systems, which do not alter its energy, the variation of its entropy shall either vanish or be negative" (J. W. Gibbs).
11. "In an adiabatic process the entropy either increases or remains unchanged:

    $$\Delta S \geqq 0$$

    where the upper sign ($>$) refers to the irreversible, the lower ($=$) to the reversible case" (P. S. Epstein).
12. "Heat cannot spontaneously pass from a colder to a warmer body" (R. J. E. Clausius).
13. "It is impossible to transfer heat from a colder system to a warmer without other simultaneous changes occurring in the two systems or in their environment" (P. S. Epstein)

14. "It is impossible for a self-acting machine, unaided by any external agency, to convey heat from one body to another at a higher temperature, or heat cannot of itself pass from a colder to a warmer body" (R. J. E. Clausius).

15. "It is impossible to take heat from a system and convert it into work without other simultaneous changes occurring in the system or its environment" (P. S. Epstein).

16. "A transformation whose only final result is to transform into work heat extracted from a source which is at the same temperature throughout is impossible" (Max Planck).

17. "The change of mechanical work into heat may be complete, but on the contrary that of heat into work must needs be incomplete, since whenever a certain quantity of heat is transformed into work, another quantity of heat must undergo a corresponding and compensating change" (Max Planck).

18. "Spontaneous processes (i.e., processes which may occur of their own accord) are those which when carried out under proper conditions, can be made to do work. If carried out reversibly, they will yield a maximum amount of work; in the natural irreversible way the maximum work is never obtained" (J. A. V. Butler).

19. "There exists a characteristic thermodynamic function called the entropy. The difference of a system in states (1) and (2) is given by the expression

$$S_2 - S_1 = \int_1^2 \frac{dq}{T} \text{ over any } \textit{reversible} \text{ path connecting the two states}$$

$$S_2 - S_1 > \int_1^2 \frac{dq}{T} \text{ over any } \textit{irreversible} \text{ path connecting the two states}$$

The entropy is a property of the state only. Its value for an isolated system can never decrease" (R. E. Gibson).

20. "The energy of the universe is constant; the entropy increases toward a maximum" (R. J. E. Clausius on the first law and second law).

21. "Gain in information is loss in entropy" (G. N. Lewis).

22. "Entropy is time's arrow" (A. Eddington).

APPENDIX **IV**

Additional Readings

The readings listed below by Chapters are selected to introduce the student to the general chemical literature if he wishes to dig deeper. Most are survey articles that have appeared since 1966, have extensive bibliographies, and are comprehensible in terms of the background given by *Chemical Systems.* They can serve as sources for class discussions, term papers, or general reading. Many deal with exciting current developments. Happy digging!

Prologue

P. M. S. Blackett, "The Ever Widening Gap," *Science,* **155,** 959 (1967).

T. C. Byerly, "Efficiency of Feed Conversion," *Science,* **157,** 890 (1967).

K. Davis, "Population Policy: Will Current Programs Succeed?," *Science,* **158,** 730 (1967).

T. Dobzhansky, "Changing Man," *Science,* **155,** 409 (1967).

L. B. Flexner, "Dissection of Memory in Mice with Antibiotics," *Am. Scientist,* **56,** 52 (1968).

R. W. Gerard, "What is Memory?," *Scientific American Offprint* 11 (September, 1953).

G. Hardin, "The Tragedy of the Commons," *Science,* **162,** 1243 (1968). Reprinted in G. Hardin, ed., *Population, Evolution, and Birth Control,* 2d ed., San Francisco, W. H. Freeman and Company, 1969, p. 367.

R. Revelle, "Pollution of the Environment," *Am. Scientist,* **XIX,** 167A (1966).

R. B. Roberts, "Memory and Learning from the Standpoint of Computer Model Building," *Am. Scientist,* **56,** 58 (1968).

L. White, Jr., "The Historical Roots of Our Ecologic Crisis," *Science,* **155,** 1203 (1967).

Chaper 1

G. Matthews, "Demonstrations of Spontaneous Endothermic Reactions," *J. Chem. Ed.,* **43,** 476 (1966).

R. C. Pinkerton and C. E. Gleit, "The Significance of Significant Figures," *J. Chem. Ed.,* **44,** 232 (1967).

R. T. Sanderson, "Principles of Chemical Reaction," *J. Chem. Ed.,* **41,** 13 (1964).

E. Schrödinger, "What Is Matter?" *Scientific American Offprint* 241 (September, 1953).

Chapter 2

H. A. Bethe, "Energy Production in Stars," *Science,* **161,** 541 (1968).

A. O. Nier, "Mass Spectroscopy—An Old Field in a New World," *Am. Scientist,* **54,** 359 (1966).

G. T. Seaborg, "Progress Beyond Plutonium," *Chem. Eng. News,* **44,** June 20, 76 (1966).

G. T. Seaborg, "Some Recollections of Early Nuclear Age Chemistry," *J. Chem. Ed.,* **45,** 278 (1968).

J. A. Swartout, "Critical Chemical Problems in the Development of Nuclear Reactors," *J. Chem. Ed.,* **45,** 304 (1968).

S. Wexler, "Destruction of Molecules by Nuclear Transformations," *Science,* **156,** 901 (1967).

J. A. Wheeler, "Our Universe: The Known and the Unknown," *Am. Scientist,* **56,** 1 (1968).

W. A. Fowler, "Origin of the Elements," *Scientific American Offprint* 210 (September, 1956).

R. Hofstadter, "The Atomic Nucleus," *Scientific American Offprint* 217 (July, 1956).

Chapter 3

S. Bashkin, "A New Method for Studying the Atom," *Science,* **148,** 1047 (1965).

J. L. Hollenberg, "The Spectrum of Atomic Hydrogen: A Freshman Laboratory Experiment," *J. Chem. Ed.,* **43,** 216 (1966).

Chapter 4

R. S. Berry, "Atomic Orbitals," *J. Chem. Ed.,* **43,** 283 (1966).

I. Cohen and T. Bustard, "Atomic Orbitals: Limitations and Variations," *J. Chem. Ed.,* **43,** 187 (1966).

N. N. Greenwood, *Principles of Atomic Orbitals.* London, Royal Institute of Chemistry, 1964.

E. A. Ogryzlo, "Atomic Orbitals and Classical Motion," *J. Chem. Ed.*, **45**, 80 (1968).

R. E. Powell, "Relativistic Quantum Chemistry: The Electrons and the Nodes," *J. Chem. Ed.*, **45**, 558 (1968).

Chapter 5

W. L. Jolly, *The Chemistry of the Non-Metals*. Englewood Cliffs, N.J., Prentice-Hall, 1966.

G. B. Kauffman, "American Forerunners of the Periodic Law," *J. Chem. Ed.*, **47**, 128 (1969).

C. E. Myers, "The Enigmatic Polymorphism of Iron," *J. Chem. Ed.*, **43**, 303 (1966).

D. M. Samuel, *Industrial Chemistry—Inorganic*. London, Royal Institute of Chemistry, 1966.

R. T. Sanderson, *Chemical Periodicity*. New York, Reinhold, 1960.

Chapter 6

A. Kalantar, "Nonideal Gases and Elementary Thermodynamics," *J. Chem. Ed.*, **43**, 477 (1966).

E. N. Lorenz, "The Circulation of the Atmosphere," *Am. Scientist*, **54**, 402 (1966).

R. W. Roberts and L. E. St. Pierre, "Ultrahigh Vacuum," *Science*, **147**, 1529 (1965).

Chapter 7

R. S. Jessup, *Precise Measurement of Heat of Combustion with a Bomb Calorimeter*, NBS Monograph 7, 1960.

L. K. Nash, "Elementary Chemical Thermodynamics," *J. Chem. Ed.*, **42**, 64 (1965).

Chapter 8

B. J. Alder and T. E. Wainwright, "Molecular Motions," *Scientific American Offprint* 265 (October, 1959).

G. M. Barrow, *The Structure of Molecules*. New York, Benjamin, 1963.

R. J. Campbell, "Gas Phase Energy Transfer Processes," *J. Chem. Ed.*, **45**, 156 (1968).

J. L. Hollenberg, "Pure Rotation Spectra of HCl and NH_3: A Physical Chemistry Experiment," *J. Chem. Ed.*, **43**, 7 (1966).

Chapter 9

J. A. Campbell, "Is ΔS Naught or Not?," *J. Chem. Ed.*, **45**, 9, 244, 340 (1968).

C. E. Hecht, "Negative Absolute Temperatures," *J. Chem. Ed.*, **44**, 124 (1967).

Chapter 10

G. C. Pimentel, "Chemical Lasers," *Scientific American Offprint* 303 (April, 1966).

Chapter 11

L. B. Borst, "Liquid Helium," *Am. Scientist*, **52**, 431 (1964).

R. Brocklehurst, "The Reactions of Ions and Excited Atoms of the Inert Gases," *Quart. Rev.*, **22**, 147 (1968).

J. E. Frey, "Discovery of the Noble Gases and Foundations of the Theory of Atomic Structure," *J. Chem. Ed.*, **43**, 371 (1966).

H. H. Hyman, "The Chemistry of Noble Gas Compounds," *Science*, **145**, 773 (1964).

Chapter 12

J. J. Katz and H. L. Crespi, "Deuterated Organisms: Cultivation and Uses," *Science*, **151**, 1187 (1966).

G. E. Pake, "Magnetic Resonance," *Scientific American Offprint* 233 (August, 1958).

L. K. Runnels, "Ice," *Scientific American Offprint* 307 (December, 1966).

R. Sanderson, "Principles of Hydrogen Chemistry," *J. Chem. Ed.*, **41**, 331 (1964).

Chapter 13

J. J. Turner, "Oxygen Fluorides," *Endeavour*, **27**, 42 (1968).

Chapter 14

H. O. Pritchard and H. A. Skinner, "The Concept of Electronegativity," *Chem. Rev.*, **55**, 745 (1955).

H. B. Thompson, "The Determination of Dipole Moments in Solution," *J. Chem. Ed.*, **43**, 66 (1966).

Chapter 15

B. V. Derjaguin, "Force Between Molecules," *Scientific American Offprint* 266 (July, 1960).

R. J. Gillespie, "The Valence-Shell Electron-Pair Repulsion Theory of Directed Valency," *J. Chem. Ed.*, **40**, 295 (1963).

E. Jaffe and W. Marshall, "Origin of Colour in Organic Compounds," *Chemistry*, **37**, 7 (1964).

W. F. Luder, "The Electron Repulsion Theory of the Chemical Bond," *J. Chem. Ed.*, **44**, 206 (1967).

W. F. Luder, "The Electron Repulsion Theory of the Chemical Bond: II. An Alternative to Resonance Hybrids," *J. Chem. Ed.*, **44**, 269 (1967).

A. L. McClellan, "The Significance of Hydrogen Bonds in Biological Structures," *J. Chem. Ed.*, **44**, 547 (1967).
E. A. Walters, "Models for the Double Bond," *J. Chem. Ed.*, **43**, 134 (1966).

Chapter 16

F. A. Cotton, "Transition-Metal Compounds Containing Clusters of Metal Atoms," *Quart. Rev.*, **20**, 389 (1966).
J. J. Gilman, "The Nature of Ceramics," *Scientific American*, **217**, 112 (1967).
G. P. Haight, Jr., "Energy Cycles," *J. Chem. Ed.*, **45**, 420 (1968).
F. W. Went, "The Size of Man," *American Scientist*, **56**, 400 (1968).

Chapter 17

H. A. Bent, "Isoelectronic Systems," *J. Chem. Ed.*, **43**, 170 (1966).
S. F. A. Kettle, "Ligand Group Orbitals of Complex Ions," *J. Chem. Ed.*, **43**, 652 (1966).
R. S. Mulliken, "Spectroscopy, Molecular Orbitals, and Chemical Bonding," *Science*, **157**, 13 (1967).
W. C. Price, "Photoionization and the Electron Structure of Molecules," *Endeavour*, **25**, 78 (1966).
C. G. Suits, "Man-Made Diamonds—A Progress Report," *Am. Scientist*, **52**, 395 (1964).
A. C. Wahl, "Molecular Orbital Densities: Pictorial Studies," *Science*, **151**, 961 (1966).
W. Weltner, Jr., "Stellar and Other High-Temperature Molecules," *Science*, **155**, 155 (1967).

Chapter 18

G. E. R. Deacon, "Chemistry of the Sea," *Chemistry in Britain*, **1**, 48 (1965).
L. J. Heidt, "The Path of Oxygen from Water to Molecular Oxygen," *J. Chem. Ed.*, **43**, 623 (1966).
R. T. Sanderson, "Principles of Oxide Chemistry," *J. Chem. Ed.*, **41**, 415 (1964).
J. M. Schlegel," Lewis Acid-Base Titration in Fused Salts," *J. Chem. Ed.*, **43**, 362 (1966).

Chapter 19

H. L. Clever, "The Ion Product Constant of Water: Thermodynamics of Water Ionization," *J. Chem. Ed.*, **45**, 231 (1968).
W. B. Guenther, "Stepwise Formation Constants of Complex Ions," *J. Chem. Ed.*, **44**, 46 (1967).
E. Haglund, D. Moss, and J. Flynn, "General Solution of Ionic Equilibria Problems: A Computer Program," *J. Chem. Ed.*, **43**, 582 (1966).

Chapter 20

L. Meites, J. Pode, and H. Thomas, "Are Solubilities and Solubility Products Related?," *J. Chem. Ed.*, **43**, 667 (1966).
S. D. Morton and G. F. Lee, "Calcium Carbonate Equilibria in Lakes," *J. Chem. Ed.*, **45**, 511 (1968).
S. D. Morton and G. F. Lee, "Calcium Carbonate Equilibria in the Oceans—Ion Pair Formation," *J. Chem. Ed.*, **45**, 513 (1968).
R. Ramette, "The Nature of Dissolved Silver Acetate," *J. Chem. Ed.*, **43**, 299 (1966).

Chapter 21

J. L. Carlos, Jr., "Molecular Symmetry and Optical Inactivity," *J. Chem. Ed.*, **45**, 248 (1968).
D. M. Samuel, *Industrial Chemistry—Organic*. London, Royal Institute of Chemistry, 1966.
H. M. Stanley, *The Petroleum-Chemicals Industry*. London, Royal Institute of Chemistry, 1963.

Chapter 22

A. B. Callear, "Flash Photolysis," *Endeavour*, **26**, 9 (1967).
D. F. DeTar, "Simplified Computer Programs for Treating Complex Reaction Mechanisms," *J. Chem. Ed.*, **44**, 191 (1967).
J. Edwards, E. Greene, and J. Ross, "From Stoichiometry and Rate Law to Mechanism," *J. Chem. Ed.*, **45**, 381 (1968).
J. E. Finholt, "The Temperature-Jump Method for the Study of Fast Reactions," *J. Chem. Ed.*, **45**, 394 (1968).
G. G. Hammes, "Very Fast Reactions in Solution," *Science*, **151**, 1507 (1966).
E. E. Muschlitz, Jr., "Metastable Atoms and Molecules," *Science*, **159**, 599 (1968).
H. J. Sanders, "Chemistry and the Atmosphere," *Chem. Eng. News*, Special Report (1966).
B. A. Thrush, "Atom Reactions in Flow Tubes," *Science*, **156**, 470 (1967).

Chapter 23

B. Agranoff, "Memory and Protein Synthesis," *Scientific American Offprint* 1077 (1967).
A. O. Allen, "Radiation Chemistry Today," *J. Chem. Ed.*, **45**, 290 (1968).
E. F. Greene and A. Kuppermann, "Chemical Reaction Cross Sections and Rate Constants," *J. Chem. Ed.*, **45**, 361 (1968).
H. Jaffe and A. Miller, "The Fates of Electronic Excitation Energy," *J. Chem. Ed.*, **43**, 469 (1966).
J. R. Jones, "Kinetic Isotope Effects," *J. Chem. Ed.*, **44**, 31 (1967).

R. A. Marcus, "Recent Developments in Theoretical Chemical Kinetics," *J. Chem. Ed.*, **45**, 356 (1968).

S. H. Massey, "Collisions Between Gas Atoms," *Endeavour*, **27**, 114–119 (1968).

Chapter 24

M. C. Caserio, "Reaction Mechanisms in Organic Chemistry," *J. Chem. Ed.*, **42**, 570 (1965).

J. O. Edwards, "Bimolecular Nucleophilic Displacement Reactions," *J. Chem. Ed.*, **45**, 386 (1968).

J. P. Idoux, "Conformational Analysis and Chemical Reactivity," *J. Chem. Ed.*, **44**, 459 (1967).

R. Weston, Jr., "Transition-State Models and Hydrogen-Isotope Effects," *Science*, **158**, 332 (1967).

Chapter 25

N. N. Greenwood, R. V. Parish, and P. Thornton, "Metal Borides," *Quart. Rev.*, **20**, 441 (1966).

M. F. Hawthorne, "Polyhedral Boranes, Carboranes, and Carbametallic Boron Hydride Derivatives," *Endeavour*, **25**, 146 (1966).

A. A. Hodgson, *Fibrous Silicates*. London: Royal Institute of Chemistry, 1965.

D. Payne, Jr., and F. Fink, "Electronegativities and Group IVA Chemistry," *J. Chem. Ed.*, **43**, 654 (1966).

C. J. Phillips, "The Strength and Weakness of Brittle Materials," *Am. Scientist*, **53**, 20 (1965).

H. F. W. Taylor, *The Chemistry of Cements*. London: Royal Institute of Chemistry, 1966.

Chapter 26

M. J. R. Dawkins and D. Hull, "The Production of Heat by Fat," *Scientific American Offprint* 1018 (August 1965).

A. L. Lehninger, "How Cells Transform Energy," *Scientific American Offprint* 91 (September 1961).

D. MacRae, "The Fundamental Assumptions of Chemical Thermodynamics," *J. Chem. Ed.*, **43**, 586 (1966).

Chapter 27

S. M. Blinder, "Mathematical Methods in Elementary Thermodynamics," *J. Chem. Ed.*, **43**, 85 (1966).

K. G. Denbigh, "The Scope and Limitations of Thermodynamics," *Chem. in Britain*, **4**, 338 (1968).

Chapter 28

R. Little, "Molecular Structure and Thermodynamic Properties of HCN and DCN," *J. Chem. Ed.*, **43**, 2 (1966).

Chapter 29

M. Barrere and A. Moutet, "Liquid-Solid Rockets," *Internat. Sci. Tech.*, **68**, 64 (1967).

R. Cockburn, "Rocket Propulsion and Space Research," *Endeavour*, **26**, 21 (1967).

C. E. Hecht, "Desalination of Water by Reverse Osmosis," *J. Chem. Ed.*, **44**, 53 (1967).

E. King, "Standard Entropy Changes in Composite Reactions," *J. Chem. Ed.*, **43**, 478 (1966).

K. J. Miller, "Prediction of Maximum Reaction Yield: Examples for Elementary Physical Chemistry," *J. Chem. Ed.*, **43**, 386 (1966).

E. Schonfeld, "Computer Calculated Concentrations in the Reactions of Nitrogen and Oxygen," *J. Chem. Ed.*, **45**, 173 (1968).

F. H. Verhoek, "Thermodynamics and Rocket Propulsion," *J. Chem. Ed.*, **46**, 140 (1969).

Chapter 30

H. Brintzinger, "Formation of NH_3 by Insertion of N_2 into Metal-Hydride Bonds," *J. Am. Chem. Soc.*, **88**, 4305 (1966).

L. F. Haber, "Fritz Haber and the Nitrogen Problem," *Endeavour*, **27**, 150–153 (1968).

A. Hantzsch and A. Werner, "On the Spatial Arrangement of Atoms in Nitrogen-Containing Molecules," *J. Chem. Ed.*, **43**, 156 (1966).

W. L. Jolly, *The Inorganic Chemistry of Nitrogen*. New York: Benjamin, 1964.

W. L. Jolly, "The Use of Oxidation Potentials in Inorganic Chemistry," *J. Chem. Ed.*, **43**, 198 (1966).

N. L. Paddock, *Structure and Reactions in Phosphorus Chemistry*. London: Royal Institute of Chemistry, 1962.

Chapter 31

L. Glasser, "Teaching Symmetry: The Use of Decorations," *J. Chem. Ed.*, **44**, 502 (1967).

W. C. Hamilton, "Structural Chemistry in the Nuclear Age," *J. Chem. Ed.*, **45**, 296 (1968).

D. C. Hodgkin, "The X-ray Analysis of Complicated Molecules," *Science*, **150**, 979 (1965).

J. Waser, "Pictorial Representation of the Fourier Method of X-Ray Crystallography," *J. Chem. Ed.*, **45**, 446 (1968).

Chapter 32

G. C. Bond, *Principles of Catalysis*. London: Royal Institute of Chemistry, 1963.

M. Boudart, "Four Decades of Active Centers," *Am. Scientist*, **57**, 91 (1969).

R. P. Eischens, "Infrared Spectroscopy and Catalysis Research," *Science*, **146**, 486 (1964).

G. Evans and K. Lordesch, "Hydrazine-Air Fuel Cells," *Science,* **158,** 1148 (1967).
H. C. Gatos, "Crystalline Structure and Surface Reactivity," *Science,* **137,** 311 (1962).
J. Huntsberger, "Wetting and Adhesion," *Chem. Eng. News,* Nov. 2, 82, (1964).
S. Kimoto and J. C. Russ, "The Characteristics and Applications of the Scanning Electron Microscope," *Am. Scientist,* **57,** 112 (1969).
H. Leidheiser, Jr., "Corrosion," *Chem. Eng. News,* April 15, 78 (1965).
W. C. Wake, "Adhesives," Royal Institute of Chemistry, Lecture Series 1966, No. 4.
J. F. Walling, "Differences in Perspective Between Electrode and Chemical Kinetics," *J. Chem. Ed.,* **45,** 109 (1968).
A. Walton, "Nucleation," *Internat. Sci. Tech.,* **60,** 28 (1966).
F. W. Went, "The Size of Man," *American Scientist,* **56,** 400 (1968).

Chapter 33

L. Brewer, "Bonding and Structures of Transition Metals," *Science,* **161,** 115 (1968).
D. M. Carlton and P. E. Cassidy, "Not Organic, Not Inorganic," *Internat. Sci. Tech.,* **68,** 78 (1967).
A. H. Cottrell, "The Nature of Metals," *Scientific American,* **217,** 90 (1967).
F. B. Cuff and L. M. Schetky, "Dislocations in Metals," *Scientific American Offprint* 204 (July, 1955).
A. Rabenau, "Chemical Problems in Semiconductor Research," *Endeavour,* **25,** 158 (1966).
F. Seitz, "The Effects of Irradiation on Metals," *Science,* **138,** 563 (1962).
A. Sharpe, "Solubility Explained," *Ed. Chem.,* **1,** 75 (1964).

Chapter 34

W. F. Claussen, "Surface Tension and Surface Structure of Water," *Science,* **156,** 1226 (1967).
J. W. Cobble, "High-Temperature Aqueous Solutions," *Science,* **152,** 1479 (1966).
E. U. Franck, "Supercritical Water," *Endeavour,* **27,** 55 May (1968).
A. V. Grosse, "High-Temperature Research," *Science,* **140,** 781 (1963).
A. Katchalsky, "Living Membranes," *Science and Tech.,* **72,** 52 (1967).
J. V. and A. L. Sengers, "The Critical Region," *Chem. Eng. News,* June 10, 104 (1968).
J. F. Thain, *Principles of Osmotic Phenomena.* London: Royal Institute of Chemistry, 1967.
E. Ungar, "Ablation Thermal Protection Systems," *Science,* **158,** 740 (1967).

Chapter 35

G. B. Alexander, "Industrial Chemistry: Tantalum Recovery by Liquid-Liquid Extraction," *J. Chem. Ed.,* **46,** 157 (1969).
M. A. Amerine, "Wine," *Scientific American Offprint* 190 (August, 1964).
J. A. Bell and W. H. Snider, "The Acetone-Chloroform System: An NMR Study," *J. Chem. Ed.,* **44,** 200 (1967).
D. Jaques, "How to Test the Thermodynamic Consistency of Liquid-Vapor Equilibrium Data," *J. Chem. Ed.,* **42,** 651 (1965).
W. G. Pfann, "Zone Melting," *Science,* **135,** 1101 (1962).

Chapter 36

E. E. Aynsley and A. B. Littlewood, *Principles of Titrimetric Analysis.* London: Royal Institute of Chemistry, 1962.
B. Crawford, "Chemical Analysis by Infrared," *Scientific American Offprint* 257 (October, 1953).
R. A. Keller, "Gas Chromatography," *Scientific American Offprint* 276 (October, 1961).
W. H. Stein and S. Moore, "Chromatography," *Scientific American Offprint* 81 (March, 1951).
J. Thomson and D. C. Abbott, "Pesticide Residues," Royal Institute of Chemistry, Lecture Series 1966, No. 3.
A. L. Turkevich, J. H. Patterson and E. J. Franzgrote, "The Chemical Analysis of the Lunar Surface," *American Scientist,* **56,** 312 (1968).
W. H. Wahl and H. H. Kramer, "Neutron-Activation Analysis," *Scientific American Offprint* 310 (April, 1967).
B. Weinstock, "The 25-Year Revolution in Hexafluoride Chemistry," *Chem. Eng. News,* Sept. 21, 86 (1964).
T. S. West, "Atomic Analysis in Flames," *Endeavour,* **26,** 44 (1967).

Chapter 37

H. B. Gray and C. H. Langford, "Ligand Substitution Dynamics," *Chem. Eng. News,* **46,** April 1, 68 (1968).
J. Halpern, "Some Aspects of Chemical Dynamics in Solution," *J. Chem. Ed.,* **45,** 372 (1968).
A. G. Sykes, *Kinetics of Inorganic Reactions.* New York: Pergamon, 1966.
H. Taube, "Mechanics of Oxidation-Reduction Reactions," *J. Chem. Ed.,* **45,** 452 (1968).
P. L. Timms, "Chemical Synthesis by means of Radicals Formed at High Temperatures," *Endeavour,* **27,** 134–137 (1968).

Chapter 38

G. A. W. Boehm, "Titanium," *Scientific American Offprint* 258 (April, 1949).

D. Grdenić, "The Structural Chemistry of Mercury," *Quart. Rev.*, **19,** 303 (1965).

D. A. Johnson, "The Standard Free Energies of Solution of Anhydrous Salts in Water," *J. Chem. Ed.*, **45,** 236 (1968).

S. R. Logan, "The Solvated Electron—the Simplest Ion and Reagent," *J. Chem. Ed.*, **44,** 344, (1967).

A. McAuley and J. Hill, "Kinetics and Mechanism of Metal-ion Complex Formation in Solution," *Quart. Rev.* **23,** 18 (1969).

L. Pokras, "On the Species Present in Aqueous Solutions of 'Salts' of Polyvalent Metals, I, II, III," *J. Chem. Ed.*, **33,** 152, 223, 282 (1956).

G. T. Seaborg and I. Perlman, "The Synthetic Elements I," *Scientific American Offprint* 242 (April, 1950).

G. T. Seaborg and A. Ghiorso, "The Synthetic Elements II," *Scientific American Offprint* 243 (December, 1956).

G. T. Seaborg and A. R. Frisch, "The Synthetic Elements III," *Scientific American Offprint* 293 (April, 1963).

G. T. Seaborg and J. L. Bloom, "The Synthetic Elements IV, *Scientific American*, **220,** 56 (1969).

S. M. Shelton, "Zirconium," *Scientific American Offprint* 259 (June, 1951).

N. Slagg, "Chemistry and Light Generation," *J. Chem. Ed.*, **45,** 103 (1968).

K. Wade, "Some Developments in Aluminum Chemistry," *Chemistry in Britain*, **4,** 503 (1968).

Chapter 39

M. and A. Bodanszky, "From Peptide Synthesis to Protein Synthesis," *Am. Scientist*, **55,** 185 (1967).

R. O. Gibson, *The Discovery of Polythene.* London: Royal Institute of Chemistry, 1964.

A. Kelly, "The Nature of Composite Materials," *Scientific American*, **217,** 160 (1967).

J. C. Kendrew, "Myoglobin and the Structure of Proteins," *Science*, **139,** 1259 (1963).

G. C. Oppenlander, "Structure and Properties of Crystalline Polymers," *Science*, **159,** 1311 (1968).

F. Rodriguez, "Simple Models for Polymer Stereochemistry," *J. Chem. Ed.*, **45,** 507 (1968).

Chapter 40

D. E. Atkinson, "Biological Feedback Control at the Molecular Level," *Science*, **150,** 851 (1965).

C. Auerback, "The Chemical Production of Mutations," *Science*, **158,** 1141 (1967).

B. R. Baker, "Interactions of Enzymes and Inhibitors," *J. Chem. Ed.*, **44,** 610 (1967).

R. V. Eck and M. O. Dayhoff, *Atlas of Protein Sequence and Structure.* Silver Spring, Maryland: Natl. Biomedical Research Foundation, 1968.

I. Hornstein and R. Teranishi, "The Chemistry of Flavor," *Chem. Eng. News*, April 3, 92 (1967).

S. Lande, "Conformation of Peptides: Speculations Based on Molecular Models," *J. Chem. Ed.*, **45,** 587 (1968).

R. B. Merrifield, "Automated Synthesis of Peptides," *Science*, **150,** 178 (1965).

H. Papkoff and C. Li, "Hormone Structure and Biological Activity: Biochemical Studies of Three Pituitary Hormones," *J. Chem. Ed.*, **43,** 41 (1966).

M. F. Perutz, "Some Molecular Controls in Biology," *Endeavour*, **26,** 3 (1967).

R. Rice, "Drug Receptors," *J. Chem. Ed.*, **44,** 565 (1967).

E. D. Robertis, "Ultrastructure and Cytochemistry of the Synaptic Region," *Science*, **156,** 907 (1967).

R. L. Sinsheimer, "The Prospect for Designed Genetic Change," *Am. Scientist*, **57,** 134 (1969).

T. M. Sonneborn, "Nucleotide Sequence of a Gene: First Complete Specification," *Science*, **148,** 1410 (1965).

J. van Overbeek, "Plant Hormones and Regulators," *Science*, **152,** 721 (1966).

H. Vogel and R. Vogel, "Some Chemical Glimpses of Evolution," *Chem. Eng. News*, Dec. 11, 90 (1967).

R. L. Wain, *Chemistry and Crop Protection.* London: Royal Institute of Chemistry, 1965.

J. and E. Weisburger, "Chemicals as Causes of Cancer," *Chem. Eng. News*, Feb. 7, 124 (1966).

E. O. Wilson, "Chemical Communication in the Social Insects," *Science*, **149,** 1064 (1965).

Index

(*Italic* numbers refer to figures. **Boldface** numbers refer to tables.)

Periodic Table of the Elements Showing Ground State Electron Structures and Common Oxidation States

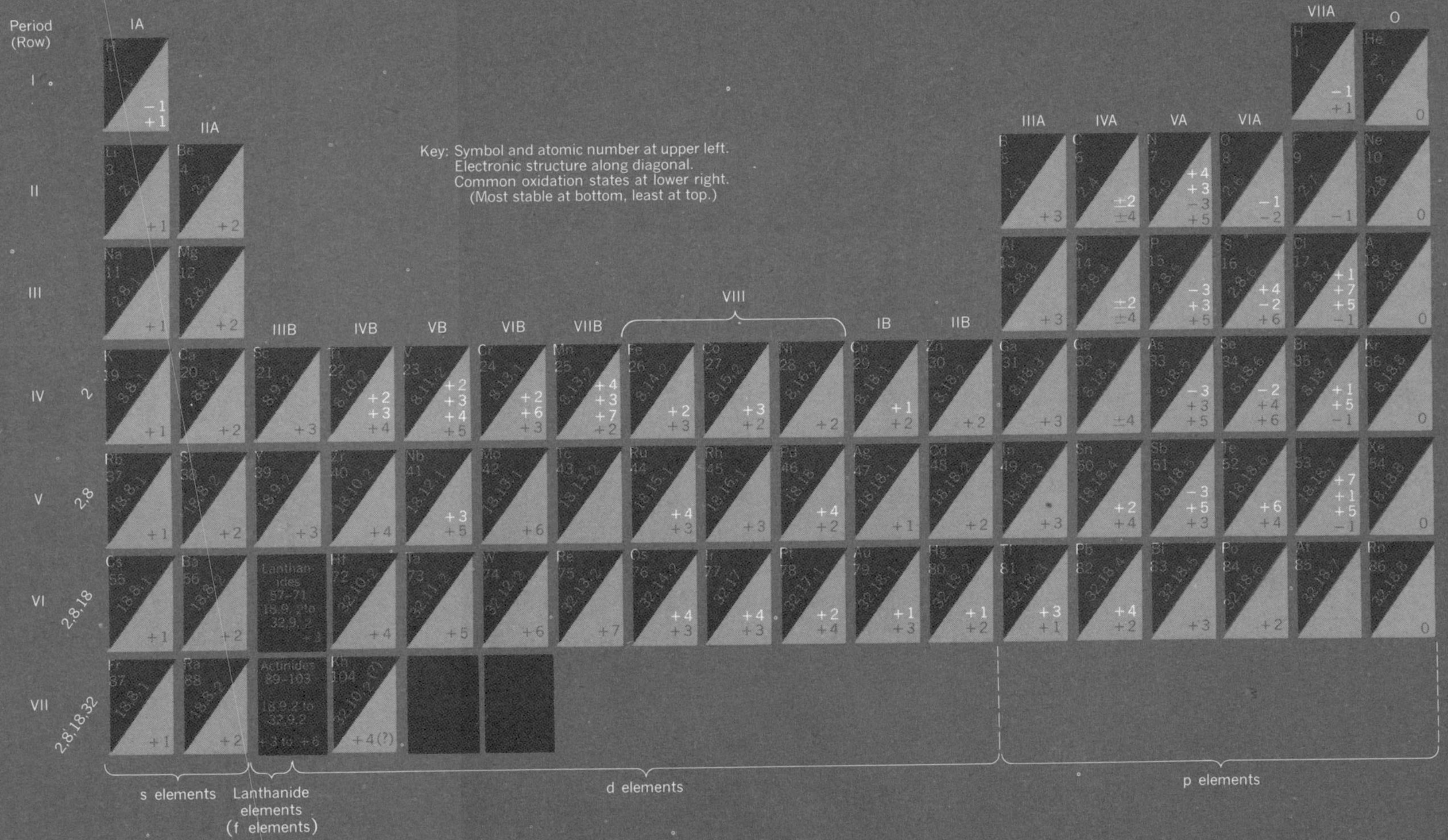